Directory of American Firms Operating in Foreign Countries

12th Edition

VOLUME 2

Alphabetical Distribution of American Corporations by Country

A-H

A World Trade Academy Press Publication
Established in 1955 by Juvenal L. Angel

Uniworld Business Publications, Inc.
50 East 42nd Street
New York, NY 10017

First Edition	1955
Second Edition	1957
Third Edition	1959
Fourth Edition	1961
Fifth Edition	1964
Sixth Edition	1966
Seventh Edition	1969
Eighth Edition	1975
Ninth Edition	1979
Tenth Edition	1984
Eleventh Edition	1987
Twelfth Edition	1991

Copyright © 1991 by
World Trade Academy Press

Published by
Uniworld Business Publications, Inc.
50 East 42nd St.
New York, N.Y. 10017

ISBN: 0-8360-0033-1

Library of Congress Catalog Card Number: 55-39067

Printed in Mexico

INTRODUCTION

For more than 35 years, the *Directory of American Firms Operating in Foreign Countries,* the only reference work of its kind, has been the authoritative source of information on American firms with foreign affiliates. As such, it has been used by public and university libraries, business, government, military and special libraries, manufacturing firms, accounting, brokerage and investment firms, airlines, transportation companies, advertising and personnel agencies, individuals seeking employment abroad, researchers, embassies and governmental agencies dealing with commerce, trade and foreign relations.

This 12th edition contains 2,600 U.S. corporations which have some 19,000 subsidiaries and affiliates in 127 countries. It is divided into three volumes:

Volume 1 lists, in alphabetical order, American firms which have operations overseas. Each entry contains the company's U.S. address and telephone number, principal product or service, number of employees, and the foreign countries in which it has a subsidiary or affiliate. Fax numbers are included when provided. Some key personnel are noted. The titles President (P), Foreign Officer (FO) and Personnel Director (Per) used in this directory are meant to be generic and are assigned to the names given to us as the chief executive officer, the person in charge of foreign operations, and the person in charge of human resources.

Volumes 2 and 3 contain listings by country—from Algeria to Zimbabwe—of the American firms' foreign operations. Each country listing includes, alphabetically, the name of the U.S. parent firm, its address, phone number and principal product or service, and the name and address of its subsidiary(ies) or affiliate(s) in that country.

The overseas companies in this directory are those in which American firms have a substantial direct capital investment and which have been identified by the parent firm as a wholly or partially owned subsidiary, affiliate or branch. Franchises and non-commercial enterprises or institutions, such as hospitals, schools, etc., financed or operated by American philanthropic or religious organizations, are not included.

Source and Accuracy of Listings

It is assumed that all companies in this directory are in good standing, but neither the compilers nor the publisher can take responsibility for their inclusion or for the correctness of the information provided as a basis for the entry. The designations and listings are not to be considered definitive as to legal status or the relationship between the American and the foreign firms.

Every effort has been made to update the information contained in the 11th edition of this directory, to delete firms which no longer maintain overseas operations or which have been acquired by foreign companies, and to add new listings. The primary sources of information were questionnaires mailed to and completed by the parent corporations, and/or annual reports provided by them. Direct telephone contact was used extensively for verification and clarification. Every firm in the last edition was sent an announcement of the new edition, along with a print-out of its previous entry, and asked to provide current data. It was stated that if we did not receive a response from a firm, and there was no evidence that it had gone out of business, the previous entry would be carried forward to this edition.

In a directory of this scope some inaccuracies are inevitable. It would be appreciated if the reader noting such would inform the publisher so corrections can be made in the next edition. Also, as extensive as this compilation may be, it does not claim to be all-inclusive. It contains only what has been disclosed to us.

Acknowledgements

Our sincerest appreciation is extended to the many company representatives who cooperated so generously in providing information for this directory, and to all who assisted in its preparation.

WORLD TRADE ACADEMY PRESS INC.

Abbreviations Used in This Book

A/C . . . . .Air Conditioning
Acces. . . . . .Accessory(ies)
Adv . . . . .Advertising
Affil. . . . . .Affiliate(d)
Agcy. . . . . .Agent/Agency
Agric . . . . .Agriculture
Arch . . . . .Architecture(al)
Assur . . . . .Assurance
Auto. . . . . .Automotive
Aux . . . . .Auxiliary
Bldg . . . . .Building(s)
Bus. . . . . .Business
Chem. . . . . .Chemical(s)
Cir . . . . .Circulation
Com . . . . .Components
Coml . . . . .Commercial
Commun . . . . .Communications
Constr . . . . .Construction
Consult. .Consultants/Consulting
Corp . . . .Corporate/Corporation
Cust . . . . .Customer
Dept . . . . .Department
Devel . . . . .Development
Diag. . . . . .Diagnostic
Dir. . . . . .Director
Dist . . . . .District
Distr. . .Distributor/Distribution
Div . . . . .Division
Dom. . . . . .Domestic

Econ. . . . . .Economic(s)
Educ . . . . .Education(al)
Elec. . . . . .Electric(al)
Electr . . . . .Electronic(s)
Emp. . . . . .Employee(s)
Engr . . . . .Engineer(ing)
Envir . . . . .Environmental
Equip . . . . .Equipment
Exch . . . . .Exchange
Exec . . . . .Executive
Exp. . . . . .Export(er)
Explor . . . . .Exploration
Fin. . . . . .Financial/Finance
Fl . . . . .Floor
Frt . . . . .Freight
Furn . . . . .Furniture
Fwdg . . . . .Forwarding
Gds . . . . .Goods
Gen . . . . .General
Gov . . . . .Governor
Hdwe . . . . .Hardware
Hos . . . . .Hospital
Imp. . . . . .Import(er)
Ind . . . . . . .Industrial/Industry
Info . . . . .Information
Ins . . . . .Insurance
Inspec. . . . . .Inspect(ion)
Instru . . . . .Instrument(s)
Intl . . . . .International

Invest . . . . .Investment	Prod. . . . . .Production
Lab . . . . .Laboratory	Prog . . . . .Programming
Liq . . . . .Liquid	Pub . . . . . .Publisher/Publishing
Mach . . . . .Machine(ry)	R&D . .Research & Development
Maint. . . . . .Maintenance	Recre. . . . . .Recreation(al)
Mat . . . . .Material(s)	Refrig . . . . .Refrigeration
Mdse . . . . .Merchandise	Rel . . . . .Relations
Mdsng. . . . . . . .Merchandising	Rep . . . . .Representative(s)
Meas. . . . . .Measurement	Res . . . . .Research
Med . . . . .Medical	Ret . . . . .Retail(er)
Mfg. . . . . .Manufacturing	Rfg . . . . .Refining
Mfr . . . . .Manufacturer	Ry . . . . .Railway
Mgmt . . . . .Management	Sci . . . . .Scientific
Mgn . . . . .Managing	Serv . . . . .Service(s)
Mgr . . . . .Manager	Spec. . . . . .Special(ty)/Specialized
Mkt. . . . . .Market	Sta . . . . .Station
Nat . . . . .Natural	Sub . . . . .Subsidiary
Oper . . . . .Operation	Super. . . . . .Supervision
Orgn . . . . .Organization(al)	Surg. . . . . .Surgical/Surgery
Pass . . . . .Passenger	Sys. . . . . .System(s)
Pct. . . . . .Percent(age)	TV . . . . .Television
Petrol . . . . .Petroleum	Tech . . . . .Technical/Technology
Pharm . . . . . .Pharmaceutical(s)	Tel . . . . .Telephone
Plt . . . . .Plant	Telecom . . .Telecommunications
Prdt. . . . . .Product(s)	Temp . . . . .Temperature
Pres. . . . . .President	Tlx . . . . .Telex
Prin . . . . .Principal	Trans . . . . .Transport(ation)
Print . . . . .Printing	Whl. . . . . .Wholesale(r)
Proc . . . . .Process(ing)	Whse. . . . . .Warehouse

Notes on Alphabetizing

Alphabetizing in this directory is by computer sort which places numerals before letters; and among names, places blanks, hyphens and ampersands before letters. Thus, 3D Co. precedes A Z Co., which precedes A-Z Co., which precedes A&Z Co., which precedes Abiz Co.

Names such as The Jones Corp., Charles Jones Inc., and L. M. Jones & Co. are alphabetized conventionally: all will be found under J.

Names which consist of initials only (e.g., LFM Co.) are in strict alphabetical order: Lewis Corp., LFM Co., Lintz Inc.

Mac/Mc names are found at the end of the M's: Mueller & Co., Myers Supply Inc., MacDougal Corp., McMurphy Electronics Co.

Table of Contents

ALGERIA

AIR EXPRESS INTL CORP   120 Tokeneke Rd, PO Box 1231, Darien, CT 06820,
Tel: (203) 655-7900
(Air frt forwarder)
   Air Express Intl., 10 Boulevard Khemisti, Algiers, Algeria

AMERICAN SERVICE CORP   2159 NW 1 Ct, Miami, FL 33137, Tel: (305) 573-0200
(Paper prdts)
   First Planning Intl. Corp., B.P. 877 Alger Gare, 6 Allee des Murier, Belcourt,
      Algiers, Algeria

BECHTEL GROUP INC   50 Beale St, PO Box 3965, San Francisco, CA 94119,
Tel: (415) 768-1234
(Engineering & constr)
   Bechtel Inc., Villa Djenane, Mouhoub 11, Chemin Acklai, B.P. 62, El Biar, Algeria

CHRISTENSEN INTL   PO Box 26135, Salt Lake City, UT 84126, Tel: (801) 487-5371
(Diamond drills)
   Christensen, 1 Blvd. Anatole France, Alger, Aldim, Algeria

COLGATE-PALMOLIVE CO   300 Park Ave, New York, NY 10022, Tel: (212) 310-2000
(Pharms, cosmetics, toiletries, detergents)
   Colgate-Palmolive Corp., 26 Blvd. Zirout Youcaf, B.P. 576, Algiers, Algeria

DRESSER INDUSTRIES INC   1600 Pacific Bldg, PO Box 718, Dallas, TX 75221,
Tel: (214) 740-6000
(Diversified supplier of equip & tech serv to energy & natural resource ind)
   Dresser Industries Inc. (ALDIA, S.A.), 4/6 Blvd. Mohamed V, Algiers, Algeria

GETTY OIL CO   3810 Wilshire Blvd, Los Angeles, CA 90010, Tel: (213) 739-2100
(Petroleum & petroleum prdts)
   Mediterranean Oil Co., 7 Rue Daguerre, Algiers, Algeria

GTE CORP   One Stamford Forum, Stamford, CT 06904, Tel: (203) 965-2000
(Electr prdts, telecom sys, publ & commun)
   GTE Intl., Factory Projects Organization, 2 Rue Isodore Tachet, Algiers, Algeria

INA CORPORATION   1600 Arch St, Philadelphia, PA 19101, Tel: (215) 523-5335
(Holding co: ins, financial serv)
   Compagnie Algerienne des Experts Maritimes et Industriels, 4 Rue Mustapha Bouhired,
      Algiers, Algeria

LE TOURNEAU INC LONGVIEW DIV   PO Box 2307, Longview, TX 75606,
Tel: (214) 753-3449
(Heavy constr, mining mach & equip)

(cont)

Blackwood-Hodge/France S.A., B.P. No.9, Z.I. Ouest-Rue des Freres Lumiere,
91162 Longjumeau Cedex, Paris, France

NCR CORP   1700 S Patterson Blvd, Dayton, OH 45479, Tel: (513) 445-2000
(Develop/mfr/sell/serv business info processing sys)
Caisse Enregistreuse Nationale-Afrique, 10 Blvd. Mohamed Khemisti, B.P. 638,
Algiers, Algeria

NORTON CO   1 New Bond St, Worcester, MA 01606, Tel: (508) 795-5000
(Abrasives, drill bits, constr & safety prdts, plastics)
Norton Co., 1 Boulevard Anatole France, Algiers, Algeria

SGS CONTROL SERVICES INC   42 Broadway, New York, NY 10004,
Tel: (212) 482-8700
(Complete range of quality & quantity control checks & related tech serv)
SGS Control Services Inc., Rue Bouzitoun Allaoua, Annaba, Algeria
SGS Control Services Inc., 6 Rue Ferroukhi Mustapha, B.P. 20, Oran, Algeria
SGS Control Services Inc., 3 Rue Hocine Asla, Skikda, Algeria
Supervise Algerie S.A.R.L., 107 Rue Didouche Mourad, B.P. 242, Alger, Algeria

UNION CARBIDE CORP   Old Ridgebury Rd, Danbury, CT 06817, Tel: (203) 794-2000
(Carbon prdts, chems, plastics, gases & related prdts, etc)
UC North Africa Ltd., 6 Rue Ali Haddad, Algiers, Algeria

WEATHERFORD INTL INC   1360 Post Oak Blvd, PO Box 27608, Houston,
TX 77227-9917, Tel: (713) 439-9400
(Tubular & cementation servs, prdts & equip; water jetting servs, mfr marine pedestal
cranes)
Weatherford Oil Tool GmbH., 63 Boulevard Bougara, El Biar, Algiers, Algeria
Weatherford Oil Tool GmbH., P.O. Box 143, Hassi Messaoud, Algeria

ANGOLA

AIR EXPRESS INTL CORP   120 Tokeneke Rd, PO Box 1231, Darien, CT 06820,
Tel: (203) 655-7900
(Air frt forwarder)
Air Express Intl., c/o Jacto Carga Ltda., Avenida dos Combatentes 42,
P.O. Box 16326, Luanda, Angola

GENERAL TIRE INTL CO   One General St, Akron, OH 44329, Tel: (216) 798-3000
(Mfr tires, rubber & associated prdts)
Manufactura Angolana de Borracha, S.A.R.L., Estrada da Conduta, Km.11,
Caixa Postal 3486, Luanda, R.P. Angola

INA CORPORATION   1600 Arch St, Philadelphia, PA 19101, Tel: (215) 523-5335
(Holding co: ins, financial serv)
Gierth & Monteiro Lda., Caixa Postal 562, Benguela, Angola

JOHNSON & JOHNSON   One Johnson & Johnson Plaza, New Brunswick, NJ 08933,
  Tel: (201) 524-0400
  (Surgical, med & baby prdts)
    Johnson & Johnson (Angola) Ltda., Luanda, Angola

MOBIL CORP   150 E 42nd St, New York, NY 10017, Tel: (212) 883-4242
  (Petroleum explor, prdts)
    Mobil Oil Portuguesa, Caixa Postal 330, Luanda, Angola

NCR CORP   1700 S Patterson Blvd, Dayton, OH 45479, Tel: (513) 445-2000
  (Develop/mfr/sell/serv business info processing sys)
    NCR Angola, Avda. Alvaro Ferreira 7-9, Caixa Postal 2203, Luanda, Angola

PFIZER INC   235 E 42nd St, New York, NY 10017, Tel: (212) 573-2323
  (Mfr pharms, hosp prdts, chems, consumer & animal health prdts)
    Pfizer Central Africa Region, c/o Angola, P.O. Box 18244, Westland, Nairobi, Kenya

TEXACO INC   2000 Westchester Ave, White Plains, NY 10650, Tel: (914) 253-4000
  (Explor/mktg crude oil & its prdts, petro-chems)
    Texaco Petroleos de Angola S.A.R.L., Caixa Postal 5897, Luanda, Angola

ARGENTINA

3M CO   3M Center, St Paul, MN 55144-1000, Tel: (612) 733-1110
  (Mfr abrasives, adhesives, chems, ind & consumer tapes/diskettes, health care prdts,
  elec connectors)
    3M Argentina S.A.I.C., Los Arboles 842, 1686-Hurligham, Buenos Aires, Argentina

ABBOTT LABORATORIES   Abbott Park, North Chicago, IL 60064,
  Tel: (312) 937-6100
  (Pharm & lab prdts)
    Abbott Laboratories Argentina S.R.L., Ruta 2, Km. 34, Florencio Varela, BS AS,
      Buenos Aires, Argentina

AFIA   110 William St, New York, NY 10038, Tel: (212) 964-4990
  (Insurance)
    American Intl. Underwriters en la Argentina S.A., Ave. Pte. Roque Saena, Pena 648,
      Buenos Aires, Argentina
    Great American Insurance Co., Suipacha 268, 2do Piso, Buenos Aires, Argentina
    The Home Insurance Co., Suipacha 268, 2do. Piso, Buenos Aires, Argentina

AIR EXPRESS INTL CORP   120 Tokeneke Rd, PO Box 1231, Darien, CT 06820,
  Tel: (203) 655-7900
  (Air frt forwarder)
    Air Express International, c/o Aero Expreso International Ave. L.N., Alem 882,
      Buenos Aires, Argentina

ALLERGAN PHARMACEUTICALS INTL INC   2525 DuPont Dr, Irvine, CA 92713,
  Tel: (714) 752-4500
  (Pharms, opthalmic & dermatological preparations)
    Allergan S.A.I.C. y F., Esmeralda 923-Dto. "A" 1007 Capital Federal, Buenos Aires,
    Argentina

ALLIED AFTERMARKET DIV   105 Pawtucket Ave, East Providence, RI 02916,
  Tel: (401) 434-7000
  (Mfr spark plugs, waste treatment sys, filters, brakes)
    Fram Argentina S.A.I.C., Cte. Lucena 1090, 1870 Avellaneda, Buenos Aires, Argentina

AMERICAN HOME PRODUCTS CORP   685 Third Ave, New York, NY 10017,
  Tel: (212) 878-5800
  (Drugs, food, household prdts)
    Kolynos S.A.C. e I, Ave. 12 de Octubre 4444 Quilmes, Buenos Aires, Argentina

AMERICAN INTL UNDERWRITERS CORP   70 Pine St, New York, NY 10270,
  Tel: (212) 770-7000
  (General ins)
    Argentina, S.A., Cangallo 648, Piso 4, Buenos Aires, Argentina

AMERICAN LIFE INSURANCE CO (ALICO)   PO Box 2226, Wilmington, DE 19899,
  Tel: (302) 594-2000
  (Life ins, pension & annuity plans, health prdts)
    La Meridional Compania Argentina de Seguros, S.A., Cangallo 646, Piso 4,
    1038 Buenos Aires, Argentina

AMP INC   470 Friendship Rd, Harrisburg, PA 17111, Tel: (717) 564-0100
  (Mfr electrical wiring devices)
    AMP S.A. Argentina, 4 de Febrero, 76, 1651 Villa San Andres, Buenos Aires, Argentina

AMPEX CORP   401 Broadway, Redwood City, CA 94063-3199, Tel: (415) 367-2011
  (Mfr professional audio/visual sys, magnetic recording media, data-memory prdts)
    Electronica Ampex S.A.C.I., Cerrito 836, Buenos Aires, Argentina

ARBOR ACRES FARM INC   41 Marlborough Rd, Glastonbury, CT 06033,
  Tel: (203) 633-4681
  (Producers of male & female broiler breeders, commercial egg layers)
    Arbor Acres Argentina S.A., Corrientes 3262-1193, Buenos Aires, Argentina

ASGROW SEED CO   7000 Portage Rd, Kalamazoo, MI 49001, Tel: (616) 385-6614
  (Growers/breeders agronomic & vegetable seeds)
    Asgrow Seed Co., C.P 1062, Buenos Aires, Argentina

ASSOCIATED METALS & MINERALS CORP   3 N Corporate Park Dr, White Plains,
  NY 10604, Tel: (914) 251-5400
  (Metals & ores)
    Asometa Compania Asociada de Metales y Minerales S.R.L., Lima 187, Buenos Aires,
    1073, Argentina

AVIS INC   900 Old Country Rd, Garden City, NY 11530, Tel: (516) 222-3000
  (Car rental serv)
    Avis Corp., Sheraton Hotel, Galeria Commeriial, Buenos Aires, Argentina
    Avis Corp., Blvd Martim 2451, Mar de Plata, Argentina

AVON PRODUCTS INC   9 W 57th St, New York, NY 10019, Tel: (212) 546-6015
  (Mfr/distr cosmetics, perfumes)
    Cosmeticos Avon S.A.C.I., Santa Rosa 4061, Florida, Buenos Aires 1602, Argentina

AYERST LABORATORIES   145 King of Prussia Rd, Radnor, PA 19087,
  Tel: (215) 688-4400
  (Biologicals & pharms)
    Ayerst Laboratories, Ayacucho 2143, Buenos Aires, Argentina

BAKER OIL TOOLS   PO Box 3048, Houston, TX 77253, Tel: (713) 923-9351
  (Oil/gas well completions equip)
    Baker Transworld Inc., Cerrito 1136, Pisos 12 y 13, 1010 Buenos Aires, Argentina

BANK OF NEW ENGLAND NA   28 State St, Boston, MA 02106, Tel: (617) 742-4000
  (Full service bank)
    Bank of New England NA, Florida 1, Piso 10, Buenos Aires, Argentina

THE BANK OF NEW YORK   48 Wall St, New York, NY 10286, Tel: (212) 530-1784
  (Banking)
    Banco Irving Austral, Tte. Gral Juan D. Peron 300, 1038 Buenos Aires, Argentina

BANKERS TRUST CO   280 Park Ave, New York, NY 10017, Tel: (212) 775-2500
  (Banking)
    B.T. Rio de la Plata, S.A.C.F., San Martin No. 128/142, piso 11, 1004 Buenos Aires,
      Argentina

BARDAHL MFG CORP   1400 N W 52nd St, PO Box 70607, Seattle, WA 98107,
  Tel: (206) 783-4851
  (Lubricating oils)
    Bardahl Lubricantes Argentina S.A.I y.C., Pedro Ignacio Rivera 3454/58,
      Buenos Aires, Argentina

BARNES GROUP INC   123 Main St, Bristol, CT 06010, Tel: (203) 583-7070
  (Mfr maint parts & supplies)
    Barnes Group, Resortes Industriales Argentina, Cordoba, Argentina

BELLSOUTH INTERNATIONAL   1155 Peachtree St NE, #400, Atlanta, GA 30367,
  Tel: (404) 249-4800
  (Mobile commun, telecom network sys)
    Compania de Radiocommunicaciones Moviles S.A. (CRM), Tucuman 744, Piso 8,
      1049 Buenos Aires, Argentina

BENTLEY LABORATORIES INC   17502 Armstrong Ave, Irvine, CA 92714,
  Tel: (714) 546-8020
  (Mfr para-med devices)
    Bentley Sorin Biomedica Argentina S.A., Ave. Santa Fe 1780, Piso 11, of 1103/8,
      1060 Buenos Aires, Argentina

BENTLY NEVADA CORP   PO Box 157, Minden, NV 89423, Tel: (702) 782-3611
  (Electronic monitoring system)
    Lix Klett S.A.I.C., Sarmiento 1236, Buenos Aires, Argentina

BLACK & DECKER CORP   701 E Joppa Road, Towson, MD 21204, Tel: (301) 583-3900
  (Mfr portable elect & pneumatic power tools, household prdts)
    Black & Decker Argentina S.A.C.I., Ave. Francisco Beiro 4689/93, Cap. Federal,
      Buenos Aires, Argentina

BORG-WARNER CORP   200 S Michigan Ave, Chicago, IL 60604', Tel: (312) 322-8500
  (Mfr A/C equip, chem & plastics, ind prdts, trans equip)
     Borg-Warner Ingersoll Agrometal (Argentina) S.A.C.I., Misiones 1830, Monte Maiz,
        Cordoba, Argentina
     Borg-Warner, Byron Jackson (Argentina) S.A.C.I., Chuquisaca 302, 5501 Godoy Cruz,
        Mendoza, Argentina

BOSTON OVERSEAS FINANCIAL CORP   100 Federal St, Boston, MA 02110,
     Tel: (617) 434-3276
     (Ind financial serv)
       Corporacion Financiera de Boston S.A.F.y C., Ave. Roque Saenz Pena 559,
          Buenos Aires, Argentina

BRUNSWICK CORP   One Brunswick Plaza, Skokie, IL 60077, Tel: (708) 470-4700
  (Mfr outboard motors & drives, bowling/fishing equip, valves & pumps)
     Medical Group Argyle & Monoject Divisions, Soldado la Independencia 1 328, Piso 7,
        Departamento B, Buenos Aires, Argentina

BULAB HOLDINGS INC   1256 N McLean Blvd, Memphis, TN 38108,
     Tel: (901) 278-0330
     (Mfr microbicides, biocides, additives, corrosion inhibitors, chems)
       Laboratorios Buckman S.A., Av. San Isidro 4602, Piso 1, 1429 Buenos Aires, Argentina

LEO BURNETT CO INC   35 West Wacker Dr, Chicago, IL 60601, Tel: (312) 220-5959
  (Advertising agency)
     Leo Burnett Co., Inc.-Sucursal Argentina, Carlos Pellegrini 1363,
        1011 Buenos Aires, Argentina

CARL BYOIR & ASSOCIATES INC   380 Madison Ave, New York, NY 10017,
     Tel: (212) 986-6100
     (Public relations consultants)
       Dirpa, Azcuenaga 1074, 1115 Buenos Aires, Agentina

CABOT CORP   950 Winter St, PO Box 9073, Waltham, MA 02254,
     Tel: (617) 890-0200
     (Mfr carbon blacks, plastics; oil & gas, info sys)
       Cabot Argentina S.A.I. y C., Sarmiento 930, 2do Piso, Buenos Aires, Argentina

CAMPBELL SOUP CO   Campbell Place, Camden, NJ 08101, Tel: (609) 342-4800
  (Food prdts)
     Swift-Armour S.A., Leandro N. Alem 986, 1001 Buenos Aires, Argentina

CANADA DRY INTL CORP   2600 Century Pkwy, Atlanta, GA 30345,
     Tel: (404) 753-2182
     (Carbonated beverages, soft drinks extract)
       Canada Dry (Western Hemisphere) Ltda., Ave. Quintana 189, 3er Piso, Buenos Alres,
          Argentina

CARGILL   PO Box 9300, Minneapolis, MN 55440, Tel: (612) 475-7575
  (Food prdts, feeds, animal prdts)
     Cargill, Casilla de Correo 2495, Buenos Aires 1000, Argentina

CARRIER INTERNATIONAL CORP   PO Box 4806, Syracuse, NY 13221,
     Tel: (315) 432-6000
     (A/C, heating, refrig & power equip)
       Carrier Lix Klett S.A., Sarmiento 1236, Pisos 20,.30 y 40, Buenos Aires, Argentina

CBI INDUSTRIES INC   800 Jorie-Blvd, Oak Brook, IL 60521, Tel: (708) 654-7000
  (Holding co: metal plate fabricating, constr, oil & gas drilling)
    CBI Argentina S.A., Salta 1212, 1872 Sarandi, Buenos Aires, Argentina

CENTRAL NATIONAL-GOTTESMAN INC   100 Park Ave, New York, NY 10017,
  Tel: (212) 532-7300
  (Pulp & paper prdts)
    Central National Argentina S.R.L., Bartolome Mitre 734, Piso 8, 1036 Buenos Aires,
    Argentina

CHEMICAL BANK   277 Park Ave, New York, NY 10172, Tel: (212) 310-6161
  (Banking & financial serv)
    Banco Generale de Negocios, S.A., Esmeralda 120, Buenos Aires, Argentina

CHESEBROUGH-POND'S INC   33 Benedict Place, Greenwich, CT 06830,
  Tel: (203) 661-2000
  (Cosmetics, consumer prdts)
    Pond's Argentina, S.A.I.C., Casilla de Correo 2880, 1000 Buenos Aires, Argentina

CHRISTENSEN INTL   PO Box 26135, Salt Lake City, UT 84126, Tel: (801) 487-5371
  (Diamond drills)
    Christensen Roder Argentina, P.O. Box 2488, Correo Central, Florida 835, Piso 3,
    Buenos Aires, Argentina

CIGNA CORP   One Liberty Place, 1650 Market St, Philadelphia, PA 19101,
  Tel: (215) 523-4000
  (Ins, invest, health care & other fin servs)
    Insurance Co. of North America, Suipacha 268- 2 Piso, 1355 Buenos Aires, Argentina

CITIBANK NA   399 Park Ave, New York, NY 10043, Tel: (212) 559-1000
  (Intl banking)
    First National City Bank, Bartolome Mitre 502-546, Buenos Aires, Argentina

COBB INC   Great Road, Littleton, MA 01460, Tel: (617) 486-3535
  (Poultry)
    Cobb's Argentina S.A., Viamonte 1326/30, Buenos Aires, Argentina

THE COCA-COLA CO   310 North Ave NW, PO Box Drawer 1734, Atlanta, GA 30313,
  Tel: (404) 676-2121
  (Mfr & sale of soft drink syrups & concentrates, juices & food prdts, motion pic & TV
  prod)
    Coca-Cola S.A.I.C. y F., Uruguay 1134, Buenos Aires 1016, Argentina

COLGATE-PALMOLIVE CO   300 Park Ave, New York, NY 10022, Tel: (212) 310-2000
  (Pharms, cosmetics, toiletries, detergents)
    Colgate-Palmolive Ltda. S.A.I., Ave. Belgrano 1670, Buenos Aires, Argentina

COLUMBIA PICTURES INDUSTRIES INC   711 Fifth Ave, New York, NY 10022,
  Tel: (212) 751-4400
  (Producer & distributor of motion pictures)
    Fox Films de la Argentina Inc., Lavalle 1876, Buenos Aires, Argentina

COMBUSTION ENGINEERING INC   900 Long Ridge Road, Stamford, CT 06902,
  Tel: (203) 329-8771
  (Tech constr)
    Combustion Engineering Vetco, Florida 577/71, Piso 14, Buenos Aires 1005, Argentina

COMPTON INTERNATIONAL   625 Madison Ave, New York, NY 10022,
   Tel: (212) 754-1100
   (Advertising)
      Blotta & Asociados, Paraguay 786, Buenos Aires 1507, Argentina

CONOCO INC   600 N Dairy Ashford Rd, Houston, TX 77079, Tel: (713) 293-1000
   (Oil, gas, coal, chems, minerals)
      PASA Petroquimica Argentina S.A., Suipacha 1111 Piso 11, Buenos Aires, Argentina

CONTINENTAL BANK NA   231 S Lasalle St, Chicago, IL 60697, Tel: (312) 828-2345
   (Coml banking servs)
      Continental Bank Corp., 25 de Mayo 537, 1002 Buenos Aires, Argentina

CORE LABORATORIES   10205 Westheimer, Houston, TX 77042, Tel: (713) 972-6312
   (Petroleum testing/analysis, analytical chem, environmental servs)
      Core Labaoratories, Estados Unidos 171, 9000 Comodoro Rivadavia, Provincia Chubut,
         Argentina
      Core Laboratories, Suipacha 268, 1355 Buenos Aires, Argentina

CPC INTERNATIONAL INC   PO Box 8000, International Plaza, Englewood Cliffs,
   NJ 07632, Tel: (201) 894-4000
   (Mfr consumer food prdts & corn refining prdts)
      Refinerias de Maiz S.A.I.C.F., Tucuman 117, 1341 Buenos Aires, Argentina

CROCKER BANK INTERNATIONAL   299 Park Ave, New York, NY 10017,
   Tel: (212) 980-5500
   (Intl banking serv)
      CNB-Argentina, Corrientes 311, Piso 3, Buenos Aires, Argentina

CROWN CORK & SEAL CO INC   Holmesburg Station, PO Box 6208, Philadelphia,
   PA 19136, Tel: (215) 698-5100
   (Cans, bottle caps; filling & packaging mach)
      Crown Cork de Argentina S.A.I.C., Laprida 4755, Villa Martell, Buenos Aires,
         Argentina
      Crown Cork de Argentina S.A.I.C., Casilla 3478, Buenos Aires 1000, Argentina

D'ARCY MASIUS BENTON & BOWLES INC (DMB&B)   1675 Broadway, New York,
   NY 10019, Tel: (212) 468-3622
   (Advertising & communications)
      Graffiti/DMB&B, Uruguay 1112, Piso 4, 1016 Buenos Aires, Argentina

DATASCOPE CORP   14 Philips Pkwy, Montvale, NJ 07645, Tel: (201) 391-8100
   (Mfr medical devices)
      InterVascular S.A., Buenos Aires, Argentina

DEERE & CO   John Deere Rd, Moline, IL 61265, Tel: (309) 752-8000
   (Mfr/sale agri/constr/utility/forestry & lawn/grounds care equip)
      Industrias John Deere Argentina S.A., Casilla de Correo 30, 2000 Rosaria, Argentina

DEKALB PLANT GENETICS   3100 Sycamore Rd, DeKalb, IL 60115,
   Tel: (815) 753-7333
   (Mfr/genetic res of hybrid corn, sorghum, sunflowers & soybeans)
      DeKalb Argentina SA, Maipu 1251- 5/F, 1006 Buenos Aires, Argentina

DEKALB-PFIZER GENETICS   3100 Sycamore Rd, De Kalb, IL 60115,
  Tel: (815) 756-7333
  (Agric seeds)
    DeKalb Argentina S.A., Maipu 1252, 5th fl., Buenos Aires 1006, Argentina

DENTSPLY INTL INC   PO Box 872, York, PA 17405, Tel: (717) 845-7511
  (Mfr dental, medical & ind supplies & equip)
    Dentsply Argentina, S.A.C.I., Zabala 3933/35, Buenos Aires, Argentina

DHJ INDUSTRIES INC   1040 Ave of the Americas, New York, NY 10018,
  Tel: (212) 944-4500
  (Mfr of knit fabrics, interlinings plastic chips & denim)
    DHJ de Argentina, S.A.C.I., Brasil 2543, 1260 Buenos Aires, Argentina

DIAMOND SHAMROCK CORP   1100 Superior Ave, Cleveland, OH 44114,
  Tel: (216) 694-5000
  (Organic & inorganic chems & specialties, agric chems)
    Nopco Argentina S.A.I.C. y F., Ave. Roque Saenz Pena 811-70, Buenos Aires, Argentina

DOW CHEMICAL CO   2030 Dow Center, Midland, MI 48640, Tel: (517) 636-1000
  (Chems, plastics, fibers, pharms)
    Indoquim S.A., Ave. L.N. Alem 896, Buenos Aires 1001, Argentina

DOW CORNING CORP   2220 W Salzburg Rd, PO Box 1767, Midland, MI 48640,
  Tel: (517) 496-4000
  (Silicones, silicon chems, solid lubricants)
    Dow Corning de Argentina S.R.L., El Cano 2853, Buenos Aires 1355, Argentina

DRESSER INDUSTRIES INC   1600 Pacific Bldg, PO Box 718, Dallas, TX 75221,
  Tel: (214) 740-6000
  (Diversified supplier of equip & tech serv to energy & natural resource ind)
    Dresser Atlas Argentinas Sampic, Suipacha 268, Buenos Aires 1355, Argentina

E I DU PONT DE NEMOURS & CO   Du Pont Bldg, 1007 Market St, Wilmington,
  DE 19898, Tel: (302) 774-1000
  (Mfr/sale diversified chems, plastics, specialty prdts & fibers)
    Ducilo S.A., E. Madero 1020, Buenos Aires 1106, Argentina

DURACELL INTL INC   Berkshire Industrial Park, Bethel, CT 06801,
  Tel: (203) 796-4000
  (Mfr batteries)
    Duracell Argentina S.A., Avenida Coronel Roca 6757/67, 1439 Buenos Aires, Argentina

EASTMAN KODAK CO   343 State St, Rochester, NY 14650-0518, Tel: (716) 724-4000
  (Devel/mfr photo & chem prdts, info mgmt/video/copier sys, fibers/plastics for
  various ind)
    Kodak Argentina Ltd., Pueyrredon 2989 Martinez, Buenos Aires 1607, Argentina

EATON CORP   100 Erieview Plaza, Cleveland, OH 44114, Tel: (216) 523-5000
  (Advanced tech prdts for transp & ind mkts)
    Eaton I.C.S.A., Avda. Cordoba 679 3rd floor, 1365 Buenos Aires, Argentina

ECHLIN INC   100 Double Beach Rd, Branford, CT 06405, Tel: (203) 481-5751
  (Mfr motor vehicle replacement parts)
    Echlin Argentina S.A., Alianza 931, 1702 Ciudadela, Buenos Aires, Argentina

ECOLAB INC   370 Wabasha St, St Paul, MN 55102, Tel: (612) 293-2233
(Ind & household detergents, cleaning agents & equip)
   Kimsa-Sape S.A.I.C., Diagonal 76, No. 1755, 1615 San Andres, Buenos Aires, Argentina

EXIM OVERSEAS INC   2121 Ponce de Leon Blvd, Coral Gables, FL 33134,
   Tel: (305) 444-6444
(Trading & sales of arms for Armco Latin Div)
   Armco Argentina, Moreno 955- Piso 9, "3" 1090 Buenos Aires, Argentina
   Minarmco SA, Moreno 955- Piso 9, "3" 1091 Buenos Aires, Argentina

EXXON CHEMICAL CO   9 Old Kings Hwy S, Darien, CT 06820, Tel: (203) 655-5200
(Mfr & sales of petrochems)
   Esso Quimica Argentina S.A., Belgrano 1580, Buenos Aires, Argentina

EXXON CORP   225 E John Carpenter Frwy, Irving, TX 75062, Tel: (214) 444-1000
(Petroleum & petroleum prdts)
   Esso S.A., Petrolero Argentina, PJE Della Paolera 297, Buenos Aires 1001, Argentina

FAHNESTOCK & CO   110 Wall St, New York, NY 10005, Tel: (212) 668-8000
(Security brokers, dealers)
   Fahnestock & Co. Argentina, San Martin 551, 1st Floor, Office 1, Buenos Aires,
      Argentina

FEDERAL-MOGUL CORP   PO Box 1966, Detroit, MI 48235, Tel: (313) 354-7700
(Mfr/distr vehicular & ind components for original market & aftermarket)
   In-De-Co H. Minoli S.A.C.I., Casilla de Correo 36,
      1900 La Plata Prov. de Buenos Aires, Argentina

FERRO CORPORATION   One Erieview Plaza, Cleveland, OH 44114,
   Tel: (216) 641-8580
(Chems, coatings, plastics, refractories)
   Ferro Enamel Argentina S.A., Casilla de Correo 2553, Correo Central,
      Buenos Aires 1000, Argentina

FIREMENS INSURANCE CO OF NEWARK   80 Maiden Lane, New York, NY 10038,
   Tel: (212) 440-3000
(Fire, marine & casualty ins)
   American Intl. Underwriters, Ave. Pte. Roque S. Pena 648, Buenos Aires, Argentina

FIRST NATIONAL BANK OF BOSTON   100 Federal St, Boston, MA 02110,
   Tel: (617) 434-2200
(Commercial banking)
   First National Bank of Boston, Florida 99, Buenos Aires, Argentina
   First National Bank of Boston, Buenos Aires 35, 5000 Cordoba, Argentina
   First National Bank of Boston, Necochea 165, 5500 Mendoza, Argentina
   First National Bank of Boston, Ave. Cordoba 1201, 2000 Rosario, Santa Fe, Argentina
   First National Bank of Boston, Avenida General Mitre 570, Avellaneda, Argentina

FLORIDA INTL FORWARDERS   6905 N W 25th St, PO Box 522085, Miami, FL 33122,
   Tel: (305) 592-6450
(Air cargo service)
   Aero Servicos Internacionales, Cerrito 1060 Local 29, Buenos Aires, Argentina
   Hueyo y Travieso, Diagonal Norte No. 729, Piso 7mo. Oficinas AYB, Buenos Aires,
      Argentina
   Prodexpo Internacional, Leandro N. Aleman 884, 1er Piso, Buenos Aires, Argentina

FMC CORP   200 E Randolph Dr, Chicago, IL 60601, Tel: (312) 861-6000
  (Mach & chem for industry, agric & govt)
    FMC Argentina S.A., Avda. Madero 1020, 1106 Buenos Aires, Argentina

FMC MATERIAL HANDLING EQUIP DIV   57 Cooper Ave, Homer City, PA 15748-9234,
  Tel: (412) 479-8011
  (Mfr bulk material handling & automation equip)
    Conveyors S.A., O'Gorman 3637, 1437 Buenos Aires, Argentina

FOOTE CONE & BELDING COMMUNICATIONS INC   101 E Erie St, Chicago,
  IL 60611-2897, Tel: (312) 751-7000
  (Advertising agency)
    Pragma/FCB Publicidad S.A., Demaria 4412, 1425 Buenos Aires, Argentina

FORD MOTOR CO   The American Road, Dearborn, MI 48121, Tel: (313) 322-3000
  (Mfr automobiles, trucks)
    Ford Motor Argentina S.A., Casilla de Correo 696, Correo Central 1000,
      Buenos Aires, Argentina

FOXBORO CO   33 Commercial St, Foxboro, MA 02035, Tel: (508) 543-8750
  (Mfr prdts/provide servs for ind automation)
    Foxboro-Argentina S.A., Casilla de Correo 4773, Correo Central,
      Ave. Pres. R. Saenz 570, 1035 Buenos Aires, Argentina

GAMLEN CHEMICAL CO   121 S Maple Ave, S San Francisco, CA 94080,
  Tel: (415) 873-1750
  (Chems, detergents & tank cleansers)
    Contact Gamlen Div. of Tanatex Argentina S.A.C.y I., Bahia Blanca, Buenos Aires,
      Argentina
    Contact Gamlen Div. of Tanatex Argentina S.A., Lavalle 1430, Piso 2,
      Buenos Aires 1048, Argentina
    Contact Gamlen Div. of Tanatex Argentina S.A., Rosario, Argentina

GENERAL TIRE INTL CO   One General St, Akron, OH 44329, Tel: (216) 798-3000
  (Mfr tires, rubber & associated prdts)
    FATE S.A.I.C.I., Ave. Alte Blanco, Encalada 3003, 1644 Victoria,
      Pcia de Buenos Aires, Argentina

THE GILLETTE CO   Prudential Tower, Boston, MA 02199, Tel: (617) 421-7000
  (Mfr/distr shaving prdts, toiletries & cosmetics, stationery prdts)
    Compania Gillette de Argentina, Casilla de Correo No. 694, Correo Central,
      Buenos Aires 1000, Argentina

GOODYEAR TIRE & RUBBER CO   1144 E Market St, Akron, OH 44316-0001,
  Tel: (216) 796-2121
  (Mfr tires, rubber prdts)
    Neumaticos Goodyear S.A., Lavalle 341 Buenos Aires 1107, Argentina

GOULD INC   10 Gould Center, Rolling Meadows, IL 60008, Tel: (708) 640-4000
  (Electric sys, batteries, etc)
    Electric Company S.A. Gould, Buenos Aires, Argentina

W R GRACE & CO   1114 Ave of the Americas, New York, NY 10036,
  Tel: (212) 819-5500
  (Specialty chems, natural resources, consumer serv)
    Darex, S.A.I.C., Primera Junta 550, Quilmes, Buenos Aires 1878, Argentina

GREY ADVERTISING INC   777 Third Ave, New York, NY 10017, Tel: (212) 546-2000
  (Advertising)
    Casares, Grey y Asociados S.R.L., Cangallo 925, Buenos Aires 1038, Argentina

GROLIER INC   Old Shereman Tpk, Danbury, CT 06816, Tel: (203) 797-3500
  (Publishers)
    W.M. Jackson Inc., Casilla de Correo 3595, Buenos Aires 1000, Argentina

GTE CORP   One Stamford Forum, Stamford, CT 06904, Tel: (203) 965-2000
  (Electr prdts, telecom sys, publ & commun)
    GTE Sylvania Argentina S.A., Cuyo 3066, Martinez, Pdo. San Isidro,
      Prov. Buenos Aires, Argentina

FRANK B HALL & CO INC   549 Pleasantville Rd, Briarcliff Manor, NY 10510,
  Tel: (914) 769-9200
  (Insurance)
    O'Grady S.A., San Martin 439, 10th fl., 1359 Buenos Aires, Argentina

HARCOURT BRACE JOVANOVICH INC   Harcourt Brace Jovanovich Bldg, Orlando,
  FL 32887, Tel: (305) 345-2000
  (Book publ, tests & related serv, journals, facisimile reprints, mgmt consult,
  operates parks/shows)
    Drake Beam Morin Argentina S.A., Viamonte 494, 1053 Buenos Aires, Argentina

THE HARPER GROUP INC   260 Townsend St, PO Box 77933, San Francisco,
  CA 94107, Tel: (415) 978-0600
  (Ocean/air freight fwdg, customs brokerage, packing & whse, logistics mgt, ins)
    Circle Freight Intl. Argentina SA, Avenida Julio A. Roca 672- Piso 3, Buenos Aires,
      Argentina

HELENE CURTIS INDUSTRIES INC   4401 W North Ave, Chicago, IL 60639,
  Tel: (312) 292-2121
  (Cosmetics, toiletries, hair preparations)
    Helene Curtis Argentina S.A.I. y C., Pringles 1089, Buenos Aires, Argentina

HEWLETT-PACKARD CO   3000 Hanover St, PO Box 10301, Palo Alto, CA 94303-0890,
  Tel: (415) 857-1501
  (Mfr measurement & computation prdts & sys)
    Hewlett-Packard Argentina S.A., Montaneses 2140, 1428 Buenos Aires, Argentina

A J HOLLANDER & CO INC   257 Park Ave So, New York, NY 10010,
  Tel: (212) 353-8000
  (Hides, skins & leather)
    A.J. Hollander y Asociados S.A., Hipolito Yrigoyen 1628, Buenos Aires, Argentina

HORWATH & HORWATH INTL   919 Third Ave, New York, NY 10022,
  Tel: (212) 980-3100
  (Public accountants & auditors)
    Canepa, Pestarino, Mazer y Asociados, Buenos Aires, Argentina
    Horwarth & Horwarth Intl. Associates, Cerrito 146, Buenos Aires 1010, Argentina

HOWE-BAKER ENGINEERS INC   PO Box 956, Tyler, TX 75710, Tel: (214) 597-0311
  (Design, fabricate, erect process sys for petroleum ind)
    Howe-Baker Argentina, Tucuman 435, 1049 Buenos Aires, Argentina

HUGHES TOOL CO   PO Box 2539, Houston, TX 77001, Tel: (713) 924-2222
  (Equip & serv to oil & gas explor & prod ind)
    Hughes Services Argentina, Esmeralda 130, Buenos Aires, Argentina

IMCO SERVICES   5950 N Course Dr, Houston, TX 70072, Tel: (713) 561-1300
  (Drilling fluids)
    Imco Services, Halliburton Argentina, S.A., Avda. Leandro N. Alen 466,
      1003 Buenos Aires, Argentina

INA CORPORATION   1600 Arch St, Philadelphia, PA 19101, Tel: (215) 523-5335
  (Holding co: ins, financial serv)
    INA Sudamericana S.A., Belgrano 321-Piso 2, 1642 San Isidro, Buenos Aires, Argentina

INSTRON CORP   100 Royall St, Canton, MA 02021, Tel: (617) 828-2500
  (Testing instru)
    Instron Ltda., Avda. Callao 555, 50B., Buenos Aires 1022, Argentina

INTERNATIONAL BUSINESS MACHINES (IBM)   Old Orchard Rd, Armonk,
  NY 10504-1783, Tel: (914) 765-1900
  (Info-handling sys, equip & serv)
    IBM Argentina S.A., Pje de las Catalinas 275, Argentina

INTERNATIONAL FLAVORS & FRAGRANCES INC   521 W 57th St, New York, NY 10019,
  Tel: (212) 765-5500
  (Create/mfr flavors, fragrances & aroma chems)
    Intl. Flavors & Fragrances S.A.C. y I., Berutti 1341, Martinez, Buenos Aires 1640,
      Argentina

INTERNATIONAL STANDARD ELECTRIC CORP   320 Park Ave, New York, NY 10022,
  Tel: (212) 752-6000
  (Telecommun equip)
    Cia. Standard Electric Argentina S.A.I. y C., San Martin 323, Piso 19,
      1004 Buenos Aires, Argentina

IRVING TRUST CO   1 Wall St, New York, NY 10015, Tel: (212) 487-2121
  (Intl banking)
    Irving Trust Co. Argentina, Corrientes 311, Buenos Aires, Argentina

ITT SHERATON CORP   60 State St, Boston, MA 02108, Tel: (617) 367-3600
  (Hotel operations)
    Buenos Aires Sheraton Hotel, San Martin 1225 at Plaza Fuerza Aerea,
      1104 Buenos Aires, Argentina

JOHN HANCOCK MUTUAL LIFE INSURANCE CO   200 Clarendon St, PO Box 111, Boston,
  MA 02117, Tel: (617) 572-6000
  (Life ins)
    Sud America Cia. de Seguros de Vida S.A., Ave., RS Pena 530, Buenos Aires, Argentina

JOHNSON & HIGGINS   125 Broad St, New York, NY 10005, Tel: (212) 574-7000
  (Ins brokerage, benefit conslt)
    Johnson & Higgins S.A., Cangallo 560, 4to Piso, Buenos Aires 1038, Argentina

JOHNSON & JOHNSON   One Johnson & Johnson Plaza, New Brunswick, NJ 08933,
  Tel: (201) 524-0400
  (Surgical, med & baby prdts)
    Cilag Farmaceutica SA, Buenos Aires, Argentina
    Janssen Farmaceutica SA, Buenos Aires, Argentina

(cont)

Johnson & Sons de Argentina S.A.C. e I., Ave. Marquez KM. 16, Pablo Podesta,
    Buenos Aires 1657, Argentina

S C JOHNSON & SON INC   1525 Howe St, Racine, WI 53403, Tel: (414) 631-2000
    (Home, auto, commercial & personal care prdts, specialty chems)
       S.C. Johnson & Son de Argentina, Casilla de Correo 4747, Correo Central,
       Buenos Aires, Argentina

JOHNSON CONTROLS INC   5757 W Green Bay Ave, PO Box 591, Milwaukee, WI 53201,
    Tel: (414) 228-1200
    (Mfr facility mgmt & control sys, auto seating, batteries & plastics)
       Penn Controls Argentina S.A.I.C., General Roca 3559, 1602 Florida, Buenos Aires,
       Argentina

KELLOGG CO   235 Porter St, Battle Creek, MI 49016, Tel: (616) 966-2000
    (Food prdts)
       Kelloggs Co. Argentina, Buenos Aires, Argentina

THE M W KELLOGG CO   3 Greenway Plaza, Houston, TX 77046-0395,
    Tel: (713) 960-2000
    (Design, engr, procurement & constr for process & energy ind)
       Kellog Pan American Corp., Ave. Cordoba 1367, Piso 10, Buenos Aires 1372, Argentina

KEPNER-TREGOE INC   Research Rd, PO Box 704, Princeton, NJ 08542,
    Tel: (609) 921-2806
    (Mgmt & organizational devel)
       Kepner-Tregoe S.A. de SYM, Ave. Rogue Saenz PE # A720, 1035 Buenos Aires, Argentina

KEYES FIBRE CO   3003 Summer St, Stamford, CT 06905, Tel: (203) 357-9100
    (Molded containers)
       Celulosa Moldeada S.A., Casilla de Correo 152, Santa Fe, Argentina

KNOLL INTL   655 Madison Ave, New York, NY 10021, Tel: (212) 826-2400
    (Furniture & fabrics)
       Interieur Forma S.A., Paraguay 541-545-555, Buenos Aires, Argentina

KORN/FERRY INTL   237 Park Ave, New York, NY 10017, Tel: (212) 687-1834
    (Executive search)
       Korn/Ferry Intl., Avda. Quintana 585, Piso 6, Buenos Aires, Argentina

LANMAN & KEMP-BARCLAY & CO INC   25 Woodland Ave, Westwood, NJ 07675,
    Tel: (201) 666-4990
    (Mfr pharms, toiletries)
       Lanman & Kemp-Barclay & Co. de la Argentina, Cordoba 3600, Buenos Aires, Argentina

ELI LILLY & CO   307 E McCarty St, Indianapolis, IN 46285, Tel: (317) 261-2000
    (Pharms, agric & cosmetic prdts)
       Eli Lilly Argentina S.A., Huipacha 664, 5th Floor, Buenos Aires 1008, Argentina
       Eli Lilly Argentina S.A., Casilla de Correo 1355, Correo Central, Argentina

LINTAS:WORLDWIDE   1 Dag Hammarskjold Plaza, New York, NY 10017,
    Tel: (212) 605-8000
    (Advertising agency)
       Colonnese:Lintas, Av. de Mayo 666, 1084 Buenos Aires, Argentina

LIQUID CARBONIC CORP   135 S LaSalle St, Chicago, IL 60603,
  Tel: (312) 855-2500
  (Compressed gases, etc)
    Liquid Carbonic Argentina S.A.I.C., Ave. Leandro N. Alen 1110, Buenos Aires 1076,
    Argentina

LONE STAR INDUSTRIES INC   One Greenwich Plaza, Greenwich, CT 06830,
  Tel: (203) 661-3100
  (Cement & bldg materials)
    Cia. Argentina de Cemento Portland S.A., Calle Defensa 113, 9no. Piso,
    Buenos Aires 1065, Argentina

MANPOWER INC   5301 N Ironwood Rd, PO Box 2053, Milwaukee, WI 53201-2053,
  Tel: (414) 961-1000
  (Temporary help)
    Cotecsud S.A.S.E., Ave. Maipu 942, P.B. Capital Federal, 1340, Buenos Aires,
    Argentina

MANUFACTURERS HANOVER TRUST CO   270 Park Ave, New York, NY 10017,
  Tel: (212) 286-6000
  (Banking)
    Manufacturers Hanover Trust Co., Aveinda Leandro N. Alem. 1110, Buenos Aires,
    Argentina
    Manufacturers Hanover Trust Co., Corrientes 311, Buenos Aires, Argentina

MANVILLE CORP   PO Box 5108, Denver, CO 80217-5108, Tel: (303) 978-2000
  (Mfr fiber glass prdts, paper & forest prdts, roofing & insulation material, ind
  minerals)
    Johns-Manville Sudamerica Ltda., Cangalo 949, Piso 13, Buenos Aires, Argentina
    Refil, S.A., Buenos Aires, Argentina

MAREMONT CORP   250 E Kehoe Blvd, Carol Stream, IL 60188, Tel: (312) 861-4000
  (Mfr automotive parts: mufflers, exhaust pipes, shock absorbers)
    Fric Rot Gabriel, Santa Fe 3544, Rosario, Sta. Fe, Buenos Aires, Argentina
    Fric Rot, S.A.I.C., Mitre 575, 2000 Rosario Santa Fe, Argentina

MARY KAY COSMETICS INC   8787 Stemmons Fwy, Dallas, TX 75247,
  Tel: (214) 630-8787
  (Cosmetics & toiletries)
    Mary Kay Cosmetics Argentina S.A., Florida 633, Piso 3, Buenos Aires, Argentina

MCI INTERNATIONAL   2 International Dr, Rye Brook, NY 10573,
  Tel: (914) 937-3444
  (Intl telecom servs)
    MCI Intl. (Argentina) SA, Viamonte 837- 2 Piso, 1053 Buenos Aires, Argentina

MEASUREX CORP   One Results Way, Cupertino, CA 95014, Tel: (408) 255-1500
  (Mfr computer integrated mfg sys)
    Measurex Intl. Corp./Aeas Aceros Especiales SA, Sarmiento 767, 1041 Buenos Aires,
    Argentina

MEDTRONIC INC   7000 Central Ave, NE, Minneapolis, MN 55432,
  Tel: (612) 574-4000
  (Mfr med devices, med serv)
    Medtronic S.A.I.C., Montaneses 2140/50, 1428 Capital Federal, Buenos Aires,
    Argentina

MELLON BANK NA   One Mellon Bank Center, Pittsburgh, PA 15258,
   Tel: (412) 234-5016
   (Commercial & trade banking, foreign exchange)
      Mellon Bank NA Argentina, Avda. Corrientes 311, 1043 Buenos Aires, Argentina

MERCK SHARP & DOHME INTL   PO Box 2000, Rahway, NJ 07065, Tel: (201) 574-4000
   (Pharms, chems & biologicals)
      Merck Sharp & Dohme (Argentina) S.A.I. y C., Ave. Libertador 1406/1410,
         Vicente Lopez, Buenos Aires, Argentina

MERGENTHALER LINOTYPE CO   201 Old Country Rd, Melville, NY 11747,
   Tel: (516) 673-4197
   (Photocomposition machs, sys & equip)
      Grafex, S.A., Casilla Correo 482, Buenos Aires 1000, Argentina

MERRILL LYNCH PIERCE FENNER & SMITH   World Financial Center, 225 Liberty St,
   New York, NY 10080, Tel: (212) 449-1000
   (Brokers, securities, commodities)
      Merrill Lynch & Co., Banco Do Brazil Bldg., San Martin 323-Piso 13,
         1004 Buenos Aires, Argentina

MONROE AUTO EQUIPMENT CO   International Dr, Monroe, MI 48161,
   Tel: (313) 243-8000
   (Automotive ride control equip)
      Monroe Argentina S.A.I.C. y F., P.O. Box NR017, 1655 Jose Leon Suarez,
         Prov. de Buenos Aires, Argentina

MONSANTO CO   800 N Lindbergh Blvd, St Louis, MO 63167, Tel: (314) 694-1000
   (Mfr chem & agric prdts, pharms, ind process equip, man-made fibers, plastics)
      Monsanto Argentina S.A.I.C., Avda. E. Madero 1020, Buenos Aires 1106, Argentina

MORGAN GUARANTY TRUST CO   23 Wall St, New York, NY 10015, Tel: (212) 483-2323
   (Banking)
      Morgan Guaranty Trust Co. Argentina, 25 de Mayo 182, Buenos Aires 1002, Argentina

MTS SYSTEMS CORP   PO Box 24012, Minneapolis, MN 55424, Tel: (612) 937-4000
   (Electrohydraulic testing & prod equip, mach controls)
      Aro S.A., Casilla de Correos 4890, Correo Central, 1092 Buenos Aires, Argentina

McCANN-ERICKSON WORLDWIDE   750 Third Ave, New York, NY 10017,
   Tel: (212) 697-6000
   (Advertising)
      McCann-Erickson, Reconquista 609, 1003 Buenos Aires, Argentina

NABISCO BRANDS INC   Nabisco Brands Plaza, East Hanover, NJ 07936,
   Tel: (201) 503-2000
   (Mfr food prdts)
      Nabisco Brands S.A., Casilla de Correo 16, 1605 Munro, Buenos Aires, Argentina

NALCO CHEMICAL CO   One Nalco Center, Naperville, IL 60566-1024,
   Tel: (708) 305-1000
   (Chems for water & waste water treatment, oil prod & refining, ind processes;
   water/energy mgmt serv)
      Nalquimica S.A., Casilla de Correo 2096, 1001 Buenos Aires, Argentina

NASHUA CORP   44 Franklin St, Nashua, NH 03061, Tel: (603) 880-2323
  (Mfr/distr/serv office copier sys & supplies)
    Nashua Argentina Inc., 11 de Septiembre 2226, 1428 Belgrano, Buenos Aires, Argentina

NCR CORP   1700 S Patterson Blvd, Dayton, OH 45479, Tel: (513) 445-2000
  (Develop/mfr/sell/serv business info processing sys)
    NCR Argentina S.A.I.C., Corrientes 1615, Casilla de Correo 2395, Buenos Aires 1000,
    Argentina

A C NIELSEN CO   Nielsen Plaza, Northbrook, IL 60062, Tel: (708) 498-6300
  (Marketing research)
    A.C. Nielsen Argentina S.A., Riva Davia 620, 1002 Buenos Aires, Argentina

NL INDUSTRIES INC   3000 N Sam Houston Pkwy E, Houston, TX 77205,
  Tel: (713) 987-4000
  (Metal prdts, chems, petroleum serv)
    National Lead Co. S.A., Ave. RS Pena 567, Buenos Aires, Argentina

NORTON CO   1 New Bond St, Worcester, MA 01606, Tel: (508) 795-5000
  (Abrasives, drill bits, constr & safety prdts, plastics)
    Abrasivos Norton S.A., Los Patos 2175, Buenos Aires 1283, Argentina

OAKITE PRODUCTS INC   50 Valley Rd, Berkeley Heights, NJ 07922,
  Tel: (201) 464-6900
  (Mfr chem prdts for ind cleaning & metal treating)
    Oakite Argentina S.A., Casilla de Correo 30, 1824 Lanus, Buenos Aires, Argentina

OGILVY & MATHER INC   2 E 48th St, New York, NY 10017, Tel: (212) 907-3400
  (Advertising agency)
    Ortiz, Scopesi y Cia., S.A., Cerrito 264, Piso 5, Buenos Aires 1010, Argentina

ONAN CORP   1400 73rd Ave NE, Minneapolis, MN 55432, Tel: (612) 574-5000
  (Electric generators, ind engines & controls)
    Bimac S.A., Maza 1122, Buenos Aires, Argentina

OTIS ELEVATOR CO   10 Farm Springs, Farmington, CT 06032, Tel: (203) 674-4047
  (Elevators & escalators)
    Ascensores Otis SAICIF, Uruguay y Ruta Panamerica, San Fernando, Buenos Aires 1644,
    Argentina
    Ascensores Otis SAICIF, Ave. Ing. Huergo 1039, Buenos Aires 1107, Argentina

PARAMOUNT INTL FILMS INC   1 Gulf & Western Plaza, New York, NY 10023,
  Tel: (212) 333-4600
  (Film prod & distr)
    Cinema Intl. Corp., S.R.L., Ayacucho 518-20, Buenos Aires 1026, Argentina

PARKER HANNIFIN CORP   17325 Euclid Ave, Cleveland, OH 44112,
  Tel: (216) 531-3000
  (Mfr motion-control prdts)
    Parker Hannifin Argentina S.A.I.C., Avda. Pte. Arturo U Illia 2064, Villa Maipu,
    1650 San Martin, Buenos Aires, Argentina

PARKER PEN CO   One Parker Place, Janesville, WI 53545, Tel: (608) 755-7000
  (Writing instru, temporary help, leisure apparel & equip)
    Parker Pen Argentina, S.A.I.C., Buenos Aires, Argentina

PEAVEY CO/CONAGRA TRADING COS   730 Second Ave, Minneapolis, MN 55402,
   Tel: (612) 370-7500
   (Flour, feeds, seeds)
      Conagra S.A., Buenos Aires, Argentina

PEPSICO INC   700 Anderson Hill Rd, Purchase, NY 10577, Tel: (914) 253-2000
   (Beverages, food prdts & servs, sporting goods)
      Pepsi-Cola Argentina S.A.C.I., Maipu 942, 14th Floor, Casilla Correo 3098, Correo,
      Central, 1340 Buenos Aires, Argentina

PFIZER INC   235 E 42nd St, New York, NY 10017, Tel: (212) 573-2323
   (Mfr pharms, hosp prdts, chems, consumer & animal health prdts)
      Pfizer S.A.C.I., Minones 2177, Casilla de Correo 3696, Buenos Aires 1000, Argentina

PIONEER HI-BRED INTL INC   700 Capital Sq, 400 Locust St, Des Moines,
   IA 50309, Tel: (515) 245-3500
   (Seed corn, feed seed, data sys & equip)
      Pioneer Argentina, S.A., Buenos Aires, Argentina

PRECISION VALVE CORP   PO Box 309, Yonkers, NY 10702, Tel: (914) 969-6500
   (Mfr aerosol valves)
      Valvulas Precision de Argentina S.A.C.I., Fondo de la Legua 936, 1640 Martinez,
      Buenos Aires, Argentina

PREMARK INTL INC   1717 Deerfield Rd, Deerfield, IL 60015, Tel: (708) 405-6000
   (Mfr/sale diversified consumer & coml prdts)
      Dart Argentina S.A., Av. del Libertador 498, 1001 Buenos Aires, Argentina
      Tupperware S.A., Av. del Libertador 498, 1001 Buenos Aires, Argentina

PUROLATOR PRODUCTS CO   2 Warren Pl, 6120 S Yale, Tulsa, OK 74136,
   Tel: (918) 492-1800
   (Mfr vehicle filters & related prdts)
      Purolator Argentina S.A.I. y C., Ave. Coronel Roca 1710-12, Burnos Aires 1437,
      Argentina

RCA GLOBAL COMMUNICATIONS INC   60 Broad St, New York, NY 10004,
   Tel: (212) 806-7000
   (Commun serv)
      RCA Ltd., Tutuman 425-2C, Buenos Aires, Argentina

READING & BATES CORP   2200 Mid-Continent Tower, Tulsa, OK 74103,
   Tel: (918) 583-8521
   (Oil & gas explor & prod, offshore contract drilling, water mgmt sys)
      Reading & Bates Drilling Co., 25 de Mayo 516, Buenos Aires, Argentina

REVLON INC   767 Fifth Ave, New York, NY 10153-0033, Tel: (212) 572-5000
   (Cosmetics, health care prdts)
      Revlon de Argentina S.A., Chiclana 3311, Buenos Aires, Argentina

ROHM & HAAS CO   Independence Mall West, Philadelphia, PA 19105,
   Tel: (215) 592-3000
   (Mfr ind & agric chems, plastics)
      Rohm & Haas Latin America Inc., Montevideo 373, Piso 1, 1019 Buenos Aires, Argentina

ROLLINS BURDICK HUNTER CO   123 N Wacker Dr, Chicago, IL 60606,
   Tel: (312) 701-4000
   (Ins brokers)
     Roilbec S.A., Cangallo 315, Piso 1, Buenos Aires, Argentina

R P SCHERER CORP   2075 W Big Beaver Rd, Troy, MI 48084, Tel: (313) 649-0900
   (Mfr soft gelatin & two-piece hard shell capsules)
     R.P. Scherer Argentina S.A.I.C., Avda. Marquez 691, Villa Loma Hermosa 1657,
       Pdo. 3 de Febrero, Buenos Aires, Argentina

SCHERING INTL   PO Box 500, Kenilworth, NJ 07033, Tel: (201) 558-4000
   (Pharms, medicines, toiletries, cosmetics, human & animal health prdts)
     Plough Essex Argentina S.A.I.C., Maipu 1300, Buenos Aires 1006, Argentina

G D SEARLE & CO   PO Box 1045, Skokie, IL 60076, Tel: (708) 982-7000
   (Pharms, health care & optical prdts, specialty chems)
     G. D. Searle Argentina S.A.C.I., Casilla de Correo 3893, Correo Central,
       Buenos Aires, Argentina
     G.D. Searle Argentina S.A.C.I., Lavalle 2107, Buenos Aires, Argentina

SELAS CORP OF AMERICA   Dreshertown Rd & Limekiln Pike, Dresher, PA 19025,
   Tel: (215) 646-6600
   (Mfr heat treating equip for metal, glass, ceramic & chem inds)
     Selas Corp. of America, Prodiseno S.A.I.C. Moreno 794-1 Piso, Buenos Aires,
       Argentina

SEVEN-UP INTL   120 Park Ave, New York, NY 10017, Tel: (212) 880-4100
   (Soft drinks)
     Seven-Up Argentina S.A., Isabel la Catolica 1644, Buenos Aires, Argentina

SGS CONTROL SERVICES INC   42 Broadway, New York, NY 10004,
   Tel: (212) 482-8700
   (Complete range of quality & quantity control checks & related tech serv)
     Supermar S.A., Cerrito 1136/40 5th Floor, C.P. 4290, Buenos Aires 1010, Argentina
     Supermar S.A., Rosario-Prov. de Santa Fe, Argentina

SHULTON INC   1 Cyanamid Plaza, Wayne, NJ 07470, Tel: (201) 831-2000
   (Health, beauty & grooming prdts)
     Shulton, Lta., J.E. Uriburu 754-40 Piso, Buenos Aires 1027, Argentina

SONOCO PRODUCTS CO   North Second St, PO Box 160, Hartsville, SC 29550,
   Tel: (803) 383-7000
   (Mfr packaging for consumer & ind mkt)
     Sonoco Argentina S.A., Calle Ferre 3260-70, Villa Soldati, Pompeya, Buenos Aires,
       Argentina

ST JOE MINERALS CORP   250 Park Ave, New York, NY 10017, Tel: (212) 953-5000
   (Coal, oil, gas, iron ore, metals & minerals)
     Cla. Minera Agullar S.A., Viamonte 1133 y R. 36 Polegrini 1069, Piso 12,
       Buenos Aires 1009, Argentina

STEINER CORP   PO Box 2317, 505 E South Temple St, Salt Lake City, UT 84102,
   Tel: (801) 328-8831
   (Linen supply service)
     ALSCO, Carlos Maria Alvear 1429, Buenos Aires, Argentina

STERLING DRUG INC   90 Park Ave, New York, NY 10016, Tel: (212) 907-2000
   (Pharms, chems, cosmetics, household cleaners & waxes)
      Cia. Argentina Sydney Ross S.A., Canning 3333, Buenos Aires, Argentina
      Farmasa-Farmaceutica Argentina S.A., Ave. de Libertador 6796, Buenos Aires 1429,
      Argentina

STOKES DIV   5500 Tabor Rd, Philadelphia, PA 19120, Tel: (215) 289-5671
   (Vacuum pumps & components, vacuum dryers, oil-upgrading equip)
      Pennwalt S.A.I.C.y F., Avda. Eduardo Madero 1020, 1106 Buenos Aires, Argentina

SULLAIR CORP   3700 E Michigan Blvd, Michigan City, IN 46360,
   Tel: (219) 879-5451
   (Refrigeration sys, vacuum pumps, generators, etc)
      Sullair Argentina S.A., Avenida Rivadavia 324, 1822 Valentin Alsina, Buenos Aires,
      Argentina

SYBRON CORP   411 E Wisconsin Ave, Milwaukee, WI 07662, Tel: (414) 274-6600
   (Professional health prdts, spec chems, instru, water & waste water treatment sys)
      Taylor Instrumentos S.A., Buenos Aires, Argentina

TAYLOR INSTRUMENT CO   99 Ames St, PO Box 110, Rochester, NY 14601,
   Tel: (716) 235-6806
   (Instru for process control inds)
      Taylor Instrumentos S.A., San Martin 390-Piso 13, 1004 Capital Federal,
      Buenos Aires, Argentina

TED BATES WORLDWIDE INC   1515 Broadway, New York, NY 10036,
   Tel: (212) 869-3131
   (Advertising agency)
      Cicero-Ted Bates Publicidad S.A., Paraguay 610, Piso 23, Buenos Aires, Argentina

TEXAS INSTRUMENTS INC   PO Box 655474, Dallas, TX 75265, Tel: (214) 995-2011
   (Mfr semiconductor devices, electr/electro-mech sys, instr & controls)
      Texas Instruments Argentina S.A.I.C.F., Ruta Panamericana Km 25.500, Don Torcuato,
      Buenos Aires, Argentina

TRANE CO   3600 Pammel Creek Rd, La Crosse, WI 54601, Tel: (608) 787-2000
   (Mfr A/C equip)
      Trane, Corrientes 1642 Of. 28, 1042 Buenos Aires, Argentina

TRANS WORLD AIRLINES INC   605 Third Ave, New York, NY 10158,
   Tel: (212) 557-6107
   (Air transp, hotel, food serv, real estate)
      Trans World Airlines, Cordoba 669, Piso 3, Buenos Aires, Argentina

TRANTER INC   1054 Claussen Rd, Augusta, GA 30907, Tel: (404) 738-7900
   (Mfr heat exchangers)
      Florcalde S.A., Sede Central y Planta, Lincoln 580-1875 Wilde, Buenos Aires,
      Argentina

UNION CARBIDE CORP   Old Ridgebury Rd, Danbury, CT 06817, Tel: (203) 794-2000
   (Carbon prdts, chems, plastics, gases & related prdts, etc)
      Union Carbide Argentina S.A.I. y C., Virrey Loreto 2481, Buenos Aires 1426,
      Argentina

UNIROYAL INC   World Headquarters, Middlebury, CT 06749, Tel: (203) 573-2000
(Tires, tubes & other rubber prdts, chems, plastics, textiles)
   Uniroyal Quimica S.A.I.C., Ave. Ing. Huergo 1439, Buenos Aires, Argentina
   Uniroyal S.A.C.I., 25 de Mayo 444, Buenos Aires, Argentina

UNISYS CORP   PO Box 500, Blue Bell, PA 19424, Tel: (215) 542-4011
(Mfg/mktg/serv electr info sys)
   Unisys S.A., Marcelo T. Dealucar 1422, 1060 Buenos Aires, Argentina

UNITED PRESS INTL   220 E 42nd St, New York, NY 10017, Tel: (212) 682-0400
(Collection & distributor of news, newspictures, fin data)
   UPI Inc., Avenida Belgrano 271, 1092 Buenos Aires, Argentina

UNITED TECHNOLOGIES CORP   United Technologies Bldg, Hartford, CT 06101,
Tel: (203) 728-7000
(Mfr aircraft engines, elevators, A/C, auto equip, space & military electr, rocket
propulsion sys)
   Ascensores Otis S.A., Ave. Ing. Huergo 1039, 1107 Buenos Aires, Argentina

UOP INC   Ten UOP Plaza, Des Plaines, IL 60016, Tel: (708) 391-2000
(Diversified research, development & mfr of ind prdts & sys mgmt studies & serv)
   UOP Inc., Canos Filtros, Johnsoh S.A., Buenos Aires, Argentina

UPJOHN CO   7000 Portage Rd, Kalamazoo, MI 49001, Tel: (616) 323-4000
(Pharms, agric prdts, ind chems)
   Laboratorios Upjohn Anodia S.A.I.C., Ruta NAC, Km 35, Florencio Varela,
      Buenos Aires 1888, Argentina

VELSICOL CHEMICAL CORP   5600 N River Rd, Rosemont, IL 60018,
Tel: (708) 698-9700
(Pesticides & ind chems)
   Velsicol Argentina S.R.L., Rodriguez Pena 243, 1020 Buenos Aires, Argentina

WACKENHUT CORP   1500 San Remo Ave, Coral Gables, FL 33146,
Tel: (305) 666-5656
(Security sys & serv)
   Search Organization de Seguridad S.A., Tronator 543, Buenos Aires 1427, Argentina

WARNER BROS INC   4000 Warner Blvd, Burbank, CA 91522, Tel: (213) 954-6000
(Prod/dist motion picture films, TV, music recording & pub)
   Warner Bros. (South) Inc., Tucuman 1938, Buenos Aires, Argentina

WEATHERFORD INTL INC   1360 Post Oak Blvd, PO Box 27608, Houston,
TX 77227-9917, Tel: (713) 439-9400
(Tubular & cementation servs, prdts & equip; water jetting servs, mfr marine pedestal
cranes)
   Weatherford Intl., c/o Petro-BACHm S.A., Florida 537, Local 494, Buenos Aires 1005,
      Argentina

WEST CHEMICAL PRODUCTS INC   1000 Herrontown Rd, Princeton, NJ 08540,
Tel: (609) 921-0501
(Sanitary equip & supplies)
   West Chemical Products Argentina S.A., Belgrano 407, Piso 4, Buenos Aires 1092,
      Argentina

WEST CO INC   West Bridge St, Phoenixville, PA 19460, Tel: (215) 935-4500
(Pharm packaging comps)
    West Argentina S.A.C.E.L., Avda. Ader 2811, 1605 Munro, Burnos Aires, Argentina

WESTERN GEOPHYSICAL   PO Box 2469, Houston, TX 77252-2469, Tel: (713) 789-9600
(Geophysical serv)
    Western Geophysical, Suipacha 268, Piso 9, Capital Federal, Buenos Aires, Argentina

WESTINGHOUSE ELECTRIC CORP   Westinghouse Bldg, Gateway Center, Pittsburgh,
  PA 15222, Tel: (412) 244-2000
(TV/radio broadcasting, mfr electr sys for ind/defense, fin & environmental servs)
    Westinghouse Electric Co. S.A., Casilla de Correo 6, Buenos Aires, Argentina

WORLD COMMUNICATIONS INC   67 Broad St, New York, NY 10004,
  Tel: (212) 607-2000
(Intl private line services)
    Comunicaciones Mundiales S.A., San Martin 299, Buenos Aires, Argentina

WORLD COURIER INC   46 Trinity Pl, New York, NY 10006, Tel: (718) 978-9400
(Intl courier serv)
    World Courier S.A. Argentina, Avenida Corrientes 327, Piso 6, Buenos Aires,
    Argentina

YOUNG & RUBICAM INTL INC   285 Madison Ave, New York, NY 10017,
  Tel: (212) 210-3000
(Advertising agency)
    Young Rubicam de Argentina S.A., Paraguay 609, Buenos Aires, Argentina

ARUBA

THE COASTAL CORP   9 Greenway Plaza, Houston, TX 77046, Tel: (713) 877-1400
  (Oil refining)
    Coastal Aruba Refining Co. N.V., P.O. Box 2150, San Nicolas, Aruba

AUSTRALIA

3M CO   3M Center, St Paul, MN 55144-1000, Tel: (612) 733-1110
  (Mfr abrasives, adhesives, chems, ind & consumer tapes/diskettes, health care prdts,
  elec connectors)
    3M Australia Pty., Ltd., P.O. Box 99, Pymble, NSW, 2073, Australia

ABBOTT LABORATORIES   Abbott Park, North Chicago, IL 60064,
  Tel: (312) 937-6100
  (Pharm & lab prdts)
    Abbott Australasia Pty., Ltd., P.O. Box 101, Cronulla, NSW 2230, Australia

ABERCROMBIE & KENT INTL INC   1420 Kensington Rd, Oak Brook, IL 60521-2106,
  Tel: (708) 954-2944
  (Tour wholesaler)
    Abercrombie & Kent (Australia) Pty. Ltd., 90 Bridport St., Albert Park,
      Melbourne 3206, Australia

ACADEMIC PRESS INC   111 Fifth Ave, New York, NY 10003, Tel: (212) 741-6800
  (Publ scientific books)
    Harcourt Brace Jovanovich Group (Australia) Pty., Ltd., 25-27 Paul St., N. Ryde,
      NSW 2113, Australia

ACCO INTL INC   770 S Acco Plaza, Wheeling, IL 60090, Tel: (708) 541-9500
  (Paper fasteners & clips, metal fasteners, binders, staplers)
    Universal Tags Pty., Ltd., 62 Whiting St., Artarmon, NSW 2064, Australia

ACCURAY CORP   650 Ackerman Rd, PO Box 02248, Columbus, OH 43202,
  Tel: (614) 261-2000
  (Computer-based process mgmt sys for forest prdts, metals rolling, textiles, tobacco
  ind)
    AccuRay Australia Pty., Ltd., NSW, Australia

ACHESON COLLOIDS CO   1600 Washington Ave, PO Box 288, Port Huron, MI 48060,
  Tel: (313) 984-5581
  (Graphite, lubricants & other specialty chems)
    Acheson A.N.Z. Pty., Ltd., P.O. Box 48, Padstow, NSW, 2211, Australia

ACME GENERAL CORP   300 E Arrow Hwy, San Dimas, CA 91773, Tel: (714) 599-6881
  (Proprietary sliding & folding door hdwe sys & access)
    Acmetrack Ltd., 46 Geddes St., Mulgrave, Vic. 3170, Australia

ACUFF-ROSE PUBLICATION INC   65 Music Square W, Nashville, TN 37203,
  Tel: (615) 321-5000
  (Music publisher)
    Acuff-Rose Publications Pty., Ltd., Suite 7A, Grosvenor House, 28 Glen St.,
      Milsons Point, NSW, 2061, Australia

ADDISON-WESLEY PUBLISHING CO   Route 128, Reading, MA 01867,
  Tel: (617) 944-3700
  (Educational textbook publ)
    Addison-Wesley Pty. Ltd., 6 Byfield St., N. Ryde, NSW, 2113, Australia

AFIA   110 William St, New York, NY 10038, Tel: (212) 964-4990
  (Insurance)
    Heartford Fire Insurance, 53-61 Walker St., P.O. Box 806, North Sydney, NSW 2060,
    Australia

AIR EXPRESS INTL CORP   120 Tokeneke Rd, PO Box 1231, Darien, CT 06820,
  Tel: (203) 655-7900
  (Air frt forwarder)
    Air Express Intl., 321 Great Eastern Highway Redeliffe, Perth, W.A., 6104, Australia
    Air Express Intl., c/o Wathen Curnow Cocks Pty., Ltd., Western Ave.,
    Eagle Farm Arpt., Brisbane, Queensland, Australia
    Air Express Intl. (lmport), AFCAB Complex, Melbourne Airport, Tullamarine,
    Vic. 3045, Australia
    Air Express Intl. Corp., Eleventh St., Mascot, NSW, 2020, Australia

AIRBORNE EXPRESS   3101 Western Ave, PO Box 662, Seattle, WA 98111,
  Tel: (206) 285-4600
  (Air transp serv)
    Australian Airborne Pty. Ltd., 42 Church Rd., Mascot, NSW 2020, Australia
    Australian Airborne Pty. Ltd., Unit 14, MIAC Bldg., P.O. Box 67, Tullamarine,
    Vic. 3043, Australia

ALADDIN INDUSTRIES INC   PO Box 100255, Nashville, TN 37210,
  Tel: (615) 748-3000
  (Vacuum bottles)
    Aladdin Industries Pty., Ltd., 43 Bridge Rd., Stanmore, NSW, 2048, Australia

ALARM DEVICE MFG CO   165 Eileen Way, Syosset, NY 11791, Tel: (516) 921-6704
  (Security, fire & burglary sys)
    Admeco Sontrix (Australia) Ltd., 41 Barry Ave., Mortdale, NSW 2223, Australia

ALBANY INTL CORP   PO Box 1907, Albany, NY 12201, Tel: (518) 445-2200
  (Paper mach clothing, engineered fabrics, plastic prdts, filtration media)
    Albany Felt Pty., Ltd., P.O. Box 417, Gosford, NSW 2250, Australia

ALBERTO-CULVER CO   2525 Armitage Ave, Melrose Park, IL 60160,
  Tel: (708) 450-3000
  (Hair sprays)
    Almond & Spragon (Australia) Pty. Ltd., Loyalty Rd., North Rocks, NSW, 2151,
    Australia

ALEXANDER & ALEXANDER INC   1211 Ave of the Americas, New York, NY 10036,
  Tel: (212) 840-8500
  (Ins brokerage, risk & human resource mgmt consult)
    Alexander Sedgwick (Services) Pty., Ltd., 422 Collins St., Melbourne, Vic. 3000,
    Australia

ALLEN-BRADLEY CO   PO Box 2086, Milwaukee, WI 53201, Tel: (414) 382-2000
  (Electrical control devices)
    Allen-Bradley Pty., Ltd., 37 Chapman St., P.O. Box 190, Blackburn, Vic. 3130,
    Australia

ALLEN-SHERMAN-HOFF CO   One Country View Rd, Malvern, PA 19355,
  Tel: (215) 647-9900
  (Design/eng material handling sys)
    Ecolaire (Australia) Pty., Ltd., 75 Miller St., North Sydney, NSW 2060, Australia

ALLERGAN PHARMACEUTICALS INTL INC   2525 DuPont Dr, Irvine, CA 92713,
  Tel: (714) 752-4500
  (Pharms, opthalmic & dermatological preparations)
    Allergan, Pharm. (Pty.,) Ltd., No. 5 George Place Artarmon, NSW, 2064, Australia

ALLIED AFTERMARKET DIV   105 Pawtucket Ave, East Providence, RI 02916,
  Tel: (401) 434-7000
  (Mfr spark plugs, waste treatment sys, filters, brakes)
    J.B. Morgan & Co., 1154-6 Sydney Rd., Fawkner, Vic., Australia

ALLIED-SIGNAL INC   Columbia Rd & Park Ave, PO Box 2245R, Morristown,
  NJ 07960, Tel: (201) 455-2000
  (Mfr aerospace & automotive prdts, engineered materials)
    Allied Corp. (Australia) Sales Ltd., 71 Queens Rd., Melbourne, Vic. 3004, Australia
    Allied-Signal Aerospace Co., Commerce House #1006, World Trade Centre, Melbourne,
      Vic. 3005, Australia
    Bendix Mintex Pty. Ltd., Elizabeth St., P.O. Box 631, Ballarat, Vic. 3350, Australia
    Garrett Aerospace Pty. Ltd., Unit B, 1020 McEvory St., Waterloo, NSW 2017, Australia
    Normalair-Garrett Mfg. (Pty.), King & Fraser Sts., Airport West, Melbourne,
      Vic. 3042, Australia

ALLIS-CHALMERS CORP   PO Box 512, Milwaukee, WI 53201, Tel: (414) 475-4011
  (Heavy mach, equip & serv)
    Allis Chalmers Australia Pty., Ltd., 140 Arthur St., North Sydney, NSW, 2060,
      Australia
    Stephens-Adamson, 140 Arthur St., North Sydney, NSW, 2060, Australia

ALUMINUM CO OF AMERICA (ALCOA)   1501 Alcoa Bldg, Pittsburgh, PA 15219,
  Tel: (412) 553-4545
  (Bauxite, alumina & aluminum prdts)
    Alcoa of Australia (W.A.) Ltd., P.O. Box 161, Kwinana, W.A., 6167, Australia
    Alcoa of Australia Ltd., 535 Bourke St., Melbourne, Vic. 3000, Australia

AM INTL INC   333 W Wacker Dr, #900, Chicago, IL 60606-1265,
  Tel: (312) 558-1966
  (Mfr/sale/serv commun graphics, info handling equip & sys)
    AM Intl. Pty., Ltd., P.O. Box 200, Mulgrave North, Victoria 3170, Australia

AMDAHL CORP   1250 East Arques Ave, PO Box 3470, Sunnyvale, CA 94088-3470,
  Tel: (408) 746-6000
  (Mfr large scale computers, complementary software storage & commun prdts)
    Amdahl Australia Pty. Ltd., 1 Pacific Hwy, North Sydney, NSW 2060, Australia

AMELCO CORP   2308 Pahounui Dr, Honolulu, HI 96819-2292, Tel: (808) 845-9324
  (Contracting)
    W.H.Y. Pty., Ltd., 301 Catherine St., Lilyfield, NSW, 2040, Australia

AMERICAN AIRLINES INC   PO Box 619616, Dallas-Ft Worth Arpt, TX 75261-9616,
  Tel: (817) 355-1234
  (Air transp)
    American Airlines, Inc., GPO Box 3261, Sydney, NSW 2001, Australia

AMERICAN COLLOID CO   1500 W Shure Dr, Arlington Hgts, IL 60004,
Tel: (708) 966-5720
(Bentonite mining)
   Volclay Standard Pty. Ltd., P.O. Box 50, Fairfield 3078, Vic., Australia

AMERICAN CYANAMID CO   1 Cyanamid Plaza, Wayne, NJ 07470, Tel: (201) 831-2000
(Pharms, chems, agric & consumer prdts)
   Cyanamid Australia Pty., Ltd., 5 Gibbon Rd., Baulkham Hills, NSW 2153, Australia
   Davis & Geck Australia Pty. Ltd., 59 Halstead St., Hurstville, NSW 2220, Australia

AMERICAN EXPRESS CO   American Express Tower, New York, NY 10285-4765,
Tel: (212) 640-2000
(Diversified fin & travel-related serv)
   American Express Intl. Inc., 380 George St., Sydney, NSW, 2000, Australia
   American Express Intl. Inc., GPO Box 1582, Sydney, NSW, 2001, Australia

AMERICAN HOME PRODUCTS CORP   685 Third Ave, New York, NY 10017,
Tel: (212) 878-5800
(Drugs, food, household prdts)
   International Home Products (Australia) Pty., Ltd., York Rd., Bellambi, NSW, 2517,
   Australia

AMERICAN INTL UNDERWRITERS CORP   70 Pine St, New York, NY 10270,
Tel: (212) 770-7000
(General ins)
   American Intl. Underwriters (Australia) Pty., Ltd., 446 Collins St., 11th Floor,
   Melbourne, Vic. 3000, Australia
   American Intl. Underwriters (Australia) Pty., Ltd., Goldfield House, 1 Alfred St.,
   Sydney Cove, NSW, 2000, Australia
   American Intl. Underwriters (Australia) Pty., Ltd., 6th Floor, IMFC House,
   33 King William St., Adelaide, 5000, South Australia
   American Intl. Underwriters (Australia) Pty., Ltd., GPO Box 139 CNR,
   Queen & Creek Sts., Brisbane, Queensland, 4001, Australia
   American Intl. Underwriters (Australia) Pty., Ltd., 26 St. Georges Terrace, Perth,
   Western, 6000, Australia

AMERICAN OPTICAL CORP   14 Mechanic St, Southbridge, MA 01550,
Tel: (617) 765-9711
(Ophthalmic lenses, frames & cases, sunglasses)
   American Optical Corp. Pty., Ltd., 22 Vic. St., Beaconsfield, NSW, 2015, Australia

AMERICAN RE-INSURANCE CO   One Liberty Plaza, 91 Liberty St, New York,
NY 10006, Tel: (212) 766-6700
(Reinsurance)
   American Re-Insurance Co., 28-34 O'Connell St., Sydney, NSW 2000, Australia
   American Re-Insurance Co., 422 Collins St., Melbourne, Vic. 3000, Australia

AMERICAN TOOL COMPANIES INC   301 S 13th St, #600, Lincoln, NE 68508,
Tel: (402) 435-3300
(Mfr hand tools)
   ATC Tools Australasia Pty. Ltd., 4A Melrich Rd., Bayswater, Victoria 3153, Australia

AMP INC   470 Friendship Rd, Harrisburg, PA 17111, Tel: (717) 564-0100
(Mfr electrical wiring devices)
   Australian AMP Pty., Ltd., P.O. Box 557. Castle Hill, NSW 2154, Australia

AMPEX CORP   401 Broadway, Redwood City, CA 94063-3199, Tel: (415) 367-2011
(Mfr professional audio/visual sys, magnetic recording media, data-memory prdts)
   Ampex Australia Pty., Ltd., 21 Terra Cotta Dr., Blackburn, Vic. 3130, Australia
   Ampex Australia Pty., Ltd., 61 Talavera Rd., North Ryde, NSW 2113, Australia

AMWAY CORP   7575 E Fulton Rd, Ada, MI 49355, Tel: (616) 676-6000
(Distr household cleaning, nutrition & diet prdts)
   Amway of Australia Pty., Ltd., 46 Carrington Rd., P.O. Box 202, Castle Hill, NSW,
   2145, Australia

ANACONDA CO   555 17th St, Denver, CO 80202, Tel: (303) 575-4000
(Copper mining)
   Anaconda Australia Inc., 9th Floor, 130 Philip St., GPI Box 2521, Sydney, NSW,
   2001., Australia

ANDREW CORP   10500 W 153rd St, Orlando Park, IL 60462, Tel: (708) 349-3300
(Antenna sys)
   Andrew Antennas, 171 Henty St., Reservoir, Vic. 3073, Australia

ANEMOSTAT PRODUCTS DIV   888 N Keyser Ave, Scranton, PA 18501,
Tel: (717) 346-6586
(Mfr air diffusers, grilles & related equip for A/C, heating & ventilation)
   Anemostat Pty., Ltd., 5-15 Cotton Ave., P.O. Box 132, Bankstown, NSW 2200, Australia

ANGLO-AMERICAN AVIATION CO   10929 Vanowen St, PO Box 3970, N Hollywood,
CA 91609, Tel: (213) 985-3500
(Aviation spare parts, hardware)
   Anglo Amerian Aviation Co., P.O. Box 92, Niddrie, Vic. 3042, Australia

ANTHONY INDUSTRIES INC   4900 S Eastern Ave, Los Angeles, CA 90040,
Tel: (213) 724-2800
(Pool constr & equip, fishing tackle, athletic apparel)
   Shakespeare Australia Pty., Ltd., Sydney, Australia

APPLE COMPUTER INC   20525 Mariani Ave, Cupertino, CA 95014,
Tel: (408) 996-1010
(Personal computers, peripherals & software)
   Apple Computer Australia Pty. Ltd., 37 Waterloo Rd., P.O. Box 371, North Ryde,
   N.S.W 2113, Australia

ARMCO INTL INC   703 Curtis St, PO Box 700, Middletown, OH 45042,
Tel: (513) 425-6541
(Sheet steel & steel prdts, constr, oil field equip, ins, finance leasing)
   Armco Australia Pty., Ltd., 127-141 Bath Rd., P.O. Box 2, Sutherland, NSW, 2232,
   Australia

ARMSTRONG WORLD INDUSTRIES INC   PO Box 3001, Lancaster, PA 17604,
Tel: (717) 397-0611
(Mfr/mkt interior furnishings & spec prdts for bldg, auto & textile inds)
   Armstrong World Industries Pty. Ltd., P.O. Box 240, N. Ryde, NSW 2113, Australia
   Armstrong-Nylex Pty. Ltd., P.O. Box 109, Mordialloc, Vic. 3195, Australia

ARVIN INDUSTRIES INC   One Noblitt Plaza, Columbus, IN 47201,
Tel: (812) 379-3000
(Mfr auto OEM & replacement parts & fabricated metal parts, R&D & testing)
   Schrader Automotive Pty., 49 Fitzroy St., Marickville, NSW 220, Australia

ASSOCIATED PRESS   50 Rockefeller Plaza, New York, NY 10020,
  Tel: (212) 621-1500
  (News gathering agency)
    The Associated Press, 364 Sussex St., Box K35, Haymarket, Sydney, NSW, Sydney,
    2001, Australia

AST RESEARCH INC   16215 Alton Parkway, PO Box 19658, Irvine, CA 92713-9658,
  Tel: (714) 727-4141
  (Mfr personal computers enhancement & data commun prdt)
    AST Australia, 45 Market St.- 8/F-#800, Sydney, NSW 2000, Australia

AT&T INTERNATIONAL   295 N Maple Ave, Basking Ridge, NJ 07920,
  Tel: (908) 221-2000
  (Telecommun)
    AT&T Intl. (Australia) Ltd., CBA Centre - 21st level, 60 Margaret St., Sydney,
    NSW 2000, Australia

AUGAT INC   89 Forbes Blvd, Mansfield, MA 02048, Tel: (508) 543-4300
  (Interconnection prdts)
    Augat Pty. Ltd., 158 S. Creek Rd., Unit 8, Dee Why West 2099, Australia

THE AUSTIN CO   3650 Mayfield Rd, Cleveland, OH 44121, Tel: (216) 382-6600
  (Conslt, design, engr & constr serv)
    Austin-Anderson (Australia) Pty., Ltd., 52-56 Atchinson St., St. Leonards, NSW,
    2065, Australia
    Austin-Anderson (Australia) Pty., Ltd., 9 Queens Rd., Melbourne, Vic. 3004,
    Australia

AUTOMATIC SWITCH CO   Hanover Rd, Florham Park, NJ 07932, Tel: (201) 966-2000
  (Valves & switches)
    Ascomation Pty., Ltd., 25 Cross St., Brookvale, NSW 2100, Australia

AVCO FINANCIAL SERVICES INC   3349 Michelson Dr, Irvine, CA 92715,
  Tel: (714) 553-1200
  (Fin serv, loans)
    Avco Financial Services Ltd., 916 Pacific Hwy., Gordon, NSW 2072, Australia

AVERY INTL CORP   150 N Orange Grove Blvd, Pasadena, CA 91103,
  Tel: (213) 304-2000
  (Mfr self-adhesive labels & marking equip)
    W.J. Cryer & Co., Ltd., 75 Union St., P.O. Box 7, Dulwich Hill, NSW 2203, Australia

AVIS INC   900 Old Country Rd, Garden City, NY 11530, Tel: (516) 222-3000
  (Car rental serv)
    Avis Rent a Car System Inc., 400 Elizabeth St., Melbourne, Australia
    Avis Rent a Car System Inc., 46 Hill St., Perth Airport, Perth, Australia
    Avis Rent a Car System Inc., 163 Mitchell St., Alexandria, Sydney NSW, Australia
    Avis Rent a Car System Inc., 86 Vic. Rd., Paramatta, Australia
    Avis Rent a Car System Inc., Terminus St. & Hume Way, Liverpool, Australia

AVON PRODUCTS INC   9 W 57th St, New York, NY 10019, Tel: (212) 546-6015
  (Mfr/distr cosmetics, perfumes)
    Avon Products Pty., Ltd., P.O. Box 180, Dee Way, NSW, 2099, Australia

AYERST LABORATORIES   145 King of Prussia Rd, Radnor, PA 19087,
  Tel: (215) 688-4400
  (Biologicals & pharms)
    Ayerst Laboratories Pty., Ltd., Parramatta, NSW, Australia

BAILEY CONTROLS CO   29801 Euclid Ave, Wickliffe, OH 44092,
  Tel: (216) 943-5500
  (Mfr analog & digital instru, controls & control sys)
    Bailey Meter Australia Pty., Ltd., 26 Auburn Rd., Regnets Park, NSW, 2143, Australia

BAKER OIL TOOLS   PO Box 3048, Houston, TX 77253, Tel: (713) 923-9351
  (Oil/gas well completions equip)
    Baker Oil Tools (Australia) Pty., Ltd., 23 Pamleula St., Regency Park, Adelaide,
      S.A. 5010, Australia

BAKER PRODUCTION TECHNOLOGY   PO Box 40129, Houston, TX 77240-0129,
  Tel: (713) 943-0170
  (Inflatable packers, instru well testing)
    Lynes Intl. Inc., 24 Little Edward Rd., Brisbane, Queensland 4000 Australia
    Lynes Intl. Inc., P.O. Box 611, Rama, Queensland 4455, Australia
    Lynes Intl. Inc., P.O. Box 39, Bentley, Perth 6102, Australia

BALTIMORE AIRCOIL CO INC   PO Box 7322, Baltimore, MD 21227,
  Tel: (301) 799-6200
  (Evaporative condensers, cooling, towers, ind fluids)
    Baltimore Aircoil (Australia) Pty., Ltd., RMB 3977, Wisemans Ferry Rd.,
      Somersby via Gosford, NSW 2250, Australia

THE BANK OF NEW YORK   48 Wall St, New York, NY 10286, Tel: (212) 530-1784
  (Banking)
    BNY Australia Ltd., 15 Castlereagh St., Sydney 2000, NSW, Australia

BANKAMERICA CORP   PO Box 37000, San Francisco, CA 94137, Tel: (415) 622-3456
  (Financial services)
    Bank of America Australia Ltd., 135 King St., Bank of America Centre, Sydney,
      NSW 2000, Australia

BANKERS TRUST CO   280 Park Ave, New York, NY 10017, Tel: (212) 775-2500
  (Banking)
    Barkers Trust Australia Pty., Ltd., Australia Square, Level 40, Sydney, NSW, 2000,
      Australia
    ORD-B.T. Co., Ltd., Level 40, Australia Square, Sydney, NSW, Australia

C R BARD INC   731 Central Ave, Murray Hill, NJ 07974, Tel: (201) 277-8000
  (Health care prdts)
    Ramsay Group Ltd., 182-206 Berkeley St., P.O. Box 124, Carlton, Vic. 3053, Australia

BARDAHL MFG CORP   1400 N W 52nd St, PO Box 70607, Seattle, WA 98107,
  Tel: (206) 783-4851
  (Lubricating oils)
    Dominion Industries Pty., Ltd., 2 Loombah Ave., Lindfield, NSW, 2070, Australia

BARNES-HIND INC   895 Kifer Rd, Sunnyvale, CA 94086, Tel: (408) 736-5462
  (Contact lenses & accessories, opthalmic & dermatology prdts)
    Barnes-Hind Pty., Ltd., 7 Dickson Ave., Artarmon, NSW, 2064, Australia

BARRY-WEHMILLER CO   4660 W Florissant Ave, St Louis, MO 63115,
   Tel: (314) 381-1504
   (Bottling mach, bottle inspection & washing)
      Barry-Wehmiller (Australia) Pty., Ltd., P.O. Box 138, 7 Walter St., Glenroy,
      Vic. 3046, Australia

BAUSCH & LOMB INC   1 Lincoln First Sq, Rochester, NY 14601-0054,
   Tel: (716) 338-6000
   (Mfr healthcare & optics prdts)
      Bausch & Lomb (Australia) Pty. Ltd., New South Wales, Australia

BAXTER TRAVENOL LABORATORIES INC   1 Baxter Pky, Deerfield, IL 60015,
   Tel: (708) 948-2000
   (Pharm & disposable med prdts)
      Travenol Laboratories Pty., Ltd., P.O. Box 88, Oaks Rd., Old Toongabbie, NSW, 2146,
      Australia

BECHTEL GROUP INC   50 Beale St, PO Box 3965, San Francisco, CA 94119,
   Tel: (415) 768-1234
   (Engineering & constr)
      Bechtel Pacific Corp., Ltd., 303 Collins St., Melbourne, Vic. 3001, Australia

BECKMAN INSTRUMENTS INC   2500 Harbor Blvd, Box 3100, Fullerton, CA 92634,
   Tel: (714) 871-4848
   (Mfr/distr/serv research & clinical lab instru, sys, software & reagents)
      Beckman Instruments (Australia) Pty., Ltd., 24 College St., Gladesville, NSW 2111,
      Australia

BEE CHEMICAL CO   2700 E 170th St, Lansing, IL 60438, Tel: (708) 758-0500
   (Coatings & finishes for plastics & metals)
      Bee Chemical Co., 594 St. Kilda Rd., Melbourne, Vic. 3004, Australia

BELL & HOWELL CO   5215 Old Orchard Rd., Skokie, IL 60077, Tel: (708) 470-7684
   (Diversified info prdts & servs)
      Bell & Howell Australia Pty., Ltd., 9 Short St., Chatswood, NSW 2067, Australia

BELLSOUTH INTERNATIONAL   1155 Peachtree St NE, #400, Atlanta, GA 30367,
   Tel: (404) 249-4800
   (Mobile commun, telecom network sys)
      Link Telecommunications, Level 8, 600 St. Kilda Rd., Melbourne, Vic. 3004, Australia

BELOIT CORP   1st Lawrence Ave, Beloit, WI 53511, Tel: (608) 365-3311
   (Paper making mach & equip)
      Beloit International Pty., Ltd., Village Gate Suite 3, 145-147 Canterbury Rd.,
      Toorak, Melbourne, Vic. 3142, Australia

BENEFICIAL CORP   1300 Market St, Wilmington, DE 19899, Tel: (302) 658-5171
   (Holding company)
      BFC Finance Ltd., 58-64 McQuarie St., P.O. Box 247, Parramatta, NSW, 2150, Australia

BENTLY NEVADA CORP   PO Box 157, Minden, NV 89423, Tel: (702) 782-3611
   (Electronic monitoring system)
      Rotor Dynamics Pty Ltd., 1 Millers Rd., P.O. Box 134, Altona, Vic. 3018, Australia
      Rotor Dynamics Pty Ltd., 28 Oatley Ave., P.O.Box 64, Oatley, NSW 2223, Australia

BERKEY-COLORTRAN INC   1015 Chestnut St, Burbank, CA 91502,
  Tel: (213) 843-1200
  (Lighting equip)
    Cine-King Motion Picture & Television Supplies, Pty., Ltd., P.O. Box 281, Artarmon,
      NSW, 2064, Australia
    Media Vision Australia, 9 Leicester Ave., Glen Waverly, Vic. 3150, Australia

BESSER CO   801 Johnson St, PO Box 336, Alpena, MI 49707, Tel: (517) 354-4111
  (Mfr equip for concrete industry)
    Besser Australia Pty., Ltd., 14 Alban St., Silverwater, 2142 NSW, Australia

BINKS MFG CO   9201 W Belmont Ave, Franklin Park, IL 60131,
  Tel: (708) 671-3000
  (Mfr of spray painting & finishing equip)
    Binks-Bellows (Australia) Pty., Ltd., 57 By the Sea Rd., P.O. Box 338, Monavale,
      NSW, 2103, Australia

BINNEY & SMITH INC   1100 Church Lane, PO Box 431, Easton, PA 18042,
  Tel: (215) 253-6271
  (Mfr art supplies, craft kits)
    Binney & Smith (Australia) Pty., Ltd., P.O. Box 296, 459 Dorset Rd., Bayswater,
      Vic. 3153, Australia

BIO-RAD LABORATORIES   2200 Wright Ave, Richmond, CA 94804,
  Tel: (415) 234-4130
  (Spec chems, clinical diagnostic prdts, test kits)
    Bio-Rad Laboratories Pty., Ltd., 8/17 Kings Rd., Hornsby 2072, NSW, Australia

BLACK & DECKER CORP   701 E Joppa Road, Towson, MD 21204, Tel: (301) 583-3900
  (Mfr portable elect & pneumatic power tools, household prdts)
    Black & Decker (Australasia) Pty., Ltd., Maroondah Highway, Croydon, Vic. 3136,
      Australia
    Rank Electric Housewares Pty., Ltd., 296 Ferntree Gully Rd., Notting Hill,
      Vic. 3168, Australia

BLACK & VEATCH INTL   PO Box 8405, Kansas City, MO 64114, Tel: (913) 339-8700
  (Engineering/architectural servs)
    GHD-Black & Veatch Pty. Ltd., P.O. Box 39, 39 Regent St., Railway Sq., Sydney,
      NSW 2000, Australia

H & R BLOCK INC   4410 Main St, Kansas City, MO 64111, Tel: (816) 753-6900
  (Income tax preparation)
    H&R Block (Australia) Ltd., P.O. Box 147, Thornleigh, NSW 2120, Australia

BLOUNT INC   4520 Executive Park Drive, Montgomery, AL 36116-1602,
  Tel: (205) 244-4370
  (Mfr cutting chain & equip, timber harvest/materials handling equip, sporting ammo,
  gen contracting)
    Omark Australia Ltd., Unit 3, 43 Herbert St., Artarmon, NSW 2064, Australia

BOOZ ALLEN & HAMILTON INC   101 Park Ave, New York, NY 10178,
  Tel: (212) 697-1900
  (Mgmt consultants)
    Booz, Allen & Hamilton (Australia) Ltd., 14th fl., 345 George St., Sydney,
      SNW 2000, Australia

BORDEN INC   420 Lexington Ave, New York, NY 10170, Tel: (212) 573-4000
   (Milk processing, dairy foods, specialty foods, chems, plastics)
      Borden Chemical Co. (Australia) Pty., Ltd., 46 Wellington Rd., P.O. Box 57,
         Granville, NSW, 2142, Australia

BORG-WARNER CORP   200 S Michigan Ave, Chicago, IL 60604, Tel: (312) 322-8500
   (Mfr A/C equip, chem & plastics, ind prdts, trans equip)
      Borg-Warner (Australia) Ltd., 52 Lisbon St., Fairfield, NSW 2165, Australia
      Borg-Warner Acceptance Corp.(Australia) Ltd., 55 Lavender St., Milsons Point,
         NSA 2061, Australia

BOSE CORP   100 The Mountain Rd, Framingham, MA 01701, Tel: (617) 879-7330
   (Electronic equip)
      Bose Australia, 11 Muriel Ave., Rydalmere 2116, NSW, Australia

BOSTITCH DIV   815 Briggs St, East Greenwich, RI 02818, Tel: (401) 884-2500
   (Stapling machs & supplies, wire)
      Bostitch Australia, P.O. Box 472, Auburn, NSW, 2144, Australia

BOYDEN ASSOCIATES INC   260 Madison Ave, New York, NY 10016,
   Tel: (212) 685-3400
   (Mgt consultants, exec search)
      Boyden Associates Intl., Suite 1004/5, The Cliveden, 4 Bridge St., Sydney,
         NSW 2000, Australia
      Boyden Associates Intl. Inc., Marland House, 570 Bourke St., Melbourne, Vic. 3000,
         Australia

W H BRADY CO   727 W Glendale Ave, PO Box 571, Milwaukee, WI 53201,
   Tel: (414) 332-8100
   (Wire markers, name plates)
      W.H. Brady Pty., Ltd., 158 Beaconsfield St., Revesby, 2212, NSW, Australia

BRIGGS & STRATTON CORP   PO Box 702, Milwaukee, WI 53201, Tel: (414) 259-5333
   (Mfr engines, auto locking devices)
      Briggs & Stratton Australia Pty. Ltd., all mail to: U.S. address

BROWN & ROOT INC   4100 Clinton Dr, Houston, TX 77020-6299,
   Tel: (713) 676-4141
   (Engr, constr & maintenance)
      Brown & Root Pty. Ltd., GPO Box 2445, Brisbane, Qld. 4001, Australia
      Dawson Brown & Root Pty. Ltd., 40 St. George's Ter., Perth, WA 6000, Australia

BUCK CONSULTANTS INC   Two Pennsylvania Plaza, New York, NY 10121,
   Tel: (212) 330-1000
   (Employee benefit, actuarial & compensation conslt serv)
      Buck Consultants Pty. Ltd., Level 2- 20 Clarke St., PO Box 412 Crows Nest,
         Sydney 2065, Australia

BUCYRUS-ERIE CO   PO Box 56, Milwaukee, WI 53172, Tel: (414) 768-4000
   (Shovels, cranes)
      Bucyrus (Australia) Pty., Ltd., 153 Walker St., North Sydney, NSW, 2060, Australia

BULAB HOLDINGS INC   1256 N McLean Blvd, Memphis, TN 38108,
   Tel: (901) 278-0330
   (Mfr microbicides, biocides, additives, corrosion inhibitors, chems)
      Buckman Laboratories Pty. Ltd., P.O. Box 161, Granville, NSW 2142, Australia

BUNDY CORP   12345 E Nine Mile, Warren, MI 48090, Tel: 313) 758) 6500
(Small diameter steel tubing, watch cases, etc)
   Bundy Tubing Co. (Australia) Pty., Ltd., 490 Churchill Rd., Adelaide, S.A., 5000,
   Australia

BURLINGTON AIR EXPRESS   18200 Van Karman Ave, Irvine, CA 92715,
Tel: (714) 752-1212
(Air freight)
   Burlington Air Express Pty. Ltd., 13 Rosebery Ave., Rosebery, NSW 2018, Australia

LEO BURNETT CO INC   35 West Wacker Dr, Chicago, IL 60601, Tel: (312) 220-5959
(Advertising agency)
   Leo Burnett Pty., Ltd., 40 Miller St., North Sydney NSW, 2060, Australia
   Leo Burnett Pty., Ltd., 225 Greenwich Hill Rd, Dulwich, Adelaide, SA 5065, Australia
   Leo Burnett Pty., Ltd., 45 Black St., Milton, Queensland 4064, Australia
   Leo Burnett Pty., Ltd., 464 St., Kilda Rd., Melbourne, Vic. 3004, Australia

BURNS & ROE INC   550 Kinderkamack Rd, Oradell, NJ 07649, Tel: (201) 265-2000
(Consulting engineers)
   Burmot Australia Pty., Ltd., 1 Chandos St., St. Leonards, NSW, 2065, Australia

BURSON-MARSTELLER   230 Park Ave, New York, NY 10003-1566, Tel: (212) 614-4000
(Public relations/public affairs consultants)
   Burson-Marsteller, 23rd fl. AGL Bldg., 111 Pacific Hwy., P.O. Box 1018,
   North Sydney, NSW 2060, Australia

BUTTERICK FASHION MARKETING CO   161 Ave of the Americas, New York, NY 10013,
Tel: (212) 620-2500
(Sewing patterns)
   Butterick Co. Pty., Ltd., 3712 M.C.L., Center, Martin Place, Sydney, NSW, 2000,
   Australia

CARL BYOIR & ASSOCIATES INC   380 Madison Ave, New York, NY 10017,
Tel: (212) 986-6100
(Public relations consultants)
   Welbeck Public Rel., 10 Dorcas St., S. Melbourne, Vic. 3205, Australia
   Welbeck Public Rel., 100 William St., Kings Cross, NSW 2011, Australia

CABOT CORP   950 Winter St, PO Box 9073, Waltham, MA 02254,
Tel: (617) 890-0200
(Mfr carbon blacks, plastics; oil & gas, info sys)
   Australian Carbon Black Pty., Ltd., P.O. Box 19, Altona 3018, Vic., Australia

CADILLAC PLASTIC & CHEMICAL CO   143 Indusco Ct, Troy, MI 48083,
Tel: (313) 583-1200
(Dist plastic basic shapes)
   Cadillac Plastic (Australia) Pty. Ltd., Silverwater, NSW 2141, Australia
   Cadillac Plastic (Australia) Pty. Ltd., P.O.Box 145, Ermington, NSW 2115, Australia

CALTEX PETROLEUM CORP   PO Box 619500, Dallas, TX 75261, Tel: (214) 830-1000
(Petroleum prdts)
   Caltex Oil (Australia) Pty. Ltd., 167 Kent St., Sydney, NSW 2000, Australia
   Caltex Refining Co. Ltd., Solander St., Kurnell, NSW 2231, Australia

CAMBRIDGE WIRE CLOTH CO   105 Goodwill Road, PO Box 399, Cambridge, MD 21613,
Tel: (301) 228-3000
(Mfr ind wire cloth, women wire conveyor belting, ind mesh)

(cont)

Locker-Cambridge Metal Belt Co., Pty., Ltd., P.O. Box 181, 125 Chesterville Rd.,
    Mordialloc, Vic. 3195, Australia

CAMP DRESSER & MCKEE INTL INC   One Center Plaza, Boston, MA 02108,
    Tel: (617) 742-5151
    (Consulting engineers)
    Camp Scott Furphy Ptd. Ltd., 47 Ord St., West Perth, W.A. 6005, Australia
    Camp Scott Furphy Pty. Ltd., 781 Pacific Hwy., Chatswood, NSW 2067, Australia
    Camp Scott Furphy Pty., Ltd., 390 St., Kilda Rd., Melbourne, 3004, Vic., Australia

CAMP INTL INC   PO Box 89, Jackson, MI 49204, Tel: (517) 787-1600
    (Mfr orthotics & prosthetics)
    The House of Jenyns, Pty., Ltd., 194-208 Melbourne St., South Brisbane,
    Queensland 4101, Australia

CAMPBELL SOUP CO   Campbell Place, Camden, NJ 08101, Tel: (609) 342-4800
    (Food prdts)
    Arnott's Biscuits Pty. Ltd., 170 Kent St., Sydney, NSW 2000, Australia
    Campbell's Soups (Australia) Pty. Ltd., 499 St. Kilda Rd., Fawkner Center,
    Melbourne, Vic. 3004, Australia
    Campbell's Soups (Australia) Pty., Ltd., P.O. Box 779, Shepparton, Vic. 3630,
    Australia

CANADA DRY INTL CORP   2600 Century Pkwy, Atlanta, GA 30345,
    Tel: (404) 753-2182
    (Carbonated beverages, soft drinks extract)
    Burnett Soft Drinks Pty., Ltd., 18 Toonburra St., Bundaberg Old, 4670, Australia
    Casino Cordials, 39-41 Johnston St., Casino, NSW, 2470, Australia
    Coca-Cola (Townsville) Pty., Ltd., 131 Ingham Rd., Townsville, QLD, 4810, Australia
    Ecks (NSW) Pty., Ltd., 31 Croydon Ave., Croydon, NSW, 2132, Australia
    Hanush's Cordials, 291 Draper St., Cairns QLD, 4870, Australia
    Matthews Cordials, 79 Arthur St., Wellington, NSW, 2820, Australia
    Nor-East Drinks Pty., Ltd., Pacific Highway, Ballina, NSW, Australia
    Passiona Btlg. Co. Ltd., 363-369 Scarborough Beach Rd., Osborne Park, W.A., Perth,
    Australia
    The Delta Spa Co., Wickham St., Ayr Old, 4807, Australia
    Unwins & Archers Soft Drinks, 50 Williams St., Bowen QLD, Australia

CANBERRA INDUSTRIES INC   One State St, Meriden, CT 06450, Tel: (203) 238-2351
    (Mfr instru for nuclear research)
    Canberra-Packard Pty. Ltd., Unit 1, 170 Forster Rd., Mt. Waverley, Vic. 3149,
    Australia

CAPITOL RECORDS INC   1750 N Vine St, Hollywood, CA 90028, Tel: (213) 462-6252
    (Phonograph records, pre-recorded tape)
    E.M.I. (Australia) Ltd., P.O. Box 352, Haymarket, NSW, 2000, Australia

CARGILL   PO Box 9300, Minneapolis, MN 55440, Tel: (612) 475-7575
    (Food prdts, feeds, animal prdts)
    Cargill Oilseeds Australia, Australia, Baranbar St., Narrabri, NSW, 2390, Australia

CARNATION INTL CO   5045 Wilshire Blvd, Los Angeles, CA 90036,
    Tel: (213) 932-6000
    (Milk prdts)
    Carnation Co., Pty., Ltd., 130 Little Collins St., Melbourne, GPO Box 2631,
    Vic. 3001, Australia

CARRIER INTERNATIONAL CORP　　PO Box 4806, Syracuse, NY 13221,
　Tel: (315) 432-6000
　(A/C, heating, refrig & power equip)
　　Carrier Air Conditioning (Holdings) Ltd., Seven Hills Rd., Seven Hills, NSW, 2147,
　　　Australia
　　Carrier International Corp. Pty., Ltd., 84 Pitt St., Sydney, NSW, 2000, Australia

CARTER-WALLACE INC　　2 Research Way, Princeton, NJ 08450-6628,
　Tel: (609) 520-3100
　(Mfr pharms, diagnostics, toiletries)
　　Carter-Wallace (Australia) Pty. Ltd., P.O. Box 216, Brookvale, NSW, 2100, Australia

CASCADE CORP　　2020 SW 4th Ave, Portland, OR 97201, Tel: (503) 227-0024
　(Lift truck attachments)
　　Cascade (Australia) Pty., Ltd., P.O. Box 67, Ermington 2115, Sydney, NSW, Australia

J I CASE CO　　700 State St, Racine, WI 53404, Tel: (414) 636-6011
　(Mfr/sale agric & constr equip)
　　J.I. Case (Australia) Pty., Ltd., Windsor Rd., Northmead, NSW, 2152, Australia

CATERPILLAR INC　　100 N E Adams St, Peoria, IL 61629, Tel: (309) 675-1000
　(Mfr earth/material-handling & constr mach & equip, engines, generators)
　　Caterpillar of Australia Ltd., 1 Sharps Rd, Private Mail Bag 4, Tullamarine,
　　　Vic. 3042, Australia

CBI INDUSTRIES INC　　800 Jorie-Blvd, Oak Brook, IL 60521, Tel: (708) 654-7000
　(Holding co: metal plate fabricating, constr, oil & gas drilling)
　　CBI Constructors Pty., Ltd., 52-54 Phillip St., Sydney, NSW, 2000, Australia
　　CBI Constructors Pty., Ltd., 5th Ave., Blacktown, NSW, 2145, Australia

CEILCOTE CO　　140 Sheldon Rd, Berea, OH 44017, Tel: (216) 243-0700
　(Mfr corrosion-resistant material, air pollution control equip, cons serv)
　　Transfield (TAS) Pty. Ltd., P.O. Box 563, Devonport, Tasmania 7310, Australia

CENTRAL NATIONAL-GOTTESMAN INC　　100 Park Ave, New York, NY 10017,
　Tel: (212) 532-7300
　(Pulp & paper prdts)
　　Central National Australia Pty. Ltd., 2 Capital City Blvd., Wantirna, Vic. 3152,
　　　Australia

CENTURY 21 REAL ESTATE CORP　　2601 SE Main, PO Box 19564, Irvine,
　CA 92713-9564, Tel: (714) 553-2100
　(Real estate)
　　Century 21 Australasia Pty. Ltd., Level 14, 221 Elizabeth St., Sydney, NSW 2000,
　　　Australia

CHAMPION SPARK PLUG CO　　PO Box 910, Toledo, OH 43661, Tel: (419) 535-2567
　(Mfr spark plugs, wiper blades & related prdts)
　　Champion Spark Plug Co. (Australia) Pty., Ltd., 83 Bourke Rd., Alexandria, NSW,
　　　2015, Australia

CHASE MANHATTAN BANK N A　　1 Chase Manhattan Plaza, New York, NY 10081,
　Tel: (212) 552-2222
　(Intl banking)
　　Chase Manhattan Regional Office, AMP Tower, 535 Bourke St., P.O. Box 5469 CC,
　　　Melbourne, 3001, Australia

CHECK TECHNOLOGY CORP   1284 Corporate Center Dr, St Paul, MN 55121,
   Tel: (612) 454-9300
   (Mfr computer controlled check/coupon print sys)
      Check Technology Pty. Ltd., 5/8 Leighton Place, Hornsby, NSW 2077, Australia

CHESEBROUGH-POND'S INC   33 Benedict Place, Greenwich, CT 06830,
   Tel: (203) 661-2000
   (Cosmetics, consumer prdts)
      Chesebrough-Pond's Intl. Ltd., P.O. Box 215, Glen Waverly, Vic. 3150, Australia

CHICAGO PNEUMATIC TOOL CO   2200 Bleeker St, Utica, NY 13501,
   Tel: (315) 792-2600
   (Mfr air tools & equip)
      Consolidated Pneumatic Tool Co. (Australia) Pty. Ltd., P.O. Box 99, 3 Bessemer St.,
      Blacktown, NSW 2148, Sydney, Australia

CHICAGO RAWHIDE MFG CO   900 N State Street, Elgin, IL 60120,
   Tel: (708) 742-7840
   (Seals & filters)
      CR Industrial Products Pty., Ltd., 25 Graham Rd., Clayton, South Melbourne, 3169,
      Australia

CHRISTENSEN INTL   PO Box 26135, Salt Lake City, UT 84126, Tel: (801) 487-5371
   (Diamond drills)
      Christensen Diamond Products Australia Pty., Ltd., 91 Briggs St., Welshpool,
      Western, 6106, Australai

CHRISTIAN SCIENCE PUBLISHING SOCIETY   1 Norway St, Boston, MA 02115,
   Tel: (617) 262-2300
   (Publishing)
      Christian Science Monitor, 57A Lucinda Ave., Wahroonga, NSW, 2076, Australia

THE CHUBB CORP   15 Mountain View Rd, Warren, NJ 07060, Tel: (201) 580-2000
   (Holding co: property/casualty ins)
      Chubb Insurance Co. Australia Ltd., Level 17, Grosvenor Pl., 225 George St.,
      Sydney, NSW, Australia

CIGNA CORP   One Liberty Place, 1650 Market St, Philadelphia, PA 19101,
   Tel: (215) 523-4000
   (Ins, invest, health care & other fin servs)
      Cigna Insurance Australia Ltd., Cigna Bldg., 28-34 O'Connell St., GPO Box 4065,
      Sydney 2000, Australia
      Cigna Intl. Investment Advisors Australia Ltd., 28-34 O'Connell St.- 12/F, Sydney,
      Australia
      Cigna Life Insurance Australia Ltd., Cigna Bldg., 28-34 O'Connell St., Sydney,
      NSW 2000, Australia
      Crusader Insurance Co. of Australia Ltd., 28-34 O'Connell St., Sydney 2000,
      Australia
      Esis Intl., Inc., 23-30 Bridge St., Sydney 2000, Australia
      Intl. Rehabilitation Associates Pty. Ltd., Sydney, Australia

CINCOM SYSTEMS INC   2300 Montana Ave, Cincinnati, OH 45211,
   Tel: (513) 662-2300
   (Computer software)
      Cincom Systems of Australia Pty. Ltd., Cincom House 6/F, 486-494 Pacific Highway,
      St. Leonards, NSW 2065, Australia

CITIBANK NA   399 Park Ave, New York, NY 10043, Tel: (212) 559-1000
  (Intl banking)
    Citibank N.A., 54 Carrington St., GPO Box 7064, Sydney, NSW, 2001, Australia
    Citibank N.A., 14th Floor, 257 Collins St., Melbourne, Vic. 3000, Australia
    Citibank N.A., 217 George St., Brisbane, QLD, 4000, Australia
    Citibank N.A., 140 St. George's Terrace, Perth, W.A., 6000, Australia
    Citicopr Australia Ltd., 63 Exhibition St., Melbourne, Vic. 3000, Australia
    Citicorp Australia Ltd., 345 King William St., Adelaide, S.A., 5000, Australia

CLEVELAND-CLIFFS IRON CO   UNion Commerce Bldg, 925 Euclid Ave, Cleveland,
  OH 44115, Tel: (216) 241-2356
  (Iron ore, timber)
    Cliffs W.A. Mining Co. Pty., Ltd., 12 St., George's Terrace, Perth, W.A., 6000,
      Australia

COBE LABORATORIES INC   1185 Oak St, Lakewood, CO 80215, Tel: (303) 232-6800
  (Mfr med equip & supplies)
    COBE Australia, Sydney, Australia

THE COLEMAN CO INC   250 N St Francis Ct, PO Box 1762, Wichita, KS 67201,
  Tel: (316) 261-3485
  (Mfr camping, outdoor & water recreation prdts)
    Australian Coleman Inc., 34 Davis Rd., Wetherill Park, NSW 2164, Australia

COLGATE-PALMOLIVE CO   300 Park Ave, New York, NY 10022, Tel: (212) 310-2000
  (Pharms, cosmetics, toiletries, detergents)
    Colgate-Palmolive Pty., Ltd., 109-113 Pitt St., Sydney, NSW, Australia

COLUMBIA PICTURES INDUSTRIES INC   711 Fifth Ave, New York, NY 10022,
  Tel: (212) 751-4400
  (Producer & distributor of motion pictures)
    Fox Columbia Film Distributors Pty., Ltd., 404-523 George St., Sydney, NSW, 2001,
      Australia

COMBINED INSURANCE CO OF AMERICA   123 N Wacker Dr, Chicago, IL 60606,
  Tel: (312) 701-3000
  (Insurance)
    Combined Insurance Co. of America, 51 Berry St., North Sydney, NSW 2060, Australia

COMBUSTION ENGINEERING INC   900 Long Ridge Road, Stamford, CT 06902,
  Tel: (203) 329-8771
  (Tech constr)
    Lummus Overseas Corp, 213-219 Miller St., North Sydney, NSW, 2060, Australia
    Natco (Australia) Pty., Ltd., P.O. Box 381, 107 Walker St., North Sydney, NSW,
      2060, Australia
    The Ramtite Co. Australia Pty., Ltd., 70 Lawrence Hargrave Drive, Austinmer, NSW,
      2514, Australia

COMMERCE CLEARING HOUSE INC   4025 W Peterson Ave, Chicago, IL 60646,
  Tel: (312) 583-8500
  (Pub topical law report, computer serv)
    CCH Australia Ltd., P.O. Box 230, North Ryde, NSW 2113, Australia

COMMERCIAL INTERTECH CORP   1775 Logan Ave, Youngstown, OH 44501,
  Tel: (216) 746-8011
  (Mfr hydraulic com, metal stampings, pre-engr metal bldgs, fluid purification prdts)

(cont)

Commercial Hydraulics Pty., Ltd., 265 Tubles St., Port Melbourne, Vic. 3207, Australia

COMMERCIAL METALS CO   PO Box 1046, Dallas, TX 75221, Tel: (214) 689-4300
  (Metal collecting/processing, steel mills, metal trading)
    CMC (Australia) Pty. Ltd., Box 113, Horstville, Sydney, NSW 2220, Australia

COMPTON INTERNATIONAL   625 Madison Ave, New York, NY 10022,
  Tel: (212) 754-1100
  (Advertising)
    Compton Advertising (Australia) Pty., Ltd., 41 McLaren St., North Sydney, NSW,
    2060, Australia
    MCR-Compton, 424 St. Kilda Rd., Melbourne, 3004, Australia
    Rose Boon Lorrigan Advertising, 220 St. George's Terrace, Perth, 6000,
    West Australia

COMPUTER ASSOCIATES INTL INC   711 Stewart Ave, Garden City, NY 11530,
  Tel: (516) 227-3300
  (Devel/mkt/mgt info mgt & bus applications software)
    Computer Associates Pty. Ltd., 55 Lavender St., Milsons Point, NSW 2061, Australia

COMPUTERVISION CORP   201 Burlington Rd, Bedford, MA 01730,
  Tel: (617) 275-1800
  (Automation sys, semiconductors)
    Computervision Australia Ltd., 62 Atchison St., St. Leonards, NSW, 2065, Australia

CONOCO INC   600 N Dairy Ashford Rd, Houston, TX 77079, Tel: (713) 293-1000
  (Oil, gas, coal, chems, minerals)
    Conoco Australia Ltd., P.O. Box 6008, Hay St., E. Perth, W. Australia
    Continental Oil Co. of Australia Ltd., IBM Center, 168 Kent St., Sydney, NSW, 2000,
    Australia

CONTINENTAL CARBON CO   10500 Richmond Ave, PO Box 42817, Houston, TX 77242,
  Tel: (713) 978-5700
  (Mfr carbon black)
    Continental Carbon Australia Pty., Ltd., Private Bag, Cronulla, NSW, 2230, Australia

CONTINENTAL INSURANCE CO   180 Maiden Lane, New York, NY 10038,
  Tel: (212) 440-3000
  (Insurance)
    Phoenix Assurance Co., Ltd., 32/34 Bridge St., Sydney NSW, Australia

THE CONTINUUM CO INC   9500 Arboretum Blvd, Austin, TX 78759,
  Tel: (512) 345-5700
  (Design & mkt software for life ins industry)
    Continuum (Australia) Ltd., Level 5- 100 Mount St., North Sydney, NSW 2060,
    Australia

CONTROL DATA CORP   8100 34th Ave S, Minneapolis, MN 55440,
  Tel: (612) 853-8100
  (Control data equip, computer sys serv & financial serv)
    Control Data Australia Pty., Ltd., 598 St. Kilda Rd., Melbourne, Vic. 3004,
    Australia

COOPERTOOLS   PO Box 30100, Raleigh, NC 27622, Tel: (919) 781-7200
  (Mfr hand tools)
    CooperTools Pty. Ltd., P.O. Box 366, 519 Nurigong St., Albury, NSW, 2640, Australia

CORDIS CORP   PO Box 025700, Miami, FL 33102-5700, Tel: (305) 824-2000
  (Mfr med devices & sys)
    Cordis Bio-Synthetics Inc., 10 Munster Ter., N. Melbourne, Vic. 3051, Australia

CORE LABORATORIES   10205 Westheimer, Houston, TX 77042, Tel: (713) 972-6312
  (Petroleum testing/analysis, analytical chem, environmental servs)
    Core Laboratories, P.O. Box 456, Hamilton Central, Brisbane 4007, Australia
    Core Laboratories, P.O. Box 785, Cloverdale, Perth 6105, Australia

CORESTATES FINANCIAL CORP   PO Box 7618, Philadelphia, PA 19101,
  Tel: (215) 973-3100
  (Banking)
    Philadelphia Natl. Bank, 143 Macquarie St., 9th Floor, Sydney, NSW 2000, Australia

CORNING CORP   Houghton Park, PO Box 2000, Corning, NY 14831,
  Tel: (617) 974-9000
  (Mfr glass, ceramic materials)
    Corning Australia Pty. Ltd., P.O. Box 540, 26 Short St., Auburn, NSW 2144, Australia

CORROON & BLACK INTL   Wall Street Plaza, New York, NY 10005,
  Tel: (212) 363-4100
  (Ins brokers)
    Minet Australia Ltd., 155 Queen St., P.O. Box 122 OK, Melbourne, Vic., Australia

COULTER ELECTRONICS INC   590 W 20th St, Hialeah, FL 33010,
  Tel: (305) 885-0131
  (Blood cell & particle counters)
    Coulter Electronics Pty., Ltd., 1-3 Dale St., Brookvale, NSW, 2100, Australia

COURTAULDS PERFORMANCE FILMS   PO Box 5068, Martinsville, VA 24115,
  Tel: (703) 629-1711
  (Mfr solar control & dyed polyester/metal window films)
    Martin Processing (Australia) Pty. Ltd., 1284 Albany Hwy., Cannington, WA 6107,
      Australia
    Martin Processing (Australia) Pty. Ltd., 12 Macewan St., Leederville, WA 6007,
      Australia

CR INDUSTRIES   900 N State St, Elgin, IL 60123, Tel: (708) 742-7840
  (Mfr shaft & face seals)
    CR Industries Pty. Ltd., 4 Shearson Crescent, Mentone, Vic. 3194, Australia

CRANE CO   757 Third Ave, New York, NY 10017, Tel: (212) 415-7300
  (Diversified mfr/distr engineered prdts for ind)
    Crane Australia Pty. Ltd., P.O. Box 101, Dunheved Circuit, St. Mary's, Sydney,
      NSW 2760, Australia

JOHN CRANE INC   6400 Oakton St, Morton Grove, IL 60053, Tel: (708) 967-2400
  (Mfr engineering seals)
    John Crane Australia Pty. Ltd., 166 Eldrige Rd., Bankstown, NSW, 2200, Australia

CRAWFORD FITTING CO   29500 Solon, Solon, OH 44139, Tel: (216) 248-4600
  (Valves, tubes, fittings)
    Australian Swagelok Pty., Ltd., 11 Stanley St., Peakhurst, NSW, 2210, Australia

CRESAP McCORMICK & PAGET INC   245 Park Ave, New York, NY 10167,
  Tel: (212) 953-7000
  (Mgmt consultants)

(cont)

Cresap, McCormick & Paget, Inc., BHP House, 140 William St., Melbourne, Vic. 3000, Australia

CROUSE-HINDS CO   PO Box 4999, Syracuse, NY 13221, Tel: (315) 477-7000
(Mfr electrical constr material)
  Crouse-Hinds (Aust.) Pty., Ltd., P.O. Box 27, Punchbowl, NSW 2196, Australia

CROWN CONTROLS CORP   40 S Washington St, New Bremen, OH 45869,
  Tel: (419) 629-2311
  (Forklift trucks, stackers)
  Crown Controls Australia Pty., Ltd., CNR. Cooper & Long Sts., Smithfield, NSW, 2164, Australia

CUMMINS ENGINE CO INC   PO Box 3005, Columbus, IN 47202, Tel: (812) 377-5000
(Mfr diesel engines)
  Cummins Diesel Australia, 2 Caribbean Dr., Scoresby, Vic. 3179, Australia

CUNA MUTUAL INSURANCE SOCIETY   5910 Mineral Point Road, PO Box 391, Madison,
  WI 53701, Tel: (608) 238-5851
  (Insurance)
  Cuna Mutual Insurance Society, P.O. Box 1418, North Sydney, NSW 2060, Australia

CURTISS-WRIGHT CORP   1200 Wall St, W Lyndhurst, NJ 07071, Tel: (201) 896-8400
(Aircraft engines)
  Dorr-Oliver Pty., Ltd., LDD, Sydney, Australia
  Service Engineers, c/o Quantas Empire Airways, Mascot, NSW, Australia

CUTLER HAMMER INC   4201 North 27th St, Milwaukee, WI 53216,
  Tel: (414) 442-7800
  (Electric control apparatus, mfr of advanced technologic prdts)
  Cutler Hammer Australia Pty., Ltd., Industrial Control Products, 27 Leeds St., P.O. Box 66, Concord West Thodes, NSW, Australia

D'ARCY MASIUS BENTON & BOWLES INC (DMB&B)   1675 Broadway, New York,
  NY 10019, Tel: (212) 468-3622
  (Advertising & communications)
  DMB&B Pty. Ltd., 499 St.Kilda Rd., Melbourne, Vic. 3004, Australia
  DMB&B Weekes Morris Osborn, 28 Richards Ave., Surry Hills, NSW 2010, Australia

D-M-E COMPANY   29111 Stephenson Highway, Madison Heights, MI 48071,
  Tel: (313) 398-6000
  (Basic tooling for plastic molding & die casting)
  Amalgamated Diemould DME Pty Ltd., 10 Warren Ave., Bankstown, NSW 2200, Australia

DAMES & MOORE   911 Wilshire Blvd, Los Angeles, CA 90017, Tel: (213) 683-1560
  (Consulting engineers)
  Australia Agricultural Consulting & Mgmt. Co. Pty. Ltd., 11-13 Bentham St., Adelaide 5000, Australia
  Dames & Moore, Unit 1B, 390 Stuart Hwy., Winnellie 0820, NT, Australia
  Dames & Moore, 25 Buckhurst St., South Melbourne, Vic. 3205, Australia
  Dames & Moore, 84 Alexander St., Crows Nest, NSW 2065, Australia
  Dames & Moore, 26 Lyall St., South Perth 6151, WA, Australia
  Groundwater Resource Consultants, 273 Stirling St., Perth, W.A. 6000, Australia
  Hollingsworth-Dames & Moore, 135 Wickham Ter., Brisbane, Qsld., Australia
  Hollingsworth-Dames & Moore, Comport & Draper Sts., Portsmith, Cairns, Qsld., Australia

DATA GENERAL CORP   4400 Computer Dr, Westboro, MA 01580, Tel: (617) 366-8911
  (Design, mfr gen purpose computer sys & peripheral prdts & servs)
    Data General Australia Pty., Ltd., 100 Dorcas St., S. Melbourne, Vic., 3205,
    Australia

DATAEASE INTL INC   7 Cambridge Dr, Trumbull, CT 06611, Tel: (203) 374-8000
  (Mfr applications devel software)
    Sapphire Australia, 166 Pacific Hwy.- Unit 4, North Sydney, NSW 2060, Australia

DATAPRODUCTS CORP   6200 Canada Ave, PO Box 746, Woodland Hills, CA 91365.
  Tel: (818) 887-8000
  (Mfr computer printers & supplies)
    Dataproducts Corp., Pacific View Business Park, Unit 2/10 Rodborough Rd.,
    Frenchs Forest, NSW 2086, Australia

DAY INTL   333 W First St, Dayton, OH 45412, Tel: (513) 226-7000
  (Diversified auto, ind & household prdts)
    Dayco Australia Pty. Ltd., Unit 2A, 16-18 Milford St., E. Vic. Park, W.A. 6106,
    Australia

DDB NEEDHAM WORLDWIDE INC   437 Madison Ave, New York, NY 10022,
  Tel: (212) 415-2000
  (Advertising)
    Ad.Link DDB Needham Pty. Ltd., 1109 Hay St., Perth, WA 6005, Australia
    DDB Needham Brisbane Pty. Ltd., Revesby House 2/F, 282 Wickham St.,
    Fortitude Valley, Brisbane, Queensland 4006, Australia
    DDB Needham Melbourne Pty. Ltd., 615 St. Kilda Rd., Melbourne, Victoria 3004,
    Australia
    DDB Needham Sydney Pty. Ltd., 76 Berry St.- 10/F, North Sydney, NSW 2060, Australia
    DDB Needham Worldwide Pty. Ltd., 615 St. Kilda Rd., Melbourne, Victoria 3004,
    Australia
    DDB Needham Worldwide Pty. Ltd., 76 Berry St.- 10/F, North Sydney, NSW 2060,
    Australia
    Leonardi & Curtis Advertising Pty. Ltd., 170 Bridport St., Albert Park,
    Victoria 3206, Australia
    Stokes King DDB Needham Pty. Ltd., 190 Fullarton Rd., Dulwich, Adelaide, SA 5065,
    Australia

DE VILBISS CO   300 Phillips Ave, Toledo, OH 43612, Tel: (419) 470-2169
  (Mfr spray painting & finishing equip)
    DeVilbiss Australasia Pty., Ltd., P.O. Box 247, 55 Capella St., Moorabbin,
    Vic. 3189, Australia

DE ZURIK CORP   250 Riverside Ave, Sartell, MN 56377, Tel: (612) 259-2000
  (Mfr manual, process & control valves)
    DeZurik of Australia Pty., Ltd., Vineyard Rd., Sunbury, Vic. 3429, Australia

DEERE & CO   John Deere Rd, Moline, IL 61265, Tel: (309) 752-8000
  (Mfr/sale agri/constr/utility/forestry & lawn/grounds care equip)
    Chamberlain John Deere Pty. Ltd., 72-82 Welshpool Rd., Welshpool, WA 6106, Australia

DEKALB PLANT GENETICS   3100 Sycamore Rd, DeKalb, IL 60115,
  Tel: (815) 753-7333
  (Mfr/genetic res of hybrid corn, sorghum, sunflowers & soybeans)
    Dekalb Shand Seed Co., Pty. Ltd., PO Box 527, Goonoo Goonoo Rd., Tamworth,
    NSW 2340, Australia

DEKALB-PFIZER GENETICS   3100 Sycamore Rd, De Kalb, IL 60115,
  Tel: (815) 756-7333
  (Agric seeds)
     DeKalb Shand Seed Co. Pty., Ltd., P.O. Box 527, Goonoo Rd., Tamworth, NSW 2340,
     Australia

DELTA DRILLING CO   PO Box 2012, Tyler, TX 75710, Tel: (214) 595-1911
  (Oil & gas explor & contract drilling)
     Delta Drilling Co., 39 Creek St., Brisbane, QLD, Australia

DENTSPLY INTL INC   PO Box 872, York, PA 17405, Tel: (717) 845-7511
  (Mfr dental, medical & ind supplies & equip)
     Dentsply (Australia) Pty. Ltd., 58-62 Rupert St., Collingwood, Melbourne,
     Vic. 3066, Australia

DEWITT INTERNATIONAL CORP   5 N Watson Rd, Taylors, SC 29687,
  Tel: (803) 244-8521
  (Mfr over-counter pharms)
     E.C. DeWitt (Australia) Pty., Ltd., P.O. Box 64, Mentone, Vic., Australia,
     Vic. 3189, Australia

DIAMOND CHAIN CO   402 Kentucky Ave, Indianapolis, IN 46225,
  Tel: (317) 638-6431
  (Mfr roller chains)
     Shawman Pty., Ltd., 8 Dalwood Ave., Seaforth, NSW, 2092, Australia

DIAMOND POWER SPECIALTY CORP   PO Box 415, Lancaster, OH 43130,
  Tel: (614) 687-6500
  (Mfr sootblowers & controls, rodding robots, drum level indicators & gauges)
     Diamond Power Australia Pty. Ltd., 5 Hereford Rd., Berkeley Vale, NSW 2259,
     Australia

DIAMOND SHAMROCK CORP   1100 Superior Ave, Cleveland, OH 44114,
  Tel: (216) 694-5000
  (Organic & inorganic chems & specialties, agric chems)
     Diamond Shamrock (Australia) Pty., Ltd., P.O. Box 66, Campbelifield, Broadmeadows,
     Vic. 4061, Australia

DIGITAL EQUIPMENT CORP   129 Parker St, Maynard, MA 01754, Tel: (617) 897-5111
  (Digital computers, digital circuit modules, memory elec- tronic system)
     Digital Equipment Australia Pty., Ltd., P.O. Box 384, Chatswood Plaza, Railway St.,
     Chatswood, NSW, 2067, Australia

DILLINGHAM CONSTRUCTION CORP   5944 Inglewood Dr, Pleasanton, CA 94566,
  Tel: (415) 847-7700
  (General contracting)
     Dillingham Construction Pty. Ltd., Suite 801, 80 Alfred St., Milsons Pt., NSW 2061,
     Australia

DO ALL COMPANY   254 N Laurel Ave, Des Plaines, IL 60016, Tel: (708) 824-1122
  (Distributors of mach tools, metal cutting tools, instru & ind supplies)
     DoAll Australia Pty. Ltd., 13-15 Cann St., Guildford, NSW,2161, Australia

DONALDSON CO INC   PO Box 1299, Minneapolis, MN 55440, Tel: (612) 887-3131
  (Filtration prdts & sys)
     Donaldson Australasia Pty., Ltd., P.O. Box 153, Wyong, NSW, 2259, Australia

DORR-OLIVER INC   612 Wheeler's Farm Rd, PO Box 3819, Milford, CT 06460,
  Tel: (203) 876-5400
  (Mfr process equip for food, pulp & paper, mineral & chem ind; & municipal/ind waste
  treatment)
    Dorr-Oliver Pty., Ltd., 28 Spring St., Chatswood, NSW, 2067, Australia

DOW CHEMICAL CO   2030 Dow Center, Midland, MI 48640, Tel: (517) 636-1000
  (Chems, plastics, fibers, pharms)
    Dow Chemical (Australia) Ltd., 1000 Miller St., N. Sydney, NSW, 2060, Australia

DOW CORNING CORP   2220 W Salzburg Rd, PO Box 1767, Midland, MI 48640,
  Tel: (517) 496-4000
  (Silicones, silicon chems, solid lubricants)
    Dow Corning Australia Pty., Ltd., 21 Tattersall Rd., Blacktown, NSW, 2148, Australia

DRAVO CORP   1 Oliver Plaza, Pittsburgh, PA 15222, Tel: (412) 777-5000
  (Material handling equip, process plants)
    Dravo Pty., Ltd., 30 Atchnson St., St. Leonards, NSW, 2065, Australia

DRESSER INDUSTRIES INC   1600 Pacific Bldg, PO Box 718, Dallas, TX 75221,
  Tel: (214) 740-6000
  (Diversified supplier of equip & tech serv to energy & natural resource ind)
    Dresser Minerals Intl. Inc., P.O. Box 443, Port Hedland, Western Australia
    Dresser Mining Products Div., 79 Spine St., Sumner Park, Queensland, Australia
    Dresser Mining Products Div., Wepco Pty., Ltd., 49 Bassendean Rd.,
      Box 1420 Bayswater, 6053, Western Australia
    Galion Pty., Ltd., P.O. Box 78, Broadmeadows 3047, Vic., Australia
    Harbision A.C.1. Pty., Ltd., P.O. Box 87, Unanderra, NSW 2526, Australia
    Marion Power Shovel Div., Dresser Australia Pty., Ltd., Box 265, Darra,
      Queensland 4076, Australia

DRIVER-HARRIS CO   308 Middlesex St, Harrison, NJ 07029, Tel: (201) 483-4800
  (Wire, cables, etc)
    Driver-Harris Australia Pty., Ltd., Childs Rd., Epping, Vic. 3076, Australia
    Driver-Harris Australia Pty., Ltd., P.O. Box 149, St. Peters, NSW, 2044, Australia

E I DU PONT DE NEMOURS & CO   Du Pont Bldg, 1007 Market St, Wilmington,
  DE 19898, Tel: (302) 774-1000
  (Mfr/sale diversified chems, plastics, specialty prdts & fibers)
    DuPont (Australia) Ltd., P.O. Box 930, N. Sydney, NSW, 2060, Australia

DURACELL INTL INC   Berkshire Industrial Park, Bethel, CT 06801,
  Tel: (203) 796-4000
  (Mfr batteries)
    Duracell Australia Pty., Ltd., P.O. Box 146, North Ryde, NSW, 2113, Australia

DURAMETALLIC CORP   2104 Factory St, Kalamazoo, MI 49001, Tel: (616) 382-8720
  (Mfr mech seals, compression packings, auxiliaries)
    Petch/Durametallic (Australia) Pty. Ltd., 24 Underwood Ave., P.O. Box 210, Botany,
      NSW 2019, Australia

DURIRON CO INC   425 N Findlay St, PO Box 1145, Dayton, OH 45401,
  Tel: (513) 226-4000
  (Mfr chem equip, pumps, valves, filters, fans, heat exchangers)
    Valtek Australia, 1 Cato St., Hawthorn, Vic., Australia

EASTMAN KODAK CO   343 State St, Rochester, NY 14650-0518, Tel: (716) 724-4000
  (Devel/mfr photo & chem prdts, info mgmt/video/copier sys, fibers/plastics for various ind)
    Kodak (Australasia) Pty., Ltd., 173-179 Elizabeth St., Coburg, Vic. 3058, Australia

EATON CORP   100 Erieview Plaza, Cleveland, OH 44114, Tel: (216) 523-5000
  (Advanced tech prdts for transp & ind mkts)
    Eaton Pty., Ltd., 33-35 Garden St., Kilsyth, Vic. 3137, Australia

ECHLIN INC   100 Double Beach Rd, Branford, CT 06405, Tel: (203) 481-5751
  (Mfr motor vehicle replacement parts)
    Echlin Australia Pty. Ltd., P.O. Box 216, S. Melbourne, Vic. 3205, Australia

ECOLAB INC   370 Wabasha St, St Paul, MN 55102, Tel: (612) 293-2233
  (Ind & household detergents, cleaning agents & equip)
    Economics Lab. Pty., Ltd., 57 Moxon Rd., Punchbowl, NSW, 2196, Australia

EG&G INC   45 William St, Wellesley, MA 02181, Tel: (617) 237-5100
  (Diversified instru, components, services)
    EG&G (Australia) Pty. Ltd., 18 Gertrude St., Arncliffe, NSW 2205, Australia

ELECTRO-NITE CO   11601 Caroline Rd, Philadelphia, PA 19154,
  Tel: (215) 464-4200
  (Expendable sensors & instru for iron & steel ind)
    Electro-Nite (Aust.) Pty. Ltd., P.O. Box 150, Caringbah 2229, NSW, Australia

ELECTRONIC ASSOCIATES INC   185 Monmouth Park Hwy, West Long Branch,
  NJ 07764, Tel: (201) 229-1100
  (Analog/hybrid computers, training simulators, energy measurement sys)
    EAI-Associates Pty., Ltd., 48 Achison St., St. Leonards, NSW, 2065, Australia

ELIZABETH ARDEN INC   55 East 52nd St, New York, NY 10055-0191,
  Tel: (212) 407-1000
  (Cosmetics, fragrances, toiletries)
    Elizabeth Arden Pty., Ltd., 4A woodcock Pl., Lane Cove, NSW 2066, Australia

EMCO WHEATON INC   50 Chamberlain Blvd, PO Box 688, Conneaut, OH 44030,
  Tel: (216) 599-8151
  (Mfr petroleum handling equip- ment)
    Wheaton Australia Pty., Ltd., 4 Stanton Rd., P.O. Box 355, Seven Hills, NSW, 2147,
    Australia

ENCYCLOPEDIA BRITANNICA INC   425 N Michigan Ave, Chicago, IL 60611,
  Tel: (312) 321-7000
  (Book publ)
    Encyclopedia Britannica, Inc., 44 Miller St., N. Sydney, NSW, 2060, Australia

ENDO LABORATORIES INC   1000 Stewart Ave, Garden City, NY 11530,
  Tel: (516) 832-2002
  (Ethical pharms)
    Endo Labs, P.O. Box 232, Gordon, NSW, 2071, Australia

ENERPAC   13000 W Silver Spring Dr, Butler, WI 53007, Tel: (414) 781-6600
  (Mfr/sale high pressure hydraulic maint tools)
    Enerpac, 29-31 O'Riordan St., Alexandria, NSW 2015, Australia

ENVIROTECH CORP   3000 Sand Hill Road, Menlo Park, CA 94025,
  Tel: (415) 854-2000
  (Supplier of equip & tech for underground mining, ind processing & pollution control)
    Eimco Mining Machinery Pty., Ltd., P.O. Box 12, 43-45 William St., Alexandria, NSW,
    2015, Australia
    Envirotech Australia Pty., Ltd., P.O. Box 221, 1 Frederick St., Artarmon, NSW,
    2064, Australia

ERIEZ MAGNETICS   PO Box 10652, Erie, PA 16514, Tel: (814) 833-9881
  (Mfr magnetic, vibratory & metal detection prdts & sys)
    Eriez Magnetics Pty., Ltd., 6-8 Malug St., P.O. Box 79, Reservoir, Vic., 3073,
    Australia

ESMARK INC   55 E Monroe St, Chicago, IL 60603, Tel: (312) 431-3600
  (Chems, dairy prdts, petroleum prdts, ins & financial serv)
    Playtex Pty. Ltd., 104 Briens Rd., Northmead, NSW 2145, Australia

ESTEE LAUDER INTL INC   767 Fifth Ave, New York, NY 10019, Tel: (212) 572-4600
  (Cosmetics)
    Estee Lauder (Australia) Pty., Ltd., G.P.O. Box 4307, Sydney, NSW, 2001, Australia

EXPLORATION LOGGING INC   PO Box 40265, Houston, TX 77240, Tel: (713) 744-3600
  (Geological engr & formation evaluation service)
    Exploration Logging of Australia Inc., 43 Planet St., Carlisle, 6101, W. Australia

EXXON CORP   225 E John Carpenter Frwy, Irving, TX 75062, Tel: (214) 444-1000
  (Petroleum & petroleum prdts)
    Exxon Chemical Ltd., 160 Row St., Eastwood 2122, Sydney, Australia

FAFNIR BEARING CO   37 Booth St, New Britain, CT 06050, Tel: (203) 225-5151
  (Ball bearings)
    Fafnir Bearing Div. of Textron Pacific Ltd., P.O. Box 41, Sutherland, NSW, 2232,
    Australia

FAIRCHILD CAMERA & INSTRUMENT CORP   PO Box 58090, Santa Clara,
  CA 95052-8090, Tel: (408) 743-3355
  (Mfr electr instru & controls)
    Fairchild Australia Pty., Ltd., 366 Whitemhorse Rd., Nunawading, Vic. 3131,
    Australia

FARAH INC   8889 Gateway Blvd W, El Paso, TX 79925, Tel: (915) 593-4000
  (Mfr wearing apparel)
    Farah Australia Pty. Ltd., P.O. Box 219, Waterloo, NSW 2017, Australia
    Farah Mfg. Australia Pty., Ltd., Box M. 4, Sydney Mail Exchange, Redfern, NSW,
    Australia

FARREL CORP   25 Main St, Ansonia, CT 06401, Tel: (203) 734-3331
  (Mfr polymer processing equip)
    A. Goninan & Co. Ltd., P.O. Box 21, Broadmeadow, NSW 2292, Australia

FEDERAL-MOGUL CORP   PO Box 1966, Detroit, MI 48235, Tel: (313) 354-7700
  (Mfr/distr vehicular & ind components for original market & aftermarket)
    Federal-Mogul Pty., Ltd., 61-63 Glenvale Crescent, Mulgrave, Vic. 3170, Australia

FELTON INTERNATIONAL INC   599 Johnson Ave, Brooklyn, NY 11237,
  Tel: (212) 497-4664
  (Essential oils & extracts, perfumes & flavor material, aromatic chems)

(cont)

Felton Intl. (Australia) Pty., Ltd., P.O. Box 889, 155 Brougham St., Pott's Point, NSW, 2001, Australia

FENWICK/WOODSTREAM   14799 Chestnut, PO Box 729, Westminster, CA 92683,
Tel: (714) 897-1066
(Fishing rods, blanks & tackle boxes)
Penn-Fenwick, 2 Angas St., Meadowbank, NSW, 2114, Australia

FERRO CORPORATION   One Erieview Plaza, Cleveland, OH 44114,
Tel: (216) 641-8580
(Chems, coatings, plastics, refractories)
Ferro Corp. (Australia) Pty., Ltd., P.O. Box 231, 105-115 Cochranes Rd., Moorabbin, Vic. 3189, Australia

FIRST BOSTON CORP   Park Avenue Plaza, New York, NY 10055, Tel: (212) 909-2000
(Underwriter, distributor & dealer in securities; financial serv)
First Boston Corp., 535 Bourke St., Melbourne, Vic. 3000, Australia

FIRST NATIONAL BANK OF BOSTON   100 Federal St, Boston, MA 02110,
Tel: (617) 434-2200
(Commercial banking)
Bank of Boston, BHP House, 140 Williams St., GPO Box 2273U, Melbourne, Vic. 3000, Australia
Boston Australia Ltd., Quantas Intl. Center, Level 28, Intl. Sq., Sydney, NSW 2000, Australia
Boston Australia Ltd., Allendale Sq., 77 St. George's Ter., Perth, W.A., Australia
Boston Australia Ltd., 127 Creek St., GPO Box 679, Brisbane, Queensland 4001, Australia

FIRST NATIONAL BANK OF CHICAGO   One First National Plaza, Chicago, IL 60670,
Tel: (312) 732-4000
(Financial services)
First Chicago Australia Ltd., First Chicago House, 33 Pitt St., GPO Box 4293, Sydney, NSW, 2000, Australia

FISCHER & PORTER CO   125 E County Line Rd, Warminster, PA 18974,
Tel: (215) 674-6000
(Design/mfr meas, recording & control instru & sys; mfr ind glass prdts)
Fisher & Porter Pty., Ltd., 474-478 Princes Highway, Noble Park, Vic. 3174, Australia

FISHER CONTROLS INTL INC   8000 Maryland Ave, Clayton, MO 63105,
Tel: (314) 694-9900
(Ind process control equip)
Fisher Controls Pty. Ltd., 102 Hassall St., Wetherill Park, NSW 2164, Australia
Fisher Controls Pty. Ltd., 212 Boundary St., Springhill, Queensland 4006, Australia
Fisher Controls Pty. Ltd., 141 Walcott St., Mt. Lawley, WA 6050, Australia
Fisher Controls Pty. Ltd., 5 Cross St., East Brunswick, Vic. 3058, Australia
Southern Controls Pty. Ltd., 4 King St., Blackburn, Vic. 3108, Australia

FLOW CONTROL   PO Box 2117, Houston, TX 77252, Tel: (713) 499-8511
(Mfr rotary drive components & drill rig handling equip)
Flow Control, Geebung, Queensland, Australia

FLOW LABORATORIES INC   7655 Old Springhouse Rd, McLean, VA 22102,
Tel: (703) 893-5900
(Mfr/distr biotechnology)

Flow Laboratories Australasia (Pty.) Ltd., Unit 12, 31 Seven Hills Rd. N.,
P.O. Box 197, Seven Hills 2147, Australia

FLUOR CORP   3333 Michelson Dr, Irvine, CA 92730, Tel: (714) 975-2000
(Engr/constr & related services; coal & lead)
Fluor Daniel Australia Ltd., Melbourne, Vic., Australia

FMC CORP   200 E Randolph Dr, Chicago, IL 60601, Tel: (312) 861-6000
(Mach & chem for industry, agric & govt)
F.M.C. (Australia) Ltd., Box 27, Clayton, Vic. 3168, Australia

FMC MATERIAL HANDLING EQUIP DIV   57 Cooper Ave, Homer City, PA 15748-9234,
Tel: (412) 479-8011
(Mfr bulk material handling & automation equip)
ICAL Ltd., P.O. Box 2, 38 South St., Rydalmere, NSW 2116, Australia

FOOTE CONE & BELDING COMMUNICATIONS INC   101 E Erie St, Chicago,
IL 60611-2897, Tel: (312) 751-7000
(Advertising agency)
FCB/Hocking Advertising Pty. Ltd., 11-13 King William St., Adelaide, SA 5000,
Australia
FCB/Shorter Pty. Ltd., 15 Ord St., West Perth, WA, Australia
Foote, Cone & Belding Pty. Ltd., 10 Quay St., Haymarket, NSW 2000, Sydney, Australia

FORD BACON & DAVIS INC   PO Box 38209, Dallas, TX 75238, Tel: (214) 238-6500
(Engineering & constr)
Ford, Bacon & Davis, Queensland Pty., Ltd., 12417 Creek St., Brisbane, Queensland,
4001, Australia

FORD MOTOR CO   The American Road, Dearborn, MI 48121, Tel: (313) 322-3000
(Mfr automobiles, trucks)
Ford Motor Co. of Australia Ltd., 1735 Sydney Rd., Campbell Field, Vic. 3601,
Australia

FOSTER WHEELER CORP   Perryville Corporate Park, Clinton, NJ 08809-4000,
Tel: (201) 730-4000
(Engr, constr, mfg)
Foster Wheeler Australia Pty., Ltd., 63 Wadham Parade, Mount Waverly, Vic. 3149,
Australia

FRANK RUSSELL CO   909 A St, PO Box 1616, Tacoma, WA 98401-9949,
Tel: (206) 572-9500
(Investment services)
Frank Russell Co., GPO Box 5291, Sydney, NSW 2001, Australia

FRANKLIN ELECTRIC CO INC   400 E Spring St, Bluffton, IN 46714,
Tel: (219) 824-2900
(Mfr fractional h.p motors, submersible motors & controls)
Franklin Electric (Australia) Pty., Ltd., Frankston Rd., P.O. Box 167, Dandenong,
Vic. 3175, , Austral-a

THE FRANKLIN MINT   Franklin Center, PA 19091, Tel: (215) 459-6000
(Creation/mfr/mktg collectible items)
Franklin Mint Pty., Ltd., 742 Springdale Rd., Mulgrave, Vic. 3170, Australia

FREEPORT MINERALS CO   200 Park Ave, New York, NY 10017, Tel: (212) 578-9200
  (Sulfur & kaolin mining, oil & gas, inorganic chems)
    Freeport of Australia Inc., P.O. Box 280, Collins St., Melbourne, Vic. 3000,
    Australia

FULLER CO   2040 Ave C, PO Box 2040, Bethlehem, PA 18001, Tel: (215) 264-6011
  (Ind processing equip & sys, conveying & blending sys, etc)
    GATX-Fuller Australasia Pty., Ltd., P.O. Box 585, Crows Nest, NSW 2065, Australia

H B FULLER CO   2400 Energy Park Dr, St Paul, MN 55108, Tel: (612) 645-3401
  (Mfr/distr adhesives, sealants, coatings, paints, waxes, sanitation chems)
    H.B. Fuller CO. Australia Pty., Ltd., P.O. Box 582, Brookvale, NSW, 2100, Australia
    H.B. Fuller CO. Australia Pty., Ltd., other locations in Australia

GAF CORP   1361 Alps Rd, Wayne, NJ 07470, Tel: (201) 628-3000
  (Chems, bldg materials, commun)
    GAF (Australasia) Pty. Ltd., P.O. Box 18, N. Melbourne 3051, Australia
    GAF Australia, P.O. Box 110, Beaconsfield, NSW 2015, Australia

GAFFNEY CLINE & ASSOCIATES INC   PO Box 796309, Dallas, TX 75379,
  Tel: (214) 733-1183
  (Consultants to energy & mineral ind)
    Gaffney, Cline & Assoc., 2 O'Connell St., 9th fl., Sydney, NSW 2000, Australia

GAMLEN CHEMICAL CO   121 S Maple Ave, S San Francisco, CA 94080,
  Tel: (415) 873-1750
  (Chems, detergents & tank cleansers)
    Gamlen Chemical Co. (Australasia) Pty., Ltd., P.O. Box 441, Lanecove, NSW, 2066,
    Australia
    Gamlen Chemical Co. (Australasia) Pty., Ltd., other locations in Australia

GARDNER-DENVER MINING & CONSTRUCTION   1700 Blue Hills Dr, NE, Roanoke,
  VA 24012-8601, Tel: (703) 343-1837
  (Mfr portable air compressors & related drilling access)
    Gardner-Denver Mining & Construction, New South Wales, Australia

GARLOCK INC   1250 Midtown Tower, Rochester, NY 14604, Tel: (214) 758-0000
  (Mechanical packings)
    Garlock Pty., Ltd., P.O. Box 54, Arncliffe, NSW, 2205, Australia

THE GATES RUBBER CO   PO Box 5887, Denver, CO 80217, Tel: (303) 744-1911
  (Mfr auto/ind belts & hose, hydraulic hose & couplings, molded rubber prdts)
    Gates Australia Pty. Ltd., 37 Dingley Ave., Dandenong, Vic. 3175, Australia

GATX CORP   120 S Riverside Plaza, Chicago, IL 60606, Tel: (312) 621-6200
  (Railcar leasing, maint & mgmt, bulk liquid storage, fin serv, shipping, mineral
  processing)
    Gatx Fuller Australia Pty. Ltd., 113 Alexander St., P.O. Box 585, Crows Nest,
    NSW 2065, Australia
    Gatx Leasing Corp., c/o Chase-NBA Group Ltd., Chase NBA House, 2 Bligh St., Sydney,
    NSW 2000, Australia

GELMAN SCIENCES INC   600 South Wagner St, Ann Arbor, MI 48106,
  Tel: (313) 665-0651
  (Laboratory prdts)
    Gelman Sciences Pty. Ltd., P.O. Box 456, Lane Cove, NSW 2066, Australia

GENERAL AUTOMATION INC   1055 S East St, Anaheim, CA 92806,
Tel: (714) 778-4800
(Computer hardware & serv)
  General Automation Australia Pty., Ltd., 127 Bowden St., Meadowbank, NSW, 2114,
  Australia

GENERAL BINDING CORP   One GBC Plaza, Northbrook, IL 60062,
Tel: (708) 272-3700
(Binding & laminating equip & associated supplies)
  GBC Australia Pty., Ltd., P.O. Box 325, 19 Victoria Rd., Castle Hill, NSW 2154,
  Australia

GENERAL DATACOMM INDUSTRIES INC   1579 Straits Turnpike, Middlebury,
CT 06762-1299, Tel: (203) 574-1118
(Mfr trans equip for commun networks)
  General DataComm Pty. Ltd., 275 Alfred St. North- #404, North Sydney, NSW 2060,
  Australia

GENERAL MOTORS ACCEPTANCE CORP   3044 West Grand Blvd, Detroit, MI 48202,
Tel: (313) 556-5000
(Automobile financing)
  GMAC Australia, 499 St. Kilda Rd., P.O. Box 6180, Melbourne, Vic. 3004, Australia
  GMAC Australia, other locations in Australia

GENERAL MOTORS CORP   3044 W Grand Blvd, Detroit, MI 48202,
Tel: (313) 556-5000
(Automotive prdts, electronics)
  General Motors-Holden's Ltd., GPO Box 1714, Melbourne 3001, Australia

GENERAL REINSURANCE CORP   PO Box 10350, Stamford, CT 06904,
Tel: (203) 328-5000
(Reinsurance)
  Reinsurance Co. of Australasia Ltd., 1 York St., Sydney, NSW, 2000, Australia
  Reinsurance Co. of Australasia Ltd., 31 Queen St., Melbourne, 3000, Vic., Australia

GEOPHYSICAL SYSTEMS CORP   3085 E Foothill Blvd, Pasadena, CA 91107-3106,
Tel: (818) 793-9511
(Mfr seismic data sys for oil/gas explor & engr surveys)
  GeoSystems Pty. Ltd., 173 Planet St., Carlisle, WA 6101, Australia

GETZ CORP   150 Post St, San Francisco, CA 94108, Tel: (415) 772-5500
(Marketing/distribution serv)
  Stelmara Biomedical Ltd., P.O. Box 588, 14 Argent Pl., Ringwood, Vic. 3134,
  Australia

GILBARCO INC   PO Box 22087, Greensboro, NC 27420, Tel: (919) 292-3011
(Service station equip)
  Gilbarco Australia Ltd., P.O. Box 63, 16-34 Talavera Rd., North Ryde, NSW, 2113,
  Australia

GILBERT COMMONWEALTH INTL INC   PO Box 1498, Reading, PA 19603,
Tel: (215) 775-2600
(Studies, engr & design, constr & project mgmt, technologies & training for ind &
govts)
  Gilbert Associates (Australia) Pty. Ltd., P.O. Box 201, 2 Thomas St., Chatswood,
  NSW 2067, Australia

(cont)

Gilbert-CMPS Engineers, P.O. Box 361, 685 Burke Rd., Camberwell, Vic. 3124, Australia

THE GILLETTE CO   Prudential Tower, Boston, MA 02199, Tel: (617) 421-7000
(Mfr/distr shaving prdts, toiletries & cosmetics, stationery prdts)
   Gillette (Australia) Pty.., Ltd., 504-520 Princes Hwy., Noble Park, Vic. 3174, Australia

GK TECHNOLOGIES INC   500 W Putnam Ave, Greenwich, CT 06830,
   Tel: (203) 661-0100
(Wire cable, electronic tech serv)
   Australia Puregas (Australia) Pty., Ltd., G.K. Technologies, Rydalmere, Sydney, Australia

GLOBAL INTERNATIONAL   500 Ygnacio Valley Rd, #175, Walnut Creek, CA 94596,
   Tel: (415) 933-2293
(Freight forwarding)
   Global Forwarding (Australia), 22 Kameruka Rd., PO Box 318, Northbridge, NSW 2063, Australia

GOODYEAR TIRE & RUBBER CO   1144 E Market St, Akron, OH 44316-0001,
   Tel: (216) 796-2121
(Mfr tires, rubber prdts)
   Goodyear Australia Ltd., 11 Grand Ave., Camellia, NSW 2142, Australia

GOULD INC   10 Gould Center, Rolling Meadows, IL 60008, Tel: (708) 640-4000
 .(Electric sys, batteries, etc)
   Imperial Eastman Pty., Ltd., Sydney, NSW, Australia

W R GRACE & CO   1114 Ave of the Americas, New York, NY 10036,
   Tel: (212) 819-5500
(Specialty chems, natural resources, consumer serv)
   Bekaert Australia Pty., Ltd., P.O. Box 408, Dandendon, Vic. 3175, Australia
   W.R. Grace Australia Ltd., 1126 Sydney Rd., Fawkner, Vic. 3060, Australia

GRAPHIC CONTROLS CORP   PO Box 1271, Buffalo, NY 14240, Tel: (716) 853-7500
(Mfr plotter supplies, ind/med recording charts, fax papers, disposable med prdts & pens)
   Miller Graphic Controls Pty. Ltd., P.O. Box 199, Clifton Hill, Vic. 3068, Australia

GREY ADVERTISING INC   777 Third Ave, New York, NY 10017, Tel: (212) 546-2000
(Advertising)
   Grey Advertising Australia Pty., Ltd., 21 Grosvenor St., P.O. Box 294,
   Neutral Bay Junction, NSW, 2089, Australia

GRIFFITH LABORATORIES INC   I Griffith Center, Alsip, IL 60658,
   Tel: (708) 371-0900
(Ind food ingredients & equip)
   Griffith Labs Pty., Ltd., 1 Griffith St., Scoresby, Vic. 3179, Australia
   Griffith Labs Pty., Ltd., 23 Britton St., Smithfield, NSW 2164, Australia

GROLIER INC   Old Shereman Tpk, Danbury, CT 06816, Tel: (203) 797-3500
(Publishers)
   Grolier Society of Australia Pty., Ltd., 1 Campbell St., Artarmon, NSW, 2064, Australia
   Grolier Society of Australia Pty., Ltd., P.O. Box 410, Crows Nest, NSW 2065, Australia

GTE CORP   One Stamford Forum, Stamford, CT 06904, Tel: (203) 965-2000
  (Electr prdts, telecom sys, publ & commun)
    GTE, Sylvania Way, P.O. Box 450, Lisarow Gofford, NSW, 2250, Australia

GUARDIAN INDUSTRIES CORP   43043 W Nine Mile Rd, Northville, MI 48167,
  Tel: (313) 349-6700
  (Mfr & fabricate flat glass prdts, insulation materials)
    Permaglass (Australia) Pty., Ltd., P.O. Box 339, Chring Bah, 2229 NSW, Australia
    Sydney Glass Co. Pty., Ltd., 578 Princes Hwy., St. Peters, NSW 2044, Australia

GULF & WESTERN INDUSTRIES INC   1 Gulf & Western Plaza, New York, NY 10023,
  Tel: (212) 333-7000
  (Widely diversified multi-industry company in consumer prdts)
    Eagle Signal Co. of Australia Pty., Ltd., 599-601 Vic. St., Abbotsford, Vic. 3067,
    Australia

FRANK B HALL & CO INC   549 Pleasantville Rd, Briarcliff Manor, NY 10510,
  Tel: (914) 769-9200
  (Insurance)
    Frank B. Hall & Co. Australia Pty. Ltd., P.O. Box 4189, 1 York St., Sydney,
    NSW 2001, Australia
    Leslie Godwin & Garroway, Box 4189, GPO 1, York St., Sydney, 2000 NSW, Australia
    Leslie Godwin & Garroway of Australia Pty., Ltd., 454-456 Collins St., Melbourne,
    Vic. 3000, Australia

HALLMARK CARDS INC   PO Box 419580, Kansas City, MO 64141, Tel: (816) 274-5100
  (Mfr greeting cards & related prdts)
    Hallmark Cards Australia, Ltd., 611 Blackburn Rd., PO Box 140, N. Clayton,
    Victoria, Australia

HARCOURT BRACE JOVANOVICH INC   Harcourt Brace Jovanovich Bldg, Orlando,
  FL 32887, Tel: (305) 345-2000
  (Book publ, tests & related serv, journals, facisimile reprints, mgmt consult,
  operates parks/shows)
    Harcourt Brace Jovanovich Group (Australia) Pty., Ltd., P.O. Box 300, North Ryde,
    NSW, 2113, Australia

HARNISCHFEGER INDUSTRIES INC   PO Box 554, Milwaukee, WI 53201,
  Tel: (414) 671-4400
  (Mfr mining & material handling equip, papermaking mach, computer sys)
    Harnischfeger of Australia Pty., Ltd., P.O. Box 231, East Brisbane, Qsld. 4169,
    Australia

HARPER & ROW PUBLISHERS INC   10 E 53rd St, New York, NY 10022,
  Tel: (212) 593-7000
  (Book publishers)
    Harper & Row Australasia Pty. Ltd., P.O. Box 226, Artarmon, NSW 2064, Australia

THE HARPER GROUP INC   260 Townsend St, PO Box 77933, San Francisco,
  CA 94107, Tel: (415) 978-0600
  (Ocean/air freight fwdg, customs brokerage, packing & whse, logistics mgt, ins)
    Circle Freight Intl. Pty. Ltd., PO Box 138, Melbourne Airport, Victoria 3045,
    Australia

HARSCO CORP   PO Box 8888, Camp Hill, PA 17011-8888, Tel: (717) 763-7064
  (Diversified mfr & serv)
    Breckett Pty. Ltd., P.O. Box 354, Wollongong East, NSW 2520, Australia

(cont)

Harsco (Australia) Pty., Ltd., c/o Coopers & Lybrand, 6 O'Connell St., Sydney,
   NSW 2000, Australia

THE HARTFORD INSURANCE GROUP   Hartford Plaza, Hartford, CT 06115,
   Tel: (203) 547-5000
   (Insurance)
   Hartford Fire INTL. lTD.Co., 27-31 Macquarie Place, sydney, NSW 2001, Australia

HCA INTL CO   1 Park Plaza, PO Box 550, Nashville, TN 37202,
   Tel: (615) 327-9551
   (Hospital & health care mgmt)
   HCA Australia, Level 3, Phillips Bldg., 15 Blue St., P.O. Box 1409, North Sydney,
   NSW 2060, Australia

HECKETT DIV   PO Box 1071, Butler, PA 16001, Tel: (412) 283-5741
   (Metal reclamation)
   Breckett Pty., Ltd., P.O. Box 354, Wollongong, NSW, Australia

HEINEMANN ELECTRIC CO   PO Box 6800, Lawrenceville, NJ 08648-0800,
   Tel: (609) 882-4800
   (Mfr circuit breakers, relays, etc.)
   Heinemann Electric (Australia) Pty., Ltd., 821-129 Springvale Rd., Box 241,
   Springvale, N. Vic. 3171, Australia

H J HEINZ CO   PO Box 57, Pittsburgh, PA 15230, Tel: (412) 456-5100
   (Food prdts)
   H.J. Heinz Co. Australia Ltd., P.O. Box 57, Dandenong, Vic. 3175, Australia

HERCULES INC   Hercules Plaza, Wilmington, DE 19894, Tel: (302) 594-5000
   (Mfr spec chems, plastics, film & fibers, coatings, resins, food ingredients)
   Australian Holdings Co. Ltd., 49-61 Stephen Rd., P.O. Box 59, Botany, NSW 2019,
   Australia

HERTZ CORP   225 Brae Blvd, Park Ridge, NJ 07656-0713, Tel: (201) 307-2000
   (Automobile rental)
   Hertz Asia Pacific Ltd., 10 Dorcas St., So. Melbourne, Vic. 3205, Australia

HEWLETT-PACKARD CO   3000 Hanover St, PO Box 10301, Palo Alto, CA 94303-0890,
   Tel: (415) 857-1501
   (Mfr measurement & computation prdts & sys)
   Hewlett-Packard Australia Pty., Ltd., P.O. Box 221, Blackburn, Vic. 3130, Australia

HILL & KNOWLTON INC   420 Lexington Ave, New York, NY 10017,
   Tel: (212) 697-5600
   (Public relations, public affairs, comm counseling)
   Eric White Associates Pty. Ltd., 115 Pitt St., Sydney, NSW, 2000, Australia
   Eric White Associates Pty. Ltd., 246 St. George' Terrace, Perth, WA 6000, Australia
   Eric White Associates Pty. Ltd., 25-27 Franklin St., Adelaide 5000, SA, Australia

HOBART BROTHERS CO   Hobart Sq, Troy, OH 45373-2928, Tel: (513) 339-6000
   (Arc/automatic welding sys, power sys)
   Hobart Mfg. Co. Pty., Ltd., P.O. Box 100, Concord, NSW, 2137, Australia

HOMELITE TEXTRON   14401 Carowinds Blvd, Charlotte, NC 28217,
   Tel: (704) 588-3200
   (Mfr pumps, generators, lawn/garden equip, outdoor power equip)
   Homelite Div. of Textron Pacific Ltd., P.O. Box 209, Blackburn, Vic. 3130, Australia

HOMESTAKE MINING CO   650 California St, San Francisco, CA 94108,
  Tel: (415) 981-8150
  (Precious metal & mineral mining)
    Homestake Iron Ore Co. of Australia Ltd., P.O. Box 338, Norwood, 5067,
      South Australia

THE HOOVER GROUP   403 W 4th St N, Newton, IA 50208, Tel: (515) 792-8000
  (Mfr floor care prdts, laundry & refrig appliances)
    Hoover (Australia Pty., Ltd., P.O. Box 101, West Ryde, NSW, 2114, Australia

HORWATH & HORWATH INTL   919 Third Ave, New York, NY 10022,
  Tel: (212) 980-3100
  (Public accountants & auditors)
    Howarth & Howarth Intl., 69 Finniss St., N. Adelaide, S.A., 5006, Australia
    Howarth & Howarth Intl., other locations in Australia

E F HOUGHTON & CO   PO Box 930, Valley Forge, PA 19482-0930,
  Tel: (215) 666-4000
  (Mfr spec chems, hydraulic fluids, lubricants)
    Paykel Oils & Chemicals NSW, Pty., Ltd., Tennyson Rd. & N. Cote St., Mortlake,
      P.O. Box 29, Concord, Sydney, NSW 2137, Australia
    Paykel Oils & Chemicals Pty. Ltd., Moorabbin, 287 Wickham Rd., Melcourne,
      Vic. 3189, Australia

HOUSEHOLD INTL INC   2700 Sanders Rd, Prospect Heights, IL 60070,
  Tel: (708) 564-5000
  (Financial services)
    Household Financial Services Ltd., 33 Herbert St., St. Leonards, NSW 2068, Australia

HOWE-BAKER ENGINEERS INC   PO Box 956, Tyler, TX 75710, Tel: (214) 597-0311
  (Design, fabricate, erect process sys for petroleum ind)
    Australian American Engineering Corp. Pty. Ltd., 25 Argyle St., Fitzroy, Vic. 3065,
      Australia

HPD INC   1717 N Naper Blvd, Naperville, IL 60540, Tel: (708) 357-7330
  (Personal processing, recovery/ pollution control sys)
    Mauri Process Equipment Co., P.O. Box 184, GPO Sydney, Australia

HUCK MFG CO   PO Box 19590, Irvine, CA 92713, Tel: (714) 855-9000
  (Mfr fasteners & fastening sys)
    Huck Australia, Private Bag 21, Mulgrave North, Vic. 3170, Australia

HUGHES TOOL CO   PO Box 2539, Houston, TX 77001, Tel: (713) 924-2222
  (Equip & serv to oil & gas explor & prod ind)
    Hughes Tool Co. of Australia Ltd., 420 George St., Brisbane, QLD, 4000, Australia

HYATT INTL CORP   200 West Madison St, Chicago, IL 60606, Tel: (312) 750-1234
  (Intl hotel mgmt)
    Hyatt Kingsgate Sydney, P.O. Box 252, Kings Cross, Sydney NSW, 2011, Australia
    Hyatt on Collins, Russell & Collins Sts., Melbourne, Australia

HYDROMATION FILTER CO   39201 Amrhein Rd, Livonia, MI 48150,
  Tel: (313) 464-0600
  (Ind filter sys)
    Hydromation Austral, Pty., Ltd., P.O. Box 54, Colchester Rd., Bayswater, Vic. 3153,
      Australia

HYSTER CO   PO Box 2902, Portland, OR 97208, Tel: (503) 280-7000
   (Fork lifts, trucks, trailers, towing winches, personnel lifts, compaction equip)
      Hyster Australia Pty., Ltd., Ashford Ave., Milperra, NSW, 2214, Australia, 2213,
      Panania P.O. Box 100

ICF KAISER ENGINEERS   1800 Harrison St, Oakland, CA 94612,
   Tel: (415) 268-6000
   (Engineering & constr)
      Kaiser Engineers, Perth, Australia
      Kaiser Engineers, Melbourne, Australia

ICS INTERNATIONAL INC   Oak St & Pawnee Ave, Scranton, PA 18515,
   Tel: (717) 342-7701
   (Correspondence courses)
      I.C.S. (Australasia) Pty., Ltd., 398 Pacific Hwy., Lane Cove, NSW 206s6 Australia

IDEAL TOY CORP   184-10 Jamaica Ave, Hollis, NY 11423, Tel: (212) 454-5000
   (Toys, games, dolls)
      Kenbrite Corp. Pty., Ltd., 1-3 Power St., S. Melbourne, Vic. 3205, Australia

ILLINOIS TOOL WORKS INC   8501 West Higgins Rd, Chicago, IL 60631,
   Tel: (312)693-3040
   (Metal cutting tools, fasteners, sealants, gear measuring instru)
      W.A. Deutsher, Pty. Ltd., P.O. Box 154, Melbourne & Sydney, 3189, Australia

IMCO CONTAINER CO   451 Florida Blvd, Baton Rouge, LA 70801,
   Tel: (504) 388-8011
   (Plastic containers)
      Australia Asia Packaging & Processing, Lysterfield Rd., Ferntree Gully, Vic.,
      Australia

IMS INTERNATIONAL INC   800 Third Ave, New York, NY 10022, Tel: (212) 371-2310
   (Market research reports)
      Intercontinental Medical Statistics (Australasia) Pty., Ltd., Administration &,
      Market Research Div., P.O. Box 372, Crows Nest, NSW, 2065, Australia

INA CORPORATION   1600 Arch St, Philadelphia, PA 19101, Tel: (215) 523-5335
   (Holding co: ins, financial serv)
      Insurance Co. of North America (Australia) Ltd., 7th Floor, Grenfell Centre,
      25 Grenfell St., GPO 1763, Adelaide, Australia
      Insurance Co. of North America (Australia) Ltd., Brisbane, Hobart, Melbourne,
      Perth, Sydney, Australia

INCOM INTERNATIONAL INC   3450 Princeton Pike, Lawrenceville, NJ 08648,
   Tel: (609) 896-7600
   (Roller & motorcycle chains, drive components, marine controls, etc)
      Teleflex Morse Pty., Ltd., P.O. Box 118, 22 Waltham St., Artarmon, NSW 2064,
      Australia

INDUCTOTHERM CORP   10 Indel Ave, Rancocas, NJ 08073, Tel: (609) 267-9000
   (Mfr induction melting furnaces)
      Dorman Equipment Pty. Ltd., 62 Bardia Ave., Seaford, Vic. 3198, Australia
      Inductotherm (Melting) Pty. Ltd., P.O. Box 171, 62 Bardia Ave., Seaford, Vic. 3198,
      Australia

INFORMATION BUILDERS INC   1250 Broadway, New York, NY 10001,
   Tel: (212) 736-4433
   (Devel/serv computer software)
      FOCUS Technologies Pty. Ltd., 22 Upton Rd., Windsor, Vic. 3181, Australia

INGERSOLL-RAND CO   200 Chestnut Ridge Rd, Woodcliff Lake, NJ 07675,
   Tel: (201) 573-0123
   (Mfr compressors, rock drills, pumps, air tools)
      Ingersoll-Rand Australia Ltd., Dandenong, 3175, Vic., Australia

INSTRON CORP   100 Royall St, Canton, MA 02021, Tel: (617) 828-2500
   (Testing instru)
      Instron Corp. Australia Pty., Factory 15, 15 Stud Rd., Bayswater, Vic. 3153,
         Australia
      Instron Corp. Australia Pty., 65 Home St., #20, Crows Nest, NSW 2065, Australia

INTERMEC CORP   6001 36th Ave West, Everett, WA 98203-9280,
   Tel: (206) 348-2600
   (Mfr automated data collection sys)
      Intermec Australia Pty. Ltd., 7-9 Gilby Rd., Mt. Waverly, Victoria 3149, Australia
      Intermec Pty. Ltd., 818 Pittwater Rd.- #14, Dee Way, NSW 2009, Australia

INTERNATIONAL BUSINESS MACHINES (IBM)   Old Orchard Rd, Armonk,
   NY 10504-1783, Tel: (914) 765-1900
   (Info-handling sys, equip & serv)
      IBM Australia Ltd., 168 Kent St., Sydney, NSW, Australia

INTERNATIONAL FLAVORS & FRAGRANCES INC   521 W 57th St, New York, NY 10019,
   Tel: (212) 765-5500
   (Create/mfr flavors, fragrances & aroma chems)
      Intl. Flavors & Fragrances Australia Pty., Ltd., 156 S. Creek Rd., Dee Way, NSW,
         2099, Australia

INTERNATIONAL PAPER   2 Manhattanville Rd, Purchase, NY 10577,
   Tel: (914) 397-1500
   (Mfr/distr container board, paper, wood prdts)
      International Paper Co. Pty. Ltd., P.O. Box H3 Australia Sq., NSW, Australia

IRVING TRUST CO   1 Wall St, New York, NY 10015, Tel: (212) 487-2121
   (Intl banking)
      Australian Intl. Finance Corp., Ltd., Dalgety House, 461 Bourke St., Melbourne,
         Vic., Australia
      Irving Trust Co., 140 William St., Melbourne, Vic. 3000, Australia

ITEL CONTAINERS INTL CORP   55 Francisco St, San Francisco, CA 94133,
   Tel: (415) 984-4400
   (Leasing, repair, storage of ocean-going containers)
      Itel Containers Corp. Intl., Level 6, Guardian Insurance Bldg., 34 Hunter St.,
         Sydney 2000, Australia

ITT CORP   1330 Ave of the Americas, New York, NY 10019, Tel: (212) 258-1000
   (Diversified mfr, tech & services)
      Standard Telephones & Cables, 552-280 Botany Rd., Alexandria, NSW 2015, Australia

ITT SHERATON CORP   60 State St, Boston, MA 02108, Tel: (617) 367-3600
   (Hotel operations)
      Sheraton Hotels in Australia, Kindersley House, 33 Bligh St., Sydney, NSW 2000,
      Australia

JOHNSON & HIGGINS   125 Broad St, New York, NY 10005, Tel: (212) 574-7000
   (Ins brokerage, benefit conslt)
      Willis Faber Johnson & Higgins Pty., Ltd., AMP Centre, 50 Bridge St., Sydney, NSW,
      2000, Australia

JOHNSON & JOHNSON   One Johnson & Johnson Plaza, New Brunswick, NJ 08933,
   Tel: (201) 524-0400
   (Surgical, med & baby prdts)
      Extal Pty. Ltd., Westbury, Tasmania, Australia
      Janssen-Cilag Pty. Ltd., Lane Cove, Australia
      Johnaon & Johnson Australia Pty. Ltd., Sydney, Australia
      Johnson & Johnson Medical Pty. Ltd., North Ryde, Australia

S C JOHNSON & SON INC   1525 Howe St, Racine, WI 53403, Tel: (414) 631-2000
   (Home, auto, commercial & personal care prdts, specialty chems)
      S.C. Johnson & Son Pty., Ltd., P.O. Box 277, Milsons Point, NSW, 2061, Australia

JOHNSON CONTROLS INC   5757 W Green Bay Ave, PO Box 591, Milwaukee, WI 53201,
   Tel: (414) 228-1200
   (Mfr facility mgmt & control sys, auto seating, batteries & plastics)
      Johnson Controls Australia Pty. Ltd., 126 Beaconsfield St., Auburn, NSW 2114,
      Australia
      Johnson Controls Australia Pty. Ltd., other locations in Australia

JOY TECHNOLOGIES INC   301 Grant St, Pittsburgh, PA 15219, Tel: (412) 562-4500
   (Mfr coal mining, air pollution control, materials mgmt & incineration equip, fans)
      Joy Manufacturing Co. (Pty.) Ltd., Vale Rd., Moss Vale, NSW 2577, Australia

K-TEL INTL INC   15525 Medina Rd, Plymouth, MN 55447, Tel: (612) 559-6800
   (Packaged consumer entertainment & convenience prdts)
      Majestic Leisure Products Pty. Ltd., 57-59 Alleyne St., Chatswood, NSW 2067,
      Australia

KAISER ALUMINUM & CHEMICAL CORP   300 Lakeside Dr, Oakland, CA 94643,
   Tel: (415) 271-3300
   (Aluminum & aluminum prdts, chems)
      Kaiser Refractories Ltd., 54-56 Adderly St., Auburn, 2144, NSW, Australia
      Kaiser Refractories Ltd., other locations in Australia

KALLESTAD DIAGNOSTICS INC   1000 Lake Hazeltine Dr, Chaska, MN 55318,
   Tel: (612) 448-4848
   (Mfr med diagnostic instru & test kits)
      Kallestad (Australia) Pty. Ltd., 140 Arthur St.- 4/F, N. Sydney, NSW 2060, Australia

KAMDEN INTL SHIPPING INC   167-41 147th Ave, Jamaica, NY 11434,
   Tel: (718) 917-8181
   (Freight forwarding servs)
      Kamden Intl. Shipping Pty. Ltd., PO Box 170, Melbourne Airport, Victoria 3045,
      Australia

KELLOGG CO   235 Porter St, Battle Creek, MI 49016, Tel: (616) 966-2000
(Food prdts)
 Kellogg (Australia) Pty., Ltd., Battle Creek, Ml 49016

KEMPER INTL INSURANCE CO   Route 22, Long Grove, IL 60049, Tel: (708) 540-2000
(Property casualty ins)
 Kemper Insurance Co. Ltd., Box H205, Australia Sq., NSW 2000, Australia

KENNAMETAL INC   PO Box 231, Latrobe, PA 15650, Tel: (412) 539-5000
(Tools, hard carbide & tungsten alloys)
 Kennametal Australia Pty., Ltd., 73 Banksia St., Botany, NSW, 2019, Australia

KENNECOTT CORP   1717 Midland Bldg, Cleveland, OH 44115, Tel: (203) 964-3000
(Minerals & metals)
 Kennecott Exploration Ltd., 60 Margaret St., P.O. Box 471, GPO Sydney, NSW 2001,
 Australia

KENNEDY VAN SAUN CORP   PO Box 500, Danville, PA 17821, Tel: (717) 275-3050
(Mineral processing & handling equip)
 McNally Australia Pty., Ltd., Centre Court, 25 Paul St., P.O. Box 142, North Ryde,
 NSW 2113, Australia

KENT-MOORE CORP   28635 Mound Rd, Warren, MI 48092, Tel: (313) 574-2332
(Mfr service equip for auto, constr, recreational, military & agric vehicles)
 Kent-Moore Australia Pty., Ltd., Unit 2, Gladstone Rd., Castle Hill, NSW 2154,
 Australia

KEPNER-TREGOE INC   Research Rd, PO Box 704, Princeton, NJ 08542,
 Tel: (609) 921-2806
(Mgmt & organizational devel)
 Kepner-Tregoe (Australia) Pty. Ltd., P.O. Box 407, Neutral Bay Jct., NSW 2087,
 Australia

KEYES FIBRE CO   3003 Summer St, Stamford, CT 06905, Tel: (203) 357-9100
(Molded containers)
 Van Leer Food Packaging, P.O. Box 215, Preston, Vic. 3072, Australia

KEYSTONE INTL INC   PO Box 40010, Houston, TX 77040, Tel: (713) 466-1176
(Mfr butterfly valves, actuators & control accessories)
 Keystone Valve, (Australia) Pty., Ltd., P.O. Box 517, Nowra, NSW, 2540, Australia

KIDDER PEABODY GROUP INC   10 Hanover Sq, New York, NY 10005,
 Tel: (212) 510-3000
(Investment banking)
 Kidder, Peabody Australia Ltd., Level 9, Grosvenor Pl., 225 George St., Sydney,
 NSW 2000, Australia

KIMBERLY-CLARK CORP   PO Box 619100, Dallas, TX 75261-1200,
 Tel: (214) 830-1200
(Mfr fiber-based prdts for personal care, pulp & forest prdts; air transport)
 Kimberly-Clark of Australia Pty., Ltd., 20 Alfred St., Milsons Point, NSW, 2061,
 Australia

KINNEY SHOE CORP   233 Broadway, New York, NY 10279, Tel: (212) 720-3700
(Mfr/sale footwear & apparel)
 The Mathers/Williams Group, 140 Melbourne St., South Brisbane, Qld. 4101, Australia

KNOGO CORP   350 Wireless Blvd, Hauppauge, NY 11788, Tel: (516) 232-2100
  (Mfr electr article surveillance sys)
     Knogo Australia Pty. Ltd., 82 Reserve Rd.- Unit 15, Artarmon, NSW 2064, Australia

KOEHRING CO   PO Box 312, Milwaukee, WI 53201, Tel: (414) 784-5800
  (Pulp mill & constr equip)
     Noyes Bros. Pty., Ltd., Frederick St., St. Leonards, NSW, 2065, Australia

KOLMAR LABORATORIES INC   123 Pike St, Port Jervis, NY 12771,
  Tel: (914) 856-5311
  (Contract mfr: cosmetics, pharms, household prdts)
     Kolmar (Australia) Pty., Ltd., 45 King Rd., Hornsby, NSW, 2077, Australia

KOPPERS CO INC   Koppers Bldg, 437 Seventh Ave, Pittsburgh, PA 15219,
  Tel: (412) 227-2000
  (Constr materiald & serv; chem & bldg prdts)
     Koppers Australia Pty., Ltd., 6th Floor, Gold Fields House, Sydney Cove,
       B.P.O. 4192, Sydney, NSW, Australia

KORN/FERRY INTL   237 Park Ave, New York, NY 10017, Tel: (212) 687-1834
  (Executive search)
     Korn/Ferry Intl. Pty. Ltd., 80 Collins St., Melbourne, Vic. 3000, Australia
     Korn/Ferry Intl. Pty. Ltd., Top of Kyle, Macquarie Pl., Sydney, NSW 2000, Australia

KRAFT INC   Kraft Court, Glenview, IL 60025, Tel: (708) 998-2000
  (Dairy prdts, processed food, chems)
     Kraft Foods Ltd., GPO Box 1673N. Melbourne, Vic. 3001, Australia

LE TOURNEAU INC LONGVIEW DIV   PO Box 2307, Longview, TX 75606,
  Tel: (214) 753-3449
  (Heavy constr, mining mach & equip)
     Morgan Equipment (Australia) Pty., Ltd., P.O. Box 213, Roklea 4106, Australia

LEEDS & NORTHRUP CO   Sumneytown Pike, North Wales, PA 19454,
  Tel: (215) 699-2000
  (Mfr process control instru & sys)
     Leeds & Northrup Australia, P.O. Box 155, Alexandria, NSW 2015, Australia

LENNOX INDUSTRIES INC   Box 809000, Dallas, TX 75380-9000, Tel: (214) 980-6000
  (Mfr heating & A/C equip)
     Lennox Australia Pty. Ltd., P.O. Box 818, Geelong, Australia

LESLIE SALT CO   7200 Central Ave, Box 364, Newark, CA 94560,
  Tel: (415) 797-1820
  (Salt, salad oils, mayonnaise)
     Leslie Salt Co., City Center Tower, 15th Floor, 44 St. George's Terrace, Perth,
       6000, Western Australia

LEVI STRAUSS & CO   1155 Battery, San Francisco, CA 94111, Tel: (415) 544-6000
  (Mfr wearing apparel)
     Levi Strauss (Australia) Pty., Ltd., 41 McLaren St., North Sydney, 2060, NSW,
       Australia

ELI LILLY & CO   307 E McCarty St, Indianapolis, IN 46285, Tel: (317) 261-2000
  (Pharms, agric & cosmetic prdts)
     Lilly Industries Pty., Ltd., Wharf Rd., West Ryde, NSW, 2114, Australia

THE LINCOLN ELECTRIC CO   22801 St Clair Ave, Cleveland, OH 44117,
  Tel: (216) 481-8100
  (Mfr arc welding equip & consumables, elec motors)
    Lincoln Electric Co. (Australia) Pty., Ltd., 35 Bryant St., Padstow 2211, Sydney,
    Ausralia

LINTAS:WORLDWIDE   1 Dag Hammarskjold Plaza, New York, NY 10017,
  Tel: (212) 605-8000
  (Advertising agency)
    Lintas:Sydney, The Denison 10/F, 65 Berry St., N. Sydney, NSW 2060, Australia

LOCKHEED CORP   2555 N Hollywood Way, Burbank, CA 91520, Tel: (213) 847-6121
  (Aircraft, missiles, etc)
    Lockheed Aircraft (Australia) Pty., Ltd., P.O. Box 359, London Circuit, Canberra,
    A.C.T., 2601, Australia

LOFFLAND BROTHERS CO   8301 E 51st St, PO Box 2847, Tulsa, OK 74101,
  Tel: (918) 622-9330
  (Oil & gas well drilling contractor)
    Loffland Bros. North Sea Inc., Box 603, Dawson St., West, Sale, Vic., 3850,
    Australia

LONGYEAR CO   PO Box 27314, Salt Lake City, UT 84127, Tel: (801) 972-1395
  (Mfr diamond drills, concrete cutting equip; drill serv)
    Longyear Australia Pty. Ltd., 919-929 Marion Rd., Mitchell Park SA, 5043, Australia

THE LOVABLE CO   2121 Peachtree Ind Blvd, Buford, GA 30518,
  Tel: (404) 945-2171
  (Mfr women's undergarments)
    Lovable Co. (Australia) Pty., Ltd., 428 George St., Sydney, NSW, Australia

LUBRIZOL CORP   29400 Lakeland Blvd, Wickliffe, OH 44092, Tel: (216) 943-4200
  (Chem additives for lubricants & fuels)
    Lubrizol Australia, 28 River St., North Lidcombe, NSW, 2144, Australia

M&T CHEMICALS INC   PO Box 1104, Rahway, NJ 07065, Tel: (201) 499-0200
  (Specialty chems & application technologies)
    M & T Products Pty., Ltd., P.O. Box 201, Princes Hwy., Springvale, Vic. 3171,
    Australia

MACK TRUCKS INC   2100 Mack Blvd, Allentown, PA 18105, Tel: (215) 439-3411
  (Truck, parts & service, fire chassis)
    Mack Trucks Australia Pty., Ltd., P.O. Box 364, Darra 4076, Qld., Australia, 4106,
    QLD, Australia

MAGELLAN PETROLEUM CORP   241 Main St, Hartford, CT 06106, Tel: (203) 525-4601
  (Oil & gas prod & explor)
    Magellan Petroleum Australia Ltd., 99 Leichhardt St., Spring Hill, Brisbane,
    Qld. 4000, Australia

C T MAIN INTL INC   Southeast Tower, Prudential Center, Boston, MA 02199,
  Tel: (617) 262-3200
  (Engineering consultants)
    Chas. T. Main Intl. Inc., 390 St. Kilda Rd., Melbourne, Vic. 3004, Australia

MALLINCKRODT INC   675 McDonnell Blvd, PO Box 5840, St Louis, MO 63134,
  Tel: (314) 895-2012
  (Med/ind chems, organics, pharms)
    Mallinckrodt Australia Pty., Ltd., Cheltenham, Australia

MANPOWER INC   5301 N Ironwood Rd, PO Box 2053, Milwaukee, WI 53201-2053,
  Tel: (414) 961-1000
  (Temporary help)
    Manpower Personnel Svcs., 34 Hunter St., Syndey 2000, NSW, Australia

MANUFACTURERS HANOVER TRUST CO   270 Park Ave, New York, NY 10017,
  Tel: (212) 286-6000
  (Banking)
    Manufacturers Hanover Trust Co., Level 21, CBA Centre, 60 Margaret St., Sydney,
      NSW, 2000, Australia

MANVILLE CORP   PO Box 5108, Denver, CO 80217-5108, Tel: (303) 978-2000
  (Mfr fiber glass prdts, paper & forest prdts, roofing & insulation material, ind
  minerals)
    Johns-Manville Australasia Pty., Ltd., 56 Berry St., 8 Floor, North Sydney, NSW,
      2060, Australia

MARMON GROUP INC   225 W Washington, Chicago, IL 60603, Tel: (312) 372-9500
  (Tank car & rail car leasing; waste water treatment)
    ATECO Holdings Ltd., Thronleigh, NSW, Australia

MARS INC   6885 Elm St, McLean, VA 22101, Tel: (703) 821-4900
  (Mfr candy, snack foods, cat food)
    Master Foods Holdings Pty., Ltd., 29-37 Smith St., Matraville, NSW, Australia
    Uncle Ben's of Australia Pty., Ltd., Kelly St., Wodonga, Vic. 3690, Australia

MARSH & McLENNAN COS INC   1221 Ave of the Americas, New York, NY 10020-1011,
  Tel: (212) 997-2000
  (Insurance)
    Marsh & McLennan Pty., Ltd., 50 Berry St., P.O. Box 1227, North Sydney, NSW 2060,
      Australia

MARSTELLER INTL   1 E Wacker Dr, Chicago, IL 60601, Tel: (312) 329-1100
  (Advertising, marketing research, sales promotion)
    Burson-Marsteller Pty., Ltd., 11 Queens Rd., Melbourne, Vic. 3004, Australia
    Burson-Marsteller Pty., Ltd., 1 York St., Sydney, NSW, 2000, Australia

MARTIN MARIETTA DATA SYSTEMS   PO Box 2392, Princeton, NJ 08540,
  Tel: (609) 799-2600
  (Computer softward, computing & professional serv)
    Mathematica Products Group Pty. Ltd., 845 Pacific Hwy., P.O. Box 999, Chatswood,
      NSW 2067, Australia
    Mathematica Products Group Pty. Ltd., City Mutual Bldg., 1284 Albany Hwy.,
      459 Collins St., Melbourne, Vic. 3000, Australia

MARTIN PROCESSING INC   PO Box 5068, Martinsville, VA 24112,
  Tel: (703) 629-1711
  (Solar control polyester window films, dyed & metallized polyester films, dyed carpet
  yarns)
    Martin Processing (Australia) Pty. Ltd., 1284 Albany Hwy., Cannington 6107, W.A.,
      Australia

Martin Processing (Australia) Pty. Ltd., 12 Macewan St., Leederville 6007, W.A., Australia

MARY KAY COSMETICS INC   8787 Stemmons Fwy, Dallas, TX 75247,
  Tel: (214) 630-8787
  (Cosmetics & toiletries)
    Mary Kay Cosmetics Pty., Ltd., 551 Burwood Highway, Knoxfield, Vic. 31801, Australia

MATTEL INC   5150 Rosecrans Ave, Hawthorne, CA 90250, Tel: (213) 644-0411
  (Toys, dolls, games, crafts & hobbies)
    Mattel Pty., Ltd., 55 Queensbridge St., South Melbourne, Vic. 3205, Australia

MAYTAG CORP   403 W 4th St N, Newton, IA 50208, Tel: (515) 792-8000
  (Mfr home appliances & floor care prdts)
    Hoover Pty. Ltd., Belmore St., Meadowbank, New South Wales, Australia

MEASUREX CORP   One Results Way, Cupertino, CA 95014, Tel: (408) 255-1500
  (Mfr computer integrated mfg sys)
    Measurex Pty., Ltd., Suites 3 & 4, 175 Boronia Rd., Boronia, Vic. 3155, Australia

MEDTRONIC INC   7000 Central Ave, NE, Minneapolis, MN 55432,
  Tel: (612) 574-4000
  (Mfr med devices, med serv)
    Medtronic Australasia Pty. Ltd., 22 Clarke St., Crow's Nest, Sydney, NSW 2065, Australia

MELLON BANK NA   One Mellon Bank Center, Pittsburgh, PA 15258,
  Tel: (412) 234-5016
  (Commercial & trade banking, foreign exchange)
    International Banking, MLC Centre, 19 Martin Pl., Sydney, NSW 2000, Australia
    Mellon Australia Ltd., 525 Collins St., Melbourne, Vic. 3000, Australia
    Mellon Bank N.A. Australia, BHP House, 140 William St., Melbourne, Vic. 3000, Australia

MEMOREX CORP   San Thomas at Central Expressway, Santa Clara, CA 95052,
  Tel: (408) 987-1000
  (Magnetic recording tapes, etc)
    Memorex Pty., Ltd., 61 Barry St. Neutral Bay, NSW 2089, Australia

MENTHOLATUM CO   1360 Niagara St, Buffalo, NY 14213, Tel: (716) 882-7660
  (Proprietary medicines, drugs)
    Mentholatum Pty., Ltd., 121 Cremorne St., Richmond, Vic., Australia

MERCK SHARP & DOHME INTL   PO Box 2000, Rahway, NJ 07065, Tel: (201) 574-4000
  (Pharms, chems & biologicals)
    Merck, Sharp & Dohme (Australia) Pty., Ltd., 54-68 Ferndell St., Granville, NSW, 2142, Australia

MERISEL INC   200 Continental Blvd, El Segundo, CA 90245, Tel: (213) 615-3080
  (Distr software & hardware)
    MicroAustralia- Softsel, #4 Sirus Rd., Lane Cove, NSW 2006, Australia

MERRILL LYNCH PIERCE FENNER & SMITH   World Financial Center, 225 Liberty St,
  New York, NY 10080, Tel: (212) 449-1000
  (Brokers, securities, commodities)
    Merrill Lynch & Co., Pty. Ltd., Collins Wales House, 360 Collins St., Melbourne,

(cont)

3000, Vic., Australia
Merrill Lynch & Co., Pty., Ltd., 143 Mac Quarie St., Sydney, 2000, NSW, Australia

METCO DIV OF PERKIN-ELMER   1101 Prospect Ave, Westbury, NY 11590,
Tel: (516) 334-1300
(Mfr/serv thermal spray coating equip & supplies)
    Metco Thermal Spray Technology, P.O. Box 307, Padstow, NSW 2211, Australia

MGM/UA COMMUNICATIONS CO   10000 W Washington Blvd, Culver City, CA 90230,
Tel: (213) 280-6000
(Motion picture, home video & pay TV prod & distr)
    MGM/UA Entertainment Co., Level 22, AGL Centre, 111 Pacific Hwy., North Sydney,
    NSW 2060, Australia

MIDLAND METALS CORP   505 Main St, Hackensack, NJ 07601-5900,
Tel: (201) 646-1115
(Imp/exp wire & cable)
    Cable Sales Group (Australia) Pte. Ltd., 422 Collins St. 6/F-#9, Melbourne,
    Victoria 3000, Australia

MIDLAND-ROSS CORP   20600 Chagrin Blvd, Cleveland, OH 44122,
Tel: (216) 491-8400
(Thermal processing sys, steelcast- ings, elect pdts, mech controls)
    Stein Atkinson Stordy (Australia) Pty., Ltd., 9 Milgate St., Oakleigh,
    South Vic. 3167, Australia

MILCHEM INC   3900 Essex Lane, PO Box 22111, Houston, TX 77027,
Tel: (214) 439-8000
(Gas & oil well drilling fluids & chem additives)
    Geofluids Pty. Ltd., GPO Box T1746, Perth 6001, Australia

MILLIPORE CORP   Ashley Rd, Bedford, MA 01730, Tel: (617) 275-9205
(Precision filters)
    Millipore Pty., Ltd., P.O. Box 303, North Ryde, NSW, 2113, Australia

MINE SAFETY APPLIANCES CO   PO Box 426, Pittsburgh, PA 15230,
Tel: (421) 273 5000
(Safety equip, ind filters)
    MSA (Australia) Pty., Ltd., 137 Gilba Rd., P.O. Box 43, Wentworthville, NSW, 2145,
    Australia

MIXING EQUIPMENT CO INC   135 Mt Read Blvd, PO Box 1370, Rochester, NY 14611,
Tel: (716) 436-5550
(Mfr ind mixing mach, aerators)
    Lightnin Mixers Pte. Ltd.., Unit 5, Block C, 391 Park Rd., Regents Park, NSW 2143,
    Australia

MOBIL CORP   150 E 42nd St, New York, NY 10017, Tel: (212) 883-4242
(Petroleum explor, prdts)
    Mobil Exploration Australia Pty., Ltd., Altona, Australia
    Mobil Exploration Australia Pty., Ltd., other locations in Australia
    Petroleum Refineries (Australia) Pty., Ltd., Altona, Australia

MOGUL CORP   PO Box 200, Chagrin Falls, OH 44022, Tel: (216) 247-5000
(Water treatment chems, equip)
    Mogul Chemicals Pty. Ltd., 19-21 Hale St., Botany, NSW 2019, Australia

MONARCH MARKING SYSTEM INC   PO Box 608, Dayton, OH 45401, Tel: (513) 865-2123
(Marking devices, tickets, tags)
   Monarch Marking Systems Australia Pty., Ltd., P.O. Box 71, Lidcombe, 2141, Australia

MONSANTO CO   800 N Lindbergh Blvd, St Louis, MO 63167, Tel: (314) 694-1000
(Mfr chem & agric prdts, pharms, ind process equip, man-made fibers, plastics)
   Monsanto Australia Ltd., 12th Fl. 600 St. Kilde Rd., Melbourne, Vic. 3004, Australia

MOOG INC   East Aurora, NY 14052-0018, Tel: (716) 652-2000
(Mfr precision control components & sys)
   Moog Australia Pty., Ltd., 53 Glenvale Crescent, Mulgrave, Vic. 3170, Australia

MORGAN EQUIPMENT CO   1550 Evans Ave, PO Box 7802, San Francisco, CA 94124,
   Tel: (415) 826-9200
(Engineers, builders)
   Morgan Equipment (Australia) Pty., Ltd., P.O. Box 213, Archerfield, Qld. 4103,
   Australia

MORGAN GUARANTY TRUST CO   23 Wall St, New York, NY 10015, Tel: (212) 483-2323
(Banking)
   AUC Holdings Ltd., 360 Collins St., Melbourne, Vic. 3000, Australia
   Morgan Guaranty Trust Co. of NY, 19 Martin Pl., Box 3536, GOP 2001, Sydney,
   NSW 2000, Australia

MOTOROLA INC   1303 E Algonquin Rd, Schaumburg, IL 60196, Tel: (708) 397-5000
(Mfr commun equip, semiconductors, cellular phones)
   Motorola Australia Pty. Ltd., 666 Wellington Rd., Mulgrave, Melbourne, Vic. 3170,
   Australia

MTS SYSTEMS CORP   PO Box 24012, Minneapolis, MN 55424, Tel: (612) 937-4000
(Electrohydraulic testing & prod equip, mach controls)
   Australian Calibrating Svcs. Pvt. Ltd., 37 Langridge St., Collingwood, Vic. 3066,
   Australia

MULTIGRAPHICS DIV   1800 W Central Rd, Mt Prospect, IL 60056,
   Tel: (708) 398-1900
(Offset duplicating & graphic commun sys)
   AM Intl. Pty., Ltd., 636-666, Wellington Rd., Mulgrave, Vic. 3170, Australia

MUNFORD INC   1860-74 Peachtree Rd, NW, Atlanta, GA 30309, Tel: (404) 352-6641
(Convenience & specialty stores)
   Majik Markets Pty. Ltd., 72 Mary St., Surry Hills, NSW 2010, Australia

MYERS TIRE SUPPLY INTL   1293 South Main St, Akron, OH 44301,
   Tel: (216) 253-5592
(Mfr polymer & metal prdts for mat handling, automotive & constr inds)
   Myers Tyre Supply Co. Australia, 24-26 Claremont St., South Yarra, Victoria 3141,
   Australia

MacDERMID INC   245 Freight St, Waterbury, CT 06702, Tel: (203) 575-5700
(Chem processing for metal ind, plastics, electronics cleaners, strippers)
   MacDermid Inc., 29 Christina Rd., Villawood 2163, NSW, Australia

E F MacDONALD CO   129 S Ludlow St, Dayton, OH 45401, Tel: (513) 226-5000
(Trading stamps, travel & sales incentives)
   E.F. Mac Donald Co. (Australia) Pty., Ltd., 608 St. Kilda Rd., Melbourne,
   Vic. 3004, Australia

(cont)

E.F. Mac Donald Co. (Australia) Pty., Ltd., 24-26 Falcon St., Crowsnest, Sydney,
   NSW, 2065, Australia
The E.F. Mac Donald Co. Intl. Motivation Pty., Ltd., 608 St., Kilda Rd., Melbourne,
   Vic. 3004, Australia

McCANN-ERICKSON WORLDWIDE   750 Third Ave, New York, NY 10017,
   Tel: (212) 697-6000
   (Advertising)
      McCann-Erickson Advertising Pty., Ltd., Northpoint, 100 Miller St., North Sydney,
      NSW 2060, Australia
      McCann-Erickson Advertising Pty., Ltd., other locations in Australia

McCORMICK & CO INC   11350 McCormick Rd, Hunt Valley, MD 21031,
   Tel: (301) 771-7301
   (Seasons, flavorings, specialty foods)
      McCormick Foods Australia Pty., Ltd., P.O. Box 342, Clayton 3168, Vic., Australia

McDERMOTT INC   1010 Common St, New Orleans, LA 70160, Tel: (504) 587-4411
   (General contractors)
      J. Ray McDermott (Australia) Pty.. Ltd., Level 46, MLC Center, 19-29 Martin Place,
      Sydney, 2000, Australia

McGRAW-HILL INC   1221 Ave of the Americas, New York, NY 10020,
   Tel: (212) 512-2000
   (Books, magazines, info sys, financial serv, b/cast operations)
      McGraw-Hill Book Co. Australia Pty., Ltd., 4 Barcoo St., East Roseville, NSW, 2026,
      Australia

McKINSEY & CO INC   55 E 52nd St, New York, NY 10022, Tel: (212) 909-8400
   (Mgmt consultants)
      McKinsey & Co., Inc., 50 Bridge St., 11th Floor, Sydney, NSW, 2000, Australia

McNALLY PITTSBURG INC   100 N Pine, PO Box 651, Pittsburg, KS 66762,
   Tel: (316) 231-3000
   (Mfr/erection of coal processing plants & material handling sys)
      McNally Australia Pty. Ltd., Centre Court, 25 Paul St., North Ryde, NSW 2113,
      Australia

NALCO CHEMICAL CO   One Nalco Center, Naperville, IL 60566-1024,
   Tel: (708) 305-1000
   (Chems for water & waste water treatment, oil prod & refining, ind processes;
   water/energy mgmt serv)
      Catoleum Pty. Ltd., Anderson St., Botany, NSW 2019, Australia

NASHUA CORP   44 Franklin St, Nashua, NH 03061, Tel: (603) 880-2323
   (Mfr/distr/serv office copier sys & supplies)
      Nashua Australia Pty., Ltd., 19 Orion Rd., Lane Cove, Sydney, NSW 2066, Australia

NATIONAL BANK OF DETROIT   611 Woodward, PO Box 116, Detroit, MI 48232,
   Tel: (313) 225-1000
   (Banking)
      Michell NBO Ltd., 70 Hindmarsh Sq., Adelaide, WA 5000, Australia

NATIONAL BULK CARRIERS INC   1345 Ave of the Americas, New York, NY 10105,
   Tel: (212) 765-3000
   (Real estate development, mgmt serv)
      Sentinel Mining Co., Inc., 181 St. George's Terrace, Perth, W.A., 6000, Australia

NATIONAL GYPSUM CO   4500 Lincoln Plaza, Dallas, TX 75201, Tel: (214) 740-4500
  (Building prdts & servs)
    Austin Australia Pty. Ltd., Sydney, Australia
    Austin Australia Pty. Ltd., Melbourne, Australia

NCR CORP   1700 S Patterson Blvd, Dayton, OH 45479, Tel: (513) 445-2000
  (Develop/mfr/sell/serv business info processing sys)
    NCR Australia Pty. Ltd., 8-20 Napier St., P.O. Box 937, North Sydney, NSW, 2060,
    Australia

NEWMONT MINING CORP   1700 Lincoln St, Denver, CO 80203, Tel: (303) 863-7414
  (Mining)
    Newmont Australia Ltd., A.P. Tower, 535 Bourke St., Melbourne 3000, Australia

NEWSWEEK INTL INC   444 Madison Ave, New York, NY 10022, Tel: (212) 350-2000
  (Publ)
    Newsweek Inc., 100 Miller St., North Sydney, NSW, 2060, Australia

A C NIELSEN CO   Nielsen Plaza, Northbrook, IL 60062, Tel: (708) 498-6300
  (Marketing research)
    A.C. Nielsen Pty., Ltd., P.O. Box 457, 50 Miller St., North Sydney, NSW, 2060,
    Australia
    A.C. Nielsen Pty., Ltd., 85 Epping Rd., North Ryde, NSW 2113, Australia

NL INDUSTRIES INC   3000 N Sam Houston Pkwy E, Houston, TX 77205,
  Tel: (713) 987-4000
  (Metal prdts, chems, petroleum serv)
    Mineral Deposits Ltd., 81 Ashmore Rd., Southport, QLD, 4215, Australia

NORDSON CORP   28601 Clemens Rd, Westlake, OH 44145, Tel: (216) 892-1580
  (Mfr ind application equip & packaging mach)
    Nordson Australia Pty. Ltd., 10 Roper St., Moorabbin, Vic. 3189, Australia
    Nordson Australia Pty. Ltd., 1 Bilston St., Stafford, Qld. 4053, Australia
    Nordson Australia Pty. Ltd., Unit 7, 780-802 South Rd., Glandore 5037, SA, Australia
    Nordson Australia Pty., Ltd., Unit 4, 6 Boden Rd., Seven Hills, NSW 2147, Australia

NORTON CO   1 New Bond St, Worcester, MA 01606, Tel: (508) 795-5000
  (Abrasives, drill bits, constr & safety prdts, plastics)
    Australian Abrasives Pty., Ltd., 302 Parramatta Rd., Auburn, NSW, 2144, Australia
    Christensen Inc., 424 North East Rd., Windsor Garden, 5087, Australia
    Norton Pty., Ltd., 25 Nyrang St., Lidcombe, NSW, 2141, Australia

NORWICH EATON PHARMACEUTICALS INC   17 Eaton Ave, Norwich, NY 13815,
  Tel: (607) 335-2111
  (Mfr pharms, chems, health prdts)
    Norwich Eaton Pty., Ltd., Lombard House, 6th Floor, 781 Pacifi.c Iwy., Chatswood,
    NSW, Australia

OAKITE PRODUCTS INC   50 Valley Rd, Berkeley Heights, NJ 07922,
  Tel: (201) 464-6900
  (Mfr chem prdts for ind cleaning & metal treating)
    TAK Chemicals Pty. Ltd., 17 Turbo Dr., Bayswater North 3153, Australia

OCCIDENTAL LIFE INSURANCE CO OF CALIFORNIA   Hill & Olive at 12th St,
  Los Angeles, CA 90015, Tel: (213) 742-2111
  (Insurance)

(cont)

OXY Metal Industries (Australia) Pty., Ltd., Canterbury Rd., Kilsyth, Vic. 3137,
   Australia

OCEANEERING INTL INC   PO Box 218130, Houston, TX 77218, Tel: (713) 578-8868
   (Underwater serv to offshore oil & gas ind)
      Oceaneering Australia Pty., Ltd., 141 Patten St., Sale, Vic. 3850, Australia

ODI   25 Mall Rd, Burlington, MA 01803, Tel: (617) 272-8040
   (Mgt & consul serv)
      ODI Australia, 214 Bay St.- #22, Brighton, Victoria, Australia

OFFSHORE NAVIGATION INC   PO Box 23504, 5728 Jefferson Hwy, Harahan,
   LA 70183, Tel: (504) 733-6790
   (Marine & airborne surveys, flight-following equip)
      Offshore Navigation Inc., 193-195 Rocky Point Rd., Ramsgate, NSW, 2217, Australia

OGILVY & MATHER INC   2 E 48th St, New York, NY 10017, Tel: (212) 907-3400
   (Advertising agency)
      Ogilvy & Mather Intl. Inc., 132 Arthur St., North Sydney, NSW, 3004, Australia
      Ogilvy & Mather Intl. Inc., other locations in Australia

OLIN CORP   120 Long Ridge Rd, Stamford, CT 06904-1355, Tel: (203) 356-2000
   (Chems, metals, applied physics in elect, defense, aerospace inds)
      Olin Australia Ltd., 1-3 Atchison St., P.O. Box 141, St. Leonards, NSW 2065,
         Australia
      Olin Australia Ltd., 2-4 Claremont St., S. Yarra, Vic. 3141, Australia
      Olin Australia Ltd., 51 Angas St., Adelaide, SA 5000, Australia
      Olin Australia Ltd., Scottish Amicable Bldg., 265 Coronation Dr., Milton, QLD 4064,
         Australia
      Olin Australia Ltd., Hays Rd., Pt. Henry 3219, Geelong, Vic., Australia
      Olin Australia Ltd., 36 Sarich Ct., Osborne Park 0617, Australia

OMARK INDUSTRIES INC   5550 SW Macadam Ave, Portland, OR 97201,
   Tel: (503) 796-1400
   (Mfr chain & accessories for chain saws, welding equip, power tools)
      Omark-Australia Ltd., P.O. Box 246, Morphett Vale 5162, S. Australia

ON-LINE SOFTWARE INTL INC   2 Executive Dr, Fort Lee, NJ 07024,
   Tel: (201) 592-0009
   (Software & related servs; consult & educ servs)
      On-Line Software Intl. Pty. Ltd., Level 3- 1 Kent St., Sydney 2000, Australia

ONAN CORP   1400 73rd Ave NE, Minneapolis, MN 55432, Tel: (612) 574-5000
   (Electric generators, ind engines & controls)
      Distragen Pty., Ltd., 4 Mitchell Rd., Brookvale, NSW, 2100, Australia
      Hawker Siddeley Eng. Pty., Ltd., Box 1967 R, GPO, Melbourne, 3001, Australia

OPPENHEIMER CASING CO   5201 W 65th St, Chicago, IL 60638, Tel: (708) 458-0333
   (Mfr sausage casings)
      Galen Pharmaceuticals Pty., Ltd., 163 Port Hacking Rd., Miranda, NSW, 2228,
         Australia

OTIS ELEVATOR CO   10 Farm Springs, Farmington, CT 06032, Tel: (203) 674-4047
   (Elevators & escalators)
      Otis Elevator Co. Pty., Ltd., 122 Canterbury Rd., Bankstown, NSW, 2200, Australia

OUTBOARD MARINE CORP   100 Sea Horse Dr, Waukegan, IL 60085,
  Tel: (708) 689-6200
  (Outboard & rotary motors, stern engines, marine parts & accessories)
    Outboard Marine (Australia) Pty., Ltd., 84 Canterbury Rd., Bankstown, NSW 2200,
    Australia

OWENS-ILLINOIS INC   PO Box 1035, Toledo, OH 43666, Tel: (419) 247-5000
  (Glass & plastic containers, house- hold & ind prdts, packaging)
    Hygienic-Lily Ltd., Alexandria, NSW, 2015, Australia
    Hygienic-Lily Ltd., 14th Floor, 213 Miller St., Sydney, 2000, Australia

PANDUIT CORP   17301 Ridgeland Ave, Tinley Park, IL 60477, Tel: (708) 532-1800
  (Mfr elec/electr wiring comps)
    Panduit Aust. Pty. Ltd., P.O. Box 153, Mordialloc, Vic. 3195, Australia

PARAMOUNT INTL FILMS INC   1 Gulf & Western Plaza, New York, NY 10023,
  Tel: (212) 333-4600
  (Film prod & distr)
    CIC Intl. Corp., Pty., Ltd., P.O. Box 4040, Aydney, NSW., 2001, Australia

PARKER HANNIFIN CORP   17325 Euclid Ave, Cleveland, OH 44112,
  Tel: (216) 531-3000
  (Mfr motion-control prdts)
    Parker-Hannifin (Australia) Pty., Ltd., 9 Carrington Rd., Castle Hill, NSW 2154,
    Australia

PARKER PEN CO   One Parker Place, Janesville, WI 53545, Tel: (608) 755-7000
  (Writing instru, temporary help, leisure apparel & equip)
    Parker Pen (Australia) Pty., Ltd., P.O. Box 52, 159 Cleveland St., Chippendale,
    NSW, 2008, Australia

PEPSICO FOOD SERVICE INTL   9111 E Douglas, Wichita, KS 67207,
  Tel: (316) 681-9793
  (Operates restaurants)
    Pizza Hut Australia Pty. Ltd., P.O. Box 231, 20 Bridge St., Pymble, NSW 2073,
    Australia

PEPSICO INC   700 Anderson Hill Rd, Purchase, NY 10577, Tel: (914) 253-2000
  (Beverages, food prdts & servs, sporting goods)
    Pepsi Cola Co. of Australia, 275 Alfred St., North Sydney, NSW, 2060, Australia

PERKIN-ELMER CORP   761 Main Ave, Norwalk, CT 06859, Tel: (203) 762-1000
  (Analytical instru, computers, semiconductor prod equip, avionics, electro-optical
  sys, etc)
    Perkin Elmer Data Systems Pty., Ltd., 3 Byfield St., North Ryde, NSW, 2113,
    Australia

PET INC   400 S 4th St, St Louis, MO 63102, Tel: (314) 622-6358
  (Process/mktg specialty foods)
    Harry Peck & Co. (Australia) Ltd., 33-37 Mentmore Ave., Rosebery 2018, Sydney, NSW,
    Australia

PFIZER INC   235 E 42nd St, New York, NY 10017, Tel: (212) 573-2323
  (Mfr pharms, hosp prdts, chems, consumer & animal health prdts)
    Pficorprod Pty. Ltd., 20 Carlotta St., Artarmon, NSW 2065, Australia
    Pfizer Pty., Ltd., 3842 Wharf Rd., P.O. Box 57, West Ryde, NSW, Australia

PHILIP MORRIS COS INC   120 Park Ave, New York, NY 10017, Tel: (212) 880-5000
  (Mfr cigarettes, foods prdts, beer)
    Philip Morris (Australia) Ltd., 252 Chesterfield Rd., Moorabbin, Vic. 3189,
    Australia

PHILLIPS PETROLEUM CO   Phillips Bldg, Bartlesville, OK 74004,
  Tel: (918) 661-6600
  (Crude oil, natural gas, liquefied petroleum gas, gasoline & petro-chems)
    Phillips Australia Chemicals Pty., Ltd., Captain Cook Dr., Kurnell, NSW, 2219,
    Australia
    Phillips Petroleum Co., GPO 73A, Brisbane, QLD, 4001, Australia

PICKANDS MATHER & CO   1100 Superior Ave, Cleveland, OH 44114,
  Tel: (216) 694-5700
  (Iron & coal mining & transport)
    Pickands Mather & Co. Intl., ANZ Bank Bldg., 7th Floor, Pitt & Hunter Sts., Sydney,
    NSW, 2000, Australia

PIONEER HI-BRED INTL INC   700 Capital Sq, 400 Locust St, Des Moines,
  IA 50309, Tel: (515) 245-3500
  (Seed corn, feed seed, data sys & equip)
    Pioneer Hi-Bred Australia Pty. Ltd., Kingaroy, QLD, Australia

PITTSBURGH NATIONAL BANK   Fifth Ave at Wood, Pittsburgh, PA 15222,
  Tel: (412) 355-2000
  (Banking)
    Pittsburgh Natl., Seldon & Co., Ltd., Barclays House, 24th Level, 25 Bligh St.,
    Sydney NSW, 2000, Australia

PITTSBURGH-DES MOINES CORP   Neville Island, Pittsburgh, PA 15225,
  Tel: (412) 331-3000
  (Water & petroleum storage sys, low temp & cryogenic tanks & sys, waste water
  treatment facilities)
    PDM Australia Pty. Ltd., 24 Davison St., Maodington, WA 6109, Australia

PLAYTEX APPAREL INC   700 Fairfield Ave, Stamford, CT 06904,
  Tel: (203) 356-8000
  (Mfr intimate apparel)
    Playtex Pty., Ltd., P.O. Box 66, Wentworthville, NSW 2145, Australia
    Playtex Pty., Ltd., 104 Briens Rd., Northmead, NSW, 2152, Australia

PLOUGH INC   PO Box 377, Memphis, TN 38151, Tel: (901) 320-2011
  (Proprietary drug & cosmetic prdts)
    Plough Australia Pty., Ltd., P.O. Box 130, North Ryde, NSW, 2113, Australia

POLAROID CORP   549 Technology Sq, Cambridge, MA 02139, Tel: (617) 577-2000
  (Photographic and optical prdts)
    Polaroid Australia Pty., Ltd., Enden Park Estate 31, Waterloo Rd., North Ryde, NSW,
    2113, Australia

R L POLK & CO   1155 Brewery Park Blvd, Detroit, MI 48207-2697,
  Tel: (313) 961-9470
  (Directories, direct mail advertising)
    R.L. Polk & Co., (Australia) Pty., Ltd., Richmond, Victoria, Australia

POLYCHROME CORP   On the Hudson, Yonkers, NY 10702, Tel: (914) 965-8800
  (Metal offset plates, coating specialties, graphic arts films)
    Polychrome A.C.P. Ltd., 193 Bouverie St., Carlton, Vic. 3053, Australia

POTTERS INDUSTRIES INC   20 Waterview Blvd, Parsippany, NJ 07054,
  Tel: (201) 299-2900
  (Mfr glass spheres for road marking & ind applications)
    Potters Industries Pty., Ltd., Lot 4 Boundary Rd., Laverton 3028, Vic., Australia

PRECISION VALVE CORP   PO Box 309, Yonkers, NY 10702, Tel: (914) 969-6500
  (Mfr aerosol valves)
    Precision Valve Australia Pty., Ltd., P.O. Box 312, Williamson Rd., Ingleburn,
      NSW 2565, Australia
    Precision Valve Corp., 1/57 Darling Point Rd., Darling Point 2027, Syndey, NSW,
      Australia

PREFORMED LINE PRODUCTS CO   PO Box 91129, Cleveland, OH 44101,
  Tel: (216) 461-5200
  (Mfr pole line hardware for elec transmission lines; splice closures & related prdts
  for telecom)
    Fanner-PLP Pty. Ltd., Sydney, Australia

PREMARK INTL INC   1717 Deerfield Rd, Deerfield, IL 60015, Tel: (708) 405-6000
  (Mfr/sale diversified consumer & coml prdts)
    Tupperware Australia Pty. Ltd., Private Bag 6, Hawthorn, Vic. 3122, Australia

PRIME COMPUTER INC   Prime Park, Natick, MA 01760, Tel: (617) 655-8000
  (Mfr minicomputers, hardware & software)
    Prime Computer of Australia, Philips Bldg., 15 Blud St., N. Sydney, NSW 2060,
      Australia

PRINCETON APPLIED RESEARCH CORP   Box 2565, Princeton, NJ 08540,
  Tel: (609) 452-2111
  (Research & analytical instru)
    PYE Industries Ltd., Tecnico Electronics, 67 Mars Rd., Lane Cove, Sydney, NSW,
      2066, Australia
    PYE Industries Ltd., Tecnico Electronics, 2 High St., Northcote, Melbourne, 3070,
      Vic., Australia

PYRONICS INC   17700 Miles Ave, Cleveland, OH 44128, Tel: (216) 662-8800
  (Mfr combustion equip, gas & oil burners)
    Metbend Engr. & Sales, 21 May St., St. Peters 2004, Australia

QUAKER CHEMICAL CORP   Elm & Lee Sts, Conshohocken, PA 19428,
  Tel: (215) 828-4250
  (Mfr chem specialties)
    Quaker Chemical (Australasia) Pty. Ltd., 8 Abbott Rd., Seven Hills, NSW 2147,
      Australia

QUAKER OATS CO   345 Merchandise Mart Plaza, Chicago, IL 60654,
  Tel: (312) 222-7111
  (Foods, pet foods, toys, chems)
    Quaker Products Australia Ltd., Sunshine Rd., West Footscray, Vic. 3012, Australia

QUIGLEY CO INC   235 E 42nd St, New York, NY 10017, Tel: (212) 573-3444
  (Mfr refractory specs, application equip)
     Pficonprod Pty. Ltd., Pfizer-Quigley Div., P.O. Box 549, Crows Nest, NSW 2065,
     Australia

RAIN BIRD SPRINKLER MFG CORP   7045 N Grand Ave, Glendora, CA 91740,
  Tel: (213) 963-9311
  (Lawn sprinklers, irrigation equip)
     Rain Bird Australia Pty., Ltd., 1/96 Levanswell Rd., Mporabbin, Vic., 3189,
     Australia

RALSTON PURINA CO   Checkerboard Sq, St Louis, MO 63164, Tel: (214) 982-1000
  (Poultry & live stock feed, cereals, food prdts)
     Robert Harper & Co., Ltd., P.O. Box 177, Dunlop & Pickering Rds., Mulgrave, 3170,
     Vic., Australia

RAMSEY TECHNOLOGY INC   1853 W County Rd, St Paul, MN 55113,
  Tel: (612) 633-5150
  (Mfr scales & mining equip)
     Ramsey Engineering Pty., Ltd., P.O. Box 228, 20-22 Box Rd., Caringbah, NSW 2229,
     Australia

RANSBURG CORP   3939 W 56th St, Indianapolis, IN 46208, Tel: (317) 298-5000
  (Mfr electrostatic coating sys)
     Ransburg Australia Pty., Ltd., 23 Ashford Ave., P.O. Box 85, Milperra, NSW 2214,
     Australia

RAPISTAN CORP   507 Plymouth Ave NE, Grand Rapids, MI 49505,
  Tel: (616) 451-6200
  (Material handling equip)
     Colby Engineering Pty. Ltd., 75 S. Creek Rd., P.O. Box 1000, Dee Why, NSW 1099,
     Australia

W T RAWLEIGH CO   223 E Main St, Freeport, IL 61032, Tel: (815) 232-4161
  (Medicines, toiletries, pet care & household prdts)
     W.T. Rawleigh Co. (Canada) Ltd., 60 Dawson St., Brunswick, Vic. 3056, Australia

RCA GLOBAL COMMUNICATIONS INC   60 Broad St, New York, NY 10004,
  Tel: (212) 806-7000
  (Commun serv)
     RCA Ltd., 11 Khartoum Rd., North Ryde, NSW, 2113, Australia

READER'S DIGEST ASSOCIATION INC   PO Box 235, Pleasantville, NY 10570,
  Tel: (914) 238-1000
  (Global publisher & direct mail marketer)
     Reader's Digest Services Pty., Ltd., 26-32 Waterloo St., Surry Hills, Sydney,
     NSW 2010, Australia

REDKEN LABORATORIES INC   6625 Variel Ave, Canoga Park, CA 91303,
  Tel: (818) 992-2700
  (Mfr hair & skin care prdts)
     Redken Labs. Pty. Ltd., Unit C, 31-33 Sirius Rd., Lane Cove, NSW 2066, Australia

REGENT SPORTS CORP   45 Ranick Rd, Hauppauge, NY 11787, Tel: (516) 234-2800
  (Sporting goods)
     Mason Green Agencies, 91-101 Leveson St., N. Melbourne, 3051, Australia

RELIANCE ELECTRIC CO   24701 Euclid Ave, Cleveland, OH 44117,
  Tel: (216) 266-7000
  (Equip & sys for ind automation, telecom equip)
    Reliance Automation Pty. Ltd., P.O. Box 312, Lane Cove, NSW 2066, Australia

REMINGTON PRODUCTS INC   60 Main St, Bridgeport, CT 06602, Tel: (203) 367-4400
  (Mfr home appliances, electric shavers)
    Remington Products Australia Pty. Ltd., 548 Clayton Rd., Clayton, Vic. 3168,
    Australia

RENA-WARE DISTRIBUTORS INC   222 112 NE St, Bellevue, WA 98004,
  Tel: (206) 453-2300
  (Cookware & china)
    Rena-Ware Distributors Pty., Ltd., 161 Broadway, Sydney, NSW, 2000, Australia

REVELL/MONOGRAM   8601 Waukegan Rd, Morton Grove, IL 60053, Tel: (708) 66-3500
  (Mfr plastic hobby kits)
    Revell (Australia) Pty. Ltd., 58 Rushdale St., Knoxfield 3180, Australia

REVLON INC   767 Fifth Ave, New York, NY 10153-0033, Tel: (212) 572-5000
  (Cosmetics, health care prdts)
    RIC Pty., Ltd., Australia
    Revlon Australia Pty., Ltd., 100 Walker St., North Sydney, NSW, 2060, Australia

REXNORD CORP   PO Box 2022, Milwaukee, WI 53201, Tel: (414) 643-3000
  (Mfr power transmission prdts)
    Rexnord Australia Pty., Ltd., P.O. Box 237, Revesby, NSW 2212, Australia

R J REYNOLDS INDUSTRIES INC   World Headquarters Bldg, 401 N Main St,
  Winston-Salem, NC 27102, Tel: (919) 773-2000
  (Tobacco prdts, holding co)
    R.J. Reynolds Tobacco Australia Pty., Ltd., 3940 GPO, Sydney, 2001, Australia

REYNOLDS INTERNATIONAL INC   6601 W Broad St, PO Box 27002, Richmond,
  VA 23261, Tel: (804) 281-2000
  (Mfr aluminum primary & fabricated prdts, plastic & paper packaging & foodservice
  prdts; gold mining)
    Reynolds Australia Ltd., Griffin Center 8/F, 28 Esplanade, Perth, WA 6000, Australia

RICHARDSON-VICKS INC   Ten Westport Rd, Wilton, CT 06897, Tel: (203) 834-5000
  (Consumer health & personal care prdts)
    Richardson-Merrell Pty., Ltd., 9 Help St., P.O. Box 469, Chatswood, NSW, 2067,
    Australia

RICHTON INTL CORP   1345 Ave of the Americas, New York, NY 10115,
  Tel: (212) 765-6480
  (Nondurable consumer wearables, active sportswear jewelry & accessories)
    Richton Intl., 95 York St., Sydney, NSW, 2000, Australia

RIDGE TOOL CO   400 Clark St, Elyria, OH 44035, Tel: (216) 323-5581
  (Hand & power tools for working pipe, drain cleaning equip, etc)
    Ridge Tool Australia Pty., Ltd., Melbourne, Australia

RIKER LABORATORIES INC   Bldg 225-1N-07, 3M Center, St Paul, MN 55144,
  Tel: (612) 733-9577
  (Specialty pharms)
    Riker Labs Australia Pty., Ltd., P.O. Box 122, Hornsby, NSW 2120, Australia

ROBERTSHAW CONTROLS CO   1701 Byrd Ave, Richmond, VA 23230,
   Tel: (804) 281-0700
   (Mfr automatic controls & control sys for ind, commercial bldgs & home)
      Robertshaw Controls Australia Pty., Ltd., 121-115 Bellandella Rd., Pendle Hill,
      NSW 2145, Australia

H H ROBERTSON CO   Two Gateway Center, Pittsburgh, PA 15222,
   Tel: (412) 281-3200
   (Mfr roof & wall prdts, cellular steel floor sys, ventilation equip)
      H.H. Robertson (Australia) Pty., Ltd., P.O. Box 194, Chatswood, NSW 2067, Australia

A H ROBINS CO INC   1407 Cummings Dr, PO Box 26609, Richmond, VA 23261-6609,
   Tel: (804) 257-2000
   (Mfr ethical pharms & consumer prdts)
      A.H. Robins, Pty., Ltd., 102 Bonds Rd., Punchbowl, NSW 2196, Australia

ROCKWELL INTL CORP   2230 E Imperial Hwy, El Segundo, CA 90245,
   Tel: (213) 647-5000
   (Prdts & serv for aerospace, automotive, electronics, graphics & automation inds)
      Collins Radio Co. (Australasia) Pty., Ltd., Maroondah Hwy., Lilydale, Vic. 3140,
      Australia
      Rockwell Standard of Australia Ltd., Berkshire Rd., Sunshine, Vic., 3020, Australia
      Rockwell-Collins Australasia Pty., Ltd., P.O. Box 200, Lilydale, Vic. 3140,
      Australia

ROHM & HAAS CO   Independence Mall West, Philadelphia, PA 19105,
   Tel: (215) 592-3000
   (Mfr ind & agric chems, plastics)
      Rohm & Haas (Australia) Pty., Ltd., 969 Burke Rd., Caberwell, Vic. 3123, Australia
      Rohm & Haas Australia Pty. Ltd., 60 Perry St., Matraville, NSW 2036, Australia

ROSEMOUNT INC   12001 Technology Dr, Eden Prairie, MN 55344,
   Tel: (612) 941-5560
   (Mfr aerospace & ind instrumentation)
      Rosemount Instruments Pty. Ltd., 471 Mountain Hwy., Bayswater, Vic. 3153, Australia

RUSSELL REYNOLDS ASSOCIATES INC   200 Park Ave, New York, NY 10166,
   Tel: (212) 351-2000
   (Exec recruiting services)
      Russell Reynolds Assoc. Inc., AMP Centre, 50 Bridge St., Sydney, NSW 2000, Australia
      Russell Reynolds Assoc. Inc., BHP House, 140 William St., Melbourne, Vic. 3000,
      Australia

SAFETY-KLEEN CORP   777 Big Timber Rd, Elgin, IL 60123, Tel: (708) 697-8460
   (Solvent based parts cleaning serv, sludge/solvent recycling serv)
      Worton Services Pty. Ltd., P.O. Box 234, 1 Jumal Pl., Smithfield, NSW 2164,
      Australia

SARA LEE CORP   3 First National Plaza, Chicago, IL 60602, Tel: (312) 726-2600
   (Mfr/distr food & consumer packaged goods)
      Sara Lee Corp. (Nicholas Kiwi Ltd.), 610 Heatherton Rd., Clayton 3169, Australia

SCHENECTADY CHEMICALS INC   PO Box 1046, Schenectady, NY 12301,
   Tel: (518) 370-4200
   (Mfr elec insulating varnishe, enamels, resins, alkylated phenol)
      Schenectady Chemicals Australia Pty. Ltd., 72 Christie St., St. Marys, NSW 2760,
      Australia

R P SCHERER CORP   2075 W Big Beaver Rd, Troy, MI 48084, Tel: (313) 649-0900
(Mfr soft gelatin & two-piece hard shell capsules)
  R.P. Scherer Pty., Ltd., 39-47 Stafford St., Huntingdale, Vic. 3166, Australia

SCHERING INTL   PO Box 500, Kenilworth, NJ 07033, Tel: (201) 558-4000
(Pharms, medicines, toiletries, cosmetics, human & animal health prdts)
  Essex Labs Pty., Ltd., P.O. Box 231, Baulkham Hills, NSW, 2153, Australia

SCHLAGE LOCK CO   2401 Bayshore Blvd, San Francisco, CA 94134,
  Tel: (415) 467-1100
(Locks, builders hardware)
  R.B. Davies Pty., Ltd., 450 lllawarra Rd., Marrickville, NSW, 2204, Australia

SCHLEGEL CORP   400 East Ave, Rochester, NY 14607, Tel: (716) 546-6260
(Engineered perimeter sealing systems for residential & commercial constr)
  Schelegel Pty., Ltd., P.O. Box 50, Broadway, Sydney, NSW, 2007, Australia

SCHOLASTIC INC   730 Broadway, New York, NY 10003, Tel: (212) 505-3000
(Pub educational magazines, books, software)
  Ashton Scholastic Pty. Ltd., P.O. Box 579, Gosford, NSW 2250, Australia
  Ashton/Scholastic, P.O. Box 579, Gosford, NSW, 2250, Australia

SEAMAN CORP   1000 Ventura Blvd, Wooster, OH 44691, Tel: (216) 262-1111
(Vinyl coated fabrics)
  Vessel Engineering Services Pty., Ltd., Citicorp House, 217 George St., Brisbane,
    4000, Australia

G D SEARLE & CO   PO Box 1045, Skokie, IL 60076, Tel: (708) 982-7000
(Pharms, health care & optical prdts, specialty chems)
  Searle Australia Pty., Ltd., P.O. Box 473, North Sydney, NSW, 2060, Australia

SECURITY PACIFIC NATIONAL BANK   333 S Hope St, Los Angeles, CA 90071,
  Tel: (213) 345-6211
(Banking)
  Security Pacific Ltd., National Australia Bank House, 255 George St., Sydney,
    NSW 2000, Australia

SGS CONTROL SERVICES INC   42 Broadway, New York, NY 10004,
  Tel: (212) 482-8700
(Complete range of quality & quantity control checks & related tech serv)
  SGS Australia Pty., Ltd., 74 McEvoy St., Alexandria, P.O. Box 163, Redfern, Sydney,
    2016, NSW, Australia
  SGS Australia Pty., Ltd., Newcastle, Melbourne, Brisbane, Gladstone,
    Adelaide & Perth

SHULTON INC   1 Cyanamid Plaza, Wayne, NJ 07470, Tel: (201) 831-2000
(Health, beauty & grooming prdts)
  Shulton (Australia) Pty., Ltd., 5 Gibbon Rd., Baulkham Hills, NSW, 2153, Australia

SIMMONS INTL   1 Gulf & Western Plaza, New York, NY 10023, Tel: (212) 333-3511
(Bedding prdts)
  Simmons Bedding Co., P.O. Box 13, Camperdown, NSW, 2050, Australia

SIMON & SCHUSTER INC   1230 Ave of the Americas, New York, NY 10020,
  Tel: (212) 245-6400
(Publisher)

(cont)

Prentice-Hall of Australia Pty. Ltd., P.O. Box 151, 7 Grosvenor Pl., Brookvale, NSW 2100, Australia

SIMPLEX TIME RECORDER CO   Simplex Plaza, Gardner, MA 01441,
  Tel: (617) 632-2500
  (Time recorders & stamps, master time sys, alarm, security, monitor & control sys)
    Simplex Intl. Time Equipment Pty., Ltd., P.O. Box 561, Brookvale, NSW, 2100, Australia

SIMPLICITY PATTERN CO INC   200 Madison Ave, New York, NY 10016,
  Tel: (212) 481-3737
  (Dress patterns)
    Simplicity Patters Pty., Ltd., 95-99 Bonds Rd., Punchbowl, NSW, 2196, Australia

SKIL CORP   4801 W Peterson Ave, Chicago, IL 60646, Tel: (312) 286-7330
  (Portable electric power tools)
    Skil-Australia Ltd., Browns Rd., Noble Park, Vic. 3174, Australia

SMITH INTL INC   16740 Hardy St, Houston, TX 77032, Tel: (713) 443-6470
  (Mfr/serv downhole drilling equip)
    Smith Intl. Australia Pty. Ltd., 26-42 Cooper Rd., Jandakot, WA 6164, Australia

SMITH TOOL   PO Box C-19511, Irvine, CA 92713, Tel: (714) 540-7010
  (Drilling bits)
    Smith Intl. Australia Pty., Ltd., Jandakot, W. Australia

SONOCO PRODUCTS CO   North Second St, PO Box 160, Hartsville, SC 29550,
  Tel: (803) 383-7000
  (Mfr packaging for consumer & ind mkt)
    Sonoco Pacific Pty. Ltd., P.O. Box 499, North Sydney, NSW 2059, Australia
    Sunoco Australia Pty. Ltd., 19 Pritchard Rd., Virginia, Zillmere, Qld. 4034, Australia
    Sunoco Australia Pty. Ltd., other locations in Australia

SPALDING & EVENFLO COS INC   5750A N Hoover Blvd, Tampa, FL 33614,
  Tel: (813) 887-5200
  (Mfr sports equip, infant & juvenile furniture & accessories)
    Spalding Australia Pty. Ltd., 969 Burke Rd., Camberwell, Vic. 3124, Australia

SPECTRAL DYNAMICS CORP   4141 Ruffin Rd, San Diego, CA 92123,
  Tel: (619) 496-3400
  (Mfr Vibration monitoring, analysis & control equip)
    Scientific-Atlantic Pty. Ltd., 2/2 Aquatic Dr., French's Forest, NSW 2086, Australia

SPS TECHNOLOGIES INC   900 Newtown-Yardley Rd, Newtown, PA 18940,
  Tel: (215) 860-3000
  (Mfr aerospace & ind fasteners, precision components, superalloys, magnetic materials, fastening sys)
    Inbrako Pty., Ltd., P.O. Box 77, Norcal Rd., Nunawading, Vic. 3131, Australia

SPX CORP   700 Terrace Point Dr, Muskegon, MI 49443, Tel: (616) 724-5000
  (Mfr spec repair equip & repair parts)
    Litchfield Tool, 334 South Rd., Croydon Park, SA, Australia
    Litchfield Tool, 334 South Rd., Croydon Park, South Australia, Australia
    Ritch Engineering, PO Box 190, Clayton, Victoria 3168, Australia
    SPX Australia Pty. Ltd., Unit 2, 8 Gladstone Rd., Castle Hill, NSW 2154, Australia
    SPX Australia Pty. Ltd., 8 Gladstone Rd.- Unit 2, Castle Hill, NSW 2154, Australia

SQUARE D CO   Executive Plaza, Palatine, IL 60067, Tel: (708) 397-2600
  (Power distribution & elec/electr ind control equip)
     Square D Co., Australia Pty., Ltd., Melbourne, Australia

SRI INTL   333 Ravenswood Ave, Menlo Park, CA 94025, Tel: (415) 326-6200
  (Intl consulting & research)
     Australian Artificial Intelligence Institution, 1 Grattan St., Carlton, Vic. 3053,
     Australia

ST JOE MINERALS CORP   250 Park Ave, New York, NY 10017, Tel: (212) 953-5000
  (Coal, oil, gas, iron ore, metals & minerals)
     Jododex Australia Pty., Ltd., 48 Albany St., Crows Nest, NSW, 2065, Australia
     Woodlawn Mines, P.O. Box 141, Goulburn, NSW, 2580, Australia

STA-RITE INDUSTRIES INC   777 E Wisconsin Ave, Milwaukee, WI 53202,
  Tel: (414) 276-6888
  (Mfr water pumps & filters, water treatment equip, fluid power components)
     Onga Pty. Ltd., P.O. Box 164, 357 Ferntree Gully Rd., Mt. Waverly, Vic. 3149,
     Australia

STANDARD COMMERCIAL CORP   PO Box 450, Wilson, NC 27893, Tel: (919) 291-5507
  (Leaf tobacco dealers/processors, wool processors)
     Standard Wool Australia (Pty.) Ltd., Fremantle, Australia

THE STANLEY WORKS   1000 Stanley Dr, PO Box 7000, New Britain, CT 06050,
  Tel: (203) 225-5111
  (Mfr hand tools & hardware)
     Stanley-Bostitch (Pty.) Ltd., P.O. Box 450, 47-55 Williamson Rd., Ingleburn,
     NSW 2565, Australia
     The Stanley Works Pty. Ltd., P.O. Box 10, 8 Moncrief Rd., Nunawading, Vic. 3131,
     Australia

STATE STREET BANK & TRUST CO   225 Franklin St, Boston, MA 02101,
  Tel: (617) 786-3000
  (Banking servs)
     State Street Australia Ltd., 141 Walker St., North Sydney, NSW 2000, Australia

STEINER CORP   PO Box 2317, 505 E South Temple St, Salt Lake City, UT 84102,
  Tel: (801) 328-8831
  (Linen supply service)
     Alsco, P.O. Box 245, Alexandria, Sydney, 2015, Australia

STEMCO INC   PO Box 1989, Longview, TX 75606, Tel: (214) 758-9981
  (Mfr automotive seals, mufflers, spec prdts for heavy duty trucks, buses, trailers)
     Stemco Truck Products Pty. Ltd., P.O. Box 277, Noble Park, Vic. 3174, Australia

STERLING DRUG INC   90 Park Ave, New York, NY 10016, Tel: (212) 907-2000
  (Pharms, chems, cosmetics, household cleaners & waxes)
     Sterling Pharmaceuticals Pty., Ltd., P.O. Box 3, 75-89 Atkins Rd., Ermington, NSW,
     2115, Australia

STERLING SOFTWARE INC   8080 N Central Expy, #1100, Dallas, TX 75206-1895,
  Tel: (214) 891-8600
  (Sales/serv software prdts; tech servs)
     Systems Sterling Software Pty. Ltd., 8 Help St.- Level 6, Chatswood, NSW 2067,
     Australia

STEWART-WARNER CORP   1826 Diversey Pkwy, Chicago, IL 60614,
   Tel: (312) 883-6000
   (Lubrication equip sys, ind tools & controls, castors, pressure switches)
      Flexdrive Industries Pty. Ltd., Private Bag 1, New Gisborne, Vic. 3438, Australia

STOKES DIV   5500 Tabor Rd, Philadelphia, PA 19120, Tel: (215) 289-5671
   (Vacuum pumps & components, vacuum dryers, oil-upgrading equip)
      Sharples-Stokes Pty. Ltd., P.O. Box 2344, N. Parramatta, NSW 2151, Australia

STORAGE TECHNOLOGY CORP   2270 S 88th St, Louisville, CO 80028-0001,
   Tel: (303) 673-5151
   (Mfr/mkt/serv info storage & retrieval sys)
      Storage Technology Corp., 174 Pacific Hwy., St. Leonards, NSW 2065, Australia

STRATOFLEX INC   220 Roberts Cut-Off Rd, PO Box 10398, Fort Worth, TX 76114,
   Tel: (817) 738-6543
   (Hose assemblies, self-sealing & quick disconnect couplings, swivels, etc)
      Stratoflex Australia Pty., Ltd., P.O. Box 143, Lidcombe, NSW 2141, Australia

SUDLER & HENNESSEY   1633 Broadway, New York, NY 10019, Tel: (212) 265-8000
   (Healthcare prdts advertising)
      Sudler & Hennessey, 572 St. Kilda St., Melbourne, Vic. 3004, Australia
      Sudler & Hennessey, 213 Miller St., N. Sydney, NSW 2060, Australia

SULLAIR CORP   3700 E Michigan Blvd, Michigan City, IN 46360,
   Tel: (219) 879-5451
   (Refrigeration sys, vacuum pumps, generators, etc)
      Sullair Australia Ltd., 1 Windsor Rd., Penrose, Vineyard, NSW, 2756, Australia

SUN ELECTRIC CORP   One Sun Pkwy, Crystal Lake, IL 60014, Tel: (815) 459-7700
   (Mfr auto tune-up, diagnostic & emission testing equip)
      Suntester (Australia) Pty., Ltd., P.O. Box 382, 31 Prince William Dr., Seven Hills,
      NSW 2147, Australia

SUNDT INTL   PO Box 26685, Tucson, AZ 85726, Tel: (602) 790-0295
   (Holding company)
      Sundt Intl. Pty., Ltd., Wynyard House, 12th Floor, 291 George St., Sydney, NSW,
      Australia

SUPERIOR BRANDS INC   122 Quincy Shore Dr, Quincy, MA 02171,
   Tel: (617) 770-0880
   (Mfr rawhide pet treats, cat litter, dog biscuits)
      Superior Pet Products (Australia) Pty., Ltd., 192 Mahoney's Rd., Thomastown,
      Vic. 3074, Australia

SYBRON CORP   411 E Wisconsin Ave, Milwaukee, WI 07662, Tel: (414) 274-6600
   (Professional health prdts, spec chems, instru, water & waste water treatment sys)
      Gamlen (Australasia) Pty., Ltd., 25 Sirius Rd., P.O. Box 441, Lane Cove, NSW, 2066,
      Sydney, Australia

SYSTEMS ENGINEERING LABS INC   6901 W Sunrise Blvd, Fort Lauderdale,
   FL 33313, Tel: (305) 587-2900
   (Digital computers)
      Systems Pacific Pty., Ltd., First Floor, 434 St. Kilda Rd., Melbourne, Vic. 3004,
      Australia

TANDY CORP   1800 One Tandy Center, Fort Worth, TX 76102, Tel: (817) 390-3700
  (Electronic & acoustic equip)
    Tandy Australia Ltd., 91 Kurrajong Ave., P.O. Box 254, Mt. Druitt, NSW, Australia

TAYLOR-WINFIELD CORP   1052 Mahoning Ave NW, Warren, OH 44482,
  Tel: (216) 399-8861
  (Metal working machs for resistance & arc welding, metal forming, automation sys)
    R.V. Dorman Co., Pty. Ltd., 78 White St., Mordialloc, Vic. 3195, Australia

TECHNICON INSTRUMENTS CORP   511 Benedict Ave, Tarrytown, NY 10591-5097,
  Tel: (914) 631-8000
  (Mfr/serv automated blook anal equip, reagents & diagnostics)
    Technicon Equipment Pty. Ltd., 80 Talavera Rd., P.O. Box 135, North Ryde,
    NSW 00115, Australia

TED BATES WORLDWIDE INC   1515 Broadway, New York, NY 10036,
  Tel: (212) 869-3131
  (Advertising agency)
    George Patterson Pty., Ltd., 252 George St., Sydney, NSW 2000, Australia
    George Patterson Pty., Ltd., 394 LaTrobe St., Melbourne, Vic. 3000, Australia
    George Patterson Pty., Ltd., 82 East Terrace, Adelaide, SA 5000, Australia
    George Patterson-Noble Bartlett Pty. Ltd., 459/461 Adelaide St., Brisbane,
    Qld. 4000, Australia
    Marketforce Pty. Ltd., 1314 Hay St., West Perth 6005, Australia

TEKNIS CORP   PO Box 3189, No Attleboro, MA 02761, Tel: (508) 695-3591
  (Sale advanced technology prdts, fiber optics, materials for semiconductor mfr)
    Teknis Pty. Ltd., P.O. Box 45, Kingswood, SA 5062, Australia

TEKTRONIX INC   PO Box 500, Beaverton, OR 97077, Tel: (503) 627-7111
  (Mfr test & meas, visual sys & commun prdts)
    Tektronix Australia Pty., Ltd., 80 Waterloo Rd., North Ryde, NSW, 2113, Australia

TELXON CORP   3330 W Market St, Akron, OH 44333, Tel: (216) 867-3700
  (Devel/mfr portable computer sys & related equip)
    Telxon Australia Pty. Ltd., Commercial Union Bldg. 3/F, 90 Arthur St., N. Sydney,
    NSW 2060, Australia

TENNANT CO   701 N Lilac Dr, Minneapolis, MN 55440, Tel: (612) 540-1200
  (Mfr ind floor maint sweepers & scrubbers, roofing machs)
    Tennant Co., Australia Pty., Ltd., 10 Hope St., Ermington, NSW 2115, Australia

C TENNANT SONS & CO OF NY   PO Box 9300, Minneapolis, MN 55440,
  Tel: (612) 475-7340
  (Ferrous & non-ferrous minerals, metals, electronic comps)
    Tennant New York Pty., Ltd., 535 Bourke St., AMP Tower, 19th Floor, Melbourne,
    Vic. 3000, Australia

TENNECO AUTOMOTIVE   100 Tri-State Intl, #300, Lincolnshire, IL 60069,
  Tel: (708) 948-0900
  (Mfr exhaust sys, ride control prdts, brake components)
    Monroe Australia Pty., Ltd., P.O. Box 61, St. Marys, SA 5042, Australia
    Walker Australia Pty., Ltd., 29 Morrow Rd., O'Sullivan Beach, SA 5166, Australia

TEXACO INC   2000 Westchester Ave, White Plains, NY 10650, Tel: (914) 253-4000
  (Explor/mktg crude oil & its prdts, petro-chems)
    Texaco Overseas Petroleum Co., GPO Box 4991, Sydney, NSW, 2001, Australia

TEXAS INSTRUMENTS INC   PO Box 655474, Dallas, TX 75265, Tel: (214) 995-2011
  (Mfr semiconductor devices, electr/electro-mech sys, instr & controls)
    Texas Instruments Australia Ltd., P.O. Box 63, Elizabeth 5112, Australia

TEXTRON INC   40 Westminster St, Providence, RI 02903, Tel: (401) 421-2800
  (Mfr aerospace tech & coml prdts; fin servs)
    Textron Pacific Ltd., 910 Pacific Hwy., Gordon, NSW 2072, Australia

THOMAS & BETTS CORP   1001 Frontier Rd, Bridgewater, NJ 08807-0993,
  Tel: (201) 685-1600
  (Mfr elect/electr connectors & accessories)
    Thomas & Betts Pty. Ltd., 10 Lucca Rd., Wyong North, NSW 2259, Australia

TIDEL SYSTEMS INC   2615 E Beltline Rd, Carrollton, TX 75006,
  Tel: (214) 416-8222
  (Mfr oil & gas monitors; cash handling equip)
    Scotch Deupty, Victory Lane 8-10, Catilina Dr., Tullamarine 3043, Australia

TIDEWATER INC   Tidewater Place, 1440 Canal St, New Orleans, LA 70112,
  Tel: (504) 568-1010
  (Marine serv & equip to companies engaged in explor, development & prod of oil, gas &
  minerals)
    Tidewater Port Jackson Marine Pty., Ltd., 1/F 391 Plummer St., Port Melbourne,
      Vic. 3207, Australia

TIME WARNER INC   Time Life Bldg, New York, NY 10020, Tel: (212) 522-1212
  (Magazine & book publ, communications)
    Time-Life Intl. (Australasia) Pty., Ltd., Sun Alliance Bldg., 22-30 Bridge St.,
      Sydney, 2000, Australia

TIMEX GROUP LTD   Waterbury, CT 06760, Tel: (203) 573-5000
  (Watches, clocks, timing instru, cameras, gyroscopes)
    TMX Australia Ltd., 86 Derby St., Pascoe Vale Coburg, Vic. 3058, Australia

THE TIMKEN CO   1835 Dueber Ave SW, Canton, OH 44706-2798, Tel: (216) 438-3000
  (Mfr tapered roller bearings & alloy steels)
    Australian Timken Prop. Ltd., 101-199 Learmonth Rd., Ballarat, Victoria 3350,
      Australia

TONKA CORP   6000 Clearwater Dr, Minnetonka, MN 55343, Tel: (612) 936-3300
  (Mfr children's toys)
    Tonka Corp. Pty. Ltd., 8-10 Leeds St., Rhodes, Sydney, NSW 2138, Australia

TOPFLIGHT CORP   200 E 9th Ave, PO Box 472, York, PA 17405,
  Tel: (717) 843-9901
  (Printed pressure-sensitive adhesive materials)
    Pacific Lables Pty., Ltd., 1615 Botany Rd., Botany, NSW, 2019, Australia

TORRINGTON/FAFNIR   200 Chestnut Ridge Rd, Woodcliff Lake, NJ 07675,
  Tel: (203) 482-9511
  (Mfr bearings, precision metal parts & assemblies, universal joints)
    The Torrington Bearing Co., 80-112 Franston Rd., PMB 43, Dandenong, Vic. 3175,
      Australia

TOWERS PERRIN FORSTER & CROSBY INC   245 Park Ave, New York, NY 10167,
  Tel: (212) 309-3400
  (Management consulting)

Towers, Perrin, Forster & Crosby, Box 85, GPO, Brisbane, Qld. 4001, Australia
Towers, Perrin, Forster & Crosby, other locations in Australia

TRADE & INDUSTRIES CORP INC   16 E 34th St, New York, NY 10016,
Tel: (212) 686-2420
(Finance)
Trade & Industry Acceptance Corp., Australia Pty., Ltd., GPO Box 117, Sydney, NSW,
2001, Australia

TRANE CO   3600 Pammel Creek Rd, La Crosse, WI 54601, Tel: (608) 787-2000
(Mfr A/C equip)
Trane Co. of Australia Pty., Ltd., 28 Forge St., Blacktown, NSW, 2146, Australia
Trane Co. of Australia Pty., Ltd., other locations in Australia

TRICO TECHNOLOGIES CORP   1995 Billy Mitchell, Brownsville, TX 78521,
Tel: (512) 544-2722
(Mfr windshield wiper sys & components)
Trico Pty., Ltd., Princess Hwy., 820-850 Springvale, Vic. 3171, Australia

TRINOVA CORP   3000 Strayer, PO Box 50, Maumee, OH 43537, Tel: (419) 867-2200
(Mfr engr components & sys for ind)
Vickers Systems Pty. Ltd., 169 Rosamond Rd., Maribyrnong, Victoria 3034, Australia

TRITON ENERGY CORP   4925 Greenville Ave, 1400 One Energy Sq, Dallas,
TX 75206, Tel: (214) 691-5200
(Energy explor & prod)
Crusader Ltd., AMP Place, 12 Creek St., Brisbane, QLD 4000, Australia

TRW INC   1900 Richmond Rd, Cleveland, OH 44124, Tel: (216) 291-7000
(Electr & energy-related prdts, automotive & aerospace prdts, tools & fasteners)
TRW Australia Ltd., P.O. Box 43, Carrington Rd., Marrickville, NSW, 2204, Australia
TRW Australia Ltd., other locations in Australia

TWIN DISC INC   1328 Racine St, Racine, WI 53403, Tel: (414) 634-1981
(Mfr ind clutches, reduction gears, transmissions)
Twin Disc (Pacific) Pty. Ltd., P.O. Box 442, Zillmere, Qld. 4034, Australia

U S LEASING INTL INC   733 Front St, San Francisco, CA 94111,
Tel: (415) 627-9000
(Equip leasing & financing)
Portfolio Leasing Australia Ltd., P.O. Box 851, North Sydney, NSW 2059, Australia

UNIBRAZE CORP   7502 W State, Rte 41, Covington, OH 45318, Tel: (513) 473-2006
(Brazing, welding & soldering alloys of copper, silver, aluminum & brass)
Unibraze, Wetherill St., Lidcombe, NSW, 2141, Australia

UNION CARBIDE CORP   Old Ridgebury Rd, Danbury, CT 06817, Tel: (203) 794-2000
(Carbon prdts, chems, plastics, gases & related prdts, etc)
Union Carbide Australia Ltd., GPO Box 5322, Sydney, NSW, 2001, Australia

UNION OIL INTL DIV   Union Oil Center, PO Box 7600, Los Angeles, CA 90017,
Tel: (213) 977-7600
(Petroleum prdts, petrochems)
Union Oil Development Corp., 8-12 Bridge St., Sydney, NSW, 2000, Australia

UNIROYAL INC   World Headquarters, Middlebury, CT 06749, Tel: (203) 573-2000
  (Tires, tubes & other rubber prdts, chems, plastics, textiles)
    Uniroyal Pty.., Ltd., 1028-1042 South Rd., Edwardstown, S.A., 5039, Australla

UNISYS CORP   PO Box 500, Blue Bell, PA 19424, Tel: (215) 542-4011
  (Mfg/mktg/serv electr info sys)
    Unisys, 30 Alfred St., P.O. Box 488, Milsons Pt., NSW 2067, Australia
    Unisys, Level 40, Northpoint, 100 Miller St., N. Sydney, NSW 2060, Australia

UNITED AIRLINES INC   PO Box 66100, Chicago, IL 60666, Tel: (708) 952-4000
  (Air transp)
    United Airlines, 11 Barrack St., Sydney, NSW 2000, Australia

UNITED CARGO CORP   40 Rector St, New York, NY 10006, Tel: (212) 766-1808
  (Containerized air & sea frt)
    United Cargo Corp., John Fletcher Pty., Ltd., Sydney, Australia

UNITED ELECTRIC CONTROLS CO   85 School St, Watertown, MA 02172,
  Tel: (617) 926-1000
  (Electro-mechanical & electronic controls & recorders)
    United Electric Controls (Australia) Pty., Ltd., P.O. Box 271, 83 Murphy, St.,
      Richmond, Vic. 3121, Australia

UNITED PRESS INTL   220 E 42nd St, New York, NY 10017, Tel: (212) 682-0400
  (Collection & distributor of news, newspictures, fin data)
    United Press Intl., 2 Holt St., Sydney, 5336, Australia

UNITEK CORP/3M   2724 S Peck Rd, Monrovia, CA 91016-7118, Tel: (818) 574-4000
  (Mfr orthodontic prdts)
    Unitek Corp./3M (Australia) Pty., Ltd., 9-15 Chilvers Rd., Thornleigh, NSW 2120,
      Australia

UOP INC   Ten UOP Plaza, Des Plaines, IL 60016, Tel: (708) 391-2000
  (Diversified research, development & mfr of ind prdts & sys mgmt studies & serv)
    Bostik Australia Pty., Ltd., P.O. Box 60, Thomastown Vt., 3074, Australia
    Bostrom Div., UOP Pty., Ltd., Melbourne, Australia
    Johnson Screen Div., UOP Pty., Ltd., Kirrawee, Australia

UPJOHN CO   7000 Portage Rd, Kalamazoo, MI 49001, Tel: (616) 323-4000
  (Pharms, agric prdts, ind chems)
    Upjohn Pty., Ltd., P.O. Box 138, Parramatta, NSW, 2150, Australia

UTAH INTL INC   550 California St, San Francisco, CA 94104,
  Tel: (415) 981-1515
  (Mining, land development, ocean shipping, oil & gas)
    Utah Development Co., 56 Pitt St., Royal Exchange Bldg., 19th Floor, Sydney, NSW,
      2000, Australia
    Utah Development Co., Box 1389, GPO, Brisbane, QLD, 4001, Australia

VALERON CORP   750 Stephenson Highway, Troy, MI 48084, Tel: (313) 589-1000
  (Cemented carbide, high speed steel, ceramic & diamond cutting tool prdts, etc)
    Valenite-Modco (Australia), 7 Acheson Place, North Coburg, Vic., 3050, Australia

VARIAN ASSOCIATES INC   611 Hansen Way, Palo Alto, CA 94304-1030,
  Tel: (415) 493-4000
  (Mfr microwave tubes & devices, analytical instru, semiconductor process & med equip,

vacuum sys)
   Varian Techtron Pty., Ltd., 679 Sprinvale Rd., Mulgravia, Vic. 3170, Australia

VEEDER-ROOT CO   125 Powder Forest Dr, PO Box 2003, Simsbury, CT 06070-2003,
   Tel: (203) 651-2700
   (Mfr counting, controlling & sensing devices)
      Veeder-Root (Australia) Pty. Ltd., 82 Herald St., Cheltenham, Vic. 3192, Australia

VELSICOL CHEMICAL CORP   5600 N River Rd, Rosemont, IL 60018,
   Tel: (708) 698-9700
   (Pesticides & ind chems)
      Velsicol Australia Ltd., P.O. Box 21, Pendle Hill, NSW 2145, Australia

VERMEER MFG CO   PO Box 200, Pella, IA 50219, Tel: (515) 628-3141
   (Mfr agri & ind equip)
      Vermeer Pacific Pty. Ltd., 3 Gratton St., Brighton, SA 4058, Australia

VF CORP   PO Box 1022, Reading, PA 19603, Tel: (215) 378-1151
   (Mfr/mktg apparel)
      H.D. Lee (Australia) Pty. Ltd, P.O. Box 571, Hume Hwy., Wodonga, Vic. 3690,
      Australia

VIACOM INTL INC   1211 Ave of the Americas, New York, NY 10036,
   Tel: (212) 575-5175
   (Diversified entertainment & commun)
      Viacom Intl. Pty. Ltd., St. Martin's Tower 16/F, 31 Market St., Sydney, NSW 2000,
      Australia

VITRAMON INC   PO Box 544, Bridgeport, CT 06601, Tel: (203) 268-6261
   (Ceramic capacitors)
      Vitramon Pty., Ltd., E58 Freder ck, P.O. Box 140, Rockdale, NSW, 2216, Australia

WALLACE & TIERNAN DIV   25 Main St, Belleville, NJ 07109, Tel: (201) 759-8000
   (Chems, instru)
      Wallace & Tiernan Pty., Ltd., 89-93 Reserve Rd., Artarmon, NSW, Australia

WANG LABORATORIES INC   1 Industrial Ave, Lowell, MA 01851,
   Tel: (508) 459-5000
   (Mfr computer info processing sys)
      Wang Computer Pty. Ltd., 10-14 Paul St., Milsons Point, NSW, 2061, Australia

WARD HOWELL INTL INC   99 Park Ave, New York, NY 10016, Tel: (212) 697-3730
   (Executive recruiting)
      Ward Howell Intl., Level 55, MLC Centle, Martin Place, Sydney, NSW, 2000, Australia

WARNER BROS INC   4000 Warner Blvd, Burbank, CA 91522, Tel: (213) 954-6000
   (Prod/dist motion picture films, TV, music recording & pub)
      Warner Bros. (Australia) Pty., Ltd., 49 Market St., Suite 3, 7th Floor, Sydney,
      NSW, 2000, Australia

WARNER ELECTRIC BRAKE & CLUTCH CO   449 Gardner St, South Beloit, IL 61080,
   Tel: (815) 389-3771
   (Automotive & ind brakes & clutches)
      Warner Electric Australia Pty., Ltd., 2 Mary Parade, Rydalmere, NSW, 2116, Australia

WARNER-LAMBERT CO   201 Tabor Road, Morris Plains, NJ 07950,
  Tel: (201) 540-2000
  (Mfr ethical & proprietary pharms, confectionary & consumer prdts)
    Parke Davis & Co., P.O. Box 42, Caringbah, Sydney, NSW 2229, Australia

WATERS CHROMATOGRAPHY DIV   34 Maple St, Milford, MA 01757,
  Tel: (617) 478-2000
  (Mfr/distr liquid chromatographic instru/accessories/tech)
    Waters Associates Pty., Ltd., 82-96 Myrtle St., Chippendale, Sydney, NSW, 2008,
    Australia

THE WAYNE GROUP LTD   244 California St, San Francisco, CA 94111,
  Tel: (415) 421-2010
  (Human resources consult)
    John P. Young & Assoc. Pty. Ltd., 2 Fordham Rd., Melbourne, Vic. 3122, Australia

WEAN INC   13 South, 3 Gateway Center, Pittsburgh, PA 15222,
  Tel: (412) 456-5300
  (Design & mfr metal working & metal producing equip)
    Wean United of Australia Pty., Ltd., 73 Barkly St., Mornington, Vic. 3931, Australia

WEATHERFORD INTL INC   1360 Post Oak Blvd, PO Box 27608, Houston,
  TX 77227-9917, Tel: (713) 439-9400
  (Tubular & cementation servs, prdts & equip; water jetting servs, mfr marine pedestal
  cranes)
    Weatherford Australia Pty., Ltd., Unit 14/2 Powell St., P.O. Box 157, Osborne Park,
    WA 6017, Australia

WEATHERHEAD DIV   6615 Brotherhood Way, Fort Wayne, IN 46825,
  Tel: (219) 481-3500
  (Mfr fluid power prdts, hose assys, tube & pipe fittings & valves)
    Dana Australia Pty. Ltd./Fluid Power Div, 585 Burwood Hwy., Knoxfield, Vic. 3180,
    Australia

WEIGHT WATCHERS INTL INC   Jericho Atrium, 500 North Broadway, Jericho,
  NY 11753-2196, Tel: (516) 939-0400
  (Weight reduction programs, food prdts)
    Weight Watchers of Australia, 309 Pitt St., 13th Floor, Sydney, NSW, 2000, Australia

WEST CO INC   West Bridge St, Phoenixville, PA 19460, Tel: (215) 935-4500
  (Pharm packaging comps)
    West Pharmapackaging Pty. Ltd., P.O. Box W123, Warringah Mall, NSW 2100, Australia

WEST POINT-PEPPERELL INC   400 W 10th St, PO Box 71, West Point, GA 31833,
  Tel: (205) 756-7111
  (Ind, household & apparel fabrics)
    Lantor of Australia Pty., Ltd., 15 Williams Rd., Coburg, Vic. 3058, Australia

WESTERN GEOPHYSICAL   PO Box 2469, Houston, TX 77252-2469, Tel: (713) 789-9600
  (Geophysical serv)
    Western Geophysical, 447-449 Belmont Ave., Perth, WA 6105, Australia

WESTINGHOUSE AIR BRAKE CO   40 W 40th St, New York, NY 10018,
  Tel: (212) 840-5440
  (Equip for transp, constr, mining inds)
    WABCO Australia Pty., Ltd., 10-16 South Street, Rydalmere, NSW, 2116, Australia

WESTINGHOUSE ELECTRIC CORP   Westinghouse Bldg, Gateway Center, Pittsburgh,
  PA 15222, Tel: (412) 244-2000
  (TV/radio broadcasting, mfr electr sys for ind/defense, fin & environmental servs)
     Tyree Industries Ltd., P.O. Box 315, Liverpool, NSW 2170, Australia

WESTVACO CORP   299 Park Ave, New York, NY 10171, Tel: (212) 688-5000
  (Mfr paper, packaging, chems)
     Westvaco Pacific Pty., Ltd., 186 Blues Point Rd., North Sydney, NSW, 2061, Australia
     Westvaco Southwest Pacific, Box 273, Milson's Point, NSW, 2016, Australia

WEYERHAEUSER CO   Tacoma, WA 98477, Tel: (206) 924-2345
  (Wood & wood fiber prdts)
     Weyerhaeuser (Australia) Pty., Ltd., Bennelong Rd., Homebush Bay, NSW, 2140,
     Austalia

WHEELABRATOR-FRYE INC   11255 N Torrey Pines Rd, La Jolla, CA 92037,
  Tel: (603) 926-5911
  (Diversified environmental & energy sys, chems, precision & ind equip)
     Wheelabrator Granowski Pty., Ltd., P.O. Box 51, Bayswater, Vic., 3153, Australia

WHITAKER CABLE CORP   PO Box 7499, Kansas City, MO 64116, Tel: (816) 474-0300
  (Electrical wire & cable assemblies for ind & auto replacement mkt)
     Whitaker Cable of Australia Pty., Ltd., 277 Milperra Rd., Revesby, NSW, 2212,
     Australia
     Whitaker Cable of Australia Pty., Ltd., P.O. Box 193, Revesby, Australia

WILBUR-ELLIS CO   320 California St, San Francisco, CA 94104,
  Tel: (415) 772-4000
  (Zippers & general merchandise)
     Canal Bros., P.O. Box 156, 6 Lambs Rd., Artarmon, NSW, 2064, Australia

JOHN WILEY & SONS INC   605 Third Ave, New York, NY 10158, Tel: (212) 850-6000
  (Publishing)
     Jacaranda Wiley Ltd., GPO Box 859, Brisbane, QLD, 4001, Australia

WILLIAMS BROS ENGINEERING CO   6600 S Yale Ave, Tulsa, OK 74136,
  Tel: (918) 496-5020
  (Engineers, contractors, mgmt serv)
     Williams Bros.-CMPS Engineers, P.O. Box 369, Seven Help St., Chatswood, NSW 2067,
     Australia

WOODWARD & DICKERSON INC   937 Haverford Road, Bryn Mawr, PA 19010,
  Tel: (215) 527-5200
  (Intl marketing)
     Woodward & Dickerson Australia, 620 St. Kilds Rd., Melbourne, Vic. 3004, Australia

WOODWARD GOVERNOR CO   5001 North 2nd St, PO Box 7001, Rockford,
  IL 61125-7001, Tel: (815) 877-7441
  (Mfr speed control governors)
     Woodward Governor Co., P.O. Box 319, Unit 1-1 Wirega Ave., Kingsgrove, NSW 2208,
     Australia

WORLD COMMUNICATIONS INC   67 Broad St, New York, NY 10004,
  Tel: (212) 607-2000
  (Intl private line services)
     World Communications System, Level 59, MLC Center, Sydney 2000, Australia

WORLD COURIER INC   46 Trinity Pl, New York, NY 10006, Tel: (718) 978-9400
  (Intl courier serv)
    World Courier Australia Pty. Ltd., 23-2S O'Connell St., Sydney, 2065, Australia

WORLD'S FINEST CHOCOLATE INC   4801 S Lawndale, Chicago, IL 60632,
  Tel: (312) 847-4600
  (Mfr chocolate)
    World's Finest Australia Pty. Ltd., 8 Bridge St., Stanmore, NSW 2048, Australia

WRIGHT LINE INC   160 Gold Star Blvd, Worcester, MA 01606, Tel: (508) 852-4300
  (Mfr filing sys)
    Datafile Pty. Ltd., 19-21 Antoine St., Rydalmere, NSW 2116, Australia

WM WRIGLEY JR CO   410 N Michigan Ave, Chicago, IL 60611-4287,
  Tel: (312) 644-2121
  (Chewing gum)
    The Wrigley Co. Pty. Ltd., P.O. Box 64, Hornsby, NSW 2077, Australia

WURLITZER CO   422 Wards Corner Rd, Loveland, OH 45140, Tel: (513) 576-4601
  (Pianos, electronic organs & pianos, vending & pay phonograph machs)
    Wurlitzer Australia Pty. Ltd., 56-58 Alexander Ave., Taren Point, NSW, 2229,
    Australia

WYNN OIL CO   2600 E Nutwood Ave, PO Box 4370, Fullerton, CA 92631,
  Tel: (714) 992-2000
  (Chem additives for oil, grease & fuels; hardware)
    Wynn Nu Performance Industries Pty., Ltd., Suite 502, Nirad House, 282 Vic. Ave.,
    Chatswood, NSW, Australia

YOUNG & RUBICAM INTL INC   285 Madison Ave, New York, NY 10017,
  Tel: (212) 210-3000
  (Advertising agency)
    Young & Rubicam Pty., Ltd., 1 York St., Sydney, NSW, 2000, Australia
    Young & Rubicam Pty., Ltd., 366 King William St., Adelaide, S.A. 5000, Australia

AUSTRIA

3M CO   3M Center, St Paul, MN 55144-1000, Tel: (612) 733-1110
  (Mfr abrasives, adhesives, chems, ind & consumer tapes/diskettes, health care prdts,
  elec connectors)
    3M Osterreich GmbH, Postfach 611, A-1011 Vienna, Austria

ABBOTT LABORATORIES   Abbott Park, North Chicago, IL 60064,
  Tel: (312) 937-6100
  (Pharm & lab prdts)
    Abbott GmbH, Diefenbachgasse 35, A-1150 Vienna, Austria

AIR EXPRESS INTL CORP   120 Tokeneke Rd, PO Box 1231, Darien, CT 06820,
  Tel: (203) 655-7900
  (Air frt forwarder)
    Air Express Intl. Cargoplan, Airport Vienna, A-1300 Vienna, Austria

ALLEN GROUP INC   534 Broadhollow Rd, Melville, NY 11747, Tel: (516) 293-5500
  (Automotive carwash & diagnostic equip)
    A. Rohe GmbH, Atzgersdorfer Str. 98, A-1230 Vienna, Austria

AMERICAN CYANAMID CO   1 Cyanamid Plaza, Wayne, NJ 07470, Tel: (201) 831-2000
  (Pharms, chems, agric & consumer prdts)
    Cyanamid GmbH, Tendlergasse 13, A-1090 Vienna, Austria
    Cyanamid GmbH, Nikolsdorfergasse 8/3, A-1050 Vienna, Austria

AMERICAN INTL UNDERWRITERS CORP   70 Pine St, New York, NY 10270,
  Tel: (212) 770-7000
  (General ins)
    National Union Fire Insurance Co. of Pittsburgh, Schwedenplatz 2, Postfach 586,
      A-1010 Vienna, Austria

AMERICAN STANDARD INC   40 W 40th St, New York, NY 10018, Tel: (212) 840-5100
  (Heating & sanitary equip)
    Ideal Standard, Abteilung der Wabco-Westinghouse GmbH, Pasettistrasse 33-35,
      1200 Vienna, Austria

AMP INC   470 Friendship Rd, Harrisburg, PA 17111, Tel: (717) 564-0100
  (Mfr electrical wiring devices)
    AMP Osterreich GmbH, Pilzgasse 31, A-1211 Vienna, Austria

AMPHENOL PRODUCTS   4300 Commerct Ct, Lisle, IL 60532, Tel: (708) 983-3500
  (Elect interconnect/penetrate sys & assemblies)
    Amphenol GmbH, Tautenhayngasse 22, A-1150 Vienna, Austria

AMWAY CORP   7575 E Fulton Rd, Ada, MI 49355, Tel: (616) 676-6000
  (Distr household cleaning, nutrition & diet prdts)
    Amway GmbH, Litfastrasse 8, A-1031 Vienna, Austria

APPLE COMPUTER INC   20525 Mariani Ave, Cupertino, CA 95014,
  Tel: (408) 996-1010
  (Personal computers, peripherals & software)
    Apple Computer GmbH, Rotenturmstrasse 1-3 top 12, A-1010 Vienna, Austria

BAKER OIL TOOLS   PO Box 3048, Houston, TX 77253, Tel: (713) 923-9351
  (Oil/gas well completions equip)
    Fagro GmbH Feur Erdoel und Bergbau, Heinstrasse 3/8, A-1020 Vienna, Austria

BANKERS TRUST CO   280 Park Ave, New York, NY 10017, Tel: (212) 775-2500
  (Banking)
    Bankers Trust Co., Claughton House, P.O. Box N 3234, Nassau, Bahamas

BARDAHL MFG CORP   1400 N W 52nd St, PO Box 70607, Seattle, WA 98107,
  Tel: (206) 783-4851
  (Lubricating oils)
    Autobedark Karlkastner, Etrichgasse 28, 6020 Innsbruck, Austria

BATTEN BARTON DURSTINE & OSBORN INC   1285 Ave of the Americas, New York,
NY 10019, Tel: (212) 459-5000
(Advertising agency)
   Team Austria, Heutteleort Strasse 65, 1150 Vienna, Austria

BAUSCH & LOMB INC   1 Lincoln First Sq, Rochester, NY 14601-0054,
Tel: (716) 338-6000
(Mfr healthcare & optics prdts)
   Bausch & Lomb GmbH, Vienna, Austria

BECKMAN INSTRUMENTS INC   2500 Harbor Blvd, Box 3100, Fullerton, CA 92634,
Tel: (714) 871-4848
(Mfr/distr/serv research & clinical lab instru, sys, software & reagents)
   Beckman Instruments Austria GmbH, Eastern European Operations,
      A-3400 Klosterneuburg, Austria

BENTLEY LABORATORIES INC   17502 Armstrong Ave, Irvine, CA 92714,
Tel: (714) 546-8020
(Mfr para-med devices)
   Bentley Labs Ltd., Gersthoferstr 160/11/8, 1180 Vienna, Austria

BLACK & DECKER CORP   701 E Joppa Road, Towson, MD 21204, Tel: (301) 583-3900
(Mfr portable elect & pneumatic power tools, household prdts)
   Black & Decker Werkzeuge, Vertriebs GmbH, Erlaaerstrasse 165, Postfach 47,
      1233 Vienna, Austria

BOISE CASCADE CORP   One Jefferson Square, PO Box 50, Boise, ID 83728,
Tel: (208) 384-6161
(Lumber, paper, related prdts)
   Duropack Wellpappe AG, Brunner Strasse 75, A-1235 Wien-Liesing, Vienna, Austria
   Duropack Wellpappe GmbH, Forsterstr. 54-62, A-8401 Kalsdorf bei Graz, Austria

BORG-WARNER CORP   200 S Michigan Ave, Chicago, IL 60604, Tel: (312) 322-8500
(Mfr A/C equip, chem & plastics, ind prdts, trans equip)
   Kalte-und Klimatechnik GmbH, Sonnleithnergasse 5, A-1100 Vienna, Austria

BULAB HOLDINGS INC   1256 N McLean Blvd, Memphis, TN 38108,
Tel: (901) 278-0330
(Mfr microbicides, biocides, additives, corrosion inhibitors, chems)
   Buckman Laboratories GmbH, Wehlistrasse 29, A-1200 Vienna, Austria

BURR-BROWN RESEARCH CORP   PO Box 11400, Tucson, AZ 85734, Tel: (602) 746-1111
(Electronic components & sys modules)
   Burr-Brown Research GmbH, Senefeldergasse 11, 1100 Vienna, Austria

BURSON-MARSTELLER   230 Park Ave, New York, NY 10003-1566, Tel: (212) 614-4000
(Public relations/public affairs consultants)
   Burson-Marsteller GmbH, Dornbacher Strasse 97, A-1170 Vienna, Austria

CARL BYOIR & ASSOCIATES INC   380 Madison Ave, New York, NY 10017,
Tel: (212) 986-6100
(Public relations consultants)
   Presseburo PR Intl., Frimmelgasse 41, A-1190 Vienna, Austria

CANBERRA INDUSTRIES INC   One State St, Meriden, CT 06450, Tel: (203) 238-2351
(Mfr instru for nuclear research)
   Canberra-Packard GmbH, Josef Zapf Gasse 2, 1210 Vienna, Austria

CHASE MANHATTAN BANK N A   1 Chase Manhattan Plaza, New York, NY 10081,
Tel: (212) 552-2222
(Intl banking)
   Chase Manhattan Bank (Austria) AG, Neuer Markt 16, Postfach 582, A-1011 Vienna,
   Austria

CHRISTENSEN INTL   PO Box 26135, Salt Lake City, UT 84126, Tel: (801) 487-5371
(Diamond drills)
   Christensen Diamond Products GmbH, Hauptstrasse 31, 2230 Ganserndorf, Austria

CIGNA CORP   One Liberty Place, 1650 Market St, Philadelphia, PA 19101,
Tel: (215) 523-4000
(Ins, invest, health care & other fin servs)
   Cigna Insurance Co. of Europe SA/NV, Direktionfuer Oesterreich,
   Alserbachstrasse 18- Postfach 4, A-1091 Vienna, Austria

CINCINNATI MILACRON INC   4701 Marburg Ave, Cincinnati, OH 45209,
Tel: (513) 841-8256
(Mfr mach tools, robots, plastic mach, metrology equip)
   Cincinnati Milacron Austria AG, Postfach 111, A-1231 Vienna, Austria

CITIBANK NA   399 Park Ave, New York, NY 10043, Tel: (212) 559-1000
(Intl banking)
   Citibank (Austria) AG, Mattiellistrasse 2-4, A-1041 Vienna, Austria

THE COCA-COLA CO   310 North Ave NW, PO Box Drawer 1734, Atlanta, GA 30313,
Tel: (404) 676-2121
(Mfr & sale of soft drink syrups & concentrates, juices & food prdts, motion pic & TV
prod)
   Coca-Cola GmbH, Niederlassung, Postfach 28, A-1232 Vienna, Austria

COLGATE-PALMOLIVE CO   300 Park Ave, New York, NY 10022, Tel: (212) 310-2000
(Pharms, cosmetics, toiletries, detergents)
   Colgate-Palmolive GmbH, Parking 10, 1010 Vienna, Austria

COLUMBIA PICTURES INDUSTRIES INC   711 Fifth Ave, New York, NY 10022,
Tel: (212) 751-4400
(Producer & distributor of motion pictures)
   Warner-Columbia Filmverleih GmbH, Postfach 115, 1071 Vienna, Austria

COMPTON INTERNATIONAL   625 Madison Ave, New York, NY 10022,
Tel: (212) 754-1100
(Advertising)
   Die Sieber Compton Intl., Kopgasse 7, Vienna, Austria

COMPUTER ASSOCIATES INTL INC   711 Stewart Ave, Garden City, NY 11530,
Tel: (516) 227-3300
(Devel/mkt/mgt info mgt & bus applications software)
   Computer Associates Intl. GmbH, Geschaftsstelle Wien, Diefenbachgasse 35,
   A-1150 Wien, Austria

CONOCO INC   600 N Dairy Ashford Rd, Houston, TX 77079, Tel: (713) 293-1000
(Oil, gas, coal, chems, minerals)
   Conoco Austria Ltd., Postfach 6008, Hay St. E Perth, Wester, Austria
   Conoco-Austria Mineraloel GmbH, A-5020 Salzburg, Austria

CONTROL DATA CORP   8100 34th Ave S, Minneapolis, MN 55440,
  Tel: (612) 853-8100
  (Control data equip, computer sys serv & financial serv)
    Control Data GmbH, Mattiellestr. 2-4, 1040 Vienna, Austria

CPC INTERNATIONAL INC   PO Box 8000, International Plaza, Englewood Cliffs,
  NJ 07632, Tel: (201) 894-4000
  (Mfr consumer food prdts & corn refining prdts)
    C.H. Knorrnahrungsmittelfabrik GmbH, A-4600 Wels, Austria

JOHN CRANE INC   6400 Oakton St, Morton Grove, IL 60053, Tel: (708) 967-2400
  (Mfr engineering seals)
    John Crane Ltd., Auhofstrasse 84/3/4/40, A-1130 Vienna, Austria

D'ARCY MASIUS BENTON & BOWLES INC (DMB&B)   1675 Broadway, New York,
  NY 10019, Tel: (212) 468-3622
  (Advertising & communications)
    DMB&B GmbH, 17 Rotenturmstrasse, A-1010 Vienna, Austria

DATA GENERAL CORP   4400 Computer Dr, Westboro, MA 01580, Tel: (617) 366-8911
  (Design, mfr gen purpose computer sys & peripheral prdts & servs)
    Data General GmbH, Sechshauerstrasse 48, A-1150 Vienna, Austria

DATAPRODUCTS CORP   6200 Canada Ave, PO Box 746, Woodland Hills, CA 91365,
  Tel: (818) 887-8000
  (Mfr computer printers & supplies)
    Dataproducts Handels GmbH, Hintere Zollamtsstr. 9/32, A-1030 Vienna, Austria

DDB NEEDHAM WORLDWIDE INC   437 Madison Ave, New York, NY 10022,
  Tel: (212) 415-2000
  (Advertising)
    DDB Needham Heye & Partner, Hietzinger Kai 169, A-1130 Vienna, Austria

DEAK & CO INC   29 Broadway, New York, NY 10006, Tel: (212) 635-0515
  (Foreign exchange specialists)
    Bankhaus Deak & Co. Ltd., A-1010 Vienna, Austria

DIGITAL EQUIPMENT CORP   129 Parker St, Maynard, MA 01754, Tel: (617) 897-5111
  (Digital computers, digital circuit modules, memory elec- tronic system)
    Digital Equipment Corp., Mariahilferstr. 136, 1150 Vienna, Austria

DOW CHEMICAL CO   2030 Dow Center, Midland, MI 48640, Tel: (517) 636-1000
  (Chems, plastics, fibers, pharms)
    Dow Chemical GmbH, Concordiapl. 2, 1010 Vienna, Austria

DOW CORNING CORP   2220 W Salzburg Rd, PO Box 1767, Midland, MI 48640,
  Tel: (517) 496-4000
  (Silicones, silicon chems, solid lubricants)
    Dow Corning GmbH, Mariahilferstrasse 180/4, 1150 Vienna, Austria

DREW CHEMICAL CORP   One Drew Plaza, Boonton, NJ 07005, Tel: (201) 263-7600
  (Spec chems for ind water & fuel treatment, chem processing)
    Drew Ameroid Intl. Corp., Rudolf Waisenhorngasse 13, A-1235, Vienna, Austria

DRG INTL INC   1167 Route 22 East, Mountainside, NJ 07092, Tel: (201) 233-2075
  (Sale/serv med diagnostic prdts & equip; biotech prdts)
    DRG Diagnostica, Geigergasse 11, A-1053 Vienna, Austria

EASTMAN KODAK CO   343 State St, Rochester, NY 14650-0518, Tel: (716) 724-4000
(Devel/mfr photo & chem prdts, info mgmt/video/copier sys, fibers/plastics for
various ind)
    Kodak GmbH, Postfach 33, A-5021 Salzburg, Austria

ECOLAB INC   370 Wabasha St, St Paul, MN 55102, Tel: (612) 293-2233
(Ind & household detergents, cleaning agents & equip)
    Soilax GmbH, Lerchenfelderstrasse 70-72, A-1080 Vienna, Austria

ELIZABETH ARDEN INC   55 East 52nd St, New York, NY 10055-0191,
Tel: (212) 407-1000
(Cosmetics, fragrances, toiletries)
    Elizabeth Arden GmbH, Seilergasse 2, A-1010 Vienna, Austria

EXXON CORP   225 E John Carpenter Frwy, Irving, TX 75062, Tel: (214) 444-1000
(Petroleum & petroleum prdts)
    Esso Austria AG, Postfach 201, Vienna, Austria

FAIRCHILD CAMERA & INSTRUMENT CORP   PO Box 58090, Santa Clara,
CA 95052-8090, Tel: (408) 743-3355
(Mfr electr instru & controls)
    Fairchild Electronics GmbH, Schwedenplatz 2, 1010 Vienna, Austria

FISCHER & PORTER CO   125 E County Line Rd, Warminster, PA 18974,
Tel: (215) 674-6000
(Design/mfr meas, recording & control instru & sys; mfr ind glass prdts)
    Fischer & Porter GmbH, Wiener Str. 17, Aa-2351 Wiener Neudorf, Austria

FISHER CONTROLS INTL INC   8000 Maryland Ave, Clayton, MO 63105,
Tel: (314) 694-9900
(Ind process control equip)
    Fisher Controls GmbH, Doblinger Haupstrasse 72, A-1190 Vienna, Austria

FMC CORP   200 E Randolph Dr, Chicago, IL 60601, Tel: (312) 861-6000
(Mach & chem for industry, agric & govt)
    FMC Chemikalien GmbH, Paulanergasse 13/3, A-1040 Vienna, Austria

FOOTE CONE & BELDING COMMUNICATIONS INC   101 E Erie St, Chicago,
IL 60611-2897, Tel: (312) 751-7000
(Advertising agency)
    Publicis/FCB, Spiegelgasse 1, 1015 Vienna, Austria

FORD MOTOR CO   The American Road, Dearborn, MI 48121, Tel: (313) 322-3000
(Mfr automobiles, trucks)
    Ford Motor Co. Austria KG, Fuerburgstrasse 51, Postfach 2, A-5021 Salzburg, Austria

FOXBORO CO   33 Commercial St, Foxboro, MA 02035, Tel: (508) 543-8750
(Mfr prdts/provide servs for ind automation)
    Inramat GmbH, Tuerkenschanzgasse 51, A-3400 Klosterneuburg, Austria
    Stahl GmbH, Postfach 33, A-1043 Vienna, Austria

THE FRANKLIN MINT   Franklin Center, PA 19091, Tel: (215) 459-6000
(Creation/mfr/mktg collectible items)
    Franklin Ming GmbH, Zillnerstr. 18, A-5020 Salzburg, Austria

GAF CORP   1361 Alps Rd, Wayne, NJ 07470, Tel: (201) 628-3000
  (Chems, bldg materials, commun)
    GAF (Oesterreich) GmbH, Hietzinger Kai 101-105, 1130 Vienna, Austria

GENERAL AUTOMATION INC   1055 S East St, Anaheim, CA 92806,
  Tel: (714) 778-4800
  (Computer hardware & serv)
    General Automation GmbH, Gnigler Strasse 5, A-5020 Salzburg, Austria

GENERAL MOTORS ACCEPTANCE CORP   3044 West Grand Blvd, Detroit, MI 48202,
  Tel: (313) 556-5000
  (Automobile financing)
    General Motors Bank GmbH, Gross-Enzersdorfer-Strasse 59, A-1226 Vienna, Austria

GENERAL MOTORS CORP   3044 W Grand Blvd, Detroit, MI 48202,
  Tel: (313) 556-5000
  (Automotive prdts, electronics)
    General Motors Austria GmbH, Gross Enzerdorferstrasse 59, A-1220 Vienna, Austria

GREY ADVERTISING INC   777 Third Ave, New York, NY 10017, Tel: (212) 546-2000
  (Advertising)
    Gramm & Grey GmbH, Gluckgasse 1, 1015 Vienna, Austria

FRANK B HALL & CO INC   549 Pleasantville Rd, Briarcliff Manor, NY 10510,
  Tel: (914) 769-9200
  (Insurance)
    Gregor, Egger & Co. GmbH, Goldschmiedgasse 6, A-1010 Vienna, Austria

HERCULES INC   Hercules Plaza, Wilmington, DE 19894, Tel: (302) 594-5000
  (Mfr spec chems, plastics, film & fibers, coatings, resins, food ingredients)
    Patex Chemie GmbH, Madlschenterweg 3, A-4050 Traun, Austria

HEWLETT-PACKARD CO   3000 Hanover St, PO Box 10301, Palo Alto, CA 94303-0890,
  Tel: (415) 857-1501
  (Mfr measurement & computation prdts & sys)
    Hewlett-Packard GmbH, Herrenbergerstrassse 110/130, D-7030 Boebligen 1, Austria

HIRSCH CO   8051 Central Park Ave, Skokie, IL 60076, Tel: (708) 673-6610
  (Shelving for home & industry)
    Hirsch & Co., GmbH, Universitaetsstrasse 5, A-1010 Vienna, Austria

HOLIDAY INNS INC   3742 Lamar Ave, Memphis, TN 38195, Tel: (901) 362-4001
  (Hotels, restaurants, casinos)
    Holiday Inns Inc., Salurner Strasse 15, Postfach 97, 6010 Innsbruck, City Centre,
    Austria

THE HOOVER GROUP   403 W 4th St N, Newton, IA 50208, Tel: (515) 792-8000
  (Mfr floor care prdts, laundry & refrig appliances)
    Hoover Austria GmbH, Foerstergasse 6/Postfach 49, A-1025 Vienna, Austria

HORWATH & HORWATH INTL   919 Third Ave, New York, NY 10022,
  Tel: (212) 980-3100
  (Public accountants & auditors)
    Auditor Treuhand GmbH, Wipplingerstrasse 34, A-1010 Vienna, Austria

ICC INDUSTRIES INC   720 Fifth Ave, New York, NY 10019, Tel: (212) 397-3300
  (Chems & plastics)
    ICC-Handels AG GmbH, Laxenburgerstrasse 35, A-1103 Vienna, Austria

INA CORPORATION   1600 Arch St, Philadelphia, PA 19101, Tel: (215) 523-5335
  (Holding co: ins, financial serv)
    Insurance Company of North America, Alserbachstrasse 18, 1090 Vienna, Austria

INCOM INTERNATIONAL INC   3450 Princeton Pike, Lawrenceville, NJ 08648,
  Tel: (609) 896-7600
  (Roller & motorcycle chains, drive components, marine controls, etc)
    Elbak Batteriewerke GmbH, Postfach 48, A-8055 Graz-Puntingam, Austria

INSTRUMENTATION LABORATORY   113 Hartwell Ave, Lexington, MA 02173-3190,
  Tel: (617) 861-0710
  (Med & sci analyzers & meas instru)
    Instrumentation Laboratory GmbH, Erlachgasse 116, A-1100 Vienna, Austria

INTERMEC CORP   6001 36th Ave West, Everett, WA 98203-9280,
  Tel: (206) 348-2600
  (Mfr automated data collection sys)
    Intermec GmbH, Pottendorferstrasse 69, A-2523 Tattendorf, Austria

INTERNATIONAL BUSINESS MACHINES (IBM)   Old Orchard Rd, Armonk,
  NY 10504-1783, Tel: (914) 765-1900
  (Info-handling sys, equip & serv)
    IBM Oesterreich Internationale Bueromaschinem GmbH, Obere Donaustrasse 95,
      Vienna 1020, Austria
    IBM Produktvertrieb GmbH, Vienna, Austria

INTERNATIONAL PAPER   2 Manhattanville Rd, Purchase, NY 10577,
  Tel: (914) 397-1500
  (Mfr/distr container board, paper, wood prdts)
    Anitec Image Warenvertriebs GmbH, Dambockgasse 413, 1060 Vienna, Austria

INTERNATIONAL STANDARD ELECTRIC CORP   320 Park Ave, New York, NY 10022,
  Tel: (212) 752-6000
  (Telecommun equip)
    Standard Telephon-Anlagenvermietung GmbH, 75 Fresener Strasse, A-1200 Vienna,
      Austria

ITT CORP   1330 Ave of the Americas, New York, NY 10019, Tel: (212) 258-1000
  (Diversified mfr, tech & services)
    ITT Austria Intl. Telephone Telegraphen GmbH, 75 Fresdner Strasse, A-1200 Vienna,
      Austria

ITT SHERATON CORP   60 State St, Boston, MA 02108, Tel: (617) 367-3600
  (Hotel operations)
    Salzburg Sheraton Hotel, Auerspergstr. 4, Salzburg A-5020, Austria

JOHNSON & JOHNSON   One Johnson & Johnson Plaza, New Brunswick, NJ 08933,
  Tel: (201) 524-0400
  (Surgical, med & baby prdts)
    Cilag GmbH, Vienna, Austria
    Janssen Pharmaceutica GmbH, Vienna, Austria
    Johnson & Johnson GmbH, Hallein, Austria

S C JOHNSON & SON INC   1525 Howe St, Racine, WI 53403, Tel: (414) 631-2000
(Home, auto, commercial & personal care prdts, specialty chems)
   Johnson's Wax GmbH, Rennbhnweg 25, A-1222 Vienna, Austria

KEITHLEY INSTRUMENTS INC   28775 Aurora Rd, Cleveland, OH 44139,
   Tel: (216) 248-0400
(Mfr electr test/meas instru, PC-based data acquisition hdwe/software)
   Keithley Instruments GmbH, Doblinger Hauptsr. 32, A-1190 Vienna, Austria

THE KENDALL CO   PO Box 10, Boston, MA 02101, Tel: (617) 423-2000
(Surgical dressings, baby prdts)
   Kenced GmbH, 4 Giessergasse, 9 Vienna, Austria

KIENBAUM INTL GROUP   110 Gibraltar Rd, PO Box 238, Horsham, PA 19044,
   Tel: (215) 674-5210
(Intl business consulting)
   Kienbaum Intl., Tuchlauben 8, A-1010 Vienna 1, Austria

KIMBALL INTERNATIONAL INC   1600 Royal St, Jasper, IN 47546,
   Tel: (812) 482-1600
(Mfr office furn & seating, pianos, wood veneers, plywood prdts)
   Bosendorfer L. Klavierfabrik AG, Bosendorferstrasse 12, A-1010 Vienna, Austria

KNOGO CORP   350 Wireless Blvd, Hauppauge, NY 11788, Tel: (516) 232-2100
(Mfr electr article surveillance sys)
   Knogo GmbH, Cervantesgasse 4, 1140 Wien, Austria

KNOLL INTL   655 Madison Ave, New York, NY 10021, Tel: (212) 826-2400
(Furniture & fabrics)
   Knoll International Austria GmbH, Baummarket 12, 1010 Vienna, Austria

LE TOURNEAU INC LONGVIEW DIV   PO Box 2307, Longview, TX 75606,
   Tel: (214) 753-3449
(Heavy constr, mining mach & equip)
   Ing. G. Schlamadinger, A-2320 Schwechat, P.B. 4, Vienna, Austria

ELI LILLY & CO   307 E McCarty St, Indianapolis, IN 46285, Tel: (317) 261-2000
(Pharms, agric & cosmetic prdts)
   Eli Lilly & Co., Hutteldorferstrasse 65, A-1150 Vienna, Austria

LINTAS:WORLDWIDE   1 Dag Hammarskjold Plaza, New York, NY 10017,
   Tel: (212) 605-8000
(Advertising agency)
   Lintas:Wein, Prinz Eugenstrasse 8, 1041 Vienna, Austria

MALLINCKRODT INC   675 McDonnell Blvd, PO Box 5840, St Louis, MO 63134,
   Tel: (314) 895-2012
(Med/ind chems, organics, pharms)
   Byk-Mallinckrodtchemische Produkte GmbH, Vienna, Austria

MANPOWER INC   5301 N Ironwood Rd, PO Box 2053, Milwaukee, WI 53201-2053,
   Tel: (414) 961-1000
(Temporary help)
   Manpower, Lugeck 1/33, A-1010 Vienna, Austria

MEAD CORP   Courthouse Plaza, NE, Dayton, OH 45463, Tel: (513) 222-6323
  (Mfr paper, packaging, pulp, lumber & other wood prdts, school & office prdts; electr
  pub, distri)
    Mead Coated Board Europe Kartonvertriebs-AG, Berggasse 7, A-1091 Vienna, Austria

MEASUREX CORP   One Results Way, Cupertino, CA 95014, Tel: (408) 255-1500
  (Mfr computer integrated mfg sys)
    Measurex Intl. GmbH, Eisgrubbengasse 2, A-2334 Voesendorf, Austria

MEDTRONIC INC   7000 Central Ave, NE, Minneapolis, MN 55432,
  Tel: (612) 574-4000
  (Mfr med devices, med serv)
    Medtronic GmbH, Donaustradtstrasse 1, 1220 Vienna, Austria

MEMOREX CORP   San Thomas at Central Expressway, Santa Clara, CA 95052,
  Tel: (408) 987-1000
  (Magnetic recording tapes, etc)
    Memorex GmbH, Gottfried Kellergass 2/16, A-1030 Vienna, Austria

MENNEN CO   Morristown, NJ 07960, Tel: (201) 631-9000
  (Health & beauty aids)
    Hamol Kosmetische Produkte AG, Postfach 41, 2320 Schwechat, Austria

MERCK SHARP & DOHME INTL   PO Box 2000, Rahway, NJ 07065, Tel: (201) 574-4000
  (Pharms, chems & biologicals)
    Merck, Sharp & Dohme GmbH, Spittelauer Lande 45, 1090 Vienna, Austria

MERRILL LYNCH PIERCE FENNER & SMITH   World Financial Center, 225 Liberty St,
  New York, NY 10080, Tel: (212) 449-1000
  (Brokers, securities, commodities)
    Merril Lynch, Pierce, Fenner Smith GmbH, Gesellschaft Passaver Platz 5,
    A-1010 Vienna, Austria

MOBIL CORP   150 E 42nd St, New York, NY 10017, Tel: (212) 883-4242
  (Petroleum explor, prdts)
    Mobil Oil Austria AG, Schwarzenbergplatz # 16, A-1011 Vienna, Austria
    Rohol-Aufsuchungs GmbH, (RAG) Schwarzenbergplatz # 16, Postfach 651, A-1011 Vienna,
    Austria

MONSANTO CO   800 N Lindbergh Blvd, St Louis, MO 63167, Tel: (314) 694-1000
  (Mfr chem & agric prdts, pharms, ind process equip, man-made fibers, plastics)
    Monsanto GmbH, Am Stadpark, Hilton Center, A-1030 Vienna, Austria

MOTOROLA INC   1303 E Algonquin Rd, Schaumburg, IL 60196, Tel: (708) 397-5000
  (Mfr commun equip, semiconductors, cellular phones)
    Motorola GmbH, Gartengasse 21, 1050 Vienna, Austria

McCANN-ERICKSON WORLDWIDE   750 Third Ave, New York, NY 10017,
  Tel: (212) 697-6000
  (Advertising)
    McCann-Erickson GmbH, Gregor Mendel-Strasse 50, Postfach 57, A-1191 Vienna 19,
    Austria

NALCO CHEMICAL CO   One Nalco Center, Naperville, IL 60566-1024,
  Tel: (708) 305-1000
  (Chems for water & waste water treatment, oil prod & refining, ind processes;

(cont)

water/energy mgmt serv)
   Nalco Chemical GmbH, Scheydgasse 34-36, A-1210 Vienna, Austria

NASH INTL CO   310 Wilson Ave, Norwalk, CT 06856, Tel: (203) 852-5700
   (Mfr vacuum pumps & compressors)
   Nash International GmbH, Nash Tuntengesnbhzeithgasse 6, 1030 Vienna, Austria

NCR CORP   1700 S Patterson Blvd, Dayton, OH 45479, Tel: (513) 445-2000
   (Develop/mfr/sell/serv business info processing sys)
   NCR Oesterreich GmbH, Hietzinger Kai 101, A-1131 Vienna, Austria

A C NIELSEN CO   Nielsen Plaza, Northbrook, IL 60062, Tel: (708) 498-6300
   (Marketing research)
   A.C. Nielsen Co. GmbH, Concordiaplatz 2, 1013 Vienna 1, Austria

NORTHERN TELECOM SYSTEMS CORP   PO Box 1222, Minneapolis, MN 55440,
   Tel: (612) 932-8000
   (Remote information processing sys)
   Data 100 GmbH, Reisnerstrasse 18, A-1030 Vienna 3, Austria

OGILVY & MATHER INC   2 E 48th St, New York, NY 10017, Tel: (212) 907-3400
   (Advertising agency)
   Ogilvy & Mather GmbH, Ferninandstrasse 4, 1021 Vienna, Austria

OTIS ELEVATOR CO   10 Farm Springs, Farmington, CT 06032, Tel: (203) 674-4047
   (Elevators & escalators)
   Freissier Otis GmbH, Oberlaaer Strasse 282, A-1232 Vienna, Austria

PANDUIT CORP   17301 Ridgeland Ave, Tinley Park, IL 60477, Tel: (708) 532-1800
   (Mfr elec/electr wiring comps)
   Panduit GmbH, Erlachplatz 2-4, 1100 Vienna, Austria

PARKER HANNIFIN CORP   17325 Euclid Ave, Cleveland, OH 44112,
   Tel: (216) 531-3000
   (Mfr motion-control prdts)
   Parker Hannifin, NmF, Handelskai 52, A-1200 Vienna, Austria
   Parker-Ermeto GmbH, Badener Str. 12, A-2700 Wiener Neustadt, Austria

PEPSICO INC   700 Anderson Hill Rd, Purchase, NY 10577, Tel: (914) 253-2000
   (Beverages, food prdts & servs, sporting goods)
   Pepsi-Cola GmbH, Link Wienzelle 234, A-1150 Vienna, Austria

PERKIN-ELMER CORP   761 Main Ave, Norwalk, CT 06859, Tel: (203) 762-1000
   (Analytical instru, computers, semiconductor prod equip, avionics, electro-optical
   sys, etc)
   Perkin-Elmer GmbH, Rotenthofgasse 17, A-1100 Vienna, Austria

PFIZER INC   235 E 42nd St, New York, NY 10017, Tel: (212) 573-2323
   (Mfr pharms, hosp prdts, chems, consumer & animal health prdts)
   Pfizer Corp. Austria GmbH, Mondscheingasse 16, A-1071 Vienna, Austria

PHILLIPS PETROLEUM CO   Phillips Bldg, Bartlesville, OK 74004,
   Tel: (918) 661-6600
   (Crude oil, natural gas, liquefied petroleum gas, gasoline & petro-chems)
   Phillips Petroleum Intl. Osthandel GmbH, Veithg. 6, 1030 Vienna, Austria

PICKER CORP   595 Minor Rd, Cleveland, OH 44143, Tel: (216) 449-3000
  (X-ray equip)
    Picker-Service-Buro, Marc Aurel Str. 4, 1010 Vienna, Austria

PIONEER HI-BRED INTL INC   700 Capital Sq, 400 Locust St, Des Moines,
  IA 50309, Tel: (515) 245-3500
  (Seed corn, feed seed, data sys & equip)
    Pioneer Overseas GmbH, Vienna, Austria
    Pioneer Saaten GmbH, Parndorf, Austria

PITNEY BOWES INC   World Headquarters, Stamford, CT 06926-0700,
  Tel: (203) 356-5000
  (Postage meters, mailroom equip, copiers, bus supplies & servs)
    Adrema Pitney Bowes GmbH, Hosnedlgaffe 35, A-1221 Vienna, Austria

PLIBRICO CO   1800 Kingsbury St, Chicago, IL 60614, Tel: (312) 549-7014
  (Refractories, engineering, constr)
    Austria-Plibrico Feuerfest-Engineering GmbH, Postfach 44, Hegelgasse 6,
      A-1015 Vienna 1, Austria

POLAROID CORP   549 Technology Sq, Cambridge, MA 02139, Tel: (617) 577-2000
  (Photographic and optical prdts)
    Polaroid GmbH, Eitnergasse 13, 1233 Vienna, Austria

PREMARK INTL INC   1717 Deerfield Rd, Deerfield, IL 60015, Tel: (708) 405-6000
  (Mfr/sale diversified consumer & coml prdts)
    Dart Industries GmbH, Muhlgasse 58, Baden A-2500, Austria

PROCTER & GAMBLE CO   One Procter & Gamble Plaza, Cincinnati, OH 45202,
  Tel: (513) 983-1100
  (Personal care, food, laundry, cleaning & ind prdts)
    Procter & Gamble Vertriebs GmbH, Ferdinandstr. 16-18, 1021 Vienna, Austria

PUROLATOR COURIER CORP   131 Morristown Rd, Basking Ridge, NJ 07980,
  Tel: (201) 953-6400
  (Time-sensitive package delivery)
    Austria Protectas GmbH, Vienna, Austria

REICHHOLD CHEMICALS INC   RCI Bldg, 525 N Broadway, White Plains, NY 10603,
  Tel: (914) 682-5700
  (Synthetic resins & specialty chems)
    Reichhold, Chemie AG, Vienna, Austria

RICHARDSON-VICKS INC   Ten Westport Rd, Wilton, CT 06897, Tel: (203) 834-5000
  (Consumer health & personal care prdts)
    Richardson GmbH, Otzeltgasse, Vosendorf, A-2331 Vienna, Austria

ROHM & HAAS CO   Independence Mall West, Philadelphia, PA 19105,
  Tel: (215) 592-3000
  (Mfr ind & agric chems, plastics)
    Rohm & Haas GmbH Austria, Diefenbachgasse 35-41, A-1150 Vienna, Austria

ROSEMOUNT INC   12001 Technology Dr, Eden Prairie, MN 55344,
  Tel: (612) 941-5560
  (Mfr aerospace & ind instrumentation)
    Rosemount Austria AG, 2346 Maria Enzersdorf/Sudstadt, Vienna, Austria

RUBBERMAID INC   1147 Akron Rd, Wooster, OH 44691, Tel: (216) 264-6464
   (Rubber & plastic home, commercial & ind prdts)
      Dupol-Rubbermaid GmbH, Teisenbergg. 35, 5013 Salzburg, Austria

RUDER FINN INC   301 E 57th St, New York, NY 10022, Tel: (212) 593-6400
   (Public relations serv, broadcast commun)
      Promota, Prinz-Eugenstrasse, A-1030 Vienna, Austria

SEA-LAND SERVICE INC   379 Thornall St, Edison, NJ 08837, Tel: (201) 558-6000
   (Container transport)
      Paul Guenther GmbH & Co., Schwedenplatz 2, 1010 Vienna, Austria

SEATRAIN LINES INC   270 Sylvan Ave, Englewood Cliffs, NJ 07632,
   Tel: (201) 871-8900
   (Containerized shipping, ship chartering)
      Seatrain GmbH, Kramergasse 3/7/22, A-1010 Vienna, Austria

SENSORMATIC ELECTRONICS CORP   500 NW 12th Ave, Deerfield Beach, BF L33341,
   Tel: (305) 427-9700
   (Electronic article surveillance equip)
      Senelco GmbH & Co., Schwedenplatz 2, 1010 Vienna, Austria

SGS CONTROL SERVICES INC   42 Broadway, New York, NY 10004,
   Tel: (212) 482-8700
   (Complete range of quality & quantity control checks & related tech serv)
      SGS Austria Control Co. GmbH, Johannesgasse 14, Postfach 52, A-1015 Vienna, Austria

SHEARSON/AMERICAN EXPRESS   American Express Tower, New York, NY 10285,
   Tel: (212) 298-2000
   (Investment banking, financial serv)
      American Express Intl. Banking Corp., Karntnerstr. 21-23, A-1015 Vienna, Austria
      American Express Intl. Banking Corp., 5 Mozartplatz, A-5010 Salzburg, Austria
      American Express Intl. Banking Corp., Karntnerstr. 21-23, A-1015 Vienna, Austria
      American Express Intl. Banking Corp., 5 Mozartplatz, A-5010 Salzburg, Austria

SKIL CORP   4801 W Peterson Ave, Chicago, IL 60646, Tel: (312) 286-7330
   (Portable electric power tools)
      Inquires to: Skil-Europe, Konijnenberg 60, Postfach 3267, 4800 DG Breda, Netherlands

SOUTHERN MUSIC PUBLISHING CO INC   810 Seventh Ave, New York, NY 10010,
   Tel: (212) 265-3910
   (Publishers of sheet music)
      Southern Music GmbH, Seilergasse 12, 1010 Vienna, Austria

SUN ELECTRIC CORP   One Sun Pkwy, Crystal Lake, IL 60014, Tel: (815) 459-7700
   (Mfr auto tune-up, diagnostic & emission testing equip)
      Sun Electric Austria GmbH, Hochtrasse 18-20, A-2380 Perchtoldsdorf, Austria

SYBRON CORP   411 E Wisconsin Ave, Milwaukee, WI 07662, Tel: (414) 274-6600
   (Professional health prdts, spec chems, instru, water & waste water treatment sys)
      Tanatex Chemical Wien GmbH, Postfach 15 (Stipcakgasse 6), Siegenhirten 23,
         1234 Vienna, Austria

TECHNICON INSTRUMENTS CORP   511 Benedict Ave, Tarrytown, NY 10591-5097,
   Tel: (914) 631-8000
   (Mfr/serv automated blook anal equip, reagents & diagnostics)
      Bayer Austria GmbH, Linke Wienzeile 236, A-1150 Vienna, Austria

TED BATES WORLDWIDE INC   1515 Broadway, New York, NY 10036,
  Tel: (212) 869-3131
  (Advertising agency)
    Dr. Puttner & Bates Worldwide GmbH, Suppegasse 11, A-1130 Vienna, Austria

TEKTRONIX INC   PO Box 500, Beaverton, OR 97077, Tel: (503) 627-7111
  (Mfr test & meas, visual sys & commun prdts)
    Tektronix GmbH, Doerenkampgasse 7, A-1100 Vienna, Austria

TEXACO INC   2000 Westchester Ave, White Plains, NY 10650, Tel: (914) 253-4000
  (Explor/mktg crude oil & its prdts, petro-chems)
    Texaco GmbH, Dr. Karl Lueger Ring 10, 1010 Vienna, Austria

TRANE CO   3600 Pammel Creek Rd, La Crosse, WI 54601, Tel: (608) 787-2000
  (Mfr A/C equip)
    Osterreichische Klima-Technik GmbH, A-2733 Gunbach, Schneeburg, Austria

TRW INC   1900 Richmond Rd, Cleveland, OH 44124, Tel: (216) 291-7000
  (Electr & energy-related prdts, automotive & aerospace prdts, tools & fasteners)
    TRW Intl. Services GmbH, Prinz Augenstrasse 8, A-1040 Vienna, Austria
    TRW Repa GmbH, A-5082 Groedig, Austria

UNION CARBIDE CORP   Old Ridgebury Rd, Danbury, CT 06817, Tel: (203) 794-2000
  (Carbon prdts, chems, plastics, gases & related prdts, etc)
    Union Carbide Austria GmbH, Diefenbachg. 35-41, 1150 Vienna, Austria

UNISYS CORP   PO Box 500, Blue Bell, PA 19424, Tel: (215) 542-4011
  (Mfg/mktg/serv electr info sys)
    Unisys GmbH, Mariahilferstr. 20, A-1071 Vienna, Austria

UNITED TECHNOLOGIES CORP   United Technologies Bldg, Hartford, CT 06101,
  Tel: (203) 728-7000
  (Mfr aircraft engines, elevators, A/C, auto equip, space & military electr, rocket
  propulsion sys)
    Freissler Otis GmbH, Oberlaaerstrasse, Postfach 104, A-1232 Vienna, Austria

VARIAN ASSOCIATES INC   611 Hansen Way, Palo Alto, CA 94304-1030,
  Tel: (415) 493-4000
  (Mfr microwave tubes & devices, analytical instru, semiconductor process & med equip,
  vacuum sys)
    Varian GmbH, Eisgrubengassse 2, Postfach 14, A-2334 Vosendorf bei Wien, Austria

WANG LABORATORIES INC   1 Industrial Ave, Lowell, MA 01851,
  Tel: (508) 459-5000
  (Mfr computer info processing sys)
    Wang Gesellschaft GmbH, Linkewienzelle 234, A-1150 Vienna, Austria

WARNER-LAMBERT CO   201 Tabor Road, Morris Plains, NJ 07950,
  Tel: (201) 540-2000
  (Mfr ethical & proprietary pharms, confectionary & consumer prdts)
    Substantia GmbH, Postfach 35, Ketzergasse 118, Vienna 1234, Austria

WATERS CHROMATOGRAPHY DIV   34 Maple St, Milford, MA 01757,
  Tel: (617) 478-2000
  (Mfr/distr liquid chromatographic instru/accessories/tech)
    Waters Associates GmbH, Schonbachstrasse 13, A-1130 Vienna, Austria

WEATHERFORD INTL INC   1360 Post Oak Blvd, PO Box 27608, Houston,
   TX 77227-9917, Tel: (713) 439-9400
   (Tubular & cementation servs, prdts & equip; water jetting servs, mfr marine pedestal
   cranes)
      Weatherford Oil Tool GmbH, Donaufelderstr. 36/II/4/12, A-1210 Vienna, Austria

WEIGHT WATCHERS INTL INC   Jericho Atrium, 500 North Broadway, Jericho,
   NY 11753-2196, Tel: (516) 939-0400
   (Weight reduction programs, food prdts)
      Weight Watchers (Austria) GmbH, Neubaubasse 3, A-1070 Vienna, Austria

WESTINGHOUSE AIR BRAKE CO   40 W 40th St, New York, NY 10018,
   Tel: (212) 840-5440
   (Equip for transp, constr, mining inds)
      WABCO Westinghouse GmbH, Hochstadtplatz 4, Postfach 49, A-1205 Vienna, Austria

WHITE STAG MFG CO   7915 Haskell Dr, Van Nuys, CA 91409, Tel: (818) 782-7568
   (Mfr sportswear & sweaters)
      Exi Modellbekleidung AG, 38 Praterstrasse, A-1020 Vienna, Austria

WM WRIGLEY JR CO   410 N Michigan Ave, Chicago, IL 60611-4287,
   Tel: (312) 644-2121
   (Chewing gum)
      Wrigley Austria GmbH, Josef Waach-Strasse 11, A-5023 Salzburg, Austria

YOUNG & RUBICAM INTL INC   285 Madison Ave, New York, NY 10017,
   Tel: (212) 210-3000
   (Advertising agency)
      Young & Rubicam GmbH, Marc Aurel-Strasse 4, Postfach 999, A-1011 Vienna, Austria

BAHAMAS

AFIA   110 William St, New York, NY 10038, Tel: (212) 964-4990
   (Insurance)
      American Foreign Insurance Assn., Nassau, Bahamas

AMERICAN AIRLINES INC   PO Box 619616, Dallas-Ft Worth Arpt, TX 75261-9616,
   Tel: (817) 355-1234
   (Air transp)
      American Airlines Inc., Nassau Intl Airport, P.O. Box N-3724, Nassau, Bahamas

AMERICAN INTL UNDERWRITERS CORP   70 Pine St, New York, NY 10270,
   Tel: (212) 770-7000
   (General ins)
      American Intl. Underwriters. Ltd., Beaumont House Bldg., P.O. Box N 8185, Nassau,
      Bahamas

AMERICAN LIFE INSURANCE CO (ALICO)   PO Box 2226, Wilmington, DE 19899,
  Tel: (302) 594-2000
  (Life ins, pension & annuity plans, health prdts)
    American Intl. Brokers Ltd., P.O. Box N 8185, Nassau, Bahamas
    American Life Insurance Co., P.O. Box F 889, Freeport, Grand Bahama, Bahamas

AVIS INC   900 Old Country Rd, Garden City, NY 11530, Tel: (516) 222-3000
  (Car rental serv)
    Avis Rent a Car, Downtown W. Bay, P.O. Box N 8300, Nassau, Bahamas
    Avis Rent a Car, Freeport Intl. Airport, Freeport, Bahamas

BANK OF VIRGINIA CO   7 North 8th St, Richmond, VA 23219, Tel: (804) 747-2000
  (Intl banking & finance)
    Bank of Virginia Ltd., Shirley St. at Victoria Ave., P.O. Box N 4901, Nassau,
    Bahamas

BANKAMERICA CORP   PO Box 37000, San Francisco, CA 94137, Tel: (415) 622-3456
  (Financial services)
    Bank America Trust & Banking Corp. Ltd., BankAmerica House, East Bay St.,
    P.O. Box N 9100, Nassau, Bahamas

CALIFORNIA FIRST BANK   350 California St, PO Box 3799, San Francisco,
  CA 94119, Tel: (415) 445-0200
  (Intl bank)
    California First Bank, P.O. Box N 100, Nassau, Bahamas

CANADA DRY INTL CORP   2600 Century Pkwy, Atlanta, GA 30345,
  Tel: (404) 753-2182
  (Carbonated beverages, soft drinks extract)
    Bahamas Beverages, P.O. Box N 756, Nassau, Bahamas

CARRIER INTERNATIONAL CORP   PO Box 4806, Syracuse, NY 13221,
  Tel: (315) 432-6000
  (A/C, heating, refrig & power equip)
    Carrier Intl. Ltd., Corn, Church & Shirley, P.O. Box 6241, Nassau, Bahamas

THE H CHAMBERS CO   1010 North Charles St, Baltimore, MD 21201,
  Tel: (301) 727-4535
  (Interior design & arch serv)
    The H. Chambers Co./ House & Garden, Lyford Cay, PO Box N7776, Nassau, Bahamas

CHASE MANHATTAN BANK N A   1 Chase Manhattan Plaza, New York, NY 10081,
  Tel: (212) 552-2222
  (Intl banking)
    Chase Manhattan Bank, Charlotte House, P.O. Box N 4921, Nassau, Bahamas

CHEMICAL BANK   277 Park Ave, New York, NY 10172, Tel: (212) 310-6161
  (Banking & financial serv)
    Bank of New Providence, Claughton House, Shirles St., Nassau, Bahamas
    Chemical Bank, Claughton House, Shirley St., Nassau, Bahamas

CIGNA CORP   One Liberty Place, 1650 Market St, Philadelphia, PA 19101,
  Tel: (215) 523-4000
  (Ins, invest, health care & other fin servs)
    Colina Insurance Co. Ltd., 12 Village Rd., PO Box N-4728, Nassau, Bahamas

CITIBANK NA   399 Park Ave, New York, NY   10043, Tel: (212) 559-1000
(Intl banking)
    Citibani N.A., Thompson Blvd. at Oakes Field, P.O. Box N 8158, Oakes Field, Nassau,
    Bahamas

THE COCA-COLA CO   310 North Ave NW, PO Box Drawer 1734, Atlanta, GA   30313,
Tel: (404) 676-2121
(Mfr & sale of soft drink syrups & concentrates, juices & food prdts, motion pic & TV
prod)
    The Coca-Cola Co. (Bahamas), all mail to: Atlanta address

CONTINENTAL BANK NA   231 S Lasalle St, Chicago, IL   60697, Tel: (312) 828-2345
(Coml banking servs)
    Continental Bank Corp., Cumberland St., Nassau, Bahamas

CORESTATES FINANCIAL CORP   PO Box 7618, Philadelphia, PA   19101,
Tel: (215) 973-3100
(Banking)
    Philadelphia National Bank, Sassoon House, P.O. Box 116313, Nassau, Bahamas

DELTA AIR LINES INC   Hartsfield Atlanta Intl Airport, Atlanta, GA   30320,
Tel: (404) 346-6011
(Air transp)
    Delta Airlines Inc., Harrison Bl, P.O. Box N 4828, Nassau, Bahamas

ECOLAB INC   370 Wabasha St, St Paul, MN   55102, Tel: (612) 293-2233
(Ind & household detergents, cleaning agents & equip)
    Economics Laboratory Ltd., 6 Terrate, Centerville, Nassau W.1., Bahamas

EXXON CORP   225 E John Carpenter Frwy, Irving, TX   75062, Tel: (214) 444-1000
(Petroleum & petroleum prdts)
    Esso Standard Oil S.A. Ltd., Bay & Armstrong, P.O. Box N 3237, Nassau, Bahamas

FEDERAL INSURANCE CO   100 William St, New York, NY   10038, Tel: (212) 285-2850
(Insurance)
    J.S. Johnson & Co. Ltd., Nassau Bank House, Collins Ave., P.O. Box N 8337, Nassau,
    Bahamas

FIDELITY BANK   135 S Broad St, Philadelphia, PA   19109, Tel: (215) 985-6000
(Investments & banking)
    Fidelity Bank, 50 Shirley, P.O. Box N 100, Nassau, Bahamas

FIRST INTERSTATE BANCORP   633 W 5th St, Los Angeles, CA   90071,
Tel: (213) 614-3001
(Banking)
    First Interstate Bank, Ltd., all mail to: PO Box 54191, Terminal Annex,
    Los Angeles, CA 90054

FIRST NATIONAL BANK OF BOSTON   100 Federal St, Boston, MA   02110,
Tel: (617) 434-2200
(Commercial banking)
    Bank of Boston Co. Ltd., Charlotte House, P.O. Box N-4294, Nassau, Bahamas

FRANK B HALL & CO INC   549 Pleasantville Rd, Briarcliff Manor, NY   10510,
Tel: (914) 769-9200
(Insurance)

Britam Insurance Brokers & Agents Bahamas Ltd., The Imperial Life Center, 21 Collins Ave., P.O. Box N-4849, Nassau, Bahamas

HERCULES INC   Hercules Plaza, Wilmington, DE 19894, Tel: (302) 594-5000
  (Mfr spec chems, plastics, film & fibers, coatings, resins, food ingredients)
    Hercules Intl. Trade Corp. Ltd., 50 Chirley St., Nassau, Bahamas

HOLIDAY INNS INC   3742 Lamar Ave, Memphis, TN 38195, Tel: (901) 362-4001
  (Hotels, restaurants, casinos)
    Holiday Inn, Freeport-Lucaya G.B., Lucaya Bch., Bahamas

HORWATH & HORWATH INTL   919 Third Ave, New York, NY 10022,
  Tel: (212) 980-3100
  (Public accountants & auditors)
    Laventhol & Horwath, P.O. Box N 3739, Centerville House, Collins Ave., Nassau, Bahamas

INA CORPORATION   1600 Arch St, Philadelphia, PA 19101, Tel: (215) 523-5335
  (Holding co: ins, financial serv)
    Collins Insurance Co. Ltd., Harrison Bldg., 12 Village Rd., P.O. Box N 4728, Malborough St., Nassau, Bahamas

INTERNATIONAL BUSINESS MACHINES (IBM)   Old Orchard Rd, Armonk,
  NY 10504-1783, Tel: (914) 765-1900
  (Info-handling sys, equip & serv)
    IBM Bahamas, Bahamas
    IBM Products Distribution (Bahamas) Ltd., Bahamas

MANUFACTURERS & TRADERS TRUST CO   654 Madison Ave, New York, NY 10021,
  Tel: (212) 832-8300
  (Bank)
    Manufacturers & Traders Trust Co., 50 Shirley St., P.O. Box N-100, Nassau, Bahamas

MANUFACTURERS HANOVER TRUST CO   270 Park Ave, New York, NY 10017,
  Tel: (212) 286-6000
  (Banking)
    Manufacturers Trust Co., Columbus House, Shirley, P.O. Box N 3209, Nassau, Bahamas

MARITEK CORP   PO Box 6755, Corpus Christi, TX 78466, Tel: (512) 851-2701
  (Holding co: consult/devel)
    Maritek Bahamas Ltd., Clarence Town, Long Island, Bahamas

MORGAN GUARANTY TRUST CO   23 Wall St, New York, NY 10015, Tel: (212) 483-2323
  (Banking)
    Morgan Guaranty Trust Co. of New York, IBM Bl, Church & Ernest, P.O. Box 3935, Nassau, Bahamas

McDERMOTT INC   1010 Common St, New Orleans, LA 70160, Tel: (504) 587-4411
  (General contractors)
    McDermott Associates Ltd., Norfolk House, Frederick, P.O. Box N 4177, Nassau, Bahamas

NCR CORP   1700 S Patterson Blvd, Dayton, OH 45479, Tel: (513) 445-2000
  (Develop/mfr/sell/serv business info processing sys)
    NCR Corp. Ltd., 406 Bay St., Nassau, Bahamas

ONAN CORP   1400 73rd Ave NE, Minneapolis, MN 55432, Tel: (612) 574-5000
   (Electric generators, ind engines & controls)
      Atlantic Equipment & Power Ltd., P.O. Box N 3238, Nassau, Bahamas

OTIS ELEVATOR CO   10 Farm Springs, Farmington, CT 06032, Tel: (203) 674-4047
   (Elevators & escalators)
      Otis Elevator Co., Miller's Court, Shirley St., Nassau, Bahamas

POLAROID CORP   549 Technology Sq, Cambridge, MA 02139, Tel: (617) 577-2000
   (Photographic and optical prdts)
      Polaroid Overseas Corp., P.O. Box 1046, Nassau, Bahamas

REPUBLIC NATIONAL BANK OF DALLAS   310 N Ervay St, Dallas, TX 75265,
   Tel: (214) 653-5000
   (Banking)
      Republic Natl. Bank of Dallas, 50 Shirley, P.O. Box N 100, Nassau, Bahamas

RESORTS INTL INC   915 N E 125th St, North Miami, FL 33161,
   Tel: (305) 891-2500
   (Ownership, development & operations of resort complexes)
      Bahamas Development Ltd., P.O. Box F 160, Freeport Grand Island, Bahamas
      Britania Beach Hotel Co., Ltd., P.O. Box N 3707, Nassau, Bahamas
      G.B. Management Ltd., P.O. Box F 787, Freeport Grand Bahama Island, Bahamas
      Paradise Enterprises Ltd., P.O. Box ES 6311, Nassau, Bahamas
      Paradise Island Ltd., P.O. Box 4777, Nassau, Bahamas

SGS CONTROL SERVICES INC   42 Broadway, New York, NY 10004,
   Tel: (212) 482-8700
   (Complete range of quality & quantity control checks & related tech serv)
      Moore Barrett & Redwood Ltd., Merport Bldg., P.O. Box 2643, Freeport Grand, Bahama,
      Bahamas

TEXACO INC   2000 Westchester Ave, White Plains, NY 10650, Tel: (914) 253-4000
   (Explor/mktg crude oil & its prdts, petro-chems)
      Texaco Bahamas Ltd., P.O. Box N 4807, Nassau, Bahamas

U S TRUST CO OF NEW YORK   45 Wall St, New York, NY 10005, Tel: (212) 425-4500
   (Invest, mgmt & commercial banking)
      United States Trust Co. of N.Y. Ltd., P.O. Box N 8327, Harrison Bldg.,
         Marlborough St., Nassau, Bahamas

WOMETCO ENTERPRISES INC   306 N Miami Ave, Miami, FL 33128,
   Tel: (305) 374-6262
   (Television broadcasting, film distribution, bottling, vending machs)
      Caribbean Bottling Co. Ltd., P.O. Box N 1123, Nassau, Bahamas
      Grand Bahama CATV, Ltd., P.O. Box F 413, Freeport Grand, Bahamas
      Grand Bahamas Theatres Ltd., P.O. Box F 413, Freeport, Bahamas

BAHRAIN

AMERADA HESS CORP   1185 Ave of the Americas, New York, NY 10036,
  Tel: (212) 997-8500
  (Crude oil, natural gas)
    Amerada Hess Inc., P.O. Box 780, Manama, Bahrain

AMERICAN EXPRESS CO   American Express Tower, New York, NY 10285-4765,
  Tel: (212) 640-2000
  (Diversified fin & travel-related serv)
    American Express, Diplomatic Area, P.O. Box 93, Manama, Bahrain

AMERICAN LIFE INSURANCE CO (ALICO)   PO Box 2226, Wilmington, DE 19899,
  Tel: (302) 594-2000
  (Life ins, pension & annuity plans, health prdts)
    American Life Insurance Co., P.O. Box 20281, Manam, Bahrain
    American Life Insurance Co., Sheikh Mubarak Bldg., Municipality Rd., Manama, Bahrain

AMPEX CORP   401 Broadway, Redwood City, CA 94063-3199, Tel: (415) 367-2011
  (Mfr professional audio/visual sys, magnetic recording media, data-memory prdts)
    Ampex World Operations, P.O. Box 26627, Diplomatic Area, Bahrain

BANKERS TRUST CO   280 Park Ave, New York, NY 10017, Tel: (212) 775-2500
  (Banking)
    Bankers Trust Co., P.O. Box 5905, Manama, Bahrain

BROWN & ROOT INC   4100 Clinton Dr, Houston, TX 77020-6299,
  Tel: (713) 676-4141
  (Engr, constr & maintenance)
    Brown & Root (Gulf) E.C., P.O. Box 780, Manama, Bahrain
    Brown & Root Middle East S.A., P.O. Box 780, Manama, Bahrain

LEO BURNETT CO INC   35 West Wacker Dr, Chicago, IL 60601, Tel: (312) 220-5959
  (Advertising agency)
    Radius Advertising, P.O. Box 2915, Manama, Bahrain

CALTEX PETROLEUM CORP   PO Box 619500, Dallas, TX 75261, Tel: (214) 830-1000
  (Petroleum prdts)
    Caltex Bahrain, P.O. Box 25125, Awali, Bahrain
    The Bahrain Petroleum Co., Bahrain Refinery, Bahrain

CANADA DRY INTL CORP   2600 Century Pkwy, Atlanta, GA 30345,
  Tel: (404) 753-2182
  (Carbonated beverages, soft drinks extract)
    Hasan & Habib Sons of Mahmood, P.O. Box 449, Bahrain

CHASE MANHATTAN BANK N A   1 Chase Manhattan Plaza, New York, NY   10081,
  Tel: (212) 552-2222
  (Intl banking)
    Chase Manhattan Bank, P.O. Box 368, Sheikh Mubarak Bldg., Manama, Bahrain

CHEMICAL BANK   277 Park Ave, New York, NY   10172, Tel: (212) 310-6161
  (Banking & financial serv)
    Chemical Bank, Bahrain Tower, Government Rd., Manama, Bahrain

CITIBANK NA   399 Park Ave, New York, NY   10043, Tel: (212) 559-1000
  (Intl banking)
    Citibank N.A., P.O. Box 548, Bab. Al-Bahrain Bldg., Government Rd., Manama, Bahrain

CONOCO INC   600 N Dairy Ashford Rd, Houston, TX   77079, Tel: (713) 293-1000
  (Oil, gas, coal, chems, minerals)
    Continental Oil Co. of Bahrain, P.O. Box 235, Manama, Bahrain

COUDERT BROTHERS   200 Park Ave, New York, NY   10166, Tel: (212) 880-4400
  (Lawyers)
    Coudert Brothers, Hawar Bldg., Diplomatic Area, P.O. Box 5366, Manama, Bahrain

DURAMETALLIC CORP   2104 Factory St, Kalamazoo, MI   49001, Tel: (616) 382-8720
  (Mfr mech seals, compression packings, auxiliaries)
    Durametallic Middle East, P.O. Box 20611, Manama, Bahrain

ECOLAB INC   370 Wabasha St, St Paul, MN   55102, Tel: (612) 293-2233
  (Ind & household detergents, cleaning agents & equip)
    Chemical Service, Salahuddin Bldg., P.O. Box 113, Manama, Bahrain

ENVIROGENICS SYSTEMS CO   9255 Telstar Ave, El Monte, CA   91731,
  Tel: (213) 573-9220
  (Water desalination sys, equip & serv)
    Sogex Intl. Ltd., P.O. Box 830, Unitag Bldg., Manama, Bahrain

EXXON CORP   225 E John Carpenter Frwy, Irving, TX   75062, Tel: (214) 444-1000
  (Petroleum & petroleum prdts)
    Esso Middle East Marketing Inc., P.O. Box 5170, Manama, Bahrain

FIRST CITY NATIONAL BANK   1001 Main St, Houston, TX   77002,
  Tel: (607) 772-2011
  (Commercial banking)
    First City National Bank of Houston, Manama Center, P.O. Box 26622, Manama, Bahrain

GAMLEN CHEMICAL CO   121 S Maple Ave, S San Francisco, CA   94080,
  Tel: (415) 873-1750
  (Chems, detergents & tank cleansers)
    Gray, Mackenzie & Co. Ltd., P.O. Box 210, Gray, Bahrain

GENERAL DYNAMICS CORP   Pierre Laclede Center, St Louis, MO   63105,
  Tel: (314) 889-8200
  (Mfr aircraft, submarines, missiles, space launch vehicles, bldg prdts, info sys)
    GD Intl. Corp., Suite 54, Diplomat Tower Bldg. 315, Road 1705, Block 317,
      Diplomatic area, Manama, Bahrain

THE HARPER GROUP INC   260 Townsend St, PO Box 77933, San Francisco,
  CA 94107, Tel: (415) 978-0600
  (Ocean/air freight fwdg, customs brokerage, packing & whse, logistics mgt, ins)
    Airlink Intl. (Bahrain) Ltd., PO Box 5069, Manama, Bahrain

HILL & KNOWLTON INC   420 Lexington Ave, New York, NY 10017,
  Tel: (212) 697-5600
  (Public relations, public affairs, comm counseling)
    Gulf Hill & Knowlton, P.O. Box 726, Manama, Bahrain

HOLIDAY INNS INC   3742 Lamar Ave, Memphis, TN 38195, Tel: (901) 362-4001
  (Hotels, restaurants, casinos)
    Holiday Inn, P.O. Box 5831, Bahrain Intl. Airport, Manama, Bahrain

INA CORPORATION   1600 Arch St, Philadelphia, PA 19101, Tel: (215) 523-5335
  (Holding co: ins, financial serv)
    Arab Commercial Enterprises, AWAL Bldg., Government Rd., P.O. Box 781, Manama,
    Bahrain

IRVING TRUST CO   1 Wall St, New York, NY 10015, Tel: (212) 487-2121
  (Intl banking)
    Irving Trust Co., Manama Centre, Manama, Bahrain

ITT CORP   1330 Ave of the Americas, New York, NY 10019, Tel: (212) 258-1000
  (Diversified mfr, tech & services)
    Intl. Telephone & Telegraph Co. Ltd., Salahuddin Bldg., Al-Fateh Rd.,
    P.O. Box 5473, Manama, Bahrain

ITT SHERATON CORP   60 State St, Boston, MA 02108, Tel: (617) 367-3600
  (Hotel operations)
    Bahrain Sheraton, P.O. Box 30, Manama, Bahrain

LOCKHEED CORP   2555 N Hollywood Way, Burbank, CA 91520, Tel: (213) 847-6121
  (Aircraft, missiles, etc)
    Lockheed Aircraft Intl., c/o Gulf Air, P.O. Box 138, Manama, Bahrain

MANUFACTURERS HANOVER TRUST CO   270 Park Ave, New York, NY 10017,
  Tel: (212) 286-6000
  (Banking)
    Manufacturers Hanover Trust Co., P.O. Box 5471, Manama, Bahrain

MARSTELLER INTL   1 E Wacker Dr, Chicago, IL 60601, Tel: (312) 329-1100
  (Advertising, marketing research, sales promotion)
    Burson-Marsteller/Intermarkets, Al-Fateh Bldg., P.O. Box 5047, Manama, Bahrain

MARTIN-DECKER CO   1200 Cypress Creek Rd, Cedar Park, TX 78613,
  Tel: (512) 331-0411
  (Oilfield & ind weight & meas sys)
    Martin Decker Co., c/o Muharraq Engineering Works, P.O. Box 8, Manama, Bahrain

MERRILL LYNCH PIERCE FENNER & SMITH   World Financial Center, 225 Liberty St,
  New York, NY 10080, Tel: (212) 449-1000
  (Brokers, securities, commodities)
    Merrill, Lynch & Co. Ltd., Bahrain Aliaa Bldg., Diplomatic Quarter, P.O. Box 5399,
    Manama, Bahrain

MILLER CHEMICAL & FERTILIZER CORP   PO Box 333, Hanover, PA 17331,
  Tel: (717) 632-8921
  (Fungicides, chems, etc)
    Millchem Intl., P.O. Box 852, Manama, Bahrain

MULLER & PHIPPS INTL CORP   Box 3994, San Francisco, CA 94119,
  Tel: (415) 772-5650
  (General merchandise)
    Muller & Phipps Ltd., P.O. Box 852, Manama, Bahrain

ONAN CORP   1400 73rd Ave NE, Minneapolis, MN 55432, Tel: (612) 574-5000
  (Electric generators, ind engines & controls)
    Bhatia & Co., P.O. Box 95, Government Rd., Bahrain

PACCAR INTL   10604 NE 38th Place, Kirkland, WA 98033, Tel: (206) 828-8872
  (Heavy duty dump trucks, military vehicles)
    PACCAR AG, Al Hasan Bldg., Suite 8, Diplomatic Area. Manama,Bahrain

PHILLIPS PETROLEUM CO   Phillips Bldg, Bartlesville, OK 74004,
  Tel: (918) 661-6600
  (Crude oil, natural gas, liquefied petroleum gas, gasoline & petro-chems)
    Phillips Petroleum, Al-Andalus Bldg., P.O. Box 5485, Manama, Bahrain

SECURITY PACIFIC NATIONAL BANK   333 S Hope St, Los Angeles, CA 90071,
  Tel: (213) 345-6211
  (Banking)
    Security Pacific National Bank, Manama Centre Bldg., Government Rd., Manama, Bahrain

TED BATES WORLDWIDE INC   1515 Broadway, New York, NY 10036,
  Tel: (212) 869-3131
  (Advertising agency)
    Fortune Promoseven, 301 Sheikh Mubarek Bldg., Government Ave., P.O. Box, 5989,
      Manama, Bahrain

UOP INC   Ten UOP Plaza, Des Plaines, IL 60016, Tel: (708) 391-2000
  (Diversified research, development & mfr of ind prdts & sys mgmt studies & serv)
    Procon, Inc., Bahrain

BANGLADESH

AMERICAN HOME PRODUCTS CORP   685 Third Ave, New York, NY 10017,
  Tel: (212) 878-5800
  (Drugs, food, household prdts)
    American Home Products, Dacca, Bangladesh

AMERICAN LIFE INSURANCE CO (ALICO)   PO Box 2226, Wilmington, DE 19899,
  Tel: (302) 594-2000
  (Life ins, pension & annuity plans, health prdts)
    American Life Insurance Co., P.O. Box 9, 18-20 Motijheel C.A., Dacca 2, Bangladesh

AMMANN & WHITNEY   Two World Trade Center, New York, NY 10048,
  Tel: (212) 524-7200
  (Consulting engineers)
    Amman & Whitney Intl. Ltd., 95 Motijheel Commercial Area, P.O. Box 348, Dacca,
    Bangladesh

BAKER OIL TOOLS   PO Box 3048, Houston, TX 77253, Tel: (713) 923-9351
  (Oil/gas well completions equip)
    Greenland Engineers & Tractors Co. Ltd., 26 Shymoli Mirpur Rd., P.O. Box 541,
    Dhaka 1207, Bangladesh

LOUIS BERGER INTL INC   100 Halsted St, East Orange, NJ 07019,
  Tel: (201) 678-1960
  (Consulting engineers, architects, economists & planners)
    Louis Berger Intl. Inc., Myani Valley Roads Project, Khagrachari, Bangladesh

CITIBANK NA   399 Park Ave, New York, NY 10043, Tel: (212) 559-1000
  (Intl banking)
    Grindlays Bank Ltd., Sheikh Muj ib Rd., P.O. Box 122, Chittagong, Bangladesh

FMC CORP   200 E Randolph Dr, Chicago, IL 60601, Tel: (312) 861-6000
  (Mach & chem for industry, agric & govt)
    FMC Intl. S.A., M.A. Hossain, GPO Box 3288, Dacca, Bangladesh

FOXBORO CO   33 Commercial St, Foxboro, MA 02035, Tel: (508) 543-8750
  (Mfr prdts/provide servs for ind automation)
    Levatus (Bangladesh) Ltd., Jahan Bldg. 1, 23 Agrabad Commercial Area, Chittagong,
    Bangladesh
    Levatus Ltd., 74 Motijheel Commercial Area, Dacca, Bangladesh

GAMLEN CHEMICAL CO   121 S Maple Ave, S San Francisco, CA 94080,
  Tel: (415) 873-1750
  (Chems, detergents & tank cleansers)
    Gamlen (A'Asia) PTY Ltd., c/o Aries Traders, 45 Court Rd, Chittagong, Bangladesh

E F HOUGHTON & CO   PO Box 930, Valley Forge, PA 19482-0930,
  Tel: (215) 666-4000
  (Mfr spec chems, hydraulic fluids, lubricants)
    S.E.A. Corp., 280, J.M. Sen Ave., Laldighi W., G.P.O. Box 208, Chittagong,
    Bangladesh

INA CORPORATION   1600 Arch St, Philadelphia, PA 19101, Tel: (215) 523-5335
  (Holding co: ins, financial serv)
    James Finlay & Co. Ltd., Finlay House, P.O. Box 118, Chittagong, Bangladesh

ITT SHERATON CORP   60 State St, Boston, MA 02108, Tel: (617) 367-3600
  (Hotel operations)
    Dhaka Sheraton Hotel, P.O. Box 504, Dhaka 2, Bangladesh

NCR CORP   1700 S Patterson Blvd, Dayton, OH 45479, Tel: (513) 445-2000
  (Develop/mfr/sell/serv business info processing sys)
    NCR Corp., 19 Dilkusha Commercial Area, G.P.O. Box 520, Dacca 2, Bangladesh

PFIZER INC   235 E 42nd St, New York, NY 10017, Tel: (212) 573-2323
  (Mfr pharms, hosp prdts, chems, consumer & animal health prdts)
     Pfizer Laboratories (Bangladesh) Ltd., 6/3 Segun Bagicha, P.O. Box 303, Ramna,
       Dhaka 2, Bangladesh

SGS CONTROL SERVICES INC   42 Broadway, New York, NY 10004,
     Tel: (212) 482-8700
  (Complete range of quality & quantity control checks & related tech serv)
     SGS Bangladesh Ltd., 19 Dilkusha Commercial Area, P.O. Box 197, Dacca, Bangladesh
     SGS Bangladesh Ltd., Taher Chamber, 10 Agrabad Commercial Area, P.O. Box 496,
       Chittagong, Bangladesh
     SGS Ltd., 20 Ahsan Ahmed Rd., P.O. Box 20, Khulna, Bangladesh
     SGS Ltd., Globe Chamber 104, Motijheel C.A., P.O. Box 197, Dacca, Bangladesh

WILBUR SMITH ASSOCS   NCNB Tower, PO Box 92, Columbia, SC 29202,
     Tel: (803) 738-0580
  (Consulting engineers)
     Wilbur Smith Associates Inc., Plot 9, Block NE(K), Road 83, Gulshan Model Town,
       Dhaka, Bangladesh

UNION CARBIDE CORP   Old Ridgebury Rd, Danbury, CT 06817, Tel: (203) 794-2000
  (Carbon prdts, chems, plastics, gases & related prdts, etc)
     Union Carbide Co. Ltd., 5/A, Bangabandhu Ave., P.O. Box 754, Dacca, Bangladesh

BARBADOS

AMERICAN AIRLINES INC   PO Box 619616, Dallas-Ft Worth Arpt, TX 75261-9616,
     Tel: (817) 355-1234
  (Air transp)
     American Airlines, Carlisle House Wharf, Bridgetown, Barbados

AMERICAN LIFE INSURANCE CO (ALICO)   PO Box 2226, Wilmington, DE 19899,
     Tel: (302) 594-2000
  (Life ins, pension & annuity plans, health prdts)
     American Life Insurance Co., P.O. Box 197, Bridgetown, Barbados
     American Life Insurance Co., Trident House, Broad St., Bridgetown, Barbados

APPLIED MAGNETICS CORP   75 Robin Hill Rd, Goleta, CA 93117,
     Tel: (805) 683-5353
  (Magnetic recording heads)
     Applied Magnetics Ltd., Newton Industrial Park, Christ Church, Bridgetown, Barbados

BARDAHL MFG CORP   1400 N W 52nd St, PO Box 70607, Seattle, WA 98107,
     Tel: (206) 783-4851
  (Lubricating oils)
     R.M. Jones & Co. Ltd., P.O. Box 241, Whitepark Rd., Bridgetown, Barbados

LOUIS BERGER INTL INC   100 Halsted St, East Orange, NJ 07019,
Tel: (201) 678-1960
(Consulting engineers, architects, economists & planners)
 Louis Berger Intl. Inc., P.O. Box 1268, Bridgetown, Barbados

CANADA DRY INTL CORP   2600 Century Pkwy, Atlanta, GA 30345,
Tel: (404) 753-2182
(Carbonated beverages, soft drinks extract)
 Bottlers Ltd., P.O. Box 257, Bridgetown, Barbados

CHASE MANHATTAN BANK N A   1 Chase Manhattan Plaza, New York, NY 10081,
Tel: (212) 552-2222
(Intl banking)
 Chase Manhattan Bank N.A., Corner Broad & Nile St., P.O. Box 699, Bridgetown,
 Barbados

CITIBANK NA   399 Park Ave, New York, NY 10043, Tel: (212) 559-1000
(Intl banking)
 Citibank N.A., Broad St., P.O. Bag 1007C, Bridgetown, Barbados

COMPTON INTERNATIONAL   625 Madison Ave, New York, NY 10022,
Tel: (212) 754-1100
(Advertising)
 Corbin-Compton Ltd., Kensington Manor, Kensington, St. Michael, Barbados

CORCOM INC   1600 Winchester Rd, Libertyville, IL 60048, Tel: (708) 680-7400
(Design & manufacturer or radio frequency interferences)
 Corcom Ltd., Newton Industrial Park, Christ Church, Bridgetown, Barbados

R R DONNELLEY & SONS CO   2223 King Dr, Chicago, IL 60616, Tel: (312) 326-8000
(Coml printing, alied commun servs)
 Donnelley Caribbean Graphics Inc., Bldg. 4, Wildey Industrial Park, St. Michael,
 Bridgetown, Barbados

ECOLAB INC   370 Wabasha St, St Paul, MN 55102, Tel: (612) 293-2233
(Ind & household detergents, cleaning agents & equip)
 K.R. Hunte & Co. Ltd., P.O. Box 677, Bridgetown, Barbados

EXXON CORP   225 E John Carpenter Frwy, Irving, TX 75062, Tel: (214) 444-1000
(Petroleum & petroleum prdts)
 Esso Standard Oil S.A., White Park Rd., Bridgetown, Barbados

HOLIDAY INNS INC   3742 Lamar Ave, Memphis, TN 38195, Tel: (901) 362-4001
(Hotels, restaurants, casinos)
 Holiday Inn, P.O. Box 639, Bridgetown, Barbados

INA CORPORATION   1600 Arch St, Philadelphia, PA 19101, Tel: (215) 523-5335
(Holding co: ins, financial serv)
 H.B. Niblock Co. Ltd., Planatation Bldg., P.O. Box 271, Bridgetown, Barbados
 INA Intl. Insurance Co. Ltd., Lower Bay St., P.O. Box 434, Bridgetown, Barbados
 Walcott & White Ltd., Walwitt House, Pinfold St., Bridgetown, Barbados

KOPPERS CO INC   Koppers Bldg, 437 Seventh Ave, Pittsburgh, PA 15219,
Tel: (412) 227-2000
(Constr materiald & serv; chem & bldg prdts)
 Long Life Timbers Ltd., Bridgetown, Barbados

MANHATTAN INTERNATIONAL   1155 Ave of the Americas, New York, NY 10036,
  Tel: (212) 221-7500
  (Mfr shirts, sweaters, sportswear, table linen)
    Juman's Garment Factory Ltd., Bridgetown, Barbados

MODUTEC INC   18 E Marshall St, Norwalk, CT 06854, Tel: (203) 853-3636
  (Electrical meters)
    Modutec Ltd., Newton Industrial Park, Christ Church, Bridgetown, Barbados

McCANN-ERICKSON WORLDWIDE   750 Third Ave, New York, NY 10017,
  Tel: (212) 697-6000
  (Advertising)
    McCann-Erickson (Barbados), Nemwil House, Collymore Rock, St. Michael, Barbados

SEQUA CORP   200 Park Ave, New York, NY 10166, Tel: (212) 986-5500
  (Aerospace prdts & sys, machinery & metal coatings, transp, spec chems, professional
  & fin serv)
    SunRise Insurance Ltd., Collymore Rock, Bridgetown, Barbados, W.I.

SIGMA INSTRUMENTS INC   170 Pearl St, S Braintree, MA 02184,
  Tel: (617) 843-5000
  (Relays & switches, electr instru)
    Sigma Ltd., Newton Industrial Park, Christ Church, Bridgetown, Barbados

U S INDUSTRIES INC   PO Box 629, Evansville, IN 47704, Tel: (812) 425-2428
  (Diversified prdts & sys for industry, agribusiness & retail markets)
    U.S. Industries Ltd., Barbados Children's Wear, Harbour Industrial Estate,
      Bridgetown, Barbados

BELGIUM

3M CO   3M Center, St Paul, MN 55144-1000, Tel: (612) 733-1110
  (Mfr abrasives, adhesives, chems, ind & consumer tapes/diskettes, health care prdts,
  elec connectors)
    3M Belgium N.V.S.A., Nieuwe Nijuerheidslaan 7, 1920 Machelen Diegem, Belgium
    3M Europe S.A., 106 B.vd. de la Woluwe, B-1200 Brussels, Belgium

ABBOTT LABORATORIES   Abbott Park, North Chicago, IL 60064,
  Tel: (312) 937-6100
  (Pharm & lab prdts)
    Abbott S.A., Rue Defacqz 113, 1050 Brussels, Belgium

ACCURAY CORP   650 Ackerman Rd, PO Box 02248, Columbus, OH 43202,
  Tel: (614) 261-2000
  (Computer-based process mgmt sys for forest prdts, metals rolling, textiles, tobacco
  ind)
    Accuray Intl., Rue de Geneve 10, B-1140 Brussels, Belgium

ACHESON COLLOIDS CO   1600 Washington Ave, PO Box 288, Port Huron, MI   48060,
   Tel: (313) 984-5581
   (Graphite, lubricants & other specialty chems)
      S.A. Huileries du Marly N.V., 20/21 Blvd. Baudouin, P.O. Box 7, 1000 brussels,
      Belgium

ACUFF-ROSE PUBLICATION INC   65 Music Square W, Nashville, TN   37203,
   Tel: (615) 321-5000
   (Music publisher)
      Acuff-Rose Benelux, Rue Fernand Neuray, 8, 1060 Brussels, Belgium

ADVANCED PRODUCTS CO   33 Defco Park Rd, North Haven, CT   06473,
   Tel: (203) 239-3341
   (Mfr metallic & PTFE seals & gaskets)
      Advanced Products N.V., Pierstraat 12, 2630 Aartselaar, Belgium

AFIA   110 William St, New York, NY   10038, Tel: (212) 964-4990
   (Insurance)
      AFIA Co., Avenue des Arts 46, Bte-15, 1040 Brussels, Belgium

AIR EXPRESS INTL CORP   120 Tokeneke Rd, PO Box 1231, Darien, CT   06820,
   Tel: (203) 655-7900
   (Air frt forwarder)
      Air Express Intl. (Belgium) N.V., Antwerp Airport, B-2-100 Deurne, Antwerp, Belgium
      Air Express Intl. (Belgium) N.V., Leuvensesteenweg 192, B-1800 Vilvoorde, Belgium
      Air Express Intl. (Belgium) S.A., Airport Liege-Bierset, B-4330, Grace Hollogne,
      Belgium
      Airsystems Courier, Rue Americaine 78, 1050 Brussels, Belgium

AIR PRODUCTS & CHEMICALS INC   7201 Hamilton Blvd, Allentown, PA   18195,
   Tel: (215) 481-4911
   (Mfr ind gases & chems)
      Air Products S.A., Le Souverain, Blvd. du Souverain 191-197, Box 1160, Brussels,
      Belgium

AIRPAX CORP   7 McKee Pl, Cheshire, CT   06450, Tel: (203) 271-6000
   (Mfr small control components)
      N.V. Airpax S.A., Rue de la Bienvenue 7, Brussels B-1070, Belgium

ALLEN-BRADLEY CO   PO Box 2086, Milwaukee, WI   53201, Tel: (414) 382-2000
   (Electrical control devices)
      Allen-Bradley Brussels S.A., Mercure Center, Rue de la Fusee 100, B-1130, Brussels,
      Belgium

ALLIED-SIGNAL INC   Columbia Rd & Park Ave, PO Box 2245R, Morristown,
   NJ 07960, Tel: (201) 455-2000
   (Mfr aerospace & automotive prdts, engineered materials)
      Bendix Wheels & Brakes Div., Airways Div., World Airways, Brussels Natl. Airport,
      B-1930 Zaventem, Belgium
      NV Allied Chemical Intl. Corp., Saifi Tower, Ave. Louise 326, Bte. 37,
      B-1050 Brussels, Belgium
      NV Allied-Signal Intl. S.A., Haasrode Research Park, Graumeer, B-3030 Heverlee,
      Belgium

ALVEY CONVEYOR INC   9301 Olive Blvd, St Louis, MO 63132, Tel: (314) 993-4700
   (Mfr conveying mach)
      Alvey Conveyor Europe N.V., Koningin Astridlaan 14, 2659 Breendonk, Belgium

AM INTL INC   333 W Wacker Dr, #900, Chicago, IL 60606-1265,
  Tel: (312) 558-1966
  (Mfr/sale/serv commun graphics, info handling equip & sys)
    AM International S.A/N.V., Leuvensesteenweg 321, 1940 St.-Stevene-Wollwe, Zaventem,
    Belgium

AMDAHL CORP   1250 East Arques Ave, PO Box 3470, Sunnyvale, CA 94088-3470,
  Tel: (408) 746-6000
  (Mfr large scale computers, complementary software storage & commun prdts)
    Amdahl Belgium S.A., 360 Blvd. du Souverain, 1160 Brussels, Belgium

AMERICAN CYANAMID CO   1 Cyanamid Plaza, Wayne, NJ 07470, Tel: (201) 831-2000
  (Pharms, chems, agric & consumer prdts)
    Cyanamid Benelux S.A./N.V, Rue du Bosquet, 15, 1348 Mont-Saint-Guibert, Belgium

AMERICAN EXPRESS CO   American Express Tower, New York, NY 10285-4765,
  Tel: (212) 640-2000
  (Diversified fin & travel-related serv)
    American Express Intl. Inc., 87 Meir, Antwerp, Belgium
    American Express Intl. Inc., 24 Place Rogier, Brussels, Belgium
    American Express Intl. Inc., Avenue Des Loisirs 2, Brussels-Evere, Belgium

AMERICAN HOME PRODUCTS CORP   685 Third Ave, New York, NY 10017,
  Tel: (212) 878-5800
  (Drugs, food, household prdts)
    American Home Products S.A., Brussels, Belgium

AMERICAN INTL UNDERWRITERS CORP   70 Pine St, New York, NY 10270,
  Tel: (212) 770-7000
  (General ins)
    American Intl. Underwriters S.A., Rue Montoyer 23, B-1040 Brussels, Belgium
    European Technical Div. of American Intl. Underwriters S.A., Blvd. de la,
      Woluwe 34, B-1200 Brussels, Belgium
    L'Union Atlantique S.A. d'Assurances, Rue Belliard 7, 1040 Brussels, Belgium

AMERICAN LIFE INSURANCE CO (ALICO)   PO Box 2226, Wilmington, DE 19899,
  Tel: (302) 594-2000
  (Life ins, pension & annuity plans, health prdts)
    Compangnie Europeenne d'Assurances sur la Vie, Rue Montoyer 31, Boite 4,
      1040 Brussels, Belgium

AMERICAN MANAGEMENT SYSTEMS INC   1777 North Kent St, Arlington, VA 22209,
  Tel: (703) 841-6000
  (Design/serv computer sys)
    AMS Management Systems Europe, SA/NV, Avenue Louise 65, 1050 Brussels, Belgium

AMERICAN STANDARD INC   40 W 40th St, New York, NY 10018, Tel: (212) 840-5100
  (Heating & sanitary equip)
    Ideal Standard Europe, 348 Blvd. du Souverain, Box 1, 1160 Brussels, Belgium
    Ideal Standard S.A. Div. of WABCO-Standard S.A., Chaussee Paul Houtart, 88,
      7070 Houdeng-Goegnies, Belgium
    WABCO Belgium, Ave. Van Volxem, 164-166, B-1190 Brussels, Belgium

AMERICAN TOOL COMPANIES INC   301 S 13th St, #600, Lincoln, NE 68508,
  Tel: (402) 435-3300
  (Mfr hand tools)
    American Tool Companies, Inc., 24 Bd Fleur de Lys- Bte. 11, B-1400 Nivelles, Belgium

AMOCO CHEMICAL CO   200 E Randolph Dr, Chicago, IL 60601, Tel: (312) 856-3200
  (Mfr/sale petrol based chems, plastics, chem/plastic prdts)
    Amoco Chemical Belgium NV, Belgium
    Amoco Fina N.V., Antwerp, Belgium

AMPEX CORP   401 Broadway, Redwood City, CA 94063-3199, Tel: (415) 367-2011
  (Mfr professional audio/visual sys, magnetic recording media, data-memory prdts)
    Ampex S.A. Nivelles, Rue de Progres 10, 1400 Nivelles, Belgium

AMSTED INDUSTRIES INC   205 N Michigan, Chicago, IL 60601, Tel: (312) 645-1700
  (Steel castings for railroad & ind use)
    Hydromation Co., Luikersteenweg, B-3700 Tongeren, Belgium

AMWAY CORP   7575 E Fulton Rd, Ada, MI 49355, Tel: (616) 676-6000
  (Distr household cleaning, nutrition & diet prdts)
    Amway Belgium Co., Bedrijfspark Keibert, Excelsiorlaan 9, bus 1, 1930 Zaventem,
      Belgium
    Amway Europe, Bedrijfspark Keibert, Excelsiorlaan 23, 1930 Zaventem, Belgium

ANGLO-AMERICAN AVIATION CO   10929 Vanowen St, PO Box 3970, N Hollywood,
  CA 91609, Tel: (213) 985-3500
  (Aviation spare parts, hardware)
    Anglo American Aviation Co., 5 Rue de la Presse, 1000 Brussels, Belgium

ANIXTER BROS INC   4711 Golf Rd, Skokie, IL 60076, Tel: (708) 677-2600
  (Dist wiring sys/prdts for voice, video, data & power applications)
    Anixter Intl. Headquarters, Avenue de Tervueren 273-Bte. 2, 1150 Brussels, Belgium

ANTHONY INDUSTRIES INC   4900 S Eastern Ave, Los Angeles, CA 90040,
  Tel: (213) 724-2800
  (Pool constr & equip, fishing tackle, athletic apparel)
    Moris Shakespeare S.A., Alleur, Belgium

APPLE COMPUTER INC   20525 Mariani Ave, Cupertino, CA 95014,
  Tel: (408) 996-1010
  (Personal computers, peripherals & software)
    Apple Computer S.A., 105A Rue Colonel Bourg, 1140 Brussels, Belgium

APPLIED MAGNETICS CORP   75 Robin Hill Rd, Goleta, CA 93117,
  Tel: (805) 683-5353
  (Magnetic recording heads)
    Applied Magnetics Belgium N.V., Industrie Zone, Raadsherenstraat 3, 2300 Turnhout,
      Belgium

ARBOR ACRES FARM INC   41 Marlborough Rd, Glastonbury, CT 06033,
  Tel: (203) 633-4681
  (Producers of male & female broiler breeders, commercial egg layers)
    Klavers P.V.B.A., Koningsstraat 22A, 2390 Ravels (Weelde), Belgium

ARMCO INTL INC   703 Curtis St, PO Box 700, Middletown, OH 45042,
  Tel: (513) 425-6541
  (Sheet steel & steel prdts, constr, oil field equip, ins, finance leasing)
    Armco Liege S.A., 55 Ave. Werihet, B-4520 Wandre (Liege), Belgium
    Armco S.A., 251 Avenue Louise, B-1050 Brussels, Belgium

ARO INTL CORP   One Aro Center, Bryan, OH 43506, Tel: (419) 636-4242
  (Mfr portable air tools, drills, motors, fluid handling pumps)
    N.V. Aro S.A., Eurolaan 3, 2690 Temse, Belgium

ASK MR FOSTER TRAVEL CORP   7833 Haskell Ave, Van Nuys, CA 91406,
  Tel: (818) 988-0181
  (Travel service)
    Ask Mr. Foster/Transcontinental, 10 Rue de la Montagne, Brussels, Belgium

ASSOCIATED PRESS   50 Rockefeller Plaza, New York, NY 10020,
  Tel: (212) 621-1500
  (News gathering agency)
    Associated Press (Belgium) S.A., Blvd. Charlemagne 1, 1040 Brussels, Belgium

AVERY INTL CORP   150 N Orange Grove Blvd, Pasadena, CA 91103,
  Tel: (213) 304-2000
  (Mfr self-adhesive labels & marking equip)
    Gasson Belgie N.V., Graatakker 92, 2300, Turnhout, Belgium

AVON PRODUCTS INC   9 W 57th St, New York, NY 10019, Tel: (212) 546-6015
  (Mfr/distr cosmetics, perfumes)
    N.V. Avon Benelux S.A., Rijksweg 22, 2680 Bornem, Belgium

AYERST LABORATORIES   145 King of Prussia Rd, Radnor, PA 19087,
  Tel: (215) 688-4400
  (Biologicals & pharms)
    N.V. Ayerst Benelux S.A., Brussels, Belgium

BALTIMORE AIRCOIL CO INC   PO Box 7322, Baltimore, MD 21227,
  Tel: (301) 799-6200
  (Evaporative condensers, cooling, towers, ind fluids)
    Baltimore Aircoil Intl. N.V., Industriepark, B-3100 Heist-op-den-Berg, Belgium

BANDAG INC   Bandag Center, Muscatine, IA 52761, Tel: (319) 262-1400
  (Mfr/sale tread rubber & related equip/supplies)
    Bandag Europe N.V., Industrieterrein, B-3650 Dilsen-Lanklaar, Belgium
    Bandag N.V., Zaventem, Belgium

BANKAMERICA CORP   PO Box 37000, San Francisco, CA 94137, Tel: (415) 622-3456
  (Financial services)
    Bank of America NT & SA, 34 Van Eycklei, B-2018 Antwerp, Belgium

BANKERS TRUST CO   280 Park Ave, New York, NY 10017, Tel: (212) 775-2500
  (Banking)
    Bankers Trust Co., Banque du Benelux S.A., Rue des Colonies 40, 1000 Brussels,
      Belgium

BAXTER TRAVENOL LABORATORIES INC   1 Baxter Pky, Deerfield, IL 60015,
  Tel: (708) 948-2000
  (Pharm & disposable med prdts)
    N.V. Travenol Laboratories S.A., Parc Industrial, Rue du Progres 7, 1400 Nivelles,
      Belgium

BECHTEL GROUP INC   50 Beale St, PO Box 3965, San Francisco, CA 94119,
  Tel: (415) 768-1234
  (Engineering & constr)
    Bechtel Intl. Co., Postbus 269, 9000 Ghent, Belgium

BELL & HOWELL CO   5215 Old Orchard Rd., Skokie, IL 60077, Tel: (708) 470-7684
  (Diversified info prdts & servs)
    Bell & Howell Benelux S.A., Leuvensesteenweg 321, B-1940 St. Stevens, Woluwe,
      Zaventem, Belgium

BELOIT CORP   1st Lawrence Ave, Beloit, WI 53511, Tel: (608) 365-3311
  (Paper making mach & equip)
    MHD S.P.R. Limitee, Avenue de SPA, 36, 4800 Verviers, Belgium

BEMIS CO INC   625 Marquette Ave, Minneapolis, MN 55402, Tel: (612) 340-6000
  (Mfr flexible packaging, spec coated & graphics prdts)
    MACtac Europe S.A., Blvd. Kennedy, B-7400 Soignies, Belgium

BENTLEY LABORATORIES INC   17502 Armstrong Ave, Irvine, CA 92714,
  Tel: (714) 546-8020
  (Mfr para-med devices)
    N.V. Bentley Labs., S.A., Aerikalei 27, 2000 Antwerp, Belgium

BETZ LABORATORIES INC   4636 Somerton Rd, Trevose, PA 19047,
  Tel: (215) 355-3300
  (Mfr spec chem for water/wastewater treatment)
    Betz Laboratories Inc., Industriepark Wolfstee Toekomstlaan, 2410 Herentals, Belgium

BINKS MFG CO   9201 W Belmont Ave, Franklin Park, IL 60131,
  Tel: (708) 671-3000
  (Mfr of spray painting & finishing equip)
    Binks Intl. S.A., Chaussee de Bruxelles 684, B-1410 Waterloo, Blegium

BIO-RAD LABORATORIES   2200 Wright Ave, Richmond, CA 94804,
  Tel: (415) 234-4130
  (Spec chems, clinical diagnostic prdts, test kits)
    Bio-Rad Laboratories Inc., 19 Dreve du Senechal, B-1180 Brussels, Belgium

BLACK & DECKER CORP   701 E Joppa Road, Towson, MD 21204, Tel: (301) 583-3900
  (Mfr portable elect & pneumatic power tools, household prdts)
    Black & Decker (Belgium) S.A., Weihoek 1, Zaventem Zuid, B-3072 Nossegem, Belgium

BLISS & LAUGHLIN INDUSTRIES INC   122 West 22nd St, Oak Brook, IL 60521,
  Tel: (708) 654-3350
  (Diversified prdts servicing ind & commercial markets)
    CTE Fischein S.A., 64 Rue Previnaire, 1070 Brussels, Belgium

E W BLISS CO   1004 E State St, Hastings, MI 49058, Tel: (616) 948-3300
  (Mfr metal-forming presses)
    Haco, S.A., Oekensestraat 120, 8810 Roeselare, Belgium

BLOUNT INC   4520 Executive Park Drive, Montgomery, AL 36116-1602,
  Tel: (205) 244-4370
  (Mfr cutting chain & equip, timber harvest/materials handling equip, sporting ammo,
  gen contracting)
    Omark Europe S.A., 8 Nouvelle rue de Buisoon des Loups, B-1400 Nivelles, Belgium

BORG-WARNER CORP   200 S Michigan Ave, Chicago, IL 60604, Tel: (312) 322-8500
  (Mfr A/C equip, chem & plastics, ind prdts, trans equip)
    Borg-Warner S.A., A.G. Building, Place de Champs de Mars, 5 Bte.4, B-1050 Brussels,
      Belgium
    S.A. Borg Warner Acceptance Corp. N.V., 165 Avenue Louise, Bte. 10,

(cont)

B-1050 Brussels, Belgium
York Europe, 15 Rue de la Loi, Bte.032, B-1040, Brussels, Belgium

BOSE CORP   100 The Mountain Rd, Framingham, MA 01701, Tel: (617) 879-7330
(Electronic equip)
Bose N.V., Avenue Brigade Piron, 23, B-1080 Brussels, Belgium

BOSTITCH DIV   815 Briggs St, East Greenwich, RI 02818, Tel: (401) 884-2500
(Stapling machs & supplies, wire)
Bostitch Belgium, Kouterveldstraat 13, Diegem, Belgium

BOYDEN ASSOCIATES INC   260 Madison Ave, New York, NY 10016,
Tel: (212) 685-3400
(Mgt consultants, exec search)
Boyden Intl. S.A., 1 Avenue de la Toison d'Or, Boite 6, B-1060 Brussels, Belgium

W H BRADY CO   727 W Glendale Ave, PO Box 571, Milwaukee, WI 53201,
Tel: (414) 332-8100
(Wire markers, name plates)
W.H. Brady N.V., Industriepark C/3, B-9140 Zele, Belgium

BRUNSWICK CORP   One Brunswick Plaza, Skokie, IL 60077, Tel: (708) 470-4700
(Mfr outboard motors & drives, bowling/fishing equip, valves & pumps)
Mercury Marine Power-Europe Inc., Parc Industrial de Petit Rechain, 4822 Verviers,
Belgium

BUCK CONSULTANTS INC   Two Pennsylvania Plaza, New York, NY 10121,
Tel: (212) 330-1000
(Employee benefit, actuarial & compensation conslt serv)
Buck Consultants SA, Rue de la Charite 15, Bte. 10, 1040 Brussels, Belgium

BULAB HOLDINGS INC   1256 N McLean Blvd, Memphis, TN 38108,
Tel: (901) 278-0330
(Mfr microbicides, biocides, additives, corrosion inhibitors, chems)
Buckman Labaoratories S.A., Wondelgemkaai 159, B-9000 Ghent, Belgium

BURLINGTON AIR EXPRESS   18200 Van Karman Ave, Irvine, CA 92715,
Tel: (714) 752-1212
(Air freight)
Burlington Air Express, Brucargo Bldg. 742, 1931 Zaventem, Brussels, Belgium

LEO BURNETT CO INC   35 West Wacker Dr, Chicago, IL 60601, Tel: (312) 220-5959
(Advertising agency)
Leo Burnett Worldwide Inc., Chaussee de la Hulpe 177, Box 6, 1170 Brussels, Belgium

BURR-BROWN RESEARCH CORP   PO Box 11400, Tucson, AZ 85734, Tel: (602) 746-1111
(Electronic components & sys modules)
Burr-Brown Intl. NV, Coghenlaan 118, B-1180 Brussels, Belgium

BURSON-MARSTELLER   230 Park Ave, New York, NY 10003-1566, Tel: (212) 614-4000
(Public relations/public affairs consultants)
Burson-Marsteller, 225 Ave. Louise, Box 5, B-1050 Brussels, Belgium

CARL BYOIR & ASSOCIATES INC   380 Madison Ave, New York, NY 10017,
Tel: (212) 986-6100
(Public relations consultants)
Comark Europe S.A./N.V., Chaussee de Charleroi 27, B-1060 Brussels, Belgium

CABOT CORP   950 Winter St, PO Box 9073, Waltham, MA 02254,
  Tel: (617) 890-0200
  (Mfr carbon blacks, plastics; oil & gas, info sys)
    Cabot Belgium S.A., Hanzestedenplaats, B-2000 Antewerp, Belgium
    Cabot Belgium S.A., Rue Emile Vandervelde 131, B-4431 Loncin, Belgium

CALCOMP   2411 W La Palma Ave, PO Box 3250, Anaheim, CA 92801,
  Tel: (714) 821-2142
  (Mfr computer graphics)
    N.V. Calcomp S.A., Saffierstraat Rue du Saphir 33.B8, 1040 Brussels, Belgium

CALGON CORP   PO Box 1346, Pittsburgh, PA 15230, Tel: (412) 777-8000
  (Mfr. cosmetic, personal care & water treatment prdts)
    Chemviron Specialty Chemicals S.A., Brusselsesteenweg 359, 1900 Overijse, Belgium

CAMERON MACHINE CO   PO Box 791, New Brunswick, NJ 08903, Tel: (201) 356-6000
  (Roll prod equip, slitting & rewinding machs)
    Cameron Machines S.A., Chemin d'Hautrage 17, Ghlin-lez-Mons, Belgium

CAMPBELL SOUP CO   Campbell Place, Camden, NJ 08101, Tel: (609) 342-4800
  (Food prdts)
    Continental Foods Co., N.V., Rijksweg 8, B-2670 Puurs, Belgium
    Godiva, S.A., Rue de L'Armistice 5, B-1010 Brussels, Belgium
    N.V. Biscuits Delacre S.A., Leuvensesteenweg, 262, B-1800 Vilvoorde, Belgium

CANADA DRY INTL CORP   2600 Century Pkwy, Atlanta, GA 30345,
  Tel: (404) 753-2182
  (Carbonated beverages, soft drinks extract)
    Bass Lamot, Van Beetjovenstraat 10, B-2800 Mechelen, Belgium

CANBERRA INDUSTRIES INC   One State St, Meriden, CT 06450, Tel: (203) 238-2351
  (Mfr instru for nuclear research)
    Canberra Semiconductor N.V., Lammerdries 25, 2430 Olen, Belgium
    Canberra-Packard Benelux ND/SA, Research Parc, Pontbeeklaan 57, B-1730 Zellik,
      Belgium

CARGILL   PO Box 9300, Minneapolis, MN 55440, Tel: (612) 475-7575
  (Food prdts, feeds, animal prdts)
    Cargill NV, Muisbroeklaan Kaai 506, B-2030 Antwerp, Belgium

CARNATION INTL CO   5045 Wilshire Blvd, Los Angeles, CA 90036,
  Tel: (213) 932-6000
  (Milk prdts)
    Carnation N.V., Vierwinden 3-5, B-1930 Zaventem, Belgium

CAT PUMPS CORP   1681 94th Lane NE, Minneapolis, MN 55434, Tel: (612) 780-5440
  (Mfr/distr pumps)
    N.V. Cat Pumps International SA, Gemzenstraat 2, Wilrijik, B-2610 Antwerp, Belgium

CATERPILLAR INC   100 N E Adams St, Peoria, IL 61629, Tel: (309) 675-1000
  (Mfr earth/material-handling & constr mach & equip, engines, generators)
    Caterpillar Belgium S.A., Boite Postale 1, B-6200 Gosselies, Belgium

CENTRAL SOYA CO   PO Box 1400, Ft Wayne, IN 46802, Tel: (219) 425-5100
  (Livestock & poultry feed, soybean meal, grain)
    N.V. Protector S.A., Kalmthoutsesteenweg 197, 2170 Wuustwezel, Belgium
    N.V. Protector S.A., Chausse de Bruxelles, 1410 Waterloo, Belgium

CHAMPION SPARK PLUG CO   PO Box 910, Toledo, OH 43661, Tel: (419) 535-2567
   (Mfr spark plugs, wiper blades & related prdts)
      Champion Spark Plug Europe S.A., Kosterstraat 209, 1920 Diegem, Belgium

CHASE MANHATTAN BANK N A   1 Chase Manhattan Plaza, New York, NY 10081,
   Tel: (212) 552-2222
   (Intl banking)
      Banque de Commerce S.A., Lange Gasthuisstraat 9, 2000 Antwerp, Belgium
      Chase Manhattan Bank S.A., 51/52 Avenue des Arts, 1040 Brussesl, Belgium
      Chase Manhattan Bank S.A., 14/15 Avenue Rogier, Liege, Belgium
      Chase Manhattan Bank S.A., Notarisstraat 1, Ghent, Belgium
      IDC-Belgium, 52 Avenue des Arts, 1040 Brussels, Belgium

CHICAGO METALLIC CORP   4849 South Austin Ave, Chicago, IL 60638,
   Tel: (312) 858-2600
   (Steel, metal prdts)
      Chicago Metallic Continental N.V., Oud Sluisstraat 5, 2110 Wljnegem, Belgium

CHICAGO PNEUMATIC TOOL CO   2200 Bleeker St, Utica, NY 13501,
   Tel: (315) 792-2600
   (Mfr air tools & equip)
      Chicago Pneumatic Tool Co., S.A., Vuurberg 18, 1920 Diegen-Machelen, Brussels,
      Belgium

THE CHUBB CORP   15 Mountain View Rd, Warren, NJ 07060, Tel: (201) 580-2000
   (Holding co: property/casualty ins)
      Chubb Insurance Co. of Europe, Square de Meeus 35, Boite 7, 1040 Brussels, Belgium

CIGNA CORP   One Liberty Place, 1650 Market St, Philadelphia, PA 19101,
   Tel: (215) 523-4000
   (Ins, invest, health care & other fin servs)
      Afia Life Insurance Co. SA/NV, Rue Belliard 9-11, 1040 Brussels, Belgium
      Cigna Insurance Co. of Europe SA/NV, Rue Belliard 9-11, 1040 Brussels, Belgium
      Cigna Reinsurance Co., SA/NV, Boulevard Du Regent 37-40, 1000 Brussels, Belgium
      Esis Intl., Inc., Rue Beillard 9-11, 1040 Brussels, Belgium

CITIBANK NA   399 Park Ave, New York, NY 10043, Tel: (212) 559-1000
   (Intl banking)
      Citibank N.A., Avenue de Tenvuren 249, P.O. Box 7, B-1150 Brussels, Belgium
      Citibank N.A., Frankrijkei 64-66, Postbus 5, B-2000 Antwerp, Belgium

CLARK EQUIPMENT CO   PO Box 7008, South Bend, IN 46634, Tel: (219) 239-0100
   (Mfr ind trucks, skid-steer loaders, heavy duty drive line components)
      Clark Automotive Europe N.V., Ten Briele 3, B-8200 Brugge, Belgium

CLAYTON INDUSTRIES   4213 N Temple City Blvd, El Monte, CA 91731,
   Tel: (213) 443-9381
   (Mfr steam generators, dynamometers, water treatment chems)
      Clayton of Belgium N.V., Rijksweg 30, 2680 Bornem, Belgium

CLEARY GOTTLIEB STEEN & HAMILTON   1 State Street Plaza, New York, NY 10004,
   Tel: (212) 344-0600
   (Law firm)
      Cleary, Gottlieb, Steen & Hamilton, Rue de la Loi 23, 1040 Brussels, Belgium

COBE LABORATORIES INC   1185 Oak St, Lakewood, CO   80215, Tel: (303) 232-6800
(Mfr med equip & supplies)
  COBE Laboratories Inc., 172 Sterrebeekstraat, 1930 Zaventem, Nossegem, Belgium

THE COCA-COLA CO   310 North Ave NW, PO Box Drawer 1734, Atlanta, GA   30313,
Tel: (404) 676-2121
(Mfr & sale of soft drink syrups & concentrates, juices & food prdts, motion pic & TV prod)
  The Coca-Cola Co. (Belgium), all mail to: Atlanta address

COLGATE-PALMOLIVE CO   300 Park Ave, New York, NY   10022, Tel: (212) 310-2000
(Pharms, cosmetics, toiletries, detergents)
  Colgate-Palmolive S.A., Rue Adolphe Lavallee 20, 1080 Brussels, Belgium

COLLINS & AIKMAN CORP   210 Madison Ave, New York, NY   10016,
Tel: (212) 578-1200
(Textile prdts)
  Painters Mill Belgium S.A., Heistraat 80, 2700 Sint-Niklaas, Belgium

COLUMBIA PICTURES INDUSTRIES INC   711 Fifth Ave, New York, NY   10022,
Tel: (212) 751-4400
(Producer & distributor of motion pictures)
  Warner Columbia Films S.N.C., Rue Royale, 326, 1030 Brussels, Belgium

COMBUSTION ENGINEERING INC   900 Long Ridge Road, Stamford, CT   06902,
Tel: (203) 329-8771
(Tech constr)
  R & I Ramtite Europe, Wandre, Belgium

COMDISCO INC   6400 Shafer Ct, Rosemont, IL   60018, Tel: (708) 698-3000
(Remarketer used computer equip)
  Comdisco Belgium S.A., Rue du Bon Pasteur 53, Bte.56, Evere, 1140 Brussels, Belgium

COMMERCIAL METALS CO   PO Box 1046, Dallas, TX   75221, Tel: (214) 689-4300
(Metal collecting/processing, steel mills, metal trading)
  Cometals Intl. S.A.   ., Chaussee de la Hulpe 181, B-1170 Brussels, Belgium

COMPTON INTERNATIONAL   625 Madison Ave, New York, NY   10022,
Tel: (212) 754-1100
(Advertising)
  VDB/Compton, Romeinsesteenweg 564, 1820 Grimbergen Brussels, Belgium

COMPUTER ASSOCIATES INTL INC   711 Stewart Ave, Garden City, NY   11530,
Tel: (516) 227-3300
(Devel/mkt/mgt info mgt & bus applications software)
  Computer Associates Products SA/NV, Woluwelaan 34 Box 13, B-1200 Brussels, Belgium

COMPUTER SCIENCES CORP   2100 E Grand Ave, El Segundo, CA   90245,
Tel: (213) 615-0311
(Software servs, sys integration)
  CSC NV/SA, 350/358 Ave. Louise, Box 1, B-1050 Brussels, Belgium
  Cegeka NV, all mail to: 350 Ave. Louise, Box 12, 1050 Brussels, Belgium
  Inforem PLC, all mail to: 350 Ave. Louise, Box 12, 1050 Brussels, Belgium

COMPUTERVISION CORP   201 Burlington Rd, Bedford, MA 01730,
   Tel: (617) 275-1800
   (Automation sys, semiconductors)
      Computervision N.V., Avenue des Arts 24,   1040 Brussels, Belgium

CONOCO INC   600 N Dairy Ashford Rd, Houston, TX 77079, Tel: (713) 293-1000
   (Oil, gas, coal, chems, minerals)
      Conoco Chemicals Europe S.A., Rue Joseph Stevens 7, 1000 Brussels, Belgium
      Societe Europeenne des Carburants (SECA), Mechelsesteenweg 520, 1800 Vilvoorde,
      Belgium

CONTAINER-STAPLING CORP   27th & ICC Tracks, Herrin, IL 62948,
   Tel: (618) 942-2125
   (Ind stapling machs & supplies)
      Container-Stapling Corp., Driekoningenstraat 150, 2700 St. Niklaas, Belgium

CONTINENTAL CAN CO   PO Box 5410, Stamford, CT 06856, Tel: (203) 357-8110
   (Packaging prdts & mach, metal, plastic & paper containers)
      N.V. Cobelplast S.A., Antwerpse Steenweg 8-10, B-9100 Loketen, Belgium

CONTINENTAL INSURANCE CO   180 Maiden Lane, New York, NY 10038,
   Tel: (212) 440-3000
   (Insurance)
      Phoenix Continental S.A., Rue de La Loi 99-101, 1040 Brussels, Belgium

CONTROL DATA CORP   8100 34th Ave S, Minneapolis, MN 55440,
   Tel: (612) 853-8100
   (Control data equip, computer sys serv & financial serv)
      Commercial Credit Europe Inc., Tour Madou Tenth Fl., Place Madou, Brussels, Belgium
      Control Data Belgium S.A., Rue de la Fusee 50, 1130 Brussels, Belgium

COPELAND CORP   Campbell Road, Sidney, OH 45365, Tel: (513) 498-3011
   (Ind refrigeration equip)
      Copeland Refrigeration Europe S.A., Rue des Trois Boudons 15, 4840 Welkenraedt,
      Belgium

CORDIS CORP   PO Box 025700, Miami, FL 33102-5700, Tel: (305) 824-2000
   (Mfr med devices & sys)
      Cordis Intl. S.A., Ave. Louise 250, 1050 Brussels, Belgium

CORNING CORP   Houghton Park, PO Box 2000, Corning, NY 14831,
   Tel: (617) 974-9000
   (Mfr glass, ceramic materials)
      N.V. Corning Benelux S.A., Doomveid 15, 1730 Zelik, Belgium

COUDERT BROTHERS   200 Park Ave, New York, NY 10166, Tel: (212) 880-4400
   (Lawyers)
      Coudert Bros., Avenue Louis 149, Bte.8, B-1050 Brussels, Belgium

CPC INTERNATIONAL INC   PO Box 8000, International Plaza, Englewood Cliffs,
   NJ 07632, Tel: (201) 894-4000
   (Mfr consumer food prdts & corn refining prdts)
      CPC Europe Consumer Foods Ltd., 300 Ave. de Tervuren, Box 7, 1150 Brussels, Belgium
      CPC Monda NV/SA, Italielei 122-124, 2000 Antwerp, Belgium

CRANE CO   757 Third Ave, New York, NY 10017, Tel: (212) 415-7300
(Diversified mfr/distr engineered prdts for ind)
    Ferguson Machine Co. S.A., 33 Parc Industriel, 1430 Braine le Chateau, Belgium

JOHN CRANE INC   6400 Oakton St, Morton Grove, IL 60053, Tel: (708) 967-2400
(Mfr engineering seals)
    S.A. John Crane Belgium N.V., 46 rue Grisar, 1070 Brussels, Belgium

CROMPTON & KNOWLES CORP   1 Station Pl Metro Center, Stamford, CT 06902,
Tel: (203) 353-5400
(Mfr dyes, colors, flavors, fragrances, spec chems, ind prdts)
    Crompton & Knowles-Tertre, S.A., Rue de Progres 323, 1000 Brussels, Belgium

CROWN CORK & SEAL CO INC   Holmesburg Station, PO Box 6208, Philadelphia,
PA 19136, Tel: (215) 698-5100
(Cans, bottle caps; filling & packaging mach)
    Crown Cork Co. (Belgium) N.V., 2 Place de L'Albertine, Bte.5, 1000 Brussels, Belgium

CULLIGAN INTL CO   One Culligan Parkway, Northbrook, IL 60062,
Tel: (708) 205-6000
(Water treatment prdts & serv)
    Culligan N.V., Culliganlaan 2, B-1920 Machelen Diegem, Belgium

CUMMINS ENGINE CO INC   PO Box 3005, Columbus, IN 47202, Tel: (812) 377-5000
(Mfr diesel engines)
    Cummins Diesel N.V., Blarenberglaan 4, Industriepark Noord 2, 2800 Mechelen, Belgium

CUTLER HAMMER INC   4201 North 27th St, Milwaukee, WI 53216,
Tel: (414) 442-7800
(Electric control apparatus, mfr of advanced technologic prdts)
    Cutler-Hammer S.A., Rue de Moorslede 237,   1020 Brussels, Belgium

D'ARCY MASIUS BENTON & BOWLES INC (DMB&B)   1675 Broadway, New York,
NY 10019, Tel: (212) 468-3622
(Advertising & communications)
    DMB&B S.A., A.G. Bldg., 5 Place du Champ de Mars, 1050 Brussels, Belgium

D-M-E COMPANY   29111 Stephenson Highway, Madison Heights, MI 48071,
Tel: (313) 398-6000
(Basic tooling for plastic molding & die casting)
    DME Europe, Industriepark Noord, B-2800 Mechelen, Belgium

DANCER FITZGERALD SAMPLE INTL   405 Lexington Ave, New York, NY 10174,
Tel: (212) 661-0800
(Advertising agency)
    JNP Communications, 454 Ave. de Terueren, Brussels, 1150 Belgium

DATA GENERAL CORP   4400 Computer Dr, Westboro, MA 01580, Tel: (617) 366-8911
(Design, mfr gen purpose computer sys & peripheral prdts & servs)
    Data General S.A., 191 Blvd. du Souverain, BTE 11, B-1160 Brussels, Belgium

DATAEASE INTL INC   7 Cambridge Dr, Trumbull, CT 06611, Tel: (203) 374-8000
(Mfr applications devel software)
    Dataleader, NV, 10 Rue de Bosquet, 1180 Brussels, Belgium

DATAGRAPHIX INC   PO Box 82449, San Diego, CA 92138, Tel: (714) 291-9960
(Mfr electronic computing equip)
   Datagraphix S.A., Avenue Lloyd George 7, 1050 Brussels, Belgium

DDB NEEDHAM WORLDWIDE INC   437 Madison Ave, New York, NY 10022,
Tel: (212) 415-2000
(Advertising)
   DDB Needham Worldwide SA, Boulevard de la Cambre 33, Bte. 4, 1050 Brussels, Belgium

DEXTER CORP   1 Elm Street, Windsor Locks, CT 06096, Tel: (203) 623-9801
(Paper & textiles)
   Dexter Intl. S.A., Avenue de Tervuren 269, 1150 Brussels, Belgium

DIAMOND LABORATORIES INC   PO Box 863, Des Moines, IA 50304,
Tel: (515) 262-9341
(Pharms)
   Diamond Laboratories S.A., Rue des Megissiers 30, 1070 Brussels, Belgium

DIAMOND SHAMROCK CORP   1100 Superior Ave, Cleveland, OH 44114,
Tel: (216) 694-5000
(Organic & inorganic chems & specialties, agric chems)
   Diamond Shamrock Europe S.A., Avenue Reine Astrid 7, 1430 Wauthier-Braine, Belgium

WALT DISNEY PRODUCTIONS   500 S Buena Vista St, Burbank, CA 91521,
Tel: (818) 560-1000
(Film/TV prod, amusement parks, land mgmt)
   Walt Disney Production (Benelux) S.A., Centre International Rogier,
      Passage International 29-Bte.67, 1000 Brussels, Belgium

DO ALL COMPANY   254 N Laurel Ave, Des Plaines, IL 60016, Tel: (708) 824-1122
(Distributors of mach tools, metal cutting tools, instru & ind supplies)
   DoAll Belgium S.P.R.L., Quai du Roi Albert, 81, 4020 Bressoux-Liege, Belgium

DONALDSON CO INC   PO Box 1299, Minneapolis, MN 55440, Tel: (612) 887-3131
(Filtration prdts & sys)
   Donaldson Europe N.V., Interleuvenlaan 1, B-3030 Leuven, Belgium

DORR-OLIVER INC   612 Wheeler's Farm Rd, PO Box 3819, Milford, CT 06460,
Tel: (203) 876-5400
(Mfr process equip for food, pulp & paper, mineral & chem ind; & municipal/ind waste
treatment)
   Dorr-Oliver S.A., Rue de l'Hospital 31, B-1000 Brussels, Belgium

DOW CHEMICAL CO   2030 Dow Center, Midland, MI 48640, Tel: (517) 636-1000
(Chems, plastics, fibers, pharms)
   Dow Chemical Europe S.A., Blvd. de Waterloo 39, 1000 Brussels, Belgium

DOW CORNING CORP   2220 W Salzburg Rd, PO Box 1767, Midland, MI 48640,
Tel: (517) 496-4000
(Silicones, silicon chems, solid lubricants)
   Dow Corning Intl. Ltd., Chaussee de la Hulpe 154, 1170 Brussels, Belgium

DOW JONES & CO INC   200 Liberty St, New York, NY 10281, Tel: (212) 416-2000
(Publisher)
   The Wall Street Journal/Europe, Hilton Tower, Boite 7A, 38 Boulevard de Waterloo,
      B-1000 Brussels, Belgium

DRAKE BEAM MORIN INC   100 Park Ave, New York, NY 10017, Tel: (212) 692-7700
(Human resource mgmt consulting & training)
   Drake Beam Morin Europe Inc., 2 Woluwe Ave., B-1150 Brussels, Belgium

DRESSER INDUSTRIES INC   1600 Pacific Bldg, PO Box 718, Dallas, TX 75221,
Tel: (214) 740-6000
(Diversified supplier of equip & tech serv to energy & natural resource ind)
   Dresser Products S.A., 63, Rue de Manage, 6548 Familleureux, Belgium
   Jeffrey Mining Machinery Operations, Dresser Europe S.A., "Le Souverain",
   Blvd. du Souverain, 191-197 (B, 3), B-1160 Brussels, Belgium

DREVER COMPANY   PO Box 98, Huntington Valley, PA 19006, Tel: (215) 947-3400
(Mfr industrial furnaces)
   Drever Intl. S.A., Parc Industriel du Sart Tilman, B-4900 Liege, Belgium

DREW CHEMICAL CORP   One Drew Plaza, Boonton, NJ 07005, Tel: (201) 263-7600
(Spec chems for ind water & fuel treatment, chem processing)
   N.V. Drew Ameroid Belgium S.A., Vosseschjnstraat Kaai 138, B-2030 Antwerp, Belgium

E I DU PONT DE NEMOURS & CO   Du Pont Bldg, 1007 Market St, Wilmington,
DE 19898, Tel: (302) 774-1000
(Mfr/sale diversified chems, plastics, specialty prdts & fibers)
   Du Pont de Nemours Belgium) S.A., Brussels, Belgium

DURAMETALLIC CORP   2104 Factory St, Kalamazoo, MI 49001, Tel: (616) 382-8720
(Mfr mech seals, compression packings, auxiliaries)
   Durametallic Benelux, Brugsesteenweg 591, B-9910 Ghent, Belgium

DURIRON CO INC   425 N Findlay St, PO Box 1145, Dayton, OH 45401,
Tel: (513) 226-4000
(Mfr chem equip, pumps, valves, filters, fans, heat exchangers)
   S.A. Durco Europe N.V., Parc Industrial 4822 Petit Rechain, Belgium

EASTMAN & BEAUDINE INC   111 W Monroe, Chicago, IL 60603, Tel: (312) 726-8195
(Investments)
   Eastman & Beaudine Inc., Boite 3, Avenue de Broqueville 44, 1200 Brussels, Belgium

EASTMAN KODAK CO   343 State St, Rochester, NY 14650-0518, Tel: (716) 724-4000
(Devel/mfr photo & chem prdts, info mgmt/video/copier sys, fibers/plastics for
various ind)
   Kodak S.A., 20 Steenstraat, 1800 Koningslo-Vilvoorde, Belgium

EATON CORP   100 Erieview Plaza, Cleveland, OH 44114, Tel: (216) 523-5000
(Advanced tech prdts for transp & ind mkts)
   Samuel Moore S.A., Chaussee de Tiriemont 100, 5800 Gembloux, Belgium

ECCA FREIGHT SYSTEMS INC   1 World Trade Center, Suite 1569, New York,
NY 10048, Tel: (212) 466-1988
(Frt consolidations)
   Euro Consolidated Container Association, 9-33 Cadixstraat, 2000 Antwerp, Belgium

ECOLAB INC   370 Wabasha St, St Paul, MN 55102, Tel: (612) 293-2233
(Ind & household detergents, cleaning agents & equip)
   Soilax Benelox S.A., Avenue de Tervuren 36, Box 18, 1040 Brussels, Belgium

EG&G INC   45 William St, Wellesley, MA   02181, Tel: (617) 237-5100
  (Diversified instru, components, services)
    EG&G Instruments, Leuvensesteenweg 613, 1930 Zaventem, Belgium

ELECTRO-NITE CO   11601 Caroline Rd, Philadelphia, PA   19154,
  Tel: (215) 464-4200
  (Expendable sensors & instru for iron & steel ind)
    Electron-Nite N.V., Grote Baan 135, 3530 Houthalen, Belgium

ELECTRONICS CORP OF AMERICA   265 Winter St, Waltham, MA   0215442,
  Tel: (617) 466-8000
  (Mfr electrical ind apparatus, electronic sys & controls)
    Electronics Corp. of America (Europe) S.A., Schepen A. Gossetlaan 20,
      1720 Groot-Bijgarden, Belgium

ELECTRONIZED CHEMICALS CORP   South Bedford St, Burlington, MA   01803,
  Tel: (617) 272-2850
  (Mfr of irradiated prdts)
    Electronized Chemicals Corp., Avenue de Tervueren 327, 1150 Brussels, Belgium

EMERSON & CUMING DEWEY & ALMY CHEMICAL CO   59 Walpole St, Canton, MA   02021,
  Tel: (617) 828-3300
  (Plastics & ceramics for electr shielding materials)
    Emerson & Cuming Europe N.V., Nijverheidstraat 24, 2431 Oevel, Belgium

EMERSON ELECTRIC CO   8000 Florissant Ave, St Louis, MO   63136,
  Tel: (314) 553-2000
  (Electrical & electronic prdts, ind components & sys, consumer, government & defense
  prdts)
    Emerson Electric Co., Avenue Adolphe Lacomle 52, Bks. 156, 1040 Brussels, Belgium

ENCYCLOPEDIA BRITANNICA INC   425 N Michigan Ave, Chicago, IL   60611,
  Tel: (312) 321-7000
  (Book publ)
    Encyclopeadia Britannica (Belgium) Ltd., Avenue des Arts 1-2, 1040 Brussels, Belgium

ERIE INTL LTD   4000 South 13th St, Milwaukee, WI   53221, Tel: (414) 483-0524
  (Mfr controls, valves & pipe fittings)
    Erie Controls-Europe N.V., Herentals, Belgium

ERIE TECHNOLOGICAL PRODUCTS INC   645 W 11th St, Erie, PA   16512,
  Tel: (814) 453-5611
  (Electronic components)
    Erie Continental S.A., Avenue Eugene Plasky 140, 1040 Brussels, Belgium

ESKIMO PIE CORP   530 E Main St, Richmond, VA   23219, Tel: (804) 782-1800
  (Frozen food prdts)
    Eskimo Europe S.A., Quai du Commerce 20, 1000 Brussels, Belgium

ETHYL CORP   330 South 4th St, Richmond, VA   23219, Tel: (804) 788-5000
  (Chems & plastics)
    Ethyl S.A., Rue Paul Lauters 1, 1050 Brussels, Belgium

ETHYL PETROLEUM ADDITIVES INC   20 S 4th St, St Louis, MO   63102-1886,
  Tel: (314) 421-3930
  (Mfr lubricant & fuel additives)
    Ethyl S.A., Ave. Louise 523, Boite 18, B-1050 Brussels, Belgium

EVERPURE INC   660 N Blackhawk Dr, Westmont, IL 60559, Tel: (708) 654-4000
  (Water purification, automatic chlorinators)
    Everpure S.A., Culliganlaan 2, Diegem, Belgium

EXXON CHEMICAL CO   9 Old Kings Hwy S, Darien, CT 06820, Tel: (203) 655-5200
  (Mfr & sales of petrochems)
    Esso-Chem Europe Inc., Nijverheidslaan 2, 1920 Diegem, Belgium

EXXON CORP   225 E John Carpenter Frwy, Irving, TX 75062, Tel: (214) 444-1000
  (Petroleum & petroleum prdts)
    Esso Belgium S.A., Frankrieklei 101, 2000 Antwerp, Belgium

FEDERAL EXPRESS CORP   PO Box 727, Memphis, TN 38194-4212, Tel: (901) 922-6900
  (Package air express svc)
    Federal Express NV/SA, Brussels National Airport, 1930 Zaventem, Belgium

FEDERAL INSURANCE CO   100 William St, New York, NY 10038, Tel: (212) 285-2850
  (Insurance)
    La Federation Europeenne, Compagnie d'Assurances S.A., Avenue Kamerdelle 14,
    1180 Brussels, Belgium

FEDERAL-MOGUL CORP   PO Box 1966, Detroit, MI 48235, Tel: (313) 354-7700
  (Mfr/distr vehicular & ind components for original market & aftermarket)
    Federal-Mogul Corp., Luithagen-Haven 2, Unit C, 2030 Anvers, Belgium

FERGUSON MACHINE CO   11820 Lockland Rd, St Louis, MO 63141,
  Tel: (314) 567-3200
  (Power transmitters, specialty mach)
    Ferguson Machine Co. S.A., Rue Bollinckx 267, 1060 Brussels, Belgium

FINKELSTEIN BROS CO   608 Fifth Ave, New York, NY 10020, Tel: (212) 246-2670
  (Diamonds)
    C.A. Finn Diamond Co., Pelikaanstraat 86, 2000 Antwerp, Belgium

FIRST NATIONAL BANK OF BOSTON   100 Federal St, Boston, MA 02110,
  Tel: (617) 434-2200
  (Commercial banking)
    Boston Leasing Belgium S.A., Avenue Louise 326, BP 22, 1050 Brussels, Belgium
    S.A. Intl. Factors N.V., Avenue de Cortenberg 71, Bte.1, 1040 Brussels, Belgium

FISCHBEIN CO   2700 30th Ave South, Minneapplis, MN 55406, Tel: (612) 721-4806
  (Mfr bag closing equip)
    Fischbein Cie. S.A., Rue Previnaire 64, 1070 Brussels, Belgium

FISCHER & PORTER CO   125 E County Line Rd, Warminster, PA 18974,
  Tel: (215) 674-6000
  (Design/mfr meas, recording & control instru & sys; mfr ind glass prdts)
    Fischer & Porter Belgium N.V., Elektronikalaan 12-14, B-2610 Wilrijk, Belgium

FISHER CONTROLS INTL INC   8000 Maryland Ave, Clayton, MO 63105,
  Tel: (314) 694-9900
  (Ind process control equip)
    Fisher Controls SA/NV, 130 Chaussee de la Hulpe, 1050 Brussels, Belgium

FISHER-PRICE   636 Girard Ave, East Aurora, NY 14052, Tel: (716) 687-3000
  (Mfr toys & games)
    Fisher-Price, Kettingbrugweg 34, 3599 Bocholt-Kaulille, Belgium

FLOW LABORATORIES INC   7655 Old Springhouse Rd, McLean, VA 22102,
   Tel: (703) 893-5900
   (Mfr/distr biotechnology)
     Flow Laboratories NV/SA, Doornveld 10, B-1730 Asse-Relegem, Brussels, Belgium

FOOTE CONE & BELDING COMMUNICATIONS INC   101 E Erie St, Chicago,
   IL 60611-2897, Tel: (312) 751-7000
   (Advertising agency)
     EMC-Brussels, 225 Avenue Moliere, 1060 Brussels, Belgium
     Park Brussels, 5 Square des Heros, 1180 Brussels, Belgium
     Publicis-FCB, Ave. de las Couronne 357, 1050 Brussels, Belgium

FORD MOTOR CO   The American Road, Dearborn, MI 48121, Tel: (313) 322-3000
   (Mfr automobiles, trucks)
     Ford Motor Co. (Belgium) NV, Kanaaldok 200, Postbus 37, B-2030 Antwerp, Belgium

FOXBORO CO   33 Commercial St, Foxboro, MA 02035, Tel: (508) 543-8750
   (Mfr prdts/provide servs for ind automation)
     Louis Welffens, S.P.R.I., 1 Meirbrug, B-2000 Antwerp, Belgium

THE FRANKLIN MINT   Franklin Center, PA 19091, Tel: (215) 459-6000
   (Creation/mfr/mktg collectible items)
     Franklin Mint S.A./N.V., Ave. du Colvert 1, 1170 Brussels, Belgium

FURON CO   29982 Ivy Glenn Dr, Laguna Niguel, CA 92677, Tel: (714) 831-5350
   (Mfr of ind components)
     Furon Samuel Moore, Chaussee de Tirlemot- #100, 5800 Gembloux, Belgium
     Furon Seals NV/SA, Helststraat 51/7, 2630 Aartselar, Belgium

GAB BUSINESS SERVICES INC   123 William St, New York, NY 10038,
   Tel: (212) 306-8000
   (Ins adjustment)
     GAB Business Services, S.A., Weber Building, Verbindingsdok Westkaai 26-30, Bus 5,
       B-2000 Antwerp, Belgium

GAF CORP   1361 Alps Rd, Wayne, NJ 07470, Tel: (201) 628-3000
   (Chems, bldg materials, commun)
     GAF (Belgium) N.V., Hodgkamerstraat 42, B-2700 Sint-Niklaas, Belgium

GAMLEN CHEMICAL CO   121 S Maple Ave, S San Francisco, CA 94080,
   Tel: (415) 873-1750
   (Chems, detergents & tank cleansers)
     Gamlen Chemical Co., Maarchalk Gerardstraat 8, Antwerp 2000, Belgium

GARLOCK INC   1250 Midtown Tower, Rochester, NY 14604, Tel: (214) 758-0000
   (Mechanical packings)
     Ets. G. Liard S.A., Rue de Marchienne 33, 6160 Roux, Belgium

THE GATES RUBBER CO   PO Box 5887, Denver, CO 80217, Tel: (303) 744-1911
   (Mfr auto/ind belts & hose, hydraulic hose & couplings, molded rubber prdts)
     Gates Europe N.V., Carlierlaan 30, 9440 Erembodegem, Belgium

GATX CORP   120 S Riverside Plaza, Chicago, IL 60606, Tel: (312) 621-6200
   (Railcar leasing, maint & mgmt, bulk liquid storage, fin serv, shipping, mineral
   processing)
     Gamatex N.V., Kanaaldok B2, Scheldelaan, 2040 Antwerp, Belgium

GENERAL AUTOMATION INC   1055 S East St, Anaheim, CA 92806,
 Tel: (714) 778-4800
 (Computer hardware & serv)
   General Automation S.A., Blvd. de la Wolvwe 34, Box 13, B-1200 Brussels, Belgium

GENERAL DATACOMM INDUSTRIES INC   1579 Straits Turnpike, Middlebury,
 CT 06762-1299, Tel: (203) 574-1118
 (Mfr trans equip for commun networks)
   General DataComm NV, Parklaan 124, 2300 Turnhout, Belgium

GENERAL DYNAMICS CORP   Pierre Laclede Center, St Louis, MO 63105,
 Tel: (314) 889-8200
 (Mfr aircraft, submarines, missiles, space launch vehicles, bldg prdts, info sys)
   General Dynamics Intl. Corp., Blvd. du Souverain 191, Box 7, B-1160 Brussels,
    Belgium

GENERAL FOODS CORP   250 North St, White Plains, NY 10625, Tel: (914) 335-2500
 (Processor, distributor & mfr of foods)
   General Foods Europe, Astro Tower, Ave. de l'Astronomie 14, B-1030 Brussels, Belgium

GENERAL INSTRUMENT CORP   767 Fifth Ave, New York, NY 10153-0082,
 Tel: (212) 207-6200
 (Electronic components & sys)
   C.P. Clare Intl. S.A., Overhaamlaan, 3700 Tongeren, Belgium
   General Instrument Europe, Ave de l'Horizon 32, B-1150 Brussels, Belgium

GENERAL MOTORS ACCEPTANCE CORP   3044 West Grand Blvd, Detroit, MI 48202,
 Tel: (313) 556-5000
 (Automobile financing)
   GMAC, Neerveldstraat 107, B-1220 Brussels Belgium
   GMAC Continental, Noorderlaan 139, Post Box 1, B-2030 Antwerp, Belgium

GENERAL MOTORS CORP   3044 W Grand Blvd, Detroit, MI 48202,
 Tel: (313) 556-5000
 (Automotive prdts, electronics)
   General Motors Continental S.A., Noorderlaan 75, Postbus 9, 2000 Antwerp, Belgium

GENERAL REFRACTORIES CO   2661 Audubon Rd, Audubon, PA 19407,
 Tel: (215) 666-0104
 (Heat-resisting materials, furnace constr)
   Dicalite Europe Nord S.A., Avenue Louise 430 Bte. 2, B-1050 Brussels, Belgium

GEORGIA BONDED FIBERS INC   1040 W 29th St, PO Box 751, Buena Vista,
 VA 24416, Tel: (703) 261-2181
 (Mfr insole & luggage material)
   Bontex S.A., Rue Slar, 4801 Stembert, Belgium

GERBER SCIENTIFIC INSTRUMENT CO   83 Gerber Rd West, So Windsor, CT 06074,
 Tel: (203) 644-1551
 (CADICAM for electronic & graphic arts ind)
   Gerber Scientific Europe S.A., Blvd. Du Souverain, 100-BTE 2, 1170 Brussels, Belgium

GK TECHNOLOGIES INC   500 W Putnam Ave, Greenwich, CT 06830,
 Tel: (203) 661-0100
 (Wire cable, electronic tech serv)
   Sprague World Trade Corp., Renaix, Belgium

THE GLEASON WORKS   1000 University Ave, Rochester, NY 14692,
   Tel: (716) 473-1000
   (Mfr mfg machines, tooling & services)
      Gleason Works S.A., Parc Industriel de Ghlin Baudour, 7420 Baudour, Belgium

GLENOIT MILLS INTL CORP   111 West 40th St, New York, NY 10018,
   Tel: (212) 391-3915
   (Synthetic pile fabrics)
      Glenoit Belgium S.A., Industriepark B3, 9140 Zele, Belgium

GORTON GROUP   327 Main Street, Gloucester, MA 01930, Tel: (617) 283-3000
   (Frozen fish)
      Viking Intl. Ltd., H. Baelskaai 24, 8400 Oostende, Belgium

GRANT THORNTON INTL   Prudential Plaza, Chicago, IL 60601, Tel: (312) 856-0001
   (Intl accountants)
      Grant Thornton Intl., Avenue Roger Vandendreissche 41, B-1150 Brussels, Belgium

GREAT LAKES CARBON INTL CORP   320 Old Briarcliff Rd, Briarcliff Manor,
   NY 10510, Tel: (914) 941-7800
   (Mfr carbon prdts, petroleum)
      Great Lakes Carbon Intl. S.A., 50 Scheepsatestraat, 9000 Ghent, Belgium

GREFCO INC   3435 W Lomita Blvd, Torrance, CA 90505, Tel: (213) 517-0700
   (Filter powders)
      Dicalite-Europe Nord S.A., Ave. Louise 430, Boite 2, B-1050 Brussels, Belgium

GREY ADVERTISING INC   777 Third Ave, New York, NY 10017, Tel: (212) 546-2000
   (Advertising)
      Belgium & Grey S.A., Avenue des Arts 20, Boite 10, 1040 Brussels, Belgium

GRIFFITH LABORATORIES INC   I Griffith Center, Alsip, IL 60658,
   Tel: (708) 371-0900
   (Ind food ingredients & equip)
      N.V. Griffith Laboratories S.A., P.O. Box 67, Wolfsteestraat, Industriepark,
         B-2410 Herentals, Belgium

GROLIER INC   Old Shereman Tpk, Danbury, CT 06816, Tel: (203) 797-3500
   (Publishers)
      Grolier Intl. (Benelux) S.A., Rue Blanche 15, 1050 Brussels, Belgium

GTE CORP   One Stamford Forum, Stamford, CT 06904, Tel: (203) 965-2000
   (Electr prdts, telecom sys, publ & commun)
      Automatic Electric S.A., Boomgaardstraat 22, 2000 Antwerp, Belgium
      GTE Sylvania N.V., Frans Timmermansstraat 119, 1730 Zellik, Belgium

GULF & WESTERN INDUSTRIES INC   1 Gulf & Western Plaza, New York, NY 10023,
   Tel: (212) 333-7000
   (Widely diversified multi-industry company in consumer prdts)
      Mattelin S.A., Route de Mons 21, 7320 Hornu, Belgium

HACH CO   PO Box 389, Loveland, CO 80539, Tel: (303) 669-3050
   (Mfr/distr water analysis & organic instru, test kits & chems)
      Hach Europe S.A., B.P. 229, 5000 Namur 1, Belgium

FRANK B HALL & CO INC   549 Pleasantville Rd, Briarcliff Manor, NY 10510,
  Tel: (914) 769-9200
  (Insurance)
    Assurances Verspieren SPRL, 7 Rue des Deux Eglises, 1040 Brussels, Belgium

HARCOURT BRACE JOVANOVICH INC   Harcourt Brace Jovanovich Bldg, Orlando,
  FL 32887, Tel: (305) 345-2000
  (Book publ, tests & related serv, journals, facisimile reprints, mgmt consult,
  operates parks/shows)
    Drake Beam Morin Europe Inc., Ave. Winston Churchill 93, 1180 Brussels, Belgium

THE HARPER GROUP INC   260 Townsend St, PO Box 77933, San Francisco,
  CA 94107, Tel: (415) 978-0600
  (Ocean/air freight fwdg, customs brokerage, packing & whse, logistics mgt, ins)
    Circle Ziegler SA Airfreight, Bldg. 726-730, Brucargo, 1931 Zaventem, Belgium

HARRIS PRC INC   300 E 42nd St, New York, NY 10017, Tel: (212) 986-2700
  (Engineering consultants)
    Frederic R. Harris S.A., 71 Rue de la Loi, 1040 Brussels, Belgium

HAYES-ALBION CORP   1999 Wildwood Ave, Jackson, MI 49202, Tel: (517) 782-9421
  (Sand or shell cast ferritic & pearlitic malleable iron prdts, hdwe & trim)
    Almet S.A., Rue de Brederode 9, 1000 Brussels, Belgium

H J HEINZ CO   PO Box 57, Pittsburgh, PA 15230, Tel: (412) 456-5100
  (Food prdts)
    H.J. Heinz Co. S.A., Chaussee de la Hulpe, Bte.6, 1170 Brussels, Belgium

HELENE CURTIS INDUSTRIES INC   4401 W North Ave, Chicago, IL 60639,
  Tel: (312) 292-2121
  (Cosmetics, toiletries, hair preparations)
    Helene Curtis S.A., Chaussee de Louvain 775, 1140 Brussels, Belgium

HERCULES INC   Hercules Plaza, Wilmington, DE 19894, Tel: (302) 594-5000
  (Mfr spec chems, plastics, film & fibers, coatings, resins, food ingredients)
    Hercules Chemicals N.V., Industrieweg Chemicals Inc., P.O. Box 1,
      B-3940 Paal-Beringen, Belgium

HERTZ CORP   225 Brae Blvd, Park Ridge, NJ 07656-0713, Tel: (201) 307-2000
  (Automobile rental)
    Hertz Europe Service Corp., Rue Col. Bourgstraat 120, 1140 Brussels, Belgium

HEWLETT-PACKARD CO   3000 Hanover St, PO Box 10301, Palo Alto, CA 94303-0890,
  Tel: (415) 857-1501
  (Mfr measurement & computation prdts & sys)
    Hewlett-Packard Belgium S.A.N.V., Blvd. de la Woluwe, 100 Woluwedal,
      B-1200 Brussels, Belgium

HEXCEL CORP   20701 Nordhoff St, Chatsworth, CA 91311, Tel: (213) 882-3022
  (Honeycomb core materials, specialty chems, resins & epoxies)
    Hexcel S.A., Rue des 3 Bourdons 50, Parc Industriel, 4840 Welkenraedt, Belgium

HILL & KNOWLTON INC   420 Lexington Ave, New York, NY 10017,
  Tel: (212) 697-5600
  (Public relations, public affairs, comm counseling)
    Hill & Knowlton Intl. Belgium S.A., Ave. Louise 430, 1050 Brussels, Belgium

HOBART INTL INC   World Headquarters Ave, Troy, OH 45374, Tel: (513) 335-7171
  (Food preparation & processing equip)
    Cie Hobart S.A., Chaussee de Wavre 1120, 1160 Brussels, Belgium

HOLIDAY INNS INC   3742 Lamar Ave, Memphis, TN 38195, Tel: (901) 362-4001
  (Hotels, restaurants, casinos)
    Holiday Inn, S.A., Boeveriestraat, 28000 Brugge, Sauna, Belgium

THE HOOVER GROUP   403 W 4th St N, Newton, IA 50208, Tel: (515) 792-8000
  (Mfr floor care prdts, laundry & refrig appliances)
    Hoover Worldwide Corp., L'Etablissement Hoover S.A., 1650 Chaussee de Haecht,
      1130 Brussels, Belgium

HORWATH & HORWATH INTL   919 Third Ave, New York, NY 10022,
  Tel: (212) 980-3100
  (Public accountants & auditors)
    Horwath & Horwath Intl., J. Van Elewyckstraat 111, (P.B.10), 1820 Strombeek, Belgium

HUGHES AIRCRAFT CO   PO Box 45066, Los Angeles, CA 90045, Tel: (213) 568-7200
  (Aircraft & aerospace sys & equip)
    Hughes Aircraft Intl. Service Co., Blvd. du Souverain Bte.3, 348, 1160 Brussels,
      Belgium

PHILIP A HUNT CHEMICAL CO   Palisades Park, NJ 07650, Tel: (201) 944-4000
  (Chem specialties for photo & graphics industries, electrosta- tics, electronics)
    Hunt Chemical N.V., Europark 9-10, 2700 Sint-Niklaas, Belgium

HYDROMATION FILTER CO   39201 Amrhein Rd, Livonia, MI 48150,
  Tel: (313) 464-0600
  (Ind filter sys)
    Hydromation (Belgium) N.V., Luikersteenweg, B-3700 Tongeren, Belgium

IDEAL TAPE CO   1400 Middlesex St, Lowell, MA 01851, Tel: (617) 458-6833
  (Pressure sensitive tapes)
    Ideal Tape Co., Oswald Ponettestraat 45, 9600 Ronse, Belgium

INA CORPORATION   1600 Arch St, Philadelphia, PA 19101, Tel: (215) 523-5335
  (Holding co: ins, financial serv)
    Insurance Co. of North America, President Bldg., Box 4, Franklin Rooseveltplants,
      12, 2000 Antwerp, Belgium
    Insurance Co. of North America, Rue Belliard 9-11, 1040 Brussels, Belgium

INDUCTOTHERM CORP   10 Indel Ave, Rancocas, NJ 08073, Tel: (609) 267-9000
  (Mfr induction melting furnaces)
    Inducto Elphiac, 79 Rue P. J. Antoine, B-4400 Herstal, Belgium

INFORMATION BUILDERS INC   1250 Broadway, New York, NY 10001,
  Tel: (212) 736-4433
  (Devel/serv computer software)
    Information Builders (Belgium), Blvd. Brand Whitlocklan 114, 1040 Brussels, Belgium

INGERSOLL-RAND CO   200 Chestnut Ridge Rd, Woodcliff Lake, NJ 07675,
  Tel: (201) 573-0123
  (Mfr compressors, rock drills, pumps, air tools)
    Ingersoll-Rand Benelux S.A., Kouterveldstraat 10-12, B-1920 Machelen, Belgium

INSTRON CORP 100 Royall St, Canton, MA 02021, Tel: (617) 828-2500
(Testing instru)
Instrol Ltd., Wouter Haecklean 110, 2100 Deurne, Belgium

INSUL-8 CORP P O Drawer 1188, San Carlos, CA 94070, Tel: (415) 595-3050
(Closed circuit TV equip)
Insul-8 Corp. (Belgium) N.V., Noorderlaan 87, 2000 Antwerp, Belgium

INTERMEC CORP 6001 36th Ave West, Everett, WA 98203-9280,
Tel: (206) 348-2600
(Mfr automated data collection sys)
Intermec Belgium, Bedrijfspark Heide 11, B-1780 Wemmel, Belgium

INTERMODAL TECHNICAL SERVICES INC 9 Campus Dr, Parsippany, NJ 07054,
Tel: (201) 993-3634
(Damage survey & inspection servs)
Intermodal Technical Services, Inc., Weber Bldg., Verbindingsdok Westkaai 26-30,
Bus 5, B-2000 Antwerp, Belgium

INTERNATIONAL BUSINESS MACHINES (IBM) Old Orchard Rd, Armonk,
NY 10504-1783, Tel: (914) 765-1900
(Info-handling sys, equip & serv)
Intl. Business Machines of Belgium, S.A., 1 Sq. Victoria Regina, Brussels,
Brabant 1030, Belgium

INTERNATIONAL PAPER 2 Manhattanville Rd, Purchase, NY 10577,
Tel: (914) 397-1500
(Mfr/distr container board, paper, wood prdts)
Anitec Image Belgium N.V., Eigenlostraat 21, B-2700 Sint-Niklaas, Belgium
Anitec Image Intl. B.V., Eigenlostraat 21, B-2700 Sint-Niklaas, Belgium
International Paper (Europe) S.A., 1150 Woluwe-Saint-Pierre, Blvd. de la Woluwe 2,
Brussels, Belgium
Veratec S.A., Blvd. de la Woluwe 58, 1200 Brussels, Belgium

INTERNATIONAL STAPLE & MACHINE CO PO Box 629, Butler, PA 16001,
Tel: (412) 287-7711
(Stapling machs, supplies)
Intl. Staple & Machine Co. S.A., Puursesteenweg 7, 2680 Bornem, Belgium

IOMEGA CORP 1821 W 4000 South, Roy, UT 84067, Tel: (801) 778-4494
(Mfr data storage prdts)
Iomega, Excelsiorlaan 39- Box 3, Zaventem, 1930 Brussels, Belgium

ITT SHERATON CORP 60 State St, Boston, MA 02108, Tel: (617) 367-3600
(Hotel operations)
Sheraton Sales Center, Brussels Sheraton Hotel, Place Rogier 3, 1000 Brussels,
Belgium

JOHN HANCOCK MUTUAL LIFE INSURANCE CO 200 Clarendon St, PO Box 111, Boston,
MA 02117, Tel: (617) 572-6000
(Life ins)
John Hancock Intl. Services S.A., Rue Montoyer 31, Boite 4, 1040 Brussels, Belgium

JOHNSON & JOHNSON One Johnson & Johnson Plaza, New Brunswick, NJ 08933,
Tel: (201) 524-0400
(Surgical, med & baby prdts)
Cilag N.V., Herentals, Belgium

(cont)

Janssen Biotech N.V., Olen, Belgium
Janssen Internationaal N.V., Beerse, Belgium
Janssen Pharmaceutica N.V., Beerse, Belgium
Ortho Diagnostic Systems N.V., Beerse, Belgium

S C JOHNSON & SON INC   1525 Howe St, Racine, WI 53403, Tel: (414) 631-2000
(Home, auto, commercial & personal care prdts, specialty chems)
    N.V. Johnson Wax Belgium S.A., Noordkustlaan 16, Groot-Bijgaarden, 1720 Brussels,
    Belgium

JOHNSON CONTROLS INC   5757 W Green Bay Ave, PO Box 591, Milwaukee, WI 53201,
Tel: (414) 228-1200
(Mfr facility mgmt & control sys, auto seating, batteries & plastics)
    Johnson Controls SA/NV, 33 Ave. Henri Dunant, 1140 Brussels, Belgium

A T KEARNEY INC   222 S Riverside Plaza, Chicago, IL 60606,
Tel: (312) 648-0111
(Mgmt consultants)
    A. T. Kearney Inc., Ave. des Arts 46, 1040 Brussels, Belgium

KEMPER INTL INSURANCE CO   Route 22, Long Grove, IL 60049, Tel: (708) 540-2000
(Property casualty ins)
    Kemper Conservasion Industrelle S.A., Rue de la Loi 227, B-1040 Brussels, Belgium
    Kemper S.A., Rue de la Loi 227, B-1040, Brussels, Belgium

KENNAMETAL INC   PO Box 231, Latrobe, PA 15650, Tel: (412) 539-5000
(Tools, hard carbide & tungsten alloys)
    Kennametal Belgium S.A., Ave. Albert Ier. 111, B-4030 Liege Grivegnee, Belgium

KEUFFEL & ESSER CO   PO Box 800, Rockaway, NJ 07866, Tel: (201) 625-9005
(Drafting & engineering supplies)
    Keuffel & Esser Intl. SA/NV, Route de Vieux Campinaire, 6220 Fleurus, Belgium

KEYES FIBRE CO   3003 Summer St, Stamford, CT 06905, Tel: (203) 357-9100
(Molded containers)
    Cartonnerie de Muno, 54 Rue Grande, 6818 Muno, Belgium

KEYSTONE INTL INC   PO Box 40010, Houston, TX 77040, Tel: (713) 466-1176
(Mfr butterfly valves, actuators & control accessories)
    Keystone Valve Belgium, Terlindenhofstraat 36, 2060 Merksem, Belgium

KNOGO CORP   350 Wireless Blvd, Hauppauge, NY 11788, Tel: (516) 232-2100
(Mfr electr article surveillance sys)
    Knogo Benelux SA, Rue Neuve 136, 1640 Rhode St., Genese, Belgium
    Knogo SA, Zoning Industriel, Route de Wallonie, 7410 Mons, Belgium

KNOLL INTL   655 Madison Ave, New York, NY 10021, Tel: (212) 826-2400
(Furniture & fabrics)
    Knoll Intl., 145 Rue Royale, Brussels, Belgium

KNOTT HOTELS CORP   840 Madison Ave, New York, NY 10021, Tel: (212) 535-2000
(Hotels)
    Knott Hotels (Belgium) S.A., Rue Cardinal Mercier 6, 1000 Brussels, Belgium

KORN/FERRY INTL   237 Park Ave, New York, NY 10017, Tel: (212) 687-1834
(Executive search)
    Korn/Ferry Intl., S.A., 523 Ave. Louise, B-1050 Brussels, Belgium

KRAFT INC   Kraft Court, Glenview, IL 60025, Tel: (708) 998-2000
  (Dairy prdts, processed food, chems)
    N.V. Kraftco S.A., Rue St. Denis 14-16, B-1190 Brussels, Belgium

KYSOR INDUSTRIAL CORP   1 Madison Ave, Cadillac, MI 49601-9785,
  Tel: (616) 779-2200
  (Mfr diversified ind prdts & sys)
    Kysor/Europe, Ave. Louise 386, B.P. 8, 1050 Brussels, Belgium

LANDAU CONSOLIDATED CORP   630 Fifth Ave, New York, NY 10020,
  Tel: (212) 247-7541
  (Rough & cut diamonds, etc)
    Continental Diamond Co. S.A., Pelikaanstraat 86, 2000 Antwerp, Belgium

LAWTER INTERNATIONAL INC   990 Skokie Blvd, Northbrook, IL 60062,
  Tel: (708) 498-4700
  (Resins, pigments, coatings)
    Lawter Chemicals S.A., Toikomstlaan 18, 9100 Lokeren, Belgium

LE TOURNEAU INC LONGVIEW DIV   PO Box 2307, Longview, TX 75606,
  Tel: (214) 753-3449
  (Heavy constr, mining mach & equip)
    Bureau Technique Bia S.A., Rameistraat 123, 1900 Overijse, Belgium

LEAF CONFECTIONERY INC   1155 N Cicero Ave, Chicago, IL 60651,
  Tel: (312) 345-6200
  (Chewing gum)
    Leaf Belgium N.V., Rijksweg 32, 2680 Bornem, Belgium

LEVI STRAUSS & CO   1155 Battery, San Francisco, CA 94111, Tel: (415) 544-6000
  (Mfr wearing apparel)
    Levi Strauss Belgium S.A., International Trade Mart, Avignon 272, Atomium Sq.,
      1020 Brussels, Belgium

ELI LILLY & CO   307 E McCarty St, Indianapolis, IN 46285, Tel: (317) 261-2000
  (Pharms, agric & cosmetic prdts)
    Eli Lilly Benelux S.A., Rue de L'Etuve 52, 1000 Brussels, Belgium

LINTAS:WORLDWIDE   1 Dag Hammarskjold Plaza, New York, NY 10017,
  Tel: (212) 605-8000
  (Advertising agency)
    Lintas:Brussels, Avenue de Tervuren 168, 1150 Brussels, Belgium

LITTLE GIANT PRODUCTS INC   201 W Oklahoma, Fairview, OK 73737,
  Tel: (405) 227-3711
  (Lift truck attachments, tractor sweepers, etc)
    Little Giant Europe S.A. N.V., Dennenlaan 8, 2340 Beerse, Belgium

ARTHUR D LITTLE INC   25 Acorn Park, Cambridge, MA 02140-2390,
  Tel: (617) 864-5770
  (Technology & mgmt consulting)
    Arthur D. Little Intl. Inc., Blvd. de la Woluwe 2, B-1150 Brussels, Belgium

LORAL INTL INC   999 Central Park Ave, Yonkers, NY 10704, Tel: (914) 964-6520
  (Comm sys, computers, instru equip)
    Loral Intl. Belgium Services Ltd., 22nd Log Wing. Bldg B35, Rue de la Fuesse 70,
      1130 Brussels, Belgium

(cont)

Loral Intl., Belgian Svcs. Ltd., 22nd Log Wing Bldg., B35 Rue de la Fuesse, 70, 1130 Brussels, Belgium

LUBRIZOL CORP   29400 Lakeland Blvd, Wickliffe, OH 44092, Tel: (216) 943-4200
(Chem additives for lubricants & fuels)
Lubrizol S.A., Avenue de Broqueville 270, 1200 Brussels, Belgium

LYKES BROS STEAMSHIP CO INC   Lykes Center, 300 Poydras St, New Orleans, LA 70130, Tel: (504) 523-6611
(Ocean frt trans)
Lykes Lines Agency Inc., Antwerp Tower, DeKeyserlei, 5- Bus 18, 2000 Antwerp, Belgium

MAGNETROL INTERNATIONAL   5300 Belmont Rd, Downers Grove, IL 60515-4499, Tel: (708) 969-4000
(Mfr level & flow process instru)
Magnetrol Intl. NV, Heikensstraat 6, B-9140 Zele, Belgium

MAND CARPET MILLS   2310 East 52nd St, Vernon, CA 90058, Tel: (213) 589-6901
(Tufted carpeting)
Jatex Mand S.A., Bissegemstraat 59, 8710 Heule, Belgium

MANPOWER INC   5301 N Ironwood Rd, PO Box 2053, Milwaukee, WI 53201-2053, Tel: (414) 961-1000
(Temporary help)
Manpower (Belgium) S.A., Rue du Lexembourg 13, 1040 Brussels, Belgium

MANUFACTURERS & TRADERS TRUST CO   654 Madison Ave, New York, NY 10021, Tel: (212) 832-8300
(Bank)
Manufacturers Hanover Trust Co., Rue de Ligne 13, 1000 Brussels, Belgium

MANVILLE CORP   PO Box 5108, Denver, CO 80217-5108, Tel: (303) 978-2000
(Mfr fiber glass prdts, paper & forest prdts, roofing & insulation material, ind minerals)
Johns-Manville Belgium N.V., Langerbruggestraat, B-9000 Ghent, Belgium
Johns-Manville Belgium N.V., Donck, B-2400 Mol, Belgium

MARS INC   6885 Elm St, McLean, VA 22101, Tel: (703) 821-4900
(Mfr candy, snack foods, cat food)
Mars Chocolate Belgium S.A., Rue des Palais 116, 1030 Brussels, Belgium

MARSH & McLENNAN COS INC   1221 Ave of the Americas, New York, NY 10020-1011, Tel: (212) 997-2000
(Insurance)
Henrijean N.V., Bd. du Souverain 2, 1170 Brussels, Belgium

MARSTELLER INTL   1 E Wacker Dr, Chicago, IL 60601, Tel: (312) 329-1100
(Advertising, marketing research, sales promotion)
Burson-Marsteller S.A., 225 Avenue Louise, Box 5, 1050 Brussels, Belgium

MAXON CORP   201 E 18th St, Muncie, IN 47302, Tel: (317) 284-3304
(Ind combustion equip & valves)
Maxon Intl. S.A., Luchthavenlaan 16-18, 1800 Vilvoorde, Belgium

MCI INTERNATIONAL   2 International Dr, Rye Brook, NY 10573,
  Tel: (914) 937-3444
  (Intl telecom servs)
    SA MCI Intl. (Belgium) NV, 391 Ave. Louise- Box 14, 1050 Brussels, Belgium

MEDTRONIC INC   7000 Central Ave, NE, Minneapolis, MN 55432,
  Tel: (612) 574-4000
  (Mfr med devices, med serv)
    Medtronic Belgium S.A., Blvd. Bischoffsheim 39, Bte. 11, 1000 Brussels, Belgium

MELROE CO   112 North University Dr, Fargo, ND 58102, Tel: (701) 241-8700
  (Mfr heavy equip)
    Melroe Europe, J. Huysmanslaan 59, 1660 Beersel (Lot), Belgium

MERCK SHARP & DOHME INTL   PO Box 2000, Rahway, NJ 07065, Tel: (201) 574-4000
  (Pharms, chems & biologicals)
    Merck, Sharp & Dohme Belgium, Chaussee de Waterloo 1135, 1180 Brussels, Belgium

MERGENTHALER LINOTYPE CO   201 Old Country Rd, Melville, NY 11747,
  Tel: (516) 673-4197
  (Photocomposition machs, sys & equip)
    Linotype Intl. S.A., 187 Rue du Biplan, 1140 Brussels, Belgium

MERRILL LYNCH PIERCE FENNER & SMITH   World Financial Center, 225 Liberty St,
  New York, NY 10080, Tel: (212) 449-1000
  (Brokers, securities, commodities)
    Merrill Lynch S.A., 221 Avenue Louise, 1050 Brussels, Belgium

METCO DIV OF PERKIN-ELMER   1101 Prospect Ave, Westbury, NY 11590,
  Tel: (516) 334-1300
  (Mfr/serv thermal spray coating equip & supplies)
    Metco Belgium N.V., Hoogmolendijk 2, B-2120 Schoten/Antwerp, Belgium

MICROMERITICS INSTRUMENT CORP   One Micromeritics Dr, Norcross,
  GA 30093-1877, Tel: (404) 662-3620
  (Mfr analytical instruments)
    N.V. Micromeritics SA, Excelsiorlaan 59, Bus 2, Zaventem, B-1930 Brussels, Belgium

MIDLAND INC   PO Box 1193, Fort Wayne, IN 46801, Tel: (219) 432-3533
  (Export mgt)
    Midland Europe, Europark Noord 1, B-2700 Sint-Niklaas, Belgium

MIDWEST RUBBER RECLAIMING CO   345 Hudson St, New York, NY 10014,
  Tel: (212) 741-8500
  (Reclaimed rubber & custom mixing)
    UMAC-Midwest N.V., Vulkaanstraat 11, 2710 Hoboken, Belgium

MILLIPORE CORP   Ashley Rd, Bedford, MA 01730, Tel: (617) 275-9205
  (Precision filters)
    Millipore Benelux S.A.N.V., 10 Heliotropes Avenue, 1030 Brussels, Belgium

MOBIL CORP   150 E 42nd St, New York, NY 10017, Tel: (212) 883-4242
  (Petroleum explor, prdts)
    S.A. Mobiloil N.V., Place de Louvain 4, 1000 Brussels, Belgium

MONROE AUTO EQUIPMENT CO   International Dr, Monroe, MI 48161,
  Tel: (313) 243-8000
  (Automotive ride control equip)
    Monroe Auto Equipment Intl. S.A., 56 Rue A. de Boeck, 1140 Brussels, Belgium
    Monroe Belgium N.V., Schuurhovenveld, B-3800 St. Truiden, Belgium

MONSANTO CO   800 N Lindbergh Blvd, St Louis, MO 63167, Tel: (314) 694-1000
  (Mfr chem & agric prdts, pharms, ind process equip, man-made fibers, plastics)
    Louvain-la-Neuve Monsanto Technical Center, Rue Laid Burniat,
      B-1348 Louvain-le-Neuve, Belgium
    Monsanto Europe SA (MESA), Ave. de Tervuren 270-272, P.O. Box 1, B-1150 Brussels,
      Belgium

SAMUEL MOORE GROUP   1199 S Cillicothe Rd, Aurora, OH 44202,
  Tel: (216) 562-9111
  (Mfr hose, tubing, wire, cables)
    Samuel Moore Europe, S.A., 100 Chaussee de Tirlemont, 5800 Gelbloux, Belgium

MOREHOUSE INDUSTRIES INC   1600 W Commonwealth Ave, Fullerton, CA 92634,
  Tel: (714) 738-5000
  (Speed mixing & dispersing equip)
    Morehouse-Cowles Intl. S.A., Parc Industriel, 4822 Petit-Rechain, Belgium

MORGAN GUARANTY TRUST CO   23 Wall St, New York, NY 10015, Tel: (212) 483-2323
  (Banking)
    Morgan Guaranty Trust Co., Frankrijklei 82, 2000 Antwerp, Belgium
    Morgan Guaranty Trust Co. of NY, Avenue des Arts 35, 1040 Brussels, Belgium

MORTON INTERNATIONAL INC   100 N Riverside Plaza, Chicago, IL 60606,
  Tel: (312) 807-2000
  (Mfr adhesives, coatings, finishes, spec chems, advanced & electr materials, auto
  safety prdts)
    N.V. Morton Intl. S.A., Chaussee de la Hulpe 130, B-1050 Brussels, Belgium
    N.V. Morton Intl. S.A., Wipstraat 5, B-2100 Brasschaat (Antwerp), Belgium
    N.V. Morton Intl. S.A., Gremelsloweg 120, B-3680 Maaseik, Belgium

MOSTEK CORP   1215 W Crosby Rd, Carrollton, TX 75006, Tel: (214) 466-6000
  (Integrated circuits, micro computer sys, semiconductors, etc)
    Mostek Intl., Ave. de Tervuren 270-272, Bte 21, B-1150 Brussels, Belgium

MOTOROLA INC   1303 E Algonquin Rd, Schaumburg, IL 60196, Tel: (708) 397-5000
  (Mfr commun equip, semiconductors, cellular phones)
    S.A. Motorola N.V., Chaussee de la Hulpe 178, 1170 Brussels, Belgium

MSI DATA CORP   340 Fischer Ave, Costa Mesa, CA 92626, Tel: (714) 549-6000
  (Portable data entry terminals)
    MSI Data Intl., 225 Avenue Louise, Bte 10, 1050 Brussels, Belgium

MULTIGRAPHICS DIV   1800 W Central Rd, Mt Prospect, IL 60056,
  Tel: (708) 398-1900
  (Offset duplicating & graphic commun sys)
    AM Intl., Rue des Chevaliers, 18, B-1050 Brussels, Belgium

McCANN-ERICKSON WORLDWIDE   750 Third Ave, New York, NY 10017,
  Tel: (212) 697-6000
  (Advertising)
    McCann-Erickson Co. S.A., 122 Chaussee de la Hulpe, 1050 Brussels, Belgium

Universal Advertising Team, 49 Britselei, 2000 Antwerp, Belgium
Universal Communication, 22 Gorenenborgerlaan, 2610 Wilrijk, Belgium

McGRAW-HILL INC   1221 Ave of the Americas, New York, NY 10020,
  Tel: (212) 512-2000
  (Books, magazines, info sys, financial serv, b/cast operations)
    DRI Europe Inc., Ave. Louise 221, Boite 5, B-1050 Brussels, Belgium
    Standard & Poor's Intl., S.A., 45 Blvd. Bischoffsheim, B-1000 Brussels, Belgium

McKINSEY & CO INC   55 E 52nd St, New York, NY 10022, Tel: (212) 909-8400
  (Mgmt consultants)
    McKinsey & Co., 18, Square de Meetus, 1040 Brussels, Belgium

NABISCO BRANDS INC   Nabisco Brands Plaza, East Hanover, NJ 07936,
  Tel: (201) 503-2000
  (Mfr food prdts)
    Van Nelle's Import-en Export MIJ B.V., Ernest van Dijekkaai 10, Bus 7,
      B-2000 Antwerp, Belgium

NASH INTL CO   310 Wilson Ave, Norwalk, CT 06856, Tel: (203) 852-5700
  (Mfr vacuum pumps & compressors)
    Nash de Belgique S.A., Chaussee de lirlemont 70, 5800 Gembloux, Belgium

NASHUA CORP   44 Franklin St, Nashua, NH 03061, Tel: (603) 880-2323
  (Mfr/distr/serv office copier sys & supplies)
    Nashua Belgium S.A., Brusselsesteenweg 345, 1900 Overijse, Belgium

NATIONAL CHEMSEARCH CORP   2727 Chemsearch Blvd, Irving, TX 75061,
  Tel: (214) 438-0211
  (Commercial chem prdts)
    National Chemsearch Benelux S.A., Rue de Bavay 109, 1800 Vilvoorde, Belgium

NATIONAL FORGE CO   Front St, Rt No 6, Irvine, PA 16329, Tel: (814) 563-7522
  (Forged & cast steel)
    National Forge Europe N.V., Industriepark 7, 2700 Sint-Niklass, Belgium

NATIONAL GYPSUM CO   4500 Lincoln Plaza, Dallas, TX 75201, Tel: (214) 740-4500
  (Building prdts & servs)
    N.V. Austin Belgium S.A., Brussels, Belgium

NATIONAL SEMICONDUCTOR CORP   2900 Semiconductor Dr, Santa Clara, CA 95051,
  Tel: (408) 721-5000
  (Semiconductors, computers & point-of-sale sys)
    National Semiconductor, Vorstiaan 100, B-1170 Brussels, Belgium

NCR CORP   1700 S Patterson Blvd, Dayton, OH 45479, Tel: (513) 445-2000
  (Develop/mfr/sell/serv business info processing sys)
    NCR Belgium S.A., Rue de la Fusee 50, B-1130 Brussels, Belgium

NEW BRUNSWICK SCIENTIFIC CO INC   44 Talmadge Rd, Edison, NJ 08818-4005,
  Tel: (201) 287-1200
  (Mfr research & production equip for life sciences)
    New Brunswick Scientific N.V./S.A., Tinklaan 2, B-1160 Brussels, Belgium

NIBCO CORP   500 Simpson Ave, PO Box 1167, Elkhart, IN 46515,
  Tel: (219) 295-3000
  (Pipe fittings, plumbing & heating valves)
    Nibco Inc. S.A., Avenue du Centre Sportif 49, 1300 Wavre, Belgium

NICO INC   345 Hudson St, New York, NY 10014, Tel: (212) 620-8200
  (Constr mgt, contracting & consult servs)
    Nico Construction PLC, Tour Louise, 149 Avenue Louise 102- 15/F, B-1050 Brussels,
      Belgium

NICOLET INSTRUMENT CORP   5225 Verona Rd, Madison, WI 53711-4495,
  Tel: (608) 271-3333
  (Mfr infrared spectrometers, oscilloscopes, med electro-diag equip)
    Nicolet Instrument Benelux, Ave. Paul Humanslaan 103, BT 12, 1200 Brussels, Belgium

A C NIELSEN CO   Nielsen Plaza, Northbrook, IL 60062, Tel: (708) 498-6300
  (Marketing research)
    A.C. Nielsen Co. (Belgium) S.A., Avenue des Arts 56, B-1040, Brussels, Belgium

NORDSON CORP   28601 Clemens Rd, Westlake, OH 44145, Tel: (216) 892-1580
  (Mfr ind application equip & packaging mach)
    Nordson Belgium S.A., Industrieterrein Zaventem-Zuid, Hoge Wei 37, Weiveld,
      1930 Zaventem (Nassegem), Belgium

NORTHERN TELECOM SYSTEMS CORP   PO Box 1222, Minneapolis, MN 55440,
  Tel: (612) 932-8000
  (Remote information processing sys)
    S.A. Data 100 N.V., Rue de la Fussee 100, B-15, 1130 Brussels, Belgium

NORTON CO   1 New Bond St, Worcester, MA 01606, Tel: (508) 795-5000
  (Abrasives, drill bits, constr & safety prdts, plastics)
    Norton Belgique S.A., Allee Verte 11, B-1000 Brussels, Belgium
    Norton S.A.N.V., Zoning Industriel de Petit, Rechain, Avenue' du Parc,
      B-4655 Chaineux, Belgium

NORWICH EATON PHARMACEUTICALS INC   17 Eaton Ave, Norwich, NY 13815,
  Tel: (607) 335-2111
  (Mfr pharms, chems, health prdts)
    Norwich Benelux S.A., Rue de la Science 7, Boite 2, 1040 Brussels, Belgium

NYNEX CORP   1113 Westchester Ave, White Plains, NY 10604, Tel: (914) 397-1200
  (Telecom & info servs)
    NYNEX Network Systems Co., Avenue Louise 106, 1050 Brussels, Belgium

OCCIDENTAL PETROLEUM CORP   10889 Wilshire Blvd, Los Angeles, CA 90024,
  Tel: (213) 879-1700
  (Petroleum & petroleum prdts, chems, plastics)
    Occidental Petroleum Belgium N.V., Frankfyklei 39, 2000 Antwerp, Belgium

OFFICE PUBLICATIONS INC   1600 Summer, Stamford, CT 06905-5112,
  Tel: (203) 327-9670
  (Publications on office equip & computer subjects)
    Office Publications Inc., Rue Veydt 65, 1050 Brussels, Belgium

OGILVY & MATHER INC   2 E 48th St, New York, NY 10017, Tel: (212) 907-3400
  (Advertising agency)
    HHD Ogilvy & Mather S.A., Avenue Louise 489, 1050 Brussels, Belgium

OLIN CORP   120 Long Ridge Rd, Stamford, CT 06904-1355, Tel: (203) 356-2000
(Chems, metals, applied physics in elect, defense, aerospace inds)
Olin Hunt Specialty Products, Euro Park Noord, 21-22 B-2700, St. Niklaas, Belgium,
Belgium

OMARK INDUSTRIES INC   5550 SW Macadam Ave, Portland, OR 97201,
Tel: (503) 796-1400
(Mfr chain & accessories for chain saws, welding equip, power tools)
Omark Europe S.A., Nouvelle Rue de Buisson des Loups, Zone Industrial,
B-1400 Nivelles, Belgium

ON-LINE SOFTWARE INTL INC   2 Executive Dr, Fort Lee, NJ 07024,
Tel: (201) 592-0009
(Software & related servs; consult & educ servs)
On-Line Software Benelux, Ltd., 221 Avenue Louise, 1050 Brussels, Belgium

ONAN CORP   1400 73rd Ave NE, Minneapolis, MN 55432, Tel: (612) 574-5000
(Electric generators, ind engines & controls)
Onan Corp., Werkhuizen Dutry, Brugse Steenweg 512, B-8800 Roeselare, Belgium

ORCHARD MACHINERY CORP   2700 Colusa Hwy, Yuba City, CA 95991,
Tel: (916) 673-2822
(Mfr tree/orchard equip)
Orchard Continental N.V., Luitenant Lippenslaan 66, 2200 Borgerhout, Belgium

OTIS ELEVATOR CO   10 Farm Springs, Farmington, CT 06032, Tel: (203) 674-4047
(Elevators & escalators)
Ascenseurs Otis S.A., Schepen A. Gossetlaan 17, B-1720 Groot-Bljgaarden, Belgium

OUTBOARD MARINE CORP   100 Sea Horse Dr, Waukegan, IL 60085,
Tel: (708) 689-6200
(Outboard & rotary motors, stern engines, marine parts & accessories)
OMC Europe, Pathoekweg 72, 8000 Brugge 1, Belgium

OVERSEAS NATIONAL AIRWAYS INC   Kennedy Intl Airport, Jamaica, NY 11430,
Tel: (212) 632-8200
(Air carrier)
Overseas National Airways S.A., Centre Intl. Rogier 1709, 1000 Brussels, Belgium

OWENS-CORNING FIBERGLAS CORP   PO Box 901, Fiberglas Tower, Toledo, OH 43659,
Tel: (419) 248-8000
(Mfr insulation, building materials, glass fiber prdts)
European Owens-Corning Fiberglas (Belgium), Belgium
N.V. Owens-Corning S.A., Battice, Belgium

PACCAR INTL   10604 NE 38th Place, Kirkland, WA 98033, Tel: (206) 828-8872
(Heavy duty dump trucks, military vehicles)
Paccar AG, 141 Rue St. Lambert, Boite 5, 1200 Brussels, Belgium

PACKAGING CORP OF AMERICA   1603 Orrington Ave, Evanston, IL 60204,
Tel: (708) 492-5713
(Mfr custom packaging, aluminum & plastic molded fibre, corrugated containers)
Ekco N.V., Henry Fordlaan 60, P.O. Box 65, 3600 Genk, Belgium

PANDUIT CORP   17301 Ridgeland Ave, Tinley Park, IL 60477, Tel: (708) 532-1800
(Mfr elec/electr wiring comps)
Panduit S.A. (PB, Avenue de la Liberte, 80, 1080 Brussels, Belgium

PARAMOUNT INTL FILMS INC   1 Gulf & Western Plaza, New York, NY 10023,
  Tel: (212) 333-4600
  (Film prod & distr)
    Films Paramount Universal S.A., Rue Royale 217, Brussels, Belgium

PARKER HANNIFIN CORP   17325 Euclid Ave, Cleveland, OH 44112,
  Tel: (216) 531-3000
  (Mfr motion-control prdts)
    Parker Hannifin-Schrader Bellows, Rue du Champ de la Couronne 29, B-1020 Brussels,
    Belgium

PEARLSON ENGINEERING CO   8970 SW 87th Ct, Miami, FL 33156,
  Tel: (305) 271-5721
  (Drydocks & transfer sys)
    General Engineering & Trading Co., Frankrijklei 70, 2000 Antwerp, Belgium

PFIZER INC   235 E 42nd St, New York, NY 10017, Tel: (212) 573-2323
  (Mfr pharms, hosp prdts, chems, consumer & animal health prdts)
    Pfizer S.A., Rue Leon Theodor 102, B-1090 Brussels, Belgium

PHELPS DODGE CORP   2600 N Central Ave, Phoenix, AZ 85004-3014,
  Tel: (602) 234-8100
  (Minerals, metals & spec engineered prdts for trans & elect mkts)
    Hudson Intl. Conductors Europe, Eeuwfeeststraat 2, 2670 Puurs, Belgium

PHILLIPS PETROLEUM CO   Phillips Bldg, Bartlesville, OK 74004,
  Tel: (918) 661-6600
  (Crude oil, natural gas, liquefied petroleum gas, gasoline & petro-chems)
    Phillips Petroleum Intl. Benelux S.A., Steeweg op, Brussels 355, 1900 Overijse,
    Belgium

PITTSBURGH CORNING CORP   800 Presque Isle Dr, Pittsburgh, PA 15239,
  Tel: (412) 327-6100
  (Mfr glass block, cellular glass insulation)
    Pittsburgh Corning Europe S.A., Avenue de Tervueren 32-38, 1040 Brussels, Belgium

PLIBRICO CO   1800 Kingsbury St, Chicago, IL 60614, Tel: (312) 549-7014
  (Refractories, engineering, constr)
    Plibrico (Belgium) S.A.N.V., Rue Arthur Maes 65, 1130 Brussels, Belgium

POLAROID CORP   549 Technology Sq, Cambridge, MA 02139, Tel: (617) 577-2000
  (Photographic and optical prdts)
    Polaroid S.A., Rue du Colonel Bourg 113, 1140 Brussels, Belgium

R L POLK & CO   1155 Brewery Park Blvd, Detroit, MI 48207-2697,
  Tel: (313) 961-9470
  (Directories, direct mail advertising)
    R.L. Polk & Co. S.A., Pieter Michielsstraat 31, 1610 Ruisbroek, Belgium

PREMARK INTL INC   1717 Deerfield Rd, Deerfield, IL 60015, Tel: (708) 405-6000
  (Mfr/sale diversified consumer & coml prdts)
    Dart Industries Belgium NV, 35 Pierre Corneliskaai, Aalst, Belgium

PROCTER & GAMBLE CO   One Procter & Gamble Plaza, Cincinnati, OH 45202,
  Tel: (513) 983-1100
  (Personal care, food, laundry, cleaning & ind prdts)
    Procter & Gamble Benelux, Rue Philippe-le-Bon 1, 1040 Brussels, Belgium

PRUDENTIAL INSURANCE CO OF AMERICA   Prudential Plaza, Newark, NJ 07101,
  Tel: (201) 877-6000
  (Life ins, health ins, annuities)
    Le Rocher Compagnie de Reassurance S.A., Arts Lux Building, Mezzanine Floor,
      Avenue des Arts 58, 1040 Brussels, Belgium

PUROLATOR COURIER CORP   131 Morristown Rd, Basking Ridge, NJ 07980,
  Tel: (201) 953-6400
  (Time-sensitive package delivery)
    Belgium Executive Air Express S.A., Brussels, Belgium

PYRONICS INC   17700 Miles Ave, Cleveland, OH 44128, Tel: (216) 662-8800
  (Mfr combustion equip, gas & oil burners)
    Pyronics Intl. S.A., Zoning Industriel de Jumet, 4-EME Rue 6040, Jumet, Belgium

RALSTON PURINA CO   Checkerboard Sq, St Louis, MO 63164, Tel: (214) 982-1000
  (Poultry & live stock feed, cereals, food prdts)
    Purina Protein Europe N.V., Zwaankofweg 1, 8900 Ieper, Belgium

RAYTHEON CO   141 Spring St, Lexington, MA 02173, Tel: (617) 862-6600
  (Mfr diversified electronics & apppliances; aviation, ind & constr services,
  publishing)
    Raytheon Overseas Ltd., Avenue Franklin D. Roosevelt 81, 1050 Brussels, Belgium

RCA GLOBAL COMMUNICATIONS INC   60 Broad St, New York, NY 10004,
  Tel: (212) 806-7000
  (Commun serv)
    RCA S.A., 1120 Chussee de Ninove, Brussels, Belgium

READER'S DIGEST ASSOCIATION INC   PO Box 235, Pleasantville, NY 10570,
  Tel: (914) 238-1000
  (Global publisher & direct mail marketer)
    Reader's Digest World Services S.A., 29 Quai du Hainaut, 1080 Brussels, Belgium

RELIANCE ELECTRIC CO   24701 Euclid Ave, Cleveland, OH 44117,
  Tel: (216) 266-7000
  (Equip & sys for ind automation, telecom equip)
    Toledo S. A., Frans Walravens Straat 84, 1660 Beersel (Lot) Belgium

RELIANCE UNIVERSAL INC   1600 Watterson Tower, 1930 Bishop Lange, Louisville,
  KY 40218, Tel: (502) 459-9110
  (Commercial highway & off-highway trailers, truck & trailer bodies)
    Reliance Universal N.V., 11 Generaal de Wittelaan, 2800 Mechelen,Belgium

RENA-WARE DISTRIBUTORS INC   222 112 NE St, Bellevue, WA 98004,
  Tel: (206) 453-2300
  (Cookware & china)
    Rena Ware Distributors S.A., Rue de Brabant 62-66, 1000 Brussels, Belgium

RESEARCH-COTTRELL COS   PO Box 1500, Somerville, NJ 08876, Tel: (201) 685-4000
  (Design/install air pollution control equip; tech servs)
    Research-Cottrell Belgium S.A., Chaussee Paul Houtart 88, 7070 LaLouviere, Belgium

REVLON INC   767 Fifth Ave, New York, NY 10153-0033, Tel: (212) 572-5000
  (Cosmetics, health care prdts)
    Revlon S.A., Avenue Michel-Ange 8, 1040 Brussels, Belgium

RICHARDSON-VICKS INC   Ten Westport Rd, Wilton, CT 06897, Tel: (203) 834-5000
(Consumer health & personal care prdts)
  Richardson-Vicks S.A., 868-870 Chaussee de Waterloo, B-1180 Brussels, Belgium

RIDGE TOOL CO   400 Clark St, Elyria, OH 44035, Tel: (216) 323-5581
(Hand & power tools for working pipe, drain cleaning equip, etc)
  Ridge Tool Europe N.V., Heverlee, Near Leuven, Belgium

RIGHT ASSOCIATES   1818 Market St, 14th Fl, Philadelphia, PA 19103-3614,
 Tel: (215) 988-1588
(Outplacement & human resources consult servs)
  Right Associates, Avenue Maurice 1, B-1050 Brussels, Belgium

ROBERT HALF INTL INC   2884 Sand Hill Rd, #200, Menlo Park, CA 94025,
 Tel: (415) 854-9700
(Personnel servs)
  Robert Half Intl., Inc., Fontaine Archer Van de Voorde, Ave. Louise 382,
    1050 Brussels, Belgium
  Robert Half- Brussels, Avenue Louise 382, 1050 Brussels, Belgium

ROCHESTER GAUGES INC   PO Box 29242, Dallas, TX 75229-0242,
 Tel: (214) 241-2161
(Liquid-level gauges, level switches, pressured gauges, electric panel gauges, etc)
  Rochester Gauges Intl. S.A., 972 Chauss Rue de Louvain, 1140 Brussels, Belgium

ROGERS CORP   One Technology Dr, Rogers, CT 06263, Tel: (203) 774-9605
(Mfr flexible, molded, die-stamped & microwave circuits; engineered polymer prdts)
  Mektron N.V., Afrikalaan 188, 9000 Gent, Belgium

ROHM & HAAS CO   Independence Mall West, Philadelphia, PA 19105,
 Tel: (215) 592-3000
(Mfr ind & agric chems, plastics)
  Rohm & Hass Benelux, Noorderlaan 111, B-9, 2030 Antwerp, Belgium

RORER GROUP INC   500 Virginia Dr, Ft Washington, PA 19034,
 Tel: (215) 628-6000
(Mfr ethical & consumer pharms)
  Pharbil-Rorer S.A., Brussels, Belgium

ROSEMOUNT INC   12001 Technology Dr, Eden Prairie, MN 55344,
 Tel: (612) 941-5560
(Mfr aerospace & ind instrumentation)
  Rosemount NV/SA, Excelsiorlaan 43, 1930 Zaventem, Belgium

RUSSELL CORP   PO Box 272, Alexander City, AL 35010, Tel: (205) 329-4000
(Mfr athletic & leisure apparel)
  Russell Intl. N.V., Baron de Vironlaan 2, 1710 Dilbeek, Brussels, Belgium

SAMSONITE CORP   11200 E 45th St, Denver, CO 80239, Tel: (303) 373-7159
(Mfr luggage & leather goods)
  Samsonite N.V., Westerring 17, 9700 Oudenaarde, Belgium

SCHLEGEL CORP   400 East Ave, Rochester, NY 14607, Tel: (716) 546-6260
(Engineered perimeter sealing systems for residential & commercial constr)
  Schlegel S.A. N.V., Industrie Zone, Rochesterlaan, 8240 Gistel, Belgium

SCHRADER BELLOWS DIV   200 W Exchange St, Akron, OH 44309, Tel: (216) 375-1263
(Pneumatic & hydraulic valves & cylinders, FRL units & accessories)
  Schrader Bellows N.V., Rue de la Procession 50, 1070 Brussels, Belgium

A SCHULMAN INC   3550 W Market St, Akron, OH 44313, Tel: (216) 666-3751
(Mfr/sale plastic resins & compounds)
  N.V. A. Schulman Plastics S.A., Industriepark, 2680 Bornem, Belgium

SCIENCE MANAGEMENT CORP   PO Box 0600, Basking Ridge, NJ 07920,
Tel: (201) 647-7000
(Human/mgmt resources, info technology, engr & technology services)
  SMC Intl. S.A., 66 Rue de Livourne, 1050 Brussels, Belgium

SCM CORP   299 Park Ave, New York, NY 10171, Tel: (212) 752-2700
(Business equip, chems, coatings & resins, foods, paper prdts)
  SCM Europe S.A., Belgium

SCOTT WORLDWIDE INC   Scott Plaza, Philadelphia, PA 19113, Tel: (215) 521-5000
(Paper & paper prdts, bleached pulp)
  Scott Graphics Intl. Div., Belgium

SEALED AIR CORP   Park 80 Plaza E, Saddle Brook, NJ 07662-5291,
Tel: (201) 791-7600
(Mfr protective packaging prdts)
  Sealed Air N.V., Brgensesteenweg 709, 1600 Sint Pieters Leeuw, Belgium

G D SEARLE & CO   PO Box 1045, Skokie, IL 60076, Tel: (708) 982-7000
(Pharms, health care & optical prdts, specialty chems)
  Laboratories Searle S.A., Avenue Van Becelaere 28B, 1170 Brussels, Belgium

SENSORMATIC ELECTRONICS CORP   500 NW 12th Ave, Deerfield Beach, BF L33341,
Tel: (305) 427-9700
(Electronic article surveillance equip)
  Senelco (Benelux) S.A., Ave. du Roi Albert 177, Bte. 12, 1080 Brussels, Belgium

SHAKESPEARE FISHING TACKLE GROUP   611 Shakespeare Rd, Columbia, SC 29204,
Tel: (803) 754-7000
(Mfr fishing tackle)
  Noris Shakespeare S.A., 10 Rue du Parc, Parc Industrial, B4430 Alleur, Belgium

SHEARSON/AMERICAN EXPRESS   American Express Tower, New York, NY 10285,
Tel: (212) 298-2000
(Investment banking, financial serv)
  Shearson/American Express, 368 Avenue Louise, Brussels, Belgium

SIGNODE PACKAGING SYSTEMS   3600 W Lake Ave, Glenview, IL 60025,
Tel: (708) 724-6100
(Mfr packaging systems)
  Signode SA/NV, E40 Business Park, Sterrebeekstraat 179 - DI & DE, 1930 Zaventem,
  Belgium

SIMPLEX TIME RECORDER CO   Simplex Plaza, Gardner, MA 01441,
Tel: (617) 632-2500
(Time recorders & stamps, master time sys, alarm, security, monitor & control sys)
  Simplex Time Recorder Co., 20 Ave. Clays, 1030 Brussels, Belgium

SONOCO PRODUCTS CO   North Second St, PO Box 160, Hartsville, SC 29550,
  Tel: (803) 383-7000
  (Mfr packaging for consumer & ind mkt)
    Sonoco Europe, 185 Chausee de la Hulpe, 1170 Brussels, Belgium

SOUTHWESTERN PETROLEUM CORP   534 N Main, Fort Worth, TX 76106,
  Tel: (817) 332-2336
  (Mfr roofing/bldg maint prdts & ind lubricants)
    Southwestern Petroleum Europe S.A., P.O. Box 3, B-2150 Oostmalle, Belgium

SPECTOR GROUP   3111 New Hyde Park Rd, North Hills, Ny 11040,
  Tel: (516) 365-4240
  (Arch & interior design servs)
    Spector Group/ Croigny, Galerie Louise 43b, Bte. 45, 1050 Brussels, Belgium

SPRAGUE ELECTRIC CO   87 Marshall St, North Adams, MA 01247,
  Tel: (413) 664-4411
  (Electronic components)
    Sprague Electromaq Belgium S.A., 2 Rue de Merode, B-9600 Ronse, Belgium

SPRINGS INDUSTRIES INC   205 N White St, Fort Mill, SC 29715,
  Tel: (803) 547-2901
  (Mfr & sales finished fabrics, home furnishings, ind fabrics)
    Clark-Schwebel Intl, S.A., Rue Chesse Roux, 23, 4651 Battice, Belgium

THE STANLEY WORKS   1000 Stanley Dr, PO Box 7000, New Britain, CT 06050,
  Tel: (203) 225-5111
  (Mfr hand tools & hardware)
    Stanley Works Belgium N.V., Dickstraat 9 P.B. 34, 9100 Lokeren, Belgium

STATE STREET BANK & TRUST CO   225 Franklin St, Boston, MA 02101,
  Tel: (617) 786-3000
  (Banking servs)
    State Street London Ltd., 36-38 Rue Joseph II, 1040 Brussels, Belgium

STERLING DRUG INC   90 Park Ave, New York, NY 10016, Tel: (212) 907-2000
  (Pharms, chems, cosmetics, household cleaners & waxes)
    Laboratories Winthrop S.A., Rue Franz Merjay 103, 1060 Brussels, Belgium

STONE CONTAINER CORP   150 N Michigan Ave, Chicago, IL 60601-7568,
  Tel: (312) 346-6600
  (Mfr paper & paper packaging)
    Cartomills SA, Route de Douvrain 19-B-7410, Ghlin, Belgium

SUN ELECTRIC CORP   One Sun Pkwy, Crystal Lake, IL 60014, Tel: (815) 459-7700
  (Mfr auto tune-up, diagnostic & emission testing equip)
    Sun Electric (Belgium) N.V., 24 Gall, Fortlei , B-2100, Deurne-Antwerp, Belgium

SUNDSTRAND CORP   PO Box 7003, Rockford, IL 61125-7003, Tel: (815) 226-6000
  (Design/mfr proprietary technology based comps & sub-sys for aerospace & ind)
    Sundstrand Intl. Corp. S.A., 8 Avenue Roger V/D Driessche, Box NR 8, 1150 Brussels,
    Belgium

SWECO INC   7120 New Buffington Rd, Florence, KY 41042, Tel: (606) 727-5100
  (Mfr vibratory process & solids control equip)
    Sweco Europe S.A., Parc Industriel,10 Chemin de la Ville, B-1400 Nivelles, Belgium

SWIFT & CO   115 W Jackson Blvd, Chicago, IL 60604, Tel: (312) 431-2000
(Meat & poultry, food prdts)
   Swift & Co. S.A., Frankrljklei 8, Bus. 7, B-2000 Antwerp, Belgium

SYBRON CORP   411 E Wisconsin Ave, Milwaukee, WI 07662, Tel: (414) 274-6600
(Professional health prdts, spec chems, instru, water & waste water treatment sys)
   Gamlen Chemicals, c/o S.A. Taylor Instrument N.V., Maarschalk Gerardstraat 8,
      B-2000 Antwerp, Belgium
   Sybron, Div. of S.A. Taylor Instrument N.V., Avenue Louis, 416- Boite 5,
      B-1050 Brussels, Belgium

SYSTEM INDUSTRIES INC   560 Cottonwood Dr, Milpitas, CA 95035,
Tel: (408) 432-1212
(Value added third party vendor high performance data storage sybsys)
   System Industries Belgium NV, Keibergpark, Minervastraat 16, 1930 Saventem, Belgium

SYSTEMS ENGINEERING LABS INC   6901 W Sunrise Blvd, Fort Lauderdale,
FL 33313, Tel: (305) 587-2900
(Digital computers)
   Systems Engineering Laboratories S.A., 50 Blvd. de la Dodaine, Boite 73,
      1400 Nivelles, Belgium

TANDY CORP   1800 One Tandy Center, Fort Worth, TX 76102, Tel: (817) 390-3700
(Electronic & acoustic equip)
   Tandy Europe, S.A., Rue du Moulin A Papier, 51, 1160 Brussels, Belgium

TAYLOR INSTRUMENT CO   99 Ames St, PO Box 110, Rochester, NY 14601,
Tel: (716) 235-6806
(Instru for process control inds)
   Taylor Instrument N.A., Maar Schalk, Gerardstraat 8, 2000 Antwerp, Belgium

TECHNICON INSTRUMENTS CORP   511 Benedict Ave, Tarrytown, NY 10591-5097,
Tel: (914) 631-8000
(Mfr/serv automated blook anal equip, reagents & diagnostics)
   Compagnie Belge Technicon S.A., Parc Industriel, Heide 15, 1810 Wemmel, Belgium
   Technicon Chemicals Co. S.A., Rue de l'Ancienne Potence, 7501 Orcq-Tournai, Belgium

TED BATES WORLDWIDE INC   1515 Broadway, New York, NY 10036,
Tel: (212) 869-3131
(Advertising agency)
   Coerten S.A., Ave des Phalenes 26. B-1050 Brussels, Belgium
   Ted Bates S.A./NV, Bd St Michel 47, 1040 Brussels, Belgium

TEEPAK INC   3 Westbrook Corp Center, Westchester, IL 60154,
Tel: (708) 409-3000
(Mfr cellulose, fibrous, collegen sausage casings & plastic packaging)
   Teepak Produktie N.V., P.O. Box 57, Industrie Park 17, 3900 Lommel, Belgium

TEKNIS CORP   PO Box 3189, No Attleboro, MA 02761, Tel: (508) 695-3591
(Sale advanced technology prdts, fiber optics, materials for semiconductor mfr)
   Landre Intechmil, Tavernierkaai 2, B-2000 Antwerp, Belgium

TEKTRONIX INC   PO Box 500, Beaverton, OR 97077, Tel: (503) 627-7111
(Mfr test & meas, visual sys & commun prdts)
   Tektronix NV/SA, Zoning Keberg, Excelsuorlsaan 3, 1930 Zaventernsseles, Belgium

TELXON CORP   3330 W Market St, Akron, OH 44333, Tel: (216) 867-3700
(Devel/mfr portable computer sys & related equip)
   Telxon Corp., Chaussee de la Hulpe 150, B-1170 Brussels, Belgium

TEMCO CORP   Electronics Ave, Danvers, MA 01923, Tel: (617) 774-8000
(Components for electr, photo typesetting industry, computers & missiles)
   Temcogas-Vulcana S.A., Avenue du Prince Heritier 176, 1150 Brussels, Belgium

C TENNANT SONS & CO OF NY   PO Box 9300, Minneapolis, MN 55440,
Tel: (612) 475-7340
(Ferrous & non-ferrous minerals, metals, electronic comps)
   Tennco Europe S.A., Rue de Livourne 7, B-1050 Brussels, Belgium

TENNECO AUTOMOTIVE   100 Tri-State Intl, #300, Lincolnshire, IL 60069,
Tel: (708) 948-0900
(Mfr exhaust sys, ride control prdts, brake components)
   Monroe Auto Equipment, 56 Rue Auguste de Boeck, 1140 Brussels, Belgium
   Monroe Belgium N.V., Industry Zone 1, 3800 St. Truiden, Belgium

TEXACO INC   2000 Westchester Ave, White Plains, NY 10650, Tel: (914) 253-4000
(Explor/mktg crude oil & its prdts, petro-chems)
   Texaco Belgium N.V., Avenue Louise 149, B-1050 Brussels, Belgium

TEXTRON INC   40 Westminster St, Providence, RI 02903, Tel: (401) 421-2800
(Mfr aerospace tech & coml prdts; fin servs)
   Textron Atlantic Belgium S.A., Avenue Louise 137, Bte. 6, 1050 Brussels, Belgium

THERMO ELECTRIC CO   109 Fifth St, Saddle Brook, NJ 07062, Tel: (201) 843-5800
(Mfr temp/meas control prdts)
   N.V. Telerex S.A., Kouwenbergdreef 6, 2230 Schilde, Belgium

THOMAS INTL PUBLISHING CO   1 Penn Plaza, New York, NY 10119,
Tel: (212) 290-7213
(Publ ind magazines & directories)
   Intl. Equipment News, N.V., Rue Verte 216, 1210 Brussels, Belgium

THOMPSON AIRCRAFT TIRE CORP   7775 NW 12th St, Miami, FL 33126,
Tel: (305) 592-3530
(Retread aircraft tires, aircraft wheel & brake servicing)
   Thompson Aircraft Tire Corp. Belgium, S.A., Route de Bavay 7230, Frameries, Belgium

TIME WARNER INC   Time Life Bldg, New York, NY 10020, Tel: (212) 522-1212
(Magazine & book publ, communications)
   Time Magazine, Clos du Manoir 9, 1150 Brussels, Belgium

THE TORO CO   8111 Lyndale Ave S, Minneapolis, MN 55420, Tel: (612) 888-8801
(Mfr outdoor beautification prdts)
   Toro Europe, Nijverheidsstraat 26, B-2431 Devel, Belgium

TOWERS PERRIN FORSTER & CROSBY INC   245 Park Ave, New York, NY 10167,
Tel: (212) 309-3400
(Management consulting)
   Towers, Perrin, Forster & Crosby, Inc., Avenue Louise 287, Box 6, 1050 Brussels,
   Belgium

TRACE MOUNTAIN   2190 Bering Dr, San Jose, CA 95131, Tel: (408) 435-7800
(Mfr diskette; tape duplication equip)
   Trace Mountain Europe, Wilrijkstraat 37-45, 2140 Borgerhout, Belgium

TRACOR INC   6500 Tracor Lane, Austin, TX 78721, Tel: (512) 926-2800
(Time & frequency prdts, gas & liquid chromatographs, eng serv, ship repair)
   Olvis, N.V., Achterpad 13-15, 2400 Mol, Belgium

TRANE CO   3600 Pammel Creek Rd, La Crosse, WI 54601, Tel: (608) 787-2000
(Mfr A/C equip)
   Societe Trane S.A., Chaussee de Watermael 38, B-1160 Brussels, Belgium

TRINOVA CORP   3000 Strayer, PO Box 50, Maumee, OH 43537, Tel: (419) 867-2200
(Mfr engr components & sys for ind)
   Aeroquip Benelux NV, Industrieterrein Klein Gent, 2420 Heventals, Belgium

TWIN DISC INC   1328 Racine St, Racine, WI 53403, Tel: (414) 634-1981
(Mfr ind clutches, reduction gears, transmissions)
   Twin Disc Intl. S.A., Chaussee de Namur 54, 1400 Nivelles, Belgium

U S GYPSUM CO   101 S Wacker Dr, Chicago, IL 60606, Tel: (312) 321-4000
(Building & constr materials)
   Gyproc-Benelux S.A., Merksemsebaan 270, 2110-Wijnegan, Belgium

U S INDUSTRIES INC   PO Box 629, Evansville, IN 47704, Tel: (812) 425-2428
(Diversified prdts & sys for industry, agribusiness & retail markets)
   Big Dutchman, Div. S.A. Unifast Manufacturing N.V., Steenweg 151, 9751 Asper,
   Belgium
   Rau Unifast, 1-3 Rue des bas Fossess, Braine le Comte, Belgium

UNION CARBIDE CORP   Old Ridgebury Rd, Danbury, CT 06817, Tel: (203) 794-2000
(Carbon prdts, chems, plastics, gases & related prdts, etc)
   UC Benelux N.V., Noorderlaan 147, B-2030 Antwerp, Belgium
   UC Benelux N.V., Scheldedijk 50, B-2730 Zqijndrecht, Belgium
   UC Benelux N.V., Avenue de la Renaissance 34, B-1040 Brussels, Belgium

UNION ELECTRIC STEEL CORP   PO Box 465, Carnegie, PA 15106,
Tel: (412) 923-1011
(Mfr forged hardened steel rolls)
   Union Electric Steel N.V., Industriepart, 3980 Tessenderlo, Belgium

UNION SPECIAL CORP   222 No LaSalle, Chicago, IL 60601, Tel: (312) 606-9500
(Mfr ind sewing machs)
   Union Special, 90 Rue de la Caserne, B-1000 Brussels, Belgium

UNIROYAL INC   World Headquarters, Middlebury, CT 06749, Tel: (203) 573-2000
(Tires, tubes & other rubber prdts, chems, plastics, textiles)
   Uniroyal Chemical Belgique S.A., Rue Charles Lemaire 1, Bte.4, 1160 Brussels,
   Belgium

UNITED CATALYSTS INC   1227 S 12th St, Louisville, KY 40210,
Tel: (502) 637-9751
(Catalysts for petroleum, chem & food inds)
   United Catalyst & Chemicals Europe S.A., Place du Champ de Mars 2, 1050 Brussels,
   Belgium

UNITED TECHNOLOGIES CORP   United Technologies Bldg, Hartford, CT 06101,
Tel: (203) 728-7000
(Mfr aircraft engines, elevators, A/C, auto equip, space & military electr, rocket
propulsion sys)
    Ascenseurs Otis S.A., Schepen A. Gossetlaan 17, B-1720 Dilbeek, Belgium
    United Technologies Inc., Avenue Lloyd George 7, B-1050 Brussels, Belgium

UOP INC   Ten UOP Plaza, Des Plaines, IL 60016, Tel: (708) 391-2000
(Diversified research, development & mfr of ind prdts & sys mgmt studies & serv)
    UOP Bostrom Belgium S.A., Rue de l'Industrie, 1400 Nivelles, Belgium

UPJOHN CO   7000 Portage Rd, Kalamazoo, MI 49001, Tel: (616) 323-4000
(Pharms, agric prdts, ind chems)
    Upjohn S.A., Lichterstraat, 2670 Kalfort-Puurs, Belgium

VARIAN ASSOCIATES INC   611 Hansen Way, Palo Alto, CA 94304-1030,
Tel: (415) 493-4000
(Mfr microwave tubes & devices, analytical instru, semiconductor process & med equip,
vacuum sys)
    NV Varian Benelux S.A., Excelsior 21, B-1930 Zaventem, Belgium

VF CORP   PO Box 1022, Reading, PA 19603, Tel: (215) 378-1151
(Mfr/mktg apparel)
    Lee Europe N.V., Industriepark-Noord 29, B-2700 Sint-Niklaas, Belgium
    Wrangler Europe S.A., Ave. Louise 66, Box 12, B-1050 Brussels, Belgium

VIRGINIA CHEMICALS INC   3340 W Norfolk Rd, Portsmouth, VA 23703,
Tel: (804) 483-7345
(Ind chems, insecticides, refrigerants, etc)
    VirChem S.A.N.V., Ave. Louise 326, 1050 Brussels, Belgium

VSI CORP   8463 Highera St, Culver City, CA 90232, Tel: (213) 202-8200
(Mold & die makers, diversified prdts for home & ind)
    VSI Intl. N.V., Antwerpsebaan, Industrie Parc Noord, 2800 Mechelen, Belgium

WANG LABORATORIES INC   1 Industrial Ave, Lowell, MA 01851,
Tel: (508) 459-5000
(Mfr computer info processing sys)
    Wang Europe S.A y N.V., 350 Ave. Louise, 1050 Brussels, Belgium

WARD HOWELL INTL INC   99 Park Ave, New York, NY 10016, Tel: (212) 697-3730
(Executive recruiting)
    Ward Howell Intl., Blvd. Saint Michel 56, Bte. 10, 1040 Brussels, Belgium

WARNER BROS INC   4000 Warner Blvd, Burbank, CA 91522, Tel: (213) 954-6000
(Prod/dist motion picture films, TV, music recording & pub)
    Warner Bros. First National Films Inc., Rue Toyale 326, 1030 Brussels, Belgium

WARNER ELECTRIC BRAKE & CLUTCH CO   449 Gardner St, South Beloit, IL 61080,
Tel: (815) 389-3771
(Automotive & ind brakes & clutches)
    Warner Electric S.A., Rue Royale 192, Bte. 39, B-1000 Brussels, Eelgium

WARNER-LAMBERT CO   201 Tabor Road, Morris Plains, NJ 07950,
Tel: (201) 540-2000
(Mfr ethical & proprietary pharms, confectionary & consumer prdts)
    Warner-Lambert Belgium, Excelsiorlaan 75-77, B-1930 Zaventem, Belgium

WATERBURY FARREL   785 W Johnson Ave, Cheshire, CT 06410, Tel: (203) 272-3271
(Machine tools, metal working mach)
    Waterbury Farrel Div., J. Huysmanslaan 59, B-1660 Lot, Belgium

WATERS CHROMATOGRAPHY DIV   34 Maple St, Milford, MA 01757,
Tel: (617) 478-2000
(Mfr/distr liquid chromatographic instru/accessories/tech)
    Millipore SA NV, Waters Chromatography Div., Rue de la Russes 60, Raketstraat,
    1130 Brussels, Belgium

ROBERT A WEAVER JR & ASSOCS   Pilot House at Lewis Wharf, Boston, MA 02110,
Tel: (617) 723-2600
(Mgmt consultants)
    Weaver-Europe S.A., Rue de Livourne 45, 1050 Brussels, Belgium

WEIGHT WATCHERS INTL INC   Jericho Atrium, 500 North Broadway, Jericho,
NY 11753-2196, Tel: (516) 939-0400
(Weight reduction programs, food prdts)
    Weight Watchers Belgium, Mechelsesteenweg 244, 1800 Vilvoorde, Belgium

WERNER MANAGEMENT CONSULTANTS   111 W 40th St, New York, NY 10018,
Tel: (212) 642-6000
(Mgmt consult to textile & ret apparel ind)
    Werner Intl., 523 Avenue Louise, 1050 Brussels, Belgium

WESTVACO CORP   299 Park Ave, New York, NY 10171, Tel: (212) 688-5000
(Mfr paper, packaging, chems)
    Westvaco Europe S.A., Avenue de Tervueren 296, Bte. 5, 1150 Brussels, Belgium

WEYERHAEUSER CO   Tacoma, WA 98477, Tel: (206) 924-2345
(Wood & wood fiber prdts)
    Weyerhaeuser Belgium S.A., 250 Ave. Louise Bte. 42, Brussels, Belgium

T D WILLIAMSON INC   PO Box 2299, Tulsa, OK 74133, Tel: (918) 254-9400
(Equip/serv for pipeline maint)
    T.D. Williamson S.A., 6 Rue du Travail, B-1400 Nivelles, Belgium

WORLD COMMUNICATIONS INC   67 Broad St, New York, NY 10004,
Tel: (212) 607-2000
(Intl private line services)
    World Communications Inc., 315 Ave. Louise, B-1050 Brussels, Belgium

WORLD COURIER INC   46 Trinity Pl, New York, NY 10006, Tel: (718) 978-9400
(Intl courier serv)
    World Courier S.A.N.V., Jan Vranckystraat 6, 3055 Neeryse, Belgium

WYNN OIL CO   2600 E Nutwood Ave, PO Box 4370, Fullerton, CA 92631,
Tel: (714) 992-2000
(Chem additives for oil, grease & fuels; hardware)
    Wynn's Belgium N.V., Industrie Park West 46, 2700 St. Niklaas, Belgium

YOUNG & RUBICAM INTL INC   285 Madison Ave, New York, NY 10017,
Tel: (212) 210-3000
(Advertising agency)
    Young & Rubicam Intl., 250 Avenue Louise B-1050 Brussels, Belgium

ZALE CORP   3000 Diamond Park, PO Box 222219, Dallas, TX 75222,
  Tel: (214) 634-4011
  (Retail jewelry, catalog showrooms, airport newsstands, etc)
    Zale (Belgium), Scheepstraat 9-11, Floor 10, 2000 Antewerp, Belgium

ZEKS INDUSTRIES INC   Malvern Industrial Park, Malvern, PA 19355,
  Tel: (215) 647-1600
  (Compressed air & gas dryers)
    Zeks Industries, Inc., Semissestraat 4, 2153 Zoersel, Belgium

BENIN

LOUIS BERGER INTL INC   100 Halsted St, East Orange, NJ 07019,
  Tel: (201) 678-1960
  (Consulting engineers, architects, economists & planners)
    Louis Berger International Inc., c/o Carder Atacora, P.B. 36, Natitingou, Benin

INA CORPORATION   1600 Arch St, Philadelphia, PA 19101, Tel: (215) 523-5335
  (Holding co: ins, financial serv)
    INA Intl., Compagnie des Experts Maritimes du Benin, B.P. 269, Cotonous, Benin

ITT SHERATON CORP   60 State St, Boston, MA 02108, Tel: (617) 367-3600
  (Hotel operations)
    Benin-Sheraton Hotel, Boulevard De La Marina, B.P. 1901, Cotonou, Benin

MOBIL CORP   150 E 42nd St, New York, NY 10017, Tel: (212) 883-4242
  (Petroleum explor, prdts)
    Mobil Oil A.O., B.P. 251, Cotonous, Benin

UNION OIL INTL DIV   Union Oil Center, PO Box 7600, Los Angeles, CA 90017,
  Tel: (213) 977-7600
  (Petroleum prdts, petrochems)
    Union Oil Co., B.P. 7600, Cotonous, Benin

BERMUDA

AFIA   110 William St, New York, NY 10038, Tel: (212) 964-4990
  (Insurance)
    American Foreign Insurance Assn., Hamilton, Bermuda

ALEXANDER & ALEXANDER INC   1211 Ave of the Americas, New York, NY 10036,
  Tel: (212) 840-8500
  (Ins brokerage, risk & human resource mgmt consult)
    Alexander Intl. Ltd., Rego Trust Bldg., P.O. Box 681, Hamilton 5, Bermuda

AMERICAN AIRLINES INC   PO Box 619616, Dallas-Ft Worth Arpt, TX 75261-9616,
  Tel: (817) 355-1234
  (Air transp)
    American Airlines Inc., Queen St., Hamilton 5, Bermuda

AMERICAN INTL UNDERWRITERS CORP   70 Pine St, New York, NY 10270,
  Tel: (212) 770-7000
  (General ins)
    American Intl. Underwriters Overseas Ltd., P.O. Box 152, Hamilton 5, Bermuda
    American Intl. Underwriters Overseas Ltd., American Intl. Bldg., Richmond Rd.,
      Pembroke 534, Bermuda

AMERICAN LIFE INSURANCE CO (ALICO)   PO Box 2226, Wilmington, DE 19899,
  Tel: (302) 594-2000
  (Life ins, pension & annuity plans, health prdts)
    American Life Insurance Co., P.O. Box 836, Hamilton 5, Bermuda
    Harnett & Richardson Ltd., 1 Front St., Hamilton 5, Bermuda

BARDAHL MFG CORP   1400 N W 52nd St, PO Box 70607, Seattle, WA 98107,
  Tel: (206) 783-4851
  (Lubricating oils)
    Tools & Equipment Unlimited, P.O. Box 266, North St., Devonshire, Bermuda

BAUSCH & LOMB INC   1 Lincoln First Sq, Rochester, NY 14601-0054,
  Tel: (716) 338-6000
  (Mfr healthcare & optics prdts)
    Bausch & Lomb (Bermuda Technology) Ltd., Hamilton, Bermuda
    Bausch & Lomb Ireland, Hamilton, Bermuda

CANADA DRY INTL CORP   2600 Century Pkwy, Atlanta, GA 30345,
  Tel: (404) 753-2182
  (Carbonated beverages, soft drinks extract)
    Canada Dry Bottling Plant, Canada Villa, Guest House, Pem., Bermuda
    Canada Dry Bottling Plant, John Barritt & Son Ltd., P.O. Box 174, Hamilton, Bermuda

CIGNA CORP   One Liberty Place, 1650 Market St, Philadelphia, PA 19101,
  Tel: (215) 523-4000
  (Ins, invest, health care & other fin servs)
    Cigna Fund Managers Ltd., Victoria Hall, Victoria St., Hamilton, Bermuda
    Cigna Intl. Asset Fund Ltd., Claredon House, Church St. West, Hamilton, Bermuda
    Cigna Intl. Insurance Co. Ltd., Victoria Hall, Victoria St., Hamilton HM11, Bermuda
    Cigna Intl. Insurance Managers Ltd., Victoria Hall, Victoria St., Hamilton HM11,
      Bermuda
    Montgomery & Collins Intl., Ltd., Victoria Hall, Victoria St., Hamilton HM11,
      Bermuda
    Riyad Insurance Co. Ltd., 30 Cedar Ave., Hamilton, Bermuda

CLARK EQUIPMENT CO   PO Box 7008, South Bend, IN 46634, Tel: (219) 239-0100
  (Mfr ind trucks, skid-steer loaders, heavy duty drive line components)
    Celfor Insurance Co. Ltd., 30 Cedar Ave., Hamilton 5, Bermuda

COBE LABORATORIES INC   1185 Oak St, Lakewood, CO 80215, Tel: (303) 232-6800
  (Mfr med equip & supplies)
    Medical Intl. Ltd., Hamilton, Bermuda

THE COCA-COLA CO   310 North Ave NW, PO Box Drawer 1734, Atlanta, GA 30313,
  Tel: (404) 676-2121
  (Mfr & sale of soft drink syrups & concentrates, juices & food prdts, motion pic & TV
  prod)
    The Coca-Cola Co., all mail to: U.S. address

COMPTON INTERNATIONAL   625 Madison Ave, New York, NY 10022,
  Tel: (212) 754-1100
  (Advertising)
    Advertising Associates-Compton Ltd., Front St. E., Hamilton 5-31, Bermuda

DELTA AIR LINES INC   Hartsfield Atlanta Intl Airport, Atlanta, GA 30320,
  Tel: (404) 346-6011
  (Air transp)
    Delta Air Lines Inc., 56 Front St., Hamilton, Bermuda

FRANK B HALL & CO INC   549 Pleasantville Rd, Briarcliff Manor, NY 10510,
  Tel: (914) 769-9200
  (Insurance)
    Parker & Co. Interocean Ltd., 189 Reid St., P.O. Box 1581, Hamilton, Bermuda

HERCULES INC   Hercules Plaza, Wilmington, DE 19894, Tel: (302) 594-5000
  (Mfr spec chems, plastics, film & fibers, coatings, resins, food ingredients)
    Curtis Bay Insurance Co., Ltd., 30 Cedar Ave., P.O. Box HM 1179, Hamilton 5-24,
      Bermuda

HOLIDAY INNS INC   3742 Lamar Ave, Memphis, TN 38195, Tel: (901) 362-4001
  (Hotels, restaurants, casinos)
    Holiday Inn, St. George, P.O. Box 59, Hamilton, Bermuda

INA CORPORATION   1600 Arch St, Philadelphia, PA 19101, Tel: (215) 523-5335
  (Holding co: ins, financial serv)
    Harnett & Richardson, 51 Front St., P.O. Box 836, Hamilton, Bermuda
    INA Intl. Insurance Co. Ltd., P.O. Box 1181, Argyle House, Victoria St.,
      Hamilton 5, Bermuda

INTERNATIONAL BUSINESS MACHINES (IBM)   Old Orchard Rd, Armonk,
   NY 10504-1783, Tel: (914) 765-1900
   (Info-handling sys, equip & serv)
      WTC Insurance Corp. Ltd., Hamilton, Bermuda

JOHN HANCOCK MUTUAL LIFE INSURANCE CO   200 Clarendon St, PO Box 111, Boston,
   MA 02117, Tel: (617) 572-6000
   (Life ins)
      John Hancock Insurance Co. of Bermuda Ltd., Reid House, Church St., Box HM 1826,
         Hamilton 5, Bermuda

KEMPER INTL INSURANCE CO   Route 22, Long Grove, IL 60049, Tel: (708) 540-2000
   (Property casualty ins)
      Kemper Management Co. Ltd., Dallas Bldg., Victoria St., P.O. Box HM 1234,
         Hamilton 5, Bermuda
      Seven Continents Insurance Co. Ltd., Dallas Bldg., Victoria St., P.O. Box HM 1234,
         Hamilton 5, Bermuda

KIMBERLY-CLARK CORP   PO Box 619100, Dallas, TX 75261-1200,
   Tel: (214) 830-1200
   (Mfr fiber-based prdts for personal care, pulp & forest prdts; air transport)
      Ridgeway Insurance Co. Ltd., Hamilton, Bermuda

MANVILLE CORP   PO Box 5108, Denver, CO 80217-5108, Tel: (303) 978-2000
   (Mfr fiber glass prdts, paper & forest prdts, roofing & insulation material, ind
   minerals)
      Rock Mountain Intl. Insurance Ltd., Hamilton, Bermuda

MARSH & McLENNAN COS INC   1221 Ave of the Americas, New York, NY 10020-1011,
   Tel: (212) 997-2000
   (Insurance)
      Marsh & McLennan Ltd., Cedar Ave., Hamilton, Bermuda

MERCK SHARP & DOHME INTL   PO Box 2000, Rahway, NJ 07065, Tel: (201) 574-4000
   (Pharms, chems & biologicals)
      Merck, Sharp & Dohme Ltd., Intl. Centre, P.O. Box 2000, Hamilton, Bermuda

MORGAN GUARANTY TRUST CO   23 Wall St, New York, NY 10015, Tel: (212) 483-2323
   (Banking)
      Morgan Guaranty Finance Ltd., Crisson Bldg., Queen St., Hamilton 5, Bermuda

OCCIDENTAL PETROLEUM CORP   10889 Wilshire Blvd, Los Angeles, CA 90024,
   Tel: (213) 879-1700
   (Petroleum & petroleum prdts, chems, plastics)
      Occidental Ltd., Boyle Bldg., Church St., Hamilton, Bermuda

OTIS ELEVATOR CO   10 Farm Springs, Farmington, CT 06032, Tel: (203) 674-4047
   (Elevators & escalators)
      Otis Elevator Co., Ashwood Hall, Church St., P.O. Box 1546, Hamilton 5, Bermuda

REVLON INC   767 Fifth Ave, New York, NY 10153-0033, Tel: (212) 572-5000
   (Cosmetics, health care prdts)
      Revlon Mfr. Ltd., Hamilton, Bermuda

SMITH INTL INC   16740 Hardy St, Houston, TX 77032, Tel: (713) 443-6470
   (Mfr/serv downhole drilling equip)
      Omega Insurance Ltd., 189 Reid St., PO Box 1179, Hamilton, Bermuda

WACKENHUT CORP   1500 San Remo Ave, Coral Gables, FL 33146,
  Tel: (305) 666-5656
  (Security sys & serv)
    Titania Insurance Co. Ltd., P.O. Box 1581, Hamilton, Bermuda

WORLD COURIER INC   46 Trinity Pl, New York, NY 10006, Tel: (718) 978-9400
  (Intl courier serv)
    World Courier Ltd., Dallas Bldg., Victoria St., Hamilton, Bermuda

BOLIVIA

ABBOTT LABORATORIES   Abbott Park, North Chicago, IL 60064,
  Tel: (312) 937-6100
  (Pharm & lab prdts)
    Laboratorios Abbott de Bolivia, Ave. 20 de Octubre 1743, Casilla 255, La Paz,
      Bolivia

AFIA   110 William St, New York, NY 10038, Tel: (212) 964-4990
  (Insurance)
    Inited States Insurance Co., Plaza Venezuela 1456, Casilla 14, La Paz, Bolivia

AMERADA HESS CORP   1185 Ave of the Americas, New York, NY 10036,
  Tel: (212) 997-8500
  (Crude oil, natural gas)
    Amerada Hess Corp. of Bolivia, Cajon Postal 2500, Santa Cruz, Bolivia

BARDAHL MFG CORP   1400 N W 52nd St, PO Box 70607, Seattle, WA 98107,
  Tel: (206) 783-4851
  (Lubricating oils)
    Cia. Importe de Automotores M. Csapek S.A., Casilla 440 Calle Fed. Zuazo 1717,
      La Paz, Bolivia

BECHTEL GROUP INC   50 Beale St, PO Box 3965, San Francisco, CA 94119,
  Tel: (415) 768-1234
  (Engineering & constr)
    Bechtel Corp., La Paz, Bolivia

LOUIS BERGER INTL INC   100 Halsted St, East Orange, NJ 07019,
  Tel: (201) 678-1960
  (Consulting engineers, architects, economists & planners)
    Louis Berger Intl. Inc., Casilla 6550, La Paz, Bolivia

CANADA DRY INTL CORP   2600 Century Pkwy, Atlanta, GA 30345,
  Tel: (404) 753-2182
  (Carbonated beverages, soft drinks extract)
    CIA Embotelladora Cristal, Ave. Villazon 5100, Casilla Postal 716, Cochabamba,
      Bolivla

Embotelladora Canada Dry Ltda., Km. 3B Carretera Norte, Casilla 1338, Santa Cruz,
  Bolivia
Embotelladora Oriental Ltda., Ave. Espana 566, Oruro, Bolivia
Embotelladora Tarlja S.R.L., Camino a Bermejo Km. 2, Tarija, Bolivia
Productos Oriental Rafael Mendoza, Colombia 520, Casilla 21042, La Paz, Bolivia

CITIBANK NA   399 Park Ave, New York, NY 10043, Tel: (212) 559-1000
  (Intl banking)
    Citibank, Calle Colon Edificio 288, Compania Boliviana de Seguros, Casilla 260,
    La Paz, Bolivia

COLUMBIA PICTURES INDUSTRIES INC   711 Fifth Ave, New York, NY 10022,
  Tel: (212) 751-4400
  (Producer & distributor of motion pictures)
    Distribuidores Asociados de Peliculas Ltda., Postosi 1007, La Paz, Bolivia

COMBUSTION ENGINEERING INC   900 Long Ridge Road, Stamford, CT 06902,
  Tel: (203) 329-8771
  (Tech constr)
    Combustion Engineering Inc., c/o Catco Ltda., Casilla 2060, Santa Cruz, Bolivia

CONTINENTAL CAN CO   PO Box 5410, Stamford, CT 06856, Tel: (203) 357-8110
  (Packaging prdts & mach, metal, plastic & paper containers)
    Fabrica Boliviana de Envases S.A., Casilla de Correos 1103, Cochababma, Bolivia

DE LEUW CATHER & CO   1133 15th St NW, Washington, DC 20005,
  Tel: (202) 775-3300
  (Consulting engineers)
    De Leuw, Cather Intl. Ltd., Calle Otero de la Vega 552, La Paz, Bolivia

DEVELOPMENT ASSOCIATES INC   2924 Columbia Pike, Arlington, VA 22204,
  Tel: (703) 979-0100
  (Mgt consulting servs)
    Development Associates, Inc., Edificio Mariscal Ballivian, Mezanine,
      Calle Mercado 1328, La Paz, Bolivia

FIRST NATIONAL BANK OF BOSTON   100 Federal St, Boston, MA 02110,
  Tel: (617) 434-2200
  (Commercial banking)
    First National Bank of Boston, Casilla de Correo 7878, Plaza Venezuela, La Paz,
      Bolivia
    First National Bank of Boston, Casilla de Correo 2482, Calle Pary #28,
      Santa Cruz de la Sierra, Bolivia

FLORIDA INTL FORWARDERS   6905 N W 25th St, PO Box 522085, Miami, FL 33122,
  Tel: (305) 592-6450
  (Air cargo service)
    Florida Intl. Forwarders Ltd., Eduardo Smith, Casilla 4041, Santa Cruz, Boliv a

FOXBORO CO   33 Commercial St, Foxboro, MA 02035, Tel: (508) 543-8750
  (Mfr prdts/provide servs for ind automation)
    Sertel Comercial Ltda., Apartado Postal 2464, Santa Cruz, Bolivia

HOLIDAY INNS INC   3742 Lamar Ave, Memphis, TN 38195, Tel: (901) 362-4001
  (Hotels, restaurants, casinos)
    Holiday Inn, Ave. San Martin, 3rd Anillo, P.O. Box 2966, Santa Cruz, Bolivia

INA CORPORATION   1600 Arch St, Philadelphia, PA 19101, Tel: (215) 523-5335
   (Holding co: ins, financial serv)
      MacDonald & Co. S.A., P.O. Box 879, La Paz, Bolivia

INTERNATIONAL BUSINESS MACHINES (IBM)   Old Orchard Rd, Armonk,
   NY 10504-1783, Tel: (914) 765-1900
   (Info-handling sys, equip & serv)
      IBM de Bolivia, S.A., La Paz, Bolivia

INTERNATIONAL MINING CORP   1271 Ave of the Americas, New York, NY 10020,
   Tel: (212) 957-3090
   (Mining, natural resources, real estate)
      Southamerican Placers, Ave. Montes 605, Edificio Linale, Casilla 939, La Paz,
      Bolivla

INTERNATIONAL STANDARD ELECTRIC CORP   320 Park Ave, New York, NY 10022,
   Tel: (212) 752-6000
   (Telecommun equip)
      Intl. Standard Electric of NY Ltd., Ave. 16 de Julio, Edificio Petrolero,
      Casilla 669, La Paz, Bolivia

LIQUID CARBONIC CORP   135 S LaSalle St, Chicago, IL 60603,
   Tel: (312) 855-2500
   (Compressed gases, etc)
      Liquid Carbonic de Bolivia S.A., Calle Salinas, Casilla 571, La Paz, Bolivia

NL INDUSTRIES INC   3000 N Sam Houston Pkwy E, Houston, TX 77205,
   Tel: (713) 987-4000
   (Metal prdts, chems, petroleum serv)
      Baroid Div. of National Lead Co., Santa Cruz, Bolivia

NUIR INTL INC   1424 LeJeune Rd, Miami, FL 33126, Tel: (305) 871-3563
   (Exporters of constr materials)
      Nuir Intl. de Bolivia, Casilla 250, La Paz, Bolivia

OCCIDENTAL PETROLEUM CORP   10889 Wilshire Blvd, Los Angeles, CA 90024,
   Tel: (213) 879-1700
   (Petroleum & petroleum prdts, chems, plastics)
      Occidental Boliviana Inc., 3ER Casilla 1296, Santa Cruz, Bolivia

ONAN CORP   1400 73rd Ave NE, Minneapolis, MN 55432, Tel: (612) 574-5000
   (Electric generators, ind engines & controls)
      Gundlach, S.A., Casilla Correo 1415, Calle Reyes Ortiz #73, La Paz, Bolivia

PARKER DRILLING CO   8 E Third St, Tulsa, OK 74103, Tel: (918) 585-8221
   (Oil well drilling)
      Parker Drilling Co., Casilla 141, Santa Cruz, Bolivia

PHILLIPS PETROLEUM CO   Phillips Bldg, Bartlesville, OK 74004,
   Tel: (918) 661-6600
   (Crude oil, natural gas, liquefied petroleum gas, gasoline & petro-chems)
      Phillips Petroleum Co., Calle Tumusla 5444, Casilla 2846, Cochabamba, Bolivia

SGS CONTROL SERVICES INC   42 Broadway, New York, NY 10004,
   Tel: (212) 482-8700
   (Complete range of quality & quantity control checks & related tech serv)
      SGS S.A., Edificio Esperanza, Ave. Mariscal Santa Cruz s/n, P.O. Box 3282, La Paz,

Bolivia
SGS S.A., Plaza Colon 5056, Cochabamba, Bolivia
SGS S.A., Edificio SACI, Oficinas 3 &4, P.O. Box 766, Santa Cruz, Bolivia

C TENNANT SONS & CO OF NY   PO Box 9300, Minneapolis, MN 55440,
Tel: (612) 475-7340
(Ferrous & non-ferrous minerals, metals, electronic comps)
Tennant S.A., Casilla 2657, La Paz, Bolivia

TESORO PETROLEUM CORP   8700 Tesoro Dr, PO Box 17536, San Antonio, TX 78286,
Tel: (512) 828-8484
(Oil, gas prod & refining)
Tesoro Bolivia Petroleum Co., Casilla 2449, Carretera Cochabamba KM 31/2,
Santa Cruz, Bolivia

TRANS WORLD AIRLINES INC   605 Third Ave, New York, NY 10158,
Tel: (212) 557-6107
(Air transp, hotel, food serv, real estate)
Trans World Airlines Inc., Ave. Arce Sheraton Hotel, La Paz, Bolivia

WESTERN GEOPHYSICAL   PO Box 2469, Houston, TX 77252-2469, Tel: (713) 789-9600
(Geophysical serv)
Western Geophysical, Calle Colon 280, Cajon Postal 2497, Santa Cruz, Bolivia

BRAZIL

3M CO   3M Center, St Paul, MN 55144-1000, Tel: (612) 733-1110
(Mfr abrasives, adhesives, chems, ind & consumer tapes/diskettes, health care prdts,
elec connectors)
3M do Brazil Ltda., Caixa Postal 123, 13100 Campinas, Sao Paulo, Brazil

ABBOTT LABORATORIES   Abbott Park, North Chicago, IL 60064,
Tel: (312) 937-6100
(Pharm & lab prdts)
Abbott Laboratories do Brazil Ltda., Caixa Postal 21111, 9808 Sao Paulo, Brazil

ACADEMIC PRESS INC   111 Fifth Ave, New York, NY 10003, Tel: (212) 741-6800
(Publ scientific books)
Academic Press do Brazil Editora Ltda., Praca Jorge de Lima 14, 05503 Sao Paulo,
SP, Brazil

ACCO INDUSTRIES INC   101 Oakview Dr, Trumbull, CT 06611, Tel: (203) 371-5439
(Testing sys, chain, castings, brakes, bridge & jib cranes)
Industrias Metalurgicas Liebau, S.A., Ave. Sete de Setembro 1370, Diadema,
Sao Paulo, Brazil

ACCURAY CORP   650 Ackerman Rd, PO Box 02248, Columbus, OH 43202,
   Tel: (614) 261-2000
   (Computer-based process mgmt sys for forest prdts, metals rolling, textiles, tobacco
   ind)
      AccuRay Systems Ltda., Sao Paulo, Brazil

ACHESON COLLOIDS CO   1600 Washington Ave, PO Box 288, Port Huron, MI 48060,
   Tel: (313) 984-5581
   (Graphite, lubricants & other specialty chems)
      Acheson do Brazil Ltda., Caixa Postal 30.816, 01000 Sao Paulo, SP, Brazil

ACTION OVERSEAS BUYING LTD   460 Nixon Rd, Allegheny Ind Park, Cheswick,
   PA 15024, Tel: (412) 782-4800
   (Distr/sale housewares, hardware, giftware, light bulbs & crystal)
      Action Overseas Buying Ltd., Rua Professor Manoel Jose Chaves 266, CEP 05463,
      Sao Paulo, Brazil

ADAMS & PORTER INC   1 World Trade Center, #8433, New York, NY 10048,
   Tel: (212) 432-0001
   (Ins brokers)
      Adams & Porter Sociedade de Corretagem de Seguros Ltda., Caixa Postal 30321,
      01051 Sao Paulo, Brazil
      Adams & Porter Sociedade de Corretagem de Seguros Ltda., Av. Beira Mar 200,
      10th andar, 20021 Rio de Janeiro, Brazil

AFIA   110 William St, New York, NY 10038, Tel: (212) 964-4990
   (Insurance)
      Home Insurance, Rua Paulo de Frontim 628, ZC-10, Caixa Postal 548, ZC-00,
      Rio de Janeiro, RJ, Brazil

AIR PRODUCTS & CHEMICALS INC   7201 Hamilton Blvd, Allentown, PA 18195,
   Tel: (215) 481-4911
   (Mfr ind gases & chems)
      Air Products Gases Industriais Ltda., Praca Radialista Manoel e Nobrega 65,
      02517-Casa Verde, Sao Paulo, SP, Brazil

AIR-SHIELDS VICKERS   330 Jacksonville Rd, Hatboro, PA 19040,
   Tel: (215) 675-5200
   (Mfr/sales/serv spec med equip, med electr prdts)
      Fanem Ltda., Av. Gal Ataliba Leonel 1790, Sao Paulo, Brazil

AJAX MAGNETHERMIC CORP   1745 Overland Ave NE, PO Box 991, Warren, OH 44482,
   Tel: (216) 372-2529
   (Electric induction heaters)
      Ajax Equipmentos Magnetermicos Ltda., Rua General Sampaio 74, Partecaju, 20.931,
      Rio de Janeiro, Brazil

ALADDIN INDUSTRIES INC   PO Box 100255, Nashville, TN 37210,
   Tel: (615) 748-3000
   (Vacuum bottles)
      M. Agostini Comercio Industria S.A., Rua Teofilo Otoni 94, ZC-00 .,
      Caixa Postal 843, ZC-00, Rio de Janeiro, RJ, Brazil

ALBANY INTL CORP   PO Box 1907, Albany, NY 12201, Tel: (518) 445-2200
   (Paper mach clothing, engineered fabrics, plastic prdts, filtration media)
      Albany Industria e Comercio Ltda., Caixa Postal No. 1015, 89100, Blumenan, S.C.,
      Brazil

ALEXANDER & ALEXANDER INC   1211 Ave of the Americas, New York, NY 10036,
  Tel: (212) 840-8500
  (Ins brokerage, risk & human resource mgmt consult)
    Alexander & Alexander Corretores de Seguros Ltda., Alameda Santos 2101, 6th Fl.,
      Caixa Postal 554, 01000, Sao Paulo, SP, Brazil

ALLEN-BRADLEY CO   PO Box 2086, Milwaukee, WI 53201, Tel: (414) 382-2000
  (Electrical control devices)
    Logicos Sistemas de Controle Ind. Ltda, Rua Dr. Silva Melo, 45-A (Santo,
      Amaro) Cepo 4675 - Sao Paulo - S.P., Brazil

ALLERGAN PHARMACEUTICALS INTL INC   2525 DuPont Dr, Irvine, CA 92713,
  Tel: (714) 752-4500
  (Pharms, opthalmic & dermatological preparations)
    Allergan Products Farmaceuticos Ltda., Ave. Bosque de Saude, 681, Sao Paulo, Brazil

ALLIED AFTERMARKET DIV   105 Pawtucket Ave, East Providence, RI 02916,
  Tel: (401) 434-7000
  (Mfr spark plugs, waste treatment sys, filters, brakes)
    Fram do Brazil Ltda., Av. Piraporinna 251, Caixa Postal 52, Sao Bernardo do Campo,
      Brazil

ALLIED-SIGNAL INC   Columbia Rd & Park Ave, PO Box 2245R, Morristown,
  NJ 07960, Tel: (201) 455-2000
  (Mfr aerospace & automotive prdts, engineered materials)
    Allied Chemical do Brasil, Avda. Paulista 688, CP 9802, Sao Paulo, Brazil
    Allied-Signal Aerospace Co., Rua Visconde de Piraja 430, 7-andar, Ipanema,
      22410 Rio de Janeiro, Brazil
    Divisao Bendix do Brasil, Rua Joao Felipe Zavier da Silva 384, 13-100 Campinas,
      Sao Paulo, Brazil
    Divisao Fram do Brazil, Ave. Piraporinha 251, Sao Bernardo do Campo,
      Sao Paulo 09890, Brazil
    Divisao Jurid do Brasil, Ave. Liberdade, S/No. Sorocaba, Sao Paulo 18100, Brazil
    Garrett Equipamentos Ltda., Ave. Julia Gaiolli 212/250, AMP da Rod. Pres. Duzra,
      CEP/07210 Guarulhos, Sao Paulo, Brazil

ALLIED-SIGNAL INTL INC   Columbia Rd & Park Ave, PO Box 2000, Morristown,
  NJ 07962, Tel: (201) 455-6034
  (Mfr advanced aerospace, automotive & engineered materials)
    Allied-Signal Intl. Inc., Rua Visconde de Piraja 450-7 Andar, Ipanema,
      22410 Rio de Janeiro, Brazil

ALLIS-CHALMERS CORP   PO Box 512, Milwaukee, WI 53201, Tel: (414) 475-4011
  (Heavy mach, equip & serv)
    Allis-Chalmers Industria e Comercio Ltda., Edificio Banco de Lohdres,
      Av. Amazonas. 311-130 andar Cidade de Belo Horizontem. ., Minas Gerais,
    Allis-Chalmers Industria e Comercio Ltda., Av. Presidente Wilson, 1716-03107,
      Sao Paulo, Brazil

ALUMINUM CO OF AMERICA (ALCOA)   1501 Alcoa Bldg, Pittsburgh, PA 15219,
  Tel: (412) 553-4545
  (Bauxite, alumina & aluminum prdts)
    Companhia Mineira de Aluminio-Alcominas, Pocos de Caldas, Minas Gerais, Brazil

AMERICAN AIR FILTER CO INC   215 Central Ave, PO Box 35690, Louisville,
KY 40277, Tel: (502) 637-0011
(Air cleaning equip)
    AAF-Controle Ambiental, Ltda., Caixa Postal 20835, Iguatemi, Sao Paulo, Brazil

AMERICAN AIRLINES INC   PO Box 619616, Dallas-Ft Worth Arpt, TX 75261-9616,
Tel: (817) 355-1234
(Air transp)
    American Airlines Inc., Av. Ipiranga 313-20. andar Conj. 21, Sao Paulo, Brazil 01046

AMERICAN BUREAU OF SHIPPING   45 Eisenhower Dr, Paramus, NJ 07653-0910,
Tel: (201) 368-9100
(Classification/certification of ships & offshore structures, devel & tech assistance)
    American Bureau of Shipping, Av. Venezuela 3, 8 andar, Caixa Postal 21142,
        20081 Rio de Janeiro, RJ, Brazil

AMERICAN CYANAMID CO   1 Cyanamid Plaza, Wayne, NJ 07470, Tel: (201) 831-2000
(Pharms, chems, agric & consumer prdts)
    Blemco Importadores e Exportadora Ltda., Av. Rio Branco 311, andar 7,
        Caixa Postal 2222, ZC-00, Rio de Janeiro, RJ, Brazil
    Cyanamid Quimica do Brazil Ltda., Av. Rio Branco 311, andar 7, LO.040,
        Caixa Postal 1039, SC-00 Rio de Janeiro, RJ, Brazil
    Formica Plasticos S.A., Av. Imperatriz Leopoldina 86 (Lapa), Sao Paulo, SP, Brazil

AMERICAN EXPRESS CO   American Express Tower, New York, NY 10285-4765,
Tel: (212) 640-2000
(Diversified fin & travel-related serv)
    Ultramax S.A., Arrendamento Mercantil, Rua Libero Badaro 377, 11 andar 01310,
        Sao Paulo, Brazil,
    Ultramax S.A., Rio Branco No. 123 F - 1106, 20040 Rio de Janeiro, Brazil

AMERICAN HOME ASSURANCE CO   70 Pine St, New York, NY 10270,
Tel: (212) 770-7000
(General ins (non-life))
    American Home Assurance Co., Rua Senador Dantas 74, andar 9, Rio de Janeiro RJ,
        Brazil

AMERICAN HOME PRODUCTS CORP   685 Third Ave, New York, NY 10017,
Tel: (212) 878-5800
(Drugs, food, household prdts)
    Industria Farmaceuticas Fontoura-Wyeth S.A., Laboratorios Anakol, Ltda.,
    Produtos Quimicos Fontoura Ltda., Rua Caetano Pinto 129, andar 3,
        Caixa Postal 8749, Sao Paulo, SP, Brazil

AMERICAN INTL UNDERWRITERS CORP   70 Pine St, New York, NY 10270,
Tel: (212) 770-7000
(General ins)
    American Intl. Underwriters, Representacoes S.A., Praca de Republica 497,
        P.O. Box 8891, ZC-0145, Sao Paulo, SP, Brazil

AMERICAN LOCKER GROUP INC   15 W Second St, Jamestown, NY 14702,
Tel: (716) 664-9600
(Mfr coin-oper locks, office furniture)
    Malex do Brasil Ltda., Av. Washington Luis 4803, CEP 04627, Sao Paulo, SP, Brazil

AMERICAN MOTORISTS INSURANCE CO   Route 22, Lake Zurich, IL 60047,
Tel: (708) 540-2000
(Insurance)
  American Motorists Insurance Co., Rua Debret 79, Caixa Postal 580, Rio de Janeiro,
  Brazil

AMERICAN OPTICAL CORP   14 Mechanic St, Southbridge, MA 01550,
Tel: (617) 765-9711
(Ophthalmic lenses, frames & cases, sunglasses)
  American Optical do Brazil Ltda., Av. Sao Luis 50, 27 andar CJ 271 A,
  B.C. 010 46 Sao Paulo, Brazil

AMERICAN STANDARD INC   40 W 40th St, New York, NY 10018, Tel: (212) 840-5100
(Heating & sanitary equip)
  Ideal Standard S.A., Ind. e Com., Av. Paulista 726, andar 10, Caixa Postal 22052,
  Sao Paulo, SP, Brazil

AMERON INC   4700 Ramona Blvd, PO Box 3000, Monterey Park, CA 91754,
Tel: (213) 268-4111
(Mfr steel pipe sys, concrete prdts, traffic & lighting poles, protective coatings)
  Ameron do Brasil, Sao Paulo, SP, Brazil

AMOCO CHEMICAL CO   200 E Randolph Dr, Chicago, IL 60601, Tel: (312) 856-3200
(Mfr/sale petrol based chems, plastics, chem/plastic prdts)
  Rhodiaco Industrias Quimicas Ltda., Brazil

AMP INC   470 Friendship Rd, Harrisburg, PA 17111, Tel: (717) 564-0100
(Mfr electrical wiring devices)
  AMP do Brazil, Rua. Ado Benatti 53, CEP 05037 Sao Paulo, Brazil

AMPEX CORP   401 Broadway, Redwood City, CA 94063-3199, Tel: (415) 367-2011
(Mfr professional audio/visual sys, magnetic recording media, data-memory prdts)
  Ampex do Brasil Elect. Ltda, Ave. Portugal 54, Urca CEP 22291,
  Rio de Janeiro RJ Brazil

ANDREW CORP   10500 W 153rd St, Orlando Park, IL 60462, Tel: (708) 349-3300
(Antenna sys)
  Andrew Antenas Ltda., Av. Victor Andrew, 585, Caixa Postal 600, 18100 Sorocaba,
  Sao Paulo, Brazil

ARBOR ACRES FARM INC   41 Marlborough Rd, Glastonbury, CT 06033,
Tel: (203) 633-4681
(Producers of male & female broiler breeders, commercial egg layers)
  Arbor Acres, S.A., Caixa Postal 400, 13500 Rio Claro, SP, Brazil

ARMCO INTL INC   703 Curtis St, PO Box 700, Middletown, OH 45042,
Tel: (513) 425-6541
(Sheet steel & steel prdts, constr, oil field equip, ins, finance leasing)
  Armco do Brazil Industrial e Comercial S.A., Av. Dr. Francisco Mesquita 1575,
  Caixa Postal 30.525, 01000, Sao Paulo, SP, Brazil

ARO INTL CORP   One Aro Center, Bryan, OH 43506, Tel: (419) 636-4242
(Mfr portable air tools, drills, motors, fluid handling pumps)
  Industria e Comercio Aro do Brazil Ltda., Av. Tiradentes 1525, 01102 Sao Paulo,
  Brazil

ARVIN INDUSTRIES INC   One Noblitt Plaza, Columbus, IN 47201,
   Tel: (812) 379-3000
   (Mfr auto OEM & replacement parts & fabricated metal parts, R&D & testing)
      Vulvulas Schrader do Brasil, Calxa Postal 21211, Sao Paulo, 01000 Brazil

ASGROW SEED CO   7000 Portage Rd, Kalamazoo, MI 49001, Tel: (616) 385-6614
   (Growers/breeders agronomic & vegetable seeds)
      Asgrow do Brasil Sementes Ltda., Caixa Postal 1564-Cambui, 13.100 Campinas,
      Sao Paulo, Brazil

ASSOCIATED METALS & MINERALS CORP   3 N Corporate Park Dr, White Plains,
   NY 10604, Tel: (914) 251-5400
   (Metals & ores)
      Sociedade Comercio de Minerios e Metais Metalora Ltda., Caixa Postal 3758,
      20.000 Rio de Janeiro, RJ, Brazil

ASSOCIATED PRESS   50 Rockefeller Plaza, New York, NY 10020,
   Tel: (212) 621-1500
   (News gathering agency)
      Associated Press, Av. Rio Branco 25, 11-andar, ZC-05, Caixa Postal 72, ZC-00,
      Rio de Janeiro, RJ, Brazil

AUTOMATIC SWITCH CO   Hanover Rd, Florham Park, NJ 07932, Tel: (201) 966-2000
   (Valves & switches)
      Ascoval Industria e Comercio Ltda., Rodovia Presidente Castelo Branco, Km. 20,
      Jardin Sta. Cecilia, Barueri, Sao Paulo, Brazil

AVON PRODUCTS INC   9 W 57th St, New York, NY 10019, Tel: (212) 546-6015
   (Mfr/distr cosmetics, perfumes)
      Avon Cosmeticos Ltda., Av. Joao Dias 1645, Santo Amaro, Caixa Postal 6781,
      01000 Sao Paulo, SF , Brazil

AYERST LABORATORIES   145 King of Prussia Rd, Radnor, PA 19087,
   Tel: (215) 688-4400
   (Biologicals & pharms)
      Laboratorios Ayerst Ltda., Rua Professor Sebastiao Soares, de Faria 27-4-11,
      Sao Paulo, SP, Brazil

BACARDI CORP   PO Box 3549, San Juan, PR 00903, Tel: (809) 784-1560
   (Distiller & exporter of rum)
      Ron Bacardi S.A., Encanta Moca, Pina, Recife, PE, Brazil

BAILEY CONTROLS CO   29801 Euclid Ave, Wickliffe, OH 44092,
   Tel: (216) 943-5500
   (Mfr analog & digital instru, controls & control sys)
      Bailey do Brazil, 1159 Av. Paulista, Conj. 613, CEP 01311, Sao Paulo, Brazil

BAIRD CORP   125 Middlesex Turnpike, Bedford, MA 01730, Tel: (617) 276-6000
   (Scientific instru)
      Baird Corp. do Brazil Ltda., Rua California 817, Cepoy 566, Sao Paulo, Brazil

BAKER OIL TOOLS   PO Box 3048, Houston, TX 77253, Tel: (713) 923-9351
   (Oil/gas well completions equip)
      Baker Hughes Equipmentos Ltda., Estrada Vigario-Geral 371, 21241 Rio de Janeiro,
      RJ, Brazil

BAKER PRODUCTION TECHNOLOGY   PO Box 40129, Houston, TX   77240-0129,
  Tel: (713) 943-0170
  (Inflatable packers, instru well testing)
    Lynes do Brazil Ltda., Rua Alcindo Guanabara 24, 20031 Rio de Janeiro, Brazil

BANDAG INC   Bandag Center, Muscatine, IA   52761, Tel: (319) 262-1400
  (Mfr/sale tread rubber & related equip/supplies)
    Bandag do Brazil Ltda., Caixa Postal 1.800, 13100 Campinas, Brazil

BANK OF NEW ENGLAND NA   28 State St, Boston, MA   02106, Tel: (617) 742-4000
  (Full service bank)
    Bank of New England NA (New England Servicos Ltda.), Rua Libero Badero 377 -,
    Conj. 2103, 01009 Sao Paulo, SP, Brazil

THE BANK OF NEW YORK   48 Wall St, New York, NY   10286, Tel: (212) 530-1784
  (Banking)
    Banco de Investimento Credibanco S.A., Av. Paulista 1294, Cep-01310 Bela Vista,
    Sao Paulo, Brazil

BANKAMERICA CORP   PO Box 37000, San Francisco, CA   94137, Tel: (415) 622-3456
  (Financial services)
    Multi-Banco Internacional de Investimentos S.A., Rua Padre Joao Manoel 923,
    01411 Sao Paulo, SP, Brazil

BANKERS TRUST CO   280 Park Ave, New York, NY   10017, Tel: (212) 775-2500
  (Banking)
    Bankers Trust Co., Rua Libero Badaru 377, 12 andar Salas 1211/1212, Sao Paulo,
    Brazil
    Bankers Trust Co., Av. Rio Branco 123, andar 5, Salas 512/51, Rio de Janeiro, Brazil

BARBER-GREENE CO   3000 Baraber-Greene Rd, DeKalb, IL   60115,
  Tel: (815) 756-5600
  (Mfr heavy road constr equip)
    Barber-Greene do Brazil Ind. e Com. S.A., Av. Dr. Renato de Andrade Maia 1430,
    C. Postal 39, 07000 Guarulhos, SP, Brazil

C R BARD INC   731 Central Ave, Murray Hill, NJ   07974, Tel: (201) 277-8000
  (Health care prdts)
    Rossifil Industria Produtos Plasticos Ltda., Caixa Postal 401, CEP 01000,
    Sao Paulo, Brazil

BARDAHL MFG CORP   1400 N W 52nd St, PO Box 70607, Seattle, WA   98107,
  Tel: (206) 783-4851
  (Lubricating oils)
    Promax Produtos Maximos S.A., C.P. 21.019 Z.P. 17, Sao Paulo, Brazil

THE BARDEN CORP   200 Park Ave, PO Box 2449, Danbury, CT   06813-2449,
  Tel: (203) 744-2211
  (Precision ball bearings)
    Rodamentos Paulista RPL S.A., Rua Pirajussara 443, 05501 Sao Paulo, Brazil

BAUSCH & LOMB INC   1 Lincoln First Sq, Rochester, NY   14601-0054,
  Tel: (716) 338-6000
  (Mfr healthcare & optics prdts)
    BL Industria Otica Ltda., Rio de Janeiro, RJ, Brazil
    Cornealent Waicon do Brasil Industria e Comercio Ltda., Rio de Janeiro, Brazil

BAXTER TRAVENOL LABORATORIES INC   1 Baxter Pky, Deerfield, IL 60015,
  Tel: (708) 948-2000
  (Pharm & disposable med prdts)
      Travenol Industrial e Commercial Ltda., Rua Mandel F. Landin, 34 CEP 04696,
      Santa Amaro, Sao Paulo, Brazil
      Travenol Produtos Hospitalares Ltda., Rua Suzano 73, CEP 01435, Jardim Paulista,
      Sao Paulo SP, Brazil

BECHTEL GROUP INC   50 Beale St, PO Box 3965, San Francisco, CA 94119,
  Tel: (415) 768-1234
  (Engineering & constr)
      Bechtel do Brasil Construcoes Ltda., Rua Haddock Lobo 578, 01414, Sao Paulo, SP,
      Brazil

BELOIT CORP   1st Lawrence Ave, Beloit, WI 53511, Tel: (608) 365-3311
  (Paper making mach & equip)
      Beloit-Rauma Industrial Ltda., Caixa Postal 1858, 13.100 Campinas, SP, Brazil
      Equipamentos Industriais Ltda., Rua Stella, 515 Bloco "E" S Andar, 04011,
      Vila Mariana, Sao Paulo, Brazil

BENTLEY LABORATORIES INC   17502 Armstrong Ave, Irvine, CA 92714,
  Tel: (714) 546-8020
  (Mfr para-med devices)
      Bentley Sorin Biomecida Industrial, Av. Paulista 509, Sao Paulo, Brazil

BENTLY NEVADA CORP   PO Box 157, Minden, NV 89423, Tel: (702) 782-3611
  (Electronic monitoring system)
      Engetec Industria e Comercio Ltda., Rua Maria Figueiredo 484, CEP 04002, Sao Paulo,
      SP, Brazil

BLACK & DECKER CORP   701 E Joppa Road, Towson, MD 21204, Tel: (301) 583-3900
  (Mfr portable elect & pneumatic power tools, household prdts)
      B & D Eletrodomesticos Ltda., Caixa Postal 2580, 09900 Sao Paulo, SP, Brazil

BLOUNT INC   4520 Executive Park Drive, Montgomery, AL 36116-1602,
  Tel: (205) 244-4370
  (Mfr cutting chain & equip, timber harvest/materials handling equip, sporting ammo,
  gen contracting)
      Omark Industrial Ltda., Av. Haras Santa Fe BP-1, 1600, Cidade Industrial,
      CEP 80000 Curitiba, Parana, Brazil

BOOZ ALLEN & HAMILTON INC   101 Park Ave, New York, NY 10178,
  Tel: (212) 697-1900
  (Mgmt consultants)
      Booz, Allen & Hamilton do Brasil Consultores Ltda., Rua Gornes de Carvalho 1765,
      5 andar, 04547 Sao Paulo SP, Brazil

BORDEN INC   420 Lexington Ave, New York, NY 10170, Tel: (212) 573-4000
  (Milk processing, dairy foods, specialty foods, chems, plastics)
      Alba S.A., Industrias Quimicas, Rua Verbo Divino, 1323 Bairro de Santo Amaro,
      Caixa Postal 438, 10100, Sao Paulo, SP, Brazil

BORG-WARNER CORP   200 S Michigan Ave, Chicago, IL 60604, Tel: (312) 322-8500
  (Mfr A/C equip, chem & plastics, ind prdts, trans equip)
      Borg Warner do Brazil Ind. e Com. Ltda., Av. Piraporinha 1000, Caixa Postal 272,
      09700 Sao Bernardo de Campo, SP, Brazil

BOYDEN ASSOCIATES INC   260 Madison Ave, New York, NY 10016,
Tel: (212) 685-3400
(Mgt consultants, exec search)
 Boyden do Brazil Ltda., Rua Bento de Andrade 421, Jardim Paulista, 04503 Sao Paulo,
 Brazil, Sao Paulo, Brazil

BRANSON ULTRASONICS CORP   Eagle Rd, Danbury, CT 06810, Tel: (203) 796-0400
(Ultrasonic & vibratory plastics assembly mach)
 Arruda Ultra-sons Ltda., Rua Vig. Taques Bittencourt, No. 63, Santa Amaro,
 04755 - Sao Paulo, Brazil

BRINK'S INC   Thorndal Circle, Darien, CT 06820, Tel: (203) 655-8781
(Security transportation)
 Brink's S.A. Transporte de Valores, Rua Joao Bricola 678, Caixa Postal 9891,
 Sao Paulo, SP, Brazil

BRISTOL BABCOCK INC   1100 Buckingham St, Watertown, CT 06795,
Tel: (203) 575-3000
(Mfr process control instru & intelligent digital prdts)
 IEF Bristol Babcock Instrumentos e Sistemas S.A., Rua das Macieiras 181,
 Casa Verde, CEP 02521, Sao Paulo, SP, Brazillo, Brazil

BROWN & ROOT INC   4100 Clinton Dr, Houston, TX 77020-6299,
Tel: (713) 676-4141
(Engr, constr & maintenance)
 Brown & Root do Brasil Servicos Maritimos Ltd., R. Senador Dantas 75,
 Rio de Janeiro, Brazil

BRUNSWICK CORP   One Brunswick Plaza, Skokie, IL 60077, Tel: (708) 470-4700
(Mfr outboard motors & drives, bowling/fishing equip, valves & pumps)
 Hydro Steam Equipamentos Industrials Ltda., Ave. Berna 230, Villa Friburgo,
 04774 Sao Paulo, SP, Brazil

BUCYRUS-ERIE CO   PO Box 56, Milwaukee, WI 53172, Tel: (414) 768-4000
(Shovels, cranes)
 Bucyrus (Brazil) Ltda., Belo Horizonte, Brazil

BULAB HOLDINGS INC   1256 N McLean Blvd, Memphis, TN 38108,
Tel: (901) 278-0330
(Mfr microbicides, biocides, additives, corrosion inhibitors, chems)
 Buckman Laboratorios Ltda., Caixa Postal 899, 13100 Campinas, SP, Brazil

BUNDY CORP   12345 E Nine Mile, Warren, MI 48090, Tel: 313) 758) 6500
(Small diameter steel tubing, watch cases, etc)
 Bundy Tubing Industria e Com., Km. 308 de Rodovia Presidente Dutra,
 Sao Jose dos Campos, SP, Brazil
 Bundy Tubing Industria e Com., Av. Santos 2152, Caixa Postal SP, Brazil

LEO BURNETT CO INC   35 West Wacker Dr, Chicago, IL 60601, Tel: (312) 220-5959
(Advertising agency)
 Leo Burnett Publicidade, Ltda., Av. Cidade Jardim 400, Sao Paulo, CEP 01454, Brazil

BURSON-MARSTELLER   230 Park Ave, New York, NY 10003-1566, Tel: (212) 614-4000
(Public relations/public affairs consultants)
 Burson-Marsteller Ltda., Av. Brig. Faria Lima 2003, 01451 Sao Paulo, SP, Brazil

CABOT CORP   950 Winter St, PO Box 9073, Waltham, MA 02254,
  Tel: (617) 890-0200
  (Mfr carbon blacks, plastics; oil & gas, info sys)
    Cabot do Brazil Ind. e Com. Ltda., Caixa Postal 22055, Av. Paulista 201-1704,
    andar CJ, 01311, Sao Paulo, SP, Brazil

CALIFORNIA PELLET MILL CO   221 Main St, #420, San Francisco, CA 94105,
  Tel: (415) 431-3800
  (Mfr mach for pelleting)
    Ingersol-Rand S.A., CPM/Brazil Div., Av. Roberto de Jesus Alfonso 351,
    14800 Araraquara, Sao Paulo, Brazil

CAMBRIDGE WIRE CLOTH CO   105 Goodwill Road, PO Box 399, Cambridge, MD 21613,
  Tel: (301) 228-3000
  (Mfr ind wire cloth, women wire conveyor belting, ind mesh)
    Cambridge do Brazil Ind. e Com. Ltda., Caixa Postal 1461, Sao Paulo, Brazil

CAMPBELL TAGGART INC   6211 Lemmon Ave, Box 222640, Dallas, TX 75209,
  Tel: (214) 358-9211
  (Mfr/mktg foods)
    Industrial Panificadora S.A., Estrada Velha da Pavuna 2890, Rio de Janeiro, Brazil

CARGILL   PO Box 9300, Minneapolis, MN 55440, Tel: (612) 475-7575
  (Food prdts, feeds, animal prdts)
    Cargill Agricola S.A., Caixa Postal 9333, 04671 Sao Paulo, SP, Brazil

CARTER AUTOMOTIVE INC   9666 Olive St Rd, St Louis, MO 63132,
  Tel: (314) 997-7400
  (Fuel sys components)
    Carter do Brazil, Rua Ferreira Viana 300, Soccono, Santo Amaro, Sao Paulo, Brazil

CATERPILLAR INC   100 N E Adams St, Peoria, IL 61629, Tel: (309) 675-1000
  (Mfr earth/material-handling & constr mach & equip, engines, generators)
    Caterpillar Brazil S.A., Caixa Postal 8239, 01000 Sao Paulo SP, Brazile
    Caterpillar Brazil S.A., SBS Edificio Case de Sao Paulo, 9 andar, 70078, Brisilia,
    DF, Brazil

L D CAULK CO   PO Box 359, Milford, DE 19963, Tel: (302) 422-4511
  (Dental material)
    Industrias Dentarias Caulk S.A., Rua Darmstadt 401, 18-andar, Caixa Postal 15,
    Petropolis, Edo. de Rio de Janeiro, RJ, Brazil

CBI INDUSTRIES INC   800 Jorie-Blvd, Oak Brook, IL 60521, Tel: (708) 654-7000
  (Holding co: metal plate fabricating, constr, oil & gas drilling)
    CBI Construcues Ltda., Rua Evaristo de Veiga, Rio de Janeiro, Brazil

CDI CORP   10 Penn Center Plaza, Philadelphia, PA 19103, Tel: (215) 569-2200
  (Engr, design, drafting & tech serv)
    Modern do Brazil Servicos e Participacoes Ltda., Rua Boa Vista 254, Sao Paulo,
    Brazil

CENTRAL NATIONAL-GOTTESMAN INC   100 Park Ave, New York, NY 10017,
  Tel: (212) 532-7300
  (Pulp & paper prdts)
    Branac Papel e Celulose S.A., Praca Ramos de Azevedo 206, 01037 Sao Paulo, Brazil
    Branac Papel e Celulose S/A, Rua Teofilo Otoni 123-A, andar 6, ZC-00,
    Caixa Postal 1864, 20090 Rio de Janeiro, RJ, Brazil

CHAMPION INTERNATIONAL CO   One Champion Plaza, Stamford, CT 06921,
  Tel: (213) 358-7000
  (Mfr/distr bldg materials)
    Champion Celulose S.A., Km 60, Rodovia Campinas -Aguas da Prata, Mogiguacu, SP,
      Brazil
    Champion Papel e Celulose S.A., Rua Libero Badaro 377, andar 8, 010 09,

CHAMPION PAPERS INC   Knightsbridge Drive, Hamilton, OH 45011,
  Tel: (513) 868-6660
  (Pulp & paper)
    Champion Celulosa S.A., Rua Libero Badaro 501, 9-andar, Sao Paulo 2, Brazil

CHASE MANHATTAN BANK N A   1 Chase Manhattan Plaza, New York, NY 10081,
  Tel: (212) 552-2222
  (Intl banking)
    Chase Manhattan Office for Southern Region, Rua Alvares Penteado, 131,
      Caixa Postal 30281, Sao Paulo, SP, Brazil
    Chase Manhattan Office-Northern States, Rua do Ouvidor, 98, Caixa Postal 221-ZC-00,
      Rio de Janeiro, Brazil

CHEMICAL BANK   277 Park Ave, New York, NY 10172, Tel: (212) 310-6161
  (Banking & financial serv)
    Banco Norveste do Investimento S.A., Rua Alvares Penteado 216, Sao Paulo, Brazil

CHESEBROUGH-POND'S INC   33 Benedict Place, Greenwich, CT 06830,
  Tel: (203) 661-2000
  (Cosmetics, consumer prdts)
    Pond's do Brazil-Productos de Beleza Ltda., Caixa Postal 30.230,
      Av. Pensilvania 1065-Brooklyn 0100, Sao Paulo, Brazil

CHEVRON CHEMICAL CO   PO Box 5047, San Ramon, CA 94583-0947,
  Tel: (415) 842-5500
  (Chemicals)
    Chevron do Brasil Ltda., Rua General Jardim, 660-6 Andar, 01223 Sao Paulo, SP 1228,
      Brazil
    Polibutenos S.A., Av. Brigadeiro Faria Lima 2020, Toree Sul - 5 andar, Cep 01452,
      Sao Paulo, Brazil

CHRISTENSEN INTL   PO Box 26135, Salt Lake City, UT 84126, Tel: (801) 487-5371
  (Diamond drills)
    Christensen Roder S.A. Produtos Diamantados, Av. Dr. Gentil de Moura 546,

CIGNA CORP   One Liberty Place, 1650 Market St, Philadelphia, PA 19101,
  Tel: (215) 523-4000
  (Ins, invest, health care & other fin servs)
    Amazonas Seguradora SA, Av. Paulo de Frontin- #628, 20001 Rio de Janeiro, Brazil
    Cigna Brasil Empreendimentos Ltda., Av. Paulo de Frontin- #628,
      20262 Rio de Janiero, Brazil
    Cigna Seguradora SA, Av. Paulo de Frontin- #628, 20001 Rio de Janeiro, Brazil
    Sumare Processamento E. Servicos SA, Av. Paulo de Frontin #628 Rio Comprido- 2/F,
      CEP 20262 Rio de Janeiro, Brazil

CITIBANK NA   399 Park Ave, New York, NY 10043, Tel: (212) 559-1000
  (Intl banking)
    Citibank NA, Av. Rio Branco 85, Caixa Postal 770, 2000, Rio de Janeiro, Brazil
    Citibank NA, Av. Ipiranga 855, Caixa Postal 8888, Sao Paulo, Brazil

CLARK EQUIPMENT CO   PO Box 7008, South Bend, IN 46634, Tel: (219) 239-0100
   (Mfr ind trucks, skid-steer loaders, heavy duty drive line components)
      Equipamentos Clark Ltda., Caixa Postal 104, 17280 Pederneiras, Sao Paulo, Brazil

CLARKSON INDUSTRIES INC   30 Buxton Farm Rd, Stamford, CT 06905-1206,
   Tel: (203) 322-3990
   (Mfr centrifugal blowers, compressors, handling equip)
      Hoffman do Brazil Sistemas de Ar e Filtragem Ltda., Rua Frederico Chopin 226,
      Sao Paulo, Brazil

THE COCA-COLA CO   310 North Ave NW, PO Box Drawer 1734, Atlanta, GA 30313,
   Tel: (404) 676-2121
   (Mfr & sale of soft drink syrups & concentrates, juices & food prdts, motion pic & TV
   prod)
      Coca-Cola Industria e Com., Ltda., Av. Nilo Pecanha 50, andar 11, Caixa Postal 860,
      ZC-00, Rio de Janeiro, RJ, Brazil
      Coca-Cola Refrescos S.A., Estrada de Itarare 1071, ZC-24, Caixa Postal 5198, ZC-05,
      Rio de Janeiro, RJ, Brazil

COLUMBIA PICTURES INDUSTRIES INC   711 Fifth Ave, New York, NY 10022,
   Tel: (212) 751-4400
   (Producer & distributor of motion pictures)
      Screen Gems-Columbia Pictures of Brazil Inc., Rua Joaquin Silva 98, Lapa,
      Caixa Postal 110, 9-ZC-00, Rio de Janeiro, Brazil

COMBUSTION ENGINEERING INC   900 Long Ridge Road, Stamford, CT 06902,
   Tel: (203) 329-8771
   (Tech constr)
      Cebrastec-Combustion Engineering do Brasil Servicos Tecnicos,
      Rua Anfilofio de Carvalho 29, andar 12, Caixa Postal 4459, ZC-21, Rio de Janeiro,
      RJ, Brazil
      Comsution Engineering do Brazil Comercio de Industria Ltda., Av. Paulista 1417,
      andar 16, 01310 Sao Paulo SP, Brazil

COMMERCIAL INTERTECH CORP   1775 Logan Ave, Youngstown, OH 44501,
   Tel: (216) 746-8011
   (Mfr hydraulic com, metal stampings, pre-engr metal bldgs, fluid purification prdts)
      Commercial Hidraulica Ltda., Rodavia Presidente Dutra, Km. 12280, Cacapava,
      Sao Paulo, Brazil

COMPTON INTERNATIONAL   625 Madison Ave, New York, NY 10022,
   Tel: (212) 754-1100
   (Advertising)
      Gang Publicidade, Rua Alves Guimaraes 115, 05410, Sao Paulo, Brazil

COMPUTER ASSOCIATES INTL INC   711 Stewart Ave, Garden City, NY 11530,
   Tel: (516) 227-3300
   (Devel/mkt/mgt info mgt & bus applications software)
      Computer Associates do Brasil Ltda., Av. Engenheiro Luiz Carlos Berrini- 1253 6/F,
      04571 Sao Paulo, Brazil

COMPUTERVISION CORP   201 Burlington Rd, Bedford, MA 01730,
   Tel: (617) 275-1800
   (Automation sys, semiconductors)
      Computervision do Brazil Industria e Com., Ltda., Sao Paulo, Brazil

CONOCO INC   600 N Dairy Ashford Rd, Houston, TX 77079, Tel: (713) 293-1000
  (Oil, gas, coal, chems, minerals)
      Conoco Quimica do Brazil Ltda., Av. Paulista 1499, 13 andar, Conj 1301, CEP 01311,
      Sao Paulo, SP, Brazil

CONTINENTAL BANK NA   231 S Lasalle St, Chicago, IL 60697, Tel: (312) 828-2345
  (Coml banking servs)
      Continenal Bank Corp., Caixa Postal 369, Avenida Paulista, 2439-6 Andar,
      01311 Sao Paulo, SP, Brazil
      Continental Banco SA, Caixa Postal 369, Avenida Paulista, 2439-6 Andar,
      01311 Sao Paulo, SP, Brazil

CONTINENTAL CAN CO   PO Box 5410, Stamford, CT 06856, Tel: (203) 357-8110
  (Packaging prdts & mach, metal, plastic & paper containers)
      Metalurgica Matarazzo S.A., Caixa Postal 2400, 01000 Sao Paulo, Brazil
      Shellmar Embalagem Moderna S.A., Via Anchieta Km. 22, 09700 Sao Bernardo, do Campo,
      Brazil

CONTROL DATA CORP   8100 34th Ave S, Minneapolis, MN 55440,
  Tel: (612) 853-8100
  (Control data equip, computer sys serv & financial serv)
      Control Data do Brazil Computadores, Ltda., Av. Pres. Vargas 962, 5th Fl.,
      Rio de Janeiro, Brazil

COOPERTOOLS   PO Box 30100, Raleigh, NC 27622, Tel: (919) 781-7200
  (Mfr hand tools)
      CooperTools Industrial Ltda., Caixa Postal 692, 18100 Sorocaba, SP, Brazil
      The Cooper Group Industria e Comercio Ltda., Caixa Postal 2744, 01000 Sao Paulo,
      SP, Brazil

CORESTATES FINANCIAL CORP   PO Box 7618, Philadelphia, PA 19101,
  Tel: (215) 973-3100
  (Banking)
      Philadelphia Natl. Bank, Rua Libero Badaro 496, 8 andar, P.O. Box 5263, Sao Paulo,
      Brazil

CORNING CORP   Houghton Park, PO Box 2000, Corning, NY 14831,
  Tel: (617) 974-9000
  (Mfr glass, ceramic materials)
      Corning Brasil-Industria e Comercio Ltda., Caixa Postal 20742,
      Av. Horacio Lafer 555, Itaim Bibi, 04538 Sao Paulo, Brazil

COUDERT BROTHERS   200 Park Ave, New York, NY 10166, Tel: (212) 880-4400
  (Lawyers)
      Ulhoa Canto, Rezende, Neviani e Guerra, Av. Almirante Barroso 81, 20,
      000 Rio de Janeiro, Brazil

CPC INTERNATIONAL INC   PO Box 8000, International Plaza, Englewood Cliffs,
  NJ 07632, Tel: (201) 894-4000
  (Mfr consumer food prdts & corn refining prdts)
      Refinacoes de Milho Brazil Ltda., Praca da Republica 468, Caixa Postal 8151,
      01031 Sao Paulo, SP, Brazil

JOHN CRANE INC   6400 Oakton St, Morton Grove, IL 60053, Tel: (708) 967-2400
  (Mfr engineering seals)
      John Crane Brasil Industrial Ltda., Av. Marechal HA Castelo Branco 600,
      Caixa Postal 14, 09700 Sao Bernardo do Campo, SP, Brazil

CROCKER BANK INTERNATIONAL   299 Park Ave, New York, NY 10017,
   Tel: (212) 980-5500
   (Intl banking serv)
     CNB-Brazil, Rua Libero Badaro 377, Rm 709, 01009 Sao Paulo, Brazil

CROWN CORK & SEAL CO INC   Holmesburg Station, PO Box 6208, Philadelphia,
   PA 19136, Tel: (215) 698-5100
   (Cans, bottle caps; filling & packaging mach)
     Crown Cork do Brazil S.A., Rua Guaranta 468, Caixa Postal 10558, Sao Paulo, SP,
     Brazil

CUMMINS ENGINE CO INC   PO Box 3005, Columbus, IN 47202, Tel: (812) 377-5000
   (Mfr diesel engines)
     Cummins Brasil S.A., P.O. Box 13, 07270 Guaruchos, Sao Paulo, Brazil

D'ARCY MASIUS BENTON & BOWLES INC (DMB&B)   1675 Broadway, New York,
   NY 10019, Tel: (212) 468-3622
   (Advertising & communications)
     Salles/Inter-Americana, R. Borges Lagoa 1328, CEP 04038, Sao Paulo, SP, Brazil

D-M-E COMPANY   29111 Stephenson Highway, Madison Heights, MI 48071,
   Tel: (313) 398-6000
   (Basic tooling for plastic molding & die casting)
     DME Polimold Ltda., Rua Vieira De Morais 311, Campo Belo 04617, Sao Paulo, Brazil

DANA CORP   4500 Dorr St, PO Box 1000, Toledo, OH 43697, Tel: (419) 535-4500
   (Mfr prdts & sys for motor vehicle ind)
     Albarus S.A. Industria e Com., Rua Joaquim Silveira 557, Caixa Postal 2181,
       Porto Alegre, RS, Brazil
     Albarus S.A. Industria e Com., Av. Henry Ford 387, Caixa Postal 9913, Sao Paulo,
       SP, Brazil
     COFAP-Cia., Fabricadora de Pecas, Av. Alexandre Gusmao 1395, Santo Andre, SP, Brazil
     Dana Equipamentos Ltda., Av. de Pinedo 394, Socorro, Santo Amaro, Sao Paulo, SP,
       Brazil

DANCER FITZGERALD SAMPLE INTL   405 Lexington Ave, New York, NY 10174,
   Tel: (212) 661-0800
   (Advertising agency)
     Esquire, Praca Pio XI 174, Jardim Botanico, CEP 22461, Rio de Janeiro, Brazil

DANIEL MANN JOHNSON & MENDENHALL   3250 Wilshire Blvd, Los Angeles, CA 90010,
   Tel: (213) 381-3663
   (Architects & engineers)
     Daniel, Mann, Johnson & Mendenhall, Rua Eng. Alfredo Duarte 440, Jardin Botanico,
       Rio de Janeiro, RJ, Brazil

DATA GENERAL CORP   4400 Computer Dr, Westboro, MA 01580, Tel: (617) 366-8911
   (Design, mfr gen purpose computer sys & peripheral prdts & servs)
     Data General Ltda., Ave. das Americas, 4430 GR, 302, CEP 22600 Barra da Tijuca,
       Rio de Janeiro, Brazil

DATAEASE INTL INC   7 Cambridge Dr, Trumbull, CT 06611, Tel: (203) 374-8000
   (Mfr applications devel software)
     Planconsult, Rua Cardeal Arcoverde 620, 05408 Sao Paulo, SP, Brazil

DAY INTL 333 W First St, Dayton, OH 45412, Tel: (513) 226-7000
(Diversified auto, ind & household prdts)
Dayco do Brazil Ind. e Com. Ltda., Ave. Marques de Sao Vincente 1205,
Caixa Postal 4738, 01139 Sao Paulo, SP, Brazil

DE VILBISS CO 300 Phillips Ave, Toledo, OH 43612, Tel: (419) 470-2169
(Mfr spray painting & finishing equip)
DeVilbiss S.A. Ind. e Com., Caixa Postal 8344, 01000 Sao Paulo, SP, Brazil

DEKALB-PFIZER GENETICS 3100 Sycamore Rd, De Kalb, IL 60115,
Tel: (815) 756-7333
(Agric seeds)
Sementes Selecionadas AD Ltd., Rodovia Assis Chateaubriand Km. 85, Caixa,
Postal 371, 14780 Barretos, SP, Brazil

DELTA DRILLING CO PO Box 2012, Tyler, TX 75710, Tel: (214) 595-1911
(Oil & gas explor & contract drilling)
PERBRAS-Empresa Brasileira de Perfuracoes Ltda., Edo. Pernambuco,
Rua Conselheiro Dantas 5, andar 9, Caixa Postal 1346, Salvador, BA, Brazil

DENTSPLY INTL INC PO Box 872, York, PA 17405, Tel: (717) 845-7511
(Mfr dental, medical & ind supplies & equip)
Dentsply Industria e Com., Ltda., Caixa Postal 90915, 25600 Rua Alice Herve 86,
Petropolis, RJ, Brazil

DHJ INDUSTRIES INC 1040 Ave of the Americas, New York, NY 10018,
Tel: (212) 944-4500
(Mfr of knit fabrics, interlinings plastic chips & denim)
Entretelas DHJ S.A., Rua Visconde de Inhauma 58, 8 andar, 20091 Rio de Janeiro,
Brazil

DIAMOND SHAMROCK CORP 1100 Superior Ave, Cleveland, OH 44114,
Tel: (216) 694-5000
(Organic & inorganic chems & specialties, agric chems)
Diamond Shamrock do Brazil, Industria e Com., Ltda., Rua Francisco Dias Velho,
66 Brooklyn, Sao Paulo, Brazil

DISTILLERIE STOCK USA LTD 58-58 Laurel Hill Blvd, Woodside, NY 11375,
Tel: (212) 651-9800
(Mfr of alcoholic beverages)
Seagers & Stock do Brazil S.A., Importadora e Industrial de, Rua Humberto 1, 961,
Caixa Postal 2606, Sao Paulo, SP, Brazil

DONALDSON CO INC PO Box 1299, Minneapolis, MN 55440, Tel: (612) 887-3131
(Filtration prdts & sys)
Donaldson do Brasil Equipamentos Industrias Ltda., Rua Gema 220, Caixa Postal 207,
09900 Diadema, Sao Paulo, Brazil

DOW CHEMICAL CO 2030 Dow Center, Midland, MI 48640, Tel: (517) 636-1000
(Chems, plastics, fibers, pharms)
Cloroquim S.A. Ind. e Com., Praca do Patriarca, Predio Conde Matarazzo, Sao Paulo,
SP, Brazil
Dow Quimica S.A., Av. Brig. Faria Lima 1541 12th-17th, Caixa Postal 30.037,
01451 Sao Paulo, SP, Brazil

DOW CORNING CORP   2220 W Salzburg Rd, PO Box 1767, Midland, MI 48640,
  Tel: (517) 496-4000
  (Silicones, silicon chems, solid lubricants)
    Dow Corning do Brazil, Caixa Postal 4102, 01000 Sao Paulo, SP, Brazil

DRESSER INDUSTRIES INC   1600 Pacific Bldg, PO Box 718, Dallas, TX 75221,
  Tel: (214) 740-6000
  (Diversified supplier of equip & tech serv to energy & natural resource ind)
    Dresser Industria e Com., Ltda., Caixa Postal 2191, 01039 Sao Paulo, SP, Brazil
    Dresser Industria e Com., Ltda., HWB-Galion Div., Caixa 2191, 01039, SP, Brazll
    Dresser Industria e Com., Ltda., Jeffrey Equipamentos Indust,
      Rua 13 de Maio 1954-10, Sao Paulo, Brazil
    Dresser Industria e Com., Ltda., Lodge-Cottrell Div., Rua 13 de Maio 1954-10,
      Sao Paulo, Brazil
    Dresser Industria e Com., Ltda., Manometros Willy Div., Caixa Postal 212,
      CEP 09500, Sao Caetano do Sul, SP, Brazil
    Dresser Industria e Com., Ltda., Wayne Div., Caixa Postal 15036/06,
      Bonsucesso (FJ), Rio de Janeiro, Brazil

E I DU PONT DE NEMOURS & CO   Du Pont Bldg, 1007 Market St, Wilmington,
  DE 19898, Tel: (302) 774-1000
  (Mfr/sale diversified chems, plastics, specialty prdts & fibers)
    DuPont do Brazil S.A., Rua de Consolacao 57, 1-andar, Caixa Postal 8112, Sao Paulo,
      SP, Brazil

DURACELL INTL INC   Berkshire Industrial Park, Bethel, CT 06801,
  Tel: (203) 796-4000
  (Mfr batteries)
    Duracell Do Brasil Ind. e Com., Ave. Eng. Eusebio Stevaux 2105, P.O. Box 12521,
      Sao Paulo, Brazil

DURAMETALLIC CORP   2104 Factory St, Kalamazoo, MI 49001, Tel: (616) 382-8720
  (Mfr mech seals, compression packings, auxiliaries)
    Durametallic do Brazil Ltda., Caixa Postal 8602, Av. Casa Grande 165o, Diadema,
      Sao Paulo, Brazil

EASTMAN & BEAUDINE INC   111 W Monroe, Chicago, IL 60603, Tel: (312) 726-8195
  (Investments)
    Eastman & Beaudine Inc., Rua Cardoso de Almeida, 788 - conj. 53, 05013, Sao Paulo,
      Brazil

EASTMAN KODAK CO   343 State St, Rochester, NY 14650-0518, Tel: (716) 724-4000
  (Devel/mfr photo & chem prdts, info mgmt/video/copier sys, fibers/plastics for
  various ind)
    Kodak Brasileira Com. e Ind., Caixa Postal 225, 01.000 Sao Paulo, SP, Brazil

EATON CORP   100 Erieview Plaza, Cleveland, OH 44114, Tel: (216) 523-5000
  (Advanced tech prdts for transp & ind mkts)
    Eaton Corp. do Brazil, Almeda Franca 84, 04222, Sao Paulo, Brazil
    Eaton S.A. Ind. de Pecas e Acessorios, Via Presidenta Dutra Km 325,
      Sao Jose dos Campos, SP, Brazil
    Eaton-Yale & Towne Ltda., Div. Fuller, Av. Capuava 603, Santo Andre, SP, Brazil

EBASCO SERVICES INC   2 World Trade Center, New York, NY 10048,
  Tel: (212) 839-2685
  (Engineering, constr)
    Ebasco Corp., Caixa Postal 883, ZC-00, Rio de Janeiro, Guanabara, Brazil

ECHLIN INC   100 Double Beach Rd, Branford, CT 06405, Tel: (203) 481-5751
  (Mfr motor vehicle replacement parts)
    Echlin do Brasil S.A., Caixa Postal 10016, CEP 01000 Sao Paulo, SP, Brazil

ECOLAB INC   370 Wabasha St, St Paul, MN 55102, Tel: (612) 293-2233
  (Ind & household detergents, cleaning agents & equip)
    Mangus-Soilax, Ind. e Com. Ltda., Rua Figueira de Melo, 237 A, ZC-08 Sao Crestovao,
    2000, Rio de Janeiro, Brazil

ELECTRO-NITE CO   11601 Caroline Rd, Philadelphia, PA 19154,
  Tel: (215) 464-4200
  (Expendable sensors & instru for iron & steel ind)
    Electro-Nite Instrumentos Ltda., Rua Salgado de Castro 495, Caixa Postal 2758,
    Diadema, CEP 09900, Sao Paulo, Brazil

EMCO WHEATON INC   50 Chamberlain Blvd, PO Box 688, Conneaut, OH 44030,
  Tel: (216) 599-8151
  (Mfr petroleum handling equip- ment)
    Emco Wheaton Ind. & Com. S.A., P.O. Box 2602, ZC-00, Rio de Janeiro, Brazil

ENCYCLOPEDIA BRITANNICA INC   425 N Michigan Ave, Chicago, IL 60611,
  Tel: (312) 321-7000
  (Book publ)
    Encyclopedia Britannica do Brazil, Praca Dom Jose Gaspar 134, andar 3,
    Caixa Postal 30127, Sao Paulo, SP, Brazil

ENGINE PRODUCTS DIV   PO Box 1166, Richmond, IN 47374, Tel: (317) 966-8111
  (Gaskets, seals, packings, etc)
    Cia. Fabricadora de Pecas, Av. Alexandre de Gusmao 1395, Caixa Postal 366,
    Santo Andre, Edo. de SP, Brazil

ENVIROTECH CORP   3000 Sand Hill Road, Menlo Park, CA 94025,
  Tel: (415) 854-2000
  (Supplier of equip & tech for underground mining, ind processing & pollution control)
    Envirotech Equipamentos Industriales Ltda., Caixa Postal 20942,
    Shopping Center Iguatemi, Sao Paulo, SP, Brazil

ERICO PRODUCTS INC   34600 Solon Road, Cleveland, OH 44139,
  Tel: (216) 248-0100
  (Mfr electric welding apparatus & hardware, metal stampings, specialty fasteners)
    Erico do Brazil, Caixa Postal 30397, Av. Santa Marina 1.588, 05036, Sao Paulo,
    Brazil

ERIEZ MAGNETICS   PO Box 10652, Erie, PA 16514, Tel: (814) 833-9881
  (Mfr magnetic, vibratory & metal detection prdts & sys)
    Equipamentos Magneticos do Brazil Ltda., Rua Salgado de Castro 657,
    CEP 09920 Diadema, SP, Brazil

ESCO CORP   2141 NW 25th Ave, Portland, OR 97210, Tel: (503) 228-2141
  (Mfr equip for mining, constr, forestry ind)
    Maquinesco, Conjunto Nacional Edif. Horsa 1, Av. Paulista 2073, Sala 1312,
    01311 Sao Paulo, SP, Brazil

EXIM OVERSEAS INC   2121 Ponce de Leon Blvd, Coral Gables, FL 33134,
  Tel: (305) 444-6444
  (Trading & sales of arms for Armco Latin Div)
    Armco do Brasil, Caixa Postal 16610, 03197 Sao Paulo, SP, Brasil

EXXON CHEMICAL CO   9 Old Kings Hwy S, Darien, CT 06820, Tel: (203) 655-5200
   (Mfr & sales of petrochems)
      Tintas Ypiranga S.A., Rua General Bruce 320, ZC-08, Caixa Postal 2454, ZC-00,
      Rio de Janeiro, RJ, Brazil

FALK CORP   3001 W Canal St, Milwaukee, WI 53208, Tel: (414) 342-3131
   (Mfr gears, geared reducers & drives, couplings)
      Sundstrand do Brasil Equipamentos Ltda., Rua Jose Martins Coelho 300, CEP 04461,
      Santo Amaro, Sao Paulo, Brazil

FERRO CORPORATION   One Erieview Plaza, Cleveland, OH 44114,
   Tel: (216) 641-8580
   (Chems, coatings, plastics, refractories)
      Ferro Enamel do Brazil Ind e Com. Ltda., Av. Senador Vergueiro 2720, Rudge Ramos,
      09740 Sao Bernardo do Campo, Sao Paulo, Brazil
      Nutriplant I.C.L., Caixa Postal 097, Avda. Constante Pavan 1155, 13140 Paulina,
      Sao Paulo, Brazil

FIGGIE INTERNATIONAL INC   4420 Sherwin Rd, Willoughby, OH 44094,
   Tel: (216) 946-9000
   (Fire protection, safety & security, consumer/recreation prdts, electrical &
   electronic instru)
      A-T-O de Brazil, Caixa Postal 1881, Aeroporto de Congonhas, Sao Paulo, Brazil

FIREMENS INSURANCE CO OF NEWARK   80 Maiden Lane, New York, NY 10038,
   Tel: (212) 440-3000
   (Fire, marine & casualty ins)
      Firemen's Insurance Co. of Newark, NJ, Rua Senador Dantas 74, andar 9, ZC-06,
      Rio de Janeiro, RJ, Brazil

FIRST NATIONAL BANK OF BOSTON   100 Federal St, Boston, MA 02110,
   Tel: (617) 434-2200
   (Commercial banking)
      First Natl. Bank of Boston, Rua Libero Badaro 487, Sao Paulo, Brazil
      First Natl. Bank of Boston, Caixa Postal 8263, Rua Libero Badaro 487, Sao Paulo,
      Brazil
      First Natl. Bank of Boston, Caixa Postal 21221, Av. Rio Branco 110, Rio de Janeiro,
      Brazil
      First Natl. Bank of Boston, Caixa Postal 040047, SCS-Quadra 06,
      Edificio Federacao do Comercio,
      First Natl. Bank of Boston, 70000 Brasilia, Brazil
      First Natl. Bank of Boston, Caixa Postal 1175, Av. Francisco Glicerio 1275,
      Campinas, Brazil

FISHER CONTROLS INTL INC   8000 Maryland Ave, Clayton, MO 63105,
   Tel: (314) 694-9900
   (Ind process control equip)
      Fisher Controls do Brasil Ltda., Rua Paes Leme 524, 05424 Sao Paulo, Brazil

FLORIDA INTL FORWARDERS   6905 N W 25th St, PO Box 522085, Miami, FL 33122,
   Tel: (305) 592-6450
   (Air cargo service)
      Transportadora Coral, S.A., Divisao Carga Aerea, Rua Padre Leandro 280, Sao Paulo,
      Brazil

FMC CORP   200 E Randolph Dr, Chicago, IL   60601, Tel: (312) 861-6000
  (Mach & chem for industry, agric & govt)
    FMC do Brazil S.A., Alameda Campinas 463 1st Fl   01404 Sao Paulo, Brazil

FMC MATERIAL HANDLING EQUIP DIV   57 Cooper Ave, Homer City, PA   15748-9234,
  Tel: (412) 479-8011
  (Mfr bulk material handling & automation equip)
    Filsan Equipamentos e Sistemas, Rua Frederico Esteban Jr. 230, 02357, Sao Paulo,
    Brazil

FOOTE CONE & BELDING COMMUNICATIONS INC   101 E Erie St, Chicago,
  IL   60611-2897, Tel: (312) 751-7000
  (Advertising agency)
    FCB/Siboney Publicidade Ltda., Av. Paulista 2073, Edif. Horsa II 25/F, Sao Paulo,
    Brazil

FORD MOTOR CO   The American Road, Dearborn, MI   48121, Tel: (313) 322-3000
  (Mfr automobiles, trucks)
    Autolatina, Rua Professor Manoelito de Ornellas 303, 04719 Sao Paulo, Brazil
    Ford Brazil S.A., Rua Profesor de Ornellas 303, 04799 Sao Paulo, Brazil

FOUR WINDS INTL INC   1 SW Columbia Ave, #1200, Portland, OR   97258,
  Tel: (503) 241-2732
  (Transp of household goods & general cargo)
    Four Winds do Brasil Mudancas Ltda., Rua Sargento Silva Nunes 538,
    21040 Rio de Janeiro, RJ, Brazil
    Four Winds do Brasil Mudancas Ltda., Av. Goncalo Maderia 209, Bairro Jaguare,
    Sao Paulo, Brazil

FOXBORO CO   33 Commercial St, Foxboro, MA   02035, Tel: (508) 543-8750
  (Mfr prdts/provide servs for ind automation)
    Foxboro Brasileira Instrumentacao Ltda., Rua Dr. Seng 235, Caixa Postal 30770,
    01331 Sao Paulo, SP, Brazil

H B FULLER CO   2400 Energy Park Dr, St Paul, MN   55108, Tel: (612) 645-3401
  (Mfr/distr adhesives, sealants, coatings, paints, waxes, sanitation chems)
    H.B. Fuller Brasil Ltda., Av. Paulista, 807, Conj. 606/607, Sao Paulo, CEP 01311,
    Brazil
    H.B. Fuller Brasil Ltda., Rua Professor Joaquim Silva 669,
    Zona Industrial Sorocaba-Sao Paulo CEP 18.000, Brazil

GAF CORP   1361 Alps Rd, Wayne, NJ   07470, Tel: (201) 628-3000
  (Chems, bldg materials, commun)
    GAF do Brasil Industria e Comercio Ltda., Rua Major Sertoria, 212-2, andar,
    Caixa Postal 9693 - V Buarque 012222, Sao Paulo SP, Brazil

GAMLEN CHEMICAL CO   121 S Maple Ave, S San Francisco, CA   94080,
  Tel: (415) 873-1750
  (Chems, detergents & tank cleansers)
    Grupo Sibron Quimca Ltda., Rua Aimara, 96, Ramos, Rio de Janeiro, Brazil
    Grupo Sibron Quimca Ltda., Sao Paulo, Brazil

THE GATES RUBBER CO   PO Box 5887, Denver, CO   80217, Tel: (303) 744-1911
  (Mfr auto/ind belts & hose, hydraulic hose & couplings, molded rubber prdts)
    Gates do Brazil S.A., Rua Cesario Alvim 602, 03054 Sao Paulo, SP, Brazil

GENERAL ELECTRIC CO   3135 Easton Tpk, Fairfield, CT 06431,
Tel: (203) 373-2211
(Diversified mfr, tech & servs)
    General Electric do Brazil S.A., Rua Antonio de Godoi 88, Sao Paulo 01034, SP,
    Brazil

GENERAL FOODS CORP   250 North St, White Plains, NY 10625, Tel: (914) 335-2500
(Processor, distributor & mfr of foods)
    Kibon S.A., Caixa Postal 30266, Sao Paulo, Brazil
    Q-Refres-Ko S.A., Caixa Postal 30700, Sao Paulo, Brazil

GENERAL MOTORS ACCEPTANCE CORP   3044 West Grand Blvd, Detroit, MI 48202,
Tel: (313) 556-5000
(Automobile financing)
    Financiadora GM, Alamedo Santos 647, Sao Paulo, SP, Brazil

GEORGIA-PACIFIC CORP   133 Peachtree St NE, Atlanta, GA 30303,
Tel: (404) 521-4000
(Lumber & paper prdts, metal prdts, chems & plastics)
    Companhia Amazonas Madeiras e Laminados, Trav. Benjamin Constant 1416, Belem, PA,
    Brazil

J GERBER & CO INC   855 Ave of the Americas, New York, NY 10001,
Tel: (212) 613-1100
(Distr steel & steel prdts, aluminum, meat)
    J. Gerber do Brasil Comercial e Exportadora Ltda., Rua Irauna 409, CEP 04518,
    Sao Paulo, Brazil

GILBARCO INC   PO Box 22087, Greensboro, NC 27420, Tel: (919) 292-3011
(Service station equip)
    Gilbarco do Brazil S.A., Caixa Postal 30.495, 01000 Sao Paulo, SP, Brazil

THE GILLETTE CO   Prudential Tower, Boston, MA 02199, Tel: (617) 421-7000
(Mfr/distr shaving prdts, toiletries & cosmetics, stationery prdts)
    Gillette do Brazil Ltda., Av. Suburbana 651 ZC-24, Caixa Postal 1797, ZC-00,
    Rio de Janeiro, RJ, Brazil

GIRARD INDUSTRIES   6531 N Eldridge Pkwy, Houston, TX 77041,
Tel: (713) 466-3100
(Mfr polyurethane foam pipeline cleaners)
    WOMA Equipamentos Ltda., Av. Ferraz Alvim, 135-Jardim Ruyce, 09980 Diadema, SP,
    Brazil

GK TECHNOLOGIES INC   500 W Putnam Ave, Greenwich, CT 06830,
Tel: (203) 661-0100
(Wire cable, electronic tech serv)
    Forest Ltda., Fabica de Condutores Electricos, Via Dutra, Km. 394,
    Guarulhos Sao Paulo, Brazil

GOODYEAR TIRE & RUBBER CO   1144 E Market St, Akron, OH 44316-0001,
Tel: (216) 796-2121
(Mfr tires, rubber prdts)
    Companhia Goodyear do Brazil, Produtos de Borracha, Av. Paulista 854, 8 through 11,
    andar 01310 Sao Paulo, SP, Brazil

GOULD INC   10 Gould Center, Rolling Meadows, IL 60008, Tel: (708) 640-4000
  (Electric sys, batteries, etc)
      Gould do Brazil Eletrica/Eletronica Ltda., Av. Brig. Faria Lima, 01451 Sao Paulo,
        SP, Brazil

GOULDS PUMPS INC   240 Fall St, Seneca Falls, NY 13148, Tel: (315) 568-2811
  (Mfr ind & water sys pumps)
      Goulds Bombas e Equipamentos Ltda., Estrada ITU-Salto Km. 40, CXP 91 Salto,
        Sao Paulo, CEP 133201, Brazil

W R GRACE & CO   1114 Ave of the Americas, New York, NY 10036,
  Tel: (212) 819-5500
  (Specialty chems, natural resources, consumer serv)
      Darex Produtos Quimicos e Plasticos Ltda., Av. Mofarrej 619, Vila Leopoldina,
        Sao Paulo, Brazil

GRAPHIC CONTROLS CORP   PO Box 1271, Buffalo, NY 14240, Tel: (716) 853-7500
  (Mfr plotter supplies, ind/med recording charts, fax papers, disposable med prdts &
  pens)
      Controles Graficos Daru, S.A., Av. Itacoa 2264, Inhauma CEP 21061, Rio de Janeiro,
        Brazil

GREY ADVERTISING INC   777 Third Ave, New York, NY 10017, Tel: (212) 546-2000
  (Advertising)
      SGB Publicidade e Promocoes S.A., Rua 19 de Fevereiro 185, Botafc.go, 20.000,
        Rio de Janeiro, Brazil
      SGB Publicidade e Promocoes S.A., Sao Paulo, Brazil

GROLIER INC   Old Shereman Tpk, Danbury, CT 06816, Tel: (203) 797-3500
  (Publishers)
      Grolier Comercio e Importacao de Livros Ltda., Rua Dr. Silva Leme 83, Sao Paulo,
        SP, Brazil

GTE CORP   One Stamford Forum, Stamford, CT 06904, Tel: (203) 965-2000
  (Electr prdts, telecom sys, publ & commun)
      Automatic Electric do Brazil S.A., Rua Conselheiro Crispiano 69, andar 6,
        Sao Paulo, SP, Brazil
      General Telephone & Electronics do Brazil S.A.,, Rua 13 de Maio 238/240,
        Caixa Postal 9212, Sao Paulo, SP, Brazil
      Sylvania Produtos Electricos, Ltda., Rua Amoipira 157, Sao Pualo, SP, Brazil

FRANK B HALL & CO INC   549 Pleasantville Rd, Briarcliff Manor, NY 10510,
  Tel: (914) 769-9200
  (Insurance)
      Frank B. Hall Corretagem de Seguros Ltda., Ave. Paulista 1106, 01310 Sao Paulo,
        Brazil
      Frank B. Hall Corretagem de Seguros Ltda., Praca Pio X 55, 20040 Rio de Janeiro,
        Brazil

M A HANNA CO   100 Erieview Plaza, Cleveland, OH 44114, Tel: (216) 589-4000
  (Iron ore, nickel & silicon, oil & gas, coal, mgmt serv)
      Mineracoes Brasileiros Reunidas, Praia de Botafoqo 300, 22259 Rio de Janeiro, Brazil
      Uniao de Industrial Petroquimicas S.A., Rua Araujo Porta Alegre 36,
        20030 Rio de Janeiro, Brazil

HARCOURT BRACE JOVANOVICH INC   Harcourt Brace Jovanovich Bldg, Orlando,
   FL 32887, Tel: (305) 345-2000
   (Book publ, tests & related serv, journals, facisimile reprints, mgmt consult,
   operates parks/shows)
      Academy Press do Brazil Editora Ltda., Praca Jorge de Lima, Sao Paulo, Brazil

HARNISCHFEGER INDUSTRIES INC   PO Box 554, Milwaukee, WI 53201,
   Tel: (414) 671-4400
   (Mfr mining & material handling equip, papermaking mach, computer sys)
      Harnischfeger do Brazil Com. e Ind. Ltda., Av. Paulista 2202, andar 7, Sao Paulo,
      SP, Brazil

HARPER & ROW PUBLISHERS INC   10 E 53rd St, New York, NY 10022,
   Tel: (212) 593-7000
   (Book publishers)
      Editora Harper & Row do Brazil Ltda., Caixa Postal - 45312, 01000 Vila, Mariana,
      Sao Paulo, SP Brazil

THE HARPER GROUP INC   260 Townsend St, PO Box 77933, San Francisco,
   CA 94107, Tel: (415) 978-0600
   (Ocean/air freight fwdg, customs brokerage, packing & whse, logistics mgt, ins)
      Circle Freight Intl. Brazil, PO Box 18.381, 04699 SP, Brazil

HCA INTL CO   1 Park Plaza, PO Box 550, Nashville, TN 37202,
   Tel: (615) 327-9551
   (Hospital & health care mgmt)
      Amico, Rua Acevedo Macedo 92, Vila Mariana, CEP 04013, Sao Paulo

HERCULES INC   Hercules Plaza, Wilmington, DE 19894, Tel: (302) 594-5000
   (Mfr spec chems, plastics, film & fibers, coatings, resins, food ingredients)
      Hercules do Brazil Produtos Quimicos, Av. Brig. Faria Lima 1664, andar 9,
      Caixa Postal 1524, 01452 Sao Paulo, SP, Brazil

HERSHEY FOODS CORP   100 Mansion Rd E, Hershey, PA 17033, Tel: (717) 534-4200
   (Chocolate, food & confectionary prdts, restaurant operations)
      Petybone Industrias Alimenticias Ltda., Rua Coriolano 1313, CEP 05047, Sao Paulo,
      Brazil

HEWLETT-PACKARD CO   3000 Hanover St, PO Box 10301, Palo Alto, CA 94303-0890,
   Tel: (415) 857-1501
   (Mfr measurement & computation prdts & sys)
      Hewlett-Packard do Brazil S.A., Alameda Rio Negro 750, Alphaville,
      06400 Barneri SP, Brazil

HILL & KNOWLTON INC   420 Lexington Ave, New York, NY 10017,
   Tel: (212) 697-5600
   (Public relations, public affairs, comm counseling)
      ACI-Assessoria de Comunicacao Integrada Ltda., Rua Cenra 142, Pacaembu 01243,
      Sao Paulo, SP, Brazil

HOBART BROTHERS CO   Hobart Sq, Troy, OH 45373-2928, Tel: (513) 339-6000
   (Arc/automatic welding sys, power sys)
      Cia. de Maquinas Hobart-Dayton do Brazil, Caixa Postal 2218, Sao Paulo, SP Brazil

HOHENBERG BROS CO   266 S Front St, Memphis, TN 38103, Tel: (901) 527-5401
   (Cotton)
      Hohenberg S.A., Comercio de Algodao, Rua Jose Bonifacio 278, Salas 406-407,
      Sao Paulo, SP, Brazil

HOLIDAY INNS INC   3742 Lamar Ave, Memphis, TN 38195, Tel: (901) 362-4001
   (Hotels, restaurants, casinos)
      Holiday Inn, Rua Aymores 501, Marilia, Sao Paulo, Brazil
      Holiday Inn, Rua Alvares Cabral 1.120, Ribeirao Preto, Brazil
      Holiday Inn, Rua Washington Luiz 399, Americana,.SP, Brazil
      Holiday Inn, Av. Ana Costa 555, Santos, SP, Brazil

HORWATH & HORWATH INTL   919 Third Ave, New York, NY 10022,
   Tel: (212) 980-3100
   (Public accountants & auditors)
      Soteconti Auditores Independentes S/C, Av. Paulista 1754, 01310, Sao Paulo, SP,
      Brazil

E F HOUGHTON & CO   PO Box 930, Valley Forge, PA 19482-0930,
   Tel: (215) 666-4000
   (Mfr spec chems, hydraulic fluids, lubricants)
      E.F. Houghton do Brazil, Caixa Postal 107, Capuava Mava, Sao Paulo, Brazil

HPD INC   1717 N Naper Blvd, Naperville, IL 60540, Tel: (708) 357-7330
   (Personal processing, recovery/ pollution control sys)
      Confab Industrial S.A., Caixa Postal 3411, Sao Paulo, Brazil

HUGHES TOOL CO   PO Box 2539, Houston, TX 77001, Tel: (713) 924-2222
   (Equip & serv to oil & gas explor & prod ind)
      Hughes Tool do Brazil, Av. Almirante Barroso, 22 -8th Floor, Caixa Postal 1597,
      Rio de Janeiro, CLP 20031, Brazil

HYSTER CO   PO Box 2902, Portland, OR 97208, Tel: (503) 280-7000
   (Fork lifts, trucks, trailers, towing winches, personnel lifts, compaction equip)
      Companhia Hyster, Av. Nacoes Unidas 22.777, Caixa Postal 4151, Santo Amaro 04795,
      01000, Sao Paulo, Brazil

ICI AMERICAS INC   Wilmington, DE 19897, Tel: (302) 575-3000
   (Chems, pharms, dyes, plastics, films, etc)
      Atlas Industrias Quimicas S.A., Rua Cons. Crispiniano 72, 7, Caixa Postal 5245,
      01037 Sao Paulo, SP, Brazil

ILLINOIS TOOL WORKS INC   8501 West Higgins Rd, Chicago, IL 60631,
   Tel: (312)693-3040
   (Metal cutting tools, fasteners, sealants, gear measuring instru)
      ITWSA Electronica e Plasticos, Av. Santa Catarina, 941 Aero Porto, Sao Paulo, SP,
      Brazil

IMCO SERVICES   5950 N Course Dr, Houston, TX 70072, Tel: (713) 561-1300
   (Drilling fluids)
      Halliburton-IMCO do Brazil Servicos Com. e Ind. Ltda., Praia do Flamengo 200,
      Rio de Janeiro, Brazil

INA CORPORATION   1600 Arch St, Philadelphia, PA 19101, Tel: (215) 523-5335
   (Holding co: ins, financial serv)
      Campanhia Colina de Seguros, Edificio Big 34th Floor, Rua Buenos Aires 68,
      Caixa Postal 1293 ZC-00, Rio de Janeiro, Brazil

(cont)

Campanhia Colina de Seguros, Rua Libero Badaro 377, 15 andar, 15th Floor,
   Caixa Postal 6698, Sao Paulo, 01000, Brazil
Campanhia Colina de Seguros, Av. Alfonso Pena 748, Valente, Caixa Postal 779,
   Belo Horizonte, Brazil
Insurance Company of North America, Rua Portugal 19, 10th Floor,
   Edificio Regente Feijo, Caixa Postal 61, Salvador, Brazil

INDUCTOTHERM CORP   10 Indel Ave, Rancocas, NJ 08073, Tel: (609) 267-9000
(Mfr induction melting furnaces)
   Inductoheat Brazil Ltda., Rua Henrique Ongari 100, 05038 Sao Paulo, Brazil
   Inductotherm Industria e Comercio Ltda., Caixa Postal 143, Av. Roberto Gordon 455,
   CEP 09900, Diadema, SP, Brazil

INSTRON CORP   100 Royall St, Canton, MA 02021, Tel: (617) 828-2500
(Testing instru)
   Equipamentes Cientificos Instron Ltda., Alameda Joaquin Eurenio de Lima 680,
   C.J. 74-01463, Sao Paulo, Brazil

INTERNATIONAL ADVERTISING SERVICE INC   90 Park Ave, New York, NY 10016,
Tel: (212) 972-4190
(Advertising)
   Intl. Advertising Service - IAS, Av. Rio Branco 251, andar 16, ZC-39,
   Caixa Postal 2818, ZC-00, Rio de Janeiro, RJ, Brazil

INTERNATIONAL FLAVORS & FRAGRANCES INC   521 W 57th St, New York, NY 10019,
Tel: (212) 765-5500
(Create/mfr flavors, fragrances & aroma chems)
   I.F.F. Essencias e Fragrancias Ltda., Av. Brazil 22351, Caixa Postal 27019, ZC-27,
   Rio de Janeiro, RJ, Brazil

INTERNATIONAL PAINT CO INC   PO Box 386, Union, NJ 07083, Tel: (212) 825-0800
(Paints)
   Tintas Intl. S.A., Caixa Postal 872, ZC-00, Rio de Janeiro, RJ, Brazil

INTERNATIONAL STANDARD ELECTRIC CORP   320 Park Ave, New York, NY 10022,
Tel: (212) 752-6000
(Telecommun equip)
   Standard Electrica S.A., Av. Rio Branco 123, andar 20, ZC-21, Rio de Janeiro, RJ,
   Brazil

IRECO INC   Crossroads Tower, 11th fl, Salt Lake City, UT 84144,
Tel: (801) 364-4800
(Explosive supplies, accessories for ind & military applications; alu- minum granules)
   Ireco Britanite Quimicas Ltda, Rua Brigadeiro Franco 1461, 8000, Curitiba PR, Brazil

IRVING TRUST CO   1 Wall St, New York, NY 10015, Tel: (212) 487-2121
(Intl banking)
   Banco de Investimento Credibanco S.A., Rua Visconde de Inhauma 38, Rio de Janeiro,
   Brazil

ITT CORP   1330 Ave of the Americas, New York, NY 10019, Tel: (212) 258-1000
(Diversified mfr, tech & services)
   Alfred Teves do Brazil Ind. e Com. Ltda., Rua 21 de Marco s/n, Varzia Paulista, SP,
   Brazil
   Cia. Intl. de Importacao e Exportacao, Av. Rio Branco 99-101, ZC-21,
   Ciaxa Postal 430, ZC-21, Rio de Janeiro, RJ, Brazil

ITT SHERATON CORP   60 State St, Boston, MA 02108, Tel: (617) 367-3600
(Hotel operations)
   Petribu Sheraton Hotel, Avda. Bernado Veira de Melo 1624, Piedade,
      Jaboatao Dos Guararapes, PE 54410, Brazil
   Sheraton Mofarrej Hotel & Towers, Alameda Santos 1437, Sao Paulo, Brazil
   Sheraton Rio Hotel & Towers, Avda. Niemeyer 121, 22450 Rio de Janeiro, Brazil

ITW MAGNAFLUX   7300 W Lawrence Ave, Chicago, IL 60656, Tel: (708) 867-8000
(Mfr testing & inspection equip)
   Kormag, Rua Carlos Weber 267, Vila Leopoldina 05303, Sao Paulo, Brazil

JOHN HANCOCK MUTUAL LIFE INSURANCE CO   200 Clarendon St, PO Box 111, Boston,
MA 02117, Tel: (617) 572-6000
(Life ins)
   John Hancock Services Internacionais Ltda., c/o Sul America Companhia,
      Nacional de Segieros de Vida, 04120 Sao Paulo, Brazil
   Sul American Companhia Nacional de Seguros de Vida, Caixa Postal 971,
      Rio de Janeiro, RJ, Brazil

JOHNSON & HIGGINS   125 Broad St, New York, NY 10005, Tel: (212) 574-7000
(Ins brokerage, benefit conslt)
   Johnson & Higgins - Eluma, Av. Rio Branco, 125, 20th Floor, 20040 ZC-00,
      Caixa Postal 205, Rio de Janeiro, RJ, Brazil
   Johnson & Higgins - Eluma, Sao Paulo, SP, Brazil

JOHNSON & JOHNSON   One Johnson & Johnson Plaza, New Brunswick, NJ 08933,
Tel: (201) 524-0400
(Surgical, med & baby prdts)
   Janssen Farmaceutica Ltda., Sao Paulo, Brazil
   Johnson & Johnson Professional Products Ltda., Sao Faulo, Brazil
   Johnson & Johnson S.A., Ind. e Com., Av. do Estado 5459, Caixa Postal 7136,
      01515 Sao Paulo, SP, Brazil

S C JOHNSON & SON INC   1525 Howe St, Racine, WI 53403, Tel: (414) 631-2000
(Home, auto, commercial & personal care prdts, specialty chems)
   Companhias Ceras Johnson, Caixa Postal 2757, Rio de Janeiro, Brazil

KAISER ALUMINUM & CHEMICAL CORP   300 Lakeside Dr, Oakland, CA 94643,
Tel: (415) 271-3300
(Aluminum & aluminum prdts, chems)
   Kaiser Aluminio do Brazil Ltda., Campinas Commercial Center Av.,
      Princesa D'Oeste 1645, Bloco a Campinas (SP), CEP 13100, Brazil

KELLOGG CO   235 Porter St, Battle Creek, MI 49016, Tel: (616) 966-2000
(Food prdts)
   Kellogg Co. do Brazil, Rua Augusto Ferreira de Moraes 650, Sao Paulo, SP, Brazil

THE KENDALL CO   PO Box 10, Boston, MA 02101, Tel: (617) 423-2000
(Surgical dressings, baby prdts)
   Kendall do Brazil Ind. e Com. Ltda., Rua Laguna 191, Santo Amaro, 04728, Sao Paulo,
      SP, Brazil

KENNEDY VAN SAUN CORP   PO Box 500, Danville, PA 17821, Tel: (717) 275-3050
(Mineral processing & handling equip)
   KVS Ltda., c/o Stroeter, Trench e Veirano, Rua Martiniano de Carvalho 1049,
      Paraiso, CEP 01321, Caixa Postal 2

KENT-MOORE CORP   28635 Mound Rd, Warren, MI 48092, Tel: (313) 574-2332
  (Mfr service equip for auto, constr, recreational, military & agric vehicles)
    Kent-Moore do Brasil Ltda., Rua Joao de Araujo 830, Sao Paulo 04462, Brazil

KEPNER-TREGOE INC   Research Rd, PO Box 704, Princeton, NJ 08542,
  Tel: (609) 921-2806
  (Mgmt & organizational devel)
    Proacao S/L Ltda., Rua Dr. Jesuino Maciel 360, CEP 04615, Sao Paulo, Brazil

KERR MANUFACTURING CO   28200 Wick Rd, Romulus, MI 48174, Tel: (313) 946-7800
  (Mfr dental supplies, jewelry mfg supplies & equip)
    Sybron Kerr Industria e Comercia Ltda., Av. Amancio Gaiolli 775,
      07000 Bonsucesso Guarulhos, Caixa Postal 193, Brazil
    Sybron Kerr Industria e Comercio Ltda., Av. Amancio Gaiolli 775h,
      07000 Bonsucesso-Guarulhos, CP 193, Sao Paulo, Brazil

KIENBAUM INTL GROUP   110 Gibraltar Rd, PO Box 238, Horsham, PA 19044,
  Tel: (215) 674-5210
  (Intl business consulting)
    Kienbaum Consultores SC Ltda., Rua Joao Pimenta 80, Caixa Postal 21378,
      04736 Sao Paulo, Brazil

KIMBERLY-CLARK CORP   PO Box 619100, Dallas, TX 75261-1200,
  Tel: (214) 830-1200
  (Mfr fiber-based prdts for personal care, pulp & forest prdts; air transport)
    K-C do Brasil, Sao Paulo, Brazil

KING RANCH INC   16825 Northchase, #1450, Houston, TX 77060,
  Tel: (713) 872-5566
  (Livestock, oil & gas)
    King Ranch do Brazil S.A. Agro-Pastoril, Rua Formosa 367, andar 9,
      Caixa Postal 4210, Sao Paulo. SP, Brazil

KNOLL INTL   655 Madison Ave, New York, NY 10021, Tel: (212) 826-2400
  (Furniture & fabrics)
    Forma S.A., Av. Faria Lima 1805, Sao Paulo, ZC-01451, Brazil

KOPPERS CO INC   Koppers Bldg, 437 Seventh Ave, Pittsburgh, PA 15219,
  Tel: (412) 227-2000
  (Constr materiald & serv; chem & bldg prdts)
    Koppers Importadora Ltda., Caixa Postal 13.273, Sao Paulo, SP, 02064, Brazil

KORN/FERRY INTL   237 Park Ave, New York, NY 10017, Tel: (212) 687-1834
  (Executive search)
    Korn/Ferry Intl. Ltda., Ave. Indianapolis 80, 04062 Sao Paulo, Brazil

LANMAN & KEMP-BARCLAY & CO INC   25 Woodland Ave, Westwood, NJ 07675,
  Tel: (201) 666-4990
  (Mfr pharms, toiletries)
    Lanman & Kemp-Barclay & Co. of Brazil, Rua Figueira de Melo 406, Sala C. ZC-15,
      Caixa Postal 1274, ZC--00, Rio de Janeiro, RJ, Brazil

LE TOURNEAU INC LONGVIEW DIV   PO Box 2307, Longview, TX 75606,
  Tel: (214) 753-3449
  (Heavy constr, mining mach & equip)
    Rimi Equipamentos Ltda., Av. Franklin Roosevelt 238, Rio de Janeiro, RJ, Brazil

LEVI STRAUSS & CO   1155 Battery, San Francisco, CA 94111, Tel: (415) 544-6000
(Mfr wearing apparel)
   Levi Strauss do Brazil Industria e Comercio Ltda., Rodovia Raposo Tavares Km. 24,
      5 Jardim da Gloria, Cotia 06700, Sao Paulo, Brazil

ELI LILLY & CO   307 E McCarty St, Indianapolis, IN 46285, Tel: (317) 261-2000
(Pharms, agric & cosmetic prdts)
   Eli Lilly do Brazil Ltda., Av. Morumbi 8264, Sao Paulo, SP, Brazil
   Eli Lilly do Brazil Ltda., Av. Morumbi 8264, Brooklyn Paulista, Caixa Postal 30861,
      01000 Sao Paulo, SP, Brazil

THE LINCOLN ELECTRIC CO   22801 St Clair Ave, Cleveland, OH 44117,
   Tel: (216) 481-8100
(Mfr arc welding equip & consumables, elec motors)
   Lincoln Brasoldas Ltda., Avda. Brasil 50.701, ZI de Palmares, Campo Grance,
      23065 Rio de Janeiro, RJ, Brazil

LINTAS:WORLDWIDE   1 Dag Hammarskjold Plaza, New York, NY 10017,
   Tel: (212) 605-8000
(Advertising agency)
   Lintas:Brazil, Rua Bela Cintra 643, 01415 Sao Paulo, Brazil

LIQUID CARBONIC CORP   135 S LaSalle St, Chicago, IL 60603,
   Tel: (312) 855-2500
(Compressed gases, etc)
   Liquid Carbonic Industrias S.A., Av. Nazareth 1299, Caixa Postal 1108, Sao Paulo,
      SP, Brazil

ARTHUR D LITTLE INC   25 Acorn Park, Cambridge, MA 02140-2390,
   Tel: (617) 864-5770
(Technology & mgmt consulting)
   Arthur D. Little Ltda., Avda. Brigadeiro Faria Lima 2003, 19 Andar, Conj. 190,
      Jarim Paulistano, Sao Paulo, Brazil

LONE STAR INDUSTRIES INC   One Greenwich Plaza, Greenwich, CT 06830,
   Tel: (203) 661-3100
(Cement & bldg materials)
   Companhia Nacional de Cimento Portland, Almirante Barroso 52, Rio de Janeiro, Brazil

LORD CORP   2000 W Grandview Blvd, Erie, PA 16514, Tel: (814) 868-0924
(Adhesives, coatings, chems, film prdts)
   Lord Industrial Ltda., R. General Jardim 770, 9 andar, Conj. 9D, CEP 01223,
      Sao Paulo, SP, Brazil

LUBRIZOL CORP   29400 Lakeland Blvd, Wickliffe, OH 44092, Tel: (216) 943-4200
(Chem additives for lubricants & fuels)
   Produtos Quimicos Lubrizol do Brazil, Av. Rio Branco 156, salas 2720/25,
      Rio de Janeiro, RJ, Brazil

LUMMUS CREST   1515 Broad St, Bloomfield, NJ 07003, Tel: (201) 893-1515
(Engr & constr)
   Setal Lummus Engenharia e Construcoes S.A., Av. Das Nacoes Unidas 18605,
      Sao Paulo 04795, Brazil

M&T CHEMICALS INC   PO Box 1104, Rahway, NJ 07065, Tel: (201) 499-0200
  (Specialty chems & application technologies)
    M & T Produtos Quimicos Ltda., Av. 9 de Julho 15617, 9 andar, CEP 01407, Sao Paulo,
    Brazil

MALLINCKRODT INC   675 McDonnell Blvd, PO Box 5840, St Louis, MO 63134,
  Tel: (314) 895-2012
  (Med/ind chems, organics, pharms)
    Mallinkrodt Produtos Diagnosticos e Quimcos Ltda., Rio de Janeiro, Brazil

MANPOWER INC   5301 N Ironwood Rd, PO Box 2053, Milwaukee, WI 53201-2053,
  Tel: (414) 961-1000
  (Temporary help)
    Manpower Brazil, Etica Servicos Temporarios Ltda., Casa Central, Rua Jupi 215,
    04753 Sao Paulo, Brazil

MARSH & McLENNAN COS INC   1221 Ave of the Americas, New York, NY 10020-1011,
  Tel: (212) 997-2000
  (Insurance)
    Tudor-Marsh & McLennan Ltda., Rua Jose Guerra 626, Sao Paulo, SP, Brazil

MARSTELLER INTL   1 E Wacker Dr, Chicago, IL 60601, Tel: (312) 329-1100
  (Advertising, marketing research, sales promotion)
    Burson-Marsteller Ltda., Av. Brigaderio Faria Lima 1451, 01451 Sao Paulo, Brazil

MEASUREX CORP   One Results Way, Cupertino, CA 95014, Tel: (408) 255-1500
  (Mfr computer integrated mfg sys)
    Measurex do Brazil, Rua Coelho Neto 329, 13100 Campinas, SP, Brazil

MEDTRONIC INC   7000 Central Ave, NE, Minneapolis, MN 55432,
  Tel: (612) 574-4000
  (Mfr med devices, med serv)
    Medtronic do Brazil Ltda., Av. Tambore 1433, Alphaville 06400, Barueri, Sao Paulo,
    Brazil

MEEHANITE METAL CORP   9909 Clayton Rd, St Louis, MO 63124,
  Tel: (314) 994-3570
  (Castings)
    Metais Meehanite S.A., Av. NS Copacabana 2, sala 401, Rio de Janeiro, RJ, Brazil

MEMOREX CORP   San Thomas at Central Expressway, Santa Clara, CA 95052,
  Tel: (408) 987-1000
  (Magnetic recording tapes, etc)
    Memorex do Brazil, Productos de Precisao Ltda., Caixa Postal 5708, Sao Paulo, Brazil

MERCK SHARP & DOHME INTL   PO Box 2000, Rahway, NJ 07065, Tel: (201) 574-4000
  (Pharms, chems & biologicals)
    Merck Sharp & Dohme Industria Quimica e Farmaceutica Ltda., Av. Brig. Faria 1-ima,
    1815, andar 12, Caixa Postal 8734, Sao Paulo, 01451, SP, Brazil

MERGENTHALER LINOTYPE CO   201 Old Country Rd, Melville, NY 11747,
  Tel: (516) 673-4197
  (Photocomposition machs, sys & equip)
    Linotypo do Brazil S.A., Caixa Postal 23019, ZC-08, Rio de Janeiro, Guanabara,
    Brazil

MERRILL LYNCH PIERCE FENNER & SMITH   World Financial Center, 225 Liberty St,
New York, NY 10080, Tel: (212) 449-1000
(Brokers, securities, commodities)
   Merrill Lynch & Co., Rua Sao Bento 365-2 andar, Sao Paulo SP, 01011, Brazil

METALLURG INC   25 E 39th St, New York, NY 10016, Tel: (212) 686-4010
(Mfr ferrous & nonferrous alloys & metals)
   Cia Industrial Fluminense, Rua Sete de Setembro 55-10 andar, CEP 20.050,
     Rio de Janeiro, RJ, Brazil
   Companhia de Estanho Minas Brasil, Rua Sete de Setembro 55-10 andar, CEP 20.050,
     Rio de Janeiro, RJ, Brazil
   Metallurg do Brasil Ltda., Rua Sete de Setembro 55-10 andar, DEP 20.050,
     Rio de Janeiro, RJ, Brazil

METCO DIV OF PERKIN-ELMER   1101 Prospect Ave, Westbury, NY 11590,
Tel: (516) 334-1300
(Mfr/serv thermal spray coating equip & supplies)
   Perkin-Elmer Ind. y Com. Ltda. Divisao Metco, Rua Major Freire 749,
     Vila Monte Alegre, CEP 04204, Sao Paulo, Brazil

MIDLAND-ROSS CORP   20600 Chagrin Blvd, Cleveland, OH 44122,
Tel: (216) 491-8400
(Thermal processing sys, steelcast- ings, elect pdts, mech controls)
   Stein Surface Combustion Ltda., Via Anhanguera, Km. 83.5, P.O. Box 353, Valinhos,
     Sao Paulo, Brazil

MILLIPORE CORP   Ashley Rd, Bedford, MA 01730, Tel: (617) 275-9205
(Precision filters)
   Millipore Ind. e Com. Ltda., Caixa Postal 19065, Sao Paulo, CEP 01000, Brazil

MINE SAFETY APPLIANCES CO   PO Box 426, Pittsburgh, PA 15230,
Tel: (421) 273 5000
(Safety equip, ind filters)
   MSA do Brasil Ltda., Caixa Postal 376, 09900 Diadema, Sao Paulo, Brazil

MINER & MINER CONSULTING ENGINEERS LTD   PO Box 548, Greeley, CO 80632,
Tel: (303) 352-3706
(Engineering consultants)
   INEAL, Av. Rio Branco 133, andar 10, sala 1003, Rio de Janeiro, RJ, Brazil

MISSION MFG CO   PO Box 40402, Houston, TX 77040, Tel: (713) 460-6200
(Oil field equip)
   TRW Mission Industrial Ltda., Rua Sargento Silvio Hollemback 151, Barros Filho,
     Rio de Janeiro, JR, Brazil

MNC INTERNATIONAL BANK   2 N Charles St, Baltimore, MD 21201,
Tel: (301) 244-6804
(Intl banking)
   Maryland National S/C Ltda., SHIS Q107, Comercio Local, Bloco C #71, Sala 203,
     71600 Brasilia, DF, Brazil

MOBIL CHEMICAL INTL LTD   150 E 42nd St, New York, NY 10017,
Tel: (212) 883-4242
(Paints & finishes)
   Mobil Tintas S.A., Rua Piratinninga 84, Santo Amaro, Caixa Postal 8989, Sao Paulo,
     SP, Brazil

MOBIL CORP   150 E 42nd St, New York, NY 10017, Tel: (212) 883-4242
   (Petroleum explor, prdts)
      Mobil Oil do Brazil Ind. e Com., Ltda., Av. Paulista 1009, andar 4,
      Caixa Postal 8121, Sao Paulo, SP, Brazil

MONROE AUTO EQUIPMENT CO   International Dr, Monroe, MI 48161,
   Tel: (313) 243-8000
   (Automotive ride control equip)
      Monroe Auto Pecas S.A., Praca Varlador Marcos Portioli 26, CEP 13, 800, Mogi Mizim,
      SP, Brazil

MONSANTO CO   800 N Lindbergh Blvd, St Louis, MO 63167, Tel: (314) 694-1000
   (Mfr chem & agric prdts, pharms, ind process equip, man-made fibers, plastics)
      Monsanto do Brasil SA (MOBRASA), Rua Paes Lerne 524, Edif. Passarelli,
      05424 Pinheiros, C.P. 61535, CEP 01000, Sao Paulo, SP, Brazil

MOOG INC   East Aurora, NY 14052-0018, Tel: (716) 652-2000
   (Mfr precision control components & sys)
      Moog do Brazil Controles Ltda., Rua Prof. Campos de Oliveira 338,
      Jurubatuba-Santo Amaro, Sao Paulo, Brazil

MORRISON KNUDSEN CORP   1 Morrison Knudsen Plaza, PO Box 73, Boise, ID 83707,
   Tel: (208) 386-5000
   (Design, procurement, constr)
      Companhia Morrison Knudsen de Engenharia, Ave. Amazonas 298, Belo Horizonte, MG,
      Brazil

MOTION PICTURE EXPORT ASSN OF AMERICA   522 Fifth Ave, New York, NY 10036,
   Tel: (212) 840-6161
   (Motion picture trade association)
      MPEAA Associacao Brasileira Cinematografica, Rua Mexico 31, Rio de Janeiro, RJ,
      Brazil

MTS SYSTEMS CORP   PO Box 24012, Minneapolis, MN 55424, Tel: (612) 937-4000
   (Electrohydraulic testing & prod equip, mach controls)
      Arotec S.A., Av. D. Joao VI 489-B, Brotas, 40000 Salvador, BA, Brazil
      Arotec S.A., Rua Turquesa 448, Bairro Prado, 30410 Belo Horizonte, MG, Brazil
      Arotec S.A., Av. Marechal Floriano Peixoto 6432, V. Hauer, 80000 Curitiba, PR,
      Brazil
      Arotec S.A., Rua Felipe Camarao 751, Sala 705, Rio Branco, 90210 Porto Alegro, RS,
      Brazil
      Arotec S.A., Av. Paulo de Frontim 667, Rio Comprido, 20260 Rio de Janeiro, RJ,
      Brazil
      Arotex S.A. Industria Comercio, Rua Howard A. Acheson, Jr. 393, 06700 Cotia, SP,
      Brazil
      MTS Sistemas do Brasil Ltda., Av. Pacaembu 8111, 01234 Sau Paulo, SP, Brazil

McCANN-ERICKSON WORLDWIDE   750 Third Ave, New York, NY 10017,
   Tel: (212) 697-6000
   (Advertising)
      McCann-Erickson Publicidade Ltda., Av. Almirante Barroso 63, 160/170 andares,
      20031 Rio de Janeiro, Brazil
      McCann-Erickson Publicidade Ltda., other locations in Brazil

McCORMICK & CO INC   11350 McCormick Rd, Hunt Valley, MD 21031,
   Tel: (301) 771-7301
   (Seasons, flavorings, specialty foods)
      McCormick do Brasil, S.A., Sao Paulo, Brazil

McGRAW-HILL INC   1221 Ave of the Americas, New York, NY 10020,
   Tel: (212) 512-2000
   (Books, magazines, info sys, financial serv, b/cast operations)
      Editora McGraw-Hill do Brazil Ltda., Ave. Paulo de Frontim 679, 20000 Rio,
      de Janeiro, Brazil

NABISCO BRANDS INC   Nabisco Brands Plaza, East Hanover, NJ 07936,
   Tel: (201) 503-2000
   (Mfr food prdts)
      Productos Alimenticios Fleischmann E Royal Ltda., Av. Pedro 11, 250 Sao Cristovao,
      Rio de Janeiro RJ, CEP 20.941, Brazil
      Productos Alimenticios Fleischmann E Royal Ltda., Rua 15 de Novembro s/no. CONCHAL,
      Sao Paulo, CEP 13.810,
      Productos Alimenticios Fleischmann E Royal Ltda., Caixa Postal 32, Brazil

NALCO CHEMICAL CO   One Nalco Center, Naperville, IL 60566-1024,
   Tel: (708) 305-1000
   (Chems for water & waste water treatment, oil prod & refining, ind processes;
   water/energy mgmt serv)
      Nalco Produtos Quimicos Ltda., Rua Americo Brasiliense, 998 04715 Sao Paulo,
      Caixa Postal 1407, 01050 Sao Paulo, SP, Brazil

NASH INTL CO   310 Wilson Ave, Norwalk, CT 06856, Tel: (203) 852-5700
   (Mfr vacuum pumps & compressors)
      Nash do Brazil Bombas Ltda., Av. das Nacoes Unidas 1550, Santo Amaro,
      Caixa Postal 636, Sao Paulo, SP, Brazil

NASHUA CORP   44 Franklin St, Nashua, NH 03061, Tel: (603) 880-2323
   (Mfr/distr/serv office copier sys & supplies)
      Nashua do Brasil S.A., Rua A #355 Quadra B - Lote 4, Campo Grande, Rio de Janeiro,
      Brazil
      Nashua do Brazil Sistemas Reprograficos, Rua Voluntarios da Patria 179, Batafogo,
      RJ, Brazil

NATIONAL BULK CARRIERS INC   1345 Ave of the Americas, New York, NY 10105,
   Tel: (212) 765-3000
   (Real estate development, mgmt serv)
      Jari Florestal e Agropecuaria Ltda., Rua 15 de Novembro 226, andar 2,
      Edificio Chamie, Belem, PA, Brazil

NATIONAL CHEMSEARCH CORP   2727 Chemsearch Blvd, Irving, TX 75061,
   Tel: (214) 438-0211
   (Commercial chem prdts)
      Natl. Chemsearch Ind. e Com. Ltda., Rua Tabatinguera 278, Caixa Postal 7023,
      Sao Paulo, SP, Brazil

NATIONAL GYPSUM CO   4500 Lincoln Plaza, Dallas, TX 75201, Tel: (214) 740-4500
   (Building prdts & servs)
      Austin Brasil Projetos e Construcoes Ltd., Sao Paulo, Brazil

NCR CORP   1700 S Patterson Blvd, Dayton, OH 45479, Tel: (513) 445-2000
(Develop/mfr/sell/serv business info processing sys)
   NCR do Brasil, S.A., Av. Marechal Floriana 96, Caixa Postal 974-ZC-00,
      Rio de Janeiro 20080, RJ, Brazil

NICHOLSON FILE CO   PO Box 728, Apex, NC 27502, Tel: (919) 362-7500
(Files, rasps, saws)
   Nicholson File do Brazil Ltda., Rua Florencio de Abrue 157, andar 1,
      Caixa Postal 4645, Sao Paulo, SP, Brazil

A C NIELSEN CO   Nielsen Plaza, Northbrook, IL 60062, Tel: (708) 498-6300
(Marketing research)
   AC Nielsen Ltda., Av. Dr. Bernardino de Campos 98, Caixa Postal 178,
      01000 Sao Paolo, Brazil

NL INDUSTRIES INC   3000 N Sam Houston Pkwy E, Houston, TX 77205,
 Tel: (713) 987-4000
(Metal prdts, chems, petroleum serv)
   Baroid do Brazil, Imp. e Exp Ltda., Rua Miguel Calmon 19, andar 11, Caixa Postal 4,
      Salvador, BA, Brazil
   Industrias Doehler do Brazil S.A., Av. Albert Schweitzer 102, 097000,
      Sao Bernardo do Campo, SP, Brazil

NORDSON CORP   28601 Clemens Rd, Westlake, OH 44145, Tel: (216) 892-1580
(Mfr ind application equip & packaging mach)
   Nordson do Brasil Ltda., Almeda Araguaia, 1350 Alphaville, CEP 06400, Barueri,
      Sao Paulo, Brazil

NORTON CO   1 New Bond St, Worcester, MA 01606, Tel: (508) 795-5000
(Abrasives, drill bits, constr & safety prdts, plastics)
   Norton do Brazil S.A., Ind. e Com., Rua Dois No. 2363, Cidade, Industrial,
      Belo Horizonte, Brazil

NORWEST BANK MINNESOTA NA   Norwest Center, 6th & Marquette, Minneapolis,
 MN 55479-0095, Tel: (612) 667-8110
(Banking)
   Norwest Bank Minnesota, NA, Cepenco Plaza, Avenida Paulista 1842, Torre Norte 1/F,
      CJ15, CEP 01310 Sao Paulo, Brazil

NUIR INTL INC   1424 LeJeune Rd, Miami, FL 33126, Tel: (305) 871-3563
(Exporters of constr materials)
   Reimportex Ltda., Caixa Postal 382, Rio de Janeiro, RJ, Brazil

OAKITE PRODUCTS INC   50 Valley Rd, Berkeley Heights, NJ 07922,
 Tel: (201) 464-6900
(Mfr chem prdts for ind cleaning & metal treating)
   Oakite Quimica Ltda., Av. Rio Branco 14 - 14 andar, 20090 Rio de Janeiro, RJ, Brazil

OCCIDENTAL PETROLEUM CORP   10889 Wilshire Blvd, Los Angeles, CA 90024,
 Tel: (213) 879-1700
(Petroleum & petroleum prdts, chems, plastics)
   Eriez Produtos Magneticos e Metalurgicos, Av. Ipirange 318, Bloco B, andar 5,
      Caixa Postal 2632, 01046 Sao Paulo, SP, Brazil
   Vulcan Material Plastico S.A., Av. Rio Branco 156, andar 20, Caixa Postal 4400,
      ZC-21, Rio de Janeiro, RJ, Brazil

OGILVY & MATHER INC   2 E 48th St, New York, NY 10017, Tel: (212) 907-3400
  (Advertising agency)
    Standar Ogilvy & Mather Publicidade Ltda., Av. Brigadeiro Faria Lima 888,
      01452 Sao Paulo, Brazil
    Standar Ogilvy & Mather Publicidade Ltda., Rio de Janeiro, Porto Alegre,
      Belo Horizonte, Curitiba, Recife
    Standar Ogilvy & Mather Publicidade Ltda., Joinville, Brazil

OLINKRAFT INC   Jonesboro Rd, PO Box 488, West Monroe, LA 71291,
  Tel: (318) 362-2000
  (Cellulose & paper)
    Olinkraft Celulose e Papel Ltda., Av. Brigadeiro Luis Antonio 4531,
      01410 Sao Paulo, SP, Brazil

OMARK INDUSTRIES INC   5550 SW Macadam Ave, Portland, OR 97201,
  Tel: (503) 796-1400
  (Mfr chain & accessories for chain saws, welding equip, power tools)
    Omark Industrial Ltda., Av. Haras Santa Fe BP-1, No. 1600, Cidade Industrial,
      CEP 800, 000, Curitiba, Parana, Brazil

OTIS ELEVATOR CO   10 Farm Springs, Farmington, CT 06032, Tel: (203) 674-4047
  (Elevators & escalators)
    Elevadores Otis S.A., Caixa Postal 2426, CEP 20030 Rio de Janeiro, RJ, Brazil
    Elevadores Otis S.A., Caixa Postal 443, CEP 09000, Santo Andre, Brazil

OWENS-CORNING FIBERGLAS CORP   PO Box 901, Fiberglas Tower, Toledo, OH 43659,
  Tel: (419) 248-8000
  (Mfr insulation, building materials, glass fiber prdts)
    Fiberglas Fibras Ltda., Rio Claro, Brazil
    OCFIBRAS Ltda. (Brasil), Guararema, Brazil

OWENS-ILLINOIS INC   PO Box 1035, Toledo, OH 43666, Tel: (419) 247-5000
  (Glass & plastic containers, house- hold & ind prdts, packaging)
    Companhia Industrial Sao Paulo e Rio (CISPER), Av. Rio Branco 80, Andares 10/13,
      Caixa Postal 601, ZC-00, Rio de Janeiro, RJ, Brazil

PARAMOUNT INTL FILMS INC   1 Gulf & Western Plaza, New York, NY 10023,
  Tel: (212) 333-4600
  (Film prod & distr)
    Paramount Films do Brazil Inc., Rua Desembargador Viriato 16, Ciaxa Postal 179,
      ZC-00, Rio de Janeiro, RJ, Brazil

PARKER HANNIFIN CORP   17325 Euclid Ave, Cleveland, OH 44112,
  Tel: (216) 531-3000
  (Mfr motion-control prdts)
    Parker Irlemp Industria e Comercio Ltda., Rua Estevan Furquim 20, 02733 Sao Paulo,
      Brazil
    Parker-Hannifin do Brazil, CP 156, 06001 Osasco, Sao Paulo, Brazil
    Schrader Bellows Industria e Comercio Ltda., Caixa Postal 1601, 01051 Sao Paulo,
      Brazil
    Schrader Bellows Industria e Comercio Ltda., other locations in Brazil

PARKER PEN CO   One Parker Place, Janesville, WI 53545, Tel: (608) 755-7000
  (Writing instru, temporary help, leisure apparel & equip)
    Parker Pen do Brazil Ind. e Com. Ltda., Rua Aninhas 1, Caixa Postal 5626, Brooklin,
      Sao Paulo, SP, Brazil

PENROD DRILLING CORP   2200 Thanksgiving Tower, Dallas, TX 75201,
  Tel: (214) 880-1700
  (Contract oil/gas well drilling)
    Penrod Drilling Corp., Rua Aloisio, de la Vasconcelos 92, CP 119-389, CEP 28700,
    Macae, RJ, Brazil

PENTAIR INC   1700 West Hwy 36, St Paul, MN 55113, Tel: (612) 636-7920
  (Diversified manufacturer)
    Invicta Delta, Caixa Postal 24, Ave. Major Jose Levy Sobrinho 2500, 3480 Limeira,
    Brazil

PEPSICO INC   700 Anderson Hill Rd, Purchase, NY 10577, Tel: (914) 253-2000
  (Beverages, food prdts & servs, sporting goods)
    Pepsico, Rua Paulo Cesar de Andrade, 222-Apt. 803, Larangeiras, Rio de Janeiro,
    Brazil

PERKIN-ELMER CORP   761 Main Ave, Norwalk, CT 06859, Tel: (203) 762-1000
  (Analytical instru, computers, semiconductor prod equip, avionics, electro-optical
  sys, etc)
    Perkin-Elmer Industria e Com. Ltda., Rua Pagev, 76 CEP 04139, Sao Paulo, SP, Brazil

PFIZER INC   235 E 42nd St, New York, NY 10017, Tel: (212) 573-2323
  (Mfr pharms, hosp prdts, chems, consumer & animal health prdts)
    Pfizer S.A., Caixa Postal 143, 07010 - Guarulhos, Sao Paulo, Brazil

PHILLIPS PETROLEUM CO   Phillips Bldg, Bartlesville, OK 74004,
  Tel: (918) 661-6600
  (Crude oil, natural gas, liquefied petroleum gas, gasoline & petro-chems)
    CCC-Companhia de Carbonos Coloidais, Rua Algibebes 6/12, andar 8, Caixa Postal 948,
    Salvador, BA, Brazil
    Produtos Petro-Quimicos "66" Ltda., Av. Brig. Luiz Antonio 1343, andar 5,
    Caixa Postal 30.818, 01317 Sao Paulo, SP, Brazil

PIONEER HI-BRED INTL INC   700 Capital Sq, 400 Locust St, Des Moines,
  IA 50309, Tel: (515) 245-3500
  (Seed corn, feed seed, data sys & equip)
    Empreendimentos Agricolas Pioneer Ltda, Santa Cruz do Sul, RS, Brazil
    Pioneer Agricultura Ltda, Santa Cruz do Sul, RS, Brazil

PITNEY BOWES INC   World Headquarters, Stamford, CT 06926-0700,
  Tel: (203) 356-5000
  (Postage meters, mailroom equip, copiers, bus supplies & servs)
    Pitney-Bowes Maqulnas Ltda., Rua Mexico 3, andar 13, ZC-39, Rio de Janeiro, RJ,
    .Brazil

PITTSBURGH NATIONAL BANK   Fifth Ave at Wood, Pittsburgh, PA 15222,
  Tel: (412) 355-2000
  (Banking)
    Pittsburgh Natl. Bank, Rua Libero Badaro 425-22 andar, Sao Paulo, Brazil

POTTERS INDUSTRIES INC   20 Waterview Blvd, Parsippany, NJ 07054,
  Tel: (201) 299-2900
  (Mfr glass spheres for road marking & ind applications)
    Potters Industrial Ltda., Via Anhanguera Km. 106, Sumare, SP, Brazil
    Potters Industrial Ltda., Avenida Prefeito Sa Lessa 381, 21.530 Rio de Janeiro, RJ,
    Brazil

PRECISION VALVE CORP   PO Box 309, Yonkers, NY 10702, Tel: (914) 969-6500
  (Mfr aerosol valves)
     Valvulas Precisho do Brazil Ltda., Caixa Postal 1570, 01051 Sao Paulo, Brazil

PREFORMED LINE PRODUCTS CO   PO Box 91129, Cleveland, OH 44101,
  Tel: (216) 461-5200
  (Mfr pole line hardware for elec transmission lines; splice closures & related prdts
  for telecom)
     PLP-Produtos Para Linhas Preformados Ltd., Sao Paulo, Brazil

PREMARK INTL INC   1717 Deerfield Rd, Deerfield, IL 60015, Tel: (708) 405-6000
  (Mfr/sale diversified consumer & coml prdts)
     Dart do Brasil Industria e Comercio Ltda., 80 Sertaozinho St., Chacara Itaim,
        Sao Paulo, Brazil

PRUDENTIAL INSURANCE CO OF AMERICA   Prudential Plaza, Newark, NJ 07101,
  Tel: (201) 877-6000
  (Life ins, health ins, annuities)
     Pruservicos Participacoes, S.A., c/o Grupa Atlantica Boavista, Av. Paulista 1415,
        Sao Paulo 01311, Brazil

QUAKER OATS CO   345 Merchandise Mart Plaza, Chicago, IL 60654,
  Tel: (312) 222-7111
  (Foods, pet foods, toys, chems)
     Produtos Alimenticios Quaker S.A., Praca da Republica 497, andar 4,
        Caixa Postal 30052, 01000, Sao Paulo, Brazil

K J QUINN & CO INC   135 Folly Mill Rd, PO Box 158, Seabrook, NH 03874,
  Tel: (603) 474-7177
  (Mfr spec coatings, adhesives, polyurethane polymers, shoe finishes, UV/EB cure
  coatings)
     K.J. Quinn do Brazil Produtos Quimicos Ltda., Caixa Postal 81-CEP 13290,
        Via Anhanguera, Km. 70.5, Trevo Louveira, SP, Brazil

RALSTON PURINA CO   Checkerboard Sq, St Louis, MO 63164, Tel: (214) 982-1000
  (Poultry & live stock feed, cereals, food prdts)
     Purina Alimentos, Av. das Naceos Unidas 13797, conj. Morumbi Bloco 111 21o,
        Sao Paulo, Brazil

RANSBURG CORP   3939 W 56th St, Indianapolis, IN 46208, Tel: (317) 298-5000
  (Mfr electrostatic coating sys)
     Ransburg Equipamentos Industrias Ltda., Av. de Putado Emilio Carlos, 520 02720,
        Sao Paulo, SP, Brazil

RAPISTAN CORP   507 Plymouth Ave NE, Grand Rapids, MI 49505,
  Tel: (616) 451-6200
  (Material handling equip)
     Rapistan-Industria e Camereo Ltda, Avda. Presidente Joscelino 642,
        CEP 09950 Diadema-Sau Paulo, Brazil

RCA GLOBAL COMMUNICATIONS INC   60 Broad St, New York, NY 10004,
  Tel: (212) 806-7000
  (Commun serv)
     RCA Electronica Ltda., Rua Dona Veridiana 203, Caixa Postal 6043, 01238, Sao Paulo,
        Brazil
     RCA Electronica Ltda., Av Presidente Vargas, 962 2/807, 20071 Rio de Janeiro, RJ,
        Brazil

RELIANCE ELECTRIC CO   24701 Euclid Ave, Cleveland, OH 44117,
   Tel: (216) 266-7000
   (Equip & sys for ind automation, telecom equip)
      Redutores Transmotecnica Ltda., Caixa Postal 30.425, 01000 Sao Paulo, Brazil

REPUBLIC STEEL CORP   PO Box 6778, Cleveland, OH 44101, Tel: (216) 622-5000
   (Alloy, carbon & stainless steel, chems, electrical conduit, etc)
      Sao Carlos Minerios S.A., Barao de Cocais, MG, Brazil

REXNORD CORP   PO Box 2022, Milwaukee, WI 53201, Tel: (414) 643-3000
   (Mfr power transmission prdts)
      Rexnord Correntes S.A., Caixa Postal 290, 93000 Sao Lepoldo, RS, Brazil

RICHARDSON-VICKS INC   Ten Westport Rd, Wilton, CT 06897, Tel: (203) 834-5000
   (Consumer health & personal care prdts)
      Quimica Moura Brazil S.A., Rua Marques de Sao Vincente 104, ZC-20, Caixa Postal 31,
      ZC-07, Rio de Janeiro, RJ, Brazil
      Richardson-Vicks do Brazil, Largo Dos Leoes 15, #2 andar, Botafogo, CEP 22260,
      Rio de Janeiro, Brazil

RIDGE TOOL CO   400 Clark St, Elyria, OH 44035, Tel: (216) 323-5581
   (Hand & power tools for working pipe, drain cleaning equip, etc)
      Ridgid Ferra mentas e Maquinas Ltda., Carapicuiba, Sao Paulo, Brazil

ROBERTSHAW CONTROLS CO   1701 Byrd Ave, Richmond, VA 23230,
   Tel: (804) 281-0700
   (Mfr automatic controls & control sys for ind, commercial bldgs & home)
      Controles Robertshaw do Brazil S.A., Caixa Postal 308, 95.100, Caixas do Sul,
      Rio Grande do Sul, Brazil

ROCKWELL INTL CORP   2230 E Imperial Hwy, El Segundo, CA 90245,
   Tel: (213) 647-5000
   (Prdts & serv for aerospace, automotive, electronics, graphics & automation inds)
      Rockwell do Brazil Ind. e Com. Ltda., Av. Brig., Faria 1-ima 888, 4 andar,
      Sao Paulo, SP, CEP 01452, Brazil
      Rockwell do Brazil Ltda., Rockwell-Collins Div., Caixa Postal 34.043,
      Rua Pio Correia 37, 22.22461 Rio de Janeiro, RJ, Brazil

ROHM & HAAS CO   Independence Mall West, Philadelphia, PA 19105,
   Tel: (215) 592-3000
   (Mfr ind & agric chems, plastics)
      Rohm & Haas Brazil Ltda., Alameda Purus 105, Alphaville, 06400 Barueri, SP, Brazil

RORER GROUP INC   500 Virginia Dr, Ft Washington, PA 19034,
   Tel: (215) 628-6000
   (Mfr ethical & consumer pharms)
      Rorer do Brazil Ltda., Sao Paulo, Brazil

SYDNEY ROSS CO   90 Park Ave, New York, NY 10016, Tel: (212) 907-2000
   (Pharms, toiletries & cosmetics)
      The Sydney Ross Co., Av. Rio Branco 251, andar 9, ZC-39, Caixa Postal 1363, ZC-00,
      Rio de Janeiro, RJ, Brazil

ROSS GEAR DIV   800 Heath St, Lafayette, IN 47904, Tel: (317) 423-5377
   (Steering gears, low speed high torque hydraulic motors)
      Industrias Gemmer do Brazil S.A., Av. Rotary 825, Sao Bernardo do Camp,
      09700 Sao Paulo, SP, Brazil

SCHENECTADY CHEMICALS INC   PO Box 1046, Schenectady, NY 12301,
  Tel: (518) 370-4200
  (Mfr elec insulating varnishe, enamels, resins, alkylated phenol)
    Schenectady Quimica do Brasil Ltda., Av. Indianopolis 3213, CEP 04063, Sao Paulo,
    SP, Brazil

R P SCHERER CORP   2075 W Big Beaver Rd, Troy, MI 48084, Tel: (313) 649-0900
  (Mfr soft gelatin & two-piece hard shell capsules)
    R. P. Scherer do Brasil Encapsulacoes Ltda., Av. Jerome Case 1277, CEP,
    18.100 Sorocaba - SP, Brazil

SCHERING INTL   PO Box 500, Kenilworth, NJ 07033, Tel: (201) 558-4000
  (Pharms, medicines, toiletries, cosmetics, human & animal health prdts)
    Industria Quimica e Farmaceutica Schering S.A., Rua Moraes e Silva 43, ZC-29,
    Caixa Postal 540, ZC-00, Rio de Janeiro, RJ, Brazil

SCHRADER BELLOWS DIV   200 W Exchange St, Akron, OH 44309, Tel: (216) 375-1263
  (Pneumatic & hydraulic valves & cylinders, FRL units & accessories)
    Scharader-Bellows & Valvulos Schrader do Brazil, Caixa Postal 21211,
    0100 Sao Paulo, Brazil

SCM CORP   299 Park Ave, New York, NY 10171, Tel: (212) 752-2700
  (Business equip, chems, coatings & resins, foods, paper prdts)
    Tintas y Piranga S.A., Rua General Bruce, 320, Caixa Postal 23.050, CZ-08,
    Rio de Janeiro, Brazil
    Tintas y Piranga S.A., Caixa Postal 856, CEP 09700, Sao Bernardo do Campo, SP,
    Brazil
    Tintas y Piranga S.A., Rua Ana Barreto, 490, Caixa Postal 2. 189, Prazeres,
    Jaboatao,
    Tintas y Piranga S.A., Recife, Pernambuco, Brazil

SCOTT WORLDWIDE INC   Scott Plaza, Philadelphia, PA 19113, Tel: (215) 521-5000
  (Paper & paper prdts, bleached pulp)
    Companhia de Papeis, Brazil

SEA-LAND SERVICE INC   379 Thornall St, Edison, NJ 08837, Tel: (201) 558-6000
  (Container transport)
    Sea-Land Services Ltda., Av. Nilo Pecanha 50, Rm 1213, 20.000, Rio de Janeiro,
    Brazil

G D SEARLE & CO   PO Box 1045, Skokie, IL 60076, Tel: (708) 982-7000
  (Pharms, health care & optical prdts, specialty chems)
    Searle Farmaceutica do Brazil Ltda., Rua Pamplona 512, Sao Paulo, Brazil

SEARS ROEBUCK & CO   Sears Towers, Chicago, IL 60684, Tel: (312) 875-2500
  (Diversified general merchandise, ins, real estate, financial serv)
    Sears Roebuck S.A. Com. e Ind., Agua Branca, Caixa Postal 7146, SP, Brazil

SECURITY PACIFIC NATIONAL BANK   333 S Hope St, Los Angeles, CA 90071,
  Tel: (213) 345-6211
  (Banking)
    Security Pacific do Brazil S/C Ltda., Alameda Santos 1800-10o andar, 01418,
    Sao Paulo, Brazil

SEVEN-UP INTL   120 Park Ave, New York, NY 10017, Tel: (212) 880-4100
  (Soft drinks)
    Seven-Up de Sao Paulo S.A., Av. Paulo Ferreira 194, Sao Paulo, SP, Brazil

SGS CONTROL SERVICES INC   42 Broadway, New York, NY 10004,
   Tel: (212) 482-8700
   (Complete range of quality & quantity control checks & related tech serv)
      S.G.S. Do Brazil S.A., 446 Av. Presidente Vargas, 13o andar, C.P. 1563-ZC-00,
      Rio de Janeiro 20071, Brazil

SHULTON INC   1 Cyanamid Plaza, Wayne, NJ 07470, Tel: (201) 831-2000
   (Health, beauty & grooming prdts)
      Shulton Cosmeticos do Brazil Ltda., Rua Conde de Confim, 604-Sij, 20.520,
      Rio de Janeiro, Brazil

SIFCO INDUSTRIES INC   970 E 64th St, Cleveland, OH 44103, Tel: (216) 881-8600
   (Forgings, tankless plating, bearings)
      Sifco do Brazil, P.O. Box 412, CEP 01009, Sao Paulo, Brazil

SIGNODE PACKAGING SYSTEMS   3600 W Lake Ave, Glenview, IL 60025,
   Tel: (708) 724-6100
   (Mfr packaging systems)
      Signode do Brasil Comercio & Servicio Ltda., P.O. Box 875, Sao Paulo 01000, Brazil

SIMMONS INTL   1 Gulf & Western Plaza, New York, NY 10023, Tel: (212) 333-3511
   (Bedding prdts)
      Industrias Simmons Epeda Ltda., Caixa Postal 13327, CEP 03169, Sao Paulo, SP, Brazil

SIMON & SCHUSTER INC   1230 Ave of the Americas, New York, NY 10020,
   Tel: (212) 245-6400
   (Publisher)
      Editora Prentice-Hall do Brazil Ltda., Travessa do Ouvidor 11/6, Rio de, Janeiro,
      RJ 20, 040 Brazil

J E SIRRINE CO   PO Box 5456, Greenvilee, SC 29606, Tel: (803) 298-6000
   (Consulting engineers, architects & planners)
      Sirrine Engenharia Ltda., Edificio das Nacde S., Av. Euzebio Matoso, 981-15 andar,
      CEP 05423, Sao Paulo, Brazil

SMITH INTL INC   16740 Hardy St, Houston, TX 77032, Tel: (713) 443-6470
   (Mfr/serv downhole drilling equip)
      Smith Equipamentos E. Servicios SA, KM 10 Highway Br-101, Eduardo Gomes,
      Rio Grande do Norte, Brazil

SMITH TOOL   PO Box C-19511, Irvine, CA 92713, Tel: (714) 540-7010
   (Drilling bits)
      Smith Intl. do Brazil Equipamentos e Servicos Ltda., Salvador, Brazil

SONAT OFFSHORE DRILLING INC   PO Box 2765, Houston, TX 77252-2765,
   Tel: (713) 871-7500
   (Offshore oil well drilling)
      Sonat Offshoure do Brasil Perfuracoes Martimas Ltda., Avda. das Americas 679,
      Grupo 109, Dep. 22600-N, Barra de Tijuca, Rio de Janeiro, Brazil

SOUTHWIRE CO   Fertilla St, Carrollton, GA 30117, Tel: (404) 832-4242
   (Electric conduits, etc)
      Empresa Produtos de Aluminio Ltda., Rodovia Dutra Km 227, Caixa Postal 3, Lorena,
      Edo. De SP, Brazil

SPS TECHNOLOGIES INC   900 Newtown-Yardley Rd, Newtown, PA 18940,
  Tel: (215) 860-3000
  (Mfr aerospace & ind fasteners, precision components, superalloys, magnetic
  materials, fastening sys)
    Metalac S.A. Industria e Com., Caixa Postal 66181, 05389 Sao Paulo, SP, Brazil

SPX CORP   700 Terrace Point Dr, Muskegon, MI 49443, Tel: (616) 724-5000
  (Mfr spec repair equip & repair parts)
    Jurubatuba, SA, Rua Joano De Araugo 830, Santo Amaro, 04469 Sao Paulo, SP, Brazil

ST JOE MINERALS CORP   250 Park Ave, New York, NY 10017, Tel: (212) 953-5000
  (Coal, oil, gas, iron ore, metals & minerals)
    St. Joe Minerals Corp., Mineracao, Sao Jose Ltda., Rua Almirante Comes, Pereira 56,
    Rio de Janeiro.. 22291, Brazil

STANDARD COMMERCIAL CORP   PO Box 450, Wilson, NC 27893, Tel: (919) 291-5507
  (Leaf tobacco dealers/processors, wool processors)
    Fumex Exportoras de Tabacos SA, Salvador, Bahia, Brazil,
    Exportadora de Tabacos Trans-Continental Ltda., Salvador, Bahia, Brazil

STANDARD OIL CO OF CALIFORNIA   225 Bush St, San Francisco, CA 94104,
  Tel: (415) 894-7700
  (Oil explor & prod, petroleum prdts)
    Asfaltos Chevron S.A., Rua Ararai, 35, Caixa Postal 12, 654, CEP 04729, Sao Paulo,
    SP, Brazil

THE STANLEY WORKS   1000 Stanley Dr, PO Box 7000, New Britain, CT 06050,
  Tel: (203) 225-5111
  (Mfr hand tools & hardware)
    Ferramentas Stanley S.A., Rua Missionarios 641, Santo Amaro, Caixa Postal 12.654,
    0.1000 Sao Paulo, SP, Brazil

STEINER CORP   PO Box 2317, 505 E South Temple St, Salt Lake City, UT 84102,
  Tel: (801) 328-8831
  (Linen supply service)
    Toalheiro Brazil Ltda., Av. Victor Manzini 470 Santo Amaro, Caixa Postal 9096,
    Sao Paulo, SP, Brazil
    Toalheiro Brazil Ltda., Rua Marques de Sabara 59, ZC-20, Rio de Janeiro, RJ. Brazil

STOKES DIV   5500 Tabor Rd, Philadelphia, PA 19120, Tel: (215) 289-5671
  (Vacuum pumps & components, vacuum dryers, oil-upgrading equip)
    Sharples-Stokes SA, Caixa Postal 2150, CEP 01000, Sao Paulo, SP, Brazil

SULLAIR CORP   3700 E Michigan Blvd, Michigan City, IN 46360,
  Tel: (219) 879-5451
  (Refrigeration sys, vacuum pumps, generators, etc)
    Sullair S.A., Alameda Joaquim Eugenio de Lima 680 Decimo andar, Salas 103 e 104,
    CEP 01403, Sao Paulo, Brazil

SUN ELECTRIC CORP   One Sun Pkwy, Crystal Lake, IL 60014, Tel: (815) 459-7700
  (Mfr auto tune-up, diagnostic & emission testing equip)
    Sun Electric do Brazil Com. e Ind. Ltda., Rua Costa Aguiar, 1639, 04204, Sao Paulo,
    SP, Brazil

SYBRON CORP   411 E Wisconsin Ave, Milwaukee, WI 07662, Tel: (414) 274-6600
  (Professional health prdts, spec chems, instru, water & waste water treatment sys)
    Kerr Industria e Commercio Ltda., Caixa Postal 12233 CEP 02070, Sao Paulo, Brazil

(cont)

Sybron-Interamericana Ind. e Com. Ltda., Alameda Fernao Cardin 84,
Caixa Postal 5638, Sao Paulo, SP, Brazil

TAYLOR INSTRUMENT CO   99 Ames St, PO Box 110, Rochester, NY 14601,
Tel: (716) 235-6806
(Instru for process control inds)
Taylor Instrumentos Ltda., Av. do Cursino 1445/9-CEP 04133, Sao Paulo, SP, Brazil

TECHNICON INSTRUMENTS CORP   511 Benedict Ave, Tarrytown, NY 10591-5097,
Tel: (914) 631-8000
(Mfr/serv automated blook anal equip, reagents & diagnostics)
Technicon Instrumentos do Brazil, Rua da Paz 2094, CEP 04713, Sao Paulo, SP, Brazil

TECUMSEH PRODUCTS CO   100 E Patterson St, Tecumseh, MI 49286,
Tel: (517) 423-8411
(Refrig & A/C compressors & units, small engines, pumps)
Sicom S.A., Caixa Postal 54, Sao Carlos, CEP, 13560, SP, Brazil

TED BATES WORLDWIDE INC   1515 Broadway, New York, NY 10036,
Tel: (212) 869-3131
(Advertising agency)
Denison Propaganda, Rua Teofilo-Otoni, 63-50 Andar, Rio de Janeiro, Brazil
Denison Propaganda S.A., Av. Brigadeiro Luiz Antonio, 2050 12o andar, Sao Paulo,
Brazil
Denison Propaganda S.A., Rua Teofilo Ottoni, 63 - 4o e 5o andares,
Caixa Postal 1703, Rio de Janeiro, Brazil
Denison Propaganda S.A., Rua Professor Americo Simas, 111 Salvador, Brazil
Denison Propaganda S.A., Rua Bulhoes Marques, 19- Salas 306/307/308 Recife, Brazil
Denison Propaganda S.A., W3, Norte Edificio Mariana, 504 Brazilia D.F., Brazil
Denison Propaganda SA, Av Brigadeiro Luiz Antonio, 2050, Sao Paulo, Brazil

TEKTRONIX INC   PO Box 500, Beaverton, OR 97077, Tel: (503) 627-7111
(Mfr test & meas, visual sys & commun prdts)
Tekronix I e C Ltda, Ave. Marechal Camara 160 Gr 605, 20020 Rio de Janeiro, RJ,
Brazil
Tektronix Industria e Com. Ltda., Rua Nebraska 459-4'CEP 04560, Sao Paulo, SP,
Brazil

TENNANT CO   701 N Lilac Dr, Minneapolis, MN 55440, Tel: (612) 540-1200
(Mfr ind floor maint sweepers & scrubbers, roofing machs)
Equipamentos Tennant Ltda., Rua Alvares Cabral 871, Diadema, CEP 09900, SP, Brazil

C TENNANT SONS & CO OF NY   PO Box 9300, Minneapolis, MN 55440,
Tel: (612) 475-7340
(Ferrous & non-ferrous minerals, metals, electronic comps)
Tennant Importacao e Exportacao Ltda., Rua Pedro Americo 32, andar 6,
Caixa Postal 7284, Sao Paulo, SP, Brazil

TENNECO AUTOMOTIVE   100 Tri-State Intl, #300, Lincolnshire, IL 60069,
Tel: (708) 948-0900
(Mfr exhaust sys, ride control prdts, brake components)
Monroe Auto Equipment, Rua Lavras 343, 3000 Bello llorizahte Minas Jirnas,
Sao Paulo, Brazil
Monroe Auto Pecas SA, CEP 13800 Nogimirim, Brazil

TENNECO INC   PO Box 2511, Houston, TX 77001, Tel: (713) 757-2812
(Natural gas pipelines, integrated oil operations, paperboard prdts, agric & land devel)
   J.I. Case do Brazil Comercio e Industria Ltda., Av. Francisco Matarazzo, 764,
      & 798/810, Caixa Postal 4204, Sao Paulo, SP, Brazil
   J.I. Case do Brazil Comercio e Industria Ltda., Sao Bernardo do Campo, Brazil

TENNECO OIL EXPLORATION & PRODUCTION   PO Box 2511, Houston, TX 77001,
   Tel: (713) 757-2131
(Oil explor & prod)
   J.I. Case do Brazil Comercio e Industria Ltda., Caixa Postal 650, 1801,
      Bairro de Eden, 18100 Sorocaba, Sao Paulo, Brazil

TENNESSEE ASSOCIATES INTL INC   337 East Broadway Ave, Maryville, TN 37801,
   Tel: (615) 983-4044
(Mgt consulting servs)
   Tennessee Associates Do Brasil, Av. Paulista 2073- 14 Andar, CEP 01311 Sao Paulo,
      SP, Brazil

TEXACO INC   2000 Westchester Ave, White Plains, NY 10650, Tel: (914) 253-4000
(Explor/mktg crude oil & its prdts, petro-chems)
   Texaco do Brazil S.A., Rua Dom Gerardo 64, andares 5/6, ZC-00, Caixa Postal 520,
      ZC-00, Rio de Janeiro, RJ. Brazil
   Texaco do Brazil S.A., Sao Paulo, Brazil

TEXAS INSTRUMENTS INC   PO Box 655474, Dallas, TX 75265, Tel: (214) 995-2011
(Mfr semiconductor devices, electr/electro-mech sys, instr & controls)
   Texas Instrumentos Electronicos do Brazil Ltda., Rua Azarias de Melo, 648/660,
      Caixa Postal 988/86, CEP-14100-Campinas, San Paulo, Brazil

THERMO ELECTRON CORP   101 First Ave, Waltham, MA 02154, Tel: (617) 890-8700
(Devel/mfr of process equip & instru for energy intensive inds)
   Lodding do Brazil Ltda., Rua Domingos Jorge No. 676, 04761, Sao Paulo, Brazil

THETFORD CORP   7101 Jackson Rd, PO Box 1285, Ann Arbor, MI 48106,
   Tel: (313) 769-6000
(Sanitation sys)
   Thetford do Brazil, Av. Samuel Aisemberg, 399, CEP 09700 Sao Bernardo Do Campo,
      .Campo, Sao Paulo, Brazil

THOMAS INTL PUBLISHING CO   1 Penn Plaza, New York, NY 10119,
   Tel: (212) 290-7213
(Publ ind magazines & directories)
   Editora Corena Ltd, Caixa Postal 30.493, 01000 Sao Paulo, SP, Brazil
   T/L Publicaroes Industriais Ltda, Caixa Postal 30.493, Rua Brigadeiroas 356,
      5 andar, 01000 Sao Paulo, SP, Brazil

TIDEWATER INC   Tidewater Place, 1440 Canal St, New Orleans, LA 70112,
   Tel: (504) 568-1010
(Marine serv & equip to companies engaged in explor, development & prod of oil, gas & minerals)
   Pan Marine do Brasil Transportes Ltda., c/o Planave S.A., Rua Costa Ferreira,
      106 Centro, 20221 Rio de Janeiro, RJ, Brazil
   Pan Marine do Brazil Transportes Ltda., Rodovia Arthur Bernardes 5511,
      Base do Tapana, Belem, Para, Brazil

TIGER EQUIPMENT & SERVICES LTD   33 W Monroe Ave, Chicago, IL 60603,
  Tel: (312) 853-5555
  (Heavy equip leasing, maint servs)
    Tiger Equipamantose Servicos Ltda., Av. Ipiranga 318, Bloca A, 12 andar, 01046,
      Sao Paulo, Brazil

THE TIMKEN CO   1835 Dueber Ave SW, Canton, OH 44706-2798, Tel: (216) 438-3000
  (Mfr tapered roller bearings & alloy steels)
    Timken do Brasil, Caixa Postal 8208, 01000 Sao Paulo, SP, Brazil

TOKHEIM CORP   1602 Wabash Ave, PO Box 360, Fort Wayne, IN 46801,
  Tel: (219) 423-2552
  (Mfr gasoline service station dispensers, access, hand & in-tank fuel pumps)
    Tokheim do Brasil, Av. Eixo Norte Sul 5359, 69083 Manaus, AM, Brazil

TORRINGTON/FAFNIR   200 Chestnut Ridge Rd, Woodcliff Lake, NJ 07675,
  Tel: (203) 482-9511
  (Mfr bearings, precision metal parts & assemblies, universal joints)
    Torrington Ind. e Com. Ltda., Av. Conselheiro Julius Arp. 440,
      28.623 Nova Friburgo, RJ, Brazil

TOWERS PERRIN FORSTER & CROSBY INC   245 Park Ave, New York, NY 10167,
  Tel: (212) 309-3400
  (Management consulting)
    Towers, Perrin Forster & Crosby Ltda., Rua Dr. Eduardo de Souza Aranha 153,
      04543 Sao Paulo, SP, Brazil

TRANE CO   3600 Pammel Creek Rd, La Crosse, WI 54601, Tel: (608) 787-2000
  (Mfr A/C equip)
    Coldex Trane Ind. e Com. S.A., Caixa Postal 362, 09900 Diadema, SP, Brazil

TRINOVA CORP   3000 Strayer, PO Box 50, Maumee, OH 43537, Tel: (419) 867-2200
  (Mfr engr components & sys for ind)
    Aeroquip Vickers do Brasil, Caixa Postal 2536, CEP 2000 Rio de Janeiro, Brazil

TRW INC   1900 Richmond Rd, Cleveland, OH 44124, Tel: (216) 291-7000
  (Electr & energy-related prdts, automotive & aerospace prdts, tools & fasteners)
    TRW Computadores, Rua Evaristo da Veiga 55, 22032 Rio de Janeiro, Brazil
    TRW Gemmer Thompson SA, Caixa Postal 8104, Sao Paulo, Brazil
    TRW Mission Industria Ltda., Rua Sargento Silvio Hollenback 151,
      Rio de Janeiro 2000, Brazil

UNION CARBIDE CORP   Old Ridgebury Rd, Danbury, CT 06817, Tel: (203) 794-2000
  (Carbon prdts, chems, plastics, gases & related prdts, etc)
    CODIM Desenvolvimento de Industrias Minerais Ltda., Rua Mexico 31, sala 150, ZC-39,
      Rio de Janeiro, RJ, Brazil
    National Carbon do Brazil S.A., Rua Formosa 367, Caixa Postal 6482, Sao Paulo, SP,
      Brazil
    S/A White Martins, Rua dos Coelhos 219, Recife, PE, Brazil
    S/A White Martins, Salvador, BA, Brazil
    Union Carbide do Brazil S.A. Ind. e Com., Av. Paulista 2073, andar 24,
      Caixa Postal 30362, Sao Paulo, SP, Brazil
    Viskings Brazil S.A. Ind. e Com., Edificio Matarazzo, Sao Paulo, SP, Brazil

UNION OIL INTL DIV   Union Oil Center, PO Box 7600, Los Angeles, CA 90017,
  Tel: (213) 977-7600
  (Petroleum prdts, petrochems)

Unionoil Exploracao de Petrolea Ltda., Praia do Flamengo 200 - 17 andar,
Rio de Janeiro, RJ, Brazil

UNIROYAL INC   World Headquarters, Middlebury, CT 06749, Tel: (203) 573-2000
(Tires, tubes & other rubber prdts, chems, plastics, textiles)
United States Rubber Intl. do Brazil S.A., Rua Dona Veridiana 158,
Caixa Postal 8041, Sao Paulo, SP, Brazil

UNISYS CORP   PO Box 500, Blue Bell, PA 19424, Tel: (215) 542-4011
(Mfg/mktg/serv electr info sys)
Burroughs Electronica Ltda., Rua Teixeira de Freitas 31-14 andar,
Rio de Janeiro 20021, Brazil
Sperry Rand do Brazil S.A., Ave. Angelica 222, 01227 Sao Paulo, SP, Brazil

UNITED PRESS INTL   220 E 42nd St, New York, NY 10017, Tel: (212) 682-0400
(Collection & distributor of news, newspictures, fin data)
UPI, Av. Paranapuan 1.793, Apt. 101, Taua-llhado Governador, Rio de Janeiro,
RJ 21910, Brazil

UPJOHN CO   7000 Portage Rd, Kalamazoo, MI 49001, Tel: (616) 323-4000
(Pharms, agric prdts, ind chems)
Asgrow do Brazil Sementes Ltda., Caixa Postal 1564, 13.100 Campinas, SP, Brazil

UTAH INTL INC   550 California St, San Francisco, CA 94104,
Tel: (415) 981-1515
(Mining, land development, ocean shipping, oil & gas)
Mineracao Colorado Ltda., Rua Barao de Lucena 67, Botafogo, Rio de Janeiro, RJ,
CEP 22260, Brazil
Utah Intl., Participacioes, Ltda., Av. Nilo Pecanho 50 - Grupo 2417 Centro,
ZC-00 CEP 20.000, Rio de Janeiro, RJ, Brazil

VALERON CORP   750 Stephenson Highway, Troy, MI 48084, Tel: (313) 589-1000
(Cemented carbide, high speed steel, ceramic & diamond cutting tool prdts, etc)
Valenite-Modco Ind. e Com., Ltda., Rua Inaga 272, Santa Amaro, Sao Paulo, Brazil

VARIAN ASSOCIATES INC   611 Hansen Way, Palo Alto, CA 94304-1030,
Tel: (415) 493-4000
(Mfr microwave tubes & devices, analytical instru, semiconductor process & med equip,
vacuum sys)
Varian Ind. e Com. Ltda., Av. Dr. Cardoso de Melo 1457, CEP 04548, Sao Paulo, Brazil

VEEDER-ROOT CO   125 Powder Forest Dr, PO Box 2003, Simsbury, CT 06070-2003,
Tel: (203) 651-2700
(Mfr counting, controlling & sensing devices)
Veeder-Root do Brazil Com. e Ind. Ltda., Rua Ado Benatti 92, Caixa Postal 8343,
01051 Sao Paulo, Brazil

VELSICOL CHEMICAL CORP   5600 N River Rd, Rosemont, IL 60018,
Tel: (708) 698-9700
(Pesticides & ind chems)
Biagro-Velskol Produtos Para Agricultural Ltda., Rua Dr. Candido Espinheira 143,
CEP 05004, Sao Paulo 5, Brazil

VETCO-GRAY INC   250 W Stanley Ave, Ventura, CA 93001, Tel: (805) 653-2500
(Offshore oilfield equip & tools, oilfield inspect & coating serv)
Cia Masa Vetco Comercio e Indus., Avenida Rio Blanco #311/208 20040,

(cont)

Rio de Janeiro, Brazil
Hughes-WKM do Brasil, Avenida Rio Branco, 85-17 Andar 200040, Rio de Janeiro, Brazil

VIACOM INTL INC   1211 Ave of the Americas, New York, NY 10036,
Tel: (212) 575-5175
(Diversified entertainment & commun)
Viacom Video Audio Comunicacoes Ltda., Caixa Postal 51521,
Alameda Jau' 1742-11 andar, 01420 Sao Paulo, Brazil

VOLKART BROS INC   120 Wall St, New York, NY 10025, Tel: (212) 422-9400
(Sale of coffee, cocoa, cotton)
Volkart Irmaos Ltda., Rua Libero Badaro 293, andar 16, Caixa Postal 7179, 01009,
Sao Paulo, SP, Brazil

WARNER COMMUNICATIONS INC   75 Rockefeller Plaza, New York, NY 10019,
Tel: (212) 484-8000
(Entertainment & commun)
Warner Bros.-First Natl. South Films, Rua Senador Dantas 19, andar 10, ZC-06,
Caixa Postal 2623, Rio de Janeiro, RJ, Brazil

WARNER-LAMBERT CO   201 Tabor Road, Morris Plains, NJ 07950,
Tel: (201) 540-2000
(Mfr ethical & proprietary pharms, confectionary & consumer prdts)
Warner-Lambert Industria e Comercio Ltda., Caixa Postal 6495, Sao Paulo, SP, Brazil

WEATHERFORD INTL INC   1360 Post Oak Blvd, PO Box 27608, Houston,
TX 77227-9917, Tel: (713) 439-9400
(Tubular & cementation servs, prdts & equip; water jetting servs, mfr marine pedestal
cranes)
Weatherford Intl., c/o Seamar, Rua Uruguaiana 39-24 andar,
CEP 20050 Rio de Janeiro, Brazil

WEIGHT WATCHERS INTL INC   Jericho Atrium, 500 North Broadway, Jericho,
NY 11753-2196, Tel: (516) 939-0400
(Weight reduction programs, food prdts)
Weight Watchers do Brazil Programas Alimentares Ltda., Rua Ataulfo de Paroa,
135/401 Liblon, Rio de Janeiro, Brazil

WELDOTRON CORP   1532 S Washington Ave, Piscataway, NJ 08854,
Tel: (201) 752-6700
(Packaging prdts & mach, audio visual sys, etc)
Weldortron do Brazil, Rua Antonio Marcordes 300, Sao Paulo, Brazil

WEST CO INC   West Bridge St, Phoenixville, PA 19460, Tel: (215) 935-4500
(Pharm packaging comps)
West do Brazil, S.A., Caixa Postal 210, Av. N.S. das Gracas, 115, Bairro, Serraria,
09900 Diadema, SP, Brazil

WESTERN GEOPHYSICAL   PO Box 2469, Houston, TX 77252-2469, Tel: (713) 789-9600
(Geophysical serv)
Western Geophysical Servicos Maritimos Ltda., Praia de Botafogo 518,
Caixa Postal 1451, Rio de Janeiro CEP 20031, Brazil

WESTINGHOUSE AIR BRAKE CO   40 W 40th St, New York, NY 10018,
Tel: (212) 840-5440
(Equip for transp, constr, mining inds)
Ideal Standard WABCO Industria E. Comercio Ltda., Caixa Postal, 1194,

13100-Campinas, Est. Sao Paulo, Brazil
Ideal Standard WABCO, Ind. e Com. Ltda., P.O. Box 22052, 01000, Sao Paulo, SP,
Brazil
WABCO Freios para Autoveiculos, Ltda., Via Anhanguera, Km. 106, Bloco A.,
13179 Sumare, SP, Brazil

WESTVACO CORP   299 Park Ave, New York, NY 10171, Tel: (212) 688-5000
(Mfr paper, packaging, chems)
Rigesa Ltda., Celulose Papel e Embalagens, Rua Atmirante Pereira Guimaraes, 349,
CEP 01250, Sao Paulo, Brazil

WHEATON INDUSTRIES   1101 Wheaton Ave, Milville, NJ 08332, Tel: (609) 825-1400
(Glass & plastic containers, glass tableware)
Wheaton do Brazil S.A., Ind. e Com., Av. Jabaquara 2979, Caixa Postal 1461,
01000 Sao Paulo, SP, Brazil

WOODWARD GOVERNOR CO   5001 North 2nd St, PO Box 7001, Rockford,
IL 61125-7001, Tel: (815) 877-7441
(Mfr speed control governors)
Woodward Governor (Reguladores) Ltda., Caixa Postal 1785, Rua Joaquin Norberto 284,
13080 Campinas, SP, Brazil

WORLD COMMUNICATIONS INC   67 Broad St, New York, NY 10004,
Tel: (212) 607-2000
(Intl private line services)
World Communications, Ave. Pres. Vargas 482, Sala 622, Rio de Janeiro, Brazil

WORLD COURIER INC   46 Trinity Pl, New York, NY 10006, Tel: (718) 978-9400
(Intl courier serv)
World Courier do Brazil, Transportes Internacionais, Rua Venezuela No. 3,
salas 905/906 Rio de Janeiro, Brazil
World Courier do Brazil, Transportes Internacionais, Sao Paulo, Brazil

YOUNG & RUBICAM INTL INC   285 Madison Ave, New York, NY 10017,
Tel: (212) 210-3000
(Advertising agency)
Young & Rubicam do Brazil Ltda., Av. Brig. Faria Lima, 1815-4 andar, CEP 01451,
Sao Paulo, SP, Brazil

BULGARIA

ITT SHERATON CORP   60 State St, Boston, MA 02108, Tel: (617) 367-3600
(Hotel operations)
Sheraton Sofia Hotel Balkan, 5 Lenin Sq., 1000 Sofia, Bulgaria

MTS SYSTEMS CORP   PO Box 24012, Minneapolis, MN 55424, Tel: (612) 937-4000
  (Electrohydraulic testing & prod equip, mach controls)
    Interpred Buro Shipka, 16 Bulgarosuvetska Drouzhba Blvd., BG-1057 Sofia, Bulgaria

CAMEROON

AMERICAN LIFE INSURANCE CO (ALICO)   PO Box 2226, Wilmington, DE 19899,
  Tel: (302) 594-2000
  (Life ins, pension & annuity plans, health prdts)
    American Life Insurance Co, B.P. 2328, Douala, Cameroon
    American Life Insurance Co, 60 Ave. General de Gaulle, Douala, Cameroon

BAKER OIL TOOLS   PO Box 3048, Houston, TX 77253, Tel: (713) 923-9351
  (Oil/gas well completions equip)
    Baker Intl. Cameroon, Base du Wouri, B.P. 3579, Douala, Cameroon

CARRIER INTERNATIONAL CORP   PO Box 4806, Syracuse, NY 13221,
  Tel: (315) 432-6000
  (A/C, heating, refrig & power equip)
    Carrier Corp., S.E.A.C, B.P. 4087, Douala, Cameroon

CHASE MANHATTAN BANK N A   1 Chase Manhattan Plaza, New York, NY 10081,
  Tel: (212) 552-2222
  (Intl banking)
    Chase Bank Cameroon S.A, B.P. 1132, 83 Boulevard de la Liberte, Douala, Cameroon

CITIBANK NA   399 Park Ave, New York, NY 10043, Tel: (212) 559-1000
  (Intl banking)
    Banque Intl. Pour l'Afrique Occidental (JV), B.P. 4001, Douala, Cameroon

THE COCA-COLA CO   310 North Ave NW, PO Box Drawer 1734, Atlanta, GA 30313,
  Tel: (404) 676-2121
  (Mfr & sale of soft drink syrups & concentrates, juices & food prdts, motion pic & TV
  prod)
    Coca-Cola Co. Cameroon, all mail to: U.S. address

EXXON CORP   225 E John Carpenter Frwy, Irving, TX 75062, Tel: (214) 444-1000
  (Petroleum & petroleum prdts)
    Esso Afrique Equatoriale, B.P. 224, Douala, Cameroon

FIRST NATIONAL BANK OF BOSTON   100 Federal St, Boston, MA 02110,
  Tel: (617) 434-2200
  (Commercial banking)
    Boston Bank Cameroon, B.P. 1784, 64 Ave. de la Liberte, Douala, Cameroon
    Boston Bank Cameroon, Ave. de l'Independence 1784, Yaunde, Cameroon

FMC CORP   200 E Randolph Dr, Chicago, IL 60601, Tel: (312) 861-6000
  (Mach & chem for industry, agric & govt)
    FMC Cameroon, S/C Caminfor, B.P. 513, Douala, Cameroon

GAMLEN CHEMICAL CO   121 S Maple Ave, S San Francisco, CA 94080,
  Tel: (415) 873-1750
  (Chems, detergents & tank cleansers)
    Gamlen Chemical, P.O. Box 336, Douala, Cameroon

GANNETT FLEMING CORDDRY & CARPENTER INC   PO Box 1963, Harrisburg, PA 17015,
  Tel: (717) 763-7211
  (Engr consulting serv)
    Gannett Fleming Transportation Engineers, B.P. 2063, Yaonde, Cameroon

GTE CORP   One Stamford Forum, Stamford, CT 06904, Tel: (203) 965-2000
  (Electr prdts, telecom sys, publ & commun)
    General Telephone & Electronics Intl, B.P. 509, Yaounde, Cameroon

FRANK B HALL & CO INC   549 Pleasantville Rd, Briarcliff Manor, NY 10510,
  Tel: (914) 769-9200
  (Insurance)
    Sogerco Cameroun, Rue Pau, B.P. 4066, Douala, Cameroon

IMCO SERVICES   5950 N Course Dr, Houston, TX 70072, Tel: (713) 561-1300
  (Drilling fluids)
    Halliburton-IMCO (Cameroon) SARL, Rue Jamot, Magazin de Cam, B.P. 5542 KDWA,
      Douala, Cameroon

LE TOURNEAU INC LONGVIEW DIV   PO Box 2307, Longview, TX 75606,
  Tel: (214) 753-3449
  (Heavy constr, mining mach & equip)
    Hamelle-Afrique, B.P. 4041, 54 Blvd. de la Liberte, Douala, Cameroon
    Hamelle-Afrique, B.P. 117, Route d'Akoloninga, Yaounde, Cameroon

MILCHEM INC   3900 Essex Lane, PO Box 22111, Houston, TX 77027,
  Tel: (214) 439-8000
  (Gas & oil well drilling fluids & chem additives)
    Milchem Cameroon SARL, B.P. 5178, Douala, Cameroon
    Milchem Minerals SABM, B.P. 5074, Douala, Cameroon

MOBIL CORP   150 E 42nd St, New York, NY 10017, Tel: (212) 883-4242
  (Petroleum explor, prdts)
    Mobil Oil, Blvd. du General Leclerc, B.P. 4058, Douala, Cameroon

McCANN-ERICKSON WORLDWIDE   750 Third Ave, New York, NY 10017,
  Tel: (212) 697-6000
  (Advertising)
    Nelson McCann, BP 12361, Douala, Cameroon

NCR CORP   1700 S Patterson Blvd, Dayton, OH 45479, Tel: (513) 445-2000
  (Develop/mfr/sell/serv business info processing sys)
    NCR Cameroon S.A., B.P. 3505, Douala, Cameroon

CANADA

3M CO   3M Center, St Paul, MN 55144-1000, Tel: (612) 733-1110
(Mfr abrasives, adhesives, chems, ind & consumer tapes/diskettes, health care prdts, elec connectors)
   3M Canada Inc., P.O. Box 5757, Terminal A, London, Ont., Canada N6A 4T1

A-Z INTL TOOL CO   PO Box 7108, Houston, TX 77248-7108, Tel: (713) 880-8888
(Mfr oil field, milling & casing cutting tools)
   A-Z/Grant/Drilex, 727 6th Ave., Calgary, Alta., Canada T2P OV1
   A-Z/Grant/Drilex, 1414 77th Ave., Edmonton, Alta., Canada T6P 1M2

AAA TRUCKING CORP   3630 Quakerbridge Rd, Trenton, NJ 08619,
   Tel: (609) 586-0700
   (Motor carrier frt serv)
   Clarke Transport Canada Inc., 1155 Dorchester Blvd. W., Montreal, Canada

ABBOTT LABORATORIES   Abbott Park, North Chicago, IL 60064,
   Tel: (312) 937-6100
   (Pharm & lab prdts)
   Abbott Laboratories Ltd., 5400 Cote de Liesse, Montreal, Que., Canada H4P 1A5
   Abbott Laboratories Ltd., P.O. Box 6150, Montreal, Que., Canada H3C 3K6

ABERDEEN MFG CORP   16 E 34th St, New York, NY 10016, Tel: (212) 889-8380
(Mfr curtains, draperies, bedspreads)
   Werner-Finkel Inc., 9500 Bond St., Laurent Section B4, Montreal, Que., Canada

ACADEMIC PRESS INC   111 Fifth Ave, New York, NY 10003, Tel: (212) 741-6800
(Publ scientific books)
   Academic Press Canada Ltd., 55 Barber Green Rd., Don Mills, Ont., Canada M3C 2A1
   Edition Etudes Vivantes Ltd., 6700 Chemin Cote de Liesse, St. Laurent, Que.,
      Canada H4T 1E8

ACCO INDUSTRIES INC   101 Oakview Dr, Trumbull, CT 06611, Tel: (203) 371-5439
(Testing sys, chain, castings, brakes, bridge & jib cranes)
   Measurement Systems of Canada, 234 Altwell Dr., Rexdale, Toronto, Ont.,
      Canada M9W 5B3

ACCO INTL INC   770 S Acco Plaza, Wheeling, IL 60090, Tel: (708) 541-9500
(Paper fasteners & clips, metal fasteners, binders, staplers)
   Acco Canadian Co. Ltd., 501 McNicoll Ave., Willowdale, Ont., Canada M2H 2E2

ACCURAY CORP   650 Ackerman Rd, PO Box 02248, Columbus, OH 43202,
   Tel: (614) 261-2000
   (Computer-based process mgmt sys for forest prdts, metals rolling, textiles, tobacco ind)
   Accuray of Canada Ltd., Ville St. Laurent, Que., Canada

ACE LONG DISTANCE CORP   39 State St, Rochester, NY 14614, Tel: (716) 987-3000
(Long distance & pvt wire telecom)
   Ace Long Distance Ltd., Toronto-Dominion Bank Tower- #2550, 55 King St., Toronto,
   Ont., Canada

ACHESON COLLOIDS CO   1600 Washington Ave, PO Box 288, Port Huron, MI 48060,
Tel: (313) 984-5581
(Graphite, lubricants & other specialty chems)
   Acheson Colloids (Canada) Ltd., P.O. Box 665, Brantford, Ont., Canada N3T 5P9

ACME GENERAL CORP   300 E Arrow Hwy, San Dimas, CA 91773, Tel: (714) 599-6881
(Proprietary sliding & folding door hdwe sys & access)
   Acmetrack Ltd., 100 Walker Dr., Brampton, Ont., Canada L6T 4H6

ACME UNITED CORP   425 Post Rd, Fairfield, CT 06430, Tel: (203) 384-1371
(Shears & scissors, sterile procedure trays)
   Acme Ruler Ltd., Mount Forest, Ont., Canada

ADC TELECOMMUNICATIONS INC   4900 W 78th St, Minneapolis, MN 55435,
Tel: (612) 835-6800
(Mfr telecom equip)
   ADC Canada, 2147 de la Province, Longueuil, Quebec J4G 1Y6, Canada

ADDISON-WESLEY PUBLISHING CO   Route 128, Reading, MA 01867,
Tel: (617) 944-3700
(Educational textbook publ)
   Addison-Wesley (Canada) Ltd., 26 Prince Andrew Place, Box 550, Don Mills, Ont.,
   Canada M3C 2T8

ADDRESSOGRAPH FARRINGTON INC   300 Pond St, Randolph, MA 02368,
Tel: (617) 963-8500
(Embossing & credit authorization sys)
   Addressograph Farrington Inc., 1660 Trinity Dr., Mississauga, Ont. Canada L5T 1L6

ADVANCE MACHINE CO   14600 21st Ave N, Plymouth, MN 55447, Tel: (612) 473-2235
(Ind floor cleaning equip)
   Advance Floor Machine Co. Canada Ltd., 1295 Crestlawn Dr., Mississauga, Ont.,
   Canada L4W 1A9

AEC INC   801 AEC Drive, Wood Dale, IL 60191, Tel: (708) 595-1090
(Mfr/serv aux equip for plastics ind)
   En-Plas, 40 Continental Plaza, Scarborough, Ont., Canada M1R 2T4

AEROFIN CORP   4621 Murray Place, PO Box 10819, Lynchburg, VA 24506,
Tel: (804) 845-7081
(Mfr heat exchangers)
   Aerofin Corp. Canada Ltd., 1020 Balmoral Rd., Cambridge, Ont., Canada N1T 1A5

AIR EXPRESS INTL CORP   120 Tokeneke Rd, PO Box 1231, Darien, CT 06820,
Tel: (203) 655-7900
(Air frt forwarder)
   Air Express Intl., Cargo Bldg. #2, Road B, Montreal Intl. Airport, Montreal, Que.,
   Canada
   Air Express Intl., Cargo Bldg. E, Air Cargo Section, Toronto Intl. Airport,
   Toronto, Ont., Canada

AIR PRODUCTS & CHEMICALS INC   7201 Hamilton Blvd, Allentown, PA 18195,
  Tel: (215) 481-4911
  (Mfr ind gases & chems)
    Air Products Canada Ltd., 2090 Steeles Ave. E., Brampton, Ont. L6T 1A7, Canada

AIR-SHIELDS VICKERS   330 Jacksonville Rd, Hatboro, PA 19040,
  Tel: (215) 675-5200
  (Mfr/sales/serv spec med equip, med electr prdts)
    Narco Scientific Ltd., 654 Petrolia Dr., Downsview, Ont., Canada M3J 2W3

AJ INDUSTRIES INC   11454 San Vicente Blvd, Los Angeles, CA 90049,
  Tel: (213) 879-0370
  (Gas heaters, heavy duty brake drums)
    A.J. Industries (Canada) Ltd., 241 S. Service Rd., Grimsby, Ont., Canada L3M 147

AJAX MAGNETHERMIC CORP   1745 Overland Ave NE, PO Box 991, Warren, OH 44482,
  Tel: (216) 372-2529
  (Electric induction heaters)
    Ajax Magnethermic Canada, 333 Station St., Ajax, Ont., Canada L1S 1S3

AKRON BRASS CO   1450 Spruce St, Wooster, OH 44691, Tel: (216) 264-5678
  (Irrigation sys)
    Akron Mfg., Box 280, Aylmer, Ont., Canada

ALADDIN INDUSTRIES INC   PO Box 100255, Nashville, TN 37210,
  Tel: (615) 748-3000
  (Vacuum bottles)
    Aladdin Industries (Canada) Ltd., 5 Maclahlan Dr., Rexdale, Ont., Canada

ALARM DEVICE MFG CO   165 Eileen Way, Syosset, NY 11791, Tel: (516) 921-6704
  (Security, fire & burglary sys)
    ABC/Ademco Security Products, 200 Benjamin Hudon, St. Laurent, Que., Canada H4N 1H8

ALBANY INTL CORP   PO Box 1907, Albany, NY 12201, Tel: (518) 445-2200
  (Paper mach clothing, engineered fabrics, plastic prdts, filtration media)
    Albany Canada, 649 Derwent Way, Annacis Industrial Estate, New Westminster,
      British Columbia, Canada V3M 5P7
    Albany Canada, 300 Westmount St., Cowansville, Que., Canada J2K 1S9
    Albany Intl. Engineered Systems Div., 805 Bancroft St., Pointe Claire, Que.,
      Canada H9R 4L6
    Albany Papermaking Products Group, 1 North St., Perth, Ont., Canada K7H 3E4

ALCO CONTROLS DIV EMERSON ELECTRIC   PO Box 12700, St Louis, MO 63141,
  Tel: (314) 569-4670
  (Mfr/sales refrig & A/C flow controls)
    Alco Controls Div., Emerson Electric Co., P.O. Box 150, Markham, Ont.,
      Canada L3P 3J6

ALCO STANDARD CORP   825 Duportail Rd, Wayne, PA 19087, Tel: (215) 296-8000
  (Diversified distr, mfg & resources)
    Alco Dispensing Canada Ltd., 23 Bay Rd., Ajax, Ont., L1S 341, Canada
    Benndorf-Verster Ltd., 380 West 2nd Ave., Vancouver, BC V57 1CB, Canada
    Big Drum Equipment Ltd., P.O. Box 676, Hamilton, Ont., Canada L8N 3M4
    Calgary Copier Ltd., 1530-27 Ave., NE, Calgary, Alb., T2E 7S6, Canada
    Halifax Office Products Ltd., 5445 Rainnie Dr., Halifax, NS B3J 1P8, Canada

ALCOLAC INTL INC   3440 Fairfield Rd, Baltimore, MD 21226, Tel: (301) 355-2600
  (Specialty chems)
    Alcolac Ltd., 490 Dufferin St., Valleyfield, Que., Canada

ALCON LABORATORIES INC   PO Box 6600, Fort Worth, TX 76115,
  Tel: (817) 293-0450
  (Mfr pharms)
    Alcon of Canada Ltd., 2 Thorncliffe Park Dr., Toronto, Ont., Canada

ALLEN-BRADLEY CO   PO Box 2086, Milwaukee, WI 53201, Tel: (414) 382-2000
  (Electrical control devices)
    Allen-Bradley (Canada) Ltd., Cambridge, Ont., Canada

ALLERGAN PHARMACEUTICALS INTL INC   2525 DuPont Dr, Irvine, CA 92713,
  Tel: (714) 752-4500
  (Pharms, opthalmic & dermatological preparations)
    Allergan Inc., 263 Labrosse Ave., Pointe Claire, Que., Canada H9R 1A3

ALLIED AFTERMARKET DIV   105 Pawtucket Ave, East Providence, RI 02916,
  Tel: (401) 434-7000
  (Mfr spark plugs, waste treatment sys, filters, brakes)
    Allied Signal Intl., 201 City Centre Dr., Mississauga, Ont., Canada L5B 3A3
    Fram Canada Ltd., P.O. Box 550, Stratford, Ont., Canada

ALLIED-SIGNAL INC   Columbia Rd & Park Ave, PO Box 2245R, Morristown,
  NJ 07960, Tel: (201) 455-2000
  (Mfr aerospace & automotive prdts, engineered materials)
    Allied Chemical Canada Inc., 201 City Center Dr., Mississauga, Ont., Canada L5B 2T4
    Barrday Inc., 75 Moorefield St., Cambridge, Ont. Canada N1R 5W6

ALLIED-SIGNAL INTL INC   Columbia Rd & Park Ave, PO Box 2000, Morristown,
  NJ 07962, Tel: (201) 455-6034
  (Mfr advanced aerospace, automotive & engineered materials)
    Allied-Signal Canada Inc., 48 St. Clair Ave. W., Toronto, Ont., Canada M4V 3A3

ALLIS-CHALMERS CORP   PO Box 512, Milwaukee, WI 53201, Tel: (414) 475-4011
  (Heavy mach, equip & serv)
    AAF-Ltd., 440 Stinson Blvd, Montreal, Que., Canada H4N 2G1
    Allis-Chalmers Canada Inc., 125 St. Joseph St., Lachine, Que., Canada H8S 2L2
    Allis-Chalmers Credit Corp. of Canada Ltd., P.O. Box 1460, Regina, Saskatchewan,
      Canada S4P 3C2
    Niagara Metals Ltd., Niagara Falls, Ont., Canada

ALTEC INDUSTRIES INC   210 Inverness Center Dr, Birmingham, AL 35242,
  Tel: (205) 991-7733
  (Mfr truck mounted aerial lifts & pole erection derricks)
    Altec Industries Ltd., 831 Nipissing Rd., Milton, Ontario L9T 4Z4, Canada

ALUMATIC CORP OF AMERICA   6353 N 64th St, Milwaukee, WI 53218,
  Tel: (414) 355-3200
  (Aluminum windows, glass)
    Alumatic of Canada Ltd., 6161 Tecumseh Rd. E., Windsor, Ont., Canada

AM INTL INC   333 W Wacker Dr, #900, Chicago, IL 60606-1265,
  Tel: (312) 558-1966
  (Mfr/sale/serv commun graphics, info handling equip & sys)
    AM Intl. Inc., 165 Milner Ave., Scarborough, Ont., Canada M1S 4G7

AMAX INC   200 Park Ave, New York, NY 10166, Tel: (212) 856-4200
(Metals & energy)
    AMAX of Canada Ltd., Box 12525, 1066 W. Hastings St., Vancouver, BC, Canada V6E 3E1

AMDAHL CORP   1250 East Arques Ave, PO Box 3470, Sunnyvale, CA 94088-3470,
Tel: (408) 746-6000
(Mfr large scale computers, complementary software storage & commun prdts)
    Amdahl Communications Inc., 2330 Millrace Ct., Mississauga, Ont. L5N 1W2, Canada
    Amdahl Communications Inc., 2330 Millrace Ct., Mississauga, Ont. L5N 1W2, Canada
    Amdahl Ltd., P.O. Box 123, 1 First Canadian Pl., #3940, Toronto, Ont.,
      Canada M5X 1A4

AMERACE CORP   Newburgh Rd, Hackettstown, NJ 07840, Tel: (201) 852-1122
(Chems, rubber prdts, plastics, electrical components & controls)
    Amerace Ltd., 10 Esna Park Dr., Markahan, Ont., Canada

AMERICAN & EFIRD INC   PO Box 507, Mt Holly, NC 28120, Tel: (704) 827-4311
(Mfr ind thread, yarn & consumer sewing prdts)
    Allied Threads Inc., 99 Rue Chabanel St. O/W, Montreal, Quebec H2N 1C3, Canada

AMERICAN AIR FILTER CO INC   215 Central Ave, PO Box 35690, Louisville,
KY 40277, Tel: (502) 637-0011
(Air cleaning equip)
    American Air Filter Ltd., 400 Stinson Blvd, Montreal, Que., Canada H4N 2G1

AMERICAN AIRLINES INC   PO Box 619616, Dallas-Ft Worth Arpt, TX 75261-9616,
Tel: (817) 355-1234
(Air transp)
    American Airlines Inc., Foster Bldg., 40 St. Clair Ave. W., Toronto, Ont.,
      Canada M4V 1M4

AMERICAN APPRAISAL ASSOCS INC   525 E Michigan St, Milwaukee, WI 53202,
Tel: (414) 271-7240
(Valuation consulting serv)
    General Appraisal of Canada Ltd., 170 University Ave., Toronto, Ont., Canada

AMERICAN BANKERS INSURANCE GROUP   11222 Quail Roost Dr, Miami, FL 33157,
Tel: (305) 253-2244
(Insurance)
    American Bankers Insurance Group, 40 Sheppard Ave. W., #501, Willowdale,
      Ont. M2N 6K9, Canada

AMERICAN BILTRITE INC   57 River St, Wellesley Hills, MA 02181,
Tel: (617) 237-6655
(Rubber prdts)
    American Biltrite (Canada) Ltd., Sherbrooke, Que., Canada J1H 5J1

AMERICAN BUILDING MAINTENANCE INDUSTRIES INC   333 Fell St, San Francisco,
CA 94102, Tel: (415) 864-5150
(Contract building serv)
    American Bldg. Maintenance Co. Ltd., 1075 Clark Dr., Vancouver, B.C., Canada V5L 3K2
    American Bldg. Maintenance Co. Ltd., 205-1039 17th Ave. SW, Calgary, Alta.,
      Canada T2T 0B1
    Associated Bldg. Maintenance Co., 112 St. Clair Ave. West., Toronto, Ont.,
      Canada M4V 2Y3

AMERICAN CHICLE CO   201 Tabor Rd, Morris Plains, NJ 07950,
  Tel: (201) 540-2000
  (Chewing gum)
    Warner Lambert Ltd., 2200 Eglinton E., Scarborough, Ont., Canada M1K 5C9

AMERICAN CYANAMID CO   1 Cyanamid Plaza, Wayne, NJ 07470, Tel: (201) 831-2000
  (Pharms, chems, agric & consumer prdts)
    Canadian Operations, Cyanamid Inc., 2255 Sheppard Ave. E., Willowdale, Ont.,
      Canada M2J 4Y5

AMERICAN EXPRESS CO   American Express Tower, New York, NY 10285-4765,
  Tel: (212) 640-2000
  (Diversified fin & travel-related serv)
    American Express Canada Inc., 225 7th Ave. SW, Calgary, Alta., Canada
    American Express Canada Inc., 647 Granville St., Vancouver, British Columbia, Canada
    American Express Canada Inc., 220 Laurier Ave. W, Ottawa, Ont., Canada
    American Express Canada Inc., 50 Bloor St. W., Toronto, Ont., Canada
    American Express Canada Inc., 1200 Peel St., Montreal, Que., Canada.

AMERICAN FILTRONA CORP   PO Box 31640, Richmond, VA 23294, Tel: (804) 346-2400
  (Diversified manufacturing)
    Filpac Inc., C.P. 148, Terrebonne, Que., Canada J6W 3L5

AMERICAN GENERAL CORP   2727 Allen Parkway, Houston, TX 77019,
  Tel: (713) 522-1111
  (Life & health ins, financial serv)
    Financial Life Assurance Co. of Canada, 10123 99th St., Edmonton, Alta., Canada

AMERICAN GREETINGS CORP   10500 American Rd, Cleveland, OH 44144,
  Tel: (216) 252-7300
  (Mfr/distr greeting cards, gift wrappings, tags, seals, ribbons & party goods)
    Carlton Cards Ltd., 1460 The Queensway, Toronto, Ortario M8Z 1S7, Canada

AMERICAN HOME PRODUCTS CORP   685 Third Ave, New York, NY 10017,
  Tel: (212) 878-5800
  (Drugs, food, household prdts)
    API Laboratory Products Ltd., St. Laurent, Que., Canada
    Ayerst, McKenna & Harrison Inc., Montreal, Que., Canada
    Boyle-Midway Canada Ltd., Toronto, Ont., Canada
    Canadian Home Products Ltd., Niagara Falls, Ont., Canada
    Dupli-Color Canada Ltd., Scarborough, Ont., Canada
    Ekco Canada Inc., Toronto, Ont., Canada
    Franklin Laboratories Ltd., Calgary, Alta., Canada
    Whitehall Laboratories Ltd., Toronto, Ont., Canada
    Wyeth Ltd., Toronto, Ont., Canada

AMERICAN INTL UNDERWRITERS CORP   70 Pine St, New York, NY 10270,
  Tel: (212) 770-7000
  (General ins)
    AIU Canada Ltd., 55 University Ave., Toronto, Ont., Canada M5J 1H7

AMERICAN LIFE INSURANCE CO (ALICO)   PO Box 2226, Wilmington, DE 19899,
  Tel: (302) 594-2000
  (Life ins, pension & annuity plans, health prdts)
    American Life Insurance Co., 55 University Ave., Toronto, Ont., Canada M57 2H7
    American Life Insurance Co., 1200 Ave. McGill College, Montreal, Que.,
      Canada H3B 4S7

AMERICAN LOCKER GROUP INC   15 W Second St, Jamestown, NY 14702,
Tel: (716) 664-9600
(Mfr coin-oper locks, office furniture)
   Canadian Locker Co., 401 Mugget Ave., Agincourt, Ont., Canada

AMERICAN MANAGEMENT SYSTEMS INC   1777 North Kent St, Arlington, VA 22209,
Tel: (703) 841-6000
(Design/serv computer sys)
   AMS Management Systems Canada Inc., 180 Elgin St., Ottawa, Ontario, Canada

AMERICAN NATIONAL CAN CO   8770 W Bryn Mawr Ave, Chicago, IL 60631,
Tel: (312) 399-3000
(Mfr metal, glass & plastic packaging prdt)
   American National Can, Canada, 180 Walker Dr., Brampton, Ont. L6P 465, Canada
   Bernadin of Canada Ltd., 853 Islington Ave., Toronto, Ont., Canada

AMERICAN OPTICAL CORP   14 Mechanic St, Southbridge, MA 01550,
Tel: (617) 765-9711
(Ophthalmic lenses, frames & cases, sunglasses)
   AO Ltd., Martin St. 564, Nicolet, Que., Canada
   AOCO Ltd., 60 Mobile Dr., Toronto, Ont., Canada M4A 2P3
   AOCO Ltd., 160 Wellington St., Belleville, Ont., Canada K8N 5C6

AMERICAN PRECISION INDUSTRIES INC   2777 Walden Ave, Buffalo, NY 14225,
Tel: (716) 684-9700
(Mfr heat transfer equip, coils, capacitors, electro-mech clutches & brakes)
   Dustex of Canada Inc., 698 Wilson Ave., Kitchener, Ont., Canada N2C 1H9

AMERICAN PRESIDENT LINES LTD   1111 Broadway, Oakland, CA 94607,
Tel: (415) 272-8000
(Intermodal shipping serv)
   American President Lines, Ltd., 231 Rue St. Jacques, Montreal, Que., Canada H2Y 1M6

AMERICAN RE-INSURANCE CO   One Liberty Plaza, 91 Liberty St, New York,
NY 10006, Tel: (212) 766-6700
(Reinsurance)
   American Re-Insurance Co., 20 Queen St. West, Box 65, Toronto, Ont., Canada M3H 3R3
   American Re-Insurance Co., 1001 Ouest Blvd. de Maisonneuve, Montreal, Que.,
   Canada H3A 3C8

AMERICAN STANDARD INC   40 W 40th St, New York, NY 10018, Tel: (212) 840-5100
(Heating & sanitary equip)
   American Standard Industrial Products (Div. of WABCO), 1 Blair Dr., Bramalea, Ont.,
   Canada L6T 2H4
   American Standard-Canada, 80 Ward St., Toronto, Ont., Canada M6H 4A7

AMERICAN STEAMSHIP CO   3200 Marine Midland Center, Buffalo, NY 14203,
Tel: (716) 854-7644
(Bulk cargo sea carrier)
   Boland & Cornelius, 830-360 Main St., Winnepeg, Man., Canada R3C 3I3

AMERICAN TOOL COMPANIES INC   301 S 13th St, #600, Lincoln, NE 68508,
Tel: (402) 435-3300
(Mfr hand tools)
   Petersen Canada Inc., 5865 Coopers Ave., Mississauga, Ontario L4Z 1R9, Canada

AMERICAN UNIFORM CO   PO Box 2130, Cleveland, TN 37311, Tel: (615) 476-6561
(Mfr work clothing, uniforms)
Canadian Uniform Ltd., 9697 St. Lawrence Blvd., Montreal, Que., Canada H3L 2N2

AMETEK INC   Station Sq, Paoli, PA 19301, Tel: (215) 647-2121
(Mfr instru, elect motors, engineered materials)
Ametek (Canada), 3085 Lenworth Dr., Mississauga, Ont., Canada L4X 2G4

AMICON CORP   182 Conant St, Danvers, MA 01923, Tel: (617) 777-3622
(Research apparatus)
Amicon Canada Ltd., 1226 White Oaks Blvd., Oakville, Ont., Canada L6H 2B9

AMPEX CORP   401 Broadway, Redwood City, CA 94063-3199, Tel: (415) 367-2011
(Mfr professional audio/visual sys, magnetic recording media, data-memory prdts)
Ampex Canada Inc., 1116-44 Ave. NE, Calgary, Alta., Canada T2E 6Y4
Ampex Canada Inc., 729 Meloche Ave., Dorval, Que., Canada H9P 2S4
Ampex Canada Inc., 1770 Argentia Rd., Mississauga, Ont., Canada L5N 3S7

AMPHENOL PRODUCTS   4300 Commerct Ct, Lisle, IL 60532, Tel: (708) 983-3500
(Elect interconnect/penetrate sys & assemblies)
Amphenol Canada, 44 Metropolitan Rd., Scarborough, Ont., Canada M1R 2T9
Amphenol Canada, 20 Melford Dr., Scarborough, Ont., Canada M1B 2X6
Amphenol Canada, 3285 Canvendish Blvd., Montreal, Que., Canada H4B 2L9
Amphenol Canada, 112 Colonnade Rd., Nepean, Ont., Canada K2E 7L6
Amphenol Canada, P.O. Box 430, Renfrew, Ont., Canada K7V 4A6
Amphenol Canada, 10711 Cambie Rd., Richmond, BC, Canada V6X 3G5

AMSCO INTL   2222 W Grandview Blvd, Erie, PA 16512, Tel: (814) 452-3100
(Hospital equip)
Ingram & Bell Ltd., 20 Bond, Don Mills, Ont., Canada

AMSTAR CORP   1251 Ave of the Americas, New York, NY 10020,
Tel: (212) 489-9000
(Sugar refining, corn milling, packaging materials & mach)
Canadian Duff-Norton Co. Ltd., 15 Lockport Ave., Toronto, Ont., Canada M82 2R6
Milwaukee Electric Tool (Canada) Ltd., 383 Midwest Rd., Scarborough, Ont.,
Canada M 1 3A6

ANACONDA CO   555 17th St, Denver, CO 80202, Tel: (303) 575-4000
(Copper mining)
Anaconda Canada Ltd., 330 University Ave., Toronto, Ont., Canada M5G 1R7

ANCHOR HOCKING CORP   109 N Broad St, PO Box 600, Lancaster, OH 43132,
Tel: (614) 687-2111
(Mfr glassware & dinnerware, plastic prdts)
Anchor Cap & Closure Corp. of Canada Ltd., 275 Wallace Ave., Toronto, Ont.,
Canada M6P 3N3
Anchor Hocking Corp., 30 Industrial St., Toronto, Ont., Canada M4G 1N9

ANDREW CORP   10500 W 153rd St, Orlando Park, IL 60462, Tel: (708) 349-3300
(Antenna sys)
Andrew Antenna Co. Ltd., 606 Beech St., Whitby, Ont., Canada L1N 5S2

ANDREW JERGENS CO   2535 Spring Grove Ave, Cincinnati, OH 45214,
Tel: (513) 421-1400
(Toiletries)
Andrew Jergens Co. Ltd., Peth, Ont., Canada

ANGELICA UNIFORM GROUP INC   700 Rosedale Ave, St Louis, MO 63112,
  Tel: (314) 889-1111
  (Uniforms & flat goods)
    Angelica-Whitewear Ltd., 5650 d'Iberville St., Montreal, Que., Canada H2G 3E4

ANGLO ENERGY LTD   233 Broadway, New York, NY 10279, Tel: (212) 619-4242
  (Constr, contract drilling, oilfield transp)
    Nabors Drilling Ltd., Home Oil Tower, T-D Square, 324 Eighth Ave. SW., Calgary,
      Alta., Canada T2P 2Z2

ANIXTER BROS INC   4711 Golf Rd, Skokie, IL 60076, Tel: (708) 677-2600
  (Dist wiring sys/prdts for voice, video, data & power applications)
    Anixter Canada, 33 City Centre Dr., Mississauga, Ont. L5B 2N5, Canada

ANTHONY INDUSTRIES INC   4900 S Eastern Ave, Los Angeles, CA 90040,
  Tel: (213) 724-2800
  (Pool constr & equip, fishing tackle, athletic apparel)
    Shakespeare Co. (Canada) Ltd., Orillia, Ont., Canada

ANTI-HYDRO WATERPROOFING CO   265-277 Badger Ave, Newark, NJ 07108,
  Tel: (201) 242-8000
  (Bldg specialties)
    Anti-Hydro of Canada Sales Ltd., 6515-B Cote de Liesse, Ville St. Laurent, Que.,
      Canada H4T 1E5

APPLE COMPUTER INC   20525 Mariani Ave, Cupertino, CA 95014,
  Tel: (408) 996-1010
  (Personal computers, peripherals & software)
    Apple Canada, 7495 Birchmount Rd., Markham, Ont., Canada L3R 5G2

ARROW MFG CO INC   567 52nd St, West New York, NJ 07093, Tel: (201) 867-4833
  (Metal & plastic jewelry & cosmetic boxes)
    Arrow Case Mfg. Co., 11 Dublin St., Toronto, Ont., Canada

ARVIN INDUSTRIES INC   One Noblitt Plaza, Columbus, IN 47201,
  Tel: (812) 379-3000
  (Mfr auto OEM & replacement parts & fabricated metal parts, R&D & testing)
    Arvin Automotive of Canada Ltd., P.O. Box 270, Concord, Ont. L4K 1B4, Canada
    Barrick AP Auto, 80 Enterprise Rd., Toronto, Ont. M9W 1C6, Canada

ASHWORTH BROTHERS INC   89 Globe Mills Ave, PO Box 670, Fall River, MA 02722,
  Tel: (617) 674-4693
  (Flexible & metallic card clothing)
    Ashworth Card Clothing Co. Ltd., 316 St. Hubert St., Granby, Que., Canada

AST RESEARCH INC   16215 Alton Parkway, PO Box 19658, Irvine, CA 92713-9658,
  Tel: (714) 727-4141
  (Mfr personal computers enhancement & data commun prdt)
    AST Research Inc., 6549-A Mississauga Rd., Missassauga, Ontario L5N 1A6, Canada

AT&T INTERNATIONAL   295 N Maple Ave, Basking Ridge, NJ 07920,
  Tel: (908) 221-2000
  (Telecommun)
    AT&T Canada Inc., 1500 Don Mills Rd., #500, Don Mills, Ont., Canada M3B 3K4

AT&T PARADYNE   8550 Ulmerton Rd, PO Box 2826, Largo, FL 34294-2826,
  Tel: (813) 530-2000
  (Mfr data commun prdts & serv)
    AT&T Paradyne, 1281 W. George St., Suite 900, Vancouver, BC V6E 3G7, Canada
    AT&T Paradyne Canada, 100 York Blvd., Suite 200, Richmond Hill, Ont. L4B 1J8, Canada
    AT&T Paradyne Canada, 155 Glendur Circle SE, Suite 105, Calgary,
      Albt. T2H 2S8 Canada
    AT&T Paradyne Canada, 2075 University St., Suite 1106, Montreal, Que. H3A 2L1,
      Canada

GUY F ATKINSON CO OF CA INC   10 W Orange Ave, South San Francisco, CA 94080,
  Tel: (415) 876-1000
  (Constr, oil & gas dev, pipe supply, light mfg)
    Comco Pipe & Supply Co., P.O. Box 5558 Station L, Edmonton, Alta., Canada V5H 3X1
    Commonwealth Construction Co., 4599 Tillicum St., Burnaby, BC, Canada V5J 3J9

AUGAT INC   89 Forbes Blvd, Mansfield, MA 02048, Tel: (508) 543-4300
  (Interconnection prdts)
    Augat Electronics Inc., 1081 Meyerside Dr., Unit 15, Mississauga, Ont.,
      Canada L5T 1M4

THE AUSTIN CO   3650 Mayfield Rd, Cleveland, OH 44121, Tel: (216) 382-6600
  (Conslt, design, engr & constr serv)
    The Austin Co. Ltd., 304 The East Mall, #701, Islington, Ont. M9B 6E2, Canada

AUTOMATIC SPRINKLER CORP OF AMERICA   1000 E Edgerton Rd, Cleveland,
  OH 44147, Tel: (216) 526-9900
  (Fire protection components & sys)
    Auto-Sentry Fire Protection Systems Ltd., 504 Iroquois Shore Rd., Oakville, Ont.,
      Canada L6H 1M4

AUTOMATIC SWITCH CO   Hanover Rd, Florham Park, NJ 07932, Tel: (201) 966-2000
  (Valves & switches)
    Ascolectric Ltd., P.O. Box 160, Brantford, Ont., Canada N3T 5M8

AVCO FINANCIAL SERVICES INC   3349 Michelson Dr, Irvine, CA 92715,
  Tel: (714) 553-1200
  (Fin serv, loans)
    Avco Financial Services Canada Ltd., 201 Queens Ave., London, Ont., Canada N6A 4T6

AVERY INTL CORP   150 N Orange Grove Blvd, Pasadena, CA 91103,
  Tel: (213) 304-2000
  (Mfr self-adhesive labels & marking equip)
    Avery Products Corp. Canada Ltd., 35 McLachlan Dr., Rexdale, Ont., Canada M9W 1E4

AVIS INC   900 Old Country Rd, Garden City, NY 11530, Tel: (516) 222-3000
  (Car rental serv)
    Aviscar Inc., 1225 Metcalfe St., Montreal, Que. H3B 2V5, Canada

AVNET INC   80 Cutter Mill Rd, Great Neck, NY 11021, Tel: (516) 466-7000
  (Mfr/distr electronic, elect & video prdts)
    Crown Controls Mfg. Ltd., 33 Gaylord Rd., St. Thomas, Ont., Canada
    Hamilton/Avnet Intl. (Canada) Ltd., 190 Colonnade Rd., Nepean, Ont., Canada K2E 7J5

AVON PRODUCTS INC   9 W 57th St, New York, NY 10019, Tel: (212) 546-6015
  (Mfr/distr cosmetics, perfumes)
    Avon Products Ltd., P.O. Box 8000, Pointe Claire-Dorvall, Que., Canada H9R 4R3

BAILEY CONTROLS CO   29801 Euclid Ave, Wickliffe, OH 44092,
   Tel: (216) 943-5500
   (Mfr analog & digital instru, controls & control sys)
      Bailey Controls, 860 Harrington Ct., Burlington, Ont., Canada L7N 3N4

J T BAKER INC   222 Red School Lane, Phillipsburg, NJ 08865,
   Tel: (201) 859-2151
   (Mfr/sale/serv lab & process chems)
      J.T. Baker, P.O. Box 355, Station A, Toronto, Ont. M5W 1C5, Canada

BALTIMORE PAINT & CHEMICAL   2325 Hollins Ferry Rd, Baltimore, MD 21230,
   Tel: (301) 837-3030
   (Paints, finishes, resins)
      Rubber Set Co. Ltd., 1951 Leslie St., Don Mills, Ont., Canada M3B 2M2

BANDAG INC   Bandag Center, Muscatine, IA 52761, Tel: (319) 262-1400
   (Mfr/sale tread rubber & related equip/supplies)
      Bandag Canada Ltd., 5230 14th Ave., Shawinigan, Que., Canada G9N 6V9

THE BANK OF NEW YORK   48 Wall St, New York, NY 10286, Tel: (212) 530-1784
   (Banking)
      The Bank of New York Canada, Sun Life Centre, Sun Life Tower, 150 King St. West,
         Toronto, Ont. M5H 1J9, Canada

BANKAMERICA CORP   PO Box 37000, San Francisco, CA 94137, Tel: (415) 622-3456
   (Financial services)
      Bank of America Canada, 4 King St. West, 18th fl., Toronto, Ont., Canada M5H 1B6

BANKERS TRUST CO   280 Park Ave, New York, NY 10017, Tel: (212) 775-2500
   (Banking)
      BT Bank of Canada, Royal Bank Plaza, North Tower, Toronto, Ont., Canada M5J 2S2

BANNER INDUSTRIES INC   24500 Chagrin Blvd, Cleveland, OH 44122,
   Tel: (216) 464-3650
   (Processing equip for chems)
      Patterson Industries Ltd., 250 Danforth Rd., Scarborough, Ont., Canada

BARBER-COLMAN CO   555 Colman Center Dr, Rockford, IL 61125,
   Tel: (815) 397-7400
   (Mfr controls, motors)
      Barber-Colman of Canada Ltd., 1875 Wilson Ave., Weston, Ont., Canada

BARBER-GREENE CO   3000 Baraber-Greene Rd, DeKalb, IL 60115,
   Tel: (815) 756-5600
   (Mfr heavy road constr equip)
      Barber-Greene Canada Ltd., P.O. Box 445, 453 Wyecroft Rd., Oakville, Ont.,
         Canada L6J 5A8

C R BARD INC   731 Central Ave, Murray Hill, NJ 07974, Tel: (201) 277-8000
   (Health care prdts)
      C.R. Bard (Canada) Ltd., 2345 Stanfield Rd., Mississauga, Ont., Canada L4Y 3Y3

BARDAHL MFG CORP   1400 N W 52nd St, PO Box 70607, Seattle, WA 98107,
   Tel: (206) 783-4851
   (Lubricating oils)
      Bardahl Inc., 6099 Trans Canada Hwy., Pointe Claire, Que., Canada H9R 1C1

BARNES GROUP INC   123 Main St, Bristol, CT 06010, Tel: (203) 583-7070
(Mfr maint parts & supplies)
Wallace Barnes Co. Ltd., Hamilton, Ont., Canada, Bowman Distribution (Canada),
Toronto, Ont., Canada

BARNES-HIND INC   895 Kifer Rd, Sunnyvale, CA 94086, Tel: (408) 736-5462
(Contact lenses & accessories, opthalmic & dermatology prdts)
Barnes-Hind Inc., 6535 Mill Creek Dr., Unit 67, Mississauga, Ont., Canada L5N 2M2

BARNWELL INDUSTRIES INC   2828 Paa St, #2085, Honolulu, HI 96819,
Tel: (808) 836-0136
(Holding co: explor/devel gas & oil, drill water sys, farming/mktg papayas)
Barnwell of Canada Ltd., 639 5th Avenue SW- #1120, Calgary, Alberta T2P 0M9, Canada

BASS CORP   P O Drawer D, Williamsburg, VA 23187, Tel: (804) 887-6000
(Ind chems, textile fibers & yarns)
Badische Canada Ltd., 1335 Carling Ave., Admiral House, Ottawa, Ont., Canada K1Z 8N8

BATTEN BARTON DURSTINE & OSBORN INC   1285 Ave of the Americas, New York,
NY 10019, Tel: (212) 459-5000
(Advertising agency)
Baker Lovick Ltd., 60 Bloor St. W., Toronto, Ont., Canada M4W 3B8

BAUSCH & LOMB INC   1 Lincoln First Sq, Rochester, NY 14601-0054,
Tel: (716) 338-6000
(Mfr healthcare & optics prdts)
Bausch & Lomb Canada Inc., Don Mills, Ont., Canada

J H BAXTER & CO   1700 S El Camino Real, PO Box 5902, San Mateo, CA 94402,
Tel: (415) 349-0201
(Pressure treated poles, piling & lumber)
J.H. Baxter & Co. Ltd., 361 Albert St., P.O. Box 278, Nanaimo, B.C., Canada

BAXTER TRAVENOL LABORATORIES INC   1 Baxter Pky, Deerfield, IL 60015,
Tel: (708) 948-2000
(Pharm & disposable med prdts)
Baxter Travenol Laboratories of Canada Ltd., 89 Centre St., Allison, Ont.,
Canada L0M 1A0
Baxter Travenol Laboratories of Canada Ltd., 6405 Northam Dr., Malton, Ont.,
Canada   L4V 1J3

D D BEAN & SONS CO   Peterborough Rd, Jaffrey, NH 03452, Tel: (603) 532-8311
(Paper book matches)
D.D. Bean & Sons (Canada) Ltd., St. Cesaire, Que., Canada

BEARIUM METALS CORP   1170 Chili Ave, Rochester, NY 14624, Tel: (716) 235-5360
(Bearium metal alloys)
Gamma Foundries Ltd., 75 Newkirk Rd., Richmond Hill, Ont., L4C 3G4 Canada

BECHTEL GROUP INC   50 Beale St, PO Box 3965, San Francisco, CA 94119,
Tel: (415) 768-1234
(Engineering & constr)
Bechtel Canada Ltd., 10123 99th St., Edmonton, Alta., Canada T5J 2P4

BECKMAN INSTRUMENTS INC   2500 Harbor Blvd, Box 3100, Fullerton, CA 92634,
Tel: (714) 871-4848
(Mfr/distr/serv research & clinical lab instru, sys, software & reagents)

(cont)

Beckman Instruments (Canada) Inc., 1045 Tristar Dr., Mississauga, Ont.,
   L5T 1W5 Canada

BELCO PETROLEUM CORP   One Dag Hammarskjold Plaza, New York, NY 10017,
   Tel: (212) 644-2200
   (Expl & prod crude oil & natural gas)
   Andex Oil Co. Ltd., 1300 700 Ninth Ave., SW, Calgary, Alta., Canada T2P 3V4

BELDEN WIRE & CABLE   2200 US Higway 27 South, PO Box 1980, Richmond,
   IN 47374, Tel: (317) 983-5200
   (Mfr electr wire & cable prdts)
   Belden Wire & Cable, Cobourg, Ontario, Canada

BELL & HOWELL CO   5215 Old Orchard Rd., Skokie, IL 60077, Tel: (708) 470-7684
   (Diversified info prdts & servs)
   Bell & Howell Ltd., 230 Barmac Dr., Weston, Ont., Canada M9L 2X5

BELL POLE LTD   PO Box 2786, New Brighton, MN 55112, Tel: (612) 633-4334
   (Mfr poles)
   Bell Pole Co. Ltd., P.O. Box 339, Lumby, B.C., Canada

BELOIT CORP   1st Lawrence Ave, Beloit, WI 53511, Tel: (608) 365-3311
   (Paper making mach & equip)
   Beloit Canada Ltd., 275 Hymus Blvd., Pointe-Claire, Que., Canada H9R 1G6
   Rader Canada Inc., Box 65567, Postal Station F, Vancouver, B.C. Canada V5N 5K5
   Rader Canada Inc., P.O. Box 925, Ville St. Laurent, Montreal, Que., Canada H4L 4W3

BELVEDERE CO   725 Columbia Ave, Belvidere, IL 61008-4296, Tel: (815) 544-3131
   (Mfr beauty salon equip)
   Belvedere Co. Canada Inc., 97 Ardelt St., Kichener, Ont., Canada H2H 6L9

BEMIS CO INC   625 Marquette Ave, Minneapolis, MN 55402, Tel: (612) 340-6000
   (Mfr flexible packaging, spec coated & graphics prdts)
   Comm-Lith, 4355 Sri Wilfrid Laurier Blvd., St. Hubert, Que., Canada J3Y 3X4
   Curwood Packaging (Canada) Ltd., 114 Armstrong Ave., Georgetown, Ont.,
      Canada L7G 4S2
   MACtac Canada Ltd., 100 Kennedy Rd. S., Brampton, Ont., Canada L6W 3E8

BENJAMIN MOORE & CO   51 Chestnut Ridge Rd, Montvale, NJ 07645,
   Tel: (201) 573-9600
   (Mfr paints & varnishes)
   Benjamin Moore & Co. Ltd., Mulock & Lloyd Aves., Toronto, Ont., Canada

BENTLEY LABORATORIES INC   17502 Armstrong Ave, Irvine, CA 92714,
   Tel: (714) 546-8020
   (Mfr para-med devices)
   Bentley Labs of Canada, 100 Amber St., Markham, Ont., Canada L3R 3A2

BENTLY NEVADA CORP   PO Box 157, Minden, NV 89423, Tel: (702) 782-3611
   (Electronic monitoring system)
   Bently Nevada Canada Ltd., P.O. Box 233, Nisku, Alta., Canada T0C 2G0
   Bently Nevada Canada Ltd., 70 Gibson Dr., Unit 4, Markham, Ont., Canada L3R 2Z3

BERKEY-COLORTRAN INC   1015 Chestnut St, Burbank, CA 91502,
   Tel: (213) 843-1200
   (Lighting equip)
   Lumitrol Ltd., 5 Walker Ave., Toronto, Ont., Canada M4V .1G3

Macphon Industries Ltd., 3600 1 9th St. NE, Calgary, Alta., Canada T2E 6V2
Rutherford Photo Ltd., 211 Laird Dr., Toronto, Ont., Canada M46 3W8
Treck Photo Ltd., 5051 Arnoldi St., Montreal, Que., Canada H4P 1X6
United Video Ltd., 1485 Triple St., Ottowa, Ont., Canada K1B 3 4

BERKLEY & CO INC   Trilene Drive, Spirit Lake, IA 51360, Tel: (712) 336-1520
 (Fishing tackle, rods, marine & cordage, Trilene, monofilament fishing line, outdoor
 prdts)
    Berkley & Co (Canada) Ltd., 815 Phillips St., Portage la Prairie, Man., Canada

BERNZ-O-MATIC CORP   Olney St, Medina, NY 14103, Tel: (716) 798-4949
 (Gas appliances & cylinders)
    BernzOmatic Ltd., 310 Judson, Toronto, Ont., Canada M82 5T6

BEROL USA   Eagle Rd, Danbury, CT 06810, Tel: (203) 744-0000
 (Writing instru, sharpeners, drafting prdts, templates)
    Berol Inc., 105 Rene Philippe St., Ville Lemoyne, St. Lambert, Que., Canada J4P 3P8

BESSER CO   801 Johnson St, PO Box 336, Alpena, MI 49707, Tel: (517) 354-4111
 (Mfr equip for concrete industry)
    Besser Canada Ltd., 387 Orenda Rd., Gramalea, Ont., Canada L6T 1G4

BETZ LABORATORIES INC   4636 Somerton Rd, Trevose, PA 19047,
 Tel: (215) 355-3300
 (Mfr spec chem for water/wastewater treatment)
    Betz Inc. (Canada), 3026 Solandt Rd., Kanata, Ont. K2K 2A5, Canada

SAMUEL BINGHAM CO   479 Business Center Dr, Mt Prospect, IL 60056,
 Tel: (708) 298-6777
 (Print & ins rollers, inks)
    Samuel Bingham (Canada) Ltd., 13 100 Blvd. Metropolitain Est., Montreal, Que.,
     Canada H1A 4A7
    Samuel Bingham Ltd., 52 Advance Rd., Toronto, Ont., Canada M82 2T7

BINKS MFG CO   9201 W Belmont Ave, Franklin Park, IL 60131,
 Tel: (708) 671-3000
 (Mfr of spray painting & finishing equip)
    Binks Mfg. Co., 14 Vansco Rd., Toronto, Ont., Canada M8Z 5J5

BINNEY & SMITH INC   1100 Church Lane, PO Box 431, Easton, PA 18042,
 Tel: (215) 253-6271
 (Mfr art supplies, craft kits)
    Binney & Smith (Canada) Ltd., 15 Mary St. W, Lindsay, Ont., Canada

BIO-RAD LABORATORIES   2200 Wright Ave, Richmond, CA 94804,
 Tel: (415) 234-4130
 (Spec chems, clinical diagnostic prdts, test kits)
    Bio-Rad Laboratories Ltd., 3140 Universal Dr., Mississauga, Ont., Canada L4X 2C8

BIW CABLE SYSTEMS INC   22 Joseph E Warner Blvd, N Dighton, MA 02764,
 Tel: (508) 822-6600
 (Mfr elect wire & cable, cable assemblies & connectors)
    Boston Insulated Wire & Cable Co. Ltd., 116 Shaw St., Hamilton, Ont., Canada

BLACK & DECKER CORP   701 E Joppa Road, Towson, MD 21204, Tel: (301) 583-3900
 (Mfr portable elect & pneumatic power tools, household prdts)
    Black & Decker Canada Inc., 100 Central Ave., Brockville, Ont., Canada K6V 5W6

BLACK SIVALLS & BRYSON INC   PO Box 27125, Houston, TX 77227,
   Tel: (713) 981-8303
   (Oil & gas prod equip, engineering serv, constr mgt)
      Black, Sivalls & Bryson Ltd., 1803 8th St., Nisku Ind. Park, Nisku, Alta.,
      Canada T0C 2G0on Ltd., 700 2nd St. SW, Scotia Center, Calgary, Alta., Canada

G S BLAKESLEE & CO   1844 S Laramie Ave, Cicero, IL 60650, Tel: (708) 242-2710
   (Food mixers, food preparation equip)
      G.S. Blakeslee & Co. of Canada Ltd., 66 Crockford Blvd., Scarborough, Ont.,
      Canada M1R 3C3

BLISS & LAUGHLIN INDUSTRIES INC   122 West 22nd St, Oak Brook, IL 60521,
   Tel: (708) 654-3350
   (Diversified prdts servicing ind & commercial markets)
      Faultless Caster Co. Ltd., 630 Weber St. N, Waterloo, Ont., Canada N2J 4B2

H & R BLOCK INC   4410 Main St, Kansas City, MO 64111, Tel: (816) 753-6900
   (Income tax preparation)
      H&R Block Inc., 3440 Pharmacy, Scarborough, Ont., Canada M1W 2P8

BLOUNT INC   4520 Executive Park Drive, Montgomery, AL 36116-1602,
   Tel: (205) 244-4370
   (Mfr cutting chain & equip, timber harvest/materials handling equip, sporting ammo,
   gen contracting)
      Omark Canada Ltd., 505 Edinburgh Rd. North, Guelph, Ont. N1H 6L4, Canada
      Omark Holdings Ltd., 505 Edinburgh Rd. North, Guelph, Ont. N1H 6L4, Canada

BLUE BIRD BODY CO   PO Box 937, Fort Valley, GA 31030, Tel: (912) 825-2021
   (Mfr buses, parts & access)
      Canadian Blue Bird Sales Co., P.O. Box 880, Brantford, Ont. Canada

BLUE GIANT EQUIPMENT CORP   One Industrial Park Dr, Pell City, AL 35125,
   Tel: (205) 884-1500
   (Mfr manual & powered lift trucks, levelers & stackers)
      Blue Giant Equipment of Canada, Ltd., 85 Heart Lake Rd. South, Brampton,
      Ontario L6W 3K2, Canada

BOISE CASCADE CORP   One Jefferson Square, PO Box 50, Boise, ID 83728,
   Tel: (208) 384-6161
   (Lumber, paper, related prdts)
      Boise Cascade Canada Ltd., 1807 Scotia Plaza, 40 King St. W., Toronto, Ont., Canada

BOND FOUNDRY & MACHINE CO   230 S Penn St, Manheim, PA 17545,
   Tel: (717) 665-2275
   (Transmission appliances)
      Bond Engineering Works Ltd., 35 Booth Ave., Toronto, Ont., Canada M5M 2M3

BONDED SERVICES   2050 Center Ave, Fort Lee, NJ 07024, Tel: (201) 592-7868
   (Storage, distribution & service of film & tape libraries)
      Bonded Services Intl. Ltd., 205 Richmond St. W, Toronto, Ont., Canada M5V 1V5

BOOK-OF-THE-MONTH CLUB INC   485 Lexington Ave, New York, NY 10017,
   Tel: (212) 867-4300
   (Retails books to mail subscribers; phonograph records, art & reading courses)
      Book-of-the-Month Club (Canada) Ltd., c/o O.E. McIntyre Ltd., 19 W. More Dr.,
      Toronto, Ont., Canada M9V 4M3

BORDEN CHEMICAL DIV   180 East Broad St, Columbus, OH 43215,
Tel: (614) 225-4000
(Chems, tapes, resins)
   Borden Chemical Div. of Borden Co. Ltd., 595 Coronation Dr., West Hill, Ont.,
   Canada M1E 4R9

BORG-WARNER CORP   200 S Michigan Ave, Chicago, IL 60604, Tel: (312) 322-8500
(Mfr A/C equip, chem & plastics, ind prdts, trans equip)
   Automotive Parts Div. Borg-Warner Canada Ltd., 6346 Viscount Rd., Mississauga,
   Ont., Canada L4V 1H3
   Borg-Warner Acceptance Canada Ltd., 2025 Sheppard Ave. E, Willowdale, Ont.,
   Canada M2J 1V6
   Borg-Warner Chemicals Canada Ltd., P.O. Box 10, Cobourg, Ont., Canada K9A 4K2
   Borg-Warner Chemicals Canada Ltd., 1351 Matheson Blvd., Mississauga, Ont.,
   Canada L4W 2A1
   Byron Jackson Div. Borg-Warner Canada Ltd., 23 Bertrand Ave., Scarborough, Ont.,
   Canada M1L 2P3
   Long Mfg. Div. Borg-Warner Canada Ltd., 3228 S. Service Rd., Burlington, Ont.,
   Canada L7N 3L3
   Morse Chain Div. Borg-Warner Canada Ltd., 385 Scond Ave., Simcoe, Ont.,
   Canada N3Y 4L5
   York Div. Borg-Warner Canada Ltd., 326 Rexdale Blvd., Rexdale, Ont., Canada M9W 1R6

BORN INC   408 N Boston Ave, PO Box 102, Tulsa, OK 74103-1404,
Tel: (918) 582-2186
(Design/mfr direct fired heaters)
   Born Heaters Canada Ltd., 409-10333 Southport Rd. SW, Calgary, Alta. T2W 4X9, Canada

BOSE CORP   100 The Mountain Rd, Framingham, MA 01701, Tel: (617) 879-7330
(Electronic equip)
   Gilles Drolet Mfg. Ltd., P.O. Box 1090, Industrial Park, Ste. Marie, Que.,
   Canada G0S 2Y0

BOSS MANUFACTURING CO   221 W First St, Kewanee, IL 61443, Tel: (309) 852-2131
(Safety prdts, protective clothing, sport/work gloves)
   Boss Canada, 53 Woodbridge Ave., Weston, Ont., Canada L4L 2S6

BOSTITCH DIV   815 Briggs St, East Greenwich, RI 02818, Tel: (401) 884-2500
(Stapling machs & supplies, wire)
   Bostitch Div. of Textron Canada Ltd., 19 Rangemore Rd., Toronto, Ont.,
   Canada M8Z 5H9

BOWEN TOOLS INC   PO Box 3186, Houston, TX 77253, Tel: (713) 869-6711
(Mfr drilling & specialty tools for oil/gas ind)
   Bowen Tools Ltd., P.O. Box 8775 Station L, Edmonton, Alta., Canada T6C 4J5

BOWES "SEAL FAST" CORP   5902 East 34th St, Indianapolis, IN 46218,
Tel: (317) 547-5245
(Automotive accessories)
   Bowes Seal-Fast Co. Ltd., 765 Woodward Ave., Box 3275, Station C, Hamilton, Ont.,
   Canada

BOZELL JACOBS KENYON & ECKHARDT INC   40 West 23rd St, New York, NY 10010,
Tel: (212) 206-5400
(Advertising agency)
   Freeman Milne Bozell & Jacobs Ltd., 70 Sanford Ave. N, Hamilton, Ont.,
   Canada L8L 7Y9

(cont)

Freeman Milne Bozell & Jacobs Ltd., 505 Dorchester Blvd. W, Montreal, Que.,
   Canada H2Z 1A8
Freeman Milne Bozell & Jacobs Ltd., 111 Avenue Rd., Toronto, Ont., Canada M5R 3M1

W H BRADY CO   727 W Glendale Ave, PO Box 571, Milwaukee, WI 53201,
Tel: (414) 332-8100
(Wire markers, name plates)
   W.H. Brady Co. of Canada Ltd., 10 Marmac Dr., Rexdale, Ont., Canada M9W 1E6

BRANSON ULTRASONICS CORP   Eagle Rd, Danbury, CT 06810, Tel: (203) 796-0400
(Ultrasonic & vibratory plastics assembly mach)
   Branson Ultrasonics Corp., 705 Progress Ave., Scarborough, Ont., Canada, M1P 3B3

C F BRAUN & CO   1000 S Fremont Ave, Alhambra, CA 91802, Tel: (213) 570-1000
(Engineering/constr/mgmt for energy & power ind)
   PCL-Braun-Simons Ltd., 1015 4th St. SW, Calgary, Alta., Canada T2R 1J4

BRK ELECTRONICS   780 McClure Rd, Aurora, IL 60504-2495, Tel: (708) 851-7330
(Mfr smoke detectors, fire extinguishers, lights, timers & sensor sys)
   BRK Canada, 6650 Finch Ave. West., Rexdale, Ont. Canada M9W 5Y6

BROCKWAY INC (NY)   McCullough Ave, Brockway, PA 15824, Tel: (814) 268-3015
(Glass, plastics, metal packaging)
   Consumers Packaging Ltd., 777 Kipling Ave., Toronto, Ont., Canada M8Z 5G6

BRODART INC   500 Arch St, Williamsport, PA 17705, Tel: (717) 326-2461
(Mfr/dist/serv books, automated sys, library supplies, equip & furniture)
   Bro-Dart of Canada Ltd., 109 Roy Blvd., Brantford, Ont., Canada

BROWN & ROOT INC   4100 Clinton Dr, Houston, TX 77020-6299,
Tel: (713) 676-4141
(Engr, constr & maintenance)
   Brown & Root Ltd., P.O. Box 5588, Edmonton, Alta., Canada T6C 4E9
   Mid-Valley Industrial Services, 910 Rowntree Dairy Rd., Unit 27, Woodbridge,
      Ont. L4L 5W6, Canada
   SRB Offshore Ltd., P.O. Box 9600, St. John's, Nfld. A1A 3C1, Canada

BROWN GROUP INC   8400 Maryland Ave, St Louis, MO 63105, Tel: (314) 854-4000
(Mfr/sale footwear; retailer of fabric)
   Brown Shoe Co. of Canada Ltd., 1857 Rogers Rd., Perth, Ont., Canada

BROWN-FORMAN CORP   PO Box 1080, Louisville, KY 40201, Tel: (502) 585-1100
(Mfr/dist distilled spirits, china, crystal, luggage)
   Canadian Mist Distillers Ltd., 202 MacDonald Rd., Collingwood, Ont., Canada L9Y 4J2

BROWNING CORP   Route 1, Morgan, UT 84050, Tel: (801) 399-3481
(Sport firearms, fishing rods, etc)
   Browning Canada Sports Ltd., 5350 Ferrer St., Montreal, Que., Canada H4P 1L9

BRUNSWICK CORP   One Brunswick Plaza, Skokie, IL 60077, Tel: (708) 470-4700
(Mfr outboard motors & drives, bowling/fishing equip, valves & pumps)
   Mercury Marine Ltd., 1156 Dundas Hwy E., P.O. Box 488, Mississauga, Ont.,
      Canada L4Y 2CZ
   Vapor Canada Ltd., 3955 Courtrai Ave., Montreal, Que., Canada H3S 1B9

BUCK CONSULTANTS INC   Two Pennsylvania Plaza, New York, NY 10121,
   Tel: (212) 330-1000
   (Employee benefit, actuarial & compensation conslt serv)
      GBB Buck Consultants Ltd., PO Box 15- #1500, 95 Wellington St. West, Toronto,
      Ont. M5J 2N7, Canada

BUCKHORN INC   55 W TechneCenter Dr, Milford, OH 45150, Tel: (513) 831-4402
   (Mfr/serv plastic containers & pallets)
      Buckhorn Canada, 2775 Slough St., Mississauga, Ontario L4T 1G2, Canada

BUCYRUS-ERIE CO   PO Box 56, Milwaukee, WI 53172, Tel: (414) 768-4000
   (Shovels, cranes)
      Bucyrus-Erie Co. of Canada Ltd., Guelph, Ont., Canada

BUFFALO FORGE CO   PO Box 985, Buffalo, NY 14240, Tel: (716) 847-5121
   (Fans, air-handling units)
      Canadian Blower/Canada Pumps, 90 Woodside Ave., Kitchener, Ont., Canada N2G 4K1

BULAB HOLDINGS INC   1256 N McLean Blvd, Memphis, TN 38108,
   Tel: (901) 278-0330
   (Mfr microbicides, biocides, additives, corrosion inhibitors, chems)
      Buckman Laboratories of Canada Ltd., 613 Orley Ave., Dorval, Que. H9P 1G1, Canada

BULOVA WATCH CO INC   Bulova Park, 75-20 Astoria Blvd, Jackson Heights,
   NY 11370, Tel: (718) 565-4200
   (Mfr timepieces, watches & clocks, watch parts, batteries, precision defense prdts)
      Bulova Watch Co. Ltd., 105 Bartley Dr., Toronto, Ont., Canada

BUNDY CORP   12345 E Nine Mile, Warren, MI 48090, Tel: 313) 758) 6500
   (Small diameter steel tubing, watch cases, etc)
      Bundy of Canada, 316 Orenda Rd., Bramalea, Ont., Canada

B H BUNN CO   2730 Drane Field Rd, Lakeland, FL 33803, Tel: (813) 647-1555
   (Package tying & strapping machs)
      Bunn Canada, 2550 Goldenridge Rd., Unit 62, Mississauga, Ont., Canada

BURLINGTON AIR EXPRESS   18200 Van Karman Ave, Irvine, CA 92715,
   Tel: (714) 752-1212
   (Air freight)
      Burlington Air Express (Canada) Ltd., 140 Thad Johnson Rd., Bay 2, Gloucester,
      Ontario K1V 0R4, Canada

BURNHAM CORP   2 Main St, Irvington, NY 10533, Tel: (914) 591-8800
   (Greenhouses, conservatories)
      Lord & Burnham Co. Ltd., St. Catharines, Ont., Canada

BURNS INTL SECURITY SERVICES   2 Campus Dr, Parsippany, NJ 07054,
   Tel: (201) 397-2000
   (Provider of security officers)
      Burns Intl. Security Services Ltd., 55 Bloor St. W., #261, Toronto, Ont.,
      Canada M4W 1A5

BURSON-MARSTELLER   230 Park Ave, New York, NY 10003-1566, Tel: (212) 614-4000
   (Public relations/public affairs consultants)
      Burson Marsteller, 80 Bloor St. W, Toronto, Ont., Canada M5S 2V1

BUSINESSLAND INC   1001 Ridder Park Dr, San Jose, CA 95131,
  Tel: (408) 437-0400
  (Distr, integration & support microcomputer sys)
    Businessland Canada Ltd., 96 Steelcase Rd. W., Markham, Ontario L3R 3J9, Canada
    Businessland Canada Ltd., other locations in Canada

BUTLER MFG CO   PO Box 917, Kansas City, MO 64141, Tel: (816) 968-3000
  (Pre-engineered steel struc sys, curtain wall & elec dist sys, grain storage &
  handling sys)
    Butler Mfg. Co. (Canada) Ltd., P.O. Box 5006, Burlington, Ont., Canada L7R 3Z3

BUTTERICK FASHION MARKETING CO   161 Ave of the Americas, New York, NY 10013,
  Tel: (212) 620-2500
  (Sewing patterns)
    Butterick Fashion Mktg. Co., 10 Butterick Rd., Toronto, Ont., Canada M8W 3Z8

BUTTES GAS & OIL CO   3040 Post Oak Blvd, Houston, TX 77056,
  Tel: (713) 627-9277
  (Natural gas, crude oil)
    Buttes Resources Canada Ltd., 1220 Aquitaine Tower, 540 5th Ave. SW, Calgary,
      Alta., Canada T2P 0M2

CARL BYOIR & ASSOCIATES INC   380 Madison Ave, New York, NY 10017,
  Tel: (212) 986-6100
  (Public relations consultants)
    FPR Communications Ltd., 496 Queen St. E., Toronto, Ont., Canada M5A 4G8
    The Houston Group Communications Ltd., 180 Dundas St., W. Suite 2000, Toronto,
      Ont., Canada M5G 1Z8

CADILLAC PLASTIC & CHEMICAL CO   143 Indusco Ct, Troy, MI 48083,
  Tel: (313) 583-1200
  (Dist plastic basic shapes)
    Cadillac Plastic (Canada) Ltd., 91 Ketfield St., Rexdale, Ont. M9W 5A4, Canada

CALCOMP   2411 W La Palma Ave, PO Box 3250, Anaheim, CA 92801,
  Tel: (714) 821-2142
  (Mfr computer graphics)
    CalComp Canada, E Tower, 1144 29th Ave. N.E., Calgary, Alta., Canada T2E 7P1
    CalComp Canada, 401 Champagne Dr., Downsview, Ont., Canada M3J 2C6
    CalComp Canada, 3466 Rue Ashby, St. Laurent, Que., Canada H4R 2C1
    CalComp Canada Ltd., 120 Hwy. 15, Millhill Bldg., Bells Corner, Ottawa, Ont.,
      Canada K2H 5Z1

CALGON CORP   PO Box 1346, Pittsburgh, PA 15230, Tel: (412) 777-8000
  (Mfr. cosmetic, personal care & water treatment prdts)
    Calgon Canada Corp., 27 Finley Rd., Bramalea, Ont., Canada L6T 1B2

CALMAQUIP ENGINEERING CORP   7240 NW 12th St, Miami, FL 33121,
  Tel: (305) 592-4510
  (Engineering)
    Calmaquip Canada Ltd., 2001 University, Montreal, Que., Canada H3A 2A6

CAMCO INC   7010 Ardmore St, Houston, TX 77021, Tel: (713) 747-4000
  (Oil field equip)
    Camco Ltd., P.O. Box 4416, Edmonton, Alta., Canada T6E 4T5

CAMP INTL INC   PO Box 89, Jackson, MI 49204, Tel: (517) 787-1600
 (Mfr orthotics & prosthetics)
   Camp Intl. Ltd., P.O. Box 495, 39 Davis St., Trenton, Ont., Canada K8V 5R6

CAMPBELL SOUP CO   Campbell Place, Camden, NJ 08101, Tel: (609) 342-4800
 (Food prdts)
   Campbell Agricultural Research Dept., 5509 Hurontario St., RR No. 6, Mississauga,
     Ont., Canada L5M 2B5
   Campbell Soup Co. Ltd., Box 69, Wellington, Ont., Canada K0K 3L0,
     with plants throughout Canada
   Campbell Soup Co. Ltd., 60 Birmingham St., Toronto, Ont., Canada M8V 2B8
   CanVin Prdts. Ltd., 409 Evans Ave., Toronto, Ont., Canada M8Z 1L1
   Gattuso Corp. Ltd., 155 Rue Authier, Montreal, Que., Canada H4M 2C7
   Georgian Bay Fruit Growers, Thronbury, Ont., Canada N0H 2P0

CARGILL   PO Box 9300, Minneapolis, MN 55440, Tel: (612) 475-7575
 (Food prdts, feeds, animal prdts)
   Cargill Canada Ltd., 300-240 Graham Ave., Winnepeg, Man. RC3C 4C5, Canada

CARPENTER TECHNOLOGY CORP   101 W Bern St, PO Box 14662, Reading, PA 19612,
 Tel: (215) 371-2000
 (Mfr specialty steel & alloy prdts)
   Carpenter Technology (Canada) Ltd., 7464 Tranmere Dr., Unit 1, Mississauga,
     Ont. L5S 1K4, Canada

CARTER AUTOMOTIVE INC   9666 Olive St Rd, St Louis, MO 63132,
 Tel: (314) 997-7400
 (Fuel sys components)
   ACF Canada Ltd., 109 East Drive, Bramalea, Ont., Canada L6T 1B6

CARTER'S INK CO   300 Howard St, Farmingham, MA 01701, Tel: (617) 890-2950
 (Inks, adhesives, ribbons)
   Carters Inc Co. of Canada Ltd., 394 Isadey, Ville St. Laurent, Montreal, Que.,
     Canada H4T 1V3

CARTER-WALLACE INC   2 Research Way, Princeton, NJ 08450-6628,
 Tel: (609) 520-3100
 (Mfr pharms, diagnostics, toiletries)
   Frank W. Horner Inc., Station A, P.O. Box 959, Montreal, Que., Canada H3C 2W6

CASHCO INC   PO Box 6, Ellsworth, KS 67439-0006, Tel: (913) 472-4461
 (Mfr pressure regulators & control valves)
   Cashco Canada Inc., 212 Wyecroft Rd., Oakville, Ont., Canada L6K 3T9

CATERPILLAR INC   100 N E Adams St, Peoria, IL 61629, Tel: (309) 675-1000
 (Mfr earth/material-handling & constr mach & equip, engines, generators)
   Caterpillar of Canada Ltd., P.O. Box 5000, Brampton, Ont., Canada L6V 3Y4

L D CAULK CO   PO Box 359, Milford, DE 19963, Tel: (302) 422-4511
 (Dental material)
   L.D. Caulk Co. of Canada Ltd., 172 John St., Toronto, Ont., Canada M5T 1X5

CBI INDUSTRIES INC   800 Jorie-Blvd, Oak Brook, IL 60521, Tel: (708) 654-7000
 (Holding co: metal plate fabricating, constr, oil & gas drilling)
   Horton CBI Ltd., 1801 McGill College Ave., Montreal, Que., Canada

CDI CORP   10 Penn Center Plaza, Philadelphia, PA 19103, Tel: (215) 569-2200
(Engr, design, drafting & tech serv)
   Comprehensive Designers of Canada Ltd., 7651 Tecumseh Rd. E, Windsor, Ont.,
      Canada N8T 3H1

CEILCOTE CO   140 Sheldon Rd, Berea, OH 44017, Tel: (216) 243-0700
(Mfr corrosion-resistant material, air pollution control equip, cons serv)
   Ceilcote Canada, 7065 Fir Tree Dr., Mississauga, Ont., Canada I5S 1G7

CENTRAL SOYA CO   PO Box 1400, Ft Wayne, IN 46802, Tel: (219) 425-5100
(Livestock & poultry feed, soybean meal, grain)
   Central Soya of Canada Ltd., Juliana Dr., P.O. Box 217, Woodstock, Ont.,
      Canada N4S 7W8
   Victory Soya Mills, 333 Lake Shore Blvd. E., Toronto, Ont., Canada M5A 1C2

CENTURY 21 REAL ESTATE CORP   2601 SE Main, PO Box 19564, Irvine,
   CA 92713-9564, Tel: (714) 553-2100
(Real estate)
   Century 21 Real Estate Canada Ltd., 135-10551 Shellbridge Way, Richmond, B.C.,
      Canada V6X 2W9

CH2M HILL INC   PO Box 428, Corvallis, OR 97339, Tel: (503) 752-4271
(Consulting engrs, planners, economists, scientists)
   CH2M Hill Intl., 640 8th Ave. SW, Calgary, Alta., Canada T2P 1G7

CHAMPION CO   401 Harrison St, PO Box 967, Springfield, OH 45501,
   Tel: (513) 324-5681
(Funeral supplies)
   The Champion Co. of Canada Ltd., 858 Millwood Rd., Toronto, Ont., Canada M4G 1W6

CHAMPION PARTS REBUILDERS INC   2525 22nd St, Oak Brook, IL 60521,
   Tel: (708) 986-6100
(Remanufacturer of automotive, truck & tractor parts)
   Champion Parts Rebuilders (Canada) Ltd., 224 Milvan Dr., Weston, Ont.,
      Canada M9L 24A

CHAMPION SPARK PLUG CO   PO Box 910, Toledo, OH 43661, Tel: (419) 535-2567
(Mfr spark plugs, wiper blades & related prdts)
   Champion Spark Plug Co. of Canada Ltd., P.O. Box 910, Windsor, Ont., Canada

CHASE MANHATTAN BANK N A   1 Chase Manhattan Plaza, New York, NY 10081,
   Tel: (212) 552-2222
(Intl banking)
   Chase Manhattan Canada Ltd., P.O. Box 301, Commerce Court Postal Station, Toronto,
      Ont., Canada M5L 1G1
   Chase Manhattan Canada Ltd., 333 Fifth Ave. SW, Calgary, Alta., Canada T2P 3B6
   Chase Manhattan Canada Ltd., 1 Place Ville Marie, Montreal, Que., Canada H3B 3M9
   Chase Manhattan Canada Ltd., P.O. Box 11581, Vancouver, B.C., Canada V6B 4N4

CHEMICAL BANK   277 Park Ave, New York, NY 10172, Tel: (212) 310-6161
(Banking & financial serv)
   Chemical Bank, 805 Fifth Ave. SW, Calgary, Alta., Canada T2P 3H5
   Chemical Bank of Canada, 150 York St., Toronto, Ont. M5H 355, Canada

CHESEBROUGH-POND'S INC   33 Benedict Place, Greenwich, CT 06830,
   Tel: (203) 661-2000
   (Cosmetics, consumer prdts)
      Chesebrough-Pond's Intl. Ltd., P.O. Box 590, Markham, Ont., Canada

A W CHESTERTON CO   Middlesex Industrial Park, Soneham, MA 02180,
   Tel: (617) 438-7000
   (Packing gaskets, sealing prdts sys, etc)
      A.W. Chesterton Co., Burlington, Ont., Canada

CHEVRON CHEMICAL CO   PO Box 5047, San Ramon, CA 94583-0947,
   Tel: (415) 842-5500
   (Chemicals)
      Chevron Chemical (Canada) Ltd., 3228 S. Service Rd., Burlington, Ont. I7N 3H8,
         Canada
      Later Chemicals Ltd., 12080 Horseshoe Way, Richmond, BC V7A 4V5, Canada

CHICAGO PNEUMATIC TOOL CO   2200 Bleeker St, Utica, NY 13501,
   Tel: (315) 792-2600
   (Mfr air tools & equip)
      Canadian Pneumatic Tool Co. Ltd., 5895 Kennedy Rd., Mississauga, Ont. L4Z 2G3,
         Canada

CHICAGO RAWHIDE MFG CO   900 N State Street, Elgin, IL 60120,
   Tel: (708) 742-7840
   (Seals & filters)
      Chicago Rawhide Products Canada Ltd., P.O. Box 707, Brantford, Ont., Canada

CHRISTENSEN INTL   PO Box 26135, Salt Lake City, UT 84126, Tel: (801) 487-5371
   (Diamond drills)
      Christensen Diamond Products Canada Ltd., 16230 112th Ave., Edmonton, Alta.,
         Canada T5M 2W1

CHRYSLER CORP   12000 Chrysler Dr, Highland Park, MI 48288-1919,
   Tel: (313) 956-5741
   (Mfr/mktg cars & light trucks, electr & aerospace prdts & sys)
      Ajax Trim Plant, 274 McKenzie Ave., Ajax on Lis 2E9, Canada
      Bramalea Assembly Plant, 2000 Williams Pkwy., Bramalea, Ont. L6T 4Y6, Canada
      Brampton Assembly Plant, 350 Kennedy Rd. South, Brampton, Ont. L6V 2M3, Canada
      Canadian Fabricated Products, 1172 Erie St., Stratford, Ont. N5A 6T3, Canada
      Etobicoke Casting Plantd., 15 Brown's Line Rd., toronto, Ont. M8W 3S3, Canada
      Guelph Products, 500 Laird Rd., Guelph, Ont. N1H 6N7, Canada
      Pillette Road Truck Assembly Plant, 3035 Pillette Rd., Windsor, Ont. N9A 4H6, Canada
      Windsor Assembly Plant, 2199 Chrysler Centre, Windsor, Ont. N9A 4H6, Canada

CHRYSLER FINANCIAL CORP   27777 Franklin Rd, Southfield, MI 48034,
   Tel: (313) 948-2890
   (Financial serv)
      Chrysler Credit Canada Ltd., 2233 Argentia Rd., Mississauga, Ont., Canada L5N 2X7

CHURCH & DWIGHT CO INC   469 N Harrison St, Princeton, NJ 08543,
   Tel: (609) 683-5900
   (Spec chems, consumer prdts)
      Church & Dwight Ltd., 25 The Donway W, Don Mills, Ont., Canada

CIGNA CORP   One Liberty Place, 1650 Market St, Philadelphia, PA 19101,
  Tel: (215) 523-4000
  (Ins, invest, health care & other fin servs)
    Cigna Insurance Co. of Canada, 100 Consilium Place- #500, Scarborough,
      Ontario M1H 3E3, Canada
    Cigna Life Insurance Co. of Canada, 20 Adelaide St. East- #1200, Toronto,
      Ontario M5C 2T6, Canada
    Connecticut General Life Insurance Co., 555 Younge St.- 6th Fl., Toronto,
      Ontario M7A 2H6, Canada
    Life Insurance Co. of North America, 141 Adelaide St. West- #709, Toronto,
      Ontario M5H 3L5, Canada

CIT FINANCIAL CORP   650 Madison Ave, New York, NY 10022, Tel: (212) 572-6500
  (Finance, ins, loans)
    B.K. Johl Inc., 3500 Cote Vertu, Montreal, Que., Canada
    Canadian Acceptance Corp. Ltd., Toronto, Ont., Canada

CITIBANK NA   399 Park Ave, New York, NY 10043, Tel: (212) 559-1000
  (Intl banking)
    Citicorp Leasing Canada Ltd., 5050 S. Service Rd., Burlington, Ont., Canada L7R 4C8
    Citicorp Ltd., First Canadian Place, 100 King St. W, Toronto, Ont., Canada M5X 1C3
    Citicorp Ltd., 1155 Sherbrooke St. W, Montreal, Que., Canada H3A 2N3
    Citicorp Ltd., Shell Centre, 400 4th Ave., SW, Calgary, Alta., Canada T2P OK4
    Citicorp Ltd., 10009 108th St., Edmonton, Alta., Canada T5J 3C5
    Citicorp Ltd., 650 W. Georgia St., Vancouver, B.C., Canada V6B 4R9

J L CLARK INC   2300 6th St, Rockford, IL 61101, Tel: (815) 962-8861
  (Lithographed metal containers & specialties, plastic molding, spiral wound &
  collapsible tubes)
    Stone Straw Corp. of Canada Ltd., 2276 Lakeshore Blvd. W, Toronto, Ont., Canada

CLARKSON INDUSTRIES INC   30 Buxton Farm Rd, Stamford, CT 06905-1206,
  Tel: (203) 322-3990
  (Mfr centrifugal blowers, compressors, handling equip)
    Hoffman Industries of Canada Ltd., 58 Bertal Rd., Toronto, Ont., Canada

CLEVELAND TWIST DRILL CO   1242 E 49 St, PO Box 6656, Cleveland, OH 44101,
  Tel: (216) 431-3120
  (Metal cutting/threading toods related prdts)
    Cleveland Twist Drill (Canada) Ltd., 23 Fasken Dr., Rexdale, Ont., Canada M9W 1K6

CLEVELAND-CLIFFS IRON CO   UNion Commerce Bldg, 925 Euclid Ave, Cleveland,
  OH 44115, Tel: (216) 241-2356
  (Iron ore, timber)
    Adams Mine, P.O. Box 877, Kirkland Lake, Ont., Canada P2N 3K7
    Sherman Mine, P.O. Box 217, Temagami, Ont., Canada POH 2HO

CLOROX CO   1221 Broadway, Oakland, CA 94612, Tel: (415) 271-7000
  (Household bleach, consumer prdts)
    Clorox Co. of Canada Ltd., 700 W. Pender St., Vancouver, B.C., Canada V6C 1G8

CLUETT PEABODY & CO INC   510 Fifth Ave, New York, NY 10036,
  Tel: (212) 930-3000
  (Wearing apparel)
    The Arrow Co.-Canada Ltd., 45 St. Clare Ave. W, Toronto, Ont., Canada M4V 1K 9

COBE LABORATORIES INC   1185 Oak St, Lakewood, CO 80215, Tel: (303) 232-6800
  (Mfr med equip & supplies)
    COBE Canada Ltd., 80 Milner Ave., Scarborough, Ont., Canada M1S 3P8

COLE BUSINESS FURNITURE CO   640 Whiteford Rd, PO Box M-26, York, PA 17405,
  Tel: (717) 854-1545
  (Mfr office furniture)
    Cole-Canada, 1865 Birchmont Rd., Scarborough, Ont., Canada M1P 2J5
    Standard Desk Ltd., 1000 St. Martin Blvd. W., Laval, Que., Canada H7S 1M7

THE COLEMAN CO INC   250 N St Francis Ct, PO Box 1762, Wichita, KS 67201,
  Tel: (316) 261-3485
  (Mfr camping, outdoor & water recreation prdts)
    Canadian Coleman Co. Ltd., 700 Kipling Ave., Toronto, Ont., Canada M8Z 5V6

COLGATE-PALMOLIVE CO   300 Park Ave, New York, NY 10022, Tel: (212) 310-2000
  (Pharms, cosmetics, toiletries, detergents)
    Colgate-Palmolive Canada, 64 Colgate Ave., Toronto, Ont., Canada M4M 1N7

COLLOIDS INC   394-400 Frelinghuysen Ave, Newark, NJ 07114,
  Tel: (201) 926-6100
  (Chem prdts)
    Colloids of Canada Ltd., 180 St. Hubert St., Granby, Que., Canada

COLSON INC   39 La Salle St, Chicago, IL 60603, Tel: (312) 372-9500
  (Material handling equip)
    Colson Casters Ltd., 1600 Bishop St. N, Cambridge-Preston, Ont., Canada N3H 4V6

COLT INDUSTRIES INC   430 Park Ave, New York, NY 10022, Tel: (212) 940-0400
  (Pumps, water sys, engines, motor arms, etc)
    Colt Industries (Canada) Ltd., P.O. Box 520, Sorel, Que., Canada J3P 5P2
    Garlock of Canada Ltd., 66 Jutland Rd., Toronto, Ont., Canada M8Z 2H3
    Menasco Canada Ltd., 3495 Cote Verto, Montreal, Que., Canada H4R 1R3

COLUMBIAN ROPE CO   501 Metcalf Plaza, Auburn, NY 13021, Tel: (315) 253-3224
  (Mfr rope, twine & ind fiber prdts)
    Canada Cordage Inc., P.O. Box 158, Kitchener, Ont., Canada N2G 3Y2

COLUMBUS McKINNON CORP   Audubon & Sylvan Pkwys, Amherst, NY 14228-1197,
  Tel: (716) 696-3208
  (Mfr chains, forgings, hoists, tire & paper shredders)
    Columbus McKinnon Ltd., P.O. Box 1106, 10 Brook Rd. North, Cobourg, Ont. K9A 4W5,
      Canada

COMBINED INSURANCE CO OF AMERICA   123 N Wacker Dr, Chicago, IL 60606,
  Tel: (312) 701-3000
  (Insurance)
    Combined Insurance Co. of America, 980 Yonge St., Toronto, Ont., Canada M4W 2J9

COMBUSTION ENGINEERING INC   900 Long Ridge Road, Stamford, CT 06902,
  Tel: (203) 329-8771
  (Tech constr)
    C-E Basic, 680 Raymur Ave. 6, Vancouver, B.C., Canada
    C-E Basic, 7600 Notre Dame St. W, Montreal, Que., Canada H4C 3K4
    C-E Bauer (Canada) Ltd., P.O. Box 910, Brantford, Ont., Canada
    C-E Canada, 99 Bank St., Ottawa, Ont., Canada K1P 6C5
    C-E Invalco, P.O. Box 850, Station T, Calgary, Alta., Canada T2H 2H3

(cont)

C-E Natco Ltd., Box 850, Station T., Calgary, Alta., Canada T2H 2H3
C-E Refractories (Canada) Ltd., Prince Charles Dr., Welland, Ont., Canada
Crest Engineering Ltd., 11012 Macleod Trail SW, Calgary, Alta., Canada T2J 6A5
The Lummus Co. Canada Ltd., 11012 Macleod Trail SW, Calgary, Alta., Canada T2J 6A5
The Lummus Co. Canada Ltd., 251 Consumers Rd., Willowdale, Ont., Canada, M2J 4H4
The W.S. Tyler Co. of Canada Ltd., P.O. Box 3006, St. Catharines, Ont., Canada

COMDISCO INC   6400 Shafer Ct, Rosemont, IL 60018, Tel: (708) 698-3000
  (Remarketer used computer equip)
    Comdisco Canada Ltd., 250 Consumers Rd., Willowdale, Ont., Canada M2J 4V6

COMMERCE CLEARING HOUSE INC   4025 W Peterson Ave, Chicago, IL 60646,
  Tel: (312) 583-8500
  (Pub topical law report, computer serv)
    CCH Canadian Ltd., 6 Garamond Ct., Don Mills, Ont., Canada M3C 1Z5
    Les Publications CCH/FM Ltee., 33 Rue Racine, Farnham, Que., Canada J2N 3A3

COMMERCIAL INTERTECH CORP   1775 Logan Ave, Youngstown, OH 44501,
  Tel: (216) 746-8011
  (Mfr hydraulic com, metal stampings, pre-engr metal bldgs, fluid purification prdts)
    Commercial Intertech Ltd., P.O. Box 450, Acton, Ont., Canada L7J 2M6

COMPTON INTERNATIONAL   625 Madison Ave, New York, NY 10022,
  Tel: (212) 754-1100
  (Advertising)
    BCP Advertising, 1010 Ste. Catherine St. W, Montreal, Que., Canada
    Ross Roy of Canada Ltd., 905-2 Carlton St., Toronto, Ont., Canada M5B 1J3

COMPUGRAPHIC CORP   200 Ballardvale St, Wilmington, MA 01887,
  Tel: (617) 658-5600
  (Mfr computerized composition & typesetting sys)
    Compugraphic Canada, 400 Brunel Rd., Mississauga, Ont., Canada L4A 2Z2

COMPUTER ASSOCIATES INTL INC   711 Stewart Ave, Garden City, NY 11530,
  Tel: (516) 227-3300
  (Devel/mkt/mgt info mgt & bus applications software)
    Computer Associates Canada Ltd., 710 Dorval Dr.- 3rd Fl., Oakville,
      Ontario L6K 3V3, Canada

CONSOLIDATED FREIGHTWAYS INC   175 Linfield Dr, Menlo Park, CA 94025,
  Tel: (415) 326-1700
  (Land, sea & air transp)
    Canadian Freightways Ltd., P.O. Box 1108 Station T, Calgary, Alta., Canada

CONSOLIDATED OIL & GAS INC   410 17th St., #440, Denver, CO 80202,
  Tel: (303) 893-1226
  (Oil & gas explor & devel)
    Consolidated Energy Resources, Calgary, Alta. T2P 0TS,
      Canada (all mail to U.S. address)

CONSTRUCTION SPECIALTIES INC   55 Winans Ave, Cranford, NJ 07016,
  Tel: (201) 272-5200
  (Aluminum architectural prdts)
    Construction Specialties Ltd., 895 Lakefront Promenade, Mississauga, Ont.,
      Canada L5E 2C2

CONTROL DATA CORP   8100 34th Ave S, Minneapolis, MN 55440,
  Tel: (612) 853-8100
  (Control data equip, computer sys serv & financial serv)
    Control Data Canada Ltd., 50 Hallcrown Pl., Willowdale, Ont., Canada

COOK-WAITE LABORATORIES INC   90 Park Ave, New York, NY 10016,
  Tel: (212) 907-2000
  (Anesthetic solutions)
    Cook-Waite Laboratories Ltd., Yonge St., Aurora, Ont., Canada

COOPER LIGHTING GROUP   400 Busse Rd, Elk Grove Village, IL 60007-2195,
  Tel: (312) 956-8400
  (Mfr indoor & outdoor lighting prdts)
    Cooper Lighting Group, Mississauga, Ontario, Canada

COOPERTOOLS   PO Box 30100, Raleigh, NC 27622, Tel: (919) 781-7200
  (Mfr hand tools)
    CooperTools, Hwy #2 East, Port Hope, Ont., Canada L1A 1CB
    CooperTools, P.O. Box 2000, Barrie, Ont., Canada L4N 3E7

COPELAND CORP   Campbell Road, Sidney, OH 45365, Tel: (513) 498-3011
  (Ind refrigeration equip)
    Copeland Refrigeration of Canada Ltd., 145 Sherwood St., Brantford, Ont., Canada

CORE LABORATORIES   10205 Westheimer, Houston, TX 77042, Tel: (713) 972-6312
  (Petroleum testing/analysis, analytical chem, environmental servs)
    Core Laboratories, 1540 25th Ave. NE, Calgary, Alta., Canada, T2E 7R2
    Core Laboratories, 463 Devonian St., PO. Box 1370, Estevan, Sask., Canada S4A 2K9
    Core Laboratories, 4777 93rd Ave., Edmonton, Alta., Canada T6B 2T6
    Core Laboratories, 10946-89 Ave., Grande Prairie, Alta., Canada T8V 4W4
    Core Laboratories, 4748-78A St., Close T4P 2J2, Canada

CORNING CORP   Houghton Park, PO Box 2000, Corning, NY 14831,
  Tel: (617) 974-9000
  (Mfr glass, ceramic materials)
    Corning Canada Inc., 135 Vanderhoof Ave., Toronto, Ont., Canada M4G 2J3

COYNE CYLINDER CO   224 Ryan Way, San Francisco, CA 94080, Tel: (415) 761-1831
  (Compressed gas cylinders)
    Canadian Cylinder Co., 63 Morton Ave. E, Brantford, Ont., Canada

CPC INTERNATIONAL INC   PO Box 8000, International Plaza, Englewood Cliffs,
  NJ 07632, Tel: (201) 894-4000
  (Mfr consumer food prdts & corn refining prdts)
    The Canada Starch Co. Inc., 401 The West Mall, Etobicoke, Ont. M9C 5H9, Canada

CR INDUSTRIES   900 N State St, Elgin, IL 60123, Tel: (708) 742-7840
  (Mfr shaft & face seals)
    CR Canada Ltd., Park Rd. & Henry St., P.O. Box 70, Brantford, Ont., Canada N3T 5M6

CRANE CO   757 Third Ave, New York, NY 10017, Tel: (212) 415-7300
  (Diversified mfr/distr engineered prdts for ind)
    Crane Canada Inc., P.O. Box 2700, St. Laurent, Montreal, Que., Canada H4L 4Y7
    Navend Ind. Co. Inc., 595 Middlefield Rd., Unit 20, Scarborough, Ont.,
    Canada M1V 3S2

JOHN CRANE INC   6400 Oakton St, Morton Grove, IL 60053, Tel: (708) 967-2400
  (Mfr engineering seals)
    John Crane Canada Inc., Box 3248, Station C, Hamilton, Ont., Canada L8H 7L3

CREAMETTE CO   428 N First St, Minneapolis, MN 55401, Tel: (612) 333-4281
  (Pasta, frozen foods)
    The Creamette Co. of Canada Ltd., 283 Stanley St., Winnipeg, Man., Canada

CROMPTON & KNOWLES CORP   1 Station Pl Metro Center, Stamford, CT 06902,
  Tel: (203) 353-5400
  (Mfr dyes, colors, flavors, fragrances, spec chems, ind prdts)
    Crompton & Knowles of Canada Ltd., 1313 Kamato Rd., Mississauga, Ont.,
      Canada L4W 2M2

CROUSE-HINDS CO   PO Box 4999, Syracuse, NY 13221, Tel: (315) 477-7000
  (Mfr electrical constr material)
    Crouse-Hinds ECM Canada Ltd., 1160 Birchmount Rd., Scarborough, Ont., Canada M1P 2B9

CROWLEY MARITIME CORP   101 California St, San Francisco, CA 94111,
  Tel: (415) 546-2300
  (Marine transp)
    Arctic Transportation Ltd., Esso Plaza E. Tower, Ste. 1900, 425 First St., SW,
      Calgary, Alta., Canada T2P 3L8
    Arctic Transportation Ltd., 5240 Calgary Trail, Edmonton, Alta., Canada T6H 5G8

CROWN CORK & SEAL CO INC   Holmesburg Station, PO Box 6208, Philadelphia,
  PA 19136, Tel: (215) 698-5100
  (Cans, bottle caps; filling & packaging mach)
    Crown Cork & Seal Co. Ltd., 7900 Keele St., Concord, Ont., Canada L4K 1B6

CROWN ZELLERBACH CORP   1 Bush St, San Francisco, CA 94119,
  Tel: (415) 951-5000
  (Pulp, paperboard & paper mills, lumber, plywood mills, mfr chems)
    Crown Zellerbach Canada Ltd., 815 W. Hastings, Vancouver, B.C., Canada V6C 1B4

CTS CORP   905 N West Blvd, Elkhart, IN 46514, Tel: (219) 293-7511
  (Electronic components & devices, metal enclosures, store fixtures)
    CTS of Canada Ltd., 80 Thomas St., Streetsville, Ont., Canada L5M 1Y9

CULLIGAN INTL CO   One Culligan Parkway, Northbrook, IL 60062,
  Tel: (708) 205-6000
  (Water treatment prdts & serv)
    Culligan of Canada Ltd., 2213 N. Sheridan Way, Sheridan Park, Mississauga, Ont.,
      Canada L5K 1A5

CURTICE BURNS FOODS   90 Linden Place, Rochester, NY 14603-0681,
  Tel: (716) 383-1850
  (Mfr food processor)
    Nalley's Canada Ltd., 1330 E. 66th Ave., Vancouver, BC V5X 2W3, Canada

CURTISS-WRIGHT CORP   1200 Wall St, W Lyndhurst, NJ 07071, Tel: (201) 896-8400
  (Aircraft engines)
    Canadian Curtiss-Wright Ltd., London, Ont., Canada
    Canadian Curtiss-Wright Ltd., Mississauga, Ont., Canada
    Dorr-Oliver Canada Ltd., Orillia, Ont., Canada
    Metal Improvement Company, Rexdale, Ont., Canada

D'ARCY MASIUS BENTON & BOWLES INC (DMB&B)   1675 Broadway, New York,
NY 10019, Tel: (212) 468-3622
(Advertising & communications)
  DMB&B Canada Inc., 2 Bloor St. W., 14th fl., Toronto, Ont., Canada M4W 3R3

D-M-E COMPANY   29111 Stephenson Highway, Madison Heights, MI 48071,
Tel: (313) 398-6000
(Basic tooling for plastic molding & die casting)
  DME of Canada Ltd., 6210 Northwest Dr., Mississauga, Ont., Canada

DAMES & MOORE   911 Wilshire Blvd, Los Angeles, CA 90017, Tel: (213) 683-1560
(Consulting engineers)
  Dames & Moore, 700 W. Pender St., 304, Vancouver, BC, Canada V6C 1G8
  V. Fournier & Associates, 1009 Rte. de L'Eglise, Ste. 305, Ste. Foy, Que.,
    Canada G1V 3V8

DANCER FITZGERALD SAMPLE INTL   405 Lexington Ave, New York, NY 10174,
Tel: (212) 661-0800
(Advertising agency)
  Ronalds-Reynolds & Co. Ltd., 40 Eglinton Ave. E., Ste. 300, Toronto, Ont.,
    Canada M4P 3A8

DARLING & CO   4650 S Racine Ave, Chicago, IL 60609, Tel: (312) 927-3000
(Animal by-prdts)
  Darling Co. of Canada Ltd., Park St., P.O. Box 97, Chatham, Ont., Canada

DARLING VALVE & MFG CO   701 First St, Williamsport, PA 17701,
Tel: (717) 323-6121
(Valves, hydrants)
  Canada Valve & Hydrant Co., P.O. Box 248, Kitchener, Ont., Canada

DATA GENERAL CORP   4400 Computer Dr, Westboro, MA 01580, Tel: (617) 366-8911
(Design, mfr gen purpose computer sys & peripheral prdts & servs)
  Data General (Canada) Ind., 2155 Leanne Blvd., Mississauga, Ont., Canada L5K 2K8

DATA I/O CORP   10525 Willows Rd NE, Redmond, WA 98053, Tel: (206) 881-6444
(Mfr computer testing devices)
  Data I/O Canada, 6725 Airport Rd.- #302, Mississauga, Ontario L4V 1V2, Canada

DATAEASE INTL INC   7 Cambridge Dr, Trumbull, CT 06611, Tel: (203) 374-8000
(Mfr applications devel software)
  Computerlinks, 4946 Dundas St. W., Toronto, Ontario M9A 1B7, Canada

DATAPRODUCTS CORP   6200 Canada Ave, PO Box 746, Woodland Hills, CA 91365,
Tel: (818) 887-8000
(Mfr computer printers & supplies)
  Dataproducts Canada, 15 W. Pearce St., Richmond Hill, Ont. L4B 1H6, Canada

DATASCOPE CORP   14 Philips Pkwy, Montvale, NJ 07645, Tel: (201) 391-8100
(Mfr medical devices)
  Datascope Medical Products, Toronto, Ont., Canada

DDB NEEDHAM WORLDWIDE INC   437 Madison Ave, New York, NY 10022,
Tel: (212) 415-2000
(Advertising)
  DDB Needham Worldwide Advertising Ltd., 77 Bloor St. W.- #1902, Toronto,
    Ontario M5S 2Z8, Canada

DE VILBISS CO   300 Phillips Ave, Toledo, OH 43612, Tel: (419) 470-2169
(Mfr spray painting & finishing equip)
   DeV. Canada Ltd., P.O. Box 3000, Barrie, Ont., Canada L4M 4V6

DEARBORN DIV   300 Genesse St, Lake Zurich, IL 60047, Tel: (708) 438-1800
(Mfr water treatment chems & serv)
   Dearborn Chemical Co. Ltd., P.O. Box 3060, Station A, Mississauga, Ont.,
   Canada L5A 3T5

DEERE & CO   John Deere Rd, Moline, IL 61265, Tel: (309) 752-8000
(Mfr/sale agri/constr/utility/forestry & lawn/grounds care equip)
   John Deere Ltd., P.O. Box 1000, South Service Road at Hunter, Grimsby,
   Ont. L3M 4H5, Canada

DEERFIELD GLASSINE CO   Main St, Monroe Bridge, MA 01350, Tel: (413) 424-5231
(Glassine papers)
   Glassine Co. Ltd., 845 Industrial Ave., Que. City, Que., Canada G1K 7K7

DEKALB PLANT GENETICS   3100 Sycamore Rd, DeKalb, IL 60115,
Tel: (815) 753-7333
(Mfr/genetic res of hybrid corn, sorghum, sunflowers & soybeans)
   DeKalb Canada Inc., PO Box 430, 585 Riverview Dr., Chatham, Ontario N7M 5K5, Canada

DEKALB-PFIZER GENETICS   3100 Sycamore Rd, De Kalb, IL 60115,
Tel: (815) 756-7333
(Agric seeds)
   DeKalb Canada., P.O. Box 430, 585 Riverview Dr., Chatham, Ont., Canada N7M 5K5

DEL MONTE CORP   1 Market Plaza, PO Box 3575, San Francisco, CA 94119,
Tel: (415) 442-5120
(Fresh/frozen foods, distribution serv)
   Canadian Canners Ltd., 44 Hughson St. S, Hamilton, Ont., Canada

DELL COMPUTER CORP   9505 Arboretum Blvd, Austin, TX 78759,
Tel: (512) 338-4400
(Design/mfr personal computers)
   Dell Computer Corp., 121 Granton Dr.- Units 6-12, Richmond Hill, Ontario L4B 3N4,
   Canada

DENNISON MFG CO   300 Howard St, Framingham, MA 01701, Tel: (617) 879-0511
(Paper prdts & office supplies)
   Dennison Mfg. Co., 200 Base Line Rd., Bowmanville, Ont., Canada L1C 1A2

DENTSPLY INTL INC   PO Box 872, York, PA 17405, Tel: (717) 845-7511
(Mfr dental, medical & ind supplies & equip)
   Dentsply Canada Ltd., 1100 Lodestar Rd., Unit 8, Downsview, Ont. M3J 2Z4 Canada

DENVER EQUIPMENT DIV   PO Box 340, Colorado Springs, CO 80901,
Tel: (303) 471-3443
(Ind process equip)
   Joy Mfg. Co. (Canada) Ltd., 235 King St. E, Kitchener, Ont., Canada N2D 4N6

DESMOND-STEPHAN MFG CO INC   317 S Walnut St, Urbana, OH 43078,
Tel: (513) 653-7181
(Mfr grinding equip)
   The Canadian Desmond-Stephen Mfg. Co., P.O. Box 83, Station B, Hamilton, Ont.,
   Canada

DETROIT DIESEL CORP   13400 Outer Dr West, Detroit, MI   48239,
Tel: (313) 592-5000
(Mfr diesel & aircraft engines, heavy-duty transmissions)
   Detroit Diesen of Canada Ltd., 150 Dufferin Ave., #701, London, Ont., Canada

DHJ INDUSTRIES INC   1040 Ave of the Americas, New York, NY   10018,
Tel: (212) 944-4500
(Mfr of knit fabrics, interlinings plastic chips & denim)
   DHJ Canada Inc., 1857 de Maisonneuve Blvd. W., Montreal, Que., Canada H3H I39

DIAMOND POWER SPECIALTY CORP   PO Box 415, Lancaster, OH   43130,
Tel: (614) 687-6500
(Mfr sootblowers & controls, rodding robots, drum level indicators & gauges)
   Diamond Canapower Ltd., P.O. Box 5051, 1122 Pioneer Rd., Burlington, Ont.,
   Canada L7R 4A7

DIAMOND SHAMROCK CORP   1100 Superior Ave, Cleveland, OH   44114,
Tel: (216) 694-5000
(Organic & inorganic chems & specialties, agric chems)
   Diamond Shamrock Canada Ltd., 251 Consumer Rd., Willowdale, Ont., Canada M2J 4R3

DICTAPHONE CORP   3191 Broadbridge Ave, Stratford, CT   06497-2559,
Tel: (203) 381-7000
(Mfr/sale dictation, tel answering & multi-channel voice commun recording sys)
   Dictaphone Canada Ltd., 630 E. Mail, Etobicoke, Ont., Canada M9B 4B2

DILLINGHAM CONSTRUCTION CORP   5944 Inglewood Dr, Pleasanton, CA   94566,
Tel: (415) 847-7700
(General contracting)
   Delta Projects Ltd., Heritage Sq. Bldg., 8500 MacLeod Trail S., P.O. Box 5244,
   Sta. A, Calgary, Alta., Canada
   Dillingham Construction Ltd., 20 Brookshank Ave., N. Vancouver, BC, Canada V7J 2B8
   Dillingham Construction Ltd., P.O. Box 5507, Postal Section L, Emondton, Alta.,
   Canada T6C 4E9

WALT DISNEY PRODUCTIONS   500 S Buena Vista St, Burbank, CA   91521,
Tel: (818) 560-1000
(Film/TV prod, amusement parks, land mgmt)
   Walt Disney Music of Canada Ltd., 270 Rexdale Blvd., Rexdale, Ont., Canada M9W 1R2

DITTO DIVISION   Main St, Whitinsville, MA   01588, Tel: (800) 225-7766
(Duplicating, copying machs)
   Ditto of Canada Ltd., 1470 Birchmount, Scarborough, Ont., Canada M1P 2G1

DIVERSIFIED INDUSTRIES INC   101 S Hanley Rd, Clayton, MO   63105,
Tel: (314) 862-8200
(Metals trading, prod & reclamation)
   Liberty Smelting Works Ltd., P.O. Box 840, Station A, Montreal, Que., Canada H3C 2V5

DIXON TICONDEROGA CO   2600 Maitland Center Pkwy, #200, Maitland, FL   32751,
Tel: (407) 875-9000
(Mfr/serv writing implements & art supplies)
   Dixon Ticonderoga Inc., 531 Davis Dr., Newmarket, Ontario L3Y 2P1, Canada
   Dixon Ticonderoga, Inc., Acton Vale, 1100 Rue Bernard, Acton Vale, Quebec J0H 1A0,
   Canada

DORCHESTER GAS CORP   5735 Pineland Dr, Dallas, TX 75231, Tel: (214) 750-3500
  (Natural gas & oil)
    Dorchester Exploration Inc., 625 Gulf Canada Sq., Calgary, Alta., Canada T2P 3C5

DOW CHEMICAL CO   2030 Dow Center, Midland, MI 48640, Tel: (517) 636-1000
  (Chems, plastics, fibers, pharms)
    Dow Canada/ Western Div., P.O. Box 759, Fort Saskatchewan, Alta., Canada T8L 2P4
    Dow Chemical of Canada Ltd., P.O. Box 1012, Sarnia, Ont., Canada N7T 7K7

DOW CORNING CORP   2220 W Salzburg Rd, PO Box 1767, Midland, MI 48640,
  Tel: (517) 496-4000
  (Silicones, silicon chems, solid lubricants)
    Dow Corning Canada Ltd., 6747 Campobello Rd., Mississauga, Ont., Canada L5N 2M2

DRAKE BEAM MORIN INC   100 Park Ave, New York, NY 10017, Tel: (212) 692-7700
  (Human resource mgmt consulting & training)
    Drake Beam Morin-Canada Inc., 440 Dorchester Blvd. W., Montreal, Que.,
      Canada H2Z 1V7
    Drake Beam Morin-Canada Inc., 77 Bloor W., Toronto, Ont., Canada M5S 1M2
    Drake Beam Morin-Canada Inc., 255 Albert St., Ottawa, Ont., Canada K1P 6A9
    Drake Beam Morin-Canada Inc., P.O. Box 11512, Vancouver, BC, Canada V6B 4N7
    Drake Beam Morin-Canada Inc., 444 St. Mary Ave., Winnipeg, Man., Canada R3C 3T1
    Drake Beam Morin-Canada Inc., 550 11th Ave. SW, Calgary, Alta., Canada T2R 1M7

DRAVO CORP   1 Oliver Plaza, Pittsburgh, PA 15222, Tel: (412) 777-5000
  (Material handling equip, process plants)
    Dravo of Canada Ltd., 4935 Kent St., Niagara Falls, Ont., Canada L2H 1J6

DRESSER INDUSTRIES INC   1600 Pacific Bldg, PO Box 718, Dallas, TX 75221,
  Tel: (214) 740-6000
  (Diversified supplier of equip & tech serv to energy & natural resource ind)
    Dresser Atlas Div., 2260, 44 5th Ave. SW, Calgary, Alta., Canada T2P 2Y8
    Dresser Clark, P.O. Box 477, Lethbridge, Alta., Canada T1J 2Z1
    Dresser Industries Canada Ltd., 6688 Kitimat Rd., Mississauga, Ont., Canada L5N 1P8
    Dresser Industries Canada Ltd., Refractories, Div., P.O. Box 1750, Station B,
      Montreal, Que., Canada H3B 3L3
    Dresser Minerals Canada, Rosalind, Alta., Canada T0B 3Y0
    Galion Mfg. Div., 6688 Kitimat Rd., Mississauga, Ont., Canada L5N 1P8
    Jeffrey Mfg. Div., P.O. Box 700, LaSalle, Que., Canada H8R 3Y4

DREW CHEMICAL CORP   One Drew Plaza, Boonton, NJ 07005, Tel: (201) 263-7600
  (Spec chems for ind water & fuel treatment, chem processing)
    Drew Chemical Ltd., Drew Ct., Ajax, Ont., Canada L1S 2E5

DRIVER-HARRIS CO   308 Middlesex St, Harrison, NJ 07029, Tel: (201) 483-4800
  (Wire, cables, etc)
    Canadian Driver-Harris Co. Ltd., 56 Bramsteel Rd., Brampton, Ont., Canada L6W 1K5

DU BOIS INTL INC   1100 DuBois Tower, Cincinnati, OH 45202,
  Tel: (513) 762-6000
  (Mfr spec chems & maintenance prdts)
    DuBois Chemicals of Canada Ltd., 64 Kenhar Dr., Weston, Ont., Canada M9L 1N3

E I DU PONT DE NEMOURS & CO   Du Pont Bldg, 1007 Market St, Wilmington,
  DE 19898, Tel: (302) 774-1000
  (Mfr/sale diversified chems, plastics, specialty prdts & fibers)
    DuPont Canada Inc., Montreal, Que., Canada

DUFF-NORTON CO   9415 Pioneer Ave, Charlotte, NC 28217, Tel: (704) 588-0510
  (Mfr ind mach & equip)
    Canadian Duff-Norton Co. Ltd., 15 Lockport Ave., Toronto, Ont., Canada

DUNHAM-BUSH INC   175 South St, West Hartford, CT 06110, Tel: (203) 249-8671
  (Ind & commercial refrigeration, heating & A/C equip)
    Dunham-Bush Ltd., 140 Wendell Ave., Weston, Ont., Canada

DURAMETALLIC CORP   2104 Factory St, Kalamazoo, MI 49001, Tel: (616) 382-8720
  (Mfr mech seals, compression packings, auxiliaries)
    Durametallic Canada Inc., 130 Edward St., St. Thomas, Ont., Canada N5P 1Z1

DURIRON CO INC   425 N Findlay St, PO Box 1145, Dayton, OH 45401,
  Tel: (513) 226-4000
  (Mfr chem equip, pumps, valves, filters, fans, heat exchangers)
    Duriron Canada Inc., 120 Vinyl Ct., Wood Bridge, Ont. L4L 4A3, Canada

DURO-TEST INTL CORP   700 Godwin Ave, Midland Park, NJ 07432,
  Tel: (201) 867-7000
  (Mfr long duration lighting prdts for ind, coml & institutional use)
    Duro-Test Electric Ltd., 419 Attwell Dr., Rexdale, Ont., Canada M9W 5W5

E-Z-EM INC   7 Portland Ave, Westbury, NY 11590, Tel: (516) 333-8230
  (Mfr prdts for med contrast media, lead protective wear & surg prdts)
    E-Z-EM Canada-Therapex, 9855 Colbert, Anjou, Quebec, Canada

EARTH TECHNOLOGY CORP   3777 Long Beach Rd, Long Beach, CA 90807,
  Tel: (213) 595-6611
  (Geotech, geoscientific & environmental consult serv)
    Nolan-Ertec Ltd., P.O. Box 1021, Armdale Postal Sta., Halifax, NS, Canada B3L 4K9

EASTERN CO   112 Bridge St, Naugatuck, CT 06770, Tel: (203) 729-2255
  (Diversified mfg metal parts, safety & security prdts, constr materials)
    Eber-East Products Inc., P.O. Box 367, Tillsonburg, Ont., Canada

EASTMAN KODAK CO   343 State St, Rochester, NY 14650-0518, Tel: (716) 724-4000
  (Devel/mfr photo & chem prdts, info mgmt/video/copier sys, fibers/plastics for
  various ind)
    Kodak Canada Ltd., 3500 Eglington Ave. W, Toronto, Ont., Canada M6M 1V3

EATON CORP   100 Erieview Plaza, Cleveland, OH 44114, Tel: (216) 523-5000
  (Advanced tech prdts for transp & ind mkts)
    Eaton Yale Ltd., 566 Riverview Dr., Chatham, Ont., Canada N7M 5L9

EBASCO SERVICES INC   2 World Trade Center, New York, NY 10048,
  Tel: (212) 839-2685
  (Engineering, constr)
    Ebasco Services of Canada Ltd., 250 Bloor St. E, Toronto, Ont., Canada

ECHLIN INC   100 Double Beach Rd, Branford, CT 06405, Tel: (203) 481-5751
  (Mfr motor vehicle replacement parts)
    Distex Industries Inc., 10500 Rue Colbert, Ville D'Anjou, Montreal, Que. H1J 2H8,
    Canada
    Echlin Canada Inc., 500 Carlingview Dr., Rexdale, Ont., Canada M9W 5H1

ECLIPSE INC   1665 Elmwood Rd, Rockford, IL 61103, Tel: (815) 877-3031
  (Mfr ind process heating equip & hdwe for natural gas utils)
     Eclipse Fuel Engineering Co. of Canada Ltd., 70 Production Dr., Scarborough,
       Ont. M1H 2X8, Canada

ECOLAB INC   370 Wabasha St, St Paul, MN 55102, Tel: (612) 293-2233
  (Ind & household detergents, cleaning agents & equip)
     Economics Laboratory Ltd., 60 Torlake Crescent, Toronto, Ont., Canada M8Z 1C2

ECONOMY FORMS CORP - EFCO   4301 NE 14th St, Des Moines, IA 50316-0386,
  Tel: (515) 266-1141
  (Mfr steel forms for concrete construction)
     Economy Forms Ltd., 30 Todd Rd., Georgetown, Ont., Canada L7G 4R7

EDMONT   1300 Walnut St, Coshocton, OH 43812, Tel: (614) 622-4311
  (Ind gloves, rubber & plas prdts, protective clothing)
     Edmont Canada Ltd., 105 Lauder, Cowansville, Que., Canada J2K 2K8

EDWARDS CO INC   195 Farmington Ave, Farmington, CT 06032, Tel: (203) 678-0410
  (Mfr fire safety equip, signaling sys)
     Edwards Intl., 6465 Airport Rd., Mississauga, Ont., Canada L4Z 1E4

EG&G INC   45 William St, Wellesley, MA 02181, Tel: (617) 237-5100
  (Diversified instru, components, services)
     EG&G Canada Ltd./Instruments Div., 205 Riviera Dr, Markham, Ont. L3R 5JB, Canada
     EG&G Sealol, 3160 Miller Ave., Dorval, Que. H9P 1K5, Canada
     EG&G Sealol, 800-D Confederation St., Sarnia, Ont. N7T 2E3, Canada
     EG&G Sealol, 975 Mid-Way Blvd., Units 10/11, Mississauga, Ont. L5T 2C6, Canada
     EG&G Sealol, 3424 78th Ave., Edmonton, Alta. T6B 2X9, Canada
     EG&G Sealol, 384-B Gregoire Dr., Ft. McMurray, Alta. T9H 3R2, Canada

ELDON INDUSTRIES INC   9920 La Cienega Blvd, Inglewood, CA 90301,
  Tel: (213) 757-2151
  (Soldering & desoldering equip, sign boards, office furniture & accessories)
     Eldon Industries of Canada Ltd., 500 Esna Park Dr., Markham, Ont., Canada L3R 1H5

ELECTRIC FURNACE CO   435 Wilson St, Salem, OH 44460, Tel: (216) 332-4661
  (Design & mfr heat treating furnaces for metals ind)
     Canefco Ltd., 50 Milne Ave., Scarborough, Ont., Canada M1L 1K3

ELECTRONICS CORP OF AMERICA   265 Winter St, Waltham, MA 0215442,
  Tel: (617) 466-8000
  (Mfr electrical ind apparatus, electronic sys & controls)
     Electrnics Corp. of America (Canada) Ltd., 520 Kipling Ave., Toronto, Ont.,
       Canada M8Z 5E5

ELIZABETH ARDEN INC   55 East 52nd St, New York, NY 10055-0191,
  Tel: (212) 407-1000
  (Cosmetics, fragrances, toiletries)
     Elizabeth Arden of Canada Ltd., 7939 Keel St. N, P.O. Box 800, Downesview,
       Ont. M3M 3C1, Canada

EMBALMERS' SUPPLY CO   1370 Honeyspot Rd Ext, Stratford, CT 06497,
  Tel: (203) 375-2984
  (Embalmers chems, equip & supplies)
     Embalmers Supply Co. Canada Ltd., 42 Haas Rd., Rexdale, Ont., Canada N9W 3A2

EMCO WHEATON INC   50 Chamberlain Blvd, PO Box 688, Conneaut, OH 44030,
  Tel: (216) 599-8151
  (Mfr petroleum handling equip- ment)
    Emco Wheaton Ltd., 136 The East Mall, Toronto, Ont., Canada M8Z 5M2

ENCYCLOPEDIA BRITANNICA INC   425 N Michigan Ave, Chicago, IL 60611,
  Tel: (312) 321-7000
  (Book publ)
    Encyclopaedia Britannica Publications, 175 Holiday Inn Dr., P.O. Box 2249,
      Cambridge, Ont., Canada N3C 3N4

ENERPAC   13000 W Silver Spring Dr, Butler, WI 53007, Tel: (414) 781-6600
  (Mfr/sale high pressure hydraulic maint tools)
    Enerpac, 6490 Vipond Dr., Mississauga, Ont L5T 1W8, Canada

ENGELHARD CORP   Menlo Park, CN 40, Edison, NJ 08818, Tel: (201) 632-6000
  (Mfr spec chem prdts & engineered materials for ind; precious metal mgmt serv)
    Engelhard of Canada Ltd., 100 Engelhard Dr., Aurora, Ont., Canada L4G 3N1

ENGINE PRODUCTS DIV   PO Box 1166, Richmond, IN 47374, Tel: (317) 966-8111
  (Gaskets, seals, packings, etc)
    Perfect Circle, Victor Div. Hayes-Dana Ltd., St. Thomas, Ont., Canada

ENVIROTECH CORP   3000 Sand Hill Road, Menlo Park, CA 94025,
  Tel: (415) 854-2000
  (Supplier of equip & tech for underground mining, ind processing & pollution control)
    Envirotech Canada Ltd., 51555 Creek Bank Rd., Mississauga, Ont., Canada L4W 1X2

EQUIFAX INC   PO Box 4081, Atlanta, GA 30302, Tel: (404) 885-8000
  (Information services)
    Equifax Canada, 7171 Jean Talon East, Anjou, Que. H1M 3N2, Canada

ERICO PRODUCTS INC   34600 Solon Road, Cleveland, OH 44139,
  Tel: (216) 248-0100
  (Mfr electric welding apparatus & hardware, metal stampings, specialty fasteners)
    Erico Inc., 46 Ingram Dr., Toronto, Ont., Canada M6M 2L6

ERIE INTL LTD   4000 South 13th St, Milwaukee, WI 53221, Tel: (414) 483-0524
  (Mfr controls, valves & pipe fittings)
    Erie Mfg. Co. (Canada) Ltd., Stouffville, Ont., Canada

ERIE TECHNOLOGICAL PRODUCTS INC   645 W 11th St, Erie, PA 16512,
  Tel: (814) 453-5611
  (Electronic components)
    Erie Technological Products of Canada Ltd., 5 Fraser Ave., Trenton, Ont.,
      Canada K8V 5S1

ERIEZ MAGNETICS   PO Box 10652, Erie, PA 16514, Tel: (814) 833-9881
  (Mfr magnetic, vibratory & metal detection prdts & sys)
    Eriez of Canada Ltd., 133 Oakdale Rd., Downsview, Ont., Canada M3N 1W2

ESCO CORP   2141 NW 25th Ave, Portland, OR 97210, Tel: (503) 228-2141
  (Mfr equip for mining, constr, forestry ind)
    ESCO Ltd., 1855 Kingsway Ave., Port Coquitlam, BC V3C 1T1, Canada

ETHYL CORP   330 South 4th St, Richmond, VA 23219, Tel: (804) 788-5000
(Chems & plastics)
    Ethyl Canada Inc., 48 St. Clair Ave. W, Toronto, Ont., Canada M4V 2Z2

EVENFLO PRODUCTS CO   771 N Freedom St, Ravenna, OH 44266, Tel: (216) 296-3465
(Infant feeding equip & care prdts)
    Evenflo Canada, 121 Roy Blvd., Brantford, Ont., Canada

EXCEL CORP   1120 N Main St, Elkhart, IN 46514, Tel: (219) 264-2131
(Automotive prdts)
    Excel Metalcraft Ltd., 95 Cousins Dr., Aurora, Ont., Canada L4G 3H1

EXOLON-ESK CO   1000 E Niagara St, PO Box 590, Tonawanda, NY 14151-0590,
Tel: (716) 693-4550
(Mfr fused aluminum oxide & silicon carbide abrasive grains)
    Exolon-Esk Co. of Canada Ltd., P.O. Box 280, Thorold, Ont., Canada L2V 3Z2

EXPLORATION LOGGING INC   PO Box 40265, Houston, TX 77240, Tel: (713) 744-3600
(Geological engr & formation evaluation service)
    Exploration Logging Canada Inc., 3700 19th. St. NE, Calgary, Alta., Canada T2E 6V2

EXQUISITE FORM INDUSTRIES INC   16 E 40th St, New York, NY 10016,
Tel: (212) 532-8160
(Foundation garments)
    Exquisite Form Brassiere (Canada) Ltd., 215 Spadina Ave., Toronto, Ont.,
    Canada M3J 2Z4

FABER-CASTELL CORP   4 Century Dr, Parsippany, NJ 07054, Tel: (201) 539-4111
(Writing, drawing & drafting instru, inks)
    Faber-Castell Canada Ltd., 77 Brown's Line, Toronto, Ont., Canada M8W 4X5

FAFNIR BEARING CO   37 Booth St, New Britain, CT 06050, Tel: (203) 225-5151
(Ball bearings)
    Fafnir Bearing (Canada) Ltd., 1 Meridian Rd., Rexdale, Ont., Canada

FAIRMONT RAILWAY MOTORS INC   415 N Main St, Fairmont, MN 56031,
Tel: (507) 235-3361
(Railway motor cars, railway maint equip, hydraulic tools)
    Fairmont Railway Motors Ltd., 6320 Northwest Dr., Mississauga, Ont., Canada L4V 1J7

FALK CORP   3001 W Canal St, Milwaukee, WI 53208, Tel: (414) 342-3131
(Mfr gears, geared reducers & drives, couplings)
    Falk of Canada Ltd., 45 Discoe Rd., Rexdale, Ont., Canada M9W 1M2

FAMILY RECORD PLAN INC   15760 Ventura Blvd, Encino, CA 91316,
Tel: (213) 990-9210
(Family photo plan)
    Canadian Family Record Plan Ltd., Vancouver, B.C., Canada

FARR CO   2301 E Rosecrans Ave, El Segundo, CA 90245, Tel: (213) 772-5221
(Filtration equip)
    Farr Co. Ltd., 2785 Francis Hughes Ave., Chomedey, Laval, Que., Canada H7L 3J6

FELTON INTERNATIONAL INC   599 Johnson Ave, Brooklyn, NY 11237,
Tel: (212) 497-4664
(Essential oils & extracts, perfumes & flavor material, aromatic chems)

Felton Intl. Inc., 601 Garyray Dr., Weston, Ont., Canada M9L 1P9
Felton Intl. Inc., 5483 Royalmount Ave., Montreal, Que., Canada H4P 1J3

FENWICK/WOODSTREAM   14799 Chestnut, PO Box 729, Westminster, CA 92683,
  Tel: (714) 897-1066
  (Fishing rods, blanks & tackle boxes)
    Woodstream Canada, Box 210, Niagara Falls, Ont., Canada L2E 6T3

FERRO CORPORATION   One Erieview Plaza, Cleveland, OH 44114,
  Tel: (216) 641-8580
  (Chems, coatings, plastics, refractories)
    Ferro Industrial Products Ltd., 354 Davis Rd., Oakville, Ont., Canada L6J 2X1
    Queen City Distributors Ltd., P.O. Box 638, Downsview, Ont. M3M 3A9, Canada

FIRST INTERSTATE BANCORP   633 W 5th St, Los Angeles, CA 90071,
  Tel: (213) 614-3001
  (Banking)
    First Interstate Bank of Canada, 2 First Canadian Pl., Exchange Tower- #800,
      PO Box 429, Toronto, Ont. M5X 1E3, Canada

FIRST NATIONAL BANK OF BOSTON   100 Federal St, Boston, MA 02110,
  Tel: (617) 434-2200
  (Commercial banking)
    Bank of Boston Canada, P.O. Box 23, 70 University Ave., Toronto, Ont.,
      Canada M5J 2M4

FIRST NATIONAL BANK OF CHICAGO   One First National Plaza, Chicago, IL 60670,
  Tel: (312) 732-4000
  (Financial services)
    First National Bank of Chicago (Canada), P.O. Box 448, Exchange Tower,
      Two First Canadian Place, Toronto, Ont. M5X 1E4, Canada

FISCHBACH & MOORE INC   485 Lexington Ave, New York, NY 10017,
  Tel: (212) 986-4100
  (Electrical & mechanical contracting)
    Fischbach & Moore of Canada Ltd., 21 Waulron, Toronto, Ont., Canada M9C 1B4

FISCHER & PORTER CO   125 E County Line Rd, Warminster, PA 18974,
  Tel: (215) 674-6000
  (Design/mfr meas, recording & control instru & sys; mfr ind glass prdts)
    Fischer & Porter (Canada) Ltd., 134 Norfinch Dr., Downsview, Ont., Canada M3N 1X7

FISHER CONTROLS INTL INC   8000 Maryland Ave, Clayton, MO 63105,
  Tel: (314) 694-9900
  (Ind process control equip)
    Fisher Controls Co. of Canada Ltd., P.O. Box 578, 1039 Dundas St., Woodstock,
      Ont., Canada N4S 7Z6
    Fisher Controls Co. of Canada Ltd., 360 Holiday Inn Dr., Cambridge, Ont. N3C 3Z9,
      Canada
    Fisher Service Co., 2122 84th Ave., Edmonton, Alta., Canada T6P 1K2

FISHER-PRICE   636 Girard Ave, East Aurora, NY 14052, Tel: (716) 687-3000
  (Mfr toys & games)
    Fisher-Price, 5300 Tomken Rd., Mississauga, Ont., Canada L4W 1P2

FLEETWOOD ENTERPRISES INC   3125 Myers St, Riverside, CA 92523,
  Tel: (714) 351-3500
  (Mobile homes, travel trailers & motor homes)
    Prowler Industries of Ont. Ltd., P.O. Box 485, Lindsay, Ont., Canada K9V 5G4

FLORASYNTH INC   410 E 62nd St, New York, NY 10021, Tel: (212) 371-7700
  (Mfr aromatic chems, fra- grances & flavors)
    Florasynth Laboratories Ltd., 29 St. Paul St. E, Montreal, Que., Canada

FLOW CONTROL   PO Box 2117, Houston, TX 77252, Tel: (713) 499-8511
  (Mfr rotary drive components & drill rig handling equip)
    Flow Control, Calgary, Alberta, Canada

FLOW LABORATORIES INC   7655 Old Springhouse Rd, McLean, VA 22102,
  Tel: (703) 893-5900
  (Mfr/distr biotechnology)
    Flow Laboratories Inc., 1246 Lorimar Dr., Unit 1, Mississauga, Ont. L5S 1R2, Canada

JOHN FLUKE MFG CO   6920 Seaway Blvd, Everett, WA 98203, Tel: (206) 347-6100
  (Electrical test & measurement instru)
    Fluke Electronics Canada Inc., 400 Britannia Rd. E., Unit 1, Mississauga,
    Ont. L4Z 1X9, Canada

FLUOR CORP   3333 Michelson Dr, Irvine, CA 92730, Tel: (714) 975-2000
  (Engr/constr & related services; coal & lead)
    Fluor Daniel Canada Ltd., Calgary, Alta., Canada
    Wright Engineers Ltd., Vancouver, BC, Canada

FMC CORP   200 E Randolph Dr, Chicago, IL 60601, Tel: (312) 861-6000
  (Mach & chem for industry, agric & govt)
    FMC of Canada Ltd., 71 Leland St., Hamilton, Ont., Canada L8S 3A1

FOOTE CONE & BELDING COMMUNICATIONS INC   101 E Erie St, Chicago,
  IL 60611-2897, Tel: (312) 751-7000
  (Advertising agency)
    Provost/Ronalds-Reynolds, 1801 McGill College #660, Montreal, Que. H3A 1W3, Canada
    Provost/Ronalds-Reynolds, other locations in Canada

FORD MOTOR CO   The American Road, Dearborn, MI 48121, Tel: (313) 322-3000
  (Mfr automobiles, trucks)
    Ford Motor Co. of Canada Ltd., P.O. Box 2000, Canadian Rd., Oakville, Ont., Canada

FOSTER REFRIGERATOR CORP   247 N Second, Hudson, NY 12534, Tel: (518) 828-3311
  (Refrigerators, freezers)
    Foster Refrigerator of Canada Ltd., P.O. Box 248, Drummondville, Ont., Canada

FOSTER WHEELER CORP   Perryville Corporate Park, Clinton, NJ 08809-4000,
  Tel: (201) 730-4000
  (Engr, constr, mfg)
    Foster Wheeler Ltd. (Canada), P.O. Box 3007, St. Catharines, Ont., Canada L2R 7B7

FOUR-PHASE SYSTEMS INC   10700 North de Anza Blvd, Cupertino, CA 95014,
  Tel: (408) 255-0900
  (Computer sys)
    Four-Phase Systems Ltd., 560 Denison St., Markham, Ont., Canada L3R 2M8

FOXBORO CO   33 Commercial St, Foxboro, MA 02035, Tel: (508) 543-8750
  (Mfr prdts/provide servs for ind automation)
    Spectrex Ltd., 5250 Ferrier, Ste. 508, Montreal, Que., Canada H4P 1L6
    The Foxboro Co. Ltd., 707 Dollar Ave., LaSalle, Que., Canada
    The Foxboro Co. Ltd., 1410 Boundary Rd., Vancouver, B.C., Canada V5K 4V3
    The Foxboro Co. Ltd., 510 Nassau Crescent, Sarnia, Ont., Canada N7S 4H0

FRANK RUSSELL CO   909 A St, PO Box 1616, Tacoma, WA 98401-9949,
  Tel: (206) 572-9500
  (Investment services)
    Frank Russell Co., P.O. Box 808, 390 Bay St., Suite 808, Toronto, Ont.,
    Canada M5H 2Y2

FRANKLIN ELECTRIC CO INC   400 E Spring St, Bluffton, IN 46714,
  Tel: (219) 824-2900
  (Mfr fractional h.p motors, submersible motors & controls)
    Franklin Electric of Canada Ltd., P.O. Box 5008, Strathroy, Ont., Canada N7G 3J3

THE FRANKLIN MINT   Franklin Center, PA 19091, Tel: (215) 459-6000
  (Creation/mfr/mktg collectible items)
    Franklin Mint Canada, 90 Royal Crest Ct., Markham, Ont. L3R 9T6, Canada

FULLER CO   2040 Ave C, PO Box 2040, Bethlehem, PA 18001, Tel: (215) 264-6011
  (Ind processing equip & sys, conveying & blending sys, etc)
    GATX-Fuller Ltd., 10 Thornmount Dr., Scarborough, Ont., Canada M1B 3J4
    GATX-Fuller Ltd., 3300 Cavendish Blvd., Montreal, Que., Canada H4B 2M8

H B FULLER CO   2400 Energy Park Dr, St Paul, MN 55108, Tel: (612) 645-3401
  (Mfr/distr adhesives, sealants, coatings, paints, waxes, sanitation chems)
    H.B. Fuller Canada Inc., 880 Rangeview Dr., Mississauga, Ont., Canada L5E 1G9
    H.B. Fuller Co. (Canada) Ltd., 88 Industrial Blvd., Boucherville, Que., Canada

GAF CORP   1361 Alps Rd, Wayne, NJ 07470, Tel: (201) 628-3000
  (Chems, bldg materials, commun)
    GAF (Canada) Inc., 1075 The Queensway E., Mississauga, Ont., Canada L4Y 4C1
    GAF (Canada) Inc., 7575 Trans Canada Hwy., Ville St. Laurent, Que., Canada 4HT IV6
    GAF (Canada) Ltd., 1075 Queensway E, Mississauga, Ont., Canada L4Y 4C1

GAMLEN CHEMICAL CO   121 S Maple Ave, S San Francisco, CA 94080,
  Tel: (415) 873-1750
  (Chems, detergents & tank cleansers)
    Gamlen Chemical Co., 1494 Powell St., Vancouver, B.C., Canada V5L 1G6
    Gamlen Chemical Co. (Canada) Ltd., 595 Guimond Blvd., Montreal, Que., Canada J4G 1L9

THE GATES RUBBER CO   PO Box 5887, Denver, CO 80217, Tel: (303) 744-1911
  (Mfr auto/ind belts & hose, hydraulic hose & couplings, molded rubber prdts)
    Gates Canada Inc., 50 Iroquois St., Brantford, Ont., N3T 5R6, Canada

GATX CORP   120 S Riverside Plaza, Chicago, IL 60606, Tel: (312) 621-6200
  (Railcar leasing, maint & mgmt, bulk liquid storage, fin serv, shipping, mineral
  processing)
    CGTX Inc., P.O. Box 70, Station A, Montreal, Que., Canada H3C 2R6
    GATX Equipment Leasing, 26 Wellington St. E., Ste. 1003, Toronto, Ont.,
    Canada M5E 1S2
    GATX Fuller Ltd., 3300 Cavendish Blvd., Montreal, Que., Canada H4B 2M8
    GATX Fuller Ltd., 10 Thornmount Dr., Scarborough, Ont., Canada M1B 3J4

GB ELECTRICAL INC   6101 N Baker Rd, Milwaukee, WI 53209, Tel: (414) 352-4160
(Mfr/sale elec consumable items & spec tools)
   GB Electrical Inc., 6490 Vipond Dr., Mississauga, Ont. L5T 1W8, Canada

GEARHART INDUSTRIES INC   1100 Everman Road, Fort Worth, TX 76140,
   Tel: (817) 293-1300
   (Mfr oil field mach & equip)
   Computerlog Gearhart Ltd., 630 Sixth Ave. SW, Calgary, Alta., Canada T2P 0S8

GELMAN SCIENCES INC   600 South Wagner St, Ann Arbor, MI 48106,
   Tel: (313) 665-0651
   (Laboratory prdts)
   Gelman Sciences Inc., 2535 DeMiniac, Ville St. Laurent, Montreal, Canada H4S 1M7

GENERAL ABRASIVE   2000 College Ave, Niagara Falls, NY 14305,
   Tel: (716) 286-1234
   (Mfr abrasives)
   General Abrasive Div. of Abrasive (Canada) Inc., 3807 Stanley Ave., Niagara Falls,
      Ont., Canada L2E 6T8

GENERAL AUTOMATION INC   1055 S East St, Anaheim, CA 92806,
   Tel: (714) 778-4800
   (Computer hardware & serv)
   GA Computer Ltd., 7225 Woodbine Ave., Markham, Ont., Canada L3R 1A3

GENERAL BINDING CORP   One GBC Plaza, Northbrook, IL 60062,
   Tel: (708) 272-3700
   (Binding & laminating equip & associated supplies)
   GBC Canada Inc., 49 Railside Rd., Don Mills, Ont., Canada M3A 1B3

GENERAL DATACOMM INDUSTRIES INC   1579 Straits Turnpike, Middlebury,
   CT 06762-1299, Tel: (203) 574-1118
   (Mfr trans equip for commun networks)
   General DataComm Ltd., 2255 Sheppard Ave. East- #410W, Willowdale, Ont. M2J 4Y3,
      Canada

GENERAL ELECTRIC CO   3135 Easton Tpk, Fairfield, CT 06431,
   Tel: (203) 373-2211
   (Diversified mfr, tech & servs)
   GE Canada, 2300 Meadowvale, Mississauga, Ont. L5N 5PG, Canada

GENERAL FOODS CORP   250 North St, White Plains, NY 10625, Tel: (914) 335-2500
   (Processor, distributor & mfr of foods)
   General Foods Inc., P.O. Box 1200, Moatfield Dr., Don Mills, Ont., Canada M3C 3J5

GENERAL INSTRUMENT CORP   767 Fifth Ave, New York, NY 10153-0082,
   Tel: (212) 207-6200
   (Electronic components & sys)
   General Instrument of Canada Ltd., 70 Wingold Ave., Toronto, Ont., Canada M6B 1P5

GENERAL LATEX & CHEMICAL CORP   666 Main St, Cambridge, MA 02139,
   Tel: (617) 864-7750
   (Latex compounds chems & dis- persions, urethanes & acrylics)
   General Latex & Chemicals Ltd., 29 Ibsen Pl., Candiac, Que., Canada

GENERAL MILLS INC   1 General Mills Blvd, PO Box 1113, Minneapolis, MN 55440,
  Tel: (612) 540-2311
  (Mfr consumer foods; restaurants)
    General Mills Canada Inc., 1330 Martin Grove Rd., P.O. Box 505, Rexdale, Ont.,
      Canada M9W 4X4
    General Mills Restaurants, 1417 Kennedy Rd., Scarborough, Ont., Canada M1P 41

GENERAL MOTORS CORP   3044 W Grand Blvd, Detroit, MI 48202,
  Tel: (313) 556-5000
  (Automotive prdts, electronics)
    Diesel Div. of GM Canada Ltd., P.O. Box 5160, London, Ont., Canada N6A 4N5.,
    Diesel Div. of GM Canada Ltd., 1000 Industrial Blvd., St. Eustache, Que.,
      Canada J7R 5A5
    General Motors of Canada Ltd., 215 William St. E, Oshawa, Ont., Canada, L1G 1K7

GENERAL REFRACTORIES CO   2661 Audubon Rd, Audubon, PA 19407,
  Tel: (215) 666-0104
  (Heat-resisting materials, furnace constr)
    General Refractories Co. of Canada Ltd., P.O. Box 160, Smithville, Ont.,
      Canada L0R 2A0

GENERAL TIME CORP   PO Box 4125, Norcross, GA 30091-4125, Tel: (404) 447-5300
  (Mfr clocks, watches)
    Westclox Canada Ltd., Peterborough, Ont., Canada

GEORGIA-PACIFIC CORP   133 Peachtree St NE, Atlanta, GA 30303,
  Tel: (404) 521-4000
  (Lumber & paper prdts, metal prdts, chems & plastics)
    Federal Packaging & Partitioning Co. Ltd., P.O. Box 148, Toronto, Ont.,
      Canada L1S 3C2

GERBER PRODUCTS CO   445 State St, Fremont, MI 49412, Tel: (616) 928-2000
  (Mfr/distr baby food & related prdts)
    Gerber (Canada) Inc., 56 Brockport Dr., Etobicoke, Ont. M9W 5N1, Canada

GETTY OIL CO   3810 Wilshire Blvd, Los Angeles, CA 90010, Tel: (213) 739-2100
  (Petroleum & petroleum prdts)
    Canadian Reserve Oil & Gas Ltd., 639 Fifth Ave. SW, Calgary, Alta., Canada T2P 0M9
    Getty Oil Canada Ltd., 715 Fifth Ave. SW, Calgary, Alta., Canada T2P 0N2

GIFT-PAX INC   25 Hempstead Gardens Dr, W Hempstead, NY 11552,
  Tel: (516) 485-0660
  (Packaging gift samples)
    Gift Pax (Canada) Ltd., 746 Warden Ave., Scarborough, Ont., Canada M1L 4A2

THE GILLETTE CO   Prudential Tower, Boston, MA 02199, Tel: (617) 421-7000
  (Mfr/distr shaving prdts, toiletries & cosmetics, stationery prdts)
    Gillette Canada Ltd., 5450 Cote de Liesse Rd., Montreal, Que., Canada H4P 1A7

GIRARD INDUSTRIES   6531 N Eldridge Pkwy, Houston, TX 77041,
  Tel: (713) 466-3100
  (Mfr polyurethane foam pipeline cleaners)
    Imperial Rubber, 708-19 Ave., Nisku, Alberta T0C 2G0, Canada

GLIDDEN-COATINGS RESINS DIV   900 Union Commerece Bldg, Cleveland, OH   44115,
    Tel: (216) 344-8167
    (Coatings, resins, adhesives, organic chems, etc)
        Gidden Co., Div. SCM (Canada) Ltd., 351 Wallace Ave., Toronto, Ont., Canada M6P 3NP

GLITSCH INC   PO Box 660053, Dallas, TX   75266, Tel: (214) 631-3841
    (Mfr mass transfer/chem separation equip, process engr)
        Glitsch Canada Ltd., P.O. Box 880, Uxbridge, Ont., Canada L0C 1K0

GOODYEAR TIRE & RUBBER CO   1144 E Market St, Akron, OH   44316-0001,
    Tel: (216) 796-2121
    (Mfr tires, rubber prdts)
        Goodyear Canada Inc., 10 Four Seasons Pl., Etobicoke, Ont. M9B 6G2, Canada
        Granford Mfg. Inc., Deregibus Blvd., St. Alphonse deGranby, Que., Canada

GORMAN-RUPP CO   305 Bowman Street, Mansfield, OH   44903, Tel: (419) 755-1011
    (Pumps, hospital equip)
        Gorman-Rupp of Canada Ltd., 70 Burwell Rd., St. Thomas, Ont., Canada N5P 3R7

GORTON GROUP   327 Main Street, Gloucester, MA   01930, Tel: (617) 283-3000
    (Frozen fish)
        Blue Water Seafood Ltd., 1640 Brandon Crescent, Lachine, Montreal, Que.,
            Canada H8T 2N1
        Canapro Ltd., Grindstone, Magdalen Islands, Que., Canada

GOULD INC   10 Gould Center, Rolling Meadows, IL   60008, Tel: (708) 640-4000
    (Electric sys, batteries, etc)
        Industrial Battery Div., Fort Erie, Ont., Canada

GOULDS PUMPS INC   240 Fall St, Seneca Falls, NY   13148, Tel: (315) 568-2811
    (Mfr ind & water sys pumps)
        Goulds Pumps Canada Inc., 185 Sheldon Dr., Cambridge, Ont., Canada N1T 1A6

W R GRACE & CO   1114 Ave of the Americas, New York, NY   10036,
    Tel: (212) 819-5500
    (Specialty chems, natural resources, consumer serv)
        Dearborn Chemicals Co. Ltd., 3451 Erindale Station Rd., Mississauga, Ont.,
            Canada L5C 2S9
        Dubois Chemicals of Canada Ltd., 64 Kenhar Drive, Weston, Ont., Canada M9L 1N3
        W.R. Grace & Co. of Canada Ltd., 294 Elements Rd. W, Ajax, Ont., Canada L1S 3C6

GRANT THORNTON INTL   Prudential Plaza, Chicago, IL   60601, Tel: (312) 856-0001
    (Intl accountants)
        Grant Thornton Canada, P.O. Box 301, Montreal, Que., Canada H4Z 1G9

GRAPHIC CONTROLS CORP   PO Box 1271, Buffalo, NY   14240, Tel: (716) 853-7500
    (Mfr plotter supplies, ind/med recording charts, fax papers, disposable med prdts &
    pens)
        Graphic Controls Canada Ltd., Herbert St., Gananoque, Ont., Canada K7G 2Y7

GREAT LAKES CARBON INTL CORP   320 Old Briarcliff Rd, Briarcliff Manor,
    NY   10510, Tel: (914) 941-7800
    (Mfr carbon prdts, petroleum)
        GLC Canada Inc., 2000 Peel St., #760, Montreal, Que., H3A 2W5, Canada

A P GREEN INDUSTRIES   Green Boulevard, Mexico, MO 65265, Tel: (314) 473-3626
(Mfr refractories & lime)
   A.P. Green Refractories (Canada) Ltd., 234 Rosemont Ave., Weston, Ont. M9N 3C4,
   Canada

GREY ADVERTISING INC   777 Third Ave, New York, NY 10017, Tel: (212) 546-2000
(Advertising)
   Grey Advertising Ltd., 2055 Peel St., Montreal, Que., Canada H3A 1W1
   Grey Advertising Ltd., 1075 Bay St., Toronto, Ont., Canada M5S 2B1

GREYHOUND CORP   Greyhound Tower, Phoenix, AZ 85077, Tel: (602) 248-4000
(Mfr consumer prdts, transportation, consumer & fin services)
   Brewster Transport Co. Ltd., P.O. Box 1140, Toloco, Alta., Canada
   Brewster Transport Co. Ltd., P.O. Box 1140, Banff, Alta. TOL OCO, Canada
   Greyhound Computer of Canada Ltd., 181 University Ave., Toronto, Ont.,
   Canada M8S 3M7
   Greyhound Lines of Canada Ltd., 877 Greyhound Way SW, Calgary, Alta. T3C 3V8, Canada
   Motor Coach Industries Inc., 1149 St. Matthews Ave., Winnipeg, Man., R3G OJ8, Canada

GRIFFITH LABORATORIES INC   I Griffith Center, Alsip, IL 60658,
   Tel: (708) 371-0900
(Ind food ingredients & equip)
   The Griffith Laboratories Ltd., 757 Pharmacy Ave., Scarborough, Ont., Canada M1L 3J8
   The Griffith Laboratories Ltd., P.O. Box 329, Howard St., South River,
   Ont. POA 1XO, Canada

GROLIER INC   Old Shereman Tpk, Danbury, CT 06816, Tel: (203) 797-3500
(Publishers)
   Grolier Ltd., 16 Overlea Blvd., Toronto., Ont., Canada M4H 1A6
   Grolier Ltd., 2405 Duncan Rd., Montreal, Que., Canada H4P 2A3

GRUEN INDUSTRIES INC   50 W 23 St, New York, NY 10010, Tel: (212) 989-1777
(Watches)
   Gruen Watch Co. of Canada Ltd., 73 Six Point Rd., Toronto, Ont.,.Canada

M GRUMBACHER INC   30 Englehard Dr, Cranbury, NJ 08512, Tel: (609) 655-8282
(Mfr artists' materials)
   M. Grumbacher of Canada Ltd., 460 Finchdene Sq., Scarborough, Ont., Canada M1X 1C4

GTE CORP   One Stamford Forum, Stamford, CT 06904, Tel: (203) 965-2000
(Electr prdts, telecom sys, publ & commun)
   British Columbia Telephone Co., Vancouver, B.C., Canada
   GTE Electrical Products, Mfg. plants & laboratories throughout Canada
   Quebec Telephone, Rimouski, Que., Canada

GTE DIRECTORIES CORP   West Airport Dr, DFW Airport, TX 75261-9810,
   Tel: (214) 453-7000
(Pub telephone directories)
   Dominion Directory Co. Ltd., 4400 Dominion St., Burnaby, BC, Canada V5G 4G4

GULTON INDUSTRIES INC   212 Durham Ave, Metuchen, NJ 08840,
   Tel: (908) 548-6500
(Electr instru & controls, commun equip)
   Gulton Industries (Canada) Ltd., 345lerbert St., Gananoque, Ont., Canada K7G 2V1

HALLMARK CARDS INC   PO Box 419580, Kansas City, MO 64141, Tel: (816) 274-5100
(Mfr greeting cards & related prdts)
   Williams E. Coutts Co., Ltd., 2 Hallcrown Pl., Willowdale, Ontario M2J 1P6, Canada

HAMILTON KENT MFG CO   2144 State Rte 59, Kent, OH 44240, Tel: (216) 673-9555
(Rubber prdts)
   Hamilton Kent of Canada Ltd., 3094 Mavis Rd., Mississauga, Ont., Canada

HANDLEMAN CO   500 Kirts Blvd, Troy, MI 48084, Tel: (313) 362-4400
(Distr pre-recorded music, books, video cassettes, computer software)
   Handleman Co. of Canada Ltd., 10 Newgale Gate, Unit 1-4, Scarborough, Ont.,
      Canada M1X 1C5

HANDY & HARMAN   850 Third Ave, New York, NY 10022, Tel: (212) 752-3400
(Precious & specialty metals for industry, refining, scrap metal)
   Handy & Harman of Canada Ltd., 290 Carlingview Dr., Rexdale, Ont., Canada, M9W 5G1

J E HANGER INC   40 Paterson St, NE, Washington, DC 20002, Tel: (202) 789-0050
(Artificial limbs)
   J.E. Hanger of Canada Ltd., 4259 St. Catherines St. W, Montreal, Que.,
      Canada H3Z 1P7

HANKSCRAFT   Reedsburg, WI 53959, Tel: (608) 524-4341
(Infant care prdts)
   Hankscraft Canada Ltd., 3310 Yonge St., Toronto, Ont., Canada

M A HANNA CO   100 Erieview Plaza, Cleveland, OH 44114, Tel: (216) 589-4000
(Iron ore, nickel & silicon, oil & gas, coal, mgmt serv)
   Iron Ore Co. of Canada, 1245 Sherbrooke St. W, Montreal, Que., Canada H3G 1G8

HARCOURT BRACE JOVANOVICH INC   Harcourt Brace Jovanovich Bldg, Orlando,
   FL 32887, Tel: (305) 345-2000
(Book publ, tests & related serv, journals, facisimile reprints, mgmt consult,
operates parks/shows)
   Academic Press Inc. Canada, 55 Barber Greene Rd., Don Mills, Ont., Canada M3C 2A1
   Drake Beam Morin Canada Inc., 80 Bloor St. W., Toronto, Ont., Canada H4T 1E3
   Editions Etudes Vivantes, 6700 Cote de Liesse Rd., Ville St. Laurent, Montreal,
      Que., Canada H4T 1E3

HARNISCHFEGER INDUSTRIES INC   PO Box 554, Milwaukee, WI 53201,
   Tel: (414) 671-4400
(Mfr mining & material handling equip, papermaking mach, computer sys)
   Harnischfeger Corp. of Canada Ltd., 875 Progress Ave., Scarborough, Ont.,
      Canada M1H 3A7
   Harnischfeger Corp. of Canada Ltd., 12391 No. 5 Rd., Richmond, BC, Canada V7A 4E9

THE HARPER GROUP INC   260 Townsend St, PO Box 77933, San Francisco,
   CA 94107, Tel: (415) 978-0600
(Ocean/air freight fwdg, customs brokerage, packing & whse, logistics mgt, ins)
   Circle Intl. Freight (Canada) Ltd., PO Box 83, Toronto AMF, Ontario L5P 1A2, Canada
   Cotrell Imperial Intl. Freight, Inc., 3061 Orlando Dr., Mississauga,
      Ontario L4V 1R4, Canada

HARRIS CORP   1025 W NASA Blvd, Melbourne, FL 32919, Tel: (305) 961-9100
(Communications & information handling equip)
   Harris Systems Ltd., Canada

HARSCO CORP   PO Box 8888, Camp Hill, PA 17011-8888, Tel: (717) 763-7064
(Diversified mfr & serv)
    Patent Scaffolding Co. Ltd., 30 Ordnance St., Toronto, Ont., Canada M6K 1A2
    Patent Scaffolding Co. Ltd., 7030 51st St., Edmondton, Alta., Canada T6B 2PH

HARSHAW/FILTRO PARTNERS   30100 Chagrin Blvd, Cleveland, OH 44124,
    Tel: (216) 292-9200
(Ind chems)
    Harshaw Chemicals of Canada Ltd., 6616 Campobello Rd., Mississauga, Ont.,
      Canada L5N 2L8
    Pembina Mt. Clays, 945 Logan Ave., Winnipeg, Man., Canada R3E IP3

HART & COOLEY MFG CO   500 E 8th St, Holland, MI 49423, Tel: (616) 392-7855
(Heating, ventilating & A/C components & accessories)
    Hart & Cooley Mfg. Co. of Canada Ltd., Wood St., Fort Erie, Ont., Canada

HARTER CORP   Prairie Ave & Albert St, Sturgis, MI 49091, Tel: (616) 651-3201
(Institutional & office furniture)
    Harter Metal Furniture Ltd., 139 Cardigan St., Guelph, Ont., Canada

HARTWELL BROTHERS   PO Box 8327, Memphis, TN 38108, Tel: (901) 452-2191
(Mfr hickory striking-tool handles)
    Elgin Handles Ltd., 21 Kains St., St. Thomas, Ont. N5P 1M8, Canada

HASBRO INDUSTRIES INC   1027 Newport Ave, Pawtucket, RI 02861,
    Tel: (401) 726-4100
(Toys, games, dolls)
    Hasbro Industries (Canada) Ltd., 2350 de la Province Longueuil, Que., Canada

HASTINGS MFG CO   300 N Hanover St, Hastings, MI 49058, Tel: (616) 945-2491
(Piston rings, spark plugs, filters)
    Hastings Ltd., 390 Richmond Rd., Toronto, Ont., Canada

HAUSERMAN INC   5711 Grant Ave, Cleveland, OH 44105, Tel: (216) 883-1400
(Steel partitions, cabinets, wall sys)
    Hauserman of Canada Ltd., 91 Yonge St., Toronto, Ont., Canada

HEAT TIMER SERVICE CORP   10 Dwight Pl, Fairfield, NJ 07006,
    Tel: (201) 575-4004
(Heating sys controls, smoke alarms, digital temp & set point controls)
    Steam & Industrial Equip. Co., 776 Halpern Ave., Dorval, Que., Canada

HECLA MINING CO   PO C-8000, Coeur d'Alene, ID 83814, Tel: (208) 769-4100
(Non-ferrous & industrial metals mining)
    Granduc Mines Ltd., 675 W. Hastings St., 15th fl., Vancouver, BC V6B 1N2, Canada

HEIN-WERNER CORP   1005 Perkins Ave, Waukesha, WI 53187, Tel: (414) 452-6611
(Hydraulic jacks & lifting equip- ment, auto body repair equip)
    Hein-Werner of Canada Ltd., 55 Mills Rd., Ajax, Ont., Canada L1S 2H2

H J HEINZ CO   PO Box 57, Pittsburgh, PA 15230, Tel: (412) 456-5100
(Food prdts)
    H.J. Heinz Co. of Canada Ltd., 250 Bloor St. E, Toronto, Ont., Canada N8H 3W8

HELENE CURTIS INDUSTRIES INC   4401 W North Ave, Chicago, IL 60639,
Tel: (312) 292-2121
(Cosmetics, toiletries, hair preparations)
    Helene Curtis Ltd., 131 Hymus Blvd., Pointe Claire, Que., Canada H9R 1E7

HERCULES INC   Hercules Plaza, Wilmington, DE 19894, Tel: (302) 594-5000
(Mfr spec chems, plastics, film & fibers, coatings, resins, food ingredients)
    Hercules Canada Ltd., Mississauga Executive Centre, 4 Robert Speck Pkwy.,
      Mississauga, Ont. L4Z 1S1, Canada

HERMETIC SEAL CORP   4232 Temple City Blvd, Rosemead, CA 91770,
Tel: (213) 283-0411
(Seals & connectors)
    Quality Hermetics Ltd., 45 Hollinger Rd., Toronto, Ont., Canada

HERSHEY FOODS CORP   100 Mansion Rd E, Hershey, PA 17033, Tel: (717) 534-4200
(Chocolate, food & confectionary prdts, restaurant operations)
    Hershey Canada Inc., 200 Ronson Dr., Ste. 7000, Rexdale, Ont., Canada M9W 5Z9

HEWLETT-PACKARD CO   3000 Hanover St, PO Box 10301, Palo Alto, CA 94303-0890,
Tel: (415) 857-1501
(Mfr measurement & computation prdts & sys)
    Hewlett-Packard (Canada) Ltd., 6877 Goreway Dr., Mississauga, Ont., Canada L4V 1M8

HILL & KNOWLTON INC   420 Lexington Ave, New York, NY 10017,
Tel: (212) 697-5600
(Public relations, public affairs, comm counseling)
    Hill & Knowlton (Canada) Ltd., 160 Bloor St. E, Toronto, Ont., Canada M4I 1B9
    Hill & Knowlton (Canada) Ltd., 202-1285 W. Bender St., Vancouver, BC, Canada V6E 4B1

HILLERICH & BRADSBY CO INC   PO Box 35700, Louisville, KY 40232-5700,
Tel: (502) 585-5226
(Golf, baseball & softball equip)
    Hillerich & Bradsby Co. Ltd., 14 Arnold St. Wallaceburg, Ont., Canada N8A 3L7

HOBART BROTHERS CO   Hobart Sq, Troy, OH 45373-2928, Tel: (513) 339-6000
(Arc/automatic welding sys, power sys)
    Hobart Brothers of Canada Ltd., P.O. Box 150, Woodstock, Ont., Canada N4S 7WB

HOKE INC   1 Tenakill Rd, Cresskill, NJ 07626, Tel: (201) 568-9100
(Valves, fittings, fluid control specialties)
    Hoke Controls, 2240 Speers Rd., Oakville, Ont., Canada L6L 2X8

HOLIDAY INNS INC   3742 Lamar Ave, Memphis, TN 38195, Tel: (901) 362-4001
(Hotels, restaurants, casinos)
    Holiday Inn, Armoury & Chestnut Sts., Toronto, Ont., Canada M5G 1R1
    Holiday Inn, 420 Sherbrooke St. W, Montreal, Que., Canada

HOLOPHANE CO INC   214 Oakwood Ave, Newark, OH 43055, Tel: (614) 345-9631
(Lighting equip)
    Holophane Co. Ltd., 1620 Steeles Ave., Bramalea, Ont., Canada

THE HOOVER GROUP   403 W 4th St N, Newton, IA 50208, Tel: (515) 792-8000
(Mfr floor care prdts, laundry & refrig appliances)
    The Hoover Co. Ltd., 4151 N. Service Rd., Burlington, Ont., Canada L7R 4A8

HORWATH & HORWATH INTL   919 Third Ave, New York, NY 10022,
   Tel: (212) 980-3100
   (Public accountants & auditors)
      Laventhol & Horwath, Box 9474 Bow Valley Sq., Calgary, Alta., Canada T2P 2W6
      Laventhol & Horwath, 120 Adelaide St. W, Toronto, Ont., Canada M5H 1T6
      Laventhol & Horwath, 805 W. Broadway, Vancouver, B.C., Canada V5Z 1K1
      Laventhol & Horwath, 1200-444 St. Mary Ave., Winnipeg, Man., Canada R3C 3T1

HOSKINS MFG CO   10776 Hall Rd, Hamburg, MI 48139, Tel: (313) 231-1900
   (Mfr elec resistance & spec alloys)
      Hoskins Alloys of Canada Ltd., 45 Racine Rd., Rexdale, Ont., Canada

E F HOUGHTON & CO   PO Box 930, Valley Forge, PA 19482-0930,
   Tel: (215) 666-4000
   (Mfr spec chems, hydraulic fluids, lubricants)
      E.F. Houghton & Co. of Canada Ltd., P.O. Box 113, Station D, Toronto, Ont.,
      Canada M6P 3J5
      E.F. Houghton & Co. of Canada Ltd., 19 E. 3rd Ave., Vancouver, B.C., an,
      Canada V5T 1C6
      E.F. Houghton & Co. of Canada Ltd., P.O. Box 188, Station C, Winnipeg, Man., Canada

HOUGHTON MIFFLIN CO   1 Beacon St, Boston, MA 02107, Tel: (617) 725-5000
   (Book publisher, computer software)
      Houghton Mifflin Canada Ltd., 150 Steelcase Rd. W., Markham, Ont., Canada L3R 1B2

HOUSEHOLD INTL INC   2700 Sanders Rd, Prospect Heights, IL 60070,
   Tel: (708) 564-5000
   (Financial services)
      HFC of Canada, 100 Sheppard Ave., Toronto, Ont. M2N 6N7, Canada
      Household Trust, 100 Sheppard Ave., Toronto, Ont. M2N 6N7, Canada

HOWE RICHARDSON CO   680 Van Houten Ave, Clifton, NJ 07015,
   Tel: (201) 471-3400
   (Ind weighing & packaging equip)
      Howe Richardson Canada Inc., 217 Brunswick Blvd., Pointe Claire, Que.,
      Canada H9R 4R7

HOWE-BAKER ENGINEERS INC   PO Box 956, Tyler, TX 75710, Tel: (214) 597-0311
   (Design, fabricate, erect process sys for petroleum ind)
      Abax Energy Services Ltd., 5929 6th St. NE, Calgary, Alta., Canada T2K 5R5

HUBBS & HOWE CO   2200 Harlem Road, Buffalo, NY 14225, Tel: (716) 895-7900
   (Paper bags, paper pdts)
      Davis & Herderson Ltd., 41 Scarsdale Rd., Don Mills, Ont., Canada

HUCK MFG CO   PO Box 19590, Irvine, CA 92713, Tel: (714) 855-9000
   (Mfr fasteners & fastening sys)
      Huck Mfg. Co. (Canada) Ltd., 326 Humber College Blvd., Rexdale, Ont., Canada M9W 5P4

HUGHES TOOL CO   PO Box 2539, Houston, TX 77001, Tel: (713) 924-2222
   (Equip & serv to oil & gas explor & prod ind)
      B.J. Hughes Service Ltd., 633 6th Ave. SW, Calgary, Alta., Canada T2P 2Y5
      B.J. Hughes Service Ltd., P.O. Box 92, Nisku, Alta., Canada TOC 2G0
      Strata-Hughes Testing, 305-635 6th Ave., Calgary, Alta., Canada T2P 2Y5

HUNT OIL CO   1401 Elm St, #2900, Dallas, TX 75202-2970, Tel: (214) 744-7911
  (Petroleum explor & prod)
  Hunt Oil Co., 801 6th Ave, S.W., Calgary, Alta. T2P 3W2, Canada

HUSSMAN INTL   12999 St Charles Rock Rd, Bridgeton, MO 63044,
  Tel: (314) 291-2000
  (Mfr refrig & environ control sys for food ind)
  Hussman Canada, P.O. Box 550, Brantford, Ont., Canada N3T 5R2

HYDE SPRING & WIRE CO   14341 Schaefer Hwy, Detroit, MI 48227,
  Tel: (313) 272-2201
  (Coil springs, wire)
  Hyde Spring & Wire Ltd., 366 Grand River Ave., Brantford, Ont., Canada

HYDRIL CO   714 W Olympic Blvd, Los Angeles, CA 90015, Tel: (213) 680-1910
  (Oil field mach & equip, rubber goods)
  Hydril Canadian Co. Ltd., 2008 Alenwood Dr., Calgary, Alta., Canada

ICN PHARMACEUTICALS INC   ICN Plaza, 3300 Hyland Ave, Costa Mesa, CA 92626,
  Tel: (714) 545-0100
  (Pharms, biochems, radioactive materials)
  ICN Canada Ltd., 1956 Bourdon St., St. Laurent, Montreal, Que., Canada H4M 1V1

ICS INTERNATIONAL INC   Oak St & Pawnee Ave, Scranton, PA 18515,
  Tel: (717) 342-7701
  (Correspondence courses)
  ICS Canadian Ltd., 7475 Sherbrooke St. W., Montreal, Que. H4B 1S4, Canada

IDEAL BASIC INDUSTRIES   950 17th St, Denver, CO 80202, Tel: (303) 623-5661
  (Masonry, white cement & potash)
  Rock Products Div., Vancouver, B.C., Canada

ILLINOIS TOOL WORKS INC   8501 West Higgins Rd, Chicago, IL 60631,
  Tel: (312)693-3040
  (Metal cutting tools, fasteners, sealants, gear measuring instru)
  Devon Corp., Scarborough, Ont., Canada

ILSCO CORP   4730 Madison Rd, Cincinnati, OH 45227, Tel: (513) 871-4000
  (Electrical connectors)
  Ilsco of Canada Ltd., 1050 Lakeshore Rd. E, Mississauga, Ont., Canada

IMCO CONTAINER CO   451 Florida Blvd, Baton Rouge, LA 70801,
  Tel: (504) 388-8011
  (Plastic containers)
  Imco Container Ltd., 3174 Mavis Rd., Mississauga, Ont., Canada

INA CORPORATION   1600 Arch St, Philadelphia, PA 19101, Tel: (215) 523-5335
  (Holding co: ins, financial serv)
  INA Insurance Co. of Canada, 9942-108th St., Edmonton, Alta., Canada T5K 2J5

INCOM INTERNATIONAL INC   3450 Princeton Pike, Lawrenceville, NJ 08648,
  Tel: (609) 896-7600
  (Roller & motorcycle chains, drive components, marine controls, etc)
  Boston Gear of Canada Ltd., 2790 Slough St., Mississauga, Ont., Canada L4T 1G2
  ESB Canada Ltd., 104 58th Ave. SE, Calgary, Alta., Canada T2H 0N7

INFOTRON SYSTEMS CORP   Cherry Hill Ind Center-9, Cherry Hill, NJ 08003,
  Tel: (609) 424-9400
  (Data commun equip)
     Infotron Canada Ltd., 755 Queensway E., Unit 107, Mississauga, Ont. Canada L4Y 4C5

INSPIRATION RESOURCES CORP   250 Park Ave, New York, NY 10177,
  Tel: (212) 503-3100
  (Agric & mining prdts & serv)
     Churchill River Power Co. Ltd., 2161 Scarth St., Regina, Sask., Canada S4P 2V4
     Hudson Bay Exploration & Development Co. Ltd., P.O. Box 1500, Flin Flon, Man.,
       Canada R8A 1N9
     Hudson Bay Exploration & Development Co. Ltd., Baffinland Iron Mines Ltd.,
       Coltan Mines Ltd., Hayes Resources Inc.,
     Hudson Bay Exploration & Development Co. Ltd., Hudson-Yukon Mining Co.,
       Hudvam Mines, Manitoba Chromium Ltd.,
     Hudson Bay Exploration & Development Co. Ltd., Tornew Mines Ltd.,
       Tantalum Mining Corp. of Canada Ltd.
     Hudson Bay Mining & Smelting Ltd., P.O. Box 1500, Flin Flon, Man., Canada R8A 1N9
     Stikine Copper Ltd., 650 W. Georgia St., Vancouver, BC, Canada

INSTRON CORP   100 Royall St, Canton, MA 02021, Tel: (617) 828-2500
  (Testing instru)
     Instron Canada Ltd., 969 Fraser Dr., Burlington, Ont., Canada L7L 4X8
     Instron Canada Ltd., CP 371, Succursale M, Montreal, Que., Canada H1V 3M5

INSTRUMENT SYSTEMS CORP   100 Jericho Quadrangle, Jericho, NY 11753,
  Tel: (516) 938-5544
  (Electronic prdts, commun sys)
     Bedford Industries, 4750 Des Grandes Prairies Blvd., Montreal, Que., Canada
     White Electronic Development Corp., Mississauga, Ont., Canada

INSUL-8 CORP   P O Drawer 1188, San Carlos, CA 94070, Tel: (415) 595-3050
  (Closed circuit TV equip)
     Insul-8 Corp. Ltd., 24 Ronson Dr., Rexdale, Ont., Canada

INTERMEC CORP   6001 36th Ave West, Everett, WA 98203-9280,
  Tel: (206) 348-2600
  (Mfr automated data collection sys)
     Intermec Systems Corp., 7065 Tranmere Dr.- #3, Mississauga, Ontario L5S 1M2, Canada
     Intermec Systems Corp., other locations in Canada

INTERMETRO INDUSTRIES CORP   651 N Washington St, Wilkes-Barre, PA 18705,
  Tel: (717) 825-2741
  (Mfr storage/material handling prdts.)
     Metropolitan Wire (Canada), Ltd., 3155 Orlando Dr., Mississauga, Ontario I4V 1C5,
       Canada

INTERNATIONAL BUSINESS MACHINES (IBM)   Old Orchard Rd, Armonk,
  NY 10504-1783, Tel: (914) 765-1900
  (Info-handling sys, equip & serv)
     IBM Canada Ldtee., Canada
     ROLM Canada Inc., Canada
     Science Research Assocs. Pty. Ltd., Canada

INTERNATIONAL DAIRY QUEEN INC   5701 Green Valley Dr, PO Box 35286,
  Minneapolis, MN 55437, Tel: (612) 830-0200
  (Mfr/sales fast foods & treats)

(cont)

Orange Julius Canada Ltd., 5245 Harvester Rd., PO Box 430, Burlington,
Ont. L7R 3Y3, Canada

INTERNATIONAL FILLER CORP   50 Bridge St, North Tonawanda, NY 14120,
Tel: (716) 693-4040
(Plastic, rubber fillers)
Intl. Filler Corp. Ltd., Hamilton, Ont., Canada

INTERNATIONAL FLAVORS & FRAGRANCES INC   521 W 57th St, New York, NY 10019,
Tel: (212) 765-5500
(Create/mfr flavors, fragrances & aroma chems)
Intl. Flavors & Fragrances Ltd., Toronto, Ont., Canada
Intl. IFlavors & Fragrances Ltd., 5990 Des Ecores, Montreal, Que., Canada

INTERNATIONAL MAILING SYSTEMS INC   19 Forest Parkway, Shelton, CT 06484,
Tel: (203) 926-1087
(Mfr gummed tape dispensers, postal meters & scales, mailing machines)
Intl. Mailing Systems of Canada Ltd., 50 Riviera Dr., Markham, Ont. L3R 5M1, Canada

INTERNATIONAL MULTIFOODS CORP   Box 2942, Minneapolis, MN 55402,
Tel: (612) 340-3300
(Food serv, grain & feed, food prdts)
Robin Hood Multifoods Ltd., P.O. Box 4000, Station A, Willowdale, Ont.,
Canada M2N 5T5

INTERNATIONAL PAINT CO INC   PO Box 386, Union, NJ 07083, Tel: (212) 825-0800
(Paints)
Intl. Paints Ltd., 6700 Park Ave., Montreal, Que., Canada

INTERNATIONAL PAPER   2 Manhattanville Rd, Purchase, NY 10577,
Tel: (914) 397-1500
(Mfr/distr container board, paper, wood prdts)
Anitec Image (Canada) Ltd., 5955 Airport Rd., Mississauga, Ont. L4V 1R9, Canada
International Paper Canada Inc., 1210 Sheppard Ave. East, Willowdale, Toronto,
Ont., Canada
Veratec (Canada) Inc., 6 Curity Ave., Toronto, Ont. M5H 3E9, Canada

INTERNATIONAL RECTIFIER CORP   233 Kansas St, El Segundo, CA 90245,
Tel: (213) 772-2000
(Mfr power semiconductors)
Intl. Rectifier Canada Ltd., 101 Bentley St., Markham, Ont., Canada L3R 3L1

INTERNORTH INC   2223 Dodge St, Omaha, NE 68102, Tel: (402) 348-4000
(Natural gas distribution)
Consolidated Gathering Systems Ltd., Calgary, Alta., Canada
Consolidated Natural Gas Ltd., 1300 L:lveden House, Calgary, Alta., Canada
Consolidated Pipe Lines Co., 1300 Elveden House, Calgary, Alta., Canada
Weskem of Canada Ltd., 1300 Elveden House, Calgary, Alta., Canada

INTEXT INC   Oak & Pawnee Sts, Scranton, PA 18515, Tel: (717) 342-7701
(Educational serv, bound books)
ICS Canadian Ltd., 791 Lajoie, Dorval, Montreal, Que., Canada

IRECO INC   Crossroads Tower, 11th fl, Salt Lake City, UT 84144,
Tel: (801) 364-4800
(Explosive supplies, accessories for ind & military applications; alu- minum granules)
Ireco Canada Inc., 6600 Trans-Canada Hwy., Pointe Claire, Que., Canada, H9R 452

IRONSIDES CO   270 W Mound St, Columbus, OH 43216, Tel: (614) 224-2228
  (Ind lubricants)
    Ironsides of Canada Ltd., Speers Rd., Trafalgar Township, Ont., Canada

IRVIN INDUSTRIES INC   630 Fifth Ave, New York, NY 10111, Tel: (212) 977-2500
  (Parachutes, cargo handling equip, life-saving devices)
    Irvin Industries Canada Ltd., 479 Central Ave., Forterie, Ont., Canada L2A 3T9

IRVING TRUST CO   1 Wall St, New York, NY 10015, Tel: (212) 487-2121
  (Intl banking)
    Irving Trust Co., Commerce Court W, Toronto, Ont., Canada M5L 1E8

ITT SHERATON CORP   60 State St, Boston, MA 02108, Tel: (617) 367-3600
  (Hotel operations)
    Halifax Sheraton, 1919 Upper Water St., Halifax, NS, Canada B3J 3JS
    Sheraton Hamilton, 116 King St. W., Hamilton, Ont., Canada L8P 4V3
    Sheraton Plaza Edmonton, 10010 104th St., Edmonton, Alta., Canada T5J 0Z1

JAEGER MACHINE CO   550 W Spring St, Columbus, OH 43216, Tel: (614) 228-4311
  (Pumps, drills, air tools, indust- rial mixers, etc)
    Jaeger Finance of Canada Ltd., St. Thomas, Ont., Canada
    Jaeger Machine Co. of Canada Ltd., St. Thomas, Ont., Canada

JAMESBURY CORP   640 Lincoln St, Worcester, MA 01605, Tel: (617) 852-0200
  (Mfr valves & accessories)
    Jamesbury Canada, 1282 Algoma Rd., Ottawa, Ont., Canada K1B 3W8

JEFFERSON LAKE SULPHUR CO   2000 S Post Oak, Houston, TX 77056,
  Tel: (713) 629-3111
  (Chems)
    Jefferson Lake Petrochemicals of Canada Ltd., Fort St. John, B.C., Canada

JESSOP STEEL CO   500 Green St, Washington, PA 15301, Tel: (412) 222-4000
  (Steel, alloys)
    Jessop Steel Co., Wallaceburg, Ont., Canada

JIM WALTER INTL SALES CORP   1500 N Dale Mabry, Tampa, FL 33607,
  Tel: (813) 871-4212
  (Bldg materials, home constr gas & oil explor, sugar growing & refining, chems,
  minerals)
    Jim Walter Intl., Celotex Ltd., Carey Canada Inc., Rte. 112E, Broth Station, Que.,
      Canada G0N 1H0

JOHN HANCOCK MUTUAL LIFE INSURANCE CO   200 Clarendon St, PO Box 111, Boston,
  MA 02117, Tel: (617) 572-6000
  (Life ins)
    Maritime Life Assurance Co., P.O. Box 1030, Halifax, NS, Canada B3S 2X5

JOHNSON & JOHNSON   One Johnson & Johnson Plaza, New Brunswick, NJ 08933,
  Tel: (201) 524-0400
  (Surgical, med & baby prdts)
    Critikon Canada Inc., Markham, Canada
    Devro Canada Ltd., Markham, Ont., Canada
    Ethicon Sutures Ltd., Peterborough, Ont., Canada
    Janssen Pharmaceutica Inc., Mississauga, Ont., Canada
    Johnson & Johnson Baby Products Co., Guelph, Ont., Canada
    Johnson & Johnson Hospital Services, Scarborough, Ont., Canada

(cont)

Johnson & Johnson Inc., Montreal, Que., Canada
Johnson & Johnson Medical Canada, Montreal, Que., Canada
LifeScan Canada Ltd., Burnaby, Canada
McNeil Laboratories (Canada) Ltd., Stouffville, Ont., Canada
Ortho Pharmaceutical (Canada) Ltd., Don Mills, Ont., Canada
Surgikos Canada Ltd., Peterborough, Ont., Canada

S C JOHNSON & SON INC   1525 Howe St, Racine, WI 53403, Tel: (414) 631-2000
(Home, auto, commercial & personal care prdts, specialty chems)
S.C. Johnson & Son Ltd., P.O. Box 520, Brantford, Ont., Canada N3T 5R1

JOHNSON CONTROLS INC   5757 W Green Bay Ave, PO Box 591, Milwaukee, WI 53201,
Tel: (414) 228-1200
(Mfr facility mgmt & control sys, auto seating, batteries & plastics)
Johnson Controls Ltd., 7400 Birchmont Rd., Markham, Ont. L3R 5V4, Canada

JOMAC INC   863 Easton Rd, Warrington, PA 18976, Tel: (215) 343-0800
(Mfr protective clothing & graphic art mat)
Jomac-Canada, 212A Wilkinson Rd., Brampton, Ontario LGT 4M4, Canada
Jomac-Canada, 15 Main St., Beebe, Quebec JOB 1EO, Canada

JOSLYN CORP   30 S Wacker Dr, Chicago, IL 60606, Tel: (312) 454-2900
(Elect transmission & distr equip & components)
Joslyn Industries (Canada) Ltd., 63 St. Joseph Blvd., Lachine, Que., Canada H8S 2K9
Joslyn Industries (Canada) Ltd., 3791 Victoria Park Ave., Scarborough, Ont.,
Canada M1W 3K6

JOSTEN'S INC   5501 Norman Center, Minneapolis, MN 55437, Tel: (612) 830-3300
(Class rings, school & graduation related prdts, awards, trophies)
Jostens National School Services Ltd., 1051 King Edward St., Winnipeg, Man.,
Canada R3C OR4

JUPITER INDUSTRIES INC   919 N Michigan, Chicago, IL 60611,
Tel: (312) 642-6000
(Diversified consumer prdts, transp, constr, energy)
Testor Corp., Weston, Ont., Canada

K-TEL INTL INC   15525 Medina Rd, Plymouth, MN 55447, Tel: (612) 559-6800
(Packaged consumer entertainment & convenience prdts)
ERA Intl. Ltd., 386 Broadway Ave., Winnipeg, Man. R3C 3R6, Canada

KALLESTAD DIAGNOSTICS INC   1000 Lake Hazeltine Dr, Chaska, MN 55318,
Tel: (612) 448-4848
(Mfr med diagnostic instru & test kits)
Kallestad Canada, Inc., 2403 Guenette, Montreal, Quebec H4R 2E9, Canada

KAMAN CORP   Old Windsor Road, Bloomfield, CT 06002, Tel: (203) 243-8311
(Aviation & aerospace prdts & serv, musical instru)
Kaman Aircraft of Canada Ltd., St. Catharines, Ont., Canada

KAMDEN INTL SHIPPING INC   167-41 147th Ave, Jamaica, NY 11434,
Tel: (718) 917-8181
(Freight forwarding servs)
Kamden Intl. Shipping (Canada), Inc., PO Box 246-AMF,
Lester B. Pearson Intl. Airport, Toronto, Ont. L5P IB1, Canada

KATY INDUSTRIES INC   853 Dundee Ave, Elgin, IL 60120, Tel: (708) 697-8900
(Holding company: transp, electronics, ind prdts)
   Bach-Simpson Ltd., P.O. Box 2484, London, Ont., Canada

KAUFMAN & BROAD HOME CORP   11601 Wilshire Blvd, Los Angeles, CA 90025,
Tel: (213) 312-1200
(Housing)
   Victoria Wood Development Corp. Inc., 2025 Sheppard Ave. E., Willowdale, Ont.,
    Canada M2J 1V7

KAUMAGRAPH CO   14th & Poplar Sts, Wilmington, DE 19899, Tel: (302) 575-1500
(Lithography)
   Kaumagraph Ltd., P.O. Box 223, Paris, Ont., Canada

KAWNEER CO INC   555 Guthridge Ct, Norcross, GA 30092, Tel: (404) 449-5555
(Mfr arch aluminum prdts for commercial constr)
   Kawneer Co. Canada Ltd., 1051 Ellesmere Rd., Scarborough, Ont. M1P 2X1, Canada

A T KEARNEY INC   222 S Riverside Plaza, Chicago, IL 60606,
Tel: (312) 648-0111
(Mgmt consultants)
   A.T. Kearney Inc., Box 10, 20 Queen St. W., Toronto, Ont., Canada M5J 3R3

KEARNEY-NATIONAL INC   5 Corporate Dr, White Plains, NY 10604,
Tel: (914) 694-6700
(Mfr elect power distr equip, elect/electr comp)
   Alomeg Div, Kearney National (Canada) Ltd., 90 Milvan Dr., Weston, Ont.,
    Canada M9L 1Z6
   Kearney National (Canada) Ltd., 280 Speedvale Ave. W., Guelph, Ont., Canada N1H 1C4

KELCO INDUSTRIES INC   9210 Country Club Rd, Woodstock, IL 60098,
Tel: (714) 292-4900
(Alginate prdts)
   Scotia Marine Products, Lower Wood Harbour, N.S., Canada

KELLOGG CO   235 Porter St, Battle Creek, MI 49016, Tel: (616) 966-2000
(Food prdts)
   Kellogg Canada Ltd., Montreal, Que., Canada
   Kellogg Canada Ltd., Toronto, Ont., Canada
   Kellogg Canada Ltd., London, Ont., Canada
   Kellogg Canada Ltd., Alliston, Ont., Canada

KELSEY-HAYES CO   38481 Huron River Dr, Romulus, MI 48174, Tel: (313) 941-2000
(Automotive & aircraft parts)
   Kelsey-Hayes Canada Ltd., Windsor, Ont., Canada
   Kelsey-Hayes Canada Ltd., Woodstock, Ont., Canada
   Kelsey-Hayes Canada Ltd., St. Catharines, Ont., Canada

THE KENDALL CO   PO Box 10, Boston, MA 02101, Tel: (617) 423-2000
(Surgical dressings, baby prdts)
   Kendall Co. Ltd., Curity Ave., Toronto, Ont., Canada

KENNECOTT CORP   1717 Midland Bldg, Cleveland, OH 44115, Tel: (203) 964-3000
(Minerals & metals)
   British Columbia Molybdenum Ltd., Vancouver, B.C., Canada
   Kennecott Canada Ltd., Toronto, Ont., Canada
   Que. Iron & Titanium Corp., P.O. Box 40, Sorel, Que., Canada

KENNEDY VAN SAUN CORP   PO Box 500, Danville, PA 17821, Tel: (717) 275-3050
(Mineral processing & handling equip)
   Kennedy Van Saun Prdts. Ltd., 11 Progress St., Unit 3, Scarborough, Ont.,
      Canada M1P 4S7

KENT-MOORE CORP   28635 Mound Rd, Warren, MI 48092, Tel: (313) 574-2332
(Mfr service equip for auto, constr, recreational, military & agric vehicles)
   Kent-Moore Canada Ltd., 178 Oakdale Rd., Downsview, Ont. M3N 1W4, Canada

KEPNER-TREGOE INC   Research Rd, PO Box 704, Princeton, NJ 08542,
   Tel: (609) 921-2806
(Mgmt & organizational devel)
   Kepner-Tregoe Associates Ltd., 45 Shepard Ave. E., Willowdale, Ont., Canada M2N 5W9
   Kepner-Tregoe Associes, Ltee., 3860 Cote Verue, St. Laurent, Que., Canada H4R 1V4

KERR-McGEE CORP   PO Box 25861, Oklahoma City, OK 73125, Tel: (405) 270-1313
(Mfr oil, gas, & refined petroleum prdts, ind chems, coal)
   Kerr-McGee Canada Ltd., 1600 250 6th Ave., SW, Calgary, Alberta T2P 3H7, Canada

KEUFFEL & ESSER CO   PO Box 800, Rockaway, NJ 07866, Tel: (201) 625-9005
(Drafting & engineering supplies)
   Keuffel & Esser Canada Inc., 124 Milner Ave., Scarborough, Ont., Canada M1S 4R6

KEYES FIBRE CO   3003 Summer St, Stamford, CT 06905, Tel: (203) 357-9100
(Molded containers)
   Canadian Keyes Fibre Co. Ltd., Hantsport, N.S., Canada B0P 1P0

KILIAN MFG CO   1728 Burnet Ave, Syracuse, NY 13201, Tel: (315) 432-0700
(Unground ball bearings, casters)
   Kilian Mfg. Corp. Ltd., 75 Torlake Crescent, Toronto, Ont., Canada

KIMBERLY-CLARK CORP   PO Box 619100, Dallas, TX 75261-1200,
   Tel: (214) 830-1200
(Mfr fiber-based prdts for personal care, pulp & forest prdts; air transport)
   Kimberly-Clark of Canada Ltd., 365 E. Bloor St., Toronto, Ont., Canada M4W 3L9
   Spruce Falls Power & Paper Co. Ltd., Kapuskasing, Ont., Canada

KINGS ELECTRONICS CO INC   40 Marbledale Rd, Tuckhahoe, NY 10707,
   Tel: (914) 793-5000
(Mfr electr coaxial connectors)
   Kings Electronics Ltd., 144 Ronald Dr., Montreal, Que., Canada

KINNEY SHOE CORP   233 Broadway, New York, NY 10279, Tel: (212) 720-3700
(Mfr/sale footwear & apparel)
   Kinney Shoes of Canada Ltd., 100 Mainshep Rd., Weston, Ont., Canada M9M 1L5

KIRSCH   309 North Prospect St, Sturgis, MI 49091, Tel: (616) 651-0211
(Mfr drapery hdwe & custom window coverings)
   Kirsch, Weston, Ontario, Canada

KIRSCH CO   309 N Prospect St, Sturgis, MI 49091, Tel: (616) 651-0339
(Drapery hardware & accessories, wood shelving, woven wood shades, etc)
   Kirsch of Canada Ltd., P.O. Box 488, Woodstock, Ont., Canada N4S 7Z1

KNAPE & VOGT MFG CO   2700 Oak Ind Dr, NE, Grand Rapids, MI 49505,
Tel: (616) 459-3311
(Builders hardware, closet & cabinet fixtures & accessories)
   Knape & Vogt Canada Ltd., Rexdale, Ont., Canada

KNOLL INTL   655 Madison Ave, New York, NY 10021, Tel: (212) 826-2400
(Furniture & fabrics)
   Klaus Neinkamper Ltd., 300 King St. E, Toronto, Ont., Canada

KNOTT HOTELS CORP   840 Madison Ave, New York, NY 10021, Tel: (212) 535-2000
(Hotels)
   Westbury Hotel, 575 Yonge St., Toronto, Ont., Canada

KOCH ENGINEERING CO INC   PO Box 8127, Wichita, KS 67208, Tel: (316) 832-5110
(Mass transfer prdts, static mixers, mist eliminator sys)
   Koch Engineering Co. Ltd., 4750 Sheppard Ave. E., Agincourt, Ont., Canada M1S 3V7

KOEHRING CO   PO Box 312, Milwaukee, WI 53201, Tel: (414) 784-5800
(Pulp mill & constr equip)
   Bomag (Canada), Mississauga, Ont., Canada
   Koehring-Waterous Ltd., Brantford, Ont., Canada

KOH-I-NOOR RAPIDOGRAPH INC   100 North St, Bloomsbury, NJ 08804,
Tel: (201) 479-4124
(Engineering & artists equip & supplies)
   Koh-I-Noor Ltd., 1815 Meyerside Dr., Mississauga, Ont., Canada L5T 1B4

THE KOHLER CO   444 Highland Dr, Kohler, WI 53044, Tel: (414) 457-4441
(Plumbing prdts, engines, generators)
   Kohler Ltd., 805 Education Rd., Cornwall, Ont., Canada K6H 6C7

KOLMAR LABORATORIES INC   123 Pike St, Port Jervis, NY 12771,
Tel: (914) 856-5311
(Contract mfr: cosmetics, pharms, household prdts)
   Kolmar of Canada Ltd., 149 Victoria St., Barrie, Ont., Canada L4N 2J6

KOMLINE-SANDERSON ENGINEERING CORP   100 Holland Ave, Peapack, NJ 07977,
Tel: (201) 234-1000
(Ind & sanitary filtration sys, metering & control devices)
   Komline-Sanderson Ltd., Orenda Rd., Brampton, Ont., Canada

KOPPERS CO INC   Koppers Bldg, 437 Seventh Ave, Pittsburgh, PA 15219,
Tel: (412) 227-2000
(Constr materiald & serv; chem & bldg prdts)
   Koppers Intl. Canada Ltd., 10106 Shellbridge Way, Richmond, B.C., Canada V6X 2W7
   Koppers Products Ltd., 19 Meteor Dr., Rexdale, Ont., Canada
   Koppers-Hickson Canada Ltd., Meadowvale Corporate Centre, Plaza One,
      2000 Agentia Rd., Mississauga, Ont. L5W 1P7
   Sprout Waldron of Canada Ltd., 160 Roger St., Waterloo, Ont., Canada N2J 1A9
   Swanson Lumber Co. Ltd., 220-6325 103rd St., Edmonton, Alta., Canada T6H 5H6

KORN/FERRY INTL   237 Park Ave, New York, NY 10017, Tel: (212) 687-1834
(Executive search)
   Korn/Ferry Intl., 40 King St. West, Toronto, Ont. M5H 3Y2, Canada

KOSS CORP   4129 N Port Washington Rd, Milwaukee, WI 53212,
Tel: (414) 964-5000
(Mfr stereophones & access, loudspeakers, portable listening prdts)
    Koss Ltd., 4112 S. Service Rd., Burlington, Ont., Canada L7L 4XS

LAFARGE CORP   12801 N Central Expy, Dallas, TX 75243, Tel: (214) 934-7400
(John D Redfern, Chmn Cement, concrete-related prdts)
    Canada Cement Lafarge, 606 Cathcart, Montreal, Que., Canada H3B 1L7

LAMBDA ELECTRONICS INC   515 Broad Hollow Rd, Melville, NY 11747,
Tel: (516) 694-4200
(Power supplies, semiconductors, test equip)
    Lambda Electronics Inc., 4125 Cousens St., St. Laurent, Que. H45 1VS, Canada

LANCASTER COLONY CORP   37 W Broad St, Columbus, OH 43215, Tel: (614) 224-7141
(Mfr/mkt automotive aftermarket prdts, glass gift & tableware)
    Lancaster Colony Canada Inc., 2531 Stanfield Rd., Mississauga, Ont., Canada L4Y 1R6

LANDER CO INC   PO Box 9610, Englewood, NJ 07631, Tel: (201) 568-9700
(Mfr health & beauty aids, cosmetics & toiletries)
    Lander Co., Canada, 275 Finchdene Sq., Agincourt, Ont. M1S 3CS, Canada

LANNON MFG CO   PO Box 550, Tullahoma, TN 37388, Tel: (615) 455-0691
(Sporting goods)
    Lannom & Wellinger, 350 Sorauren, Toronto, Ont., Canada

LAU DIV OF PHILIPS INDUSTRIES INC   2027 Home Ave, Dayton, OH 45401,
Tel: (513) 263-3591
(Air moving equip)
    Lau Products Ltd., 385 Block Line Rd., Kitchener, Ont., Canada

LAWTER INTERNATIONAL INC   990 Skokie Blvd, Northbrook, IL 60062,
Tel: (708) 498-4700
(Resins, pigments, coatings)
    Lawter Chemicals (Canada) Ltd., 29 Iron St., Rexdale, Ont., Canada

LEAF CONFECTIONERY INC   1155 N Cicero Ave, Chicago, IL 60651,
Tel: (312) 345-6200
(Chewing gum)
    Leaf Confections Ltd., Toronto, Ont., Canada

LEEDS & NORTHRUP CO   Sumneytown Pike, North Wales, PA 19454,
Tel: (215) 699-2000
(Mfr process control instru & sys)
    Leeds & Northrup Canada, 1344 Fewster Dr., Mississauga, Ont., Canada L4W 1A4

LEHN & FINK PRODUCTS CO   225 Summit Ave, Montvale, NJ 07645,
Tel: (201) 391-8500
(Cosmetics, pharms)
    Lehn & Fink Ltd., 37 Hanna Ave., Toronto, Ont., Canada

LEIGH PRODUCTS INC   2627 E Beltline, SE, Grand Rapids, MI 49506,
Tel: (616) 942-1440
(Ceiling sys, ventilators, wire hdwe)
    Leigh Metal Products Ltd., 101 Brookside, London, Ont., Canada

LENNOX INDUSTRIES INC   Box 809000, Dallas, TX 75380-9000, Tel: (214) 980-6000
(Mfr heating & A/C equip)
   Lennox Industries Ltd., 400 Norris Glen Rd., Etobicoke, Ont., Canada

LESLIE FAY INC   1400 Broadway, New York, NY 10018, Tel: (212) 221-4000
(Wearing apparel)
   Leslie Fay Ltd., 1470 Peel St., Montreal, Que., Canada

LEVI STRAUSS & CO   1155 Battery, San Francisco, CA 94111, Tel: (415) 544-6000
(Mfr wearing apparel)
   Levi Strauss of Canada, 80 Allstate Pkwy., Markham, Ont. L3R 8X6, Canada

LEWIS-HOWE CO   319 South 4th St, St Louis, MO 63102, Tel: (314) 621-2304
(Pharms)
   Lewis-Howe Co., 1415 Janette Ave., Windsor, Ont., Canada

LIGHTOLIER   100 Lighting Way, Secaucus, NJ 07096, Tel: (201) 864-3000
(Mfr lighting fixtures, portable lamps)
   Canlyte/Lightolier, 3015 Rue Louis A. Amos, Lachine, Que., Canada H8T 1C4

ELI LILLY & CO   307 E McCarty St, Indianapolis, IN 46285, Tel: (317) 261-2000
(Pharms, agric & cosmetic prdts)
   Eli Lilly & Co. (Canada) Ltd., 3650 Danforth Ave.,.Scarborough, Ont., Canada M1N 2E8

THE LINCOLN ELECTRIC CO   22801 St Clair Ave, Cleveland, OH 44117,
Tel: (216) 481-8100
(Mfr arc welding equip & consumables, elec motors)
   Lincoln Electric Co. of Canada Ltd., 179 Wicksteed Ave., Toronto, Ont.,
   Canada M4G 2B9

LINTAS:WORLDWIDE   1 Dag Hammarskjold Plaza, New York, NY 10017,
Tel: (212) 605-8000
(Advertising agency)
   MacLaren:Lintas, 20 Dundas St. W., Toronto, Ont., Canada M5G 2H1

LITTLE GIANT PRODUCTS INC   201 W Oklahoma, Fairview, OK 73737,
Tel: (405) 227-3711
(Lift truck attachments, tractor sweepers, etc)
   Little Giant Products Ltd., 1196 Speers Rd., Oakville, Ont., Canada

ARTHUR D LITTLE INC   25 Acorn Park, Cambridge, MA 02140-2390,
Tel: (617) 864-5770
(Technology & mgmt consulting)
   Arthur D. Little of Canada Ltd., 67 Yonge St. #200, Toronto, Ont. M5E 1J8, Canada

LITTON INDUSTRIES INC   360 N Crescent Dr, Beverly Hills, CA 90210,
Tel: (213) 859-5000
(Elec sys, ind automation, resource explor)
   Kester Solder Co. of Canada Ltd., 1 Prince Charles, Brantford, Ont., Canada N3T 5N9
   Litton Systems Ltd., 25 City View Dr., Rexdale, Ont., Canada M9W 5A7
   Western Geophysical Co. of Canada Ltd., 530 71st Ave. SE, Calgary, Alta.,
   Canada T2H 1X6

LOCKHEED CORP   2555 N Hollywood Way, Burbank, CA 91520, Tel: (213) 847-6121
(Aircraft, missiles, etc)
   Lockheed Aircraft Corp. of Canada Ltd., 255 Albert St., Ottawa, Ont., Canada K1P 6A9

LOCKPORT FELT CO   Highway 12 West, Starkville, MS 39759, Tel: (601) 323-4064
(Papermakers' felts)
   Lockport-Pacific Ltd., Vancouver, B.C., Canada
   Lockport-Warwick Ltd., Warwick, Que., Canada

LONGYEAR CO   PO Box 27314, Salt Lake City, UT 84127, Tel: (801) 972-1395
(Mfr diamond drills, concrete cutting equip; drill serv)
   Canadian Longyear Ltd., P.O. Box 330, 1111 Main St. W., North Bay, Ont.,
      Canada P1B 8H6
   N. Morissette Diamond Drilling Ltd., P.O. Box 789, Haileybury, Ont., Canada P0J 1K0

LORAIN PRODUCTS CORP   122 F St, Lorain, OH 44052, Tel: (216) 288-1122
(Telecommun equip)
   Lorain Products Ltd., 122 Edward St., St. Thomas, Ont., Canada

LORD & BURNHAM DIV   2 Main St, Irvington, NY 10533, Tel: (914) 591-8800
(Glass & plastic enclosures, greenhouses)
   Lord & Burnham, 325 Welland Ave., St. Catharines, Ont., Canada

LOUISIANA LAND & EXPLORATION CO   PO Box 60350, 909 Poydras St, New Orleans,
LA 70160, Tel: (504) 566-6500
(Oil & gas explor)
   Candex Development Ltd., Calgary, Alta., Canada
   LL&E Canada Ltd., Calgary, Alta., Canada

LOUISIANA-PACIFIC CORP   111 SW 6th Ave, Portland, OR 97204,
Tel: (503) 221-0800
(Mfr lumber & lumber prdts)
   Louisiana-Pacific Canada, Ltd., Pulp Mill, PO Box 900, Chetwynd, BC V0C 1J0, Canada

THE LOVABLE CO   2121 Peachtree Ind Blvd, Buford, GA 30518,
Tel: (404) 945-2171
(Mfr women's undergarments)
   Lovable Brassiere Co. Ltd., 590 King St. W, Toronto, Ont., Canada

LTV ENERGY PRODUCTS CO   2441 Forest Lane, Garland, TX 75042,
Tel: (214) 487-3000
(Mfr tubular gds, mach, & supplies for drilling; oil & gas inds servs)
   LTV Energy Products, Ltd., PO Box 4012, Station C, Calgary, Alberta T2T 5V2, Canada

LUBRIZOL CORP   29400 Lakeland Blvd, Wickliffe, OH 44092, Tel: (216) 943-4200
(Chem additives for lubricants & fuels)
   Lubrizol of Canada Ltd., 1800 Thorold Stone Rd., Niagara Falls, Ont., Canada

LUKENS STEEL CO   Coatesville, PA 19320, Tel: (215) 383-2000
(Plate steel & plate steel prdts)
   Canadian Lukens Ltd., 50 Taber Rd., Rexdale, Ont., Canada

LUMMUS CREST   1515 Broad St, Bloomfield, NJ 07003, Tel: (201) 893-1515
(Engr & constr)
   Lummus Canada, 6715 Airport Rd., Mississauga, Ont. L4V 1V9, Canada

M&T CHEMICALS INC   PO Box 1104, Rahway, NJ 07065, Tel: (201) 499-0200
(Specialty chems & application technologies)
   M&T Chemicals Ltd., 670 Strathearne Ave. N, Hamilton, Ont., Canada L8H 7N7

MAGNETIC METALS CORP   Box 351, Camden, NJ 08105, Tel: (609) 964-7842
  (Magnetic alloys, shields; lamina- tions & special stampings)
    Magnetic Metals of Canada Ltd., 10 Spaulding Dr., Brantford, Ont., Canada

MAGNETROL INTERNATIONAL   5300 Belmont Rd, Downers Grove, IL 60515-4499,
  Tel: (708) 969-4000
  (Mfr level & flow process instru)
    Magnetrol Intl., Ltd., 6291-18 Dorman Rd., Mississagua, Ontario L4V 1H2, Canada

MAINE PUBLIC SERVICE CO   209 State St, Presque Isle, ME 04769,
  Tel: (207) 768-5811
  (Electricity)
    Maine & New Brunswick Electrical Power Co. Ltd., Aroostook Junction, N.B., Canada

MALLINCKRODT INC   675 McDonnell Blvd, PO Box 5840, St Louis, MO 63134,
  Tel: (314) 895-2012
  (Med/ind chems, organics, pharms)
    Bowers Printing Inc. Co. of Canada Ltd., Montreal, Que., Canada
    Bowers Printing Inc. Co. of Canada Ltd., Vancouver,13.C., Canada
    Bowers Printing Inc. Co. of Canada Ltd., Toronto, Ont., Canada
    Fries & Fries Ltd., Toronto, Ont., Canada
    Mallinckrodt Canada Inc., Pointe Claire, Que., Canada

MANPOWER INC   5301 N Ironwood Rd, PO Box 2053, Milwaukee, WI 53201-2053,
  Tel: (414) 961-1000
  (Temporary help)
    Manpower Services Ltd., P.O. Box 370, Station F, 980 Yonge St., Toronto, Ont.,
      Canada M4Y 2L8

MANVILLE CORP   PO Box 5108, Denver, CO 80217-5108, Tel: (303) 978-2000
  (Mfr fiber glass prdts, paper & forest prdts, roofing & insulation material, ind
  minerals)
    Manville-Canada Ltd., 295 The West Mall, Etobicoke, Ont., Canada M9C 4Z7

MAREMONT CORP   250 E Kehoe Blvd, Carol Stream, IL 60188, Tel: (312) 861-4000
  (Mfr automotive parts: mufflers, exhaust pipes, shock absorbers)
    Goderich Steel & Tube Co. Ltd., 89 Mills Rd., Ajax, Ont., Canada
    Van Der Hout Assoc. Ltd., 3600 Lake Shore Blvd., Toronto, Ont., Canada M8W 1N8

MARKEM CORP   150 Congress St, Keene, NH 03431, Tel: (603) 352-1130
  (Marking and printing mach; hot stamping foils)
    Markem Products Ltd., 149 Manitou Dr., Kitchener, Ont., Canada N2C 1L4

MARLEY CO   1900 Johnson Dr, Mission Woods, KS 66205, Tel: (913) 362-5440
  (Cooling & heating towers, waste treatment sys)
    Ajax Engineers Ltd., Acton, Ont., Canada
    Marley Canadian Ltd., 260 Merton, Toronto, Ont., Canada

MARSH INSTRUMENT CO   PO Box 1011, Skokie, IL 60076, Tel: (708) 673-4300
  (Pressure gauges, valves, etc)
    Marsh Instrument & Valve Co. Ltd., 8407 103rd St., Edmonton, Alta., Canada

MARSTELLER INTL   1 E Wacker Dr, Chicago, IL 60601, Tel: (312) 329-1100
  (Advertising, marketing research, sales promotion)
    Burson-Marsteller, 1155 Blvd. Dorchester W, Montreal, Que., Canada H3B 3T6
    Burson-Marsteller, 80 Bloor St. W, Toronto, Ont., Canada M5S 2V1

J B MARTIN CO   10 E 53rd St, #3100, New York, NY 10022, Tel: (212) 421-2020
(Mfr velvets)
    J.B. Martin Canada Ltd., 445 Rue St. Jacques, St. Jean, Que., Canada J3B QM1

MARTIN MARIETTA CORP   6801 Rockledge Dr, Bethesda, MD 20817,
Tel: (301) 897-6000
(Design/mfr/mgmt of sys in fields of space, defense, energy, electronics, commun)
    Martin Marietta Canada Ltd., 50 O'Connor St., Ottawa, Ont., Canada K1P 6L2

MARTIN MARIETTA DATA SYSTEMS   PO Box 2392, Princeton, NJ 08540,
Tel: (609) 799-2600
(Computer softward, computing & professional serv)
    Mathematica Canada Ltd., 300 Fifth Ave. SW, Ste 2050, Calgary, Alta., Canada T2P 3C4
    Mathematica Canada Ltd., 100 Alexis Nihon Blvd., St. Laurent, Que., Canada H4M 2P4
    Mathematica Canada Ltd., 106 Colonnade Rd., Ste. 220, Nepean, Ont., Canada K2E 7P4
    Mathematica Canada Ltd., 5915 Airport Rd., Mississauga, Ont., Canada L4V 1T1

MARTIN-DECKER CO   1200 Cypress Creek Rd, Cedar Park, TX 78613,
Tel: (512) 331-0411
(Oilfield & ind weight & meas sys)
    Martin-Decker (Canada), 9835 42nd Ave., Edmonton, Alta., Canada T63 0A3

MARY KAY COSMETICS INC   8787 Stemmons Fwy, Dallas, TX 75247,
Tel: (214) 630-8787
(Cosmetics & toiletries)
    Mary Kay Cosmetics Inc., 5600 Ambler Dr., Mississauga, Ont., Canada L4W 2K2

MASCO CORP   21001 Van Born Rd, Taylor, MI 48180, Tel: (313) 274-7400
(Mfr building, energy, cold extruded prdts)
    Auto-Flo Corp of Canada Ltd., Windsor, Ont., Canada
    Delta Faucet Corp. of Canada Ltd., Windsor, Ont., Canada

MASONEILAN DIV   275 Turnpike St, Canton, MA 02021, Tel: (617) 821-5100
(Mfr control, safety & safety relief valves)
    Masoneilan, Burlington, Ont., Canada

MATHESON GAS PRODUCTS   30 Seaview Dr, Secaucus, NJ 07073, Tel: (201) 867-4100
(Specialty gases & equip)
    Matheson Gas Products Canada, P.O. Box 89, Whitby, Ont., Canada

MATTEL INC   5150 Rosecrans Ave, Hawthorne, CA 90250, Tel: (213) 644-0411
(Toys, dolls, games, crafts & hobbies)
    Mattel Canada Ltd., Box 902, Station U, Toronto, Ont., Canada M8Z 5R5

GEORGE S MAY INTL CO   303 S Northwest Hwy, Park Ridge, IL 60068-4255,
Tel: (708) 825-8806
(Mgmt consulting)
    George S May Intl. Co. - Canada, 615 Rene Levesque #1100, Montreal, Que.,
    Canada H3B 1PS

MAYFRAN INC   PO Box 43038, Cleveland, OH 44143, Tel: (216) 461-4100
(Conveyors for metal working & refuse)
    Mayfran Canada Ltd., 5955 Airport Rd., Mississauga, Ont., Canada L4V 1R9

MEAD CORP   Courthouse Plaza, NE, Dayton, OH 45463, Tel: (513) 222-6323
(Mfr paper, packaging, pulp, lumber & other wood prdts, school & office prdts; electr
pub, distri)

Dataline Inc., 67 Richmond St. W., Toronto, Ont., Canada M5H 1Z57
Packagemaster Ltd., 281 Fairall St., Ajax, Ont., Canada

MEASUREX CORP   One Results Way, Cupertino, CA 95014, Tel: (408) 255-1500
  (Mfr computer integrated mfg sys)
     Measurex Inc., 981 Pierre Dupuy St., Longueuil, Que., Canada J4K 1A1
     Measurex Inc., 20216 Fraser Hwy., Langley, B.C., Canada V3A 4E6
     Measurex Inc., 2180 Steeles Ave. W., Concord, Ont., Canada L4K 2Z5
     Measurex Inc., 1000 de Serigny St., Longueuil, Que., Canada J4K 5B1
     Measurex Inc., Div. MSD, 75 Hymus Blvd., Point Claire, Que, Canada H9R 1E2
     Measurex Sales & Service, 100 de Serigny St., Longueuil, Que., Canada J4K 5B1

MEDTRONIC INC   7000 Central Ave, NE, Minneapolis, MN 55432,
  Tel: (612) 574-4000
  (Mfr med devices, med serv)
     Medtronic of Canada Ltd., 6733 Kitimat Rd., Mississauga, Ont., Canada L5N 1W3

MELLON BANK NA   One Mellon Bank Center, Pittsburgh, PA 15258,
  Tel: (412) 234-5016
  (Commercial & trade banking, foreign exchange)
     Mellon Bank Canada, One First Canadian Pl., Toronto, Ont., Canada M5X 1A4

MEMOREX CORP   San Thomas at Central Expressway, Santa Clara, CA 95052,
  Tel: (408) 987-1000
  (Magnetic recording tapes, etc)
     Memcrex Canada Ltd., 230 Lesmill Rd., Don Mills, Ont., Canada M3B 2T5

MENNEN CO   Morristown, NJ 07960, Tel: (201) 631-9000
  (Health & beauty aids)
     Mennen Canada Inc., 6400 Northwest Dr., Mississauga, Ont., Canada L4V 1K1

MENTHOLATUM CO   1360 Niagara St, Buffalo, NY 14213, Tel: (716) 882-7660
  (Proprietary medicines, drugs)
     The Mentholatum Co. of Canada Ltd., 20 Lewis St., Fort Erie, Ont., Canada L7A 5M6

MERCK SHARP & DOHME INTL   PO Box 2000, Rahway, NJ 07065, Tel: (201) 574-4000
  (Pharms, chems & biologicals)
     Merck, Sharp & Dohme of Canada Ltd., 16701 Trans-Canada Hwy., Kirkland, Que.,
     Canada H9H 3L1

MERISEL INC   200 Continental Blvd, El Segundo, CA 90245, Tel: (213) 615-3080
  (Distr software & hardware)
     Merisel-Canada, 731 Millway Ave., Concord, Ontario L4K 3S8, Canada

MERLE NORMAN COSMETICS INC   9130 Bellance Ave, Los Angeles, CA 90045,
  Tel: (213) 641-3000
  (Cosmetics)
     Merle Norman Cosmetics (Canada) Ltd., 346 Orenda, Bramalea, Ont., Canada

METAL IMPROVEMENT CO   10 Forest Ave, Paramus, NJ 07652, Tel: (201) 843-7800
  (Shot peening)
     Metal Improvement Co., 105 Alfred Kuehne Blvd., Brampton, Ont., Canada L6T 4K3

METALLURG INC   25 E 39th St, New York, NY 10016, Tel: (212) 686-4010
  (Mfr ferrous & nonferrous alloys & metals)
     Metallurg (Canada) Ltd., 40 University Ave. #1066, Toronto, Ont. M5J 1T1, Canada

METCO DIV OF PERKIN-ELMER   1101 Prospect Ave, Westbury, NY 11590,
  Tel: (516) 334-1300
  (Mfr/serv thermal spray coating equip & supplies)
    Metco Canada Div., 7956 Torbram Rd., Unit 9, Brampton, Ont., Canada L6T 4M1

METROPOLITAN LIFE INSURANCE CO   1 Madison Ave, New York, NY 10010,
  Tel: (212) 578-2211
  (Insurance)
    Metropolitan Life Insurance Co., 99 Bank St., Ottawa, Ont., Canada K1P 5A3

MGM/UA COMMUNICATIONS CO   10000 W Washington Blvd, Culver City, CA 90230,
  Tel: (213) 280-6000
  (Motion picture, home video & pay TV prod & distr)
    MGM/UA Communications Co., 45 Charles St. E., Toronto, Ont., Canada M4Y 1S2
    MGM/UA Communications Co., 3015 12th St. NE #230, Hampshire Ct., Calgary,
      Alta. T2E 7J2, Canada
    MGM/UA Communications Co., 3290 Cavendish Blvd., Montreal, Que., Canada H4B 2M7
    MGM/UA Communications Co., 720 King St. W., #611, Toronto, Ont. M5V 2T3, Canada

MID-WEST ABRASIVE DIV   510 S Washington St, Owosso, MI 48867,
  Tel: (517) 725-7161
  (Honing stones, bonded coated abrasives, etc)
    Mid-West Abrasive Co., 620 Albert St., Strathroy, Ont., Canada

MIDLAND-ROSS CORP   20600 Chagrin Blvd, Cleveland, OH 44122,
  Tel: (216) 491-8400
  (Thermal processing sys, steelcast- ings, elect pdts, mech controls)
    Midland-Ross of Canada Ltd., 304 St. Patrick St., La Salle, Que., Canada
    Robotron of Canada Ltd., Malden Rd., Windsor, Ont., Canada N9C 3Z1

MILCHEM INC   3900 Essex Lane, PO Box 22111, Houston, TX 77027,
  Tel: (214) 439-8000
  (Gas & oil well drilling fluids & chem additives)
    Milchem Canada Ltd., 102 Century Sq III, 309 Second Ave. SW, Calgary, Alta., Canada

HERMAN MILLER INC   8500 Byron Rd, Zeeland, MI 49464, Tel: (616) 772-3300
  (Office furnishings)
    Herman Miller Canada Ltd., 2360 Argentia Rd., Mississauga, Ont., Canada L5N 4G9

MILLIPORE CORP   Ashley Rd, Bedford, MA 01730, Tel: (617) 275-9205
  (Precision filters)
    Millipore Ltd., 3688 Nashua Dr., Mississauga, Ont., Canada L4V 1M5

MINE SAFETY APPLIANCES CO   PO Box 426, Pittsburgh, PA 15230,
  Tel: (421) 273 5000
  (Safety equip, ind filters)
    Mine Safety Appliances Co. of Canada Ltd., 148 Norfinch Dr., Downsview, Ont.,
      Canada M3N 1X8

MMOS INC   15219 Michigan Ave, Dearborn, MI 48126, Tel: (313) 582-9480
  (Marine accessories)
    M.M.O.S. Inc., 250 St. Helen's Ave., Toronto, Ont., Canada M6H 4A4

MOBIL CORP   150 E 42nd St, New York, NY 10017, Tel: (212) 883-4242
  (Petroleum explor, prdts)
    Mobil Chemical Canada Ltd., Chemical Coatings Div., P.O. Box 200, West Hill, Ont.,
      Canada

Mobil Chemical Canada Ltd., Plastics Div., 321 University Ave., Belleville, Ont.,
    Canada K8M 5A2
Mobil Paint Co., 645 Coronation Dr., West Hill, Ont., Canada

MOEN INC   377 Woodland Ave, Elyria, OH 44036, Tel: (216) 323-3341
    (Diesel fuel sys, hydraulic tappets, plumbing prdts)
    Moen Inc., 1677 Aimco Blvd., Mississauga, Ont. L4W 1H7, Canada

MOGUL CORP   PO Box 200, Chagrin Falls, OH 44022, Tel: (216) 247-5000
    (Water treatment chems, equip)
    Mogul Canada, 2065 Dundas St. E., Unit 105, Mississauga, Ont., Canada L4X 2W1

MOHAWK RUBBER CO   2560 W Market St, Akron, OH 44313, Tel: (216) 666-8177
    (Mfr tires, tubes, rubber prdts)
    MTR Inc., Toronto, Ont., Canada

MONARCH MARKING SYSTEM INC   PO Box 608, Dayton, OH 45401, Tel: (513) 865-2123
    (Marking devices, tickets, tags)
    Monarch Marking Systems Ltd., 895 Brock Rd., Pickering, Ont., Canada L1W 3C1

MONMOUTH PLASTICS INC   PO Box 921, Asbury Park, NJ 07712, Tel: (201) 775-5100
    (Flame retardant concentrates, thermoplastic sys, spec formulations)
    Shuman Plastics, 115 Main St., Hamilton, Ont., Canada

MONSANTO CO   800 N Lindbergh Blvd, St Louis, MO 63167, Tel: (314) 694-1000
    (Mfr chem & agric prdts, pharms, ind process equip, man-made fibers, plastics)
    Monsanto Canada Inc., Box 787, Streetsville Postal Station, Mississauga, Ont.,
        Canada L5M 2G4

MONTANA POWER CO   40 E Broadway, Butte, MT 59701, Tel: (406) 723-5421
    (Energy, mining, telecommun, electronics, waste mgmt)
    Altana Exploration Co., 520 Britannia Bldg., 703 6th Ave. SW, Calgary, Alta.,
        Canada T2P 0T9
    Canadian Montana Gas Co. Ltd., (same address)
    Canadian Montana Pipeline Co., (same address)
    Intercontinental Energy Corp., (same address)

MONTGOMERY ELEVATOR CO   30 20th St, Moline, IL 61265, Tel: (309) 764-6771
    (Mfr/install elevators & escalators)
    Montgomery Elevator Ltd., 150 E. Cordova, Vancouver, B.C., Canada

MOORE PRODUCTS CO   Summeytown Pike, Spring House, PA 19477,
    Tel: (215) 646-7400
    (Mfr process control instru)
    Moore Instruments Ltd/Ltee., P.O. Box 370, Brampton, Ont., Canada L6V 2L3

MORGAN ADHESIVES CO   4260 Darrow Rd, Stow, OH 44224, Tel: (216) 688-1111
    (Self-adhesive print stock & emblem materials)
    Morgan Adhesives of Canada Ltd., 101 Kennedy Rd., Brampton, Ont., Canada

MORRISON KNUDSEN CORP   1 Morrison Knudsen Plaza, PO Box 73, Boise, ID 83707,
    Tel: (208) 386-5000
    (Design, procurement, constr)
    Northern Construction Co. Ltd., 1304 Hornby St., Vancouver, B.C., Canada V6Z 1W6

MORTON INTERNATIONAL INC   100 N Riverside Plaza, Chicago, IL 60606,
Tel: (312) 807-2000
(Mfr adhesives, coatings, finishes, spec chems, advanced & electr materials, auto safety prdts)
    Morton Intl. Ltd., 430 Finley Ave., P.O. Box 100, Ajax, Ont. L1S 3C2, Canada
    Morton Intl. Ltd., 5800 Ambler Dr., Unit 105, Mississauga, Ont. L4W 4J4, Canada

MOSLER INC   1561 Grand Blvd, Hamilton, OH 45012, Tel: (513) 867-4000
(Mfr security prdts, sys, & servs to fin, coml, & govt mkt)
    Mosler Canada, 280 Brittannia Rd. East, Mississauga, Ontario L4Z 1S6, Canada

MOTOROLA COMPUTER SYSTEMS DIV   10700 N De Anza Blvd, Cupertino, CA 95014,
Tel: (408) 255-0900
(Mfr computer sys)
    Motorola Information Systems Ltd., 9445 Airport Rd., Brampton, Ontario L6S 4J3, Canada

MOTOROLA INC   1303 E Algonquin Rd, Schaumburg, IL 60196, Tel: (708) 397-5000
(Mfr commun equip, semiconductors, cellular phones)
    Mobile Data Intl. Inc., 11411 Number Five Rd., Richmond, BC, Canada V7A 423
    Motorola Canada Ltd., 4000 Victoria Park Ave., North York, Ont., Canada M2H 3P4

MUELLER BRASS CO   1925 Lapeer Ave, Port Huron, MI 48060, Tel: (313) 987-4000
(Mfr plumbing/heating prdts, refrig/A/C components, copper/copper alloy, metal forgings & extrusions)
    Streamline Copper & Brass Ltd., 290 Ellor St., P.O. Box 5003, Strathray, Ont., Canada N7G 3J3

MULTIGRAPHICS DIV   1800 W Central Rd, Mt Prospect, IL 60056,
Tel: (708) 398-1900
(Offset duplicating & graphic commun sys)
    AM Intl. Inc., 165 Milner Ave., Scarborough, Ont., Canada M1S 4G7

F E MYERS & CO   400 Orange St, Ashland, OH 44805, Tel: (419) 322-1544
(Pumps, water sys)
    The F.E. Myers Co., 808 Courtland Ave., Kitchener, Ont., Canada

MYERS TIRE SUPPLY INTL   1293 South Main St, Akron, OH 44301,
Tel: (216) 253-5592
(Mfr polymer & metal prdts for mat handling, automotive & constr inds)
    Eastern Tire Equipment & Supplies, 2807 Rue Botham, Ville St. Laurent, Montreal, Quebec, Canada
    Myers Tire Supply (Canada) Ltd., 517 McCormick Blvd., London, Ontario H5W 4C8, Canada

MacDERMID INC   245 Freight St, Waterbury, CT 06702, Tel: (203) 575-5700
(Chem processing for metal ind, plastics, electronics cleaners, strippers)
    MacDermid Chemicals Inc., 1275 Crestlawn Dr., Mississauga, Ont., Canada L4W 1W2
    MacDermid Chemicals Inc., 2737 Louis A. Amos St., Lachine, Que., Canada H8T 1C3

McCALL PATTERN CO   230 Park Ave, New York, NY 10017, Tel: (212) 880-2899
(Fashion patterns)
    McCall Pattern Co., 1406 Birchmount Rd., Scarborough, Ont., Canada

McCANN-ERICKSON WORLDWIDE   750 Third Ave, New York, NY 10017,
Tel: (212) 697-6000
(Advertising)

Foster/McCann-Erickson, 40 St. Clair Ave. W., Toronto, Ont., Canada M4V 1M6
McCann-Erickson Adv. of Canada Ltd., 10 Bay St., Toronto, Ont. Canada M5S 1S8
McCann-Erickson Adv. of Canada Ltd., other locations in Canada

McCORMICK & CO INC   11350 McCormick Rd, Hunt Valley, MD 21031,
Tel: (301) 771-7301
(Seasons, flavorings, specialty foods)
Club House Foods Inc., London, Ont., Canada
Stange Canada Inc., Mississauga, Ont., Canada

McDONNELL DOUGLAS CORP   Box 516, St Louis, MO 63166, Tel: (314) 232-0232
(Military & comm aircraft, space vehicles, electronics, missiles, data processing)
McDonnell Douglas Canada Ltd., P.O. Box 6013, Toronto, Ont., Canada L5P 1B7

McGRAW-HILL INC   1221 Ave of the Americas, New York, NY 10020,
Tel: (212) 512-2000
(Books, magazines, info sys, financial serv, b/cast operations)
DRI of Canada, Nu-West Center, 80 Bloor St. W., Toronto, Ont., Canada M5S 2V1
McGraw-Hill Ryerson Ltd., 330 Progress Ave., Scarborough, Ont., Canada M1P 2Z5

McKINSEY & CO INC   55 E 52nd St, New York, NY 10022, Tel: (212) 909-8400
(Mgmt consultants)
McKinsey & Co. Inc., Nu-West Center, 80 Bloor St. W, Toronto, Ontario,
Canada M5S 2V1

NABISCO BRANDS INC   Nabisco Brands Plaza, East Hanover, NJ 07936,
Tel: (201) 503-2000
(Mfr food prdts)
Standard Brands Ltd. (Canada), 1 Dundas St. W, Toronto, Ont., Canada M5G 2A9

NALCO CHEMICAL CO   One Nalco Center, Naperville, IL 60566-1024,
Tel: (708) 305-1000
(Chems for water & waste water treatment, oil prod & refining, ind processes;
water/energy mgmt serv)
Alchem Inc., P.O. Box 5002, Burlington, Ont., Canada L7R 3Y9

NALLEY'S FINE FOODS INC   3303 S 35th St W, Tacoma, WA 98411,
Tel: (206) 383-1621
(Mfr food prdts)
Nalley's Ltd., 1330 E. 66th St., Vancouver, B.C., Canada

NASH MFG CO   PO Box 296, Long Branch, NJ 07740, Tel: (201) 222-6200
(Aluminum awnings, doors, etc)
Nash Aluminum Ltd., 95 Athol St., Oshawa, Ont., Canada

NASHUA CORP   44 Franklin St, Nashua, NH 03061, Tel: (603) 880-2323
(Mfr/distr/serv office copier sys & supplies)
Nashua Canada, 3755 Hickmore, Ville St. Laurent, Que. H4T 155, Canada
Nashua Canada Ltd., 195 The West Mall, #900, Toronto, Ont. M9C 5K1, Canada
Nashua Canada Ltd., 349 Evans Ave., Toronto, Ont. M8Z 1K3, Canada
Nashua Photo Products, 209 Ave. D South, Saskatoon, Sask., Canada

NATCO   PO Box 1710, Tulsa, OK 74101, Tel: (918) 663-9100
(Mfr/sale/serv oil & gas prdts)
NATCO Canada, P.O. Box 850, Station T, Calgary, Alta., Canada T2H 2H3

NATIONAL BANK OF DETROIT   611 Woodward, PO Box 116, Detroit, MI 48232,
 Tel: (313) 225-1000
 (Banking)
    National Bank of Detroit, Canada, Royal Bank Plaza, North Tower Suite 1601,
      P.O. Box 112, Toronto, Ont. M5J 2J3, Canada

NATIONAL BANNER CO   11938 Harry Hines Blvd, Dallas, TX 95234,
 Tel: (214) 241-2131
 (Banners, pennants, flags, etc)
    National Banner Co. Inc., 120 Judge Rd., Toronto, Ont., Canada

NATIONAL CAR RENTAL SYSTEM INC   7700 France Ave S, Minneapolis, MN 55435,
 Tel: (612) 830-2121
 (Car rental)
    Tilden Car Rental, 1485 Stanley St., Montreal, Que., Canada H3A 1P6

NATIONAL DATA CORP   National Data Plaza, Atlanta, GA 30329,
 Tel: (404) 728-2000
 (Provider of info & transaction serv to fin, retail, health care & commun sectors)
    National Data Corp. of Canada Ltd., 1 Concorde Gate #700, Don Mills, Ont. M3C 3N6,
      Canada

NATIONAL ELECTRIC COIL DIV   11510 S Alameda St, Los Angeles, CA 90059,
 Tel: (614) 459-1200
 (Electric coils, lifting magnets)
    National Electric Coil Div., McGraw-Edison of Canada Ltd., St. John's- Que., Canada

NATIONAL GYPSUM CO   4500 Lincoln Plaza, Dallas, TX 75201, Tel: (214) 740-4500
 (Building prdts & servs)
    The Austin Co. Ltd., Toronto, Ont., Canada

NATIONAL KINNEY CORP   60 Madison Ave, New York, NY 10010, Tel: (212) 683-9191
 (Real estate devel, bldg components & supplies)
    Jespersen-Kay Systems Ltd., 109 Railside, Don Mills, Ont., Canada

NAVISTAR INTL CORP   455 N Cityfront Plaza Dr, Chicago, IL 60611,
 Tel: (312) 836-2000
 (Mfr medium & heavy trucks, diesel engines)
    Navistar Intl. Corp. Canada, 120 King St W., Hamilton, Ont., Canada L8N 3S5

NCR CORP   1700 S Patterson Blvd, Dayton, OH 45479, Tel: (513) 445-2000
 (Develop/mfr/sell/serv business info processing sys)
    NCR Canada Ltd., 6865 Century Ave., Mississauga, Ont., Canada L5N 2E2

NEW YORK AIR BRAKE CO   Starbuck Ave, Watertown, NY 13601, Tel: (315) 782-7000
 (Hydraulic pumps)
    The New York Air Brake Co. Ltd., 25 Shaft Rd., Rexdale, Ont., Canada

NEW YORK LIFE INSURANCE CO   51 Madison Ave, New York, NY 10010,
 Tel: (212) 576-7000
 (Insurance)
    New York Li&e Insurance Co., 443 University Ave., Toronto, Ont., Canada

NEWCOR INC   3270 W Big Beaver Rd, Troy, MI 48084, Tel: (313) 643-7730
 (Mfr spec mach & precision parts)
    Newcor Canada Ltd., P.O. Box 129, Windsor, Ont., Canada N9A 6K1

THE NEWELL CO   29 E Stephenson St, Freeport, IL 61032, Tel: (815) 235-4171
  (Mfr hdwe & housewares)
    Newell Industries Canada Inc., 387 Bloor East, #202, Toronto, Ont. M4W 1H7, Canada

NIAGARA MOHAWK POWER CORP   300 Erie Blvd West, Syracuse, NY 13202,
  Tel: (315) 474-1511
  (Electricity & gas utility)
    Opinac Exploration Ltd., Suite 1000, 530 Eighth Ave. SW, Calgary,
    Alta. T2P 3S8 Canada

NIAGARA THERAPY MFG CORP   Adamsville, PA 16110, Tel: (412) 932-7131
  (Electrical massage equip)
    Monarch Massage Equipment Ltd., P.O. Box 1969, Fort Erie, Ont., Canada

NICOLET INSTRUMENT CORP   5225 Verona Rd, Madison, WI 53711-4495,
  Tel: (608) 271-3333
  (Mfr infrared spectrometers, oscilloscopes, med electro-diag equip)
    Nicolet Instrument Canada Inc., 1-1200 Aerowood Dr., Mississauga, Ont.,
    Canada L4W 2S7

A C NIELSEN CO   Nielsen Plaza, Northbrook, IL 60062, Tel: (708) 498-6300
  (Marketing research)
    A.C. Nielsen Co. of Canada Ltd., 160 McNabb St., Markham, Ont., Canada L3R 4B8
    A.C. Nielsen Co. of Canada Ltd., 100 Alexis Nihon Blvd., St. Laurent, Que.,
    Canada H4M 2N7
    A.C. Nielsen Co. of Canada Ltd., 6011 Westminster Hwy., Richmond, BC, Canada V7C 4V4
    A.C. Nielsen Co. of Canada Ltd., 661 Millidge Ave., St.John, NB, Canada E2L 4A5
    A.C. Nielsen Co. of Canada Ltd., 925 7th Ave. SW, Calgary, Alta., Canada T1P 1A5

NOMA INTERNATIONAL INC   7400 W Industrial Dr, Forest Park, IL 60130,
  Tel: (708) 771-9400
  (Mfr decorative Christmas & patio lighting)
    Noma Industries, 4211 Yonge St., Willowdale, Ont. M2P 2A9, Canada

NORDSON CORP   28601 Clemens Rd, Westlake, OH 44145, Tel: (216) 892-1580
  (Mfr ind application equip & packaging mach)
    Nordson Canada Ltd., 849 Progress Ave., Scarborough, Ont., Canada M1H 2X4
    Nordson Canada Ltd., 2670 Rue Paulus, Ville St. Laurent, Que. H4S 1G1, Canada

NORRIS FLOW PRODUCTS   PO Box 1739, Tulsa, OK 74112, Tel: (918) 584-4241
  (Mfr butterfly valves, fittings, plugs)
    W.C. Norris Co. Ltd., Edmonton, Alta., Canada

NORRIS INDUSTRIES INC   1 Golden Shore, Long Beaah, CA 90802,
  Tel: (213) 435-6676
  (Bldg prdts, hdwe, vehicular components, military prdts)
    The Fyer-Fyter Co. of Canada, 19 Victoria Crescent, Bramalea, Ont., Canada
    Weiser Lock Co. Ltd., Burnaby, B.C., Canada

NORTEK INC   50 Kennedy Plaza, Providence, RI 02903, Tel: (401) 751-1600
  (Mfr residential & coml bldg prdts)
    Broan, Ltd., 1140 Tristar Dr., Mississauga, Ontario, Canada

NORTH AMERICAN REFRACTORIES CO   1228 Euclid Ave, Cleveland, OH 44115-1809,
  Tel: (216) 621-5200
  (Mfr firebrick, refractories)
    North American Refractories Co., P.O. Box 339, Caledonia, Ont., Canada

NORTH AMERICAN VAN LINES INC   5001 US 30 West, Fort Wayne, IN 46818,
  Tel: (219) 429-2511
  (Household goods movers, trucking, frt forwarding, brokerage serv)
    North American Van Lines Ltd., 1150 Champlain Ct., Whitby, Ont., Canada L1N 6A8

NORTH LILY MINING CO   1111 Bayhill Dr, #210, San Bruno, CA 94066-3035,
  Tel: (415) 742-0133
  (Mining gold & silver)
    International Mahogany Corp, #2470-609 Howe St., Vancouver, Canada

NORTHERN ENGINEERING CORP   210 Chene St, Detroit, MI 48207,
  Tel: (313) 259-3280
  (Cranes & hoists)
    Northern Crane & Hoist Works Ltd., 1428 Argyle Rd., Windsor, Ont., Canada

NORTHERN TELECOM SYSTEMS CORP   PO Box 1222, Minneapolis, MN 55440,
  Tel: (612) 932-8000
  (Remote information processing sys)
    Northern Telecom Systems Ltd., 4 Place du Commerce, Nun's Island, Verdun, Que.,
      Canada H3E 1J4

NORTON CO   1 New Bond St, Worcester, MA 01606, Tel: (508) 795-5000
  (Abrasives, drill bits, constr & safety prdts, plastics)
    Canadian Koebel Diamond Tools Ltd., 1 Towns Rd., Toronto, Ont., Canada M8Z 1A2
    Christiansen Diamond Products (Canada) Ltd., 16230-112 Ave., Edmonton, Alta., Canada
    Norton Chemical Process Products, 1170 Blair Rd., Burlington, Ont., Canada L7M 1K9
    Norton Co., P.O. Box 37, Cap-de-la Madeleine, Que., Canada
    Norton Co., 8001 Daly St., Niagara Falls, Ont., Canada
    Norton Co. of Canada Ltd., P.O. Box 908, Brantford, Ont., Canada
    Norton Co. of Canada Ltd., P.O. Box 3008, Station B, Hamilton, Ont., Canada
    Norton Research Corp. (Canada) Ltd., 8001 Daly St., Niagara Falls, Ont., Canada
    Norton Safety Products Ltd., 396 Humberline Dr., Rexdale, Ont., Canada
    Produits de Securite Norton (Que.) Ltee., Rachel St. E, Montreal, Que., Canada
    Produits de Securite Norton (Que.) Ltee., 551 Gabriel St., St. Tite, Que., Canada

NOXELL CORP   PO Box 1799, Baltimore, MD 21203, Tel: (301) 628-7300
  (Cosmetics, medications)
    Noxzema Chemical Co. of Canada Ltd., 77 Park Lawn, Toronto, Ont., Canada

NUMATICS INC   1450 N Milford Rd, Highland, MI 48031, Tel: (313) 887-4111
  (Mfr control valves & manifolds)
    Numatics Ltd., 363 Sovereign Rd., London, Ont. N6M 1A3, Canada

NUTONE INC   Madison at Red Bank Rd, Cincinnati, OH 45227, Tel: (513) 527-5100
  (Residential spec prdts, elec appliances)
    Nutone Electrical Mfg. Co. Ltd., 2 St. Lawrence Ave., Toronto, Ont., Canada M8Z 5T8

NVF CO   Yorklyn Rd, Yorklyn, DE 19736, Tel: (302) 239-5281
  (Metal containers, steel prdts, laminated plastics, papers)
    NFV Industries of Canada Ltd., Rexdale, Ont., Canada

OAKITE PRODUCTS INC   50 Valley Rd, Berkeley Heights, NJ 07922,
  Tel: (201) 464-6900
  (Mfr chem prdts for ind cleaning & metal treating)
    Oakite Products of Canada Ltd., 115 East Dr., Bramalea, Ont., Canada

OCCIDENTAL PETROLEUM CORP   10889 Wilshire Blvd, Los Angeles, CA 90024,
  Tel: (213) 879-1700
  (Petroleum & petroleum prdts, chems, plastics)
    Canadian Occidental Petroleum Ltd., 700 Fourth Ave. SW, Calgary, Alta.,
      Canada T2P 3T5

ODI   25 Mall Rd, Burlington, MA 01803, Tel: (617) 272-8040
  (Mgt & consul serv)
    ODI Canada, 45 St. Clair Ave. W.- #602, Toronto, Ontario M4V 1L3, Canada

C M OFFRAY & SON INC   Route #24, Box 601, Chester, NJ 07930-0601,
  Tel: (201) 879-4700
  (Mfr narrow fabrics)
    Offray Ribbon Canada Inc., 160 Maden St., Valleyfield, Que., Canada J6S 4V7

OFFSHORE NAVIGATION INC   PO Box 23504, 5728 Jefferson Hwy, Harahan,
  LA 70183, Tel: (504) 733-6790
  (Marine & airborne surveys, flight-following equip)
    Ocean Navigation Ltd., P.O. Box 5340, St. Johns, Newfoundland, Canada A1C 5W2
    Offshore Navigation (Canada) Ltd., P.O. Box 858, Calgary, Alta., Canada T2P 2J6

OGILVY & MATHER INC   2 E 48th St, New York, NY 10017, Tel: (212) 907-3400
  (Advertising agency)
    Ogilby & Mather (Canada) Ltd., 88 University Ave., Toronto, Ont., Canada M5J 1V5
    Ogilvy & Mather (Canada) Ltd., Place du Canada, Montreal, Ouebec, Canada H3B 2P6

OGLEBAY NORTON CO   1100 Superior Ave, Cleveland, OH 44114,
  Tel: (216) 861-3300
  (Raw materials & transport for steel, glass & oil industries; iron castings)
    Canadian Ferro Hot-Metal Specialties Ltd., 345 Stoney Creek, Ont., Canada L8E 2M6

OIL-DRI CORP OF AMERICA   520 N Michigan Ave, Chicago, IL 60611,
  Tel: (312) 321-1515
  (Oil & grease absorbants, soil conditioners, etc)
    Favorite Products Co., Laval, Que., Canada

OMARK INDUSTRIES INC   5550 SW Macadam Ave, Portland, OR 97201,
  Tel: (503) 796-1400
  (Mfr chain & accessories for chain saws, welding equip, power tools)
    KSM Canada Ltd., 425 Attwell Dr., Rexdale, Ont., Canada
    Omark Canada Ltd., 505 Edinburgh Rd. N., Guelph, Ont., Canada

ONAN CORP   1400 73rd Ave NE, Minneapolis, MN 55432, Tel: (612) 574-5000
  (Electric generators, ind engines & controls)
    Onan Americas Inc., Canadian Operations, P.O. Box 32146, Minneapolis, MN   55432

ORGANIZATIONAL DYNAMICS INC   5 Burlington Woods Dr, Burlington, MA 01803,
  Tel: (617) 272-8040
  (Quality/productivity consultants)
    Organizational Dynamics Inc., 130 Adelaide St. W., Toronto, Ont., Canada M5H 3P5

OTIS ELEVATOR CO   10 Farm Springs, Farmington, CT 06032, Tel: (203) 674-4047
  (Elevators & escalators)
    Otis Elevator Co. Ltd., 414 Victoria Ave. N, Hamilton, Ont., Canada L8N 3M 1

OUTBOARD MARINE CORP   100 Sea Horse Dr, Waukegan, IL 60085,
  Tel: (708) 689-6200
  (Outboard & rotary motors, stern engines, marine parts & accessories)
    Outboard Marine Canada, 910 Monaghan Rd., Peterborough, Ont. Canada K9J 7B6

OWENS-ILLINOIS INC   PO Box 1035, Toledo, OH 43666, Tel: (419) 247-5000
  (Glass & plastic containers, house- hold & ind prdts, packaging)
    Owens-lllinois of Canada Ltd., 50 Belfield Rd., Rexdale, Ont., Canada

PACIFIC GAS & ELECTRIC CO   77 Beale St, San Francisco, CA 94106,
  Tel: (415) 972-7000
  (Electric & natural gas serv)
    Alberta & Southern Gas Co. Ltd., West Tower, Esso Plaza, 425 1st St., Calgary,
    Alta., Canada
    Alberta Natural Gas Co. Ltd., East Tower, Esso Plaza, 425 1st St., Calgary, Alta.,
    Canada

PACKAGING CORP OF AMERICA   1603 Orrington Ave, Evanston, IL 60204,
  Tel: (708) 492-5713
  (Mfr custom packaging, aluminum & plastic molded fibre, corrugated containers)
    PCA Canada, 3471 McNicoll Ave., Scarborough, Ont. M1V 4B8, Canada

PALL CORP   30 Sea Cliff Ave, Glen Cove, NY 11542, Tel: (516) 671-4000
  (Filters & related fluid clarification equip)
    Pall (Canada) Ltd., 1380 California Ave., Brockville, Ont., Canada K6V 5Y6

PANALARM DIV   7401 N Hamlin Ave, Skokie, IL 60076, Tel: (708) 675-2500
  (Elec alarm sys, temp monitors, display sys, sensors)
    Ametek (Canada) Ltd., 3085 Lenworth Dr., Mississauga, Ont., Canada L4X 2G4

PANDUIT CORP   17301 Ridgeland Ave, Tinley Park, IL 60477, Tel: (708) 532-1800
  (Mfr elec/electr wiring comps)
    Panduit Canada Ltd., 140 Amber St., Markham, Ont., Canada L3R 358

PANELFOLD INC   10700 NW 36th Ave, Miami, FL 33167, Tel: (305) 688-3501
  (Mfr folding doors & partitions, operable & relocatable partition sys)
    Panelfold Doors S.A., Alemania 36-38, 08201 Sabadell (Barcelona), Spain

PANGBORN CO   Pangborn Blvd, PO Box 380, Hagerstown, MD 21740,
  Tel: (301) 739-3500
  (Blast cleaning sys)
    Pangborn CES Canada Ltd., 2345 Stanfield Rd., Mississauga, Ont., Canada L4Y 3Y3

PAPER NOVELTY MFG CO   200 Harvard Ave, Stamford, CT 06902,
  Tel: (203) 325-2671
  (Holiday decorations)
    Paper Novelty Mfg. Co. Ltd., 306 Front St. W, Toronto, Ont., Canada

PAPERCRAFT CORP   Papercraft Park, Pittsburgh, PA 15238, Tel: (412) 362-8000
  (Gift wrappings, greeting cards)
    Papercraft of Canada Ltd., 1440 Jules Poltras, Montreal, Que., Canada

PARK CHEMICAL CO   8074 Military Ave, Detroit, MI 48204, Tel: (213) 895-7215
  (Heat treating materials, automotive chems)
    Park Thermal Ltd., 62 Todd Rd., Georgetown, Ont., Canada

PARKER HANNIFIN CORP   17325 Euclid Ave, Cleveland, OH 44112,
   Tel: (216) 531-3000
   (Mfr motion-control prdts)
      Parker Hannefin Refrig. & Air Conditioning Group, 94 Union St., Beamsville,
         Ont. LOR 1B0, Canada
      Parker Hannifin Fluid Connectors Group, P.O. Box 158, Grimsby, Ont. L3M 4G4, Canada
      Parker Hannifin Fluidpower Group, 530 Kipling Ave., Toronto, Ont. M82 5E6, Canada
      Parker Hannifin Seal Group, 5935 Ambler Dr., Mississauga, Ont. L4W 2K2, Canada

PARKER PEN CO   One Parker Place, Janesville, WI 53545, Tel: (608) 755-7000
   (Writing instru, temporary help, leisure apparel & equip)
      Parker Pen Co. Ltd., 9 Codeco Ct., Don Mills, Ont., Canada

PARSONS & WHITTEMORE INC   666 Third Ave, New York, NY 10017,
   Tel: (212) 972-2000
   (Pulp & paper mfg, constr pulp & paper mills, engr)
      St. Anne Nackawic Pulp Co. Ltd., Main Rd., Nackawic, NB EOH 1P0, Canada
      St. Anne Pulp Sales Ltd., 250 Bloor St. E. #1420, Toronto, Ont. M4W 1E6, Canada

THE PEELLE CO   50 Inez Pathway, Bay Shore, NY 11706, Tel: (516) 231-6000
   (Elevator, fire & specially engineered doors)
      The Peelle Co. Ltd., Torbram Dr., Malton, Ont., Canada

PENNZOIL CO   PO Box 2967, Houston, TX 77001, Tel: (713) 546-4000
   (Producer, refiner, marketer of oil, natural gas, sulphur)
      Pennzoil Exploration & Production Co., MdFarlane Tower, 4th Ave. SW, Calgary,
         Alta., Canada T2P 3I4

PENTAIR INC   1700 West Hwy 36, St Paul, MN 55113, Tel: (612) 636-7920
   (Diversified manufacturer)
      Delta Intl. Machinery Corp., 644 Imperial Rd., Guelph, Ontario N1H 6M7, Canada
      F.E. Myers Co., 269 Trillium Dr., PO Box 38, Kitchener, Ontario N2G 3W9, Canada
      Lincoln Canada, 7017 Fir Tree Dr., Mississauga, Ontario L5S 1J7, Canada

PEPSICO FOOD SERVICE INTL   9111 E Douglas, Wichita, KS 67207,
   Tel: (316) 681-9793
   (Operates restaurants)
      PepsiCo Food Service Intl., 10 Four Seasons Place #500, Etobicoke, Ont. M9B 6H7,
         Canada

PEPSICO INC   700 Anderson Hill Rd, Purchase, NY 10577, Tel: (914) 253-2000
   (Beverages, food prdts & servs, sporting goods)
      Pepsi-Cola Canada Ltd., 9245 Blau Blvd., St. Leonard, Montreal, Que., Canada H1R 2V7
      Pepsi-Cola Canada Ltd., 1255 Bay St., Toronto, Ont., Canada M5R 2A9

PERKIN-ELMER CORP   761 Main Ave, Norwalk, CT 06859, Tel: (203) 762-1000
   (Analytical instru, computers, semiconductor prod equip, avionics, electro-optical
   sys, etc)
      Perkin-Elmer (Canada) Ltd., 10123 99th St., Edmonton, Alta., Canada T5J 3H1
      Perkin-Elmer (Canada) Ltd., 8250 Mountain Sights Ave., Montreal, Que.,
         Canada H4P 2B7
      Perkin-Elmer (Canada) Ltd., 335 MacLaren St., Ottawa, Ont., Canada K2P OM5
      Perkin-Elmer (Canada) Ltd., 120 Norfinch Dr., Downsview, Ont., Canada M3N 1X3
      Perkin-Elmer (Canada) Ltd., 310-10991 Shellbridge Way, Richmond, B.C.,
         Canada V6X 3C6
      Perkin-Elmer (Canada) Ltd., 1000 Windmill Rd., Dartmouth, N.S., Canada B3B 1L7

PET INC   400 S 4th St, St Louis, MO 63102, Tel: (314) 622-6358
(Process/mktg specialty foods)
   Van Kirk Chocolate Corp., Toronto, Ont., Canada
   Wm. Underwood Co. (Canada) Ltd., 190 Attwell Dr., Rexdale, Ont., Canada M9W 6H8

PETTIBONE CORP   5401 W Grand Ave, Chicago, IL 60631, Tel: (312) 399-1550
(Foundry equip, heavy mach, loaders, mining & crushing equip)
   Pettibone Canada Ltd., 1666 Shawson Dr. E., Mississauga, Ont., Canada

PFIZER INC   235 E 42nd St, New York, NY 10017, Tel: (212) 573-2323
(Mfr pharms, hosp prdts, chems, consumer & animal health prdts)
   Pfizer Canada Inc., P.O. Box 800, Pointe Claire/Dorval, Que. H9R 4V2, Canada

PHELPS DODGE CORP   2600 N Central Ave, Phoenix, AZ 85004-3014,
   Tel: (602) 234-8100
(Minerals, metals & spec engineered prdts for trans & elect mkts)
   Accuride Canada Inc., 31 Firestone Blvd., London, Ont. N6A 4H7, Canada
   Phelps Dodge Corp. of Canada, Ltd., 120 Adelaide St. W., #912, Toronto,
      Ont. M5H 1T1, Canada

PHILIP MORRIS COS INC   120 Park Ave, New York, NY 10017, Tel: (212) 880-5000
(Mfr cigarettes, foods prdts, beer)
   General Foods Inc., 95 Moatfield Dr., Don Mills, Ont M3B 3L6, Canada
   Kraft Ltd., 8600 Devonshire Rd., Mount Royal, Que. H4P 2K9, Canada
   Rothmans, Benson & Hedges Inc., Place du Canada, 1010 Lagauchetiere St. W,
      Montreal, Que., Canada H3B 2P4

PHILLIPS DRILL CO INC   PO Box 364, Michigan City, IN 46360,
   Tel: (219) 874-4217
(Concrete anchor sys for constr ind)
   Phillips Anchors of Canada, 108 Doncaster Ave., Thornhill, Ont., Canada L3T 1L3

PICKANDS MATHER & CO   1100 Superior Ave, Cleveland, OH 44114,
   Tel: (216) 694-5700
(Iron & coal mining & transport)
   Pickands Mather & Co., Wabush Mines, Wabush, Labrador, Canada
   Pickands Mather & Co., Wabush Mines, Pointe Noire, Que., Canada
   Pickands Mather & Co., The Griffith Mine, Red Lake, Ont., Canada

PIERCE & STEVENS CORP   710 Ohio St, Buffalo, NY 14203, Tel: (716) 856-4910
(Mfr coatings, adhesives & chem specs for packaging, graphic arts & gen mfg)
   Pierce & Stevens Canada Ltd., Catherine St. & Concession Rd., Fort Erie, Ont.,
      Canada

PILLSBURY CO   Pillsbury Center, Minneapolis, MN 55402, Tel: (612) 330-4966
(Baking mixes, canned & frozen foods, restaurants & food shops)
   Pillsbury Canada Ltd., 234 Eglinton E, Toronto, Ont., Canada

PINKERTON'S INC   6727 Odessa Ave, Van Nuys, CA 91406, Tel: (818) 373-8800
(Security & investigations)
   Pinkerton's of Canada Ltd., 1980 Sherbrooke St. W, Montreal, Que., Canada H3G 2L1

PITNEY BOWES INC   World Headquarters, Stamford, CT 06926-0700,
   Tel: (203) 356-5000
(Postage meters, mailroom equip, copiers, bus supplies & servs)
   Pitney-Bowes of Canada Ltd., 909 Yonge St., Toronto, Ont., Canada

PITTSTON CO   1 Pickwick Plaza, Greenwich, CT 06830, Tel: (203) 622-0900
(Trucking, warehousing, armored car serv)
   Brinks' Canada Ltd., 55 Logan, Toronto, Ont., Canada
   Metropolitan Plt. Ltd., Montreal, Que., Canada
   Montreal Terminals Ltd., 10000 Notre Dame E, Montreal, Que., Canada

PLANTERS PEANUTS   Suffolk, VA 23434, Tel: (804) 539-2345
(Nut prdts, peanut oil, candy)
   Planters Nut & Chocolate Co. Ltd., 672 Dupont St., Toronto, Ont., Canada

PLASTIGLIDE MFG CORP   2701 W E Segundo Blvd, Hawthorne, CA 90250,
Tel: (213) 777-8108
(Furniture component parts, indus- trial plastic & metal parts)
   Plastiglide Ltd., 150 Norfinch Ave., Downsview, Ont., Canada

PLAYTEX APPAREL INC   700 Fairfield Ave, Stamford, CT 06904,
Tel: (203) 356-8000
(Mfr intimate apparel)
   Playtex Apparel Canada Ltd., 550 Hall St., Renfrew, Ont. K7V 2S9, Canada

PLIBRICO CO   1800 Kingsbury St, Chicago, IL 60614, Tel: (312) 549-7014
(Refractories, engineering, constr)
   Plibrico (Canada) Ltd., P.O. Box 910, Burlington, Ont., Canada L7R 3Y7

PNEUMATIC SCALE CORP   65 Newport Ave, Quincy, MA 02171, Tel: (617) 328-6100
(Packaging & bottling mach)
   Delamere & Williams Co. Ltd., 21 Carson St., Toronto, Ont., Canada

PNEUMO ABEX CORP   485 Frontage Rd, Burr Ridge, IL 60521, Tel: (708) 323-4446
(Mfr aerospace & automotive friction materials & equip)
   Abex Industries Ltd., 50 Colborne St. E., Lindsay, Ont., Canada K9V 4R8
   Canparts Ltd., 177 Pinebush Rd., Cambridge, Ont., Canada N1R 7H8

POLAROID CORP   549 Technology Sq, Cambridge, MA 02139, Tel: (617) 577-2000
(Photographic and optical prdts)
   Polaroid Corp. Ltd., 350 Carlingview Dr., Rexdale, Ont., Canada

R L POLK & CO   1155 Brewery Park Blvd, Detroit, MI 48207-2697,
Tel: (313) 961-9470
(Directories, direct mail advertising)
   B.C. Directories, 100 E. 4th Ave., Vancouver, B.C., Canada V5T 1G3
   Canadian Advertising Distributors, 1 Cleopatra Dr., Ottawa, Ont., Canada K2G 3M9
   Henderson Directories, 419 McMillan Ave., Winnipeg, Man., Canada R3L 0N3
   Might Directories, Box 1005, Postal Station 0, Toronto, Ont., Canada M4A 2N4
   R.L. Polk & Co. Ltd., 9-6143 4th St., Calgary, Alta., Canada
   R.L. Polk & Co. Ltd., 12506 128th St., Edmonton, Alta., Canada
   R.L. Polk & Co. Ltd., 500 Bechard St., Ville Vanier, Que., Canada G1M 2E9

POMEROY INC   PO Box 1377, Stamford, CT 06904, Tel: (203) 324-6775
(Building hardware)
   Andre Trudel, Unique Sash, 7590 19th Ave., Montreal, Que., Canada H2A 2M4

POPE & TALBOT INC   1500 S W First Ave, Portland, OR 97201,
Tel: (503) 228-9161
(Mfr paper, pulp & wood prdts)
   Pope & Talbot, Ltd., PO Box 39, 570 68th Ave., Grand Forks V0H 1H0, Canada

PORTEC INC   300 Windsor Dr, Oak Brook, IL 60521-1553, Tel: (708) 573-4600
(Mfr engineered prdts for constr equip, material handling & railroad inds)
    Portec Ltd., 2044 32nd Ave., Lachine, Que. H8T 3H7, Canada

PORTER PRECISION PRODUCTS CO   2734 Banning Rd, Cincinnati, OH 45239,
    Tel: (513) 923-3777
    (Mfr piercing punches & die supplies for metal stamping & tool/die ind)
    Porter Precision Products Canada Ltd., 45 Durward Pl., Waterloo, Ont.,
    Canada N2L 4E5

POWERS REGULATOR CO   3400 Oakton St, Skokie, IL 60076, Tel: (708) 673-6700
(Control devices)
    The Powers Regulator Co. Ltd., 15 Torbarrie Rd., Downsview, Ont., Canada

PPG INDUSTRIES   One PPG Place, Pittsburgh, PA 15272, Tel: (412) 434-3131
(Mfr flat glass, fiber glass, chems, coatings, med electr)
    PPG Canada Inc., 50 St. Clair Ave. W, Toronto, Ont., Canada M4V 1M9

PRATT & LAMBERT INC   PO Box 22, Buffalo, NY 14240-0022, Tel: (716) 873-6000
(Mfr paints, coatings, adhesives)
    Pratt & Lambert Inc., 254 Courtwright St., Fort Erie, Ont., Canada

PRC/NC   1500 Planning Research Dr, McLean, VA 22102, Tel: (703) 556-1000
(Computer sys & servs)
    PRC Public Management Services, 405 The West Mall- #700, Etobicoke, Ontario, Canada

PRECISION RUBBER PRODUCT CORP   Hartman Dr, Lebanon, TN 37087,
    Tel: (615) 444-0191
    (Rings, seals & custom molded rubber prdts)
    Precision Rubber Products Corp., Precision Dr., Orillia, Ont., Canada L3V 2M3

PRECISION VALVE CORP   PO Box 309, Yonkers, NY 10702, Tel: (914) 969-6500
(Mfr aerosol valves)
    Precision Valve Canada Ltd., 85 Fuller Rd., Ajax, Ont., Canada L1S 2EI

PREFORMED LINE PRODUCTS CO   PO Box 91129, Cleveland, OH 44101,
    Tel: (216) 461-5200
    (Mfr pole line hardware for elec transmission lines; splice closures & related prdts
    for telecom)
    Foundation Instruments Inc., Ottawa, Ont., Canada
    Preformed Line Products (Canada) Ltd., Cambridge, Ont., Canada

PREMARK INTL INC   1717 Deerfield Rd, Deerfield, IL 60015, Tel: (708) 405-6000
(Mfr/sale diversified consumer & coml prdts)
    Premark Canada Inc., Toronto Dominion Bank Tower #2400, 66 Wellington St. W.,
    Toronto, Ont., Canada M5K 1E7

PRETTY PRODUCTS INC   Cambridge Rd, Coshocton, OH 43812, Tel: (614) 622-3522
(Rubber & plastic prdts)
    Pretty Ware Ltd., 40 Racine Rd., Toronto, Ont., Canada

PRIMAC COURIER INC   114 E 32nd St, New York, NY 10016, Tel: (212) 684-7200
(Air Courier)
    Primac Courier (Canada) Inc., 2289 Fairview St., Unit 206, Burlington, Ont., Canada
    Primac Courier (Canada) Inc., 1157 Wellington St., Montreal, Que., Canada

PRIME COMPUTER INC   Prime Park, Natick, MA   01760, Tel: (617) 655-8000
  (Mfr minicomputers, hardware & software)
    Prime Computer of Canada Ltd., 5915 Airport Rd., Mississauga, Ont., Canada L4V 1T1

PROCTER & GAMBLE CO   One Procter & Gamble Plaza, Cincinnati, OH   45202,
  Tel: (513) 983-1100
  (Personal care, food, laundry, cleaning & ind prdts)
    Procter & Gamble Inc., 2 St. Clair Ave. W., Toronto, Ont., Canada M5W 1C5

PRODUCT RESEARCH & CHEMICAL CORP   5430 San Fernando Rd, Glendale, CA   91203,
  Tel: (213) 240-2060
  (Sealants, coatings & adhesives)
    PRC Canada Inc., 266 Humberline Dr., Rexdale, Ont., Canada M9W 5X1

PRODUCTO MACHINE CO   990 Housatonic Ave, PO Box 780, Bridgeport, CT   06601,
  Tel: (203) 367-8675
  (Mfr machine tools, die sets & diemakers accessories)
    Producto Diemakers Supplies Ltd., 620 Supertest Rd., Downsview, Ont., Canada M3J 2M8

PRUDENTIAL INSURANCE CO OF AMERICA   Prudential Plaza, Newark, NJ   07101,
  Tel: (201) 877-6000
  (Life ins, health ins, annuities)
    Prudential Insurance Co. of America, 4 King St. W, Toronto, Ont., Canada M5H 1B7

PUROLATOR COURIER CORP   131 Morristown Rd, Basking Ridge, NJ   07980,
  Tel: (201) 953-6400
  (Time-sensitive package delivery)
    Purolator Courier Ltd., 304 The East Mall, Toronto, Ont., Canada M9B 6E2

PUROLATOR PRODUCTS CO   2 Warren Pl, 6120 S Yale, Tulsa, OK   74136,
  Tel: (918) 492-1800
  (Mfr vehicle filters & related prdts)
    Purolator Products Ltd., 304 The East Mall, Toronto, Ont., Canada M9B 6E2

PYLE-NATIONAL INC   1334 N Kostner Ave, Chicago, IL   60651-1697,
  Tel: (312) 342-6300
  (Mfr elec, electr & military specification connectors)
    Pyle-National/Canada, 2650 S. Sheridan Way, Mississauga, Ont., Canada L5J 2M9

QUAKER CHEMICAL CORP   Elm & Lee Sts, Conshohocken, PA   19428,
  Tel: (215) 828-4250
  (Mfr chem specialties)
    QuakerChem Canada Ltd., 6800 Kitimat Rd., Unit 32, Mississauga, Ont., Canada L5N 5M1

QUAKER STATE OIL REFINING CORP   255 Elm St, Oil City, PA   16301,
  Tel: (814) 676-7676
  (Mfr motor oil, lubricants, automotive chems, waxes)
    Quaker State Inc., 1101 Blair Rd., Burlington, Ont. L7M 1T3, Canada

QUIGLEY CO INC   235 E 42nd St, New York, NY   10017, Tel: (212) 573-3444
  (Mfr refractory specs, application equip)
    Quigley Canada Inc., 1870 Blvd. des Sources, Pointe-Claire, Que. H9R 5N4, Canada

RADIATOR SPECIALTY CO   PO Drawer 34689, Charlotte, NC   28234,
  Tel: (704) 377-6555
  (Plumbing/heating supplies)
    Radiator Specialty Co. Ltd., 1711 Amico Blvd., Mississauga, Ont. Canada

RAIN BIRD SPRINKLER MFG CORP   7045 N Grand Ave, Glendora, CA 91740,
   Tel: (213) 963-9311
   (Lawn sprinklers, irrigation equip)
      Rain Bird Sprinkler Mfg. Co. (Canada) Ltd., 5337 180th St., Surrey, B.C.,
      Canada V3S 4K5

RALSTON PURINA CO   Checkerboard Sq, St Louis, MO 63164, Tel: (214) 982-1000
   (Poultry & live stock feed, cereals, food prdts)
      Ralston Purina Co. of Canada Ltd., 118 Guibault St., Longueuil, Que., Canada J4H 2T3

RAMSEY TECHNOLOGY INC   1853 W County Rd, St Paul, MN 55113,
   Tel: (612) 633-5150
   (Mfr scales & mining equip)
      Ramsey REC Ltd., 385 Enford Rd., Richmond Hill, Ont., Canada L4C 3G2

RANCO INC   555 Metro Pl N, PO Box 248, Dublin, OH 43017, Tel: (614) 764-3733
   (Controls for appliance, automotive, comfort, commercial & consumer mkts)
      Ranco Controls Canada Ltd., 221 Evans Ave., Toronto, Ont., Canada M8Z 1J5

RAPID-AMERICAN CORP   888 Seventh Ave, New York, NY 10019, Tel: (212) 399-4500
   (Wearing apparel, retail stores, alcoholic beverages)
      Canadian Schenley Distilleries Ltd., Valleyfield, Que., Canada

W T RAWLEIGH CO   223 E Main St, Freeport, IL 61032, Tel: (815) 232-4161
   (Medicines, toiletries, pet care & household prdts)
      The W.T. Rawleigh Co. Ltd., 354 Isaby St., St. Laurent, Que., Canada H4T 1W1

RAYMOND CORP   S Canal St, Greene, NY 13778, Tel: (607) 656-2311
   (Mfr elec fork lift trucks, material handling sys)
      Raymond Industrial Equipment Ltd., 406 Elgin St., Brantford, Ont., Canada

RAYOVAC CORP   601 Rayovac Dr, Madison, WI 53711, Tel: (608) 275-3340
   (Mfr batteries & lighting devices)
      Rayovac Canada, 5448 Timberlea Blvd., Mississauga, Ont., Canada

RAYTHEON CO   141 Spring St, Lexington, MA 02173, Tel: (617) 862-6600
   (Mfr diversified electronics & apppliances; aviation, ind & constr services,
   publishing)
      D.C. Heath Canada Ltd., 100 Adelaide St. W, #1600, Toronto, Ont., Canada M5H 1S9
      Raytheon Canada Ltd., 400 Phillip St., Waterloo, Ont., Canada N2J 4K6

RCA GLOBAL COMMUNICATIONS INC   60 Broad St, New York, NY 10004,
   Tel: (212) 806-7000
   (Commun serv)
      RCA Ltd. Canada, 21001 Trans Canada Hwy., Bellevue, Que., Canada

READER'S DIGEST ASSOCIATION INC   PO Box 235, Pleasantville, NY 10570,
   Tel: (914) 238-1000
   (Global publisher & direct mail marketer)
      Reader's Digest, 215 Redfern Ave., Montreal, Que., Canada H3Z 2V9

REDKEN LABORATORIES INC   6625 Variel Ave, Canoga Park, CA 91303,
   Tel: (818) 992-2700
   (Mfr hair & skin care prdts)
      Redken Laboratories (Canada) Ltd., 151 Carlingview Dr., Rexdale, Ont.,
      Canada M9W 5S4

THE REECE CORP   800 South St, Waltham, MA 02254-9168, Tel: (617) 894-9220
  (Mfr apparel mach)
    The Reece Machinery Co. of Canada Ltd., 9440 Charles de Latour St., Montreal, Que.,
    Canada W4N IM2

REEVES BROTHERS INC   1271 Ave of the Americas, New York, NY 10020,
  Tel: (212) 573-8600
  (Woven cotton & synthetic fabrics, textile job finishing, filter cloth, ind fabric
  prdts)
    Reeves Hardifoam Ltd., 415 Evans Ave., Toronto, Ont., Canada
    Reeves Hardifoam Ltd., 5675 des Grandes Prairies, St. Leonard, Que., Canada

REICHHOLD CHEMICALS INC   RCI Bldg, 525 N Broadway, White Plains, NY 10603,
  Tel: (914) 682-5700
  (Synthetic resins & specialty chems)
    Sterling Varnish Co. (Canada) Ltd., P.O. Box 554, St. Catherine, Ont.,
    Canada L2R 6X1

RELIANCE ELECTRIC CO   24701 Euclid Ave, Cleveland, OH 44117,
  Tel: (216) 266-7000
  (Equip & sys for ind automation, telecom equip)
    Reliable Communications & Power Prdts. Ltd., 6810 F6 St., Calgary, Alta.,
    Canada T2H 2K4
    Reliance Electric Canada Ltd., 5220 Creek Bank Rd., Mississauga, Ont.,
    Canada L4W 1X1
    Reliance Telecommunications Prdts. Ltd., 122 Edward St., St. Thomas, Ont.,
    Canada N5P 1Z2

RELIANCE UNIVERSAL INC   1600 Watterson Tower, 1930 Bishop Lange, Louisville,
  KY 40218, Tel: (502) 459-9110
  (Commercial highway & off-highway trailers, truck & trailer bodies)
    Reliance Universal Inc., 1001 Daniel Johnson Blvd., St. Jerome, Que., Canada
    Reliance Universal Inc., 20100 Number 10 Hwy., Langley, B.C., Canada V3A 5E7

REMINGTON ARMS CO INC   1800 Washington Rd, Pittsburgh, PA 05241,
  Tel: (412) 831-4000
  (Mfr sporting firearms & ammunition)
    Remington Arms of Canada Ltd., 172 Sheldon Dr., Cambridge, Ont., Canada

REMINGTON PRODUCTS INC   60 Main St, Bridgeport, CT 06602, Tel: (203) 367-4400
  (Mfr home appliances, electric shavers)
    Remington Omar Inc., 2254 S. Sheridan Way, Mississauga, Ont., Canada

REPUBLIC STEEL CORP   PO Box 6778, Cleveland, OH 44101, Tel: (216) 622-5000
  (Alloy, carbon & stainless steel, chems, electrical conduit, etc)
    Union Drawn Steel Co. Ltd., Burlington St. E, Hamilton, Ont., Canada

RESORTS INTL INC   915 N E 125th St, North Miami, FL 33161,
  Tel: (305) 891-2500
  (Ownership, development & operations of resort complexes)
    Intl. Intelligence (Canada) Ltd., Valhalla Executive Centre, 300 East Mall,
    Toronto, Ont., Canada M9B 6B7

REVLON INC   767 Fifth Ave, New York, NY 10153-0033, Tel: (212) 572-5000
  (Cosmetics, health care prdts)
    Revlon Intl. Corp. (Canada), 2501 Stanfield Rd., Mississauga, Ont., Canada L4Y 1R9

REXNORD CORP   PO Box 2022, Milwaukee, WI 53201, Tel: (414) 643-3000
  (Mfr power transmission prdts)
    Rexnord Canada Ltd., 81 Maybrook Dr., Scarborough, Ont. M1V 3Z2, Canada

REYNOLDS & REYNOLDS CO   800 Germantown St, PO Box 1005, Dayton, OH 45407,
  Tel: (513) 443-2000
  (Business forms, sys & EDP serv)
    Reynolds & Reynolds Co., Brampton, Ont., Canada L6T 3X1

R J REYNOLDS INDUSTRIES INC   World Headquarters Bldg, 401 N Main St,
  Winston-Salem, NC 27102, Tel: (919) 773-2000
  (Tobacco prdts, holding co)
    Chun King Corp. of Canada Ltd., Windsor, Ont., Canada
    RJR Foods Ltd., 750 Laurentien, Montreal, Que., Canada

REYNOLDS INTERNATIONAL INC   6601 W Broad St, PO Box 27002, Richmond,
  VA 23261, Tel: (804) 281-2000
  (Mfr aluminum primary & fabricated prdts, plastic & paper packaging & foodservice
  prdts; gold mining)
    Canadian Reynolds Metals Co. Ltd., 1420 Sherbrooke St. W., 10th Fl., Montreal,
      Que., Canada H3G 1K9

M H RHODES INC   99 Thompson Rd, Avon, CT 06001, Tel: (203) 673-3281
  (Mfr timers, time switches & parking meters)
    M.H. Rhodes Ltd., 10 Kimway Crescent, Ottawa, Ont., Canada

RICHARDSON-VICKS INC   Ten Westport Rd, Wilton, CT 06897, Tel: (203) 834-5000
  (Consumer health & personal care prdts)
    Richardson Vicks Ltd., 2 Norelco Dr., Weston, Ont., Canada M9L 1R9

RICHTON INTL CORP   1345 Ave of the Americas, New York, NY 10115,
  Tel: (212) 765-6480
  (Nondurable consumer wearables, active sportswear jewelry & accessories)
    Richton Intl. Canada Ltd., 186 Bartley Dr., Toronto, Ont., Canada M4A 1E4

RIEKE CORP   500 W 7th St, Auburn, IN 46706, Tel: (219) 925-3700
  (Steel drum closures, plugs, seals, faucets, rings, combination pail spout & closure,
  etc)
    Rieke Canada Ltd., 125 Orenda Rd., Brampton, Ont., Canada L6W 1W3

RIGHT ASSOCIATES   1818 Market St, 14th Fl, Philadelphia, PA 19103-3614,
  Tel: (215) 988-1588
  (Outplacement & human resources consult servs)
    Right Associates, 144 4th Ave. SW- #2580, Calgary, Alberta T2P 3N4, Canada
    Right Associates, other locations in Canada

RIKER LABORATORIES INC   Bldg 225-1N-07, 3M Center, St Paul, MN 55144,
  Tel: (612) 733-9577
  (Specialty pharms)
    Riker Pharmaceutical Co. Ltd., 3241 Wharton Way, Cooksville, Ont., Canada

ROBERT HALF INTL INC   2884 Sand Hill Rd, #200, Menlo Park, CA 94025,
  Tel: (415) 854-9700
  (Personnel servs)
    Robert Half Intl., Inc., 603 7th Ave. SW, Calgary, Alberto T2P 2T5, Canada
    Robert Half Intl., Inc., other locations in Canada

ROBERTS-GORDON APPLIANCE CORP   44 Central Ave, Buffalo, NY 14206,
Tel: (716) 892-8400
(Gas conversion burners, ind gas burners, ind space heaters, etc)
    Roberts-Gordon Appliance Corp. Ltd., Grimsby, Ont., Canada

ROBERTSHAW CONTROLS CO   1701 Byrd Ave, Richmond, VA 23230,
Tel: (804) 281-0700
(Mfr automatic controls & control sys for ind, commercial bldgs & home)
    Robertshaw Controls Canada Inc., 41 Medulla Ave., Toronto, Ont., Canada M82 5W1

H H ROBERTSON CO   Two Gateway Center, Pittsburgh, PA 15222,
Tel: (412) 281-3200
(Mfr roof & wall prdts, cellular steel floor sys, ventilation equip)
    Robertson Building Systems Ltd., P.O. Box 100, Station A, Hamilton, Ont.,
    Canada L8N 3B6

A H ROBINS CO INC   1407 Cummings Dr, PO Box 26609, Richmond, VA 23261-6609,
Tel: (804) 257-2000
(Mfr ethical pharms & consumer prdts)
    A. H. Robins Co. Ltd., Mississauga, Ont., Canada

ROCHESTER INSTRUMENT SYSTEMS INC   255 N Union St, Rochester, NY 14605,
Tel: (716) 263-7700
(Electronic alarms & monitors in- cluding annunciators, event recorders, etc)
    Rochester Instrument Systems Ltd., 915 Kipling Ave., Toronto, Ont., Canada M8Z 5H4

ROCHESTER MIDLAND CORP   PO Box 1515, Rochester, NY 14603, Tel: (716) 266-2250
(Mfr specialty chems for ind cleaning/maint, water treatment, personal hygiene)
    Rochester Midland Ltd., 851 Progress Ct., Oakville, Ont. L6J 5A8, Canada

ROCK OF AGES CORP   PO Box 482, Barre, VT 05641, Tel: (802) 476-3115
(Quarrier; mfr granite prdts)
    Rock Of Ages Canada, Beebe, Quebec, Canada

ROCKWELL INTL CORP   2230 E Imperial Hwy, El Segundo, CA 90245,
Tel: (213) 647-5000
(Prdts & serv for aerospace, automotive, electronics, graphics & automation inds)
    Rockwell Intl. of Canada Ltd., 150 Bartley Dr., Toronto, Ont., Canada M4A 1C7

ROHM & HAAS CO   Independence Mall West, Philadelphia, PA 19105,
Tel: (215) 592-3000
(Mfr ind & agric chems, plastics)
    Rohm & Haas Canada Inc., 2 Manse Rd., West Hill, Ont., Canada M1E 3T9

RORER GROUP INC   500 Virginia Dr, Ft Washington, PA 19034,
Tel: (215) 628-6000
(Mfr ethical & consumer pharms)
    Rorer Canada Inc., Bramalea, Ont., Canada

ROSEMOUNT INC   12001 Technology Dr, Eden Prairie, MN 55344,
Tel: (612) 941-5560
(Mfr aerospace & ind instrumentation)
    Rosemount Instruments Ltd., 808 55th Ave. NE, Calgary, Alta., Canada T2E 6Y4

ROSPATCH CORP   3101 Walkent Dr NW, Walker, MI 49504, Tel: (616) 784-1000
(Printed cloth labels & label processing mach, paper cutting machs)
    Thermopatch (Canada) Inc., St. Laurent, Que., Canada

ROSS ROY GROUP INC   100 Bloomfield Hills Pkwy, Bloomfield Hills, MI 48304,
Tel: (313) 433-6000
(Advertising agency)
  Ross Roy Communications, Inc., 1737 Walker Rd., Windsor, Ontario N8Y 4R8, Canada
  Ross Roy of Canada, Ltd., Renaissance Ct., 162 Cumberland St.- #300, Toronto,
  Ontario M5R 1A8, Canada

ROSTONE CORP   2450 Sagamore Pkwy S, PO Box 7497, Lafayette, IN 47902,
Tel: (317) 474-2421
(Custom molded glass, reinforced thermoset polyester prdts)
  Relmech Mfg. Ltd., 3 Industrial Dr., Elmira, Ont., Canada

RPM INC   2628 Pearl Rd, Medina, OH 44256, Tel: (216) 225-3192
(Protective coatings, paint)
  RPM Canada, 12 Finley Rd., Bramalea, Ont., Canada L6T 1A9

RUBBERMAID INC   1147 Akron Rd, Wooster, OH 44691, Tel: (216) 264-6464
(Rubber & plastic home, commercial & ind prdts)
  Rubbermaid (Canada) Ltd., Mississauga, Ont., Canada

RUST-OLEUM CORP   11 Hawthorne Parkway, Vernon Hill, IL 60061,
Tel: (708) 367-7700
(Rust preventive coatings)
  Rust-Oleum (Canada) Ltd., 590 Supertest Rd., Downsview, Ont., Canada M3J 2M5

RYDER SYSTEM INC   3600 NW 82nd Ave, Miami, FL 33166, Tel: (305) 593-3726
(Truck leasing & rental, common & contract truck carriage, truck-stops & ins)
  Ryder Truck Rental Ltd., 672 Kipling, Toronto, Ont., Canada

S&C ELECTRIC CO   6601 Ridge Blvd, Chicago, IL 60626, Tel: (312) 338-1000
(Mfr high voltage power equip)
  S&C Electric Canada Ltd., 90 Belfield Rd., Toronto, Ont., Canada M5W 1G4

SAFETY-KLEEN CORP   777 Big Timber Rd, Elgin, IL 60123, Tel: (708) 697-8460
(Solvent based parts cleaning serv, sludge/solvent recycling serv)
  Safety-Kleen Canada Ltd., 1110 Sherbrooke St. W., Montreal, Que., Canada H3A 1G8

SAFEWAY STORES INC   201 4th St, Oakland, CA 94660, Tel: (415) 891-3000
(Food marketing)
  Safeway Stores Canada, P.O. Box 864, Station M, Calgary, Alta., Canada T2P 2J6

SALANT CORP   1155 Ave of the Americas, New York, NY 10036,
Tel: (212) 221-7500
(Diversified apparel)
  Buckeye-Peerless Textile Products Co. Ltd., 2301 Keele St., Toronto, Ont.,
  Canada M6M 3Z9

SALEM CORP   PO Box 2222, Pittsburgh, PA 15230, Tel: (412) 923-2200
(Mfr ind furnaces, coal processing equip, metal finishing equip)
  Salem Industries Canada Ltd., 41 Enterprise Rd., Rexdale, Ont., Canada

SAMSONITE CORP   11200 E 45th St, Denver, CO 80239, Tel: (303) 373-7159
(Mfr luggage & leather goods)
  Samsonite Canada, 753 Ont. St., Stratford, Ont., Canada

SARA LEE CORP   3 First National Plaza, Chicago, IL 60602, Tel: (312) 726-2600
  (Mfr/distr food & consumer packaged goods)
    Canadelle, P.O. Box 850, Montreal, Que., Canada

SARGENT MANUFACTURING CO   100 Sargent Dr, New Haven, CT 06511,
  Tel: (203) 562-2151
  (Mfr architectural builders hdwe, locks)
    Sargent of Canada, 900 Water St., Peterborough, Ont., Canada K9J 6Z3

SARGENT-WELCH SCIENTIFIC CO   7300 N Linder Ave, Skokie, IL 60077,
  Tel: (708) 677-0600
  (Laboratory & scientific equip & supplies)
    Sargent-Welch Scientific of Canada Ltd., 285 Garyway Dr., Weston, Ont.,
      Canada M9L 1P3

W B SAUNDERS CO   W Washington Sq, Philadelphia, PA 19105, Tel: (215) 574-4700
  (Med & tech book publishers)
    W.B. Saunders Co. Ltd., 1 Goldthorn Ave., Toronto, Ont., Canada M8Z 5T9

SCHENECTADY CHEMICALS INC   PO Box 1046, Schenectady, NY 12301,
  Tel: (518) 370-4200
  (Mfr elec insulating varnishe, enamels, resins, alkylated phenol)
    Schenectady Chemicals Canada Ltd., 319 Comstock Rd., Scarborough, Ont.,
      Canada M1L 2H3

R P SCHERER CORP   2075 W Big Beaver Rd, Troy, MI 48084, Tel: (313) 649-0900
  (Mfr soft gelatin & two-piece hard shell capsules)
    Pharmaphil, 3190 Devon Rd., Windsor, Ont., Canada N8X 4L2
    R.P. Scherer (Canada), 1370 Argyle Rd., Windsor, Ont., Canada N8Y 3K7

SCHERING INTL   PO Box 500, Kenilworth, NJ 07033, Tel: (201) 558-4000
  (Pharms, medicines, toiletries, cosmetics, human & animal health prdts)
    Schering Corp. Ltd., 3535 Trans-Canada Hwy., Point Claire, Que., Canada H9R 1B4

SCHLAGE LOCK CO   2401 Bayshore Blvd, San Francisco, CA 94134,
  Tel: (415) 467-1100
  (Locks, builders hardware)
    Schlage Lock Co. Ltd., 1290 Marine Dr. N, Vancouver, B.C., Canada

SCHOLASTIC INC   730 Broadway, New York, NY 10003, Tel: (212) 505-3000
  (Pub educational magazines, books, software)
    Scholastic TAB Publications Ltd., 123 Newkirk Rd., Richmond Hill, Ont., Canada,
      L4C 3G5

SCHRADER BELLOWS DIV   200 W Exchange St, Akron, OH 44309, Tel: (216) 375-1263
  (Pneumatic & hydraulic valves & cylinders, FRL units & accessories)
    Schrader Bellows, 530 Kipling Ave., Toronto, Ont., Canada M8Z 5E6

A SCHULMAN INC   3550 W Market St, Akron, OH 44313, Tel: (216) 666-3751
  (Mfr/sale plastic resins & compounds)
    A. Schulman Canada Ltd., 400 S. Edgeware Rd., St. Thomas, Ont., Canada N5P 3Z5
    A. Schulman Canada Ltd., 170 Attwell Dr., #503, Rexdale (Toronto), Ont.,
      Canada M9W 5Z5

SCIENCE MANAGEMENT CORP   PO Box 0600, Basking Ridge, NJ 07920,
  Tel: (201) 647-7000
  (Human/mgmt resources, info technology, engr & technology services)
    SMC Management Services Group, 142 Islington Ave., Toronto, Canada

SCIENTIFIC ATLANTA INC   1 Technology Pkwy, PO Box 105600, Atlanta, GA 30348,
  Tel: (404) 441-4000
  (Telecommun instru & equip, energy mgmt & home security equip, test & measurement
  instru)
    Scientific Atlanta Ltd., 1640 Bonhill Rd., Mississauga, Ont., Canada L5T 1C8

SCM CORP   299 Park Ave, New York, NY 10171, Tel: (212) 752-2700
  (Business equip, chems, coatings & resins, foods, paper prdts)
    Proctor-Silex Ltd., 239 McRae Dr., Toronto, Ont., Canada
    SCM Canada Ltd., 29 Gervais Dr., Don Mills, Ont., Canada

THE SCOTT & FETZER CO   28800 Clemens Rd, Westlake, OH 44145,
  Tel: (216) 892-3000
  (Electrical & lighting fixtures, leisure prdts)
    SFZ Intl., c/o McMillan Binch, P.O. Box 38, Toronto, Ont., Canada M51 2J7

SCOTT WORLDWIDE INC   Scott Plaza, Philadelphia, PA 19113, Tel: (215) 521-5000
  (Paper & paper prdts, bleached pulp)
    Scott Paper Ltd., P.O. Box 760, New Westminster, B.C., Canada

SCRIPTURE PRESS PUBLICATIONS INC   1825 College Ave, Wheaton, IL 60187,
  Tel: (708) 668-6000
  (Publ Christian education materials)
    Scripture Press Publications Ltd., P.O. Box 2000, Paris, Ont. N3L 3X5, Canada

SEA-LAND SERVICE INC   379 Thornall St, Edison, NJ 08837, Tel: (201) 558-6000
  (Container transport)
    Intl. Sea-Land Shipping Service Ltd., 7403 Newman Blvd., Lasalle, Que.,
      Canada H8M 1X4
    Intl. Sea-Land Shipping Service Ltd., 297 Rutherford Rd. S, Brampton, Ont.,
      Canada L6W 3J8
    Intl. Sea-Land Shipping Service Ltd., 2010 Glen Dr., Vancouver, B.C., Canada V5T 4B2
    Intl. Sea-Land Shipping Service Ltd., P.O. Box 955, Montreal, Que., Canada H2W 2N1
    Intl. Sea-Land Shipping Service Ltd., 1401 W. Eighth Ave., Vancouver, B.C. V6H 1C9

SEALED AIR CORP   Park 80 Plaza E, Saddle Brook, NJ 07662-5291,
  Tel: (201) 791-7600
  (Mfr protective packaging prdts)
    Sealed Air of Canada Ltd., 95 Glidden Rd., Brampton, Ont., Canada L6T 2H8

SEAQUIST DIV   1160 N Silver Lake Rd, Cary, IL 60013, Tel: (708) 639-2126
  (Aerosol valves, closures, pump dispensers)
    Seaquist Canada, 42 Lepage Ct., Downsview, Ont., Canada M3J 1Z9

G D SEARLE & CO   PO Box 1045, Skokie, IL 60076, Tel: (708) 982-7000
  (Pharms, health care & optical prdts, specialty chems)
    G.D. Searle & Co. of Canada Ltd., 400 Iroquois Rd., Oakville, Ont., Canada L6H 1M5

SEARS ROEBUCK & CO   Sears Towers, Chicago, IL 60684, Tel: (312) 875-2500
  (Diversified general merchandise, ins, real estate, financial serv)
    Simpson-Sears Ltd., 222 Jarvis St., Toronot, Ont., Canada M5B 2B8

SEATTLE FIRST NATIONAL BANK   1001 4th Ave, PO Box 3586, Seattle, WA 98124,
   Tel: (206) 583-3131
   (Bank holding company, financial serv)
      Seafirst Financial Services Canada Ltd., 10024 Jasper Ave., Edmonton, Alta.,
         Canada T5J 1R9
      Seafirst Financial Services Canada Ltd., 1050 W. Pender, Vancouver, B.C.,
         Canada V6E 3S7
      Seafirst Financial Services Canada Ltd., 5920 Macleod Trail S, Calgary, Alta.,
         Canada T2H OK2

SELLSTROM MFG CO   Sellstrom Industrial Park, PO Box 355, Palatine, IL 60078,
   Tel: (708) 358-2000
   (Mfr safety prdts for eyes, ears, face & head)
      Sellstrom Mfg. (Canada) Ltd., 160 St. Viateur St. E, Montreal, Que., Canada H2T 1A8

SENCO PRODUCTS INC   8485 Broadwell Rd, Cincinnati, OH 45244,
   Tel: (513) 388-2000
   (Mfr ind nailers, staplers, fasteners & accessories)
      Senco Products (Canada) Ltd., 258 Attwell Dr., Rexdale, Ont., Canada M9W 5B2

SERVICEMASTER INDUSTRIES INC   2399 Warrensville Rd, Downers Grove, IL 60515,
   Tel: (708) 964-1300
   (Mgmt serv to health care, school & ind facilities; home, ind & commercial cleaning
   serv)
      Servicemaster of Canada Ltd.., All inquiries to U.S. address

SEVEN-UP INTL   120 Park Ave, New York, NY 10017, Tel: (212) 880-4100
   (Soft drinks)
      Dominion Seven-Up Co. Ltd., 12 Cranfield Rd., Toronto, Ont., Canada M4B 5G8

SGS CONTROL SERVICES INC   42 Broadway, New York, NY 10004,
   Tel: (212) 482-8700
   (Complete range of quality & quantity control checks & related tech serv)
      SGS Supervision Services Inc., 355 Burrard St., Vancouver, B.C., Canada V6C 2G8
      SGS Supervision Services Inc., 7020 Farrell Rd. SE, Calgary, Alta., Canada T2H 0T2
      SGS Supervision Services Inc., 300 St. Sacrement St., Montreal, Que., Canada H2Y 1X4

SHEAFFER EATON INC   1 Crown Mark Dr, Lincoln, RI 02865, Tel: (401) 333-0303
   (Mfr writing instruments)
      Sheaffer Pen, 6700 Century Rd., #104, Mississauga, Ont., Canada L59 2V8

SHEARSON/AMERICAN EXPRESS   American Express Tower, New York, NY 10285,
   Tel: (212) 298-2000
   (Investment banking, financial serv)
      Shearson/American Express, 622 Fifth Ave. SW, Calgary, Alta., Canada T2P OM6
      Shearson/American Express, 1200 McGill College Ave., Montreal, Que., Canada H3B 4G7
      Shearson/American Express, 55 University Ave., Toronto, Ont., Canada M5J 2H7

SHELLER-GLOBE CORP   1641 Porter St, Detroit, MI 48216, Tel: (313) 962-7311
   (Mfr auto components, ind prdts)
      Sheller-Globe of Canada, 253 Queen St., Brampton, Ont., Canada L6W 2B8
      Sheller-Globe of Canada, P.O. Box 489, Windsor, Ont., Canada N9A 6M8

J R SHORT MILLING CO INC   500 W Madison, Chicago, IL 60606,
   Tel: (312) 559-5450
   (Corn & soybean prdts)
      J.R. Short Canadian Mills Ltd., 70 Wicksteed Ave., Leaside, Ont., Canada

SHULTON INC   1 Cyanamid Plaza, Wayne, NJ 07470, Tel: (201) 831-2000
(Health, beauty & grooming prdts)
Shulton of Canada Ltd., 2031 Kennedy Rd., Scarborough, Ont., Canada M7P 2M4

SIGMA INSTRUMENTS INC   170 Pearl St, S Braintree, MA 02184,
Tel: (617) 843-5000
(Relays & switches, electr instru)
Sigma Instruments (Canada) Ltd., 55 Six Point, Toronto, Ont., Canada M8Z Q3X

SIGNODE PACKAGING SYSTEMS   3600 W Lake Ave, Glenview, IL 60025,
Tel: (708) 724-6100
(Mfr packaging systems)
Signode Canada Ltd., 115 Ridgetop Rd., Scarborough, Ont., Canada M1P 2K3

SIMMONS INTL   1 Gulf & Western Plaza, New York, NY 10023, Tel: (212) 333-3511
(Bedding prdts)
Simmons Ltd., 6900 Airport Rd., Mississauga, Ont., Canada L4V 1E8

SIMPLEX TIME RECORDER CO   Simplex Plaza, Gardner, MA 01441,
Tel: (617) 632-2500
(Time recorders & stamps, master time sys, alarm, security, monitor & control sys)
Simplex Intl. Time Equipment Co. Ltd., 6300 Viscount Rd., Mississauga, Ont.,
Canada L4V 1H3

SIMPLICITY PATTERN CO INC   200 Madison Ave, New York, NY 10016,
Tel: (212) 481-3737
(Dress patterns)
Dominion Simplicity Patterns Ltd., 120 Mack Ave., Scarborough, Ont., Canada M1L 2N3

SINCLAIR & VALENTINE LP   2520 Pilot Knob Rd, St Paul, MN 55120,
Tel: (612) 452-8010
(Mfr printing inks, pigment & related prdts)
Sinclair & Valentine, L.P., 4590 Dufferin, Downsview, Ont., Canada M3H 5S5

SIRCO INTL CORP   700-718 S Fulton Ave, Mt Vernon, NY 10550,
Tel: (914) 664-4400
(Imp of handbags, totes, wallets)
Sirco Intl. Canada Ltd., 1321 Blundell Rd., Mississauga, Ont., Canada

J E SIRRINE CO   PO Box 5456, Greenvilee, SC 29606, Tel: (803) 298-6000
(Consulting engineers, architects & planners)
LGL-Wardrop-Sirrine, 1400 Ouest rue Sauve, Montreal, Que., Canada H4N 1C5
LGL-Wardrop-Sirrine, 77 Main St., Winnipeg, Man., Canada R3C-3H1

SLANT/FIN CORP   100 Forest Dr at East Hills, Greenvale, NY 11548,
Tel: (516) 484-2600
(Heating & A/C sys & comps)
Slant/Fin Ltd., 6450 Northan Dr., Mississauga, Ont., Canada

WILBUR SMITH ASSOCS   NCNB Tower, PO Box 92, Columbia, SC 29202,
Tel: (803) 738-0580
(Consulting engineers)
Lawrence Flemming & Associates Ltd., 365 Evans Ave. #604, Toronto, Ont.,
Canada M8Z 1K2

A O SMITH CORP   PO Box 584, Milwaukee, WI 53201, Tel: (414) 447-4000
(Auto & truck frames, motors, water heaters, computer serv, etc)
   A.O. Smith Corp., 768 Erie St., Stratford, Ont., Canada
   Sterling Electric, P.O. Box 3313, Station F, Hamilton, Ont., Canada

SMITH INTL INC   16740 Hardy St, Houston, TX 77032, Tel: (713) 443-6470
(Mfr/serv downhole drilling equip)
   Smith Intl. Canada Ltd., 1400 Elveden House, Calgary, Alberta, Canada

SMITH TOOL   PO Box C-19511, Irvine, CA 92713, Tel: (714) 540-7010
(Drilling bits)
   Smith Intl. Canada Ltd., Calgary, Alta., Canada

SNAP-ON TOOLS CORP   2801 80th St, Kenosha, WI 53141-1410, Tel: (414) 656-5200
(Mfr automotive & ind maint serv tools)
   Snap-On Tools of Canada Ltd., 2325 Skymark Ave., Mississauga, Ont., Canada L4W 5A9

SOLIDYNE INC   60 Spence St, Bay Shore, NY 11706, Tel: (516) 231-7800
(Heat sealing generators, dielectric equip)
   Solidyne Canada Ltd., 59 Portland St., Etobicoke, Ont., Canada

SOLO CUP CO   1505 E Main St, Urbana, IL 61801, Tel: (217) 384-1800
(Paper & plastic cups)
   Solo Cup Canada, 525 Stinson Blvd., Ville St. Laurent, Que., Canada M4N 2E1

SONOCO PRODUCTS CO   North Second St, PO Box 160, Hartsville, SC 29550,
Tel: (803) 383-7000
(Mfr packaging for consumer & ind mkt)
   Domtar Sonoco Containers Inc., 6591 Kitimat Rd., Mississauga, Ont., Canada L5N 3T4
   Sonoco Ltd., P.O. Box 1208, Brantford, Ont., Canada N3T 5T5
   Sonoco Ltd., other locations in Canada

SOUTHWESTERN PETROLEUM CORP   534 N Main, Fort Worth, TX 76106,
Tel: (817) 332-2336
(Mfr roofing/bldg maint prdts & ind lubricants)
   Southwestern Petroleum Canada Ltd., 87 West Dr., Brampton, Ont., Canada L6T 2J6

SPALDING & EVENFLO COS INC   5750A N Hoover Blvd, Tampa, FL 33614,
Tel: (813) 887-5200
(Mfr sports equip, infant & juvenile furniture & accessories)
   Spalding & Evenflo Canada Inc., 470 Norfinch Dr., Downsview, Ont., Canada M3N 1Y4

SPRAGUE ELECTRIC CO   87 Marshall St, North Adams, MA 01247,
Tel: (413) 664-4411
(Electronic components)
   Sprague Electric of Canada Ltd., 49 Bertal Rd., Toronto, Ont., Canada M6M 4M7

SPS TECHNOLOGIES INC   900 Newtown-Yardley Rd, Newtown, PA 18940,
Tel: (215) 860-3000
(Mfr aerospace & ind fasteners, precision components, superalloys, magnetic
materials, fastening sys)
   Standco Inc., 101 Spinnaker Way, Concord, Ont. L4K 2T2, Canada

SQUARE D CO   Executive Plaza, Palatine, IL 60067, Tel: (708) 397-2600
(Power distribution & elec/electr ind control equip)
   Square D Canada Electrical Equipment Inc., 6303 Airport Rd., Mississauga, Ont.,
   Canada L4V 1S2

ST JOE MINERALS CORP   250 Park Ave, New York, NY 10017, Tel: (212) 953-5000
(Coal, oil, gas, iron ore, metals & minerals)
    CanDel Oil Ltd., 330 Fifth Ave. SW, Calgary, Alta., Canada T1Z 0L4

STA-RITE INDUSTRIES INC   777 E Wisconsin Ave, Milwaukee, WI 53202,
    Tel: (414) 276-6888
(Mfr water pumps & filters, water treatment equip, fluid power components)
    Filtersoft Ltd., 1221 Gateway Rd., Winnipeg, Man., Canada R2G 1E6

STACKPOLE CORP   201 Stackpole St, St Mary's, PA 15857, Tel: (814) 781-1234
(Carbon & graphite specialties)
    Stackpole Ltd., 550 Evans Ave., Toronto, Ont., Canada M8W 2V6

A E STALEY MFG CO   2200 E Eldorado St, Decatur, IL 62525, Tel: (217) 423-4411
(Corn & soybean prdts, food & ind starches, retail consumer prdts)
    Staley (Canada) Ltd., 385 The West Mall, Etobiocoke, Ont., Canada

STANBEL INC   100 Tapley St, Springfield, MA 01104, Tel: (413) 732-3312
(Mfr twines, ice packs)
    Stanbel Ltd., 11600 Albert Hudon, Montreal, Que., Canada H1G 3K2

STANDARD COMMERCIAL CORP   PO Box 450, Wilson, NC 27893, Tel: (919) 291-5507
(Leaf tobacco dealers/processors, wool processors)
    Standard Commercial Tobacco Co. of Canada Ltd., Chatham, Ont., Canada

STANDARD OIL CO OF CALIFORNIA   225 Bush St, San Francisco, CA 94104,
    Tel: (415) 894-7700
(Oil explor & prod, petroleum prdts)
    Chevron Asphalt Ltd., 43 Industrial St., Toronto, Ont., Canada M4G 1Z2
    Chevron Canada Ltd., 1050 W. Pender St., Vancouver, B.L., Canada E6E 3T4
    Chevron Standard Ltd., 400 5th Ave., Calgary, Alta., Canada T2P 0L7
    Irving Oil Ltd., P.O. Box 1421, St. John, NB, Canada L:1L 4H6

STANDARD PRODUCTS CO   2130 W 110th St, Cleveland, OH 44102,
    Tel: (216) 281-8300
(Molded & extruded rubber & plastic prdts, cartage & warehousing)
    Standard Products (Canada) Ltd., 346 Guelph St., Georgetown, Ont., Canada,
        Canada L7G 4B5
    Standard Products (Canada) Ltd., 1030 Erie St., Stratford, Ont., Canada N5A 6V7

STANGE CO   342 N Western Ave, Chicago, IL 60612, Tel: (312) 733-6945
(Seasonings, food colors & flavorings)
    Club House Foods Ltd., London, Ont., Canada

THE STANLEY WORKS   1000 Stanley Dr, PO Box 7000, New Britain, CT 06050,
    Tel: (203) 225-5111
(Mfr hand tools & hardware)
    Stanley Automatic Openers, P.O. Box 789, Windsor, Ont., Canada N8W 5A7
    Stanley Canada Inc., P.O. Box 66, Station B, Hamilton, Ont., Canada L8L 7V2
    Stanley Door Systems, 42 Queen Elizabeth Blvd., Toronto, Ont., Canada M8Z 1M1
    Stanley Hardware, P.O. Box 3001, Station B, Hamilton, Ont., Canada L8L 7X9
    Stanley Tools, 1100 Corporate Dr., Burlington, Ont., Canada L7L 5R6
    Stanley-Bostitch, 19 Rangemoor Rd., Toronto, Ont., Canada M8Z 5H9

STATE STREET BANK & TRUST CO   225 Franklin St, Boston, MA 02101,
  Tel: (617) 786-3000
  (Banking servs)
    State Street Canada Inc., 40 King St. W. #5700, Toronto, Ont., Canada M5H 3Y8

STEBBINS ENGINEERING & MFG CO   363 Eastern Blvd, Watertown, NY 13601,
  Tel: (315) 782-3000
  (Engineering & constr)
    Canadian Stebbins Engineering & Mfg. Co. Ltd., 2700 Lancaster Rd., Ottawa, Ont.,
      Canada K1B 4T7

STEINER CORP   PO Box 2317, 505 E South Temple St, Salt Lake City, UT 84102,
  Tel: (801) 328-8831
  (Linen supply service)
    Nelson's, 5 W. 4th Ave., Vancouver, B.C., Canada V5Y 1G2

STEMCO INC   PO Box 1989, Longview, TX 75606, Tel: (214) 758-9981
  (Mfr automotive seals, mufflers, spec prdts for heavy duty trucks, buses, trailers)
    Stemco Canada, 400 Traders Blvd., Mississauga, Ont., Canada L42 1W7

STEPAN CO   22 W Frontage Rd, Northfield, IL 60093, Tel: (708) 446-7500
  (Mfr basic & intermediate chems)
    Stepan Canada, Longford Mills, Canada

STERLING DIV   1977 Ohio River Rd, Sewickley, PA 15143, Tel: (412) 766-7600
  (Elect varnishes, epoxy compounds, resins, protective coatings)
    The Sterling Varnish Co. Ltd., St. Catharine's, Ont., Canada

STERLING DRUG INC   90 Park Ave, New York, NY 10016, Tel: (212) 907-2000
  (Pharms, chems, cosmetics, household cleaners & waxes)
    Gray Laboratories Div., Sterling-Canada Group, Toronto, Ont., Canada
    Sterling Products Div., Sterling-Canada Group, Aurora, Ont., Canada
    Winthrop Laboratories Div., Sterling-Canada Group, Aurora, Ont., Canada

STERLING SOFTWARE INC   8080 N Central Expy, #1100, Dallas, TX 75206-1895,
  Tel: (214) 891-8600
  (Sales/serv software prdts; tech servs)
    Asyst Technologies, Inc., 1061 St. Alexandre- #100, Montreal, Quebec H2Z 1P4, Canada
    Sterling Software Intl., Inc., 2235 Sheppard Ave. East- #901, Willowdale,
      Ontario M2J 5A6, Canada
    Zanthe Systems Division, 500-36 Antares Dr., Nepean, Ontario K2E 7V2, Canada

J P STEVENS & CO INC   1185 Ave of the Americas, New York, NY 10036,
  Tel: (212) 930-2000
  (Mfr bed linens & accessories, terry prdts)
    J.P. Stevens Co. (Canada) Ltd., 474 Attwell Dr., Rexdale, Ont., Canada M9W 1M4

STONE & WEBSTER ENGINEERING CORP   245 Summer St, Boston, MA 02107,
  Tel: (617) 973-5111
  (Engineering, constr & consulting serv)
    Stone & Webster Canada Ltd., 2300 Yonge St., Toronto, Ont., Canada M4P 2W6

STONE CONTAINER CORP   150 N Michigan Ave, Chicago, IL 60601-7568,
  Tel: (312) 346-6600
  (Mfr paper & paper packaging)
    Macmillan Bathurst, 2070 Hadwen Rd., Mississauga, Ont., Canada L5K 2C9
    Stone Consolidated Inc, 800 Rene Levesque Blvd. W., Montreal, Que., Canada H3C 2R5

STORAGE TECHNOLOGY CORP   2270 S 88th St, Louisville, CO 80028-0001,
  Tel: (303) 673-5151
  (Mfr/mkt/serv info storage & retrieval sys)
    StorageTek Canada Inc., 51 International Blvd., Rexdale, Ont. M9W 6H3, Canada

STRATOFLEX INC   220 Roberts Cut-Off Rd, PO Box 10398, Fort Worth, TX 76114,
  Tel: (817) 738-6543
  (Hose assemblies, self-sealing & quick disconnect couplings, swivels, etc)
    Stratoflex of Canada Inc., P.O. Box 44, Station U, Toronto, Ont., Canada M8Z 5N2

STREETER RICHARDSON DIV   680 Van Houten Ave, Clifton, NJ 07015,
  Tel: (201) 471-3400
  (Ind weighing & packaging equip)
    Howe Richardson Scale of Canada, 217 Brunswick Blvd., Pointe Claire, Que.,
      Canada H9R 4R7

SUDLER & HENNESSEY   1633 Broadway, New York, NY 10019, Tel: (212) 265-8000
  (Healthcare prdts advertising)
    Sudler & Hennessey, 60 Bloor St. W., Toronto, Ont., M4W 1J2, Canada

SUN CO INC   100 Matsonford Rd, Radnor, PA 19087, Tel: (215) 293-6000
  (Petroleum & petroleum prdts)
    Suncor Inc., 36 York Mills Rd., North York, Ont. M2P 2C5, Canada

SUN ELECTRIC CORP   One Sun Pkwy, Crystal Lake, IL 60014, Tel: (815) 459-7700
  (Mfr auto tune-up, diagnostic & emission testing equip)
    Sun Automotive Eqipment (Canada) Ltd., 5466 Timerlea Blvd., Mississauga, Ont.,
      Canada L4W 2T7

SUNBEAM-OSTER INTL   5055 N Lydell Ave, Milwaukee, WI 53217,
  Tel: (414) 361-8223
  (Mfr small houseware prdts)
    Sunbeam Corp. (Canada) Ltd., 1040 Islington Ave.., Toronto, Ont., Canada. M8Z 4R5

SUNRISE MEDICAL INC   2355 Crenshaw Blvd, #150, Torrance, CA 90501,
  Tel: (213) 328-8018
  (Mfr medical prdts)
    Sunrise Medical Canada, 265 Hood Rd.- Unit 3, Markham, Ontario L3R 4N3, Canada

SUNSHINE BISCUITS INC   100 Woodbridge Centre Dr, Woodbridge, NJ 07095,
  Tel: (908) 855-4000
  (Mfr crackers & cookies)
    Humpty Dumpty Foods Ltd., 2100 Norman St., Lachine, Que., Canada H8S 1B1
    Sunshine Biscuits Ltd., 195 Rexdale Blvd., Toronto, Ont., Canada M9W 1P7

THE SUPERIOR ELECTRIC CO   383 Middle St, Bristol, CT 06010,
  Tel: (203) 582-9561
  (Mfr voltage regulators/conditioners, transformers, motion control prdts)
    The American Superior Electric Co. Ltd., 38 Torlake Crescent, Toronto, Ont.,
      Canada M8Z 1B3

SUPERIOR INDUSTRIES INTL INC   7800 Woodley Ave, Van Nuys, CA 91406,
  Tel: (213) 781-4973
  (Mfr automotive prdts)
    Superior Performance Products Ltd., P.O. Box 179, Newmarket, Ont., Canada

SWECO INC   7120 New Buffington Rd, Florence, KY 41042, Tel: (606) 727-5100
  (Mfr vibratory process & solids control equip)
    Sweco Canada Inc., 40 Titan Rd., Toronto, Ont., Canada M8Z 2J8

M SWIFT & SONS INC   10 Love Lane, Hartford, CT 06141, Tel: (203) 522-1181
  (Gold leaf & hot die stamping foil in all finishes)
    M. Swift & Sons (Canada) Ltd., 1801 Favard St., Montreal, Que., Canada

SYBRON CORP   411 E Wisconsin Ave, Milwaukee, WI 07662, Tel: (414) 274-6600
  (Professional health prdts, spec chems, instru, water & waste water treatment sys)
    Ando Laboratories Ltd., P.O. Box 550, Calgary, Alta., Canada T2P 2J2
    Ando Laboratories Ltd., P.O. Box-2123, Vancouver, B.C., Canada V6B 3T5
    Dental Products Div. of Sybron Canada Ltd., 6845 Rexwood Rd., Mississauga, Ont.,
      Canada L4V 1R2
    Gamlen Chemical Co., 595 Guimond Blvd., Longueuil, Que., Canada
    Medical Products Div. of Sybron Canada Ltd., 75 Tycos Dr., Toronto, Ont.,
      Canada M6B 1W4
    Tanatex Canada Co., 120 Norfinch Dr., Downsview, Ont.,. Canada M3N 1X3
    Taylor Instrument Div., Sybron Canada Ltd., 75 Tycos Dr., Toronto, Ont.,
      Canada M6B 1W4

SYSTEM INDUSTRIES INC   560 Cottonwood Dr, Milpitas, CA 95035,
  Tel: (408) 432-1212
  (Value added third party vendor high performance data storage sybsys)
    System Industries, 718 12th Ave., SW 101, Calgary, Alta., Canada T2R OH7
    System Industries, 237 Argyle St., Ottawa, Ont., Canada K2P 1B8
    System Industries, 1281 West Georgia #900, Vancouver, BC, Canada V6E 3J7
    System Industries, 2 Roberts Speck Parkway, Mississauga, Ont., Canada L4Z 1HB

SYSTEMS ENGINEERING LABS INC   6901 W Sunrise Blvd, Fort Lauderdale,
  FL 33313, Tel: (305) 587-2900
  (Digital computers)
    Selcan Ltd., 205 5th Ave. SW, Calgary, Alta., Canada T2P 2V7
    Selcan Ltd., 100 Alexis Nihon Blvd., St. Laurent, Que., Canada H4M 2N6

TACO INC   1160 Cranston St, Cranston, RI 02920, Tel: (401) 942-8000
  (Hydronic & solar system equip)
    Taco Heaters of Canada Ltd., 3090 Lenworth Dr., Mississauga, Ont., Canada

TANDEM COMPUTERS INC   19333 Vallco Parkway, Cupertino, CA 95014,
  Tel: (408) 725-6000
  (Computer sys)
    Tandem Computers Canada Ltd., Edmonton, Alta., Canada
    Tandem Computers Canada Ltd., Montreal, Que., Canada
    Tandem Computers Canada Ltd., Vancouver, B.C., Canada
    Tandem Computers Canada Ltd., Toronto, Ont., Canada

TANDY CORP   1800 One Tandy Center, Fort Worth, TX 76102, Tel: (817) 390-3700
  (Electronic & acoustic equip)
    Radio Shack Canada, P.O. Box 34000, 279 Bayview Dr., Barrie, Ont., Canada L4M 4W5

THE TAPECOAT CO INC   1527 Lyons St, Evanston, IN 60204-0631,
  Tel: (708) 866-8500
  (Mfr protective coatings for buried metal structures)
    The Tapecoat Co. Ltd., 25 Haas Rd., Rexdale, Ont., Canada M9W 3A1

TATE ACCESS FLOORS INC   7510 Montevideo Rd, Jessup, MD 20794,
Tel: (301) 799-4200
(Mfr access flooring for computers & offices)
   Tate Access Floors Inc., 960 Kamato Rd., Mississauga, Ont., Canada L4W 2R6

TAYLOR INSTRUMENT CO   99 Ames St, PO Box 110, Rochester, NY 14601,
Tel: (716) 235-6806
(Instru for process control inds)
   Taylor Instrument Co. of Canada Ltd., 75 Tycos Dr., Toronto, Ont., Canada

TECHNICAL TAPE INC   LeFevre Lane, New Rochelle, NY 10801, Tel: (914) 235-1000
(Pressure sensitive tapes, poly-ethylene prdts)
   Dominion Tape of Canada Ltd., 104 William St., Cornwall, Ont., Canada K6H 5T6

TECUMSEH PRODUCTS CO   100 E Patterson St, Tecumseh, MI 49286,
Tel: (517) 423-8411
(Refrig & A/C compressors & units, small engines, pumps)
   Tecumseh Products of Canada Ltd., Box 2033, Terminal A, London, Ont., Canada

TED BATES WORLDWIDE INC   1515 Broadway, New York, NY 10036,
Tel: (212) 869-3131
(Advertising agency)
   Publicite Bates Inc., 1425 Blvd. Dorchester W., Montreal, Que, Canada H3G 1T7
   Sptizer, Mills & Bates Ltd., 780 Bay St., Toronto, Ont., Canada M5G 1N9
   Ted Bates Advertising Inc., 790 Bay St., Toronto, Ont., Canada M5G 1N9

TEEPAK INC   3 Westbrook Corp Center, Westchester, IL 60154,
Tel: (708) 409-3000
(Mfr cellulose, fibrous, collegen sausage casings & plastic packaging)
   Teepak Industries Ltd., 3471 McNicoll Ave., Unit 2, Scarborough, Ont.,
   Canada M1V 4B8

TEKTRONIX INC   PO Box 500, Beaverton, OR 97077, Tel: (503) 627-7111
(Mfr test & meas, visual sys & commun prdts)
   Tektronix Canada Ltd., P.O. Box 6500, Barrie, Ont., Canada L4M 4V3
   Tektronix Canada Ltd., 3016 19th St. NE, Calgary, Alta., Canada T2E 4Y3
   Tektronix Canada Ltd., 900 Selkirk St., Pointe Claire, Que., Canada H9R 3S3
   Tektronix Canada Ltd., 1642 Woodward Dr., Ottawa, Ont., Canada K2C 2B8
   Tektronix Canada Ltd., 4519 Canada Way, Burnaby, BC, Canada V5G 1K1

TELEDYNE FIRTH STERLING INC   470 Streets Run Rd, Pittsburgh, PA 15236,
Tel: (412) 464-5200
(Sintered tungsten carbides for metal cutting, metal forming, etc)
   Teledyne Canada Firth Sterling, 43 Spalding Dr., Brantford, Ont., Canada N.3T 5P9

TELEFLEX INC   155 S Limerick Rd, Limerick, PA 19468, Tel: (215) 948-5100
(Designs/mfr/mkt mech & electro-mech sys, meas sys)
   Teleflex (Canada) Ltd., 1650 W. Second Ave., Vancouver, B.C., Canada V6J 1H4

TELEX COMMUNICATIONS INC   9600 Aldrich Ave S, Minneapolis, MN 55420,
Tel: (612) 884-4051
(Mfr audio-visual equip)
   Telex Communications Ltd. Canada, 705 Progress Ave., Unit 10, Scarborough, Ont.,
   Canada M1H 2X1

TELXON CORP   3330 W Market St, Akron, OH 44333, Tel: (216) 867-3700
(Devel/mfr portable computer sys & related equip)
   Telxon Canada Corp., Inc., 80 Microcourt- #100, Markham, Ontario L3R 9Z5, Canada

TENNANT CO   701 N Lilac Dr, Minneapolis, MN 55440, Tel: (612) 540-1200
(Mfr ind floor maint sweepers & scrubbers, roofing machs)
   Tennant Co., 1329 Cardiff Blvd., Mississauga, Ont., Canada L5S 1R2

TENNESSEE ASSOCIATES INTL INC   337 East Broadway Ave, Maryville, TN 37801,
Tel: (615) 983-4044
(Mgt consulting servs)
   Tennessee Associates Intl., Ltd., 319 Lakeshore Rd. East, Mississauga,
   Ontario L5G 1H3, Canada

TEXACO INC   2000 Westchester Ave, White Plains, NY 10650, Tel: (914) 253-4000
(Explor/mktg crude oil & its prdts, petro-chems)
   Texaco Canada Inc., 90 Wynford Dr., Don Mills, Ont., Canada M3C 1K5

TEXAS EASTERN TRANSMISSION CORP   PO Box 2521, Houston, TX 77252,
Tel: (713) 759-3131
(Energy pipeliner, oil/gas explor & prod)
   Texas Eastern Exploration of Canada Ltd., 1502 49th St. SE, Calgary, Alta., Canada

TEXAS INSTRUMENTS INC   PO Box 655474, Dallas, TX 75265, Tel: (214) 995-2011
(Mfr semiconductor devices, electr/electro-mech sys, instr & controls)
   Texas Instruments Canada, 280 Centre St. E., Richmond Hill, Ont., Canada L4C 1B1

TEXAS IRON WORKS INC   12300 S Main St, PO Box 35729, Houston, TX 77235,
Tel: (713) 729-2110
(Mfr liner hanger equip, production packers, safety & kelly valves)
   TIW Canada Ltd., 507 12th Ave., Nisky, Alta., Canada T0C 2G0

TEXAS REFINERY CORP   1 Refinery Pl, Fort Worth, TX 76101, Tel: (817) 332-1161
(Mfr bldg. maintenance prdts & spec lubricants)
   Texas Refinery Corp. of Canada, Ltd., all mail to: 1 Refinery Pl., Fort Worth,
   TX 76101

TEXON INC   Crescent Mills St, Russell, MA 01071, Tel: (413) 862-3652
(Latex & resin impregnated fibre prdts)
   Texon, Inc., Cornwall, Ont., Canada

TEXTRON INC   40 Westminster St, Providence, RI 02903, Tel: (401) 421-2800
(Mfr aerospace tech & coml prdts; fin servs)
   Textron Canada Ltd., Scotia Plaza, 40 King St. W., Toronto, Ont., Canada M5H 3Y4

THERM-O-DISC INC   1320 S Main St, Mansfield, OH 44907-0538,
Tel: (419) 525-8500
(Mfr thermostats, controls, sensor & thermal cutoffs, switches)
   Therm-O-Disc Canada Ltd., 95 Edgeware Rd., St. Thomas, Ont., Canada N5P 4C4

THERMO ELECTRIC CO   109 Fifth St, Saddle Brook, NJ 07662, Tel: (201) 843-5800
(Mfr temp/meas control prdts)
   Thermo Electric (Canada) Ltd., 12 Rutherford Rd. S, Brampton, Ont., Canada L6W 3J2
   Thermo Electric (Canada) Ltd., 3005 DeBaene St., Ville St. Laurent, Montreal, Que.,
   Canada H4S 1K8
   Thermo Electric (Canada) Ltd., c/o Norman Columbia Process Equip., 1234 Marine Dr.,
   N. Vancouver,

(cont)

Thermo Electric (Canada) Ltd., B.C., Canada V7P 1T2
Thermo Electric (Canada) Ltd., 8425 Argyll Rd., Edmonton, Alta., Canada T6C 4B2
Thermo Electric (Canada) Ltd., c/o Electro Systems Group, 532 Berry St., Winnipeg,
   Man., Canada R3H OR9

THERMO ELECTRON CORP   101 First Ave, Waltham, MA 02154, Tel: (617) 890-8700
   (Devel/mfr of process equip & instru for energy intensive inds)
   Holcroft & Co. (Canada) Ltd., 94 Bessemer Ct., London, Ont., Canada N6E 1K7
   Thermo Electron (Canada) Inc., 6875 Bombardier St., St. Leonard, Que.,
      Canada H1P 3A1

THETFORD CORP   7101 Jackson Rd, PO Box 1285, Ann Arbor, MI 48106,
   Tel: (313) 769-6000
   (Sanitation sys)
   Thetford Sanitation Ltd., 2299 Drew Rd., Unit 12, Mississauga, Ont., Canada L5S 1A1

THOMAS & BETTS CORP   1001 Frontier Rd, Bridgewater, NJ 08807-0993,
   Tel: (201) 685-1600
   (Mfr elect/electr connectors & accessories)
   Thomas & Betts Ltd., P.O. Box 30700, Iberville, Que., Canada J2X 2M9

THOMAS BUILT BUSES INC   1408 Courtesy Rd, PO Box 2450, High Point, NC 27261,
   Tel: (919) 889-4871
   (Mfr buses)
   Thomas Built Buses of Canada Ltd., P.O. Box 580, Woodstock, Ont., Canada

THOMAS INDUSTRIES INC   4360 Brownsboro Rd, #300, Louisville, KY 40207,
   Tel: (502) 893-4600
   (Mfr lighting fixtures, compressors, vacuum pumps, spec prdts)
   Lumec Inc., 618 Cure Boivin Blvd., Boisbrand, Que., Canada J7G 2A7
   Thomas Lighting Inc., 189 Bullock Dr., Markham, Ont., Canada L3P 1W4

THOR POWER TOOL CO   72 Bayside Rd, Virginia Beach, VA 23455,
   Tel: (804) 323-5666
   (Mfr portable air-operated & elect tools)
   Thor Power Tool Co., 1715 Meyerside Dr., Mississauga, Ont., Canada

TIDELAND SIGNAL CORP   4310 Directors Row, PO Box 52430, Houston,
   TX 77052-2430, Tel: (713) 681-6101
   (Mfr aids to navigation)
   Tideland Signal Canada Ltd., 105-3650 Bonneville Pl., Burnaby, BC V3N 4T7, Canada

THE TIMKEN CO   1835 Dueber Ave SW, Canton, OH 44706-2798, Tel: (216) 438-3000
   (Mfr tapered roller bearings & alloy steels)
   Canadian Timken, 1055 Talbot St., St. Thomas, Ontario N5P 1G5, Canada

TOKHEIM CORP   1602 Wabash Ave, PO Box 360, Fort Wayne, IN 46801,
   Tel: (219) 423-2552
   (Mfr gasoline service station dispensers, access, hand & in-tank fuel pumps)
   Tokheim of Canada Ltd., 5988 Ambler Dr., Mississauga, Ont., Canada L4W 2P2

TONKA CORP   6000 Clearwater Dr, Minnetonka, MN 55343, Tel: (612) 936-3300
   (Mfr children's toys)
   Tonka Corp. Canada, 7630 Airport Rd., Mississauga, Ont., Canada L4T 2H6

TOOTSIE ROLL INDUSTRIES INC   7401 S Cicero Ave, Chicago, IL 60629,
  Tel: (312) 581-6100
  (Mfr candies, chocolate prdts)
    Tootsie Roll of Canada Ltd., 260 Brimley Rd., Scarborough, Ont., Canada

TOWERS PERRIN FORSTER & CROSBY INC   245 Park Ave, New York, NY 10167,
  Tel: (212) 309-3400
  (Management consulting)
    TPF&C Limited, 150 6th Ave. SW, Calgary, Alta., Canada T2P 3Y7
    TPF&C Limited, 1800 McGill College Ave., Montreal, Que., Canada H3A 3J6
    TPF&C Limited, 250 Bloor St. E., #1100, Toronto, Ont., Canada M4W 3N3
    TPF&C Limited, 1100 Melville St., Vancouver, B.C., Canada V6E 4A6

TRANE CO   3600 Pammel Creek Rd, La Crosse, WI 54601, Tel: (608) 787-2000
  (Mfr A/C equip)
    Trane Co. of Canada Ltd., 401 Horner Ave., Toronto, Ont., Canada M8W 2A5

TRANS-LUX CORP   110 Richards Ave, Norwalk, CT 06854, Tel: (203) 853-4321
  (Telecom terminals, facsimile equip, moving-msg displays)
    Canadian Trans-Lux Corp. Ltd., 5446 Gorvan Dr., Mississauga, Ont., Canada L4W 3E8

TRANSCONTINENTAL GAS PIPE LINE CORP   2700 Post Oak Blvd, Houston, TX 77056,
  Tel: (713) 871-8000
  (Purchase, transmission & sale of natural gas)
    Transco Production of Canada Ltd., 565 Bow Valley Sq., Calgary, Alta., Canada

TREMCO INC   10701 Shaker Blvd, Cleveland, OH 44104, Tel: (216) 229-3000
  (Protective coatings & sealants for building, maint & constr)
    Tremco Mfg. Co. Ltd., 220 Wicksteed Ave., Toronto, Ont., Canada

TRINOVA CORP   3000 Strayer, PO Box 50, Maumee, OH 43537, Tel: (419) 867-2200
  (Mfr engr components & sys for ind)
    Aeroquip (Canada) Ltd., 287 Bridgeland Ave., Toronto, Ontario M6A 1ZT, Canada
    Vickers Systems Inc., 280 Attwell Dr., Etobicoke, Ontario M9W 5B6, Canada

TRION INC   101 McNeil Rd, PO Box 760, Sanford, NC 27330, Tel: (919) 775-2201
  (Mfr air cleaners & electrostatic fluid depositors)
    Trion Canada Inc., 130 Otonabee Dr., Kitchener, Ontario N2C 1L6, Canada

TRW INC   1900 Richmond Rd, Cleveland, OH 44124, Tel: (216) 291-7000
  (Electr & energy-related prdts, automotive & aerospace prdts, tools & fasteners)
    Nelson Stud Welding Div., TRW Canada Ltd., 2 Meridian Rd., Rexdale, Ont.,
      Canada M9W 4Z7
    TRW Canada Ltd., Thompson Products Div., P.O. Box 3004, St. Catharine's, Ont.,
      Canada L2R 7B5
    TRW Data Systems, 270 Yorkland Blvd., Willowdale, Ont., Canada M2J 1R8
    TRW Electronics, Tuner Operations, 72 Gervais Dr., Don Mills, Ont., Canada M3C 3H2
    TRW Pleuger of Canada Ltd., 6650 Finch Ave., Rexdale, Ont., Canada M9W 5Y6
    TRW Reda Pump Co. of Canada, 324 Eighth Ave. SW, Calgary, Alta., Canada T2P 2Z2
    United-Carr Div. of TRW Canada Ltd., 455 Arvin Ave., Stoney Creek, Ont.,
      Canada L8G 4A2

TULTEX INTL   22 E Church St, PO Box 215, Martinsville, VA 24114,
  Tel: (703) 632-2961
  (Mfr sporting goods/apparel)
    Tultex Canada Inc., 11417 163rd St., Edmonton, Alberta T5M 3Y3, Canada

W S TYLER INC   PO Box 8900, Gastonia, NC 28053-9065, Tel: (704) 868-3374
(Mfr vibrating screens, lab equip & related screening media)
　　W.S. Tyler Inc., P.O. Box 3006, St. Catharines, Ont. L2R 7B6, Canada

U S GYPSUM CO   101 S Wacker Dr, Chicago, IL 60606, Tel: (312) 321-4000
(Building & constr materials)
　　Canadian Gypsum Co. Ltd., 790 Bay St., Toronto, Ont., Canada M5W 1K8

U S INDUSTRIES INC   PO Box 629, Evansville, IN 47704, Tel: (812) 425-2428
(Diversified prdts & sys for industry, agribusiness & retail markets)
　　Maple Credit Ltd., 1216 Centre St. N, Calgary, Alta., Canada T2E 2R4
　　Maple Credit Ltd., 10054 112th St. E, Edmonton, Alta., Canada T5K 1L9
　　Maple Credit Ltd., 3044 Flint St., Port Coquitlain, B.C., Canada V3B 4H4
　　Maple Credit Ltd., 604 Oxford St., London, Ont., Canada N5Y 3J1
　　Maple Financial Services Ltd., P.O. Box 50, First Canadian Place, Toronto, Ont.,
　　　Canada M5X 1B8
　　Rau of Canada Ltd., 1255 Des Carrieres, Montreal, Que., Canada
　　Sun Lite Industries, 100 Louvain W, Montreal, Que., Canada

U S PLAYING CARD CO   Beech St at Park Ave, Cincinnati, OH 45212,
Tel: (513) 396-5700
(Mfr playing cards & accessories, board games)
　　Intl. Playing Card Co. Ltd., P.O. Box 188, Windsor, Ont., Canada N9A 6K1

UARCO INC   W County Line Rd, Barrington, IL 60010, Tel: (708) 381-7000
(Mfr business forms)
　　Crain-Drummond Inc., 210 Montarville, Boucherville, Que., Canada J4B 6T3

UNIBRAZE CORP   7502 W State, Rte 41, Covington, OH 45318, Tel: (513) 473-2006
(Brazing, welding & soldering alloys of copper, silver, aluminum & brass)
　　Unibraze Corp., 99 Columbus St., Pointe Claire, Que., Canada H9R 4K3

UNION CAMP CORP   1600 Valley Rd, Wayne, NJ 07470, Tel: (201) 628-2000
(Flavors, fragrances, essential oils, aroma chems, corrugated containers)
　　Bush Boake Allen Corp Ltd., 312 St. Patrick St., La Salle, Que., Canada H8N 2H2

UNION OIL INTL DIV   Union Oil Center, PO Box 7600, Los Angeles, CA 90017,
Tel: (213) 977-7600
(Petroleum prdts, petrochems)
　　Union Oil Co. of Canada Ltd., 335 Eighth Ave. SW, Calgary, Alta., Canada T2P 2K6

UNION PACIFIC CORP   Eighth & Eaton Aves, Bethlehem, PA 18018,
Tel: (215) 861-3200
(Holding co: railroad, crude oil, natural gas, petroleum refining, metal mining serv,
real estate)
　　Union Pacific Railroad, 6 Lansing Sq., Willowdale, Ont. M2J 1T5, Canada
　　Union Pacific-Spokane Intl. Railroads, 717-304 Eighth Ave. SW, Calgary, Alta.,
　　　Canada

UNION SPECIAL CORP   222 No LaSalle, Chicago, IL 60601, Tel: (312) 606-9500
(Mfr ind sewing machs)
　　Union Special of Canada Ltd., 9495 Charles de Latour St., Montreal, Que.,
　　　Canada H4N 1M5
　　Union Special of Canada Ltd., 2410 Tedlo St., Unit 1, Mississauga, Ont.,
　　　Canada L5A 3V3

UNISYS CORP   PO Box 500, Blue Bell, PA 19424, Tel: (215) 542-4011
  (Mfg/mktg/serv electr info sys)
    Unisys, 55 City Centre Dr., Mississauga, Ont., Canada L5B 1M4

UNITED CALIFORNIA BANK   PO Box 54191, Los Angeles, CA 90054,
  Tel: (213) 624-0111
  (Banking)
    UCB Financial Services Ltd., Royal Bank Plaza, P.O. Box 3, Toronto, Ont.,
      Canada M5J 2J1

UNITED INDUSTRIAL SYNDICATE INC   600 Fifth Ave, New York, NY 10020,
  Tel: (212) 581-7660
  (Auto parts, movie projectors, steel fabrication, furniture & wood prdts, etc)
    Automotive Accessory Co. Ltd., 771 Main, Winnipeg, Man., Canada
    Wells Mfg. Co. Canada Ltd., 14 Plastics Ave., Toronto, Ont., Canada

UNITED PRESS INTL   220 E 42nd St, New York, NY 10017, Tel: (212) 682-0400
  (Collection & distributor of news, newspictures, fin data)
    United Press Intl. Ltd., 366 Adelaide St. E, Toronto, Ont., Canada M5A 1N4

UNITEK CORP/3M   2724 S Peck Rd, Monrovia, CA 91016-7118, Tel: (818) 574-4000
  (Mfr orthodontic prdts)
    Inter-Unitek Canada Ltd., 20 Standish Crescent, Markham, Ont., Canada L3 4A3

UNIVAR CORP   801 Second Ave, #1600, Seattle, WA 98104, Tel: (206) 447-5911
  (Chemical distributor)
    Van Waters & Rogers Ltd., 9800 Van Horne Way, Richmond, BC V6X 1W5, Canada

UNIVERSAL LEAF TOBACCO CO   PO Box 25099, Richmond, VA 23260,
  Tel: (804) 359-9311
  (Leaf tobaccos, fertilizer)
    Canadian Leaf Tobacco Co. Ltd., P.O. Box 280, Simcoe, Ont., Canada N3Y 4L1

UOP INC   Ten UOP Plaza, Des Plaines, IL 60016, Tel: (708) 391-2000
  (Diversified research, development & mfr of ind prdts & sys mgmt studies & serv)
    Flexonics Div., UOP Ltd., Brampton, Ont., Canada
    Forest Products Div., UOP Ltd., North Bay, Ont., Canada
    Forest Products Div., UOP Ltd., Tee Lake, Que., Canada
    Forest Products Div., UOP Ltd., Mattawa, Ont., Canada
    Forest Products Div., UOP Ltd., Rutherglen, Ont., Canada
    Forest Products Div., UOP Ltd., Deu Rivieres, Quebec, Canada
    Johnson Div., UOP Ltd., Ajax, Ont., Canada
    Shawinigan Procon Co., Toronto, Ont., Canada
    Shawinigan Procon Co., Calgary, Alta., Canada
    Wolverine Div., UOP Ltd., London, Ont., Canada

UPJOHN CO   7000 Portage Rd, Kalamazoo, MI 49001, Tel: (616) 323-4000
  (Pharms, agric prdts, ind chems)
    The Upjohn Co. of Canada Ltd., 865 York Mills Rd., Don Mills, Ont., Canada M3B 1Y6

UPSON CO   Upson Point, Lockport, NY 14094, Tel: (716) 434-8881
  (Bldg materials, laminated wood fire panels)
    The Upson Co. of Canada Ltd., 61 Catherine St., St. Catharines, Ont.,
      Canada   L2R 5E9

USG CORP   101 S Wacker Dr, Chicago, IL 60606, Tel: (312) 606-4122
   (Holding co: bldg prdts ind)
      Canadian Gypsum Co., 777 Bay St., PO Box 4034/ Terminal A, Toronto,
         Ontario M5W 1K8, Canada

USX ENGINEERS & CONSULTANTS INC   600 Grant St, Pittsburgh, PA 15219,
   Tel: (412) 391-8115
   (Engr & consulting serv)
      Met-Chem Canada Inc., 425 Blvd. de Maisonneuve W., Montreal, Que., Canada H3A 3G5

UTAH INTL INC   550 California St, San Francisco, CA 94104,
   Tel: (415) 981-1515
   (Mining, land development, ocean shipping, oil & gas)
      Utah Mines Ltd., 1050 W. Pender St., Vancouver, B.C., Canada V6E 3S7
      Utah Mines Ltd., 4 King St. W, Toronto, Ont., Canada M5H 1B6

UTILICORP UNITED INC   PO Box 13287, Kansas City, MO 64199,
   Tel: (816) 421-6600
   (Electric & gas utility)
      West Kootenay Power Ltd., Waneta Plaza, 8100 Rock Island Highway, Trail,
         BC V1R 4N7, Canada

VALERON CORP   750 Stephenson Highway, Troy, MI 48084, Tel: (313) 589-1000
   (Cemented carbide, high speed steel, ceramic & diamond cutting tool prdts, etc)
      Valenite Modco Ltd., 1456 Wallace Rd., Oakville, Ont., Canada L6L 2Y2

VALSPAR CORP   1101 South Third St, PO Box 1461, Minneapolis, MN 55415,
   Tel: (612) 332-7371
   (Paint, varnish & allied prdts)
      Valspar Inc., 5669 Casgrain Ave., Montreal, Que., Canada

VAN STRAATEN CHEMICAL CO   630 W Washington Blvd, Chicago, IL 60606,
   Tel: (312) 454-1000
   (Metalworking fluids, ind cleaners, rust preventives, etc)
      Van Straaten of Canada Inc., 514 Carlingview Dr., Rexcale, Ont., Canada M9W 5R3

VAPOR CORP   6420 W Howard St, Chicago, IL 60648, Tel: (708) 967-8300
   (Mfr railway passenger car heating & A/C equip)
      Vapor Canada Ltd., 10655 Henri-Bourassa West, Ville St. Laurent, Montreal, Que.,
         Canada

VAREL MFG CO   9230 Denton Rd, PO Box 20156, Dallas, TX 75220,
   Tel: (214) 351-6487
   (Oil, mining, geophysical, water-well & constr equip)
      Varel Canada Ltd., 11-6120 3rd St. SE, Calgary, Alta., Canada T2H 1K4

VARIAN ASSOCIATES INC   611 Hansen Way, Palo Alto, CA 94304-1030,
   Tel: (415) 493-4000
   (Mfr microwave tubes & devices, analytical instru, semiconductor process & med equip,
   vacuum sys)
      Varian Canada Ltd., 45 River Dr., Georgetown, Ont., Canada L7G 2J4

VEEDER-ROOT CO   125 Powder Forest Dr, PO Box 2003, Simsbury, CT 06070-2003,
   Tel: (203) 651-2700
   (Mfr counting, controlling & sensing devices)
      Veeder-Root of Canada Ltd., 26 Fieldway Rd., Toronto, Ont., Canada M8Z 3L2

VELSICOL CHEMICAL CORP   5600 N River Rd, Rosemont, IL 60018,
Tel: (708) 698-9700
(Pesticides & ind chems)
Velsicol Corp. of Canada Ltd., 1360 Blundell Rd., Mississauga, Ont., Canada L4Y 1M5

VETCO-GRAY INC   250 W Stanley Ave, Ventura, CA 93001, Tel: (805) 653-2500
(Offshore oilfield equip & tools, oilfield inspect & coating serv)
Vetco Offshore Inc., 205 5th Ave. SW, Calgary, Alta., Canada T2P 2W7

VIACOM INTL INC   1211 Ave of the Americas, New York, NY 10036,
Tel: (212) 575-5175
(Diversified entertainment & commun)
Viacom Enterprises Canada, 45 Charles St. E, Toronto, Ont., Canada M4Y 1S2

THE VIKING CORP   210 N Ind Rd, Hastings, MI 49058, Tel: (616) 945-9501
(Mfr fire extinguishing equip)
Viking Fire Protection Ltd., 3005 Pitfield Blvd., St. Laurent, Que., Canada M4S 1H4

VIRGINIA CHEMICALS INC   3340 W Norfolk Rd, Portsmouth, VA 23703,
Tel: (804) 483-7345
(Ind chems, insecticides, refrigerants, etc)
Virchem Canada Inc., 323 Church St., Oakville, Ont., Canada L6J 1P2

VIVITAR CORP   9350 Desoto Ave, Chatsworth, CA 91313, Tel: (818) 700-2890
(Photographic equip, electr supplies)
Vivitar Canada Ltd., 5211 Creekbank Rd., Mississauga, Ontraio, Canada L4W 1R3

VSI CORP   8463 Highera St, Culver City, CA 90232, Tel: (213) 202-8200
(Mold & die makers, diversified prdts for home & ind)
D-M-E Canada Ltd., 6210 Northwest Dr., Mississauga, Ontarlo, Canada L4V 1J6

WACKENHUT CORP   1500 San Remo Ave, Coral Gables, FL 33146,
Tel: (305) 666-5656
(Security sys & serv)
Wackenhut of Canada Ltd., 1 East Mall Crescent, Toronto, Ont., Canada M9B 6G9
Wackenhut of Canada Ltd., other locations in Canada

WAGNER BRAKE DIVISION   3700 Forest Park Blvd, St Louis, MO 63108,
Tel: (314) 537-8700
(Mfr automotive brakes)
Wagner Brake Division, Bramalea, Ontario, Canada

WAHL CLIPPER CORP   2902 N Locust St, Sterling, IL 61081, Tel: (815) 625-6525
(Mfr clippers, soldering irons)
Wahl Clipper Corp. Ltd., 80 Orfus Rd., Toronto, Ont., Canada M6A 1M7

WALBAR INC   Peabody Ind Center, PO Box 3369, Peabody, MA 01960,
Tel: (508) 532-6999
(Mfr turbine components for engines; repair & coating serv)
Walbar Canada Inc., 1303 Aerowood Dr., Mississauga, Ont., Canada L4W 2P6

WALKER MFG CO   1201 Michigan Blvd, Racine, WI 53402, Tel: (414) 632-8871
(Automotive parts, exhaust sys, service equip)
Walker Canada, 500 Conestoga Blvd., Cambridge, Ont., Canada N1R 5T7

WALL COLMONOY CORP   30261 Stephenson Hwy, Madison Hghts, MI 48071,
  Tel: (313) 585-6400
  (Mfr metallizing & welding equip, alloys, casting, brazing, aircraft engine parts)
    Wall Colmonoy (Canada) Inc., 210-1 Willmott St., P.O. Box 787, Cobourg, Ont.,
      Canada K9A 4S3

WALLACE & TIERNAN DIV   25 Main St, Belleville, NJ 07109, Tel: (201) 759-8000
  (Chems, instru)
    Wallace & Tiernan Ltd., 925 Warden Ave., Scarborough, Ont., Canada M1L 4C5

WANG LABORATORIES INC   1 Industrial Ave, Lowell, MA 01851,
  Tel: (508) 459-5000
  (Mfr computer info processing sys)
    Wang Laboratories (Canada) Ltd., 66 Leek Crescent, Wang Way, Richmond Hill, Ont.,
      Canada L4B 1J7

WARNACO INC   350 Lafayette St, Bridgeport, CT 06601, Tel: (203) 579-8272
  (Intimate apparel, men's & women's shirts, ski & sportswear)
    Warnaco of Canada Ltd., St. Lawrence St., Prescott, Ont., Canada K0E IT0

WARNER-LAMBERT CO   201 Tabor Road, Morris Plains, NJ 07950,
  Tel: (201) 540-2000
  (Mfr ethical & proprietary pharms, confectionary & consumer prdts)
    Warner-Lambert Canada Inc., 2200 Eglinton E, Toronto, Ont., Canada M1L 2N3

WATERS CHROMATOGRAPHY DIV   34 Maple St, Milford, MA 01757,
  Tel: (617) 478-2000
  (Mfr/distr liquid chromatographic instru/accessories/tech)
    Millipore Ltd., Waters Chromat. Div., 3688 Nashua Dr., Mississauga, Ont.,
      Canada L4V 1M5
    Waters Associates Scientific Ltd., 6480 Viscount Rd., Mississauga, Ont.,
      Canada L4V 1H3

WATKINS INC   150 Liberty St, Winona, MN 55987, Tel: (507) 457-3300
  (Mfr cosmetics, medicines, spices & extracts, household cleaning prdts)
    Watkins Inc., 30-5 Scurfield Blvd., Winnipeg, Man., Canada R3Y 1G3

WAXMAN INDUSTRIES INC   24460 Aurora Rd, Bedford Heights, OH 44146,
  Tel: (216) 439-1830
  (Assemble/distr plumbing, electrical & hardware prdts)
    H. Belanger Plumbing Accessories Ltd., 6445 De Maisonneuve West, Montreal,
      Quebec H4B 2Z1, Canada
    Ideal Plumbing Group, Inc., 2905 Industrial Blvd., Laval, Quebec H7L 3W9, Canada

WEAN INC   13 South, 3 Gateway Center, Pittsburgh, PA 15222,
  Tel: (412) 456-5300
  (Design & mfr metal working & metal producing equip)
    Wean Canada Ltd., Box 366, Cambridge, Ont., Canada N1R 5V6

WEATHERFORD INTL INC   1360 Post Oak Blvd, PO Box 27608, Houston,
  TX 77227-9917, Tel: (713) 439-9400
  (Tubular & cementation servs, prdts & equip; water jetting servs, mfr marine pedestal
  cranes)
    Weatherford Intl. Inc., 14435 - 116 Ave., Edmonton, Alta., Canada T5M 3E8
    Weatherford Intl. Inc., other locations in Canada

JERVIS B WEBB CO   34375 W Twelve Mile Rd, Farmington Hills, MI 48331,
  Tel: (313) 553-1000
  (Integrators of material handling sys)
    Jervis B. Webb Co. of Canada Ltd., 1647 Burlington St. E, Hamilton, Ont.,
      Canada L8H 7M5

WEBER COSTELLO CO   200 Academic Way, Troy, MO 63379, Tel: (314) 528-9500
  (Mfr office & school prdts)
    Weber Costello Canada, 2000 Drew Rd., Mississauga, Ont., Canada L5S 1S4

WEBER MARKING SYSTEMS INC   711 W Algonquin Rd, Arlington Heights, IL 60005,
  Tel: (708) 364-8500
  (Mfr label printing sys, custom labels)
    Weber Marking Systems (Canada) Ltd., 2728 Slough St., Mississauga, Ont.,
      Canada L4T 1G3

WEIL-McLAIN   Blaine St, Michigan City, IN 46360, Tel: (219) 879-6561
  (Hot water & steam boilers)
    Wylain Canada Ltd., 126 East Dr., Brampton, Ont., Canada L6T 1C2

THE WEST BEND CO   400 Washington St, West Bend, WI 53095, Tel: (414) 334-2311
  (Mfr small elec appliances, cookware, water distillers, timers)
    West Bend of Canada, P.O. Box 6000, 191 John St., Barrie, Ont., Canada L4M 4V3

WESTERN GEOPHYSICAL   PO Box 2469, Houston, TX 77252-2469, Tel: (713) 789-9600
  (Geophysical serv)
    Western Geophysical Co. of Canada Ltd., 2612 37th Ave. NE, Station A, Box 5250,
      Calgary, Alta., Canada T2H 1X6

WESTERN PUBLISHING CO   1220 Mound Ave, Racine, WI 53404, Tel: (414) 633-2431
  (Pub children's & adult books; games, educational prdts)
    Whitman Golden Ltd., 200 Sheldon Dr., Cambridge, Ont., Canada N1R 5X2

WESTINGHOUSE AIR BRAKE CO   40 W 40th St, New York, NY 10018,
  Tel: (212) 840-5440
  (Equip for transp, constr, mining inds)
    Benn Iron Foundry, P.O. Box 130, Wallaceburg, Ont., Canada N8A 4L5
    Canadian Cardwell Div., 1875 46th Ave., Lachine, Que., Canada H8T 2N8
    Canadian Cardwell Div., 1845 46th Ave., Lachine, Que., Canada H8T 2N8
    WABCO Ltd., P.O. Box 2050, Hamilton, Ont., Canada L8N 3T5
    WABCO Ltd., 475 Seaman St., Stoney Creek, Ont., Canada L8E 2R2

WESTINGHOUSE ELECTRIC CORP   Westinghouse Bldg, Gateway Center, Pittsburgh,
  PA 15222, Tel: (412) 244-2000
  (TV/radio broadcasting, mfr electr sys for ind/defense, fin & environmental servs)
    Westinghouse Canada Inc., P.O. Box 510, Hamilton, Ont., Canada L8N 3K2

WEYERHAEUSER CO   Tacoma, WA 98477, Tel: (206) 924-2345
  (Wood & wood fiber prdts)
    Weyerhaeuser Canada Ltd., P.O. Box 800, Kamloops, BC, Canada V2C 5M7

WHEATON INDUSTRIES   1101 Wheaton Ave, Milville, NJ 08332, Tel: (609) 825-1400
  (Glass & plastic containers, glass tableware)
    Wheaton Industries of Canada Ltd., Brampton, Ont., Canada

WHEEL TRUEING TOOL CO   PO Box 1317, Columbia, SC 29202, Tel: (803) 788-8860
  (Diamond drill bits)
    Aqua Tech Mfg., 1860 Sismet Rd., Mississauga, Ont., Canada L4W 1W9
    Wheel Trueing Tool Co. Ltd., P.O. Box 33, Windsor, Ont., Canada N9A 6J5

WHEELABRATOR-FRYE INC   11255 N Torrey Pines Rd, La Jolla, CA 92037,
  Tel: (603) 926-5911
  (Diversified environmental & energy sys, chems, precision & ind equip)
    Sinclair & Valentine of Canada Ltd., Downsview, Ont., Canada
    Wheelabrator of Canada Ltd., 230 Speers Rd., Oakville, Ont., Canada

WHIRLPOOL CORP   2000 M63, Benton Harbor, MI 49022, Tel: (616) 926-5000
  (Mfr appliances)
    Inglis Ltd., 1901 Minnesota Ct., Mississauga, Ont., Canada L5N 3A7

WHITAKER CABLE CORP   PO Box 7499, Kansas City, MO 64116, Tel: (816) 474-0300
  (Electrical wire & cable assemblies for ind & auto replacement mkt)
    Whitaker Cable of Canada Ltd., P.O. Box 608, Owen Sound, Ont., Canada N4K 5R4
    Whitaker Cable of Canada Ltd., P.O. Box 638, Guelph, Ont., Canada N1H 6L3

WHITE CONSOLIDATED INDUSTRIES INC   11770 Berea Rd, Cleveland, OH 44111,
  Tel: (216) 252-3700
  (Major household appliances, ind mach & equip)
    Franklin Mfg. Co. (Canada) Ltd., 501 Franklin Blvd, Cambridge, Ont., Canada N1R 5W5
    Hupp Canada Ltd., L'Assumption, Que., Canada J0K 1G0

WHITE MOP WRINGER CO   PO Box 277, Fultonville, NJ 12072, Tel: (518) 853-3451
  (Mop wringers)
    White Mop Wringer Co. of Canada, 2 Scot Ave., Paris, Ont., Canada N31 3E7

WHITING CORP   15700 Lathrop Ave, Harvey, IL 60426-5098, Tel: (708) 331-4000
  (Mfr EOT cranes, metallurgical & railroad shop equip)
    Whiting Equipment Ltd., 350 Alexander St., Welland, Ont., Canada L3B 3B4

WICKES COS INC   3340 Ocean Park Blvd, Santa Monica, CA 90405,
  Tel: (213) 452-0161
  (Lumber & bldg supplies, steel bldgs, motor homes)
    Behlan-Wickes Bldg. Systems, 5100 Harvester Rd., Burlington, Ont., Canada L7L 4X2
    Behlen-Wickes Co. Ltd., P.O. Box 1120, Brandon, Man., Canada R7A 6A4

JOHN WILEY & SONS INC   605 Third Ave, New York, NY 10158, Tel: (212) 850-6000
  (Publishing)
    John Wiley & Sons Canada Ltd., 22 Worcester Rd., Rexdale, Ont., Canada M9W 1L1

WILLIAM E WRIGHT CO   South St, W Warren, MA 01092, Tel: (413) 436-7762
  (Tapes, braids, apparel & furnishing trims)
    Wm. E. Wright Co. of Canada Ltd., 1123 Leslie St., Don Mills, Ont., Canada M3C 2K1

WILLIAMHOUSE-REGENCY INC   28 W 23rd St, New York, NY 10010,
  Tel: (212) 691-2000
  (Paper converting, thermography)
    Rainbow Thermographers Co., 7400 Victoria Park Ave., Markham, Ont., Canada L3P 3S7
    Rainbow Thermographers Co., 9200 Park Ave., Montreal, Que., Canada H2N 1Z8
    Williamhouse (Ont.) Ltd., 17 Laidlaw Blvd., Markham, Ont., Canada L3P 1W5

WILLIS DIV   2508 E Palm Dr, Long Beach, CA 90807, Tel: (213) 426-4411
  (Oil tools & equip)
    SII Willis, 8620 18th St., Edmonton, Alta., Canada

WILSON JONES CO   6150 W Touhy Ave, Chicago, IL 60648, Tel: (312) 774-7700
  (Business forms, office & school supplies)
    Wilson Jones Div., Swingline of Canada, 7 Engram Dr., Toronto, Ont., Canada M6M 2L8

WITCO CORP   520 Madison Ave, New York, NY 10022-4236, Tel: (212) 605-3800
  (Mfr chem & petroleum prdts)
    Surpass Ltd., 250 Consumers Rd., Willowdale, Ont., Canada M2J 4V6
    Witco Canada Ltd., 2 Lansing Sq., Willowdale, Ont., Canada M2J 4Z4

WOMETCO ENTERPRISES INC   306 N Miami Ave, Miami, FL 33128,
  Tel: (305) 374-6262
  (Television broadcasting, film distribution, bottling, vending machs)
    KVOS-TV, 1345 Burrard St., Vancouver, B.C., Canada V6Z 2A2
    Wometco (B.C.) Ltd., 2471 Viking Way, Richmond, B.C., Canada V6V 1N3
    Wometco Newfoundland Ltd., 60 O'Leary Ave., St. Johns, Newfoundland, Canada A1B 3V8

WOODHEAD INDUSTRIES INC   3411 Woodhead Drive, Northbrook, IL 60062,
  Tel: (708) 272-7990
  (Elect, mech & telecomm prdts for ind)
    Woodhead Industries (Canada) Ltd., 1090 Brevik Pl., Mississauga, Ont.,
      Canada L4W 3Y5

WOODWARD & DICKERSON INC   937 Haverford Road, Bryn Mawr, PA 19010,
  Tel: (215) 527-5200
  (Intl marketing)
    Petrosul Intl. Ltd., 100 Park Royal S., W. Vancouver, BC, Canada V7T 1A2

WOOLWORTH CORP   Woolworth Bldg, 233 Broadway, New York, NY 10279,
  Tel: (212) 553-2000
  (Retail stores)
    F.W. Woolworth Co. Ltd., 33 Adelaide St. W, Toronto, Ont., Canada M5H 1P5

WORK WEAR CORP INC   1768 E 25th St, Cleveland, OH 44114, Tel: (216) 771-4040
  (Mfr uniforms & work apparel, disposables for health care, food service, transp &
  other inds)
    Anchor Textiles, 17 Benton Rd., Toronto, Ont., Canada M6M 3G3
    Ella Skinner, 67 Ingram Dr., Toronto, Ont., Canada M6M 2L7
    Ella Skinner Uniforms Ltd., 57 Ingram Dr., Toronto, Ont., Canada M6M 2L7
    La Corporation Work Wear du Quebec, 6910 Clark St., Montreal, Que., Canada H2S 3G3
    Sainlee Industries Ltd., 100 Broadview Ave., Toronto, Ont., Canada M4M 2E8
    Work Wear Corp. of Canada Ltd., 17 Benton Rd., Toronto, Ont., Canada M6M 3G3
    Work Wear Corp. of Canada Ltd., 17 Benton Rd., Toronto, Ont., Canada M6M 3G3

WORLD COURIER INC   46 Trinity Pl, New York, NY 10006, Tel: (718) 978-9400
  (Intl courier serv)
    World Courier of Canada Ltd., 212 N. Queen St., Etobicoke, Ont., Canada
    World Courier of Canada Ltd., 300 St. Sacrement St., Montreal, Que., Canada

WORLD'S FINEST CHOCOLATE INC   4801 S Lawndale, Chicago, IL 60632,
  Tel: (312) 847-4600
  (Mfr chocolate)
    World's Finest Chocolate Canada Ltd., 2nd St., Campbellford, Ont. K0L 1L0, Canada

WRIGHT LINE INC   160 Gold Star Blvd, Worcester, MA 01606, Tel: (508) 852-4300
  (Mfr filing sys)
    Datafile/Wright Line of Candad Ltd., 130 Sparks Ave., Willowdale, Ont.,
    Canada M2H 2S4

WM WRIGLEY JR CO   410 N Michigan Ave, Chicago, IL 60611-4287,
  Tel: (312) 644-2121
  (Chewing gum)
    Wm. Wrigley Jr. Co. Ltd., 1123 Leslie St., Don Mills, Ont., Canada M3C 2K1

WURLITZER CO   422 Wards Corner Rd, Loveland, OH 45140, Tel: (513) 576-4601
  (Pianos, electronic organs & pianos, vending & pay phonograph machs)
    Wurlitzer Ltd., 560 McNicoll Ave., Willowdale, Ont., Canada M2H 2E1

WYNN OIL CO   2600 E Nutwood Ave, PO Box 4370, Fullerton, CA 92631,
  Tel: (714) 992-2000
  (Chem additives for oil, grease & fuels; hardware)
    Wynn's Canada, 23 Racine Rd., Rexdale, Ont., Canada

YORK INTERNATIONAL CORP   PO Box 1592, York, PA 17405-1592,
  Tel: (715) 771-7890
  (Mfr A/C, heating & refrig sys & equip)
    York Air Conditioning Ltd., 375 Matheson Blvd. E., Mississauga, Ont., Canada L4Z 1X8

YORK-SHIPLEY INC   693 North Hills Rd, York, PA 17402, Tel: (717) 755-1081
  (Mfr automatic heating & processing equip)
    York-Shipley of Canada, 1297 Industrial Rd., P.O. Box 3131, Cambridge, Ont.,
    Canada N3H 4S6

YOUNG & RUBICAM INTL INC   285 Madison Ave, New York, NY 10017,
  Tel: (212) 210-3000
  (Advertising agency)
    Young & Rubicam Ltd., 1155 Dorchester Blvd. W, Montreal, Que., Canada H3B 3T2
    Young & Rubicam Ltd., 60 Bloor St. W, Toronto, Ont., Canada M4W 1J2

ZAPATA CORP   Zapata Tower, PO Box 4240, Houston, TX 77001,
  Tel: (713) 226-6000
  (Offshore drilling & petroleum explor)
    Ocean Maid Foods, P.O. Box 2800, St. Laurent, Montreal, Que., Canada H4L 4Y7

ZENITH ELECTRONICS CORP   1000 Milwaukee Ave, Glenview, IL 60025,
  Tel: (708) 391-7000
  (Mfr consumer electr, cable prdts, electr components)
    Zenith Radio Canada Ltd., 900 St. Martin Blvd. W., Chomedey, Laval, Que.,
      Canada H7S 2B6
    Zenith Radio Canada Ltd., 1020 Islington Ave., Toronto, Ont., Canada M8Z 5X5

ZIEBART INTL CORP   1290 E Maple Rd, Troy, MI 48084, Tel: (313) 588-4100
  (Auto aftermarket servs)
    Ziebart Canada Inc., 150 Oakdale Rd., Downsview, Ontario M3N 1W1, Canada

ZIPPO MFG CO   33 Barbour St, Bradford, PA 16701, Tel: (814) 362-4541
  (Mfr cigarette lighters)
    Zippo Mfg Co. of Canada Ltd., 6158 Allen Ave., Niagara Falls, Ont., Canada L2E 6V9

CAYMAN ISLANDS

THE BANK OF NEW YORK   48 Wall St, New York, NY 10286, Tel: (212) 530-1784
(Banking)
   The Bank of New York, P.O. Box 500, Grand Cayman, Cayman Islands
   The Bank of New York Trust Co. (Cayman) Ltd., P.O. Box 705, Georgetown,
     Grand Cayman, Cayman Islands

BANKAMERICA CORP   PO Box 37000, San Francisco, CA 94137, Tel: (415) 622-3456
(Financial services)
   BankAmerica Trust & Banking Corp. (Cayman) Ltd., Anchorage Center, Harbour Dr.,
     P.O. Box 1092, Grand Cayman, Cayman Islands

BROWN BROTHERS HARRIMAN & CO   59 Wall St, New York, NY 10005,
Tel: (212) 483-1818
(Financial serv)
   Brown Brothers Harriman & Co., P.o. Box 694, Grand Cayman, Cayman Islands

THE M W KELLOGG CO   3 Greenway Plaza, Houston, TX 77046-0395,
Tel: (713) 960-2000
(Design, engr, procurement & constr for process & energy ind)
   Kellogg Intl. Services Ltd., Box 1038, Cayman Islands 92110

OWENS-CORNING FIBERGLAS CORP   PO Box 901, Fiberglas Tower, Toledo, OH 43659,
Tel: (419) 248-8000
(Mfr insulation, building materials, glass fiber prdts)
   Owens-Corning Cayman Ltd., Cayman Islands

STATE STREET BANK & TRUST CO   225 Franklin St, Boston, MA 02101,
Tel: (617) 786-3000
(Banking servs)
   State Street Cayman Trust Co. Ltd., P.O. Box 1984, Georgetown, Grand Cayman,
     Cayman Islands

TOOTSIE ROLL INDUSTRIES INC   7401 S Cicero Ave, Chicago, IL 60629,
Tel: (312) 581-6100
(Mfr candies, chocolate prdts)
   World Trade & Marketing Ltd., P.O. Box 1751, Grand Cayman, Cayman Islands

CENTRAL AFRICAN REPUBLIC

LOUIS BERGER INTL INC   100 Halsted St, East Orange, NJ 07019,
  Tel: (201) 678-1960
  (Consulting engineers, architects, economists & planners)
    Louis Berger Intl. Inc., B.P. 2030, Bangui, Central African Republic

DIAMOND DISTRIBUTORS INTL   589 Fifth Ave, New York, NY 10017,
  Tel: (212) 759-8383
  (Diamonds)
    Cie. Centrafricaine de Mines (Centramines), Boite Postale 4, Berberati,
    Central African Republic

INA CORPORATION   1600 Arch St, Philadelphia, PA 19101, Tel: (215) 523-5335
  (Holding co: ins, financial serv)
    INA Intl., B.P. 513, Bangui, Central African Republic

MOBIL CORP   150 E 42nd St, New York, NY 10017, Tel: (212) 883-4242
  (Petroleum explor, prdts)
    Mobil Oil S.A., B.P. 576, Bangui, Central African Republic

CHAD

LOUIS BERGER INTL INC   100 Halsted St, East Orange, NJ 07019,
  Tel: (201) 678-1960
  (Consulting engineers, architects, economists & planners)
    Louis Berger Intl. Inc., B.P. 1191, N'Djamena, Chad

CITIBANK NA   399 Park Ave, New York, NY 10043, Tel: (212) 559-1000
  (Intl banking)
    Banque Internationale pour l'Afrique Occidentale (BIAO), Boite Postale 87,
    Fort Lamy, Chad

CONOCO INC   600 N Dairy Ashford Rd, Houston, TX 77079, Tel: (713) 293-1000
  (Oil, gas, coal, chems, minerals)
    Continental Oil Co. of Chad, Boite Postale 694, N'Djamena, Chad

EXXON CORP   225 E John Carpenter Frwy, Irving, TX 75062, Tel: (214) 444-1000
   (Petroleum & petroleum prdts)
      Esso West Africa, Boite Postale 744, Fort Lamy, Chad

GANNETT FLEMING CORDDRY & CARPENTER INC   PO Box 1963, Harrisburg, PA 17015,
   Tel: (717) 763-7211
   (Engr consulting serv)
      Gannett Fleming Transportation Engineers, c/o USAID, B.P. 413, N'Diamena, Chad

INA CORPORATION   1600 Arch St, Philadelphia, PA 19101, Tel: (215) 523-5335
   (Holding co: ins, financial serv)
      INA Intl., Boite Postale 12, N'Djamena, Chad

WESTERN GEOPHYSICAL   PO Box 2469, Houston, TX 77252-2469, Tel: (713) 789-9600
   (Geophysical serv)
      Western Geophysical, Box 799, N'Djamena, Chad

CHANNEL ISLANDS

BANKAMERICA CORP   PO Box 37000, San Francisco, CA 94137, Tel: (415) 622-3456
   (Financial services)
      BankAmerica Trust Co. (Jersey) Ltd., Union House, Union St., P.O. Box 120,
        St. Helier, Jersey, Channel Islands

BROWN BROTHERS HARRIMAN & CO   59 Wall St, New York, NY 10005,
   Tel: (212) 483-1818
   (Financial serv)
      BBH Advisory Services Ltd., Westbourne, The Grance, St. Peter Port, Guernsey,
        Channel Islands

CHEMICAL BANK   277 Park Ave, New York, NY 10172, Tel: (212) 310-6161
   (Banking & financial serv)
      Chemical Bank & Howard de Walden Ltd., St. Julian's Ct., St. Peter Port, Guernsey,
        Channel Islands

CIGNA CORP   One Liberty Place, 1650 Market St, Philadelphia, PA 19101,
   Tel: (215) 523-4000
   (Ins, invest, health care & other fin servs)
      Cigna Intl. Fund Managers (CI) Ltd., St. Julian's House, St. Peter Port, Guernsey,
        Channel Islands

FIRST NATIONAL BANK OF CHICAGO   One First National Plaza, Chicago, IL 60670,
   Tel: (312) 732-4000
   (Financial services)
      First National Bank of Chicago (CI) Ltd., St. Peter Port House, Saumarcz St.,
        St. Peter Port, Guernsey, Channel Islands

NASHUA CORP   44 Franklin St, Nashua, NH 03061, Tel: (603) 880-2323
  (Mfr/distr/serv office copier sys & supplies)
     Nashua Intl. Ltd., P.O. Box 268, St. Peter Port, Guernsey, Channel Islands

CHILE

3M CO   3M Center, St Paul, MN 55144-1000, Tel: (612) 733-1110
  (Mfr abrasives, adhesives, chems, ind & consumer tapes/diskettes, health care prdts,
  elec connectors)
     3M Chile S.A., Casilla 3068, Las Hortensias 650 Maipo, Santiago, Chile

ABBOTT LABORATORIES   Abbott Park, North Chicago, IL 60064,
  Tel: (312) 937-6100
  (Pharm & lab prdts)
     Abbott Laboratories de Chile Ltda., Casilla 169-D, Santiago, Chile

AFIA   110 William St, New York, NY 10038, Tel: (212) 964-4990
  (Insurance)
     Home Insurance Co., Moneda 1123, Casilla 987, Santiago, Chile

AIR EXPRESS INTL CORP   120 Tokeneke Rd, PO Box 1231, Darien, CT 06820,
  Tel: (203) 655-7900
  (Air frt forwarder)
     Air Express Intl., c/o Decapack, Antonio Bellet 258, Providencia, Santiago, Chile

AMERICAN EXPRESS CO   American Express Tower, New York, NY 10285-4765,
  Tel: (212) 640-2000
  (Diversified fin & travel-related serv)
     Turismo Colcha (R), Agustinas 1356-1360, Casilla 379, Santiago, Chile

AMERICAN HOME PRODUCTS CORP   685 Third Ave, New York, NY 10017,
  Tel: (212) 878-5800
  (Drugs, food, household prdts)
     American Home Products Corp., Santiago, Chile

AMERICAN LIFE INSURANCE CO (ALICO)   PO Box 2226, Wilmington, DE 19899,
  Tel: (302) 594-2000
  (Life ins, pension & annuity plans, health prdts)
     La Interamericana Compania de Seguros de Vida S.A., Mira Flores 178, Casilla 111,
       Santiago, Chile

AMERICAN RE-INSURANCE CO   One Liberty Plaza, 91 Liberty St, New York,
  NY 10006, Tel: (212) 766-6700
  (Reinsurance)
     Reaseguradora Bernardo O'Higgins, Bandera 206, Piso 7, Santiago, Chile

ARBOR ACRES FARM INC   41 Marlborough Rd, Glastonbury, CT 06033,
Tel: (203) 633-4681
(Producers of male & female broiler breeders, commercial egg layers)
Agricola Ariztia Ltda., Casilla 90, Melipilla, Chile

ARMCO INTL INC   703 Curtis St, PO Box 700, Middletown, OH 45042,
Tel: (513) 425-6541
(Sheet steel & steel prdts, constr, oil field equip, ins, finance leasing)
Armco Chile S.A.M.I., Camino Industrias, Casilla 68C, Concepcion, Talcahuano, Chile

GUY F ATKINSON CO OF CA INC   10 W Orange Ave, South San Francisco, CA 94080,
Tel: (415) 876-1000
(Constr, oil & gas dev, pipe supply, light mfg)
Guy F. Atkinson Ltda., Huerfamos 669, Oficina 412, Santiago, Chile

AVIS INC   900 Old Country Rd, Garden City, NY 11530, Tel: (516) 222-3000
(Car rental serv)
Avis Rent a Car System Inc., Elidoro Yanez 869, Santiago, Chile

AVON PRODUCTS INC   9 W 57th St, New York, NY 10019, Tel: (212) 546-6015
(Mfr/distr cosmetics, perfumes)
Cosmeticos Avon Ltda., Santiago, Chile

BAKER OIL TOOLS   PO Box 3048, Houston, TX 77253, Tel: (713) 923-9351
(Oil/gas well completions equip)
Baker Transworld Inc. y Cia. Ltda., Avenida Colon 602, P.O. Box 76-D, Punta Arenas, Chile

BANKAMERICA CORP   PO Box 37000, San Francisco, CA 94137, Tel: (415) 622-3456
(Financial services)
Bank of America, Agustinas 1465, Casilla 117, Santiago, Chile

BANKERS TRUST CO   280 Park Ave, New York, NY 10017, Tel: (212) 775-2500
(Banking)
Bankers Trust Co., Estado 359, Santiago, Chile

BARDAHL MFG CORP   1400 N W 52nd St, PO Box 70607, Seattle, WA 98107,
Tel: (206) 783-4851
(Lubricating oils)
Leon Kaplun S.A.C., Arturo Prat 179, Casilla 4180, Santiago, Chile

BENTLY NEVADA CORP   PO Box 157, Minden, NV 89423, Tel: (702) 782-3611
(Electronic monitoring system)
Turbomecanica Ltda., C.A.S. 90-C, Concepcion, Chile

SAMUEL BINGHAM CO   479 Business Center Dr, Mt Prospect, IL 60056,
Tel: (708) 298-6777
(Print & ins rollers, inks)
Davis Graphics Ltda., Paraguan 486, Santiago, Chile

BLACK & DECKER CORP   701 E Joppa Road, Towson, MD 21204, Tel: (301) 583-3900
(Mfr portable elect & pneumatic power tools, household prdts)
Maquinas y Herramientas, Black & Decker de Chile S.A., P.O. Box 437 V, Santiago 21, Chile

BOYLES BROS DRILLING CO   PO Box 25068, Salt Lake City, UT 84125,
  Tel: (801) 972-3333
  (Contract drilling)
    Geotec Boyles Bros. S.A., La Violetas 5931, Santiago, Chile

BUCYRUS-ERIE CO   PO Box 56, Milwaukee, WI 53172, Tel: (414) 768-4000
  (Shovels, cranes)
    Bucyrus Chile Ltda., Santiago, Chile

LEO BURNETT CO INC   35 West Wacker Dr, Chicago, IL 60601, Tel: (312) 220-5959
  (Advertising agency)
    Leo Burnett Chile, Suecia 791, Santiago, Chile

CANADA DRY INTL CORP   2600 Century Pkwy, Atlanta, GA 30345,
  Tel: (404) 753-2182
  (Carbonated beverages, soft drinks extract)
    Establecimientos Nobis, S.A.I., Ave. Domingo Santa Maria #1946, Casilla 1361,
      Santiago, Chile

CARGILL   PO Box 9300, Minneapolis, MN 55440, Tel: (612) 475-7575
  (Food prdts, feeds, animal prdts)
    Cargill Chile, Teatinos 333, piso 5, Santiago, Chile

CHASE MANHATTAN BANK N A   1 Chase Manhattan Plaza, New York, NY 10081,
  Tel: (212) 552-2222
  (Intl banking)
    Chase Manhattan Bank N.A., Casilla de Correos 9192, Centro Comercial de la, Merced,
      MacIver y Huerfanos, Santiago, Chile

CIGNA CORP   One Liberty Place, 1650 Market St, Philadelphia, PA 19101,
  Tel: (215) 523-4000
  (Ins, invest, health care & other fin servs)
    Cigna Compania de Seguros (Chile) SA, Calle Nueva York #80- 9th Fl., PO Box 493,
      Santiago, Chile
    Cigna Compania de Seguros de Vida (Chile) SA, Calle Nueva York #80- 9th Fl.,
      PO Box 493, Santiago, Chile
    Cigna Salud Isapre SA, Nueva York 80- Piso 11/Casilla 493, Santiago, Chile
    Esis Intl. Asesorias Ltda., Moneda 1123- Casilla #987, Santiago, Chile
    Institucion de Salud Luis Pasteur SA, Almirante Lorenzo Gotuzzo 70, Santiago, Chile
    Inversiones INA Ltda., Calle Nueva York #80- 9/F, Santiago, Chile

CITIBANK NA   399 Park Ave, New York, NY 10043, Tel: (212) 559-1000
  (Intl banking)
    Citibank N.A., Ahumada 40, Casilla 2125, Santiago, Chile

THE COCA-COLA CO   310 North Ave NW, PO Box Drawer 1734, Atlanta, GA 30313,
  Tel: (404) 676-2121
  (Mfr & sale of soft drink syrups & concentrates, juices & food prdts, motion pic & TV
  prod)
    Coca-Cola Corp., Requests that all inquiries be made to Atlanta address

COLUMBIA PICTURES INDUSTRIES INC   711 Fifth Ave, New York, NY 10022,
  Tel: (212) 751-4400
  (Producer & distributor of motion pictures)
    Columbia Pictures of Chile Inc., Asociacion Twentieth Fox In, Huerfanos 786,
      Casilla 9003, Santiago, Chile

COMBUSTION ENGINEERING INC   900 Long Ridge Road, Stamford, CT 06902,
  Tel: (203) 329-8771
  (Tech constr)
    Combustion Engineering, c/o Dimtel Ltda., Matias Cousino 82, Santiago, Chile

CONTINENTAL BANK NA   231 S Lasalle St, Chicago, IL 60697, Tel: (312) 828-2345
  (Coml banking servs)
    Chicago Continental Capital Markets Ltd., Casilla 414-V, Correo 21, Moneda 1138,
      Santiago, Chile
    Continental Bank Corp., Chicago Continental Bank, Casilla 414-V, Correo 21,
      Moneda 1138, Santiago, Chile

CPC INTERNATIONAL INC   PO Box 8000, International Plaza, Englewood Cliffs,
  NJ 07632, Tel: (201) 894-4000
  (Mfr consumer food prdts & corn refining prdts)
    Industrias de Maiz y Alimentos S.A., Torre Santa Maria, piso 16,
      Av. Los Conquistadores 1.700, Casilla de Correo 837, Santiago, Chile

CROWN CORK & SEAL CO INC   Holmesburg Station, PO Box 6208, Philadelphia,
  PA 19136, Tel: (215) 698-5100
  (Cans, bottle caps; filling & packaging mach)
    Crown Cork de Chile S.A.I., Camino de Milipilla 10, 700, Casilla 9342, Casilla 108,
      Santiago, Chile

CROWN ZELLERBACH CORP   1 Bush St, San Francisco, CA 94119,
  Tel: (415) 951-5000
  (Pulp, paperboard & paper mills, lumber, plywood mills, mfr chems)
    Laja Crown S.A., Agustina 1357, Casilla 108, Santiago, Chile

DAMES & MOORE   911 Wilshire Blvd, Los Angeles, CA 90017, Tel: (213) 683-1560
  (Consulting engineers)
    Dames & Moore, Av. 11 de Septiembre 1860, Santiago, Chile

DANCER FITZGERALD SAMPLE INTL   405 Lexington Ave, New York, NY 10174,
  Tel: (212) 661-0800
  (Advertising agency)
    Israel & de Bianchi, Hindenburgh 674, Providencia, Santiago, Chile

DATA GENERAL CORP   4400 Computer Dr, Westboro, MA 01580, Tel: (617) 366-8911
  (Design, mfr gen purpose computer sys & peripheral prdts & servs)
    Data General Chile Ltda., Suecia 392, Providencia, Santiago, Chile

DHJ INDUSTRIES INC   1040 Ave of the Americas, New York, NY 10018,
  Tel: (212) 944-4500
  (Mfr of knit fabrics, interlinings plastic chips & denim)
    DHJ Industries Chile Ltda., Alberto Pepper, Renca, Santiago, Chile

DIAMOND SHAMROCK CORP   1100 Superior Ave, Cleveland, OH 44114,
  Tel: (216) 694-5000
  (Organic & inorganic chems & specialties, agric chems)
    Diamond Shamrock Chile S.A.I., Casilla 9711, Correo Central, Santiago, Chile

DORR-OLIVER INC   612 Wheeler's Farm Rd, PO Box 3819, Milford, CT 06460,
  Tel: (203) 876-5400
  (Mfr process equip for food, pulp & paper, mineral & chem ind; & municipal/ind waste
  treatment)
    Dorr-Oliver de Chile Ltda., Casilla 14711, Moneda 1040, Santiago, Chile

DOW CHEMICAL CO   2030 Dow Center, Midland, MI 48640, Tel: (517) 636-1000
(Chems, plastics, fibers, pharms)
    Dow Quimica Chilena S.A., Suecia 281, P.O. Box 14590, Providencia, Santiago, Chile

DRESSER INDUSTRIES INC   1600 Pacific Bldg, PO Box 718, Dallas, TX 75221,
    Tel: (214) 740-6000
    (Diversified supplier of equip & tech serv to energy & natural resource ind)
    Refractarios Chilenos S.A., Carretera Panamericana Norte 3076, Casilla 63,
      Santiago, Chile
    Triconos Mineros S.A., Lo Ruiz 2880, Casilla 1335, Santiago, Chile

DURACELL INTL INC   Berkshire Industrial Park, Bethel, CT 06801,
    Tel: (203) 796-4000
    (Mfr batteries)
    Duracell Chile, Roman Diaz 1271, Providencia, Santiago, Chile

EASTMAN KODAK CO   343 State St, Rochester, NY 14650-0518, Tel: (716) 724-4000
    (Devel/mfr photo & chem prdts, info mgmt/video/copier sys, fibers/plastics for
    various ind)
    Kodak Chilena S.A.F., Alonso Ovalle 1180, Casilla 2797, Santiago, Chile

ERICO PRODUCTS INC   34600 Solon Road, Cleveland, OH 44139,
    Tel: (216) 248-0100
    (Mfr electric welding apparatus & hardware, metal stampings, specialty fasteners)
    Erico-Chile Ltda., Grajales 2948, Casilla 16.666, Santiago, Chile

EXIM OVERSEAS INC   2121 Ponce de Leon Blvd, Coral Gables, FL 33134,
    Tel: (305) 444-6444
    (Trading & sales of arms for Armco Latin Div)
    Armco Chile, Casilla 16217, Santiago 9, Chile

EXXON CORP   225 E John Carpenter Frwy, Irving, TX 75062, Tel: (214) 444-1000
    (Petroleum & petroleum prdts)
    Esso Industrial Ltda., Avenida Bdo. O'Higgins 1170, Casilla 50D, Santiago, Chile

FEDERAL-MOGUL CORP   PO Box 1966, Detroit, MI 48235, Tel: (313) 354-7700
    (Mfr/distr vehicular & ind components for original market & aftermarket)
    Federal-Mogul World Trade (Chile) Ltda., Argomedo 494 (Esquina Carmen),
      Casilla 475V, Santiago, Chile

FIRST NATIONAL BANK OF BOSTON   100 Federal St, Boston, MA 02110,
    Tel: (617) 434-2200
    (Commercial banking)
    Bank of Boston, Moneda 799, Casilla 1946, Santiago, Chile
    Bank of Boston, Prat 863, Valparaiso, Chile
    Bank of Boston, Ave. Libertad 101, Vina del Mar, Chile

FLORIDA INTL FORWARDERS   6905 N W 25th St, PO Box 522085, Miami, FL 33122,
    Tel: (305) 592-6450
    (Air cargo service)
    OCSER Ltda., Casilla Postal 2858, Correo Central, Santiago, Chile

FOXBORO CO   33 Commercial St, Foxboro, MA 02035, Tel: (508) 543-8750
    (Mfr prdts/provide servs for ind automation)
    Pullen & Juppet Ltda., Casilla de Correo 10202, Santiago, Chile

H B FULLER CO   2400 Energy Park Dr, St Paul, MN 55108, Tel: (612) 645-3401
(Mfr/distr adhesives, sealants, coatings, paints, waxes, sanitation chems)
    H.B. Fuller Chile S.A., Santa Rosa 7576, Correo 3, Santiago, Chile

GENERAL CABLE CORP   50 Tice Blvd, Woodcliff Lake, NJ 07675,
    Tel: (201) 573-8200
(Mfr wire, cord & cable, associated prdts)
    Manufacturas de Cobre S.A., Ureta Cox 930, Santiago, Chile

GENERAL MOTORS ACCEPTANCE CORP   3044 West Grand Blvd, Detroit, MI 48202,
    Tel: (313) 556-5000
(Automobile financing)
    GMAC Comercial Automotriz Chile S.A., Once de Septiembre 2606, Casilla 366,
        Correo 21, Santiago, Chile

GENERAL MOTORS CORP   3044 W Grand Blvd, Detroit, MI 48202,
    Tel: (313) 556-5000
(Automotive prdts, electronics)
    General Motors Chile S.A., P.O. Box 14370, Santiago, Chile

GOODYEAR TIRE & RUBBER CO   1144 E Market St, Akron, OH 44316-0001,
    Tel: (216) 796-2121
(Mfr tires, rubber prdts)
    Goodyear de Chile S.A.I.C., P.O. Box 3607, Santiago, Chile

GRAY TOOL CO   PO Box 2291, Houston, TX 77001, Tel: (713) 747-1240
(Oil field equip, pipe connectors, etc)
    Dimitel Ltda., Matias Cousine 82, Santiago, Chile

GREY ADVERTISING INC   777 Third Ave, New York, NY 10017, Tel: (212) 546-2000
(Advertising)
    Publicidad Fabres de Heeckeren Casares & Grey S.A., Ernesto Pinto, Lagarrigue 148,
        Santiago, Chile

FRANK B HALL & CO INC   549 Pleasantville Rd, Briarcliff Manor, NY 10510,
    Tel: (914) 769-9200
(Insurance)
    Andueza y Compania, Corredores de Seguros S.A., Ahumada 179, Santiago, Chile

THE HARPER GROUP INC   260 Townsend St, PO Box 77933, San Francisco,
    CA 94107, Tel: (415) 978-0600
(Ocean/air freight fwdg, customs brokerage, packing & whse, logistics mgt, ins)
    Circle Freight Intl., La Concepcion 281, PO Box 9328- Correo Central, Santiago,
        Chile

HORWATH & HORWATH INTL   919 Third Ave, New York, NY 10022,
    Tel: (212) 980-3100
(Public accountants & auditors)
    Ramon A. Espelo F. y Asociados Ltda., P.O. Box 3577, Huerfanos, 682, Santiago, Chile

HUGHES TOOL CO   PO Box 2539, Houston, TX 77001, Tel: (713) 924-2222
(Equip & serv to oil & gas explor & prod ind)
    Hughes Tool Co., Chile Ltda., Huerfanos 1376, Casilla 14450, Correo 21, Santiago,
        Chile

INA CORPORATION   1600 Arch St, Philadelphia, PA 19101, Tel: (215) 523-5335
  (Holding co: ins, financial serv)
    Ina-Kappes Compania de Seguros Generales, S.A., Calle Nueva York #80, Casilla 493,
    Correo Central, Santiago, Chile

INTERNATIONAL BUSINESS MACHINES (IBM)   Old Orchard Rd, Armonk,
  NY 10504-1783, Tel: (914) 765-1900
  (Info-handling sys, equip & serv)
    Compania Standard Electric S.A.C., Vicuma Mackenna 3939, Casilla 444, Santiago,
    Chile
    IBM de Chile S.A.C., Los Conquistadores 1700, Santiago, Chile

IRECO INC   Crossroads Tower, 11th fl, Salt Lake City, UT 84144,
  Tel: (801) 364-4800
  (Explosive supplies, accessories for ind & military applications; alu- minum granules)
    Ireco Chile Ltda., Mons. Sanz 182, Santiago, Chile

ITT CORP   1330 Ave of the Americas, New York, NY 10019, Tel: (212) 258-1000
  (Diversified mfr, tech & services)
    ITT Commucations Mudiales S.A., Huerfanos 1546, Casilla 262V, Santiago, Chile

ITT SHERATON CORP   60 State St, Boston, MA 02108, Tel: (617) 367-3600
  (Hotel operations)
    Sheraton San Cristobal Hotel, P.O. Box 16058, Santiago, Chile

JOHNSON & HIGGINS   125 Broad St, New York, NY 10005, Tel: (212) 574-7000
  (Ins brokerage, benefit conslt)
    Johnson & Higgins Ltda., Huerfanos 1178-40, Piso Casilla 14220, Santiago 5, Chile

JOHNSON & JOHNSON   One Johnson & Johnson Plaza, New Brunswick, NJ 08933,
  Tel: (201) 524-0400
  (Surgical, med & baby prdts)
    Johnson & Johnson de Chile S.A., Santiago, Chile

S C JOHNSON & SON INC   1525 Howe St, Racine, WI 53403, Tel: (414) 631-2000
  (Home, auto, commercial & personal care prdts, specialty chems)
    Quimica S.A., Chilena & Cia, Ltda., 1 Norte 3250, Vina del Mar, Chile
    S.C. Johnson & Son Inc., Lasilla 99D, Santiago, Chile

KEYES FIBRE CO   3003 Summer St, Stamford, CT 06905, Tel: (203) 357-9100
  (Molded containers)
    Chilena de Moldeados S.A., Casilla 208, Puente Alto, Chile

KNOLL INTL   655 Madison Ave, New York, NY 10021, Tel: (212) 826-2400
  (Furniture & fabrics)
    Sergio Roccay Cia. Ltda., Ave. Vicuna MacKenna 1704, Casilla 628722, Santiago, Chile

KOPPERS CO INC   Koppers Bldg, 437 Seventh Ave, Pittsburgh, PA 15219,
  Tel: (412) 227-2000
  (Constr materiald & serv; chem & bldg prdts)
    Koppers Hickson (Chile) Ltd., Santiago, Chile

LE TOURNEAU INC LONGVIEW DIV   PO Box 2307, Longview, TX 75606,
  Tel: (214) 753-3449
  (Heavy constr, mining mach & equip)
    Contact Chile: Wajax Intl. Ltd., 716 Gordon Baker Rd., Willowdale, Ont. M2H 3B4,
    Canada

ELI LILLY & CO   307 E McCarty St, Indianapolis, IN 46285, Tel: (317) 261-2000
(Pharms, agric & cosmetic prdts)
  Eli Lilly & Co., Casilla 426V, Correo 21, Santiago, Chile

LINTAS:WORLDWIDE   1 Dag Hammarskjold Plaza, New York, NY 10017,
Tel: (212) 605-8000
(Advertising agency)
  Lintas:Chile, Ave. Ricardo Lyon 1623, Providencia, Chile

LONGYEAR CO   PO Box 27314, Salt Lake City, UT 84127, Tel: (801) 972-1395
(Mfr diamond drills, concrete cutting equip; drill serv)
  Longyear Co., Casilla 15118, Las Dalias 2900, Macul, Santiago, Chile

MANPOWER INC   5301 N Ironwood Rd, PO Box 2053, Milwaukee, WI 53201-2053,
Tel: (414) 961-1000
(Temporary help)
  Manpower de Chile Ltda., Estados Unidos 395, Sz'ntiago, Chile

MARCO   2300 W Commodore Way, Seattle, WA 98199, Tel: (206) 285-3200
(Shipbldg & repair, coml fishing equip & sys, hydraulic pumps)
  Marco Chilena, S.A., Casilla 62-D, Iquique, Chile

MARRIOTT CORP   Marriott Dr, Washington, DC 20058, Tel: (301) 897-9000
(Lodging, contract food & beverage serv, restaurants)
  Marriott de Chile Ltda., Aeropuerto Intl. Antonio Merino Benitez, Santiago, Chile

MARY KAY COSMETICS INC   8787 Stemmons Fwy, Dallas, TX 75247,
Tel: (214) 630-8787
(Cosmetics & toiletries)
  Mary Kay (Chile) Ltda., Europa 2035, Providencia, Santiago, Chile

MEASUREX CORP   One Results Way, Cupertino, CA 95014, Tel: (408) 255-1500
(Mfr computer integrated mfg sys)
  Measurex Corp., Av. Bernardo O'Higgins 142, Oficina 185, Santiago, Chile

MENNEN CO   Morristown, NJ 07960, Tel: (201) 631-9000
(Health & beauty aids)
  Mennen de Cihile Ltda., Casilla 9358, Santiago, Chile

MENTHOLATUM CO   1360 Niagara St, Buffalo, NY 14213, Tel: (716) 882-7660
(Proprietary medicines, drugs)
  Laboratorios Mentholatum Ltda., Carrascal 3585, Casilla 37D, Santiago, Chile

MGM/UA COMMUNICATIONS CO   10000 W Washington Blvd, Culver City, CA 90230,
Tel: (213) 280-6000
(Motion picture, home video & pay TV prod & distr)
  MGM/UA Communications Co., Providencia 929, 5/F, Santiago 9, Chile

MINE SAFETY APPLIANCES CO   PO Box 426, Pittsburgh, PA 15230,
Tel: (421) 273 5000
(Safety equip, ind filters)
  MSA de Chile Ltda., Casilla 16647, Santiago 9, Chile

MOBIL CORP   150 E 42nd St, New York, NY 10017, Tel: (212) 883-4242
(Petroleum explor, prdts)
  Mobil Oil de Chile Ltda., Amunategui 178, Casilla 2060, Santiago, Chile

MYERS TIRE SUPPLY INTL   1293 South Main St, Akron, OH 44301,
   Tel: (216) 253-5592
   (Mfr polymer & metal prdts for mat handling, automotive & constr inds)
      Myers De Chile Ltda., Chacabuco #745, Casilla 14130, Santiago, Chile

McCANN-ERICKSON WORLDWIDE   750 Third Ave, New York, NY 10017,
   Tel: (212) 697-6000
   (Advertising)
      McCann-Erickson S.A. de Publicidad, Eliodoro Yanez 2290, Casilla 2428, Providencia,
      Santiago, Chile

NABISCO BRANDS INC   Nabisco Brands Plaza, East Hanover, NJ 07936,
   Tel: (201) 503-2000
   (Mfr food prdts)
      Nabisco, Camino de Melipilla 13250, Maipu, Chile
      Nabisco, Casilla 50, Correo Los Cerrltos, Santiago, Chile

NALCO CHEMICAL CO   One Nalco Center, Naperville, IL 60566-1024,
   Tel: (708) 305-1000
   (Chems for water & waste water treatment, oil prod & refining, ind processes;
   water/energy mgmt serv)
      Nalco Productos Quimicos de Chile S.A., Aptdo. Postal 16477, Santiago 9, Chile

NATIONAL CAR RENTAL SYSTEM INC   7700 France Ave S, Minneapolis, MN 55435,
   Tel: (612) 830-2121
   (Car rental)
      National Car Rental, Ave. de la Concepcion 212, Santiago, Chile

NCR CORP   1700 S Patterson Blvd, Dayton, OH 45479, Tel: (513) 445-2000
   (Develop/mfr/sell/serv business info processing sys)
      NCR de Chile S.A., MacIver 370, Casilla 115-D, Santiago, Chile

NIBCO CORP   500 Simpson Ave, PO Box 1167, Elkhart, IN 46515,
   Tel: (219) 295-3000
   (Pipe fittings, plumbing & heating valves)
      Industrias Nibco SGM Sudamerica Ltd., Juan Griego 4429, San Miguel, Chile

NORTH LILY MINING CO   1111 Bayhill Dr, #210, San Bruno, CA 94066-3035,
   Tel: (415) 742-0133
   (Mining gold & silver)
      Minera Northern Resources Ltd., Avenida El Bosque Sur 175, Providencia, Santiago,
      Chile

NORTON CO   1 New Bond St, Worcester, MA 01606, Tel: (508) 795-5000
   (Abrasives, drill bits, constr & safety prdts, plastics)
      Christensen Diamond Products de Chile S.A., Casilla 1150, Santiago, Chile

ONAN CORP   1400 73rd Ave NE, Minneapolis, MN 55432, Tel: (612) 574-5000
   (Electric generators, ind engines & controls)
      Montero y Cia., S.A.C., Casilla 312, Alameda B O'Higgins # 1493, Santiago, Chile

OSMOSE INTL INC   980 Ellicott St, Buffalo, NY 14209, Tel: (716) 882-5905
   (Maint & inspec utility poles, railroad track & marine piling)
      Osmose Chile Ltda., Luis Thayer Ojeda 0115, Oficina 604, P.O. Box 4178, Santiago,
      Chile

PARAMOUNT INTL FILMS INC   1 Gulf & Western Plaza, New York, NY 10023,
  Tel: (212) 333-4600
  (Film prod & distr)
    Cinema Intl. Corp. Ltda., Casilla 3462, Santiago, Chile

PARSONS CORP   100 W Walnut St, Pasadena, CA 91124, Tel: (818) 440-2000
  (Engineering & constr)
    Parsons Overseas Co. (Chile) Ltd., Galvarino Gallardo 2125, Providencia, Santiago,
    Chile

PEPSICO INC   700 Anderson Hill Rd, Purchase, NY 10577, Tel: (914) 253-2000
  (Beverages, food prdts & servs, sporting goods)
    Pepci-Cola Consultores Ltda., Pedro de Valdivia 0193, Casilla 13540, Correo 21,
    Santiago, Chile

PFIZER INC   235 E 42nd St, New York, NY 10017, Tel: (212) 573-2323
  (Mfr pharms, hosp prdts, chems, consumer & animal health prdts)
    Laboratorios Pfizer de Chile, Camino a Melipilla 9978, Casilla 3529, Santiago, Chile

PHELPS DODGE CORP   2600 N Central Ave, Phoenix, AZ 85004-3014,
  Tel: (602) 234-8100
  (Minerals, metals & spec engineered prdts for trans & elect mkts)
    Cia Minera Ojos del Salado, Roger de Flor No. 2996, Las Condes, Santiago, Chile
    Cobre Cerrillos S.A., Camino a Melipilla 6307, Casilla 100, Correo Los Cerrillos,
    Santiago, Chile
    Minera Phelps Dodge de Chile, SA, Roger de Flor No. 2996, Las Condes, Santiago,
    Chile

PIONEER HI-BRED INTL INC   700 Capital Sq, 400 Locust St, Des Moines,
  IA 50309, Tel: (515) 245-3500
  (Seed corn, feed seed, data sys & equip)
    Semillas Pioneer Chile Ltda., Santiago, Chile

PROCTER & GAMBLE CO   One Procter & Gamble Plaza, Cincinnati, OH 45202,
  Tel: (513) 983-1100
  (Personal care, food, laundry, cleaning & ind prdts)
    Laboratorio Reka S.A., Avda. Portugal 1198, Santiago, Chile

RCA GLOBAL COMMUNICATIONS INC   60 Broad St, New York, NY 10004,
  Tel: (212) 806-7000
  (Commun serv)
    RCA Corp., Moneda 920, Santiago, Chile

ROHM & HAAS CO   Independence Mall West, Philadelphia, PA 19105,
  Tel: (215) 592-3000
  (Mfr ind & agric chems, plastics)
    Rohm & Haas Chile Ltd., Ahumada 11, Oficina 207, Santiago, Chile

SYDNEY ROSS CO   90 Park Ave, New York, NY 10016, Tel: (212) 907-2000
  (Pharms, toiletries & cosmetics)
    Sydney Ross Co. y Cia. Ltda., Casilla 163D, Santiago, Chile

SECURITY PACIFIC NATIONAL BANK   333 S Hope St, Los Angeles, CA 90071,
  Tel: (213) 345-6211
  (Banking)
    Banco Security Pacific de Chile, Agustinas 621, Santiago de Chile, Chile
    Security Pacific Valaores S.A., Ahumada 11, Office 601, Santiago de Chile, Chile

SGS CONTROL SERVICES INC   42 Broadway, New York, NY 10004,
   Tel: (212) 482-8700
   (Complete range of quality & quantity control checks & related tech serv)
      SGS Chile Ltda., Moneda 973, P.O. Box 3067, Santiago, Chile

ST JOE MINERALS CORP   250 Park Ave, New York, NY 10017, Tel: (212) 953-5000
   (Coal, oil, gas, iron ore, metals & minerals)
      Compania Minera San Jose Ltda., Clasificador #45, Correo 9, Santiago, Chile

SYSTEMS ENGINEERING LABS INC   6901 W Sunrise Blvd, Fort Lauderdale,
   FL 33313, Tel: (305) 587-2900
   (Digital computers)
      Texas de Chile Ltda., Div. Sistemas Digitales, Avenida Leon 1660, Casilla 13505,
      Santiago, Chile

TED BATES WORLDWIDE INC   1515 Broadway, New York, NY 10036,
   Tel: (212) 869-3131
   (Advertising agency)
      Publicitaria Epoca/Ted Bates S.A., Carlos Charlin, 1599 Santiago, Chile

C TENNANT SONS & CO OF NY   PO Box 9300, Minneapolis, MN 55440,
   Tel: (612) 475-7340
   (Ferrous & non-ferrous minerals, metals, electronic comps)
      Tennant Chilena Ltda., Agustinas 972, Santiago, Chile

TEXACO INC   2000 Westchester Ave, White Plains, NY 10650, Tel: (914) 253-4000
   (Explor/mktg crude oil & its prdts, petro-chems)
      Texaco S.A.C., Casilla 13345, Correo 21, Santiago, Chile

TOPFLIGHT CORP   200 E 9th Ave, PO Box 472, York, PA 17405,
   Tel: (717) 843-9901
   (Printed pressure-sensitive adhesive materials)
      Topflight Chile Ltda., Berlioz 5550, Santiago, Chile

TRANS WORLD AIRLINES INC   605 Third Ave, New York, NY 10158,
   Tel: (212) 557-6107
   (Air transp, hotel, food serv, real estate)
      Trans World Airlines Inc., Phillips #451, Sao Miguel, Azores, Chile

U S WHEAT ASSOCIATES   200 Market Bldg Suite 1020, Portland, OR 97201,
   Tel: (503) 223-8123
   (Market development for wheat prdts)
      U.S. Wheat Associates Inc., Casilla 16616, Santiago 9, Chile

UNION CARBIDE CORP   Old Ridgebury Rd, Danbury, CT 06817, Tel: (203) 794-2000
   (Carbon prdts, chems, plastics, gases & related prdts, etc)
      Union Carbide Comercial Chile Ltda., Ahumada 11, Casilla 14184, Correo 21,
      Santiago, Chile

UNION OIL INTL DIV   Union Oil Center, PO Box 7600, Los Angeles, CA 90017,
   Tel: (213) 977-7600
   (Petroleum prdts, petrochems)
      Moly Corp. Inc., Minera Union Oil Chile Ltda., Ave. Providencia 1072, Torre A,
      Dento 1203, Santiago, Chile

UNITEK CORP/3M   2724 S Peck Rd, Monrovia, CA 91016-7118, Tel: (818) 574-4000
  (Mfr orthodontic prdts)
    Unitek/3M Chile S.A., Casilla 3068, Las Hortensias 650, Maipu, Santiago, Chile

UPJOHN CO   7000 Portage Rd, Kalamazoo, MI 49001, Tel: (616) 323-4000
  (Pharms, agric prdts, ind chems)
    Upjohn Compania Ltda., Casilla 42D, Correo Central, Santiago, Chile

UTAH INTL INC   550 California St, San Francisco, CA 94104,
  Tel: (415) 981-1515
  (Mining, land development, ocean shipping, oil & gas)
    Minera Utah de Chile Inc., Isidora Goyenechea 2925, Santiago, Chile

WACKENHUT CORP   1500 San Remo Ave, Coral Gables, FL 33146,
  Tel: (305) 666-5656
  (Security sys & serv)
    Wackenhut Chile S.A., Calle Capullo 2240, Santiago, Chile

WARNER-LAMBERT CO   201 Tabor Road, Morris Plains, NJ 07950,
  Tel: (201) 540-2000
  (Mfr ethical & proprietary pharms, confectionary & consumer prdts)
    Empresas Warner-Lambert S.A., Cailla 1991-D, Santiago, Chile

CHINA
(PEOPLE'S REPUBLIC OF CHINA)

3M CO   3M Center, St Paul, MN 55144-1000, Tel: (612) 733-1110
  (Mfr abrasives, adhesives, chems, ind & consumer tapes/diskettes, health care prdts,
  elec connectors)
    3M China Ltd., 1486 Nanjing Rd. W., 3/F Bldg. #2, Shanghai 200040, PRC

A-Z INTL TOOL CO   PO Box 7108, Houston, TX 77248-7108, Tel: (713) 880-8888
  (Mfr oil field, milling & casing cutting tools)
    Asia-America Oil Tools & Svce. Ltd., Chiwan Petroleum Supply Base, Chiwan,
      Shenzhen, PRC

ALLEN-SHERMAN-HOFF CO   One Country View Rd, Malvern, PA 19355,
  Tel: (215) 647-9900
  (Design/eng material handling sys)
    BET Trading Associates, Beijing Hotel, Rm. 1209, Beijing, PRC
    BET Trading Associates, Beijing Hotel, Room 1209, Beijing, PRC

ALLIED-SIGNAL INC   Columbia Rd & Park Ave, PO Box 2245R, Morristown,
  NJ 07960, Tel: (201) 455-2000
  (Mfr aerospace & automotive prdts, engineered materials)
    Allied-Signal Aerospace Co., Lido Commercial Center, Block 2A, 5/F, Jichang Rd.,
      Jiany Tai Rd., Beijing, PRC

ALLIED-SIGNAL INTL INC   Columbia Rd & Park Ave, PO Box 2000, Morristown,
  NJ 07962, Tel: (201) 455-6034
  (Mfr advanced aerospace, automotive & engineered materials)
    Allied-Signal China Inc., 5th fl., Lido Commercial Centre, Jichang Rd.,
      Jiangtai Rd., Beijing, PRC

AMERICAN EXPRESS CO   American Express Tower, New York, NY 10285-4765,
  Tel: (212) 640-2000
  (Diversified fin & travel-related serv)
    American Express Co., Hotel Beijing, Rm. 410, East Chang An Ave., Beijing (Peking),
      PRC

AMERICAN INTL GROUP   70 Pine St, New York, NY 10270, Tel: (212) 770-7000
  (Insurance)
    China-America Insurance, Peking Hotel, Peking, PRC

ASSOCIATED MERCHANDISING CORP   1440 Broadway, New York, NY 10018,
  Tel: (212) 536-4000
  (Retail service organization)
    Associated Merchandising Corp., 58 Mai Ming Rd. S., Shanghai, PRC

BAILEY CONTROLS CO   29801 Euclid Ave, Wickliffe, OH 44092,
  Tel: (216) 943-5500
  (Mfr analog & digital instru, controls & control sys)
    Bailey Beijing Controls Ltd., 64 Gulou West St., Beijing, PRC

BAKER OIL TOOLS   PO Box 3048, Houston, TX 77253, Tel: (713) 923-9351
  (Oil/gas well completions equip)
    Baker Hughes Inc., Suite 1907 Noble Tower, 22 Gangua men wei Dajie, Beijing, PRC

BANKAMERICA CORP   PO Box 37000, San Francisco, CA 94137, Tel: (415) 622-3456
  (Financial services)
    Bank of America NT & SA, China World Trade Centre, 1 Jian Guo Men Wai Ave.,
      Beijing 100004, PRC

BARDAHL MFG CORP   1400 N W 52nd St, PO Box 70607, Seattle, WA 98107,
  Tel: (206) 783-4851
  (Lubricating oils)
    Bardahl Intl. Oil Corp. (HK) Ltd., all mail to: 27 Ashley Rd., 10th Floor, Kowloon,
      Hong Kong

BENTLY NEVADA CORP   PO Box 157, Minden, NV 89423, Tel: (702) 782-3611
  (Electronic monitoring system)
    Qing Hua Technical Services, Qing Hua Yuan, West Suburg, Beijing, PRC

LOUIS BERGER INTL INC   100 Halsted St, East Orange, NJ 07019,
  Tel: (201) 678-1960
  (Consulting engineers, architects, economists & planners)
    Louis Berger Intl. Inc., Sherator Hotel, Zi Jin Shan Rd., Tianjiin, PRC

BROWN & ROOT INC   4100 Clinton Dr, Houston, TX 77020-6299,
  Tel: (713) 676-4141
  (Engr, constr & maintenance)
    Brown & Root Overseas Ltd., Lido Commercial Center, Jichang Rd., Beijing, PRC
    COES-Brown & Root Marine Engineering & Construction Co. Ltd., 536 Bin Jiang Rd. E.,
      Guangznou, Guangdong, PRC
    COESK-Taylor Diving Co., Rms. 912/914, 536 Bin Jiang Rd. E., Guangznou, Guangdong,

PRC
China Brown & Root Marine Engineering & Construction Ltd., 10 Yuetan Beixiaojie, Beijing, PRC

CALTEX PETROLEUM CORP   PO Box 619500, Dallas, TX 75261, Tel: (214) 830-1000
(Petroleum prdts)
   Caltex China Ltd., all mail to: Caltex Oil Hong Kong, Box 147, Hong Kong

COMMERCIAL METALS CO   PO Box 1046, Dallas, TX 75221, Tel: (214) 689-4300
(Metal collecting/processing, steel mills, metal trading)
   Cometals China Inc., Beijing Exhibition Hall, Nanlou Ermen 2107-2109, Beijing, PRC

CONNELL BROTHERS CO LTD   320 California St, San Francisco, CA 94104,
Tel: (415) 772-4000
(Exp/imp chems, commodities, minerals, cons materials)
   Connell Bros. Co. Ltd., Shanghai Union Bldg., Rm. 1405, 100 Yanan Lu E, Shanghai, PRC

CONTROL DATA CORP   8100 34th Ave S, Minneapolis, MN 55440,
Tel: (612) 853-8100
(Control data equip, computer sys serv & financial serv)
   Control Data Corp., Room 3009, Peking Hotel, Peking, PRC

CORE LABORATORIES   10205 Westheimer, Houston, TX 77042, Tel: (713) 972-6312
(Petroleum testing/analysis, analytical chem, environmental servs)
   China Corelab Ltd., 1 Shang Yie Warehouse, Unit D, Tai Zi Rd.,
      CMSN Shekou Ind. Zone, Shenzhen, Shekou, PRC

COUDERT BROTHERS   200 Park Ave, New York, NY 10166, Tel: (212) 880-4400
(Lawyers)
   Coudert Brothers, Room 1009, Beijing Hotel, Beijing, PRC

JOHN CRANE INC   6400 Oakton St, Morton Grove, IL 60053, Tel: (708) 967-2400
(Mfr engineering seals)
   Tianjin Crane Seals Ltd., Mi Yun 1st Branch Rd., Nan Kai District, Tianjin, PRC

CUMMINS ENGINE CO INC   PO Box 3005, Columbus, IN 47202, Tel: (812) 377-5000
(Mfr diesel engines)
   Cummins Corp., Nationalities Cultural Palace, Rm. 304, Beijing, PRC

DIAMOND POWER SPECIALTY CO   PO Box 415, Lancaster, OH 43130,
Tel: (614) 687-6500
(Mfr sootblowers & controls, rodding robots, drum level indicators & gauges)
   Diamond Power Hubei Machine Co. Ltd., 139 Cheng Bei Lu, Xinshi Zhen,
      Jingshan County, Hubei, PRC

DRAVO CORP   1 Oliver Plaza, Pittsburgh, PA 15222, Tel: (412) 777-5000
(Material handling equip, process plants)
   Dravo Corp., c/o East Asiatic Co., Minzu Wen Hua, Gong Ju, LaBu Xi, Dan, Peking, PRC

DRESSER INDUSTRIES INC   1600 Pacific Bldg, PO Box 718, Dallas, TX 75221,
Tel: (214) 740-6000
(Diversified supplier of equip & tech serv to energy & natural resource ind)
   Dresser Peking, Room 1522, Peking Hotel, Peking, PRC

EG&G INC   45 William St, Wellesley, MA 02181, Tel: (617) 237-5100
   (Diversified instru, components, services)
      EG&G China, Rm. 408, 4th fl., Noble Tower, 22 Jianguomen Wai Da Jie, Beijing, PRC

FINNIGAN CORP   355 River Oaks Parkway, San Jose, CA 95134-1991,
   Tel: (408) 433-4800
   (Mfr mass spectrometers, data handling sys, methodology devel)
      Finnigan MAT China Inc., Friendship Hotel, Suite 3702, Beijing, PRC

FLEXTRONICS INC   34551 Ardenwood Blvd, Fremont, CA 94555, Tel: (415) 794-3539
   (Contract mfr for electronics ind)
      Flextronics Computer (Shekou) Ltd., 5/F, Nan Shan Bldg., Shekou, Shenzhen, PRC

FOXBORO CO   33 Commercial St, Foxboro, MA 02035, Tel: (508) 543-8750
   (Mfr prdts/provide servs for ind automation)
      Shanghai-Foxboro Co. Ltd., 161 Cao Bao Rd., Shanghai, PRC

GENERAL RAILWAY SIGNAL CO   PO Box 20600, Rochester, NY 14602-0600,
   Tel: (716) 783-2000
   (Railway, rapid transit & vehicle control sys)
      Casco Signal Ltd., 1150 Qiu Jiang Rd., Zha Bei District, Shanghai, PRC

GETZ CORP   150 Post St, San Francisco, CA 94108, Tel: (415) 772-5500
   (Marketing/distribution serv)
      The Getz Corp., c/o The Getz Corp (HK) Ltd., 8/F Wyler Centre, 210 Lai Lin Pai Rd.,
      Kwai Chung, NT, Hong Kong

THE GLEASON WORKS   1000 University Ave, Rochester, NY 14692,
   Tel: (716) 473-1000
   (Mfr mfg machines, tooling & services)
      Gleason Intl. Marketing Corp., Room 1310, Noble Tower, No. 22, Beijing, PRC

H J HEINZ CO   PO Box 57, Pittsburgh, PA 15230, Tel: (412) 456-5100
   (Food prdts)
      Heinz-UFE Ltd., Heinz-UFE Mansion, 33 Tienho Rd., Guangzhou, Guangdong, PRC

HEWLETT-PACKARD CO   3000 Hanover St, PO Box 10301, Palo Alto, CA 94303-0890,
   Tel: (415) 857-1501
   (Mfr measurement & computation prdts & sys)
      China Hewlett-Packard Co. Ltd., Beijing Second Watch Factory, Shuang Yu Shu,
      Bei San Huan Rd., Hai Dian Dist., Beijing, PRC
      China Hewlett-Packard Co. Ltd., 1A Lane 2, Luchang St., Beiwei Rd., Xanwu Dist.,
      Beijing, PRC

HILL & KNOWLTON INC   420 Lexington Ave, New York, NY 10017,
   Tel: (212) 697-5600
   (Public relations, public affairs, comm counseling)
      Hill & Knowlton Asia Ltd., Jinglun Hotel, Suite 3045, Jianguo Men Wai Ave.,
      Beijing, PRC

INGERSOLL-RAND CO   200 Chestnut Ridge Rd, Woodcliff Lake, NJ 07675,
   Tel: (201) 573-0123
   (Mfr compressors, rock drills, pumps, air tools)
      Ingersoll-Rand Co., Room 5044, Peking Hotel, Peking, PRC

INSTRON CORP   100 Royall St, Canton, MA   02021, Tel: (617) 828-2500
(Testing instru)
   Instron Corp. Beijing, Friendship Hotel, Room 71043, P.O. Box 300, Beijing, PRC

ITT SHERATON CORP   60 State St, Boston, MA   02108, Tel: (617) 367-3600
(Hotel operations)
   Hua Ting Sheraton Hotel, Cao Xi Bei Lu, Shanghai, PRC
   The Great Wall Sheraton Hotel, North Donghuan Rd., Beijing, PRC

JEEP CORP   27777 Franklin Rd, Southfield, MI   48034, Tel: (313) 827-1000
(Automobiles, trucks, utility vehicles)
   Beijing Jeep Corp., Chuelyawgliu, Chaoyang Dist., Beijing, PRC

JOHNSON & JOHNSON   One Johnson & Johnson Plaza, New Brunswick, NJ   08933,
Tel: (201) 524-0400
(Surgical, med & baby prdts)
   Shanghai Johnson & Johnson Ltd., Shanghai, PRC
   Xian-Janssen Pharmaceutical Ltd., Xian, Shaanxi Province, PRC

THE M W KELLOGG CO   3 Greenway Plaza, Houston, TX   77046-0395,
Tel: (713) 960-2000
(Design, engr, procurement & constr for process & energy ind)
   Kellogg China Inc., CITIC Bldg., Suite 2403, 19 Jianguomenwai Dajie, Beijing, PRC

LOCKHEED CORP   2555 N Hollywood Way, Burbank, CA   91520, Tel: (213) 847-6121
(Aircraft, missiles, etc)
   Lockheed Corp., Room 6036, Peking Hotel, Peking, PRC

LUMMUS CREST   1515 Broad St, Bloomfield, NJ   07003, Tel: (201) 893-1515
(Engr & constr)
   Hua Lu Engineering Co. Ltd., Xue Yuan Rd. & Shi Huan Rd., Hai Dian District,
      P.O. Box 949, Beijing, PRC
   Lummus Crest, Rm. 1601 International Bldg., 19 Jian Guo Men Wai Da Jie, Beijing, PRC

MICROMERITICS INSTRUMENT CORP   One Micromeritics Dr, Norcross,
GA 30093-1877, Tel: (404) 662-3620
(Mfr analytical instruments)
   Micromeritics China, Xi Yuan Hotel- #609, Xi Jiao, Beijing, PRC

MTS SYSTEMS CORP   PO Box 24012, Minneapolis, MN   55424, Tel: (612) 937-4000
(Electrohydraulic testing & prod equip, mach controls)
   MTS Systems China Inc., Xi Yuan Hotel, Suites 674-5-6 691, Bldg. No. 6, Er Li Gou,
      Zi Jiao, Beijing, PRC
   MTS Systems China Inc., Room 2219, Rui Jing Bldg., 205 Mao Ming Road (South),
      Shanghai, PRC

McCANN-ERICKSON WORLDWIDE   750 Third Ave, New York, NY   10017,
Tel: (212) 697-6000
(Advertising)
   McCann-Erickson Inc., Room 5035, Peking Hotel, Peking, PRC

McCORMICK & CO INC   11350 McCormick Rd, Hunt Valley, MD   21031,
Tel: (301) 771-7301
(Seasons, flavorings, specialty foods)
   Shanghai McCormick Seasoning & Food Stuffs Co. Ltd., Shanghai, PRC

McDONNELL DOUGLAS CORP   Box 516, St Louis, MO 63166, Tel: (314) 232-0232
(Military & comm aircraft, space vehicles, electronics, missiles, data processing)
McDonnell-Douglas China Tech. Services Ltd., P.O. Box 7840, Shanghai, PRC
McDonnell-Douglas Corp., Room 3012, Peking Hotel, Peking, PRC

PHILIPP BROTHERS CHEMICALS INC   1 Parker Plaza, Fort Lee, NJ 07029,
Tel: (201) 944-6020
(Mfr ind & agric chems)
Philipp Brothers Chemicals Inc., P.O. Box 9028, Intl. Club, Sanlitun Branch,
Peking, PRC

PPG INDUSTRIES   One PPG Place, Pittsburgh, PA 15272, Tel: (412) 434-3131
(Mfr flat glass, fiber glass, chems, coatings, med electr)
Guangdong Glass Co. Ltd., Shekou Industrial Zone, Shenzen, Guangdong Province, PRC
PPG-Nan Chang Chemical Technology Development Corp. Ltd., 57 Fifta Jiao Tong Ave.,
Nan Chang City, Jiangxi Province, PRC

READING & BATES CORP   2200 Mid-Continent Tower, Tulsa, OK 74103,
Tel: (918) 583-8521
(Oil & gas explor & prod, offshore contract drilling, water mgmt sys)
China Nanhai Reading & Bates Drilling Corp. Ltd., China Hotel Office Tower,
Rms. 506-508, Lui Hua Lu, Guangzhou, PRC

ROCKWELL INTL CORP   2230 E Imperial Hwy, El Segundo, CA 90245,
Tel: (213) 647-5000
(Prdts & serv for aerospace, automotive, electronics, graphics & automation inds)
Rockwell Intl. Overseas Corp., 5/F A-2 Block, 502 Lido Center, Jichang Rd.,
Dong Jiao, Beijing, PRC

ROSEMOUNT INC   12001 Technology Dr, Eden Prairie, MN 55344,
Tel: (612) 941-5560
(Mfr aerospace & ind instrumentation)
Rosemount China, Minzu Hotel, Room 2117, 51 Fuxingmennei Dajie, Beijing, PRC

SIGNODE PACKAGING SYSTEMS   3600 W Lake Ave, Glenview, IL 60025,
Tel: (708) 724-6100
(Mfr packaging systems)
Signode, Room 1570, Dong Fang Hotel, Liu Hua Rd., Guangzhou, PRC

STOKES DIV   5500 Tabor Rd, Philadelphia, PA 19120, Tel: (215) 289-5671
(Vacuum pumps & components, vacuum dryers, oil-upgrading equip)
Connell Co. Ltd., 1405 Shanghai Union Bldg., 100 Yanan East Rd., Shanghai, PRC

SUN EXPLORATION & PRODUCTION CO   PO Box 2880, Dallas, TX 75221-2880,
Tel: (214) 890-2300
(Oil & gas explor & prod)
Sun Orient Exploration Co., P.O. Box 23 Potou, Foreign Corp. Bldg., Zhanjiang Ritz,
Guangdong Prov., PRC

TEKTRONIX INC   PO Box 500, Beaverton, OR 97077, Tel: (503) 627-7111
(Mfr test & meas, visual sys & commun prdts)
Tektronix China Ltd., Xiyuan Hotel #102, Erligou Western Suburb, Beijing, PRC

VARIAN ASSOCIATES INC   611 Hansen Way, Palo Alto, CA 94304-1030,
Tel: (415) 493-4000
(Mfr microwave tubes & devices, analytical instru, semiconductor process & med equip,

vacuum sys)
    Varian China Ltd., Room 907/908 Beijing Yanshan Hotel, 56 Haidian Rd., Beijin, PRC

WARNER-LAMBERT CO   201 Tabor Road, Morris Plains, NJ 07950,
    Tel: (201) 540-2000
    (Mfr ethical & proprietary pharms, confectionary & consumer prdts)
      Harbin Warner-Lambert Confectionery Co. Ltd., Daoli District, Shangjiang Rd. 66,
      Harbin City, PRC

WAXMAN INDUSTRIES INC   24460 Aurora Rd, Bedford Heights, OH 44146,
    Tel: (216) 439-1830
    (Assemble/distr plumbing, electrical & hardware prdts)
      CWI Intl. China, Inc., #6 Xing-Hua Rd, Xiamen Economic Spec. Zone, Fujian, PRC

WEATHERFORD INTL INC   1360 Post Oak Blvd, PO Box 27608, Houston,
    TX 77227-9917, Tel: (713) 439-9400
    (Tubular & cementation servs, prdts & equip; water jetting servs, mfr marine pedestal
    cranes)
      Weatherford Intl. Inc., c/o Nan Hai West Oil Corp., Shekou Industrial Zone,
      Shenzhen, PRC

COLOMBIA

3M CO   3M Center, St Paul, MN 55144-1000, Tel: (612) 733-1110
    (Mfr abrasives, adhesives, chems, ind & consumer tapes/diskettes, health care prdts,
    elec connectors)
      3M Colombia S.A., Aptdo. Aereo 11091, y 12693, Diagonal 6A, Bis No. 5-95, Soacha,
      Cundina Marca, Bogota, Colombia

ABBOTT LABORATORIES   Abbott Park, North Chicago, IL 60064,
    Tel: (312) 937-6100
    (Pharm & lab prdts)
      Abbott Labs de Colombia S.A., Carrera 3, No. 10-20, Cali, Colombia
      Abbott Labs de Colombia S.A., Autopista al Aeropuerto El Dorado, Bogota, Colombia

AEROGLIDE CORP   PO Box Aeroglide, Raleigh, NC 27626-0505, Tel: (919) 851-2000
    (Rotary driers, dehydrators, roasters, grain & coffee driers)
      Empresa Metalurgica Colombiana S.A., Carrera 19, No. 16-75, Bucaramanga, Colombia

AFIA   110 William St, New York, NY 10038, Tel: (212) 964-4990
    (Insurance)
      La Continental Compania de Seguros Generales S.A., Intl. Bldg., Carrera 13, #26-45,
      Aptdo. Aereo 3802, Bogota, Colombia

ALLEN-SHERMAN-HOFF CO   One Country View Rd, Malvern, PA 19355,
Tel: (215) 647-9900
(Design/eng material handling sys)
   Ing. Victor M. Tejada Ltda., Edif. Zaccour, Calle 11, Cali, Colombia

ALLERGAN PHARMACEUTICALS INTL INC   2525 DuPont Dr, Irvine, CA 92713,
Tel: (714) 752-4500
(Pharms, opthalmic & dermatological preparations)
   Allergan de Colombua S.A., Aptdo. Aereo 29699, Bogota, D.E., Colombia

AMERICAN BROADCASTING COS INC   1330 Ave of the Americas, New York, NY 10019,
Tel: (212) 887-7777
(Radio/TV prod & broadcast)
   Producciones Tecnicas, Ltda., Calle 22, No. 6-27, Piso 6, Bogota, Colombia

AMERICAN CYANAMID CO   1 Cyanamid Plaza, Wayne, NJ 07470, Tel: (201) 831-2000
(Pharms, chems, agric & consumer prdts)
   Cyanamid de Colombia S.A., Carrera 64, No. 12-51, Bogota, Colombia
   Cyanamid de Colombia S.A., Mamonal, Cartagena, Colombia

AMERICAN HOME PRODUCTS CORP   685 Third Ave, New York, NY 10017,
Tel: (212) 878-5800
(Drugs, food, household prdts)
   Home Products, Inc., Calle 29 Norte, No. 64-34, Cali, Colombia

AMERICAN INTL UNDERWRITERS CORP   70 Pine St, New York, NY 10270,
Tel: (212) 770-7000
(General ins)
   American Intl Underwriters de Colombia Ltda., P.O.Box 92381, Edif. La,
     Interamericana de Seguros, Calle 79 No. 9-57, 5th Floor, Bogota, Colombia
   American Intl Underwriters de Colombia Ltda., other locations in Colombia

AMERICAN LIFE INSURANCE CO (ALICO)   PO Box 2226, Wilmington, DE 19899,
Tel: (302) 594-2000
(Life ins, pension & annuity plans, health prdts)
   Interamericana Compania de Seguros de Vida S.A., Aptdo. Aereo 92381, Bogota,
   Colombia

AMERICAN RE-INSURANCE CO   One Liberty Plaza, 91 Liberty St, New York,
NY 10006, Tel: (212) 766-6700
(Reinsurance)
   American Re-Insurance Co., Carrera 7, No. 32-33, Bogota, Colombia

AMERON INC   4700 Ramona Blvd, PO Box 3000, Monterey Park, CA 91754,
Tel: (213) 268-4111
(Mfr steel pipe sys, concrete prdts, traffic & lighting poles, protective coatings)
   American Pipe & Construction Intl., Aptdo. Aereo No. 90087, Bogota, D.E., Colombia

AMPEX CORP   401 Broadway, Redwood City, CA 94063-3199, Tel: (415) 367-2011
(Mfr professional audio/visual sys, magnetic recording media, data-memory prdts)
   Ampex de Colombia S.A., Carrera 16A 79-25, Bogota, Colombia

ARBOR ACRES FARM INC   41 Marlborough Rd, Glastonbury, CT 06033,
Tel: (203) 633-4681
(Producers of male & female broiler breeders, commercial egg layers)
   Avicola Colombiana Ltda., Carrere 74, No. 48-B-7, Medellin, Colombia

ARMCO INTL INC 703 Curtis St, PO Box 700, Middletown, OH 45042,
Tel: (513) 425-6541
(Sheet steel & steel prdts, constr, oil field equip, ins, finance leasing)
Armco Colombiana S.A., Calle 15 No. 41-54, Aptdo. Aereo 120-22, Bogota, Colombia

AYERST LABORATORIES 145 King of Prussia Rd, Radnor, PA 19087,
Tel: (215) 688-4400
(Biologicals & pharms)
Ayerst Labs, Inc., Calle 18 No. 44-A-00, Edif. No. 3, Bogota, Colombia

BAKER OIL TOOLS PO Box 3048, Houston, TX 77253, Tel: (713) 923-9351
(Oil/gas well completions equip)
Baker Transworld Inc., Calle 18, No. 44A-40, Bogota, Colombia

BANKAMERICA CORP PO Box 37000, San Francisco, CA 94137, Tel: (415) 622-3456
(Financial services)
Banco Colombo Americano, Edificio Avianca, Carrera 7a, No. 16-36,
Aptdo. Aereo 12327, Bogota, Colombia

BANKERS TRUST CO 280 Park Ave, New York, NY 10017, Tel: (212) 775-2500
(Banking)
Bankers Trust Co., Aptdo. Aereo 3497, Bogota, Colombia

BARDAHL MFG CORP 1400 N W 52nd St, PO Box 70607, Seattle, WA 98107,
Tel: (206) 783-4851
(Lubricating oils)
Glanton Ltda., P.O. Box 27660, Cra, 20 #21-35, Bogota, Colombia

BENTLY NEVADA CORP PO Box 157, Minden, NV 89423, Tel: (702) 782-3611
(Electronic monitoring system)
Vibran Cia. Ltda., Cra. 9, No. 80-15, Aptdo. Aereo 92077, Bogota, Colombia

BEROL USA Eagle Rd, Danbury, CT 06810, Tel: (203) 744-0000
(Writing instru, sharpeners, drafting prdts, templates)
Berol S.A., Aptdo. Aereo 7571, Bogota 1, Colombia

BLACK & DECKER CORP 701 E Joppa Road, Towson, MD 21204, Tel: (301) 583-3900
(Mfr portable elect & pneumatic power tools, household prdts)
Black & Decker de ColombiaS.A., Aptdo. Aereo 12108, Bogota, Colombia

BOYDEN ASSOCIATES INC 260 Madison Ave, New York, NY 10016,
Tel: (212) 685-3400
(Mgt consultants, exec search)
Boyden/Consultores Ejecutivox Ltda., Calle 71, No. 3-74, Bogota, Colombia

BRISTOL BABCOCK INC 1100 Buckingham St, Watertown, CT 06795,
Tel: (203) 575-3000
(Mfr process control instru & intelligent digital prdts)
Singer Products Co., Inc. & Cia Ltda., Carrera 9A, No. 91-2, Aptdo. Aereo 054902,
Bogota, D.E., Colombia

LEO BURNETT CO INC 35 West Wacker Dr, Chicago, IL 60601, Tel: (312) 220-5959
(Advertising agency)
Leo Burnett Colombia S.A., Carrera 13 No. 89-59, Bogota 8, D.E., Colombia

BURNS INTL SECURITY SERVICES   2 Campus Dr, Parsippany, NJ 07054,
  Tel: (201) 397-2000
  (Provider of security officers)
    Seguridad Burns de Colombia S.A., Carrera 17 No. 36-62, Bogota, D.E., Colombia

CABOT CORP   950 Winter St, PO Box 9073, Waltham, MA 02254,
  Tel: (617) 890-0200
  (Mfr carbon blacks, plastics; oil & gas, info sys)
    Cabot Colombiana S.A., Aptdo. Aereo No. 14471, Carrera 13 No. 2700 of 703, Bogota,
      Colombia
    Cabot Colombiana S.A., Edif. Seguros Bolivia, Carrera 4A #12-41 of 413, Cali,
      Colombia
    Cabot Colombiana S.A., Aptdo. Aereo 2903, Edif. Banco de America Latina,
      Oficina 8-05 & 8-06, Cartagena, Colombia

CANADA DRY INTL CORP   2600 Century Pkwy, Atlanta, GA 30345,
  Tel: (404) 753-2182
  (Carbonated beverages, soft drinks extract)
    Canada Dry Ltda., Calle 12 # 1-12 of 408 (Downtown), Aptdo. Aereo #2126, Cali,
      Colombia
    Gaseosas Posado Tobon S.A., Carrera 52, Calle 50 #20 Piso 15,
      Aptdo. Aereo #683 (Ave. Guayabal 24-96), Medellin, Colombia

CARGILL   PO Box 9300, Minneapolis, MN 55440, Tel: (612) 475-7575
  (Food prdts, feeds, animal prdts)
    Cargill Colombia, Apartado Aereo 5276, Bogota, Colombia

CENTRAL NATIONAL-GOTTESMAN INC   100 Park Ave, New York, NY 10017,
  Tel: (212) 532-7300
  (Pulp & paper prdts)
    Central National Andina Ltda., Apartado Aereo 14431, Bogota, D.E., Colombia

CHASE MANHATTAN BANK N A   1 Chase Manhattan Plaza, New York, NY 10081,
  Tel: (212) 552-2222
  (Intl banking)
    Banco del Commercio (Associated Bank), Main Office, Calle Trece 8-52/56,
      Aptdo. Aereo 4749, Bogota, Colombia
    Chase Manhattan Bank, N.A., Edif. Seguros Fenix, Carrera 7, No. 32-33, Piso 29A,
      Aptdo. Aereo 16192, Bogota, Colombia

CHEVRON CHEMICAL CO   PO Box 5047, San Ramon, CA 94583-0947,
  Tel: (415) 842-5500
  (Chemicals)
    Chevron Chemical Intl. Sales Inc., Apartado Aereo 3631, Bogota, Colombia

CIGNA CORP   One Liberty Place, 1650 Market St, Philadelphia, PA 19101,
  Tel: (215) 523-4000
  (Ins, invest, health care & other fin servs)
    Cigna Seguros de Colombia SA, Calle 72- #10-51/ Pisos 6, 7Y 8, Bogota, Colombia
    Grancol, Asesoramiento y Servicios Ltda., Carrera 13, #26-45/ of. 13-06,
      Bogota D.E., Colombia

CITIBANK NA   399 Park Ave, New York, NY 10043, Tel: (212) 559-1000
  (Intl banking)
    Banco Intl. de Colombia S.A., Carrera 9, No. 14-10, Aptdo. Aereo 4134, Bogota,
      Colombia
    Representaciones Financieras S.A., Citibank, N.A., Carrera 9, No. 14-10,

Aptdo. Aereo 4134, Bogota, Colombia
Representaciones Financieras S.A., in: Barranquilla, Bucaramanga, Cali, Cartegena, Cacata
Representaciones Financieras S.A., Medellin, Pereira, Villairicencio

CITIZENS & SOUTHERN NATL BANK   35 Broad St, Atlanta, GA 30399,
Tel: (404) 581-2121
(Banking)
Banco de Occidente, Carrera 5A, No. 12-50, Cali, Colombia

THE COCA-COLA CO   310 North Ave NW, PO Box Drawer 1734, Atlanta, GA 30313,
Tel: (404) 676-2121
(Mfr & sale of soft drink syrups & concentrates, juices & food prdts, motion pic & TV prod)
Coca-Cola Colombia S.A., all mail to: U.S. address

COLGATE-PALMOLIVE CO   300 Park Ave, New York, NY 10022, Tel: (212) 310-2000
(Pharms, cosmetics, toiletries, detergents)
Colgate Palmolive Cia., Carrera 1, No. 41-06, Cali, Colombia

COLUMBIA PICTURES INDUSTRIES INC   711 Fifth Ave, New York, NY 10022,
Tel: (212) 751-4400
(Producer & distributor of motion pictures)
Fox/Columbia Pictures of Columbia Inc., Carrera 5, No. 22-85, Piso 5, Bogota, Colombia

COMBUSTION ENGINEERING INC   900 Long Ridge Road, Stamford, CT 06902,
Tel: (203) 329-8771
(Tech constr)
Combustion Engineering, c/o Sudamerica de Perforaciones y Servicios S.A., Aptdo. Aereo 7940, Bogota, Colombia

COOPERTOOLS   PO Box 30100, Raleigh, NC 27622, Tel: (919) 781-7200
(Mfr hand tools)
Empresa Andina de Herramientas, S.A., Aptdo. Aereo 8041, Cali, Colombia

CORE LABORATORIES   10205 Westheimer, Houston, TX 77042, Tel: (713) 972-6312
(Petroleum testing/analysis, analytical chem, environmental servs)
Core Laboratories, Aptdo. Aereo 80347, Bogota, Colombia

CPC INTERNATIONAL INC   PO Box 8000, International Plaza, Englewood Cliffs, NJ 07632, Tel: (201) 894-4000
(Mfr consumer food prdts & corn refining prdts)
Maizena S.A., Calle 72 No. 13-23, Aptdo. Aereo 92483, Bogota 8, Colombia

CROWN CORK & SEAL CO INC   Holmesburg Station, PO Box 6208, Philadelphia, PA 19136, Tel: (215) 698-5100
(Cans, bottle caps; filling & packaging mach)
Crown Litometal S.A., Aptdo. Aereo 4084, Bogota, D.E., Colombia

CUMMINS ENGINE CO INC   PO Box 3005, Columbus, IN 47202, Tel: (812) 377-5000
(Mfr diesel engines)
Cummins de Colombia S.A., Aptdo. Aereo 90988, Botoga, Colombia

D'ARCY MASIUS BENTON & BOWLES INC (DMB&B)   1675 Broadway, New York,
  NY 10019, Tel: (212) 468-3622
  (Advertising & communications)
      Procesos Creativos, Calle 93A #19-84, Bogota, Colombia

DANCER FITZGERALD SAMPLE INTL   405 Lexington Ave, New York, NY 10174,
  Tel: (212) 661-0800
  (Advertising agency)
      Contacto Publicidad Ltda., Ave. 5A Norte 20-83, Aptdo. Aereo 010138, Cali, Colombia

DATAEASE INTL INC   7 Cambridge Dr, Trumbull, CT 06611, Tel: (203) 374-8000
  (Mfr applications devel software)
      Iris Software, Calle 26, NTE #4 N-17, Cali, Colombia

DHJ INDUSTRIES INC   1040 Ave of the Americas, New York, NY 10018,
  Tel: (212) 944-4500
  (Mfr of knit fabrics, interlinings plastic chips & denim)
      Entretelas DHJ-Unica Ltda., Carrera 10, No. 2-35, Parque Industrial Villamaria,
      Manizales, Colombia

DOW CHEMICAL CO   2030 Dow Center, Midland, MI 48640, Tel: (517) 636-1000
  (Chems, plastics, fibers, pharms)
      Dow Colombiana S.A., Manonal, Aptdo. Aereo 1651, Cartagena, Colombia
      Dow Quimica de Colombia S.A., Calle 37, No. 8-47, Bogota, Colombia
      Dow Quimica de Colombia S.A., Carrera 56, 50-40, Aptdo. Aereo 3715, Medellin,
      Colombia

DOW CORNING CORP   2220 W Salzburg Rd, PO Box 1767, Midland, MI 48640,
  Tel: (517) 496-4000
  (Silicones, silicon chems, solid lubricants)
      Dow Corning Latin America Ltd., Aptdo. Aereo 91079, Bogota 8, Colombia

E I DU PONT DE NEMOURS & CO   Du Pont Bldg, 1007 Market St, Wilmington,
  DE 19898, Tel: (302) 774-1000
  (Mfr/sale diversified chems, plastics, specialty prdts & fibers)
      DuPont de Colombia S.A., Via 40, No. 85-85, Aptdo. Aereo 1386, Barranquilla,
      Colombia

EASTMAN KODAK CO   343 State St, Rochester, NY 14650-0518, Tel: (716) 724-4000
  (Devel/mfr photo & chem prdts, info mgmt/video/copier sys, fibers/plastics for
  various ind)
      Kodak Colombiana, Ltda., Avenida El Dorado 78A-93, Botota, Colombia

EATON CORP   100 Erieview Plaza, Cleveland, OH 44114, Tel: (216) 523-5000
  (Advanced tech prdts for transp & ind mkts)
      Eaton Intl., Inc., Aptdo. Aereo 32258, Bogota, D.E., Colombia

EBERHARD FABER INC   PO Box 760, Wilkes-Barre, PA 18773, Tel: (717) 474-6711
  (Art materials, pencils, visual aids)
      Industria Colombiana de Lapices S.A., Aptdo. Aereo 2200, Cali, Colombia

ENDO LABORATORIES INC   1000 Stewart Ave, Garden City, NY 11530,
  Tel: (516) 832-2002
  (Ethical pharms)
      Endo Pan American Corp., Aptdo. Aereo 29674, Bogota, Colombia

ENVIROTECH CORP   3000 Sand Hill Road, Menlo Park, CA 94025,
   Tel: (415) 854-2000
   (Supplier of equip & tech for underground mining, ind processing & pollution control)
      Envirotech Latin America, Aptdo. Aereo 7076, Cali, Colombia

EXIM OVERSEAS INC   2121 Ponce de Leon Blvd, Coral Gables, FL 33134,
   Tel: (305) 444-6444
   (Trading & sales of arms for Armco Latin Div)
      Armco Colombiana, Apartado Aereo 094359, Bogota, Colombia

EXQUISITE FORM INDUSTRIES INC   16 E 40th St, New York, NY 10016,
   Tel: (212) 532-8160
   (Foundation garments)
      Exquisite Form Brassiere de Colombia, Ltda., Carrera 34-A, No. 7-06, Bogota,
      Colombia

EXXON CORP   225 E John Carpenter Frwy, Irving, TX 75062, Tel: (214) 444-1000
   (Petroleum & petroleum prdts)
      Amonaicos del Caribe S.A. (AMOCAR), Carrera 7, No. 35-45, Bogota, Colombia,
         Intl. Petroleum Colombia, Ltda., Carrera 7, No. 36-45, Bogot
      Exxon Colombiana S.A., Carrera 44, No. 35-31, Edif. Banco Cafetero, Barranquilla,
      Colombia
      Exxon Colombiana S.A., other locations in Colombia

FLAGSHIP NATIONAL BANK OF MIAMI   777 Brickell Ave, Miami, FL 33131,
   Tel: (305) 674-5111
   (Banking)
      Flagship Natl. Bank of Miami, Aptdo. Aereo 33966, Bogota, Colombia

FLORIDA INTL FORWARDERS   6905 N W 25th St, PO Box 522085, Miami, FL 33122,
   Tel: (305) 592-6450
   (Air cargo service)
      Mundo Carga Ltda., Edif. Zaccour, Carrera 3-A, No. 11-32, Of. 730, Cali, Colombia
      Mundo Carga Ltda., Carrera 10 #15-22, Suite 702, Bogota, Colombia

FMC CORP   200 E Randolph Dr, Chicago, IL 60601, Tel: (312) 861-6000
   (Mach & chem for industry, agric & govt)
      FMC Corp., Aptdo. Aereo 5511, Cali, Colombia

FOOTE CONE & BELDING COMMUNICATIONS INC   101 E Erie St, Chicago,
   IL 60611-2897, Tel: (312) 751-7000
   (Advertising agency)
      FCB/Puma, Carrera 43A, No. 14109, Oficina 403, Medellin, Colombia

FOXBORO CO   33 Commercial St, Foxboro, MA 02035, Tel: (508) 543-8750
   (Mfr prdts/provide servs for ind automation)
      Equipos y Controles Industriales Ltda., Aptdo. Aereo 9128, Bogota 1, Colombia
      Equipos y Controles Industriales Ltda., Aptdo. Aereo 10465, Cali, Colombia
      Equipos y Controles Industriales Ltda., Aptdo. Aereo No. 50383, Medellin, Colombia

GAMLEN CHEMICAL CO   121 S Maple Ave, S San Francisco, CA 94080,
   Tel: (415) 873-1750
   (Chems, detergents & tank cleansers)
      Cabarria y Cia S.C.A., Calle Larga No. 10C-82, Cartagena, Colombia
      Cabarria y Cia S.C.A., Calle 14 No. 6-22, Cali, Colombia
      Gamlen Chemicals Co., Cabarria y Cia S.C.A., Paseo Boliva No. 43-54, Barranquilla,
      Colombia

GENERAL CABLE CORP   50 Tice Blvd, Woodcliff Lake, NJ 07675,
  Tel: (201) 573-8200
  (Mfr wire, cord & cable, associated prdts)
    Ceat General de Colombia S.A., Ciudadela ACOPI, Yumbo, Colombia

GENERAL FOODS CORP   250 North St, White Plains, NY 10625, Tel: (914) 335-2500
  (Processor, distributor & mfr of foods)
    Colombiana General Foods S.A., Aptdo. Aereo 8037, Cali, Colombia
    General Foods de Colombia S.A., Aptdo. Aereo 8037, Cali, Colombia

GENERAL MOTORS ACCEPTANCE CORP   3044 West Grand Blvd, Detroit, MI 48202,
  Tel: (313) 556-5000
  (Automobile financing)
    GMAC Colombia S.A., Centro Comercial Granahorrar, Calle 100 #11A-35,
      Aptdo. Aereo 28280, Bogota 1, Colombia

GENERAL REFRACTORIES CO   2661 Audubon Rd, Audubon, PA 19407,
  Tel: (215) 666-0104
  (Heat-resisting materials, furnace constr)
    Empresa de Refractorios Colombianos S.A. (ERECOS), Aptdo. Aereo 865, Medellin,
      Colombia

THE GILLETTE CO   Prudential Tower, Boston, MA 02199, Tel: (617) 421-7000
  (Mfr/distr shaving prdts, toiletries & cosmetics, stationery prdts)
    Gillette de Colombia S.A., Aptdo. Aereo 87, Cali, Calle 55 #IN-45, Cali, Colombia

GLOBAL INTERNATIONAL   500 Ygnacio Valley Rd, #175, Walnut Creek, CA 94596,
  Tel: (415) 933-2293
  (Freight forwarding)
    Global Servicios, SA, Calle 18A- #32-13, Bogota 1, DE, Colombia

GOODYEAR TIRE & RUBBER CO   1144 E Market St, Akron, OH 44316-0001,
  Tel: (216) 796-2121
  (Mfr tires, rubber prdts)
    Goodyear de Colombia S.A., Apartado 8020, Cali, Colombia

GRIFFITH LABORATORIES INC   I Griffith Center, Alsip, IL 60658,
  Tel: (708) 371-0900
  (Ind food ingredients & equip)
    Laboratorios Griffith de Colombia S.A., Aptdo. Aereo 8589, Medellin, Colombia

GROLIER INC   Old Shereman Tpk, Danbury, CT 06816, Tel: (203) 797-3500
  (Publishers)
    Editorial Camilo Torres S.A., Calle 22 No. 6-27, Bogota, Colombia
    Editorial Camilo Torres S.A., Aptdo. Aereo 3686, Bogota, Colombia
    W.M. Jackson, Inc., Calle 22 No. 6-27, Bogota, Colombia

GTE CORP   One Stamford Forum, Stamford, CT 06904, Tel: (203) 965-2000
  (Electr prdts, telecom sys, publ & commun)
    GTE Electric S.A., Calle 13, No. 46-52, Bogota, Colombia

FRANK B HALL & CO INC   549 Pleasantville Rd, Briarcliff Manor, NY 10510,
  Tel: (914) 769-9200
  (Insurance)
    AIS Ltda., Calle 79, No. 7-16, Aptdo. Aereo 90299, Bogota, Colombia

M A HANNA CO   100 Erieview Plaza, Cleveland, OH 44114, Tel: (216) 589-4000
  (Iron ore, nickel & silicon, oil & gas, coal, mgmt serv)
    Cerro Matoso S.A., Carrera 10 No. 27-27, Piso 4, Aptdo. Aereo 6823, Bogota, Colombia

THE HARPER GROUP INC   260 Townsend St, PO Box 77933, San Francisco,
  CA 94107, Tel: (415) 978-0600
  (Ocean/air freight fwdg, customs brokerage, packing & whse, logistics mgt, ins)
    Circle Freight Intl. De Colombia SA, Carrera 103- #47-85 Oficina 306, Bogota,
    Colombia

HUGHES TOOL CO   PO Box 2539, Houston, TX 77001, Tel: (713) 924-2222
  (Equip & serv to oil & gas explor & prod ind)
    Hughes Tool Co. S.A., Edif. Seguros Fenix, Of. 1204, Carrera 7, No. 32-33,
    Aptdo. Aereo 29697, Bogota 1, Colombia

IMCO SERVICES   5950 N Course Dr, Houston, TX 70072, Tel: (713) 561-1300
  (Drilling fluids)
    IMCO Services, Carrera 90A, No. 62-37, Bogota, Colombia

INA CORPORATION   1600 Arch St, Philadelphia, PA 19101, Tel: (215) 523-5335
  (Holding co: ins, financial serv)
    Seguros Colona S.A., Edif. Camara de Comercio, Calle 40, No. 44-39, Of. 3F,
    Aptdo. Aereo 2937, Barranquilla, Colombia
    Seguros Colona S.A., other locations in Colombia

INTERNATIONAL BUSINESS MACHINES (IBM)   Old Orchard Rd, Armonk,
  NY 10504-1783, Tel: (914) 765-1900
  (Info-handling sys, equip & serv)
    IBM de Colombia S.A., Bogota, Colombia

INTERNATIONAL MINERALS & CHEMICALS CORP   2315 Sanders Rd, Northbrook,
  IL 60062, Tel: (708) 564-8600
  (Fertilizers, chems, ind materials)
    Compania de Productos Quimicos Nacionales Sulfacidos S.A., Residencias, Nutibara,
    Piso M, Aptdo. Aereo 921, Medellin, Colombia

INTERNATIONAL PAPER   2 Manhattanville Rd, Purchase, NY 10577,
  Tel: (914) 397-1500
  (Mfr/distr container board, paper, wood prdts)
    Productora de Papeles S.A., Apartado Aereo 4412, Cali, Colombia

ITT CORP   1330 Ave of the Americas, New York, NY 10019, Tel: (212) 258-1000
  (Diversified mfr, tech & services)
    ITT Standard Electric de Colombia S.A., Carrera 7, No. 33-92, Bogota, Colombia

JOHNSON & HIGGINS   125 Broad St, New York, NY 10005, Tel: (212) 574-7000
  (Ins brokerage, benefit conslt)
    Johnson & Higgins Colombia, Ltda., Carrera 7, No. 32-33 Piso 70,
    Aptdo. Aereo No. 7248, Bogota, Colombia

JOHNSON & JOHNSON   One Johnson & Johnson Plaza, New Brunswick, NJ 08933,
  Tel: (201) 524-0400
  (Surgical, med & baby prdts)
    Janssen Farmaceutica S.A., Bogota, Colombia
    Johnson & Johnson de Colombia S.A., Cali, Colombia

S C JOHNSON & SON INC   1525 Howe St, Racine, WI 53403, Tel: (414) 631-2000
(Home, auto, commercial & personal care prdts, specialty chems)
   S.C. Johnson & Son Colombiana S.A., Aptdo. Aereo 29632, Bogota, D.E., Colombia

THE KENDALL CO   PO Box 10, Boston, MA 02101, Tel: (617) 423-2000
(Surgical dressings, baby prdts)
   Industrias Kendall de Colombia, Ltda., Carrera 44, No. 12-A, 13, Bogota, Colombia

KEYES FIBRE CO   3003 Summer St, Stamford, CT 06905, Tel: (203) 357-9100
(Molded containers)
   Colombiana de Modleados S.A., Calle 47 Nte., 5AN-21, Aptdo. Aereo 6880, Cali,
   Colombia

KIMBERLY-CLARK CORP   PO Box 619100, Dallas, TX 75261-1200,
   Tel: (214) 830-1200
(Mfr fiber-based prdts for personal care, pulp & forest prdts; air transport)
   Colombiana Kimberly S.A., Carrera 51, No. 50-51, Of. 806, Aptdo. Aereo 51906,
   Medellin, Colombia
   Colombiana Universal de Papeles S.A., Pereira, Colombia

KNOLL INTL   655 Madison Ave, New York, NY 10021, Tel: (212) 826-2400
(Furniture & fabrics)
   Trama Ltda., Carrera 7A 24-89 Piso 45, Bogota, Colombia

LANMAN & KEMP-BARCLAY & CO INC   25 Woodland Ave, Westwood, NJ 07675,
   Tel: (201) 666-4990
(Mfr pharms, toiletries)
   Lanman & Kemp-Barclay & Co. of Colombia, Calle 32 No. 44-85, Aptdo. Aereo 696,
   Barranquilla, Colombia

ELI LILLY & CO   307 E McCarty St, Indianapolis, IN 46285, Tel: (317) 261-2000
(Pharms, agric & cosmetic prdts)
   Eli Lilly & Co. of Colombia, Inc., Calle 25, No. 5-72, Cali, Colombia
   Eli Lilly Interamerica Inc., Edif. Carvajal, 4th & 5th Floors, Calle 13 No. 4-25,
   Cali, Colombia
   Eli Lilly Interamerica Inc., Aptdo. Aereo No. 4365, Cali, Colombia
   Eli Lilly Interamerica Inc., other locations in Colombia

LINTAS:WORLDWIDE   1 Dag Hammarskjold Plaza, New York, NY 10017,
   Tel: (212) 605-8000
(Advertising agency)
   Lintas:Colombia, Calle 80 #8-10, Bogota, Colombia

LIQUID CARBONIC CORP   135 S LaSalle St, Chicago, IL 60603,
   Tel: (312) 855-2500
(Compressed gases, etc)
   Liquido Carbonico Colombianao S.A., Carrera 7, No. 34-61, Bogota, Colombia
   Liquido Carbonico de Colombia S.A., Via 40-Siape, Aptdo. Aereo 938, Barranquilla,
   Colombia

LOUISIANA LAND & EXPLORATION CO   PO Box 60350, 909 Poydras St, New Orleans,
   LA 70160, Tel: (504) 566-6500
(Oil & gas explor)
   LL & E Colombia, Inc., Aptdo. Aereo 91001, Bogota 8, Colombia

MANUFACTURERS HANOVER TRUST CO 270 Park Ave, New York, NY 10017,
Tel: (212) 286-6000
(Banking)
Manufacturers Hanover Trust Bank, Calle 16 No. 6-66, Aptdo. Aereo 28127, Bogota,
Colombia

MAREMONT CORP 250 E Kehoe Blvd, Carol Stream, IL 60188, Tel: (312) 861-4000
(Mfr automotive parts: mufflers, exhaust pipes, shock absorbers)
Gabriel de Colombia S.A., c/o Chaid Neme Hermanos, Aptdo. Aereo 4895, Bogota,
Colombia

MERCK SHARP & DOHME INTL PO Box 2000, Rahway, NJ 07065, Tel: (201) 574-4000
(Pharms, chems & biologicals)
Laboratorios Merck, Sharp & Dohme Quimica de Colombia S.A., Calle 30, No. 6-38,
Piso 6, Bogota, Colombia

MILCHEM INC 3900 Essex Lane, PO Box 22111, Houston, TX 77027,
Tel: (214) 439-8000
(Gas & oil well drilling fluids & chem additives)
Milchem Western Hemisphere Inc., Aptdo. Aereo 9313, Bogota, Colombia

MOBIL CORP 150 E 42nd St, New York, NY 10017, Tel: (212) 883-4242
(Petroleum explor, prdts)
Mobil AMI S.A., Aptdo. Aereo 8401, Bogota, Colombia
Mobil Oil Co. de Colombia, Aptdo. Aereo 052973 Zona 2, Bogota, Colombia

MONSANTO CO 800 N Lindbergh Blvd, St Louis, MO 63167, Tel: (314) 694-1000
(Mfr chem & agric prdts, pharms, ind process equip, man-made fibers, plastics)
Monsanto Colombiana Inc., Edif. Multifinanciera, Piso 16, Calle 71A 6-30,
Aptdo. Aereo 56014, Bogota, Colombia

MTS SYSTEMS CORP PO Box 24012, Minneapolis, MN 55424, Tel: (612) 937-4000
(Electrohydraulic testing & prod equip, mach controls)
Arotec Colombiana S.A., Carrera 25 No. 38-23, Apto. Aereo 050862, Bogota D.E.,
Colombia

MYERS TIRE SUPPLY INTL 1293 South Main St, Akron, OH 44301,
Tel: (216) 253-5592
(Mfr polymer & metal prdts for mat handling, automotive & constr inds)
Industrias E. Inversiones Myers, SA, Ave. 13 #10540, Apartado Aereo 82542, Bogota,
Colombia

McCANN-ERICKSON WORLDWIDE 750 Third Ave, New York, NY 10017,
Tel: (212) 697-6000
(Advertising)
McCann-Erickson Corp. S.A., Edif. Colgas, Calle 38 8-43, Bogota, D.E., Colombia
McCann-Erickson Corp. S.A., Calle 22 Norte No. 3-21, Apartado 976, Cali, Valle,
Colombia

NABISCO BRANDS INC Nabisco Brands Plaza, East Hanover, NJ 07936,
Tel: (201) 503-2000
(Mfr food prdts)
Nabisco Brands, Inc., Aptdo. Aereo 214, Palmira, Colombia

NALCO CHEMICAL CO One Nalco Center, Naperville, IL 60566-1024,
Tel: (708) 305-1000
(Chems for water & waste water treatment, oil prod & refining, ind processes;

(cont)

water/energy mgmt serv)
    Quimica Nalco de Colombia S.A., Aptdo. Aereo 92219, Bogota D.E., Colombia

NCR CORP   1700 S Patterson Blvd, Dayton, OH 45479, Tel: (513) 445-2000
(Develop/mfr/sell/serv business info processing sys)
    NCR de Colombia, S.A., Carrera 37 No. 30-20, Apartado Aereo 3933, Bogota, Colombia

A C NIELSEN CO   Nielsen Plaza, Northbrook, IL 60062, Tel: (708) 498-6300
(Marketing research)
    A.C. Nielsen de Colombia S.A., Calle 80 No. 5-81, Bogota, Colombia

NORWICH EATON PHARMACEUTICALS INC   17 Eaton Ave, Norwich, NY 13815,
Tel: (607) 335-2111
(Mfr pharms, chems, health prdts)
    Norwich Colombiana, D.E. Transversaal 42B 19-77, Aptdo. Aereo 13902, Bogota,
      Colombia

OCCIDENTAL PETROLEUM CORP   10889 Wilshire Blvd, Los Angeles, CA 90024,
Tel: (213) 879-1700
(Petroleum & petroleum prdts, chems, plastics)
    Island Creek de Colombia, Inc., Aptdo. Aereo 2524, Bogota, Colombia
    Occidental de Colombia, Inc., Calle 79, No. 8-70, Bogota, Colombia

OLIN CORP   120 Long Ridge Rd, Stamford, CT 06904-1355, Tel: (203) 356-2000
(Chems, metals, applied physics in elect, defense, aerospace inds)
    Quimica Saga S.A., Calle 26, No. 4 A 45, Aptdo. Aereo 19905, Bogota, Colombia

ONAN CORP   1400 73rd Ave NE, Minneapolis, MN 55432, Tel: (612) 574-5000
(Electric generators, ind engines & controls)
    Peter Santa Maria & Cia Ltd., Almacen Universal, Calle 50, No. 53-2,
      Aptdo. Aereo 910, Medellin, Colombia

OTIS ELEVATOR CO   10 Farm Springs, Farmington, CT 06032, Tel: (203) 674-4047
(Elevators & escalators)
    Otis Elevator Co., Aptdo. Aereo 8584, Bogota, Colombia

OWENS-ILLINOIS INC   PO Box 1035, Toledo, OH 43666, Tel: (419) 247-5000
(Glass & plastic containers, house- hold & ind prdts, packaging)
    Cristaleria Peldar S.A., Carrera 13, No. 27-75, Bogota, Colombia
    Cristaleria Peldar S.A., other locations in Colombia

PAN-AMERICAN LIFE INSURANCE CO   Pan American Life Center, New Orleans,
LA 70130, Tel: (504) 566-1300
(Insurance)
    Pan-American de Colombia, Cia de Seguros de Vida S.A., Carrera 7 No. 75-09,
      Edificio Bogota, Bogota, Colombia

PARAMOUNT INTL FILMS INC   1 Gulf & Western Plaza, New York, NY 10023,
Tel: (212) 333-4600
(Film prod & distr)
    Paramount Films of Colombia, Inc., Carrera 5, No. 22-85, Piso 4, Bogota, Colombia

PEABODY BARNES INC   651 N Main St, Mansfield, OH 44902, Tel: (419) 522-1511
(Mfr water/waste water pumps & sys)
    Barnes de Colombia S.A., Apartado 12098, Calle 15 No. 41-17, Bogota, Colombia

PEPSICO INC 700 Anderson Hill Rd, Purchase, NY 10577, Tel: (914) 253-2000
(Beverages, food prdts & servs, sporting goods)
Pepsi-Cola Panamericana S.A., Aptdo. Aereo 7462, Bogota, Colombia

PFIZER INC 235 E 42nd St, New York, NY 10017, Tel: (212) 573-2323
(Mfr pharms, hosp prdts, chems, consumer & animal health prdts)
Pfizer S.A., Aptdo. Aereo 5641, Bogota, D.E., Colombia

PHILLIPS PETROLEUM CO Phillips Bldg, Bartlesville, OK 74004,
Tel: (918) 661-6600
(Crude oil, natural gas, liquefied petroleum gas, gasoline & petro-chems)
Phillips Petroleum Co., Carrera 13, No. 26-49, Piso 12, Cali, Colombia
Phillips Petroleum Ventas S.A., Carrera 13, No. 26-45, Cali, Colombia
Phillips Petroquimica S.A., Calle 11, No. 3-58, Cali, Colombia
Phillips Quimica Ventas Colombia S.A., Calle 11, No. 3-58, Cali, Colombia

PROCTER & GAMBLE CO One Procter & Gamble Plaza, Cincinnati, OH 45202,
Tel: (513) 983-1100
(Personal care, food, laundry, cleaning & ind prdts)
Norwich Colombiana, S.A., Colombia

QUAKER OATS CO 345 Merchandise Mart Plaza, Chicago, IL 60654,
Tel: (312) 222-7111
(Foods, pet foods, toys, chems)
Productos Quaker S.A., Aptdo. Aereo 2074, Cali, Colombia

RALSTON PURINA CO Checkerboard Sq, St Louis, MO 63164, Tel: (214) 982-1000
(Poultry & live stock feed, cereals, food prdts)
Purina Colombiana S.A., Calle 58 No. 10-42, Of. 303, Bogota 2, Colombia

RAPISTAN CORP 507 Plymouth Ave NE, Grand Rapids, MI 49505,
Tel: (616) 451-6200
(Material handling equip)
Rapistan de Colombia - Rapiscol S.A., Aptdo. 9564, Bogota, Colombia

RCA GLOBAL COMMUNICATIONS INC 60 Broad St, New York, NY 10004,
Tel: (212) 806-7000
(Commun serv)
Ocampo Vargas e Cia., Carrera 10 No. 22-65, Bogota, Colombia

RICHARDSON-VICKS INC Ten Westport Rd, Wilton, CT 06897, Tel: (203) 834-5000
(Consumer health & personal care prdts)
Richardson-Vicks Internamericas Inc., Carrera 7 No. 23-12, Cali, Colombia

A H ROBINS CO INC 1407 Cummings Dr, PO Box 26609, Richmond, VA 23261-6609,
Tel: (804) 257-2000
(Mfr ethical pharms & consumer prdts)
A.H. Robins Intl. S.A., Carrera 27, No. 8-46 a 8-70, Bogota, D.E., Colombia
Instituto Medico Tecnico Sanicol S.A., Carrera 27, No. 8-46 a 8-70, Bogota, D.E.,
Colombia

ROHM & HAAS CO Independence Mall West, Philadelphia, PA 19105,
Tel: (215) 592-3000
(Mfr ind & agric chems, plastics)
Rohm & Haas Colombia S.A., Calle 72 No. 12-65, Fl 6-7-8, Bogota, Colombia

RORER GROUP INC   500 Virginia Dr, Ft Washington, PA 19034,
  Tel: (215) 628-6000
  (Mfr ethical & consumer pharms)
    Rorer S.A., Bogota, Colombia

SGS CONTROL SERVICES INC   42 Broadway, New York, NY 10004,
  Tel: (212) 482-8700
  (Complete range of quality & quantity control checks & related tech serv)
    Sociedad General De Supervisiones S.A., Carrera 9A, No. 72-25, Aptdo. Aereo 7205,
      Bogota 1, D.E., Colombia
    Sociedad General De Supervisiones S.A., other locations in Colombia

SONOCO PRODUCTS CO   North Second St, PO Box 160, Hartsville, SC 29550,
  Tel: (803) 383-7000
  (Mfr packaging for consumer & ind mkt)
    Sonoco Colombiana S.A., Aptdo. Aereo 695, Cali, Valle, Colombia

STANDARD OIL CO OF CALIFORNIA   225 Bush St, San Francisco, CA 94104,
  Tel: (415) 894-7700
  (Oil explor & prod, petroleum prdts)
    Chevron Petroleum Co. of Colombia, Carrera 13, No. 27-75, Bogota, Colombia

THE STANLEY WORKS   1000 Stanley Dr, PO Box 7000, New Britain, CT 06050,
  Tel: (203) 225-5111
  (Mfr hand tools & hardware)
    Herramientas Stanley S.A., Aptdo. Aereo 241, Palmira, Colombia

SUN EXPLORATION & PRODUCTION CO   PO Box 2880, Dallas, TX 75221-2880,
  Tel: (214) 890-2300
  (Oil & gas explor & prod)
    Sun Colombia Oil Co., Edif. Seguros Aurora, Carrera 7 No. 74-21, Bogota, Colombia

SYBRON CORP   411 E Wisconsin Ave, Milwaukee, WI 07662, Tel: (414) 274-6600
  (Professional health prdts, spec chems, instru, water & waste water treatment sys)
    Tanatex Colombiana Ltda., Aptdo. Aereo 5967, Carrera 12, No. 15-95, Piso 10,
      Bogota, Colombia

SYSTEMS ENGINEERING LABS INC   6901 W Sunrise Blvd, Fort Lauderdale,
  FL 33313, Tel: (305) 587-2900
  (Digital computers)
    Instrumentation, Aptdo. Aereo 6287, Bogota 1, D.E., Colombia

TED BATES WORLDWIDE INC   1515 Broadway, New York, NY 10036,
  Tel: (212) 869-3131
  (Advertising agency)
    G. Meza/Ted Bates Ltda., Calle 93 No. 12-65, Bogota, Colombia

TENNECO OIL EXPLORATION & PRODUCTION   PO Box 2511, Houston, TX 77001,
  Tel: (713) 757-2131
  (Oil explor & prod)
    Houston Oil Colombiana S.A., Calle 72 7-96, Bogota 58106, Colombia

TEXACO INC   2000 Westchester Ave, White Plains, NY 10650, Tel: (914) 253-4000
  (Explor/mktg crude oil & its prdts, petro-chems)
    Texas Petroleum Co., Aptdo. Aereo 3622, Bogota 1, D.E., Colombia

TOPFLIGHT CORP   200 E 9th Ave, PO Box 472, York, PA 17405,
  Tel: (717) 843-9901
  (Printed pressure-sensitive adhesive materials)
    Arclad S.A., Aptdo. Aereo 11561, Medellin, Colombia
    Topflight-Andina S.A., Aptdo. Aereo 3425, Medellin, Colombia

TORRINGTON/FAFNIR   200 Chestnut Ridge Rd, Woodcliff Lake, NJ 07675,
  Tel: (203) 482-9511
  (Mfr bearings, precision metal parts & assemblies, universal joints)
    Ingersoll Rand de Colombia SA, Apartado Aereo 7451, Bogota, Colombia

TRANS WORLD AIRLINES INC   605 Third Ave, New York, NY 10158,
  Tel: (212) 557-6107
  (Air transp, hotel, food serv, real estate)
    Trans World Airlines, Calle 70 53-74, Of. 402, Barranquilla, Colombia

UNION CARBIDE CORP   Old Ridgebury Rd, Danbury, CT 06817, Tel: (203) 794-2000
  (Carbon prdts, chems, plastics, gases & related prdts, etc)
    UC Colombia S.A., Aptdo. Aereo 4704, Bogota, Colombia
    Union Carbide Colombia S.A., Carrera 13, No. 26-45, Piso 10, Aptdo. Aereo, 4704,
      Bogota, Colombia

UNIROYAL INC   World Headquarters, Middlebury, CT 06749, Tel: (203) 573-2000
  (Tires, tubes & other rubber prdts, chems, plastics, textiles)
    Uniroyal Croydon S.A., Carretera del Sur, No. 61-51, Aptdo. Aereo 14509,
      Apartado National 4980, Bogota, Colombia

UNISYS CORP   PO Box 500, Blue Bell, PA 19424, Tel: (215) 542-4011
  (Mfg/mktg/serv electr info sys)
    Unisys, Bogota, Colombia

UNITED BRANDS CO   1271 Ave of the Americas, New York, NY 10020,
  Tel: (212) 397-4000
  (Food prdts)
    Campania Frutera de Sevilla, Edif. Furatena, Medellin, Colombia
    Campania Frutera de Sevilla, Carrera 5, Calle 26, Aptdo. Aereo 50309, Santa Marta,
      Colombia
    CompaniaPetrolera de Nueva Granada, Carrera 10, No. 14-33, Bogota, Colombia

UOP INC   Ten UOP Plaza, Des Plaines, IL 60016, Tel: (708) 391-2000
  (Diversified research, development & mfr of ind prdts & sys mgmt studies & serv)
    UOP Process Intl., Bogota, Colombia

UPJOHN CO   7000 Portage Rd, Kalamazoo, MI 49001, Tel: (616) 323-4000
  (Pharms, agric prdts, ind chems)
    Compania Upjohn S.A., Calle 37, No. 8-47, Bogota, Colombia

WACKENHUT CORP   1500 San Remo Ave, Coral Gables, FL 33146,
  Tel: (305) 666-5656
  (Security sys & serv)
    Seguridatecnica S.A. (SETECSA), Calle 34 #14-57, Bogota, Colombia
    Wackenhut de Colombia S.A., Carrera 5 #35-27, Aptdo. Aereo #4008, Bogota, Colombia
    Wackenhut de Colombia S.A., other locations in Colombia

WARNER-LAMBERT CO   201 Tabor Road, Morris Plains, NJ 07950,
  Tel: (201) 540-2000
  (Mfr ethical & proprietary pharms, confectionary & consumer prdts)

(cont)

Chicle Adams S.A., Calle 62, No. 1N-80, Cali, Colombia
Parke-Davis & Co., Edif. Colpatria, Carrera #7-24-89, Piso 21, Bogota, Colombia

WEST CO INC   West Bridge St, Phoenixville, PA 19460, Tel: (215) 935-4500
(Pharm packaging comps)
West Rubber de Colombia, Aptdo. Aereo 144-26, Bogota, D.E., Colombia

WESTERN GEOPHYSICAL   PO Box 2469, Houston, TX 77252-2469, Tel: (713) 789-9600
(Geophysical serv)
Western Geophysical Co. of America, Aptdo. Aereo 91014 Z8, Calle 42, #101-61,
Bogota, Colombia

WORLD COMMUNICATIONS INC   67 Broad St, New York, NY 10004,
Tel: (212) 607-2000
(Intl private line services)
World Communications Inc., Calle 19 No. 7-48 Of. 306, P.O. Box 18567, Bogota,
Colombia

CONGO

GAMLEN CHEMICAL CO   121 S Maple Ave, S San Francisco, CA 94080,
Tel: (415) 873-1750
(Chems, detergents & tank cleansers)
Gamlen Chemical Co., P.O. Box 95, Pointe Noire, Congo

INA CORPORATION   1600 Arch St, Philadelphia, PA 19101, Tel: (215) 523-5335
(Holding co: ins, financial serv)
INA Intl., Les Commissaires d'Avaries Reunis, Boite Postale 130, Brazzaville, Congo

WEATHERFORD INTL INC   1360 Post Oak Blvd, PO Box 27608, Houston,
TX 77227-9917, Tel: (713) 439-9400
(Tubular & cementation servs, prdts & equip; water jetting servs, mfr marine pedestal
cranes)
Weatherford Intl. Inc., BP 807, Pointe Noire, Congo

WESTERN GEOPHYSICAL   PO Box 2469, Houston, TX 77252-2469, Tel: (713) 789-9600
(Geophysical serv)
Western Geophysical, BP 824, Pointe Noire, Congo

COSTA RICA

3M CO   3M Center, St Paul, MN 55144-1000, Tel: (612) 733-1110
(Mfr abrasives, adhesives, chems, ind & consumer tapes/diskettes, health care prdts,
elec connectors)
   3M Centroamerica S.A., Aptdo. 10119, San Jose, Costa Rica

AMERICAN & EFIRD INC   PO Box 507, Mt Holly, NC 28120, Tel: (704) 827-4311
(Mfr ind thread, yarn & consumer sewing prdts)
   Hilos A & E de Costa Rica SA, Edificio 48C-2, Zona Franca,
      Parque Industrial Cartago, Costa Rica

AMERICAN STANDARD INC   40 W 40th St, New York, NY 10018, Tel: (212) 840-5100
(Heating & sanitary equip)
   INCESA, Aptdo. 4120, San Jose, Costa Rica

AVIS INC   900 Old Country Rd, Garden City, NY 11530, Tel: (516) 222-3000
(Car rental serv)
   Avis Rental Office, Avenida Las Americas Sabana Norte, San Jose, Costa Rica

BARDAHL MFG CORP   1400 N W 52nd St, PO Box 70607, Seattle, WA 98107,
Tel: (206) 783-4851
(Lubricating oils)
   Comercial Tecnica S.A., Aptdo. 5113, San Jose, Costa Rica
   Repuestos Kabe S.A., Aptdo. 3629, San Jose, Costa Rica

BLACK & DECKER CORP   701 E Joppa Road, Towson, MD 21204, Tel: (301) 583-3900
(Mfr portable elect & pneumatic power tools, household prdts)
   B&D Costa Rica S.A., 100 Mts. sur de Acuaductos y Alcantarrilados, Calle 9,
      Ave. 12, San Jose, Costa Raca

BOSTON OVERSEAS FINANCIAL CORP   100 Federal St, Boston, MA 02110,
Tel: (617) 434-3276
(Ind financial serv)
   Financiera de America S.A., Aptdo. 10144, San Jose, Costa Rica

BOURNS INC   1200 Columbia Ave, Riverside, CA 92507, Tel: (714) 781-5960
(Mfr resistive com & networks, precision potentiometers, panel controls)
   Trimpot Electronics S.A., Sptdo. Postal 45, San Antonio de Belen, Heredia,
      Costa Rica

BROWN & WILLIAMSON TOBACCO CORP   1600 W Hill St, Louisville, KY 40201,
Tel: (502) 771-7011
(Tobacco)
   Republic Tobacco Co., Aptdo. 896, San Jose, Costa Rica

LEO BURNETT CO INC   35 West Wacker Dr, Chicago, IL 60601, Tel: (312) 220-5959
   (Advertising agency)
      Comunica Leo Burnett-Costa Rica, Aptdo. 2316-1000, San Jose, Costa Rica

CALMAQUIP ENGINEERING CORP   7240 NW 12th St, Miami, FL 33121,
   Tel: (305) 592-4510
   (Engineering)
      Reifi S.A., Aptdo. 3156, San Jose, Costa Rica

CANADA DRY INTL CORP   2600 Century Pkwy, Atlanta, GA 30345,
   Tel: (404) 753-2182
   (Carbonated beverages, soft drinks extract)
      Canada Dry Bottling Co. of Costa Rica S.A., Aptdo. 532, San Jose, Costa Rica

CHEVRON CHEMICAL CO   PO Box 5047, San Ramon, CA 94583-0947,
   Tel: (415) 842-5500
   (Chemicals)
      Quimicas Ortho de California Ltda., Apartado Postal 2560, Loma Linda Sabana Sur 35,
      San Jose, Costa Rica

CITIBANK NA   399 Park Ave, New York, NY 10043, Tel: (212) 559-1000
   (Intl banking)
      Citibank NA (Costa Rica) S.A., Aptdo. 10277, San Jose, Costa Rica

THE COCA-COLA CO   310 North Ave NW, PO Box Drawer 1734, Atlanta, GA 30313,
   Tel: (404) 676-2121
   (Mfr & sale of soft drink syrups & concentrates, juices & food prdts, motion pic & TV
   prod)
      Coca Cola Corp., Request all inquiries be made to Atlanta address

COLGATE-PALMOLIVE CO   300 Park Ave, New York, NY 10022, Tel: (212) 310-2000
   (Pharms, cosmetics, toiletries, detergents)
      Colgate-Palmolive (Costa Rica) S.A., Aptdo. 860, San Jose, Costa Rica

CROWN CORK & SEAL CO INC   Holmesburg Station, PO Box 6208, Philadelphia,
   PA 19136, Tel: (215) 698-5100
   (Cans, bottle caps; filling & packaging mach)
      Crown Cork Centro Americana S.A., Aptdo. 504, San Jose, Costa Rica

DOW CHEMICAL CO   2030 Dow Center, Midland, MI 48640, Tel: (517) 636-1000
   (Chems, plastics, fibers, pharms)
      Dow Quimica de Centro America S.A., Aptdo. 10207, San Jose, Costa Rica

EATON CORP   100 Erieview Plaza, Cleveland, OH 44114, Tel: (216) 523-5000
   (Advanced tech prdts for transp & ind mkts)
      Cutles Hammes Centro America S.A., Aptdo. 10156, San Jose, Costa Rica

EXIM OVERSEAS INC   2121 Ponce de Leon Blvd, Coral Gables, FL 33134,
   Tel: (305) 444-6444
   (Trading & sales of arms for Armco Latin Div)
      Anamarcala, Centro Colon- #4/4-10, Paseo Colon, Calles 38 & 40, 1007 San Jose,
      Costa Rica

EXXON CORP   225 E John Carpenter Frwy, Irving, TX 75062, Tel: (214) 444-1000
   (Petroleum & petroleum prdts)
      Exxon Corp. S.A., Aptdo. 23, San Jose, Costa Rica

FIRST NATIONAL BANK OF BOSTON   100 Federal St, Boston, MA 02110,
  Tel: (617) 434-2200
  (Commercial banking)
    Corporacion Intl. de Boston S.A., Edif. Arinza, Aptdo. 6370, San Jose, Costa Rica

FLORIDA INTL FORWARDERS   6905 N W 25th St, PO Box 522085, Miami, FL 33122,
  Tel: (305) 592-6450
  (Air cargo service)
    SICSA, Aptdo. 3045, San Jose, Costa Rica

FMC CORP   200 E Randolph Dr, Chicago, IL 60601, Tel: (312) 861-6000
  (Mach & chem for industry, agric & govt)
    FMC Intl., Aptdo. 2847, Correo Central 1000, San Jose, Costa Rica

FOOTE CONE & BELDING COMMUNICATIONS INC   101 E Erie St, Chicago,
  IL 60611-2897, Tel: (312) 751-7000
  (Advertising agency)
    FCB/Siboney S.A., De la Pops en la Sabana 300 Mts Oests, 100 Sur 7 100 Este,
    San Jose, Costa Rica

FOXBORO CO   33 Commercial St, Foxboro, MA 02035, Tel: (508) 543-8750
  (Mfr prdts/provide servs for ind automation)
    Instrumentos Industriales Centro America S.A., Aptdo. 271, San Jose, Costa Rica

H B FULLER CO   2400 Energy Park Dr, St Paul, MN 55108, Tel: (612) 645-3401
  (Mfr/distr adhesives, sealants, coatings, paints, waxes, sanitation chems)
    Kativo Chemical Industries S.A., Aptdo. 4178, San Jose, Costa Rica

GERBER PRODUCTS CO   445 State St, Fremont, MI 49412, Tel: (616) 928-2000
  (Mfr/distr baby food & related prdts)
    Productos Gerber de Centroamerica S.A., Aptdo. 1811, San Jose, Costa Rica

GLIDDEN-COATINGS RESINS DIV   900 Union Commerece Bldg, Cleveland, OH 44115,
  Tel: (216) 344-8167
  (Coatings, resins, adhesives, organic chems, etc)
    Pinturas Centroamericanias Costa Rica S.A., Aptdo. 10260, San Jose, Costa Rica

GRIFFITH LABORATORIES INC   I Griffith Center, Alsip, IL 60658,
  Tel: (708) 371-0900
  (Ind food ingredients & equip)
    Laboratorios Griffith de Centro America S.A., Aptdo. 7-2820, 1000 San Jose,
    Costa Rica

GROLIER INC   Old Shereman Tpk, Danbury, CT 06816, Tel: (203) 797-3500
  (Publishers)
    Grolier Intl. Inc., Aptdo. 458, San Jose, Costa Rica

GTE DIRECTORIES CORP   West Airport Dr, DFW Airport, TX 75261-9810,
  Tel: (214) 453-7000
  (Pub telephone directories)
    Compania General de Directorios Telefonicos, Aptdo. 5932, San Jose, Costa Rica

INA CORPORATION   1600 Arch St, Philadelphia, PA 19101, Tel: (215) 523-5335
  (Holding co: ins, financial serv)
    Tecni Seguros de Centro America S.A., Aptdo. 469, San Jose, Costa Rica

INTERNATIONAL BUSINESS MACHINES (IBM)   Old Orchard Rd, Armonk,
NY 10504-1783, Tel: (914) 765-1900
(Info-handling sys, equip & serv)
    IBM de Costa Rica S.A., San Jose, Costa Rica

ITT SHERATON CORP   60 State St, Boston, MA 02108, Tel: (617) 367-3600
(Hotel operations)
    Sheraton Herradura Hotel & Spa, Aptdo. 7-1880, Ciudad Cariari, San Jose, Costa Rica

JOHNSON & JOHNSON   One Johnson & Johnson Plaza, New Brunswick, NJ 08933,
Tel: (201) 524-0400
(Surgical, med & baby prdts)
    Johnson & Johnson de Costa Rica S.A., Heredia, Costa Rica

S C JOHNSON & SON INC   1525 Howe St, Racine, WI 53403, Tel: (414) 631-2000
(Home, auto, commercial & personal care prdts, specialty chems)
    S.C. Johnson de Centroamerica S.A., Aptdo. 4971, San Jose, Costa Rica

LOCTITE CORP   705 North Mountain Rd, Newington, CT 06111, Tel: (203) 278-1280
(Adhesives, sealants)
    Permatec de Centro America S.A., Aptdo. 956, San Jose, Costa Rica

LONGYEAR CO   PO Box 27314, Salt Lake City, UT 84127, Tel: (801) 972-1395
(Mfr diamond drills, concrete cutting equip; drill serv)
    Longyear Co., Aptdo. 5235, San Jose, Costa Rica

MENNEN CO   Morristown, NJ 07960, Tel: (201) 631-9000
(Health & beauty aids)
    Mennen de Costa Rica S.A., Aptdo. 1044, San Jose, Costa Rica

MERCK SHARP & DOHME INTL   PO Box 2000, Rahway, NJ 07065, Tel: (201) 574-4000
(Pharms, chems & biologicals)
    Merck, Sharp & Dohme (IA) Corp., Aptdo. 10135, San Jose, Costa Rica

MICRODOT INC   Two First National Plaza, 20 S Clark St, Chicago, IL 60603,
Tel: (312) 899-1925
(Connectors, cables, automotive fasteners)
    Microdot Costa Rica S.A., Aptdo. 8-5570, San Jose, Costa Rica

MONSANTO CO   800 N Lindbergh Blvd, St Louis, MO 63167, Tel: (314) 694-1000
(Mfr chem & agric prdts, pharms, ind process equip, man-made fibers, plastics)
    Monsanto de Costa Rica S.A., P.O. Box 987, 1007 Centro Colon, San Jose, Costa Rica

MOTOROLA INC   1303 E Algonquin Rd, Schaumburg, IL 60196, Tel: (708) 397-5000
(Mfr commun equip, semiconductors, cellular phones)
    Motorola de Centro America S.A., Aptdo. 442, Guadalupe, Costa Rica

MYERS TIRE SUPPLY INTL   1293 South Main St, Akron, OH 44301,
Tel: (216) 253-5592
(Mfr polymer & metal prdts for mat handling, automotive & constr inds)
    Myers Servicios Tecnicos, Apartado Postal 853, San Jose, Costa Rica

McCANN-ERICKSON WORLDWIDE   750 Third Ave, New York, NY 10017,
Tel: (212) 697-6000
(Advertising)
    McCann-Erickson Centroamericana (Costa Rica) Ltda., Autopista General Canas,
    Contiquo Canal 6, Apt. 4505, San Jose, Costa Rica

NABISCO BRANDS INC   Nabisco Brands Plaza, East Hanover, NJ 07936,
   Tel: (201) 503-2000
   (Mfr food prdts)
      Alant Golden S.A., Aptdo. 1465, San Jose, Costa Rica
      Pan American Standard Brands Inc., Aptdo. 1465, San Jose, Costa Rica

ONAN CORP   1400 73rd Ave NE, Minneapolis, MN 55432, Tel: (612) 574-5000
   (Electric generators, ind engines & controls)
      Alberto L. Arce S.A., Aptdo. 296, San Jose, Costa Rica

PET INC   400 S 4th St, St Louis, MO 63102, Tel: (314) 622-6358
   (Process/mktg specialty foods)
      Cinta Azul S.A., Aptdo 2905, San Jose, Costa Rica

PFIZER INC   235 E 42nd St, New York, NY 10017, Tel: (212) 573-2323
   (Mfr pharms, hosp prdts, chems, consumer & animal health prdts)
      Pfizer S.A., Aptdo. 10202, 1000 San Jose, Costa Rica

PHELPS DODGE CORP   2600 N Central Ave, Phoenix, AZ 85004-3014,
   Tel: (602) 234-8100
   (Minerals, metals & spec engineered prdts for trans & elect mkts)
      Conducen S.A. (COCESA), Aptdo. 10274, San Jose, Costa Rica

PHILLIPS PETROLEUM CO   Phillips Bldg, Bartlesville, OK 74004,
   Tel: (918) 661-6600
   (Crude oil, natural gas, liquefied petroleum gas, gasoline & petro-chems)
      Productos Plasticos S.A., Aptdo. 271, San Jose, Costa Rica

ROHM & HAAS CO   Independence Mall West, Philadelphia, PA 19105,
   Tel: (215) 592-3000
   (Mfr ind & agric chems, plastics)
      Laboratorios Quimicos Industriales S.A. (LAQUINSA), Llorente de Tibas, San Jose,
         Costa Rica
      Rohm & Haas Centro America S.A. (ROHACA), Llorente de Tibas, San Jose, Costa Rica

SCM CORP   299 Park Ave, New York, NY 10171, Tel: (212) 752-2700
   (Business equip, chems, coatings & resins, foods, paper prdts)
      Compania Agricola Myristica S.A., San Jose, Costa Rica
      Pinturas Centroamericanas Costa Rica S.A., San Jose, Costa Rica

SCOTT WORLDWIDE INC   Scott Plaza, Philadelphia, PA 19113, Tel: (215) 521-5000
   (Paper & paper prdts, bleached pulp)
      Scott Paper Co. de Costa Rica, Aptdo. 10271, San Jose, Costa Rica

SEA-LAND SERVICE INC   379 Thornall St, Edison, NJ 08837, Tel: (201) 558-6000
   (Container transport)
      Colina & Cia. S.A., Aptdo. 10259, San Jose, Costa Rica
      Sea-Land Service Inc., Aptdo. 10259, San Jose, Costa Rica

R G SLOANE MFG CO INC   7660 N Clybourn Ave, Sun Valley, CA 91352,
   Tel: (213) 767-4726
   (Mfr plastic pipe, fittings, valves)
      Accesorios Plasticos Centroamericana S.A., San Jose, Costa Rica

SQUARE D CO   Executive Plaza, Palatine, IL 60067, Tel: (708) 397-2600
   (Power distribution & elec/electr ind control equip)
      Square D Co. Centroamericana, S.A., Aptdo. 4123, San Jose, Costa Rica

STANDARD FRUIT & STEAMSHIP CO   50 California St, San Francisco, CA 94111,
  Tel: (415) 986-3000
  (Shipping, banana & pineapple production & distr)
     Envases Industriales de Costa Rica S.A., Aptdo. 151, Puerto Limon, Costa Rica,
        Standard Fruit Co., Aptdo. N, San Jose, Costa Rica
     Standard Fruit Co., Puerto Limon, Costa Rica

TEXACO INC   2000 Westchester Ave, White Plains, NY 10650, Tel: (914) 253-4000
  (Explor/mktg crude oil & its prdts, petro-chems)
     Texaco Caribbean Inc., Aptdo. 10090, San Jose, Costa Rica

TRANS WORLD AIRLINES INC   605 Third Ave, New York, NY 10158,
  Tel: (212) 557-6107
  (Air transp, hotel, food serv, real estate)
     Trans World Airlines, Calle 1 Avenida Oy 1, San Jose, Costa Rica

UNION CARBIDE CORP   Old Ridgebury Rd, Danbury, CT 06817, Tel: (203) 794-2000
  (Carbon prdts, chems, plastics, gases & related prdts, etc)
     Union Carbide Centro America S.A., Aptdo. 10160, San Jose, Costa Rica

UNITED BRANDS CO   1271 Ave of the Americas, New York, NY 10020,
  Tel: (212) 397-4000
  (Food prdts)
     Polymer United S.A., Aptdo. 5123, San Jose, Costa Rica
     Unimar S.A., Aptdo. 3657, San Jose, Costa Rica
     United Fruit Group, Aptdo. 30, San Jose, Costa Rica,
        Compania Bananera de Costa Rica, Aptdo. 30, San Jose, Costa Rica

VELSICOL CHEMICAL CORP   5600 N River Rd, Rosemont, IL 60018,
  Tel: (708) 698-9700
  (Pesticides & ind chems)
     Velsicol de Centro America S.A., Aptdo. 6554, San Jose, Costa Rica

VF CORP   PO Box 1022, Reading, PA 19603, Tel: (215) 378-1151
  (Mfr/mktg apparel)
     Confecciones H.D. Lee S.A., Omni Bldg., San Jose, Costa Rica

WACKENHUT CORP   1500 San Remo Ave, Coral Gables, FL 33146,
  Tel: (305) 666-5656
  (Security sys & serv)
     Costa Rica Wackenhut S.A., Aptdo. 923, Escazu, San Jose, Costa Rica

ZAPATA CORP   Zapata Tower, PO Box 4240, Houston, TX 77001,
  Tel: (713) 226-6000
  (Offshore drilling & petroleum explor)
     Sardimar S.A., Aptdo. 8-4430, San Jose, Costa Rica

CYPRUS

AMERICAN LIFE INSURANCE CO (ALICO)   PO Box 2226, Wilmington, DE 19899,
  Tel: (302) 594-2000
  (Life ins, pension & annuity plans, health prdts)
    Alico Middle East Ltd., 86 Ayias Phylaxeos St., P.O. Box 1162, Limassol, Cyprus

BARBER-GREENE CO   3000 Baraber-Greene Rd, DeKalb, IL 60115,
  Tel: (815) 756-5600
  (Mfr heavy road constr equip)
    Barber-Green Cyprus Ltd., P.O. Box 3796, Nicosia, Cyprus

BARDAHL MFG CORP   1400 N W 52nd St, PO Box 70607, Seattle, WA 98107,
  Tel: (206) 783-4851
  (Lubricating oils)
    Lubrico, 120 Makarias Ave., Box 16, Limassol, Cyprus

CANADA DRY INTL CORP   2600 Century Pkwy, Atlanta, GA 30345,
  Tel: (404) 753-2182
  (Carbonated beverages, soft drinks extract)
    Kean Soft Drinks Ltd., P.O. Box 300, Limassol, Cyprus

ECOLAB INC   370 Wabasha St, St Paul, MN 55102, Tel: (612) 293-2233
  (Ind & household detergents, cleaning agents & equip)
    Economics Laboratory Inc., P.O. Box 5128, Nicosia, Cyprus

EXXON CORP   225 E John Carpenter Frwy, Irving, TX 75062, Tel: (214) 444-1000
  (Petroleum & petroleum prdts)
    Esso Standard Inc., P.O. Box 1340, Nicosia, Cyprus

FOREST OIL CORP   1500 Colorado Natl Bldg, Denver, CO 80202,
  Tel: (313) 629-1916
  (Crude oil & natural gas)
    Forest Oil Corp., Nicosia, Cyprus

INA CORPORATION   1600 Arch St, Philadelphia, PA 19101, Tel: (215) 523-5335
  (Holding co: ins, financial serv)
    Francoudi & Stephanou Ltd., New Port Rd., P.O. Box 1490, Limassol, Cyprus
    Mickys Michaelides Ltd., Mitsis Bldg., One Stassinos Ave., P.O. Box 1057, Nicosia,
      Cyprus

INTERMEC CORP   6001 36th Ave West, Everett, WA 98203-9280,
  Tel: (206) 348-2600
  (Mfr automated data collection sys)
    Intermec Middle East, 38 Makarios St., Karaouana Court- Flat 41, Larnaca, Cyprus

INTRACO CORP   1410 Allen Dr, Troy, MI 48083-4001, Tel: (313) 585-6900
  (Export mgmt & mktg consultants)
    Intech (USA) Ltd., P.O. Box 3417, Limassol, Cyprus

ITT SHERATON CORP   60 State St, Boston, MA 02108, Tel: (617) 367-3600
  (Hotel operations)
    Limassol Sheraton Resort & Pleasure Harbour, Amathus Ave., P.O. Box 1064, Limassol,
    Cyprus

MOBIL CORP   150 E 42nd St, New York, NY 10017, Tel: (212) 883-4242
  (Petroleum explor, prdts)
    Mobil Oil, Ltd., P.O. Box 1344, Nicosia 107, Cyprus

NCR CORP   1700 S Patterson Blvd, Dayton, OH 45479, Tel: (513) 445-2000
  (Develop/mfr/sell/serv business info processing sys)
    NCR (Cyprus) Ltd., 16, Griva Dighenis Ave., P.O. Box 1823, Nicosia, Cyprus

PEPSICO INC   700 Anderson Hill Rd, Purchase, NY 10577, Tel: (914) 253-2000
  (Beverages, food prdts & servs, sporting goods)
    Beverages, Food & Service Ind. Inc., Apartment #6, Veronica Court #2, 85,
    Kennedy Ave., Nicosia, Cyprus

TELLABS INC   4951 Indiana Ave, Lisle, IL 60532, Tel: (708) 969-8800
  (Mfr telecom equip)
    Tellabs Intl., Inc., 3 Plovtona St., PO Box 3945, Strovolos, Nicosia, Cyprus

UNION CARBIDE CORP   Old Ridgebury Rd, Danbury, CT 06817, Tel: (203) 794-2000
  (Carbon prdts, chems, plastics, gases & related prdts, etc)
    Eveready Batteries Ltd., Alpha House, Makarios 111 Ave. #50, Nicosia, Cyprus

CZECHOSLOVAKIA

INA CORPORATION   1600 Arch St, Philadelphia, PA 19101, Tel: (215) 523-5335
  (Holding co: ins, financial serv)
    INA Intl., State Insurance Institute, Spalena 16, P.O. Box 841, Prague Nove Mesto,
    Czechoslovakia

LE TOURNEAU INC LONGVIEW DIV   PO Box 2307, Longview, TX 75606,
  Tel: (214) 753-3449
  (Heavy constr, mining mach & equip)
    Le Tourneau Ltd., all mail to: A-2320 Schwechat P.B 4, Vienna, Austria

DENMARK

3M CO   3M Center, St Paul, MN 55144-1000, Tel: (612) 733-1110
(Mfr abrasives, adhesives, chems, ind & consumer tapes/diskettes, health care prdts, elec connectors)
  3/M A/S, Fabriksparken 15, 2600 Glostrup, Denmark

A L LABORATORIES INC   One Executive Drive, PO Box 1399, Fort Lee, NJ 07024,
 Tel: (201) 947-7774
(Devel/mfr spec pharm & animal health micro-nutrients)
  A/S Dumex, 37 Prags Boulevard, DK-2300 Copenhagen S., Denmark

AAR CORP   1111 Nicholas Blvd, Elk Grove Village, IL 60007,
 Tel: (708) 439-3939
(Aircraft prdts & serv, aviation serv)
  Avia Radio A/S, Hangar 141, Copenhagen Airport, 2791 Dragor, Denmark

ABBOTT LABORATORIES   Abbott Park, North Chicago, IL 60064,
 Tel: (312) 937-6100
(Pharm & lab prdts)
  Abbott Laboratories S/A, Bygstubben 15, 2950 Vedbaek, Denmark

ACUFF-ROSE PUBLICATION INC   65 Music Square W, Nashville, TN 37203,
 Tel: (615) 321-5000
(Music publisher)
  Acuff-Rose Scandia, Chr. D, 1X Gade 7, 1111 Copenhagen K, Denmark

AFIA   110 William St, New York, NY 10038, Tel: (212) 964-4990
(Insurance)
  American Foreign Insurance Association, Copenhagen, Denmark

AIR EXPRESS INTL CORP   120 Tokeneke Rd, PO Box 1231, Darien, CT 06820,
 Tel: (203) 655-7900
(Air frt forwarder)
   Olson & Wright AEI, A/S, Old Administration Bldg., Copenhagen Airport, DK-2770,
    Kastrup, Denmark

AMDAHL CORP   1250 East Arques Ave, PO Box 3470, Sunnyvale, CA 94088-3470,
 Tel: (408) 746-6000
(Mfr large scale computers, complementary software storage & commun prdts)
   Amdahl Danmark Computer Systems A/S, Sundkrogsgade 2, 2100 Copenhagen, Denmark

AMERICAN CYANAMID CO   1 Cyanamid Plaza, Wayne, NJ 07470, Tel: (201) 831-2000
(Pharms, chems, agric & consumer prdts)
   Cyanamid Denmark, St. Kongensgade 68, 2 DK-1264, Copenhagen K, Denmark

AMERICAN EXPRESS CO   American Express Tower, New York, NY 10285-4765,
   Tel: (212) 640-2000
   (Diversified fin & travel-related serv)
      American Express, Kobmagergade 60, 1150 Copenhagen, Denmark

AMERICAN HOME ASSURANCE CO   70 Pine St, New York, NY 10270,
   Tel: (212) 770-7000
   (General ins (non-life))
      American Intl. Underwriters agentur Denmark A/S, 4 H.C., Andersens Blvd., DK 1553,
         Copenhagen V, Denmark

AMERICAN INTL UNDERWRITERS CORP   70 Pine St, New York, NY 10270,
   Tel: (212) 770-7000
   (General ins)
      American Home Assurance Co. Denmark, A/S, H.C. Andersens Blvd., 4, DK 1553,
         Copenhagen V, Denmark

AMERICAN METER CO   13500 Philmont Ave, Philadelphia, PA 19116,
   Tel: (215) 673-2100
   (Meas & control serv for natural gas inds)
      International Gas Apparatus A/S, 1 Anholvej, DK-9800 Hjorring, Denmark

AMP INC   470 Friendship Rd, Harrisburg, PA 17111, Tel: (717) 564-0100
   (Mfr electrical wiring devices)
      AMP Danmark, Gunnar Clausensvej 32, 8260 Vibyj, Denmark

ANALOG DEVICES INC   1 Technology Way, Box 9106, Norwood, MA 02062,
   Tel: (617) 329-4700
   (Analog digital converters)
      Analog Devices Aps, Horkaer 20, 2730 Herlev, Denmark

ASSOCIATED MERCHANDISING CORP   1440 Broadway, New York, NY 10018,
   Tel: (212) 536-4000
   (Retail service organization)
      Associated Merchandising Corp., Tornsangerveg 5, D-3600 Frederikssund, Denmark

AVERY INTL CORP   150 N Orange Grove Blvd, Pasadena, CA 91103,
   Tel: (213) 304-2000
   (Mfr self-adhesive labels & marking equip)
      Avery Etikettering A/S, Tjaerbyvej 90, P.O. Box 320, 8900 Randers, Denmark

BAKER OIL TOOLS   PO Box 3048, Houston, TX 77253, Tel: (713) 923-9351
   (Oil/gas well completions equip)
      Baker Oil Tools Denmark, Handaerkerej 2, DK-6710 Esbjerg V, Denmark

BAKER PRODUCTION TECHNOLOGY   PO Box 40129, Houston, TX 77240-0129,
   Tel: (713) 943-0170
   (Inflatable packers, instru well testing)
      Baker Production Services (Denmark), Handvaerkervej 4, DK-6710 Esbjerg V, Denmark

BANKERS TRUST CO   280 Park Ave, New York, NY 10017, Tel: (212) 775-2500
   (Banking)
      Bankers Trust Co., Admiralgade 24, 1066, Copenhagen K, Denmark

BAUSCH & LOMB INC   1 Lincoln First Sq, Rochester, NY 14601-0054,
  Tel: (716) 338-6000
  (Mfr healthcare & optics prdts)
    Bausch & Lomb Denmark A/S, Copenhagen S., Denmark

BENTLEY LABORATORIES INC   17502 Armstrong Ave, Irvine, CA 92714,
  Tel: (714) 546-8020
  (Mfr para-med devices)
    Bentley Labs, APS, Fredericiagade 16, 1310 Copenhagen K, Denmark

BLACK & DECKER CORP   701 E Joppa Road, Towson, MD 21204, Tel: (301) 583-3900
  (Mfr portable elect & pneumatic power tools, household prdts)
    Black & Decker A/S, Bistrupvej 172, DK-3460 Birkerod, Denmark

BORDEN INC   420 Lexington Ave, New York, NY 10170, Tel: (212) 573-4000
  (Milk processing, dairy foods, specialty foods, chems, plastics)
    Borden Co. A/S, P.O. Box 4202, 6715 Esbjerg, Denmark

BOSE CORP   100 The Mountain Rd, Framingham, MA 01701, Tel: (617) 879-7330
  (Electronic equip)
    Bose Denmark, Falconer Alle, 2000 Frederiksberg, Denmark

BRANSON ULTRASONICS CORP   Eagle Rd, Danbury, CT 06810, Tel: (203) 796-0400
  (Ultrasonic & vibratory plastics assembly mach)
    Branson Sonic Power A/S, 112 Lerso Parkalle, 2100 Copenhagen, Denmark
    Branson Sonic Power-Scandinavia, Lojtegardsvej 155, DK-2770 Kastrup, Copenhagen,
    Denmark

LEO BURNETT CO INC   35 West Wacker Dr, Chicago, IL 60601, Tel: (312) 220-5959
  (Advertising agency)
    Leo Burnett Denmark, Vesterbrogade 2B, 1620 Copenhagen V, Denmark

BURSON-MARSTELLER   230 Park Ave, New York, NY 10003-1566, Tel: (212) 614-4000
  (Public relations/public affairs consultants)
    Burson-Marsteller A/S, 24C Oestergade, DK-1100 Copenhagen K, Denmark

BUSSMANN   PO Box 14460, St Louis, MO 63178-4460, Tel: (314) 394-2877
  (Mfr electr fuses & acces, terminal strips, interconnect devices & circuit breakers)
    Bussmann, Copenhagen, Denmark

CANBERRA INDUSTRIES INC   One State St, Meriden, CT 06450, Tel: (203) 238-2351
  (Mfr instru for nuclear research)
    Canberra-Pack AB, Greveager 7, DK-2670 Greve AB, Denmark

CHASE MANHATTAN BANK N A   1 Chase Manhattan Plaza, New York, NY 10081,
  Tel: (212) 552-2222
  (Intl banking)
    Chase Manhattan Bank N.A., Vognmagergade 10, 1120 Copenhagen, Denmark

THE CHUBB CORP   15 Mountain View Rd, Warren, NJ 07060, Tel: (201) 580-2000
  (Holding co: property/casualty ins)
    Chubb Insurance Co. of Europe, Denmark

CIGNA CORP   One Liberty Place, 1650 Market St, Philadelphia, PA 19101,
  Tel: (215) 523-4000
  (Ins, invest, health care & other fin servs)
    Cigna Insurance Co. of Europe SA/NV, Amargeriorv 24, DK-1160 Copenhagen K, Denmark

(cont)

Insurance Co. of North America, c/o PFA Skade, Marina Park, Sundkrogsgade 4, DK-2100 Copenhagen 0, Denmark

CITIBANK NA   399 Park Ave, New York, NY 10043, Tel: (212) 559-1000
(Intl banking)
Citibank N.A., Industriens Hus, Vesterbrogade 1B, 1620 Copenhagen, Denmark

THE COCA-COLA CO   310 North Ave NW, PO Box Drawer 1734, Atlanta, GA 30313,
Tel: (404) 676-2121
(Mfr & sale of soft drink syrups & concentrates, juices & food prdts, motion pic & TV prod)
Coca-Cola Corp., Request that all inquiries be made to Altanta address.

COLGATE-PALMOLIVE CO   300 Park Ave, New York, NY 10022, Tel: (212) 310-2000
(Pharms, cosmetics, toiletries, detergents)
Colgate-Palmolive A/S, 9 Smedeland, 26000 Glostrup, Denmark

COLUMBIA PICTURES INDUSTRIES INC   711 Fifth Ave, New York, NY 10022,
Tel: (212) 751-4400
(Producer & distributor of motion pictures)
Columbia-Fox, C. Hauchsvej 13, 1825 Frederiksberg, Denmark

COMBUSTION ENGINEERING INC   900 Long Ridge Road, Stamford, CT 06902,
Tel: (203) 329-8771
(Tech constr)
Gray Tool Co. Ltd., 6700 Esbjerg, Androp, Denmark

COMPTON INTERNATIONAL   625 Madison Ave, New York, NY 10022,
Tel: (212) 754-1100
(Advertising)
Compton Denmark, Kronprinsensgade 13, 1114 Copenhagen, Denmark

COMPUTER ASSOCIATES INTL INC   711 Stewart Ave, Garden City, NY 11530,
Tel: (516) 227-3300
(Devel/mkt/mgt info mgt & bus applications software)
Computer Associates Scandinavia A/S, Ryttermarken 10, DK-3520 Farum, Denmark

CONTROL DATA CORP   8100 34th Ave S, Minneapolis, MN 55440,
Tel: (612) 853-8100
(Control data equip, computer sys serv & financial serv)
Control Data A/S, 35 Sonder Blvd., 1720 Copenhagen V, Denmark

COOK INC   925 South Curry Pike, PO Box 489, Bloomington, ID 47402,
Tel: (812) 339-2235
(Instru for cardiovascular diagnosis)
Willam Cook A/S, Sandet 6, 4632 Bjaeverskov, Denmark

CPC INTERNATIONAL INC   PO Box 8000, International Plaza, Englewood Cliffs,
NJ 07632, Tel: (201) 894-4000
(Mfr consumer food prdts & corn refining prdts)
CPC Foods A/S, Skovlyoften 33, DK 2840, Holte, Denmark

CROWN CORK & SEAL CO INC   Holmesburg Station, PO Box 6208, Philadelphia,
PA 19136, Tel: (215) 698-5100
(Cans, bottle caps; filling & packaging mach)
Crown Cork Co., A/S, Hoerskaetten 13, DK 2630, Taastrup, Denmark

D'ARCY MASIUS BENTON & BOWLES INC (DMB&B)   1675 Broadway, New York,
   NY 10019, Tel: (212) 468-3622
   (Advertising & communications)
      DMB&B Reklamebureau A/S, Sankt Knuds VEJ 41, 1903 Frederiksberg C, Denmark
      DMM/Ipsen & Parmo A/S, Brostes Gaard, Ovengaden oven Vandet 10, 1415 Copenhagen K,
      Denmark

DANCER FITZGERALD SAMPLE INTL   405 Lexington Ave, New York, NY 10174,
   Tel: (212) 661-0800
   (Advertising agency)
      Bergenholz & Arnesen, Bjerregardsvej 16, Copenhagen, DK-2500 Valby, Denmark

DATA GENERAL CORP   4400 Computer Dr, Westboro, MA 01580, Tel: (617) 366-8911
   (Design, mfr gen purpose computer sys & peripheral prdts & servs)
      Data General A/S, Fabriksparken 38, DK-2600 Glostrup, Denmark

DDB NEEDHAM WORLDWIDE INC   437 Madison Ave, New York, NY 10022,
   Tel: (212) 415-2000
   (Advertising)
      DDB Needham Worldwide, Montergarden, Gothersgade 49, 1123 Copenhagen K, Denmark

DIGITAL EQUIPMENT CORP   129 Parker St, Maynard, MA 01754, Tel: (617) 897-5111
   (Digital computers, digital circuit modules, memory elec- tronic system)
      Digital Equipment Corp. A/S, Sandtoften 9, 2820 Gentofte, Denmark

WALT DISNEY PRODUCTIONS   500 S Buena Vista St, Burbank, CA 91521,
   Tel: (818) 560-1000
   (Film/TV prod, amusement parks, land mgmt)
      Walt Disney Productions A/S, Ostergade 24B, 1100 Copenhagen, Denmark

DOW CHEMICAL CO   2030 Dow Center, Midland, MI 48640, Tel: (517) 636-1000
   (Chems, plastics, fibers, pharms)
      Dow Chemical A/S, 171 Strandvejen, 2900 Hellerup, Denmark

EASTMAN KODAK CO   343 State St, Rochester, NY 14650-0518, Tel: (716) 724-4000
   (Devel/mfr photo & chem prdts, info mgmt/video/copier sys, fibers/plastics for
   various ind)
      Kodak A/S, 16 Roskildevej, 2620 Albertslund, Denmark

ECOLAB INC   370 Wabasha St, St Paul, MN 55102, Tel: (612) 293-2233
   (Ind & household detergents, cleaning agents & equip)
      Soilax A/S, 22 Hoffdingsvej, 2500 Valby, Denmark

ELIZABETH ARDEN INC   55 East 52nd St, New York, NY 10055-0191,
   Tel: (212) 407-1000
   (Cosmetics, fragrances, toiletries)
      Elizabeth Arden A/S, Tommerup Stationsvej 10, 2770 Kastrup, Denmark

ESTEE LAUDER INTL INC   767 Fifth Ave, New York, NY 10019, Tel: (212) 572-4600
   (Cosmetics)
      Estee Lauder Cosmetics A/S, 7-A Norregade, 1165 Copenhagen K, Denmark

EXXON CORP   225 E John Carpenter Frwy, Irving, TX 75062, Tel: (214) 444-1000
   (Petroleum & petroleum prdts)
      Dansk Esso A/S, 13 Skt. Annae Plads, 1298 Copenhagen K, Denmark
      Dansk Esso A/S, Raffinaderiet, 4400 Kalundborg, Denmark

FIRST NATIONAL BANK OF BOSTON   100 Federal St, Boston, MA 02110,
  Tel: (617) 434-2200
  (Commercial banking)
    First National Bank of Boston, International Factors S.A., Bredgade 29,
      1260 Copenhagen K, Denmark

FOOTE CONE & BELDING COMMUNICATIONS INC   101 E Erie St, Chicago,
  IL 60611-2897, Tel: (312) 751-7000
  (Advertising agency)
    FCB/Hiort, Stenius & Walter, Amaliegade 3-5, DK 1256 Copenhagen K, Denmark

FORD MOTOR CO   The American Road, Dearborn, MI 48121, Tel: (313) 322-3000
  (Mfr automobiles, trucks)
    Ford Motor Co. A/S, 1 Sluseholmen, 2450, Copenhagen SV, Denmark

FOXBORO CO   33 Commercial St, Foxboro, MA 02035, Tel: (508) 543-8750
  (Mfr prdts/provide servs for ind automation)
    F. Henriques, Brudelysvej 26, DK 2880, Bagsvaerd, Copenhagen, Denmark

THE FRANKLIN MINT   Franklin Center, PA 19091, Tel: (215) 459-6000
  (Creation/mfr/mktg collectible items)
    Franklin Mint A/S, Lyngbyvej 293B, 2900 Hellerup, Denmark

GAMLEN CHEMICAL CO   121 S Maple Ave, S San Francisco, CA 94080,
  Tel: (415) 873-1750
  (Chems, detergents & tank cleansers)
    Gamlen Chemical Co., Siljangade 7, 2300 Copenhagen, Denmark

GENERAL AUTOMATION INC   1055 S East St, Anaheim, CA 92806,
  Tel: (714) 778-4800
  (Computer hardware & serv)
    General Automation, Sortedams Dosseringen 416, 2200 Copenhagen, Denmark

GENERAL FOODS CORP   250 North St, White Plains, NY 10625, Tel: (914) 335-2500
  (Processor, distributor & mfr of foods)
    General Foods Denmark, Teknikerbjen 1, DK-2830, Virum, Denmark

GENERAL MOTORS ACCEPTANCE CORP   3044 West Grand Blvd, Detroit, MI 48202,
  Tel: (313) 556-5000
  (Automobile financing)
    GMAC Continental, Klampenborgvej 232, DK 2800 Lyngby, Denmark

GENERAL MOTORS CORP   3044 W Grand Blvd, Detroit, MI 48202,
  Tel: (313) 556-5000
  (Automotive prdts, electronics)
    General Motors Denmark A/S, Tobaksvejen 22, DK-2860 Soeborg, Denmark

W R GRACE & CO   1114 Ave of the Americas, New York, NY 10036,
  Tel: (212) 819-5500
  (Specialty chems, natural resources, consumer serv)
    W.R. Grace A/S, 200 Islevdalvej, DK 2610, Roedvre, Denmark

GRAY TOOL CO   PO Box 2291, Houston, TX 77001, Tel: (713) 747-1240
  (Oil field equip, pipe connectors, etc)
    Gray Tool Co. Ltd., 6700 Esbjerg, Androp, Denmark

GREY ADVERTISING INC   777 Third Ave, New York, NY 10017, Tel: (212) 546-2000
(Advertising)
  Grey Denmark A/S, Bodums Gaard, Nyhavn 63, 1051 Copengagen, Denmark, Copenhagen,
  Denmark

FRANK B HALL & CO INC   549 Pleasantville Rd, Briarcliff Manor, NY 10510,
Tel: (914) 769-9200
(Insurance)
  Frank B. Hall (Scandinavia) A/S, Vesterbrogade 15, DK-1620 Copenhagen, Denmark

THE HARPER GROUP INC   260 Townsend St, PO Box 77933, San Francisco,
CA 94107, Tel: (415) 978-0600
(Ocean/air freight fwdg, customs brokerage, packing & whse, logistics mgt, ins)
  Circle Leman Air Freight, 149 Amager Landevej, PO Box 110, 2770 Kastrup, Denmark

HERCULES INC   Hercules Plaza, Wilmington, DE 19894, Tel: (302) 594-5000
(Mfr spec chems, plastics, film & fibers, coatings, resins, food ingredients)
  A/S Kobenhavns Pektinfabrik, Ved Banen 16, 4623 Lille Skensved, Denmark

HERTZ CORP   225 Brae Blvd, Park Ridge, NJ 07656-0713, Tel: (201) 307-2000
(Automobile rental)
  Hertz Biludlejnign A/S, Vesterbrogade 6D, 1620 Copenhagen V, Denmark

HEWLETT-PACKARD CO   3000 Hanover St, PO Box 10301, Palo Alto, CA 94303-0890,
Tel: (415) 857-1501
(Mfr measurement & computation prdts & sys)
  Hewlett-Packard A/S, Datavej 52, 3460 Birkerod, Denmark

HILLERICH & BRADSBY CO INC   PO Box 35700, Louisville, KY 40232-5700,
Tel: (502) 585-5226
(Golf, baseball & softball equip)
  Ib Steen Rasmussen, Spangsbjerggade 20, 6700 Esbejerg, Denmark

HORWATH & HORWATH INTL   919 Third Ave, New York, NY 10022,
Tel: (212) 980-3100
(Public accountants & auditors)
  Revi-consult Odense Intl. Auditing APS, Iramsherred, Svendborg 5700, Denmark

E F HOUGHTON & CO   PO Box 930, Valley Forge, PA 19482-0930,
Tel: (215) 666-4000
(Mfr spec chems, hydraulic fluids, lubricants)
  E.F. Houghton & Co., Rodkjaer & Tvedes Eftf., Esplanaden 5A, 1263, Copenhagen K,
  Denmark

IMCO SERVICES   5950 N Course Dr, Houston, TX 70072, Tel: (713) 561-1300
(Drilling fluids)
  Halliburton Co., Kanalen 1, DK-6700 Esbjerg, Denmark

INA CORPORATION   1600 Arch St, Philadelphia, PA 19101, Tel: (215) 523-5335
(Holding co: ins, financial serv)
  Danks Forening for International Motorkoretojsforsikring, Amaliegade 10, DK 1256,
    Copenhagen K, Denmark
  Hecksher & Son Succsrs., Finladesgade 25, P.O. Box 233, Aarhus, Denmark
  Hecksher & Sons Succsrs., 63 Bredgade, Denmark
  Hecksher & Sons Succsrs., Cort Adelersgade 2, Esbjerg 700, Denmark
  INA, Dyrehaveve 180, 6000 Kolding, Denmark

(cont)

INA, Forsikrings Aktieselskab H.C., Andersens Boulevard 6, DK 1553, Copenhagen V, Denmark

INTERMEC CORP   6001 36th Ave West, Everett, WA   98203-9280,
Tel: (206) 348-2600
(Mfr automated data collection sys)
   B.B. Data Gentofte ApS, Ryvangs Alle 28, 2900 Hellerup, Denmark

INTERNATIONAL BUSINESS MACHINES (IBM)   Old Orchard Rd, Armonk,
NY 10504-1783, Tel: (914) 765-1900
(Info-handling sys, equip & serv)
   IBM Danmark A/S, Nymollevej 91, Lyngby, Aarhus 2800, Denmark
   IBM Danmark Produkt Dist. Selskab A/S, Copenhagen, Denmark

INTERNATIONAL STANDARD ELECTRIC CORP   320 Park Ave, New York, NY 10022,
Tel: (212) 752-6000
(Telecommun equip)
   ITT Standard Electric A/S, Fabriksparken 31, 2600 Glostrup, Denmark

INTERNATIONAL TOBACCO CO INC   PO Box 1824, Greenville, NC 27834,
Tel: (919) 752-4730
(Tobacco)
   International Tobacco Co. A/S, Amtsvej 5, 8450 Allerod, Denmark

INTRALOX INC   PO Box 50699, New Orleans, LA 70150, Tel: (504) 733-0463
(Mfr plastic, modular conveyor belts & access)
   Intralox A/S, Egholmverj 3, 9800 Hjorring, Denmark

ITEL CONTAINERS INTL CORP   55 Francisco St, San Francisco, CA 94133,
Tel: (415) 984-4400
(Leasing, repair, storage of ocean-going containers)
   Itel Containers Corp. Intl., 11B Amaliegade, DK-1256, Cogenhage, Denmark

ITT SHERATON CORP   60 State St, Boston, MA 02108, Tel: (617) 367-3600
(Hotel operations)
   Sheraton Copenhagen Hotel, 6 Vester Sogade, DK-1601 Copenhagen V, Denmark

JBL INTERNATIONAL   8500 Balboa Blvd, Northridge, CA 91329,
Tel: (818) 893-8411
(Mfr loudspeakers, sound reinforcement equip)
   Lydig Marketing A/S, Rugmarken 27 A, 3520 Farum, Denmark

JOHNSON & JOHNSON   One Johnson & Johnson Plaza, New Brunswick, NJ 08933,
Tel: (201) 524-0400
(Surgical, med & baby prdts)
   Janssenpharma A/S, Hammerbakken 21, 3460 Birkerod, Denmark

S C JOHNSON & SON INC   1525 Howe St, Racine, WI 53403, Tel: (414) 631-2000
(Home, auto, commercial & personal care prdts, specialty chems)
   Johnson Wax A/S, Midtager 18, 2600 Glostrup, Denmark

KELLOGG CO   235 Porter St, Battle Creek, MI 49016, Tel: (616) 966-2000
(Food prdts)
   Nordisk Kellog's A/S, Ostre Havnevej 25, 5700 Svendborg, Denmark

KEPNER-TREGOE INC   Research Rd, PO Box 704, Princeton, NJ 08542,
  Tel: (609) 921-2806
  (Mgmt & organizational devel)
    P. Kokholm A/S, Norrevaenget 7, DK-3500 Vaerlose, Denmark

KIRKWOOD INDUSTRIES INC   4855 W 130th St, Cleveland, OH 44135,
  Tel: (216) 267-6200
  (Mfr elect components, commutators, mica insulation, slip rings, carbon brushes)
    S&A-Kirkwood A/S, Tolderlundavej 3, 5000 Odense C, Denmark

KNOGO CORP   350 Wireless Blvd, Hauppauge, NY 11788, Tel: (516) 232-2100
  (Mfr electr article surveillance sys)
    Knogo Denmark APS, Kystvej 2, 3100 Hornbaek, Denmark

KRAFT INC   Kraft Court, Glenview, IL 60025, Tel: (708) 998-2000
  (Dairy prdts, processed food, chems)
    Kraft Foods A/S, Vasbyqade 45. DK 2450, Copenhagen SV, Denmark

LAMSON & SESSIONS CO   25701 Science Park Dr, Cleveland, OH 44122,
  Tel: (216) 464-3400
  (Mfr thermoplastic electrical conduit & related prdts; prdts for transp equip ind)
    Lamson & Sessions APS, Rojrupveg 15, DK-5550 Langeskov, Denmark

LEVI STRAUSS & CO   1155 Battery, San Francisco, CA 94111, Tel: (415) 544-6000
  (Mfr wearing apparel)
    Levi Strauss Denmark, Store Kirkestraede 1, 1073 Copenhagen K, Denmark

ELI LILLY & CO   307 E McCarty St, Indianapolis, IN 46285, Tel: (317) 261-2000
  (Pharms, agric & cosmetic prdts)
    Eli Lilly & Co. A/S, Tommerup Stationsvej 10, DK 2770 Kastrup, Denmark

LINCOLN ST LOUIS DIVISION   1 Lincoln Way, St Louis, MO 63120,
  Tel: (314) 679-4200
  (Lubrication equip, materials dispensing equip)
    Lincoln GmbH Novdan A/S, 31 Vallensbaekvej, DK-2600 Glostrup, Denmark

LINTAS:WORLDWIDE   1 Dag Hammarskjold Plaza, New York, NY 10017,
  Tel: (212) 605-8000
  (Advertising agency)
    Lintas:GR/Kopenhavn, Kobmagergase 60, DK-1500 Copenhagen K, Denmark

R H MACY & CO INC   51 West 34th St, New York, NY 10001, Tel: (212) 560-3600
  (Department stores, importers)
    R.H. Macy & Co. Inc., Chr. Winthersvej 5, 1860 Copenhagen V, Denmark

MANPOWER INC   5301 N Ironwood Rd, PO Box 2053, Milwaukee, WI 53201-2053,
  Tel: (414) 961-1000
  (Temporary help)
    Manpower A/S, Vesterbrogade 12, 1620 Copenhagen, Denmark

MARSH & McLENNAN COS INC   1221 Ave of the Americas, New York, NY 10020-1011,
  Tel: (212) 997-2000
  (Insurance)
    Marsh & McLennan Bowring A/S, P.O. Box 821, 2100 Copenhagen, Denmark

MEMOREX CORP   San Thomas at Central Expressway, Santa Clara, CA 95052,
   Tel: (408) 987-1000
   (Magnetic recording tapes, etc)
      MRX A/S, Vallensbaekvej 25, DK 2600 Glostrup, Copenhagen, Denmark

MERCK SHARP & DOHME INTL   PO Box 2000, Rahway, NJ 07065, Tel: (201) 574-4000
   (Pharms, chems & biologicals)
      Merck, Sharp & Dohme, Marielundvej 46C, 1625 Copenhagen, Denmark

MOBIL CORP   150 E 42nd St, New York, NY 10017, Tel: (212) 883-4242
   (Petroleum explor, prdts)
      Mobil Oil A/S, H.C. Andersens Blvd. 1, DK 1553 Copenhagen V, Denmark

MONSANTO CO   800 N Lindbergh Blvd, St Louis, MO 63167, Tel: (314) 694-1000
   (Mfr chem & agric prdts, pharms, ind process equip, man-made fibers, plastics)
      Monsanto A/S, Smedeland 6, DK-2600 Glostrop, Denmark

MOTOROLA INC   1303 E Algonquin Rd, Schaumburg, IL 60196, Tel: (708) 397-5000
   (Mfr commun equip, semiconductors, cellular phones)
      Storno A/S, 126 Artillerivej, DK-2300 Copenhagen 5, Denmark

MULLER & PHIPPS INTL CORP   Box 3994, San Francisco, CA 94119,
   Tel: (415) 772-5650
   (General merchandise)
      Muller & Phipps Corp., Maldahlgade 3, 1613 Copenhagen, Denmark, Copenhagen V,
      Denmark

MULTIGRAPHICS DIV   1800 W Central Rd, Mt Prospect, IL 60056,
   Tel: (708) 398-1900
   (Offset duplicating & graphic commun sys)
      AM Intl. A/S, Carl Jacobsensvej 16, DK 2500, Copenhagen, Valby, Denmark

McCANN-ERICKSON WORLDWIDE   750 Third Ave, New York, NY 10017,
   Tel: (212) 697-6000
   (Advertising)
      McCann-Erickson A/S, Toldbodgade 19B, 1253 Copenhagen K, Denmark

McKINSEY & CO INC   55 E 52nd St, New York, NY 10022, Tel: (212) 909-8400
   (Mgmt consultants)
      McKinsey & Co., Ved Stranden 14, 1061 Copenhagen, Denmark

NABISCO BRANDS INC   Nabisco Brands Plaza, East Hanover, NJ 07936,
   Tel: (201) 503-2000
   (Mfr food prdts)
      Oxford Biscuit Fabrik A/S, Parallelvej 11, 9800 Hjorring, Denmark

NASHUA CORP   44 Franklin St, Nashua, NH 03061, Tel: (603) 880-2323
   (Mfr/distr/serv office copier sys & supplies)
      Nashua Denmark A/S, Naverland 2, DK-2600 Glostrup, Denmark

NATIONAL CAR RENTAL SYSTEM INC   7700 France Ave S, Minneapolis, MN 55435,
   Tel: (612) 830-2121
   (Car rental)
      National Car Rental System A/S, Gammel Kongevej 70, 1850 Copenhagen V, Denmark

NATIONAL CHEMSEARCH CORP   2727 Chemsearch Blvd, Irving, TX 75061,
Tel: (214) 438-0211
(Commercial chem prdts)
National Chemsearch Aps., Industribuen 7E, 2635 Ishoj, Denmark

NATIONAL SEMICONDUCTOR CORP   2900 Semiconductor Dr, Santa Clara, CA 95051,
Tel: (408) 721-5000
(Semiconductors, computers & point-of-sale sys)
National Semiconductor Ltd., Ringager 4A 3, DK-2605 Brandby, Denmark

NCR CORP   1700 S Patterson Blvd, Dayton, OH 45479, Tel: (513) 445-2000
(Develop/mfr/sell/serv business info processing sys)
NCR Denmark A/S, Teglvaerksgade 31, DK-2100 Copenhagen, Denmark

A C NIELSEN CO   Nielsen Plaza, Northbrook, IL 60062, Tel: (708) 498-6300
(Marketing research)
A/S Markeds-Data, 16 Ahlefeldtsgade, DK-1359, Copenhagen, Denmark

NORTON CO   1 New Bond St, Worcester, MA 01606, Tel: (508) 795-5000
(Abrasives, drill bits, constr & safety prdts, plastics)
Norton B.V. Holland, Fynsvej 73, 6000 Kolding, Denmark

OGILVY & MATHER INC   2 E 48th St, New York, NY 10017, Tel: (212) 907-3400
(Advertising agency)
Ogilvy & Mather Reklamebureau A/S, Martinsvej 7-9, DK 1926, Copenhagen V, Denmark

ONAN CORP   1400 73rd Ave NE, Minneapolis, MN 55432, Tel: (612) 574-5000
(Electric generators, ind engines & controls)
Con Mec-EFTF, APS, P.O. Box 39, Ringstedvej 556, DK 4632, Bjaeverskov, Denmark

OVERSEAS NATIONAL AIRWAYS INC   Kennedy Intl Airport, Jamaica, NY 11430,
Tel: (212) 632-8200
(Air carrier)
Overseas National Airways, Vester Farimagsgade 1, 1606 Copenhagen V, Denmark

OWENS-CORNING FIBERGLAS CORP   PO Box 901, Fiberglas Tower, Toledo, OH 43659,
Tel: (419) 248-8000
(Mfr insulation, building materials, glass fiber prdts)
Dansk-Svensk Glasfiber S/A (Denmark), Denmark

PACKAGING CORP OF AMERICA   1603 Orrington Ave, Evanston, IL 60204,
Tel: (708) 492-5713
(Mfr custom packaging, aluminum & plastic molded fibre, corrugated containers)
A/S Haustrup-Ekco Aluminium-Emballage, P.O. Box 929, DK-5000 Odense, Denmark
Omni-Pac ApS, Retortvej 36, DK-2500 Copenhagen Valby, Denmark

PANTASOTE INC   PO Box 1800, Greenwich, CT 06830, Tel: (203) 661-0400
(Mfr rubber & plastic)
ILPEA A/S, Egeskovej 8, 3490 Kvistgard, Denmark

PARAMOUNT INTL FILMS INC   1 Gulf & Western Plaza, New York, NY 10023,
Tel: (212) 333-4600
(Film prod & distr)
Cinema Intl. Corp., APS, Hauchsvej 13, 1825 Copenhagen V, Denmark

PARKER HANNIFIN CORP   17325 Euclid Ave, Cleveland, OH 44112,
Tel: (216) 531-3000
(Mfr motion-control prdts)
    Parker Hannifin Denmark A/S, Industribuen 8, DK 2635 Ishoj, Denmark

PERKIN-ELMER CORP   761 Main Ave, Norwalk, CT 06859, Tel: (203) 762-1000
(Analytical instru, computers, semiconductor prod equip, avionics, electro-optical
sys, etc)
    Perkin-Elmer A/S, Birkerod Kongevej 137F, DK 3460 Birkerod, Denmark

PFIZER INC   235 E 42nd St, New York, NY 10017, Tel: (212) 573-2323
(Mfr pharms, hosp prdts, chems, consumer & animal health prdts)
    Pfizer A/S, Vestre Gade 18, P.O. Box 149, DK 2650 Huidovre, Denmark

PHILLIPS PETROLEUM CO   Phillips Bldg, Bartlesville, OK 74004,
Tel: (918) 661-6600
(Crude oil, natural gas, liquefied petroleum gas, gasoline & petro-chems)
    Phillips Industri & Handel, Postbox 1919, 2300 Copenhagen, Denmark

PLIBRICO CO   1800 Kingsbury St, Chicago, IL 60614, Tel: (312) 549-7014
(Refractories, engineering, constr)
    Plibrico A/S, Cirkelhuset, Christianshusvej 2, DK-2970 Horsholm, Denmark

POLAROID CORP   549 Technology Sq, Cambridge, MA 02139, Tel: (617) 577-2000
(Photographic and optical prdts)
    Polaroid A/S, Postboks 9, Blokken 75, DK-3460 Birkerod, Denmark
    Polaroid A/S, Postbox 9, Blokken 75, 3460 Birkerod, Denmark

PREMARK INTL INC   1717 Deerfield Rd, Deerfield, IL 60015, Tel: (708) 405-6000
(Mfr/sale diversified consumer & coml prdts)
    Rexall Scandinavia A/S, Rygards Alle 104, DK-2900 Hellerup, Denmark

PUROLATOR COURIER CORP   131 Morristown Rd, Basking Ridge, NJ 07980,
Tel: (201) 953-6400
(Time-sensitive package delivery)
    Courier of Denmark, Copenhagen, Denmark

QUAKER OATS CO   345 Merchandise Mart Plaza, Chicago, IL 60654,
Tel: (312) 222-7111
(Foods, pet foods, toys, chems)
    OTA A/S, Islands Brygge 41, 2300 Copenhagen S, Denmark

RAYTHEON CO   141 Spring St, Lexington, MA 02173, Tel: (617) 862-6600
(Mfr diversified electronics & apppliances; aviation, ind & constr services,
publishing)
    Raytheon-Copenhagen, Siljangade 6, 2300 Copenhagen S, Denmark

READER'S DIGEST ASSOCIATION INC   PO Box 235, Pleasantville, NY 10570,
Tel: (914) 238-1000
(Global publisher & direct mail marketer)
    Forlaget Det Bedste A/S, Jagtvej 169B, Postboks 810, DK-2100 Copenhagen, Denmark

RESEARCH-COTTRELL COS   PO Box 1500, Somerville, NJ 08876, Tel: (201) 685-4000
(Design/install air pollution control equip; tech servs)
    Reeco Stroem A/S, Federiciavej 99, DK-7100 Vejile, Denmark

RMS GROUP INC   43-59 10th St, Long Island City, NY 11101, Tel: (718) 361-9756
(Intl market devel)
Pak-Item Aps, 16 Fredericiagade, DK-1310 Copenhagen K, Denmark

H H ROBERTSON CO   Two Gateway Center, Pittsburgh, PA 15222,
Tel: (412) 281-3200
(Mfr roof & wall prdts, cellular steel floor sys, ventilation equip)
H.H. Robertson Nordisk A/S, Bernhard Bangs Alle 25, 2000, Copenhagen F, Denmark

ROSEMOUNT INC   12001 Technology Dr, Eden Prairie, MN 55344,
Tel: (612) 941-5560
(Mfr aerospace & ind instrumentation)
Rosemount A/S, Hejrevang 11, 3450 Allerod, Denmark

SEA-LAND SERVICE INC   379 Thornall St, Edison, NJ 08837, Tel: (201) 558-6000
(Container transport)
Sealand Transport, Nyholmsvej 7, DK 2000, Copenhagen,F, Denmark

SEATRAIN LINES INC   270 Sylvan Ave, Englewood Cliffs, NJ 07632,
Tel: (201) 871-8900
(Containerized shipping, ship chartering)
Seatrain A/B, Wilsonterminalen Stilla Haven, Skandiahammen S, 41734, Goteborg,
Denmark
Seatrain A/B, Nadirgatan, Skaneterminalen, Box 11064, Helsinborg 25011, Denmark
Seatrain Denmark, Gluckstadtsvej 2, 2100 Copenhagen, Denmark
Seatrain Denmark, Olandsgade, 8000 Aarhus C, Denmark

SGS CONTROL SERVICES INC   42 Broadway, New York, NY 10004,
Tel: (212) 482-8700
(Complete range of quality & quantity control checks & related tech serv)
SGS Inspection A/S, 2 A.L. Drewsensvej, DK 2100, Copenhagen, Denmark
SGS Inspection A/S, 4 Havnegade, DK 8000, Aarhus C, Denmark
SGS Inspection A/S, M Vej, Provestenen, DK 2300, Copenhagen S, Denmark

W S SHAMBAN & CO   2951 28th St, #2010, Santa Monica, CA 90405,
Tel: (213) 450-0020
(Tech plastics prdts)
W.S. Shamban & Co. A/S, Falbriksvej 15, 3000 Helsingor, Denmark

SPS TECHNOLOGIES INC   900 Newtown-Yardley Rd, Newtown, PA 18940,
Tel: (215) 860-3000
(Mfr aerospace & ind fasteners, precision components, superalloys, magnetic
materials, fastening sys)
Unbrako ApS, Generatorvej 6A.2, DK-2730 Herlev, Denmark

STANDARD COMMERCIAL CORP   PO Box 450, Wilson, NC 27893, Tel: (919) 291-5507
(Leaf tobacco dealers/processors, wool processors)
Leafco A/S, Tordenskjoldsjade 24, DK 1055, Copenhagen, Denmark

STANDARD OIL CO OF CALIFORNIA   225 Bush St, San Francisco, CA 94104,
Tel: (415) 894-7700
(Oil explor & prod, petroleum prdts)
Chevron Oil A/S, Amaliegade 33B, 1256 Copenhagen, Denmark

THE STANLEY WORKS   1000 Stanley Dr, PO Box 7000, New Britain, CT   06050,
  Tel: (203) 225-5111
  (Mfr hand tools & hardware)
    Stanley Vaerktoj & Beslag A/S, Generatorvej 6A, 2730 Herlev, Denmark

SYSTEMS ENGINEERING LABS INC   6901 W Sunrise Blvd, Fort Lauderdale,
  FL   33313, Tel: (305) 587-2900
  (Digital computers)
    Systems Associated AB, Fredericagade 16, Copenhagen, Denmark

TANDEM COMPUTERS INC   19333 Vallco Parkway, Cupertino, CA   95014,
  Tel: (408) 725-6000
  (Computer sys)
    Tandem Computers A/S, Helgeshoj Alle 55, 2630 Tastrup, Denmark

TED BATES WORLDWIDE INC   1515 Broadway, New York, NY   10036,
  Tel: (212) 869-3131
  (Advertising agency)
    Ted Bates A/S, Landemaerket 29, DK-1119 Copenhagen K, Denmark

TEKTRONIX INC   PO Box 500, Beaverton, OR   97077, Tel: (503) 627-7111
  (Mfr test & meas, visual sys & commun prdts)
    Tektronix A/S, Postboks 144, DK-2750 Ballerup, Denmark

TENNECO AUTOMOTIVE   100 Tri-State Intl, #300, Lincolnshire, IL   60069,
  Tel: (708) 948-0900
  (Mfr exhaust sys, ride control prdts, brake components)
    Walker Danmark A/S, Falstersvej, Middelfart 5500, Denmark

TEXACO INC   2000 Westchester Ave, White Plains, NY   10650, Tel: (914) 253-4000
  (Explor/mktg crude oil & its prdts, petro-chems)
    Texaco A/S, Borgergade 13, 1300 Copenhagen, Denmark

THERMO ELECTRIC CO   109 Fifth St, Saddle Brook, NJ   07662, Tel: (201) 843-5800
  (Mfr temp/meas control prdts)
    Telemetric Instrument Aps, Gl. Hovedgade 10E, 2970 Horsholm, Denmark

UNION CAMP CORP   1600 Valley Rd, Wayne, NJ   07470, Tel: (201) 628-2000
  (Flavors, fragrances, essential oils, aroma chems, corrugated containers)
    Bush Boake Allen A/S, Maglebergvej 5A, 2800 Lyngby, Denmark

UNION CARBIDE CORP   Old Ridgebury Rd, Danbury, CT   06817, Tel: (203) 794-2000
  (Carbon prdts, chems, plastics, gases & related prdts, etc)
    Unifos Kemi A/S, Falkonercentret, Falkoner alle 7, DK 2000, Copenhagen, Denmark

UNISYS CORP   PO Box 500, Blue Bell, PA   19424, Tel: (215) 542-4011
  (Mfg/mktg/serv electr info sys)
    Unisys, Oesterbrogade 125, DK-2100 Copenhagen, Denmark

UNITED TECHNOLOGIES CORP   United Technologies Bldg, Hartford, CT   06101,
  Tel: (203) 728-7000
  (Mfr aircraft engines, elevators, A/C, auto equip, space & military electr, rocket
  propulsion sys)
    Nielson-Otis Elevator A/S, Hoerkaer 7-9, DK 2730 Harlev, Denmark

URSCHEL LABORATORIES INC   2503 Calumet Ave, PO Box 2200, Valparaiso,
 IN 46384-2200, Tel: (219) 464-4811
 (Design & mfr precision food processing equip)
   Urschel Intl., Pilevej 24, Taulov, 700 Fredericia, Denmark

VARIAN ASSOCIATES INC   611 Hansen Way, Palo Alto, CA 94304-1030,
 Tel: (415) 493-4000
 (Mfr microwave tubes & devices, analytical instru, semiconductor process & med equip,
 vacuum sys)
   Varian Electronics APS, 9 Lyskaer, DK-2730 Herlev, Denmark

VF CORP   PO Box 1022, Reading, PA 19603, Tel: (215) 378-1151
 (Mfr/mktg apparel)
   H.D. Lee Danmark Aps., Mileparken 20A, 2740 Skovlunde, Denmark

WALKER MFG CO   1201 Michigan Blvd, Racine, WI 53402, Tel: (414) 632-8871
 (Automotive parts, exhaust sys, service equip)
   Lydex A/S, Falstervej 11, DK-5500 Middelfart, Denmark

WATERS CHROMATOGRAPHY DIV   34 Maple St, Milford, MA 01757,
 Tel: (617) 478-2000
 (Mfr/distr liquid chromatographic instru/accessories/tech)
   Millipore A/S, Roskildevej 342, 2630 Tastrup, Denmark
   Waters Associates A/S, Sondre Ringvej 24, DK 4000, Roskilde, Denmark

WEATHERFORD INTL INC   1360 Post Oak Blvd, PO Box 27608, Houston,
 TX 77227-9917, Tel: (713) 439-9400
 (Tubular & cementation servs, prdts & equip; water jetting servs, mfr marine pedestal
 cranes)
   Weatherford Intl., c/o DOGIS APS, Made Engvej 7, DK-6701 Esbjerg, Denmark

WEIGHT WATCHERS INTL INC   Jericho Atrium, 500 North Broadway, Jericho,
 NY 11753-2196, Tel: (516) 939-0400
 (Weight reduction programs, food prdts)
   Weight Watchers A/S, Buddingevej 85D, 2800 KG, Lyngby, Denmark

WORLD COURIER INC   46 Trinity Pl, New York, NY 10006, Tel: (718) 978-9400
 (Intl courier serv)
   World Courier Copenhagen, Fuzlebaekvej 3, DK 2770, Kastrup, Denmark

YOUNG & RUBICAM INTL INC   285 Madison Ave, New York, NY 10017,
 Tel: (212) 210-3000
 (Advertising agency)
   Young & Rubicam, Norre Sogade 35, 1370 Copenhagen K, Denmark

DOMINICAN REPUBLIC

3M CO   3M Center, St Paul, MN 55144-1000, Tel: (612) 733-1110
(Mfr abrasives, adhesives, chems, ind & consumer tapes/diskettes, health care prdts, elec connectors)
  3M Dominicana S.A., Aptdo. 103-2, Ave. Luperon, Zona Industrial de Herrera, Santo Domingo, Dominican Republic

ABBOTT LABORATORIES   Abbott Park, North Chicago, IL 60064, Tel: (312) 937-6100
(Pharm & lab prdts)
  Abbott Laboratories Intl., P.O. Box 846, Santo Domingo, Dominican Republic

AFIA   110 William St, New York, NY 10038, Tel: (212) 964-4990
(Insurance)
  AFIA Home Insurance Co., P.O. Box 162, Santo Domingo, Dominican Republic

AMERICAN AIRLINES INC   PO Box 619616, Dallas-Ft Worth Arpt, TX 75261-9616, Tel: (817) 355-1234
(Air transp)
  American Airlines, P.O. Box 1295, El Conde #401, Edificio Copello, Santo Domingo, Dominican Republic

AMERICAN NATIONAL CAN CO   8770 W Bryn Mawr Ave, Chicago, IL 60631, Tel: (312) 399-3000
(Mfr metal, glass & plastic packaging prdt)
  Envases Antillanos, C. por A., Calle 11, Altos de Virella, Santiago, Dominican Republic

AMERICAN STANDARD INC   40 W 40th St, New York, NY 10018, Tel: (212) 840-5100
(Heating & sanitary equip)
  Sanitarios Dominicanos S.A., P.O. Box 910, Santiago de Los Caballeros, Dominican Republic

BARDAHL MFG CORP   1400 N W 52nd St, PO Box 70607, Seattle, WA 98107, Tel: (206) 783-4851
(Lubricating oils)
  Suami Tractor C. por A., Aptdo. 70-9, Santo Domingo, Dominican Republic

LEO BURNETT CO INC   35 West Wacker Dr, Chicago, IL 60601, Tel: (312) 220-5959
(Advertising agency)
  Leo Burnett Inc., Prolongacion Arabia 13, Arroyo Hondo, Santo Domingo, Dominican Republic

BURNS & ROE INC   550 Kinderkamack Rd, Oradell, NJ 07649, Tel: (201) 265-2000
(Consulting engineers)
  Burns & Roe, Santo Domingo, Dominican Republic

CALMAQUIP ENGINEERING CORP   7240 NW 12th St, Miami, FL 33121,
  Tel: (305) 592-4510
  (Engineering)
    Calmest S.A., Abraham Lincoln, Esquina Modesto Diaz, Aptdo. 1693, Santo Domingo,
      Dominican Republic

CANADA DRY INTL CORP   2600 Century Pkwy, Atlanta, GA 30345,
  Tel: (404) 753-2182
  (Carbonated beverages, soft drinks extract)
    Refrescos Nacionales C. por A., P.O. Box 283, Santo Domingo, Dominican Republic

CARNATION INTL CO   5045 Wilshire Blvd, Los Angeles, CA 90036,
  Tel: (213) 932-6000
  (Milk prdts)
    Dominicana de Alimentos Lacteos S.A., P.O. Box 900, Santo Domingo,
      Dominican Republic

CHASE MANHATTAN BANK N A   1 Chase Manhattan Plaza, New York, NY 10081,
  Tel: (212) 552-2222
  (Intl banking)
    Chase Manhattan Bank NA., Avenida John F. Kennedy y Tiradentes, Aptdo. 1408,
      Santo Domingo, Dominican Republic

CIGNA CORP   One Liberty Place, 1650 Market St, Philadelphia, PA 19101,
  Tel: (215) 523-4000
  (Ins, invest, health care & other fin servs)
    Insurance Co. of North America, Edificio Torre BHD- 2 Piso,
      Ave. Winston Churchill/Esq. 27 de Feb., Santo Dom., Dominican Republic

CITIBANK NA   399 Park Ave, New York, NY 10043, Tel: (212) 559-1000
  (Intl banking)
    Citibank NA., Avenida John F. Kennedy No. 1, Aptdo. 1492, Santo Domingo,
      Dominican Republic
    Citibank NA., Calle el Sol, Esquina Mella, Aptdo. 17, Santiago de los Cabaelleros,
      Dominican Republic

COLUMBIA PICTURES INDUSTRIES INC   711 Fifth Ave, New York, NY 10022,
  Tel: (212) 751-4400
  (Producer & distributor of motion pictures)
    Columbia Film Trading Corp., Avenida Independencia #310, Zona 1, P.O. Box 1459],
      Santo Domingo, Dominican Republic

COSCO INTERNATIONAL INC   1845 Oak St, #9, Northfield, IL 60093,
  Tel: (708) 446-9390
  (Flavoring extracts, chem spec, franchised soft drinks)
    Sabores Cosco Domicano C.por A., Aptdo. 524, Santo Domingo, Dominican Republic

DEVELOPMENT ASSOCIATES INC   2924 Columbia Pike, Arlington, VA 22204,
  Tel: (703) 979-0100
  (Mgt consulting servs)
    Development Associates, Inc., Jose Joaquin Perez #203 (Altos), Santo Domingo,
      Dominican Republic

ECOLAB INC   370 Wabasha St, St Paul, MN 55102, Tel: (612) 293-2233
  (Ind & household detergents, cleaning agents & equip)
    Quimo Caribe S.A., Ave. Independencia 278, Aptdo. Postal 1611-158-2, Santo Domingo,
      Dominican Republic

ECUADORIAN FRUIT IMPORT CORP   19 Rector St, New York, NY 10006,
  Tel: (212) 344-1370
  (Fruit)
    Exportadora Dominicana de Guneos C. por A., Calle Beler No. 98, Santiago,
      Dominican Republic

EXXON CORP   225 E John Carpenter Frwy, Irving, TX 75062, Tel: (214) 444-1000
  (Petroleum & petroleum prdts)
    Esso Standard Oll S.A., P.O. Box 1026., Santo Domingo, Dominican Republic

FOOTE CONE & BELDING COMMUNICATIONS INC   101 E Erie St, Chicago,
  IL 60611-2897, Tel: (312) 751-7000
  (Advertising agency)
    FCB/Siboney, Aptdo. Postal 295-2, Santo Domingo, Dominican Republic

H B FULLER CO   2400 Energy Park Dr, St Paul, MN 55108, Tel: (612) 645-3401
  (Mfr/distr adhesives, sealants, coatings, paints, waxes, sanitation chems)
    Industrial Quimicas Nacionales C. por A., Piedra Bianca, Haina, Dominican Republic

GROLIER INC   Old Shereman Tpk, Danbury, CT 06816, Tel: (203) 797-3500
  (Publishers)
    Cobranzas S.A., Ave. Alma Mater #33, Esq. 27 de Febrero, Santo Domingo,
      Dominican Republic

GULF & WESTERN INDUSTRIES INC   1 Gulf & Western Plaza, New York, NY 10023,
  Tel: (212) 333-7000
  (Widely diversified multi-industry company in consumer prdts)
    Gulf & Western Americas Corp., P.O. Box 891, Santo Domingo, Dominican Republic

HOLIDAY INNS INC   3742 Lamar Ave, Memphis, TN 38195, Tel: (901) 362-4001
  (Hotels, restaurants, casinos)
    Holiday Inn, Avenida Anacaona, Santo Domingo, Dominican Republic

HORWATH & HORWATH INTL   919 Third Ave, New York, NY 10022,
  Tel: (212) 980-3100
  (Public accountants & auditors)
    Horwath & Horwath, Sotero Peralta y Asscociados, Aptdo. Postal 355-2,
      Ave. Winston Churchill, Edificio Lama, Dominican Republic

INA CORPORATION   1600 Arch St, Philadelphia, PA 19101, Tel: (215) 523-5335
  (Holding co: ins, financial serv)
    Compania de Seguros Qulsqueyana S.A., Isabel la Catolica & Restauricion St.,
      P.O. Box 1076, Santo Domingo, Dominican Republic

INTERNATIONAL PAPER   2 Manhattanville Rd, Purchase, NY 10577,
  Tel: (914) 397-1500
  (Mfr/distr container board, paper, wood prdts)
    Impresora del Yaque, C. por A., Autopista Santiago Navarrete, Kilometro 2 1/2,
      Santiago/Navarrete, Dominican Republic

ITT SHERATON CORP   60 State St, Boston, MA 02108, Tel: (617) 367-3600
  (Hotel operations)
    Santo Domingo Sheraton Hotel & Casino, Ave. George Washington 365, Aptdo. 1493,
      Santo Domingo, Dominican Republic

JOHNSON & JOHNSON   One Johnson & Johnson Plaza, New Brunswick, NJ 08933,
Tel: (201) 524-0400
(Surgical, med & baby prdts)
   Johnson & Johnson (Dominicana) C. por A., Santo Domingo, Dominican Republic

S C JOHNSON & SON INC   1525 Howe St, Racine, WI 53403, Tel: (414) 631-2000
(Home, auto, commercial & personal care prdts, specialty chems)
   Ceras Johnson Dominicana S.A., Ave. San Martin No. 296, Santo Domingo,
      Dominican Republic

McCANN-ERICKSON WORLDWIDE   750 Third Ave, New York, NY 10017,
Tel: (212) 697-6000
(Advertising)
   McCann-Erickson Dominicana S.A., Moises Garcia 17, Gazque, Santo Domingo,
      Dominican Republic

NABISCO BRANDS INC   Nabisco Brands Plaza, East Hanover, NJ 07936,
Tel: (201) 503-2000
(Mfr food prdts)
   Nabisco Inc. Tamara C. por A., Aptdo. Postal No, 1146, Santo Domingo,
      Dominlcan Republic

NATIONAL CAR RENTAL SYSTEM INC   7700 France Ave S, Minneapolis, MN 55435,
Tel: (612) 830-2121
(Car rental)
   National Car Rental System Inc., A. Lincoln 1056, P.O. Box 800, Santo Domingo,
      Dominican Republic

NCR CORP   1700 S Patterson Blvd, Dayton, OH 45479, Tel: (513) 445-2000
(Develop/mfr/sell/serv business info processing sys)
   NCR Dominicana C. por A., John F. Kennedy-Ortega & Gasset, Apartado 2720,
      Santo Domingo, Dominican Republic

ONAN CORP   1400 73rd Ave NE, Minneapolis, MN 55432, Tel: (612) 574-5000
(Electric generators, ind engines & controls)
   Curacao Trading Co. C. por A., Leopoldo Navarro, Esq. San Francisco, Aptdo. 1358,
      Santo Domingo, Dominican Republic

OTIS ELEVATOR CO   10 Farm Springs, Farmington, CT 06032, Tel: (203) 674-4047
(Elevators & escalators)
   Otis Elevator Co., Avenida Abraham Lincoln 355, Aptdo. No. 307, Santo Domingo,
      Dominican Republic

PAN-AMERICAN LIFE INSURANCE CO   Pan American Life Center, New Orleans,
LA 70130, Tel: (504) 566-1300
(Insurance)
   Cia de Seguros PALIC, S.A., Abraham Lincoln esq. Jose Amado Soler, Santo Domingo,
      Dominican Republic

RCA GLOBAL COMMUNICATIONS INC   60 Broad St, New York, NY 10004,
Tel: (212) 806-7000
(Commun serv)
   RCA Global Dominicana S.A., Aptdo. 1027, Edif. Diez, Calle el Conde 203-1,
      Santo Domingo, Dominican Republic

RICHARDSON-VICKS INC   Ten Westport Rd, Wilton, CT 06897, Tel: (203) 834-5000
(Consumer health & personal care prdts)
  Richardson-Vicks, Eduardo Vicioso 1, Santo Domingo, Dominican Republic

ROHM & HAAS CO   Independence Mall West, Philadelphia, PA 19105,
Tel: (215) 592-3000
(Mfr ind & agric chems, plastics)
  Rohm & Haas Caribe Inc., Ave. J. F. Kennedy 57, Esq. Calle Del Carmen,
    Edif. Brugal 209, Santo Domingo, Dominican Republic

SEA-LAND SERVICE INC   379 Thornall St, Edison, NJ 08837, Tel: (201) 558-6000
(Container transport)
  Sea-Land Service, P.O. Box 1431, Santo Domingo, Dominican Republic

TEXACO INC   2000 Westchester Ave, White Plains, NY 10650, Tel: (914) 253-4000
(Explor/mktg crude oil & its prdts, petro-chems)
  Texaco Caribbean Inc., Aptdo. 779, Santo Domingo, Dominican Republic

UNION SPECIAL CORP   222 No LaSalle, Chicago, IL 60601, Tel: (312) 606-9500
(Mfr ind sewing machs)
  Productos Textiles S.A., Gaspar Hernandez No. 15, Aptdo. No. 442, Santo Domingo,
    Dominican Republic

VELSICOL CHEMICAL CORP   5600 N River Rd, Rosemont, IL 60018,
Tel: (708) 698-9700
(Pesticides & ind chems)
  Velsicol Dominicana S.A., Gustavo Mejia Ricart No.79, Aptdo. 201, Ensanche Pantini,
    Santo Domingo, Dominican Republic

WACKENHUT CORP   1500 San Remo Ave, Coral Gables, FL 33146,
Tel: (305) 666-5656
(Security sys & serv)
  Wackenhut Dominicana S.A., Paseo de los Locutores #36, Ensanche Piantini,
    Aptdo. #1677, Zona 1, Santo Domingo, Dominican Repub

WARNER-LAMBERT CO   201 Tabor Road, Morris Plains, NJ 07950,
Tel: (201) 540-2000
(Mfr ethical & proprietary pharms, confectionary & consumer prdts)
  Laboratories Warner-Chilcott/Adams Dominicana S.A., Ramon Santana 12,
    Santo Domingo, Dominican Republic

WEST CHEMICAL PRODUCTS INC   1000 Herrontown Rd, Princeton, NJ 08540,
Tel: (609) 921-0501
(Sanitary equip & supplies)
  West S.A., P.O. Box 428, Santo Domingo, Dominican Republic

WOMETCO ENTERPRISES INC   306 N Miami Ave, Miami, FL 33128,
Tel: (305) 374-6262
(Television broadcasting, film distribution, bottling, vending machs)
  Operadora Filmica S.A., P.O. Box 1396, Ave. Bolivar 453, Zona 2, Santo Domingo,
    Dominican Republic

YOUNG & RUBICAM INTL INC   285 Madison Ave, New York, NY 10017,
Tel: (212) 210-3000
(Advertising agency)
  Young & Rubicam Damaris C. por A., Ave. de Los Proceres, Esq. Camino del Oeste,
    Arroya Hondo, Santo Domingo, Dominican Republic

ECUADOR

3M CO   3M Center, St Paul, MN 55144-1000, Tel: (612) 733-1110
(Mfr abrasives, adhesives, chems, ind & consumer tapes/diskettes, health care prdts, elec connectors)
   3M Ecuador C.A., Km. 1.5 Via Duran Tambo, P.O. Box 6137, Guayaquil, Ecuador

ABBOTT LABORATORIES   Abbott Park, North Chicago, IL 60064,
   Tel: (312) 937-6100
(Pharm & lab prdts)
   Abbott Labs del Ecuador S.A., 1 de Mayo 610, P.O. Box 3423, Guayaquil, Ecuador

AMERICAN BROADCASTING COS INC   1330 Ave of the Americas, New York, NY 10019,
   Tel: (212) 887-7777
(Radio/TV prod & broadcast)
   Primera Television Ecuatoriana S.A., 9 de Octubre 1200, P.O. Box 5063, Guayaquil, Ecuador
   Primera Television Ecuatoriana S.A., Calle Padre Aguirre y Nueva Tola, P.O. Box 70, Quito, Ecuador
   Telesistema del Ecuador S.A., Palacio Municipal, P.O. Box 400, Cuenca, Ecuador

AMERICAN INTL UNDERWRITERS CORP   70 Pine St, New York, NY 10270,
   Tel: (212) 770-7000
(General ins)
   American Intl. Underwriters del Ecuador S.A., Edif. Soto Mayor, 7 Piso, Avenida 9 de Octubre 415, P.O. Box 4537, Guayaquil, Ecuador
   American Intl. Underwriters del Ecuador S.A., P.O. Box 303-A, Ave. Amazonas 540 & Carrion, Edif. Londres 4-5 Piso,
   American Intl. Underwriters del Ecuador S.A., Quito, Ecuador

ARBOR ACRES FARM INC   41 Marlborough Rd, Glastonbury, CT 06033,
   Tel: (203) 633-4681
(Producers of male & female broiler breeders, commercial egg layers)
   Ecuador Farms, S.A., Casilla 2042, Quito, Ecuador

ARMCO INTL INC   703 Curtis St, PO Box 700, Middletown, OH 45042,
   Tel: (513) 425-6541
(Sheet steel & steel prdts, constr, oil field equip, ins, finance leasing)
   Armco Industrial S.A., Ave. Elay Alfaro 1234, Casilla de Correo 540, Quito, Ecuador
   Productos Metalicos Armco S.A., Ave. Robles 653 y Amazonas, Edif. Proinco-Calisto, Casilla 540, Quito, Ecuador

AVIS INC   900 Old Country Rd, Garden City, NY 11530, Tel: (516) 222-3000
(Car rental serv)
   Avis Rent A Car System Inc, P. Icaza 425 y Cordova, Guayaquil, Ecuador

BADGER METER INC   4545 W Brown Deer Rd, PO Box 23099, Milwaukee, WI 53223,
Tel: (414) 355-0400
(Liquid meters & controls)
   Badger del Ecuador A.S., P.O. Box 3353, Quito, Ecuador

MICHAEL BAKER CORP   4301 Dutch Ridge Rd, Beaver, PA 15009,
Tel: (412) 391-9526
(Consulting engineering)
   Michael Baker, Jr., Inc., Fco. de P. Ycaza 107, P.O. Box 4746, Guayaquil, Ecuador

BALSA ECUADOR LUMBER CORP   10 Fairway Court, PO Box 195, Northvale,
NJ 07647, Tel: (201) 767-1400
(Light lumber)
   Compania Ecuatoriana de Balsa S.A., Robles 301, P.O. Box 3842, Guayaquil, Ecuador

BELCO PETROLEUM CORP   One Dag Hammarskjold Plaza, New York, NY 10017,
Tel: (212) 644-2200
(Expl & prod crude oil & natural gas)
   Belco Petroleum Ecuador Inc., Cordova 808 y V.M. Rendon, Edif. Torres de,
   la Merced, Guayaquil, Ecuador

SAMUEL BINGHAM CO   479 Business Center Dr, Mt Prospect, IL 60056,
Tel: (708) 298-6777
(Print & ins rollers, inks)
   Comercial Stimgraf S.A., Casilla 6540,Guayaquil, Ecuador

BLACK & DECKER CORP   701 E Joppa Road, Towson, MD 21204, Tel: (301) 583-3900
(Mfr portable elect & pneumatic power tools, household prdts)
   Black & Decker Ecuatoriana S.A., Robles 653, Quito, Ecuador

BRANSON ULTRASONICS CORP   Eagle Rd, Danbury, CT 06810, Tel: (203) 796-0400
(Ultrasonic & vibratory plastics assembly mach)
   Suquin, Casilla 9612, Guayaquil, Ecuador

CALMAQUIP ENGINEERING CORP   7240 NW 12th St, Miami, FL 33121,
Tel: (305) 592-4510
(Engineering)
   Calmaquip Engineering del Ecuador S.A., Aptdo. 56, Edif. Torres de Colon,
   Av. Colon #1346, Quito, Ecuador

CANADA DRY INTL CORP   2600 Century Pkwy, Atlanta, GA 30345,
Tel: (404) 753-2182
(Carbonated beverages, soft drinks extract)
   Bebidasy Refrescos de Quito, Cia. Ltd., Villa Lengua y San Francisco, Casilla 260,
   Quito, Ecuador

CHASE MANHATTAN BANK N A   1 Chase Manhattan Plaza, New York, NY 10081,
Tel: (212) 552-2222
(Intl banking)
   Chase Manhattan Overseas Corp., 18 de Septiembre 332y, Juan Leon Mera, Piso 7,
   P.O. Box 9439, Sucursal 7, Quito, Ecuador

CHEVRON CHEMICAL CO   PO Box 5047, San Ramon, CA 94583-0947,
Tel: (415) 842-5500
(Chemicals)
   Plastigama S.A., Km. 4, Av. Cj, Arosemena, Guayaquil, Ecuador

CIGNA CORP   One Liberty Place, 1650 Market St, Philadelphia, PA 19101,
  Tel: (215) 523-4000
  (Ins, invest, health care & other fin servs)
    Cigna Worldwide Insurance Co., Idificio Antisana- 4 Piso, Av. Amazonas 3655,
      Catalina Herrera, Quito, Ecuador
    Indi Servicios C. Ltda., Av. Eloy Alfaro 939 y Amazonas, Quito, Ecuador

CITIBANK NA   399 Park Ave, New York, NY 10043, Tel: (212) 559-1000
  (Intl banking)
    Citibank N.A., Ave. 10 de Agosto No. 345, P.O. Box 1393, Quito, Ecuador
    Citibank N.A., Sucres 14-57 y Mera, P.O. Box 600, Ambato, Ecuador
    Citibank N.A., Ave. 9 de Octobre y Chile, Aptdo. 5885, Guayaquil, Ecuador
    Citibank N.A., Gran Colombia 757, P.O. Box 443, Cuenca, Ecuador

THE COCA-COLA CO   310 North Ave NW, PO Box Drawer 1734, Atlanta, GA 30313,
  Tel: (404) 676-2121
  (Mfr & sale of soft drink syrups & concentrates, juices & food prdts, motion pic & TV
  prod)
    Coca-Cola, Request that all inquiries be made to Atlanta address.

COLUMBIA PICTURES INDUSTRIES INC   711 Fifth Ave, New York, NY 10022,
  Tel: (212) 751-4400
  (Producer & distributor of motion pictures)
    Productora Filmica Nacional del Ecuador Cia, Ltda., Calle 9 de Octobre 424,
      P.O. Box 3445, Guayaquil, Ecuador

COMBUSTION ENGINEERING INC   900 Long Ridge Road, Stamford, CT 06902,
  Tel: (203) 329-8771
  (Tech constr)
    Gray Tool Co., c/o Lliniza Cia, Ltd. Aptdo. 6010, Paz 471 Roca, Ecuador

CROWN CORK & SEAL CO INC   Holmesburg Station, PO Box 6208, Philadelphia,
  PA 19136, Tel: (215) 698-5100
  (Cans, bottle caps; filling & packaging mach)
    Crown Cork del Ecuador C.A., P.O. Box 5401 & 8888, Guayaquil, Ecuador

DEVELOPMENT ASSOCIATES INC   2924 Columbia Pike, Arlington, VA 22204,
  Tel: (703) 979-0100
  (Mgt consulting servs)
    Development Associates, Inc., 12 de Octobre 532, Esq. Andrade de Coello, Ecuador

DOW CHEMICAL CO   2030 Dow Center, Midland, MI 48640, Tel: (517) 636-1000
  (Chems, plastics, fibers, pharms)
    Dow Chemical Intl., Inc., Circunvalacion Calle 6a., Urdesa, P.O. Box 6560,
      Guayaquil, Ecuador
    LIFE (Laboratorios Industriales Faramceuticos Ecuatorianos), Edif. LIFE,
      Avda. Zumaco y de la Prensa, P.O. Box 458, Quito, Ecuador
    LIFE (Laboratorios Industriales Faramceuticos Ecuatorianos), V.M. Rendon 408,
      P.O. Box 3783, Guayaquil, Ecuador

EAGLE ELECTRIC MFG CO INC   45-31 Court Sq, Long Island City, NY 11101,
  Tel: (718) 937-8000
  (Mfg electrical wiring devices)
    Eagle Andina, Apartado 9900, Guayaquil, Ecuador

EXIM OVERSEAS INC   2121 Ponce de Leon Blvd, Coral Gables, FL 33134,
Tel: (305) 444-6444
(Trading & sales of arms for Armco Latin Div)
Armco Paxi, Casilla 546, Quito, Ecuador
Productos Metalicos Armco, Casilla 540, Quito, Ecuador

EXXON CORP   225 E John Carpenter Frwy, Irving, TX 75062, Tel: (214) 444-1000
(Petroleum & petroleum prdts)
Compania Ecuatoriana de Petroleo S.A., Francisco de Pedro Ycaza 445, P.O. Box 3341,
Guayaquil, Ecuador
Esso Andina, Inc., C.A., P.O. Box 1309, Guayaquil, Ecuador

FERRO CORPORATION   One Erieview Plaza, Cleveland, OH 44114,
Tel: (216) 641-8580
(Chems, coatings, plastics, refractories)
Ferro Ecuatoriana S.A., P.O. Box 1188, Cuenca, Ecuador

FLORIDA INTL FORWARDERS   6905 N W 25th St, PO Box 522085, Miami, FL 33122,
Tel: (305) 592-6450
(Air cargo service)
Transpack-Guayaquil, Box 5932, Guayaquil, Ecuador
Transpack-Guayaquil, Quito Ave. Amazonas 877, 3 Piso Of. 301, Quito, Ecuador

FOOTE CONE & BELDING COMMUNICATIONS INC   101 E Erie St, Chicago,
IL 60611-2897, Tel: (312) 751-7000
(Advertising agency)
FCB/Artefilme, Avda. 10 de Agosto 103 y Malecon, Edif. Valra, Guayaquil, Ecuador

FOXBORO CO   33 Commercial St, Foxboro, MA 02035, Tel: (508) 543-8750
(Mfr prdts/provide servs for ind automation)
Foxboro Co., Tecniequipos, P.O. Box 348-A, Quito, Ecuador

H B FULLER CO   2400 Energy Park Dr, St Paul, MN 55108, Tel: (612) 645-3401
(Mfr/distr adhesives, sealants, coatings, paints, waxes, sanitation chems)
H.B. Fuller Ecuador S.A., Casilla 7441, Guayaquil, Ecuador

GENERAL MOTORS CORP   3044 W Grand Blvd, Detroit, MI 48202,
Tel: (313) 556-5000
(Automotive prdts, electronics)
Autos y Maquinas del Ecuador S.A., Quito, Ecuador
Omnibus BB Transportes S.A., Quito, Ecuador

GENERAL TIRE INTL CO   One General St, Akron, OH 44329, Tel: (216) 798-3000
(Mfr tires, rubber & associated prdts)
Compania Ecuatoriana del Caucho S.A., Aptdo. 1594, Cuenca, Ecuador

GLIDDEN-COATINGS RESINS DIV   900 Union Commerece Bldg, Cleveland, OH 44115,
Tel: (216) 344-8167
(Coatings, resins, adhesives, organic chems, etc)
Pinturas Ecuatorianas S.A., P.O. Box 186, Guayaquil, Ecuador
Pinturas Ecuatorianas S.A., Avda. de las Americas, P.O. Box 7041, Guayaquil, Ecuador

GLOBAL INTERNATIONAL   500 Ygnacio Valley Rd, #175, Walnut Creek, CA 94596,
Tel: (415) 933-2293
(Freight forwarding)
Global Transports, Ltd., Veintimilla 878, Ave. Amazonas- Piso 3, PO Box 3458,
Quito, Ecuador

GROLIER INC   Old Shereman Tpk, Danbury, CT 06816, Tel: (203) 797-3500
(Publishers)
  Editora Volcan S.A., Paez 844 y Cordero, Edif. Interandina, Dept. 5A, 5 Piso,
    Quito, Ecuador

FRANK B HALL & CO INC   549 Pleasantville Rd, Briarcliff Manor, NY 10510,
  Tel: (914) 769-9200
(Insurance)
  Uniseguros C.A., Juan Leon Mera 565, P.O. Box 343A, Quito, Ecuador
  Uniseguros C.A., Calle 1, Condo. 2001, Ciudadela Kennedy, P.O. Box 2399, Guayaquil,
    Ecuador

THE HARPER GROUP INC   260 Townsend St, PO Box 77933, San Francisco,
  CA 94107, Tel: (415) 978-0600
(Ocean/air freight fwdg, customs brokerage, packing & whse, logistics mgt, ins)
  Circle Intercarga SA, Avda. Brasil 1708, El Condor Esq., Quito, Ecuador

HORWATH & HORWATH INTL   919 Third Ave, New York, NY 10022,
  Tel: (212) 980-3100
(Public accountants & auditors)
  Juan Seif y Asociados Cia. Ltda., Casilla 2675, Pasaje Farget 155, (Sta.Prisca),
    Edif. America 2 Piso, Oficina 202, Quito, Ecuador

INA CORPORATION   1600 Arch St, Philadelphia, PA 19101, Tel: (215) 523-5335
(Holding co: ins, financial serv)
  Liquidadores e Inspectores de Averla C Ltda., c/o Amazonas C.A. de Seguros,
    Edif. Gran Pasaje, Casilla 3285, Guayaquil, Ecuador

INTERNATIONAL BUSINESS MACHINES (IBM)   Old Orchard Rd, Armonk,
  NY 10504-1783, Tel: (914) 765-1900
(Info-handling sys, equip & serv)
  IBM del Ecuador, C.A., Quito, Ecuador

ITT CORP   1330 Ave of the Americas, New York, NY 10019, Tel: (212) 258-1000
(Diversified mfr, tech & services)
  Intl. Standard Electric of New York, Ltd., Edif. Banco de Prestamos, 4o Piso,
    Oficina D, P.O. Box 2754, Quito, Ecuador

JOHNSON & JOHNSON   One Johnson & Johnson Plaza, New Brunswick, NJ 08933,
  Tel: (201) 524-0400
(Surgical, med & baby prdts)
  Johnson & Johnson del Ecuador S.A., Mons. Domingo Comin 135, P.O. Box 487,
    Guayaquil, Ecuador

KNOLL INTL   655 Madison Ave, New York, NY 10021, Tel: (212) 826-2400
(Furniture & fabrics)
  Industrias Artectum S.A., Jorge Washington No. 718 y Amazonas, Quito, Ecuador

MANPOWER INC   5301 N Ironwood Rd, PO Box 2053, Milwaukee, WI 53201-2053,
  Tel: (414) 961-1000
(Temporary help)
  Manpower, Casilla 6530 CCI, Quito, Ecuador

MERCK SHARP & DOHME INTL   PO Box 2000, Rahway, NJ 07065, Tel: (201) 574-4000
(Pharms, chems & biologicals)
  Merck, Sharp & Dohme Intl., Carretera al Tingo, Guayaquil, Ecuador

MILCHEM INC   3900 Essex Lane, PO Box 22111, Houston, TX 77027,
  Tel: (214) 439-8000
  (Gas & oil well drilling fluids & chem additives)
    Milchem Western Hemisphere, Inc., Aptdo. Postal 4143, Quito, Ecuador

MOBIL CORP   150 E 42nd St, New York, NY 10017, Tel: (212) 883-4242
  (Petroleum explor, prdts)
    Mobil Oil Co. del Ecuador, P.O. Box 169, Quito, Ecuador

MTS SYSTEMS CORP   PO Box 24012, Minneapolis, MN 55424, Tel: (612) 937-4000
  (Electrohydraulic testing & prod equip, mach controls)
    Digitec Cia. Ltda., Av. Shyris 2281 y El Telografo, Box 408A, Suc. 3, Quito, Ecuador

McCANN-ERICKSON WORLDWIDE   750 Third Ave, New York, NY 10017,
  Tel: (212) 697-6000
  (Advertising)
    McCann Erickson Corp., Publicidad S.A., Malecon 1401, P.O. Box 5809, Guayaquil,
      Ecuador
    McCann Erickson Corp., Publicidad S.A., Leonidas Plaza 150, 18 de Septiembre,
      P.O. Box 3491, Quito, Ecuador

McKESSON CORP   One Post St, San Francisco, CA 94104, Tel: (415) 983-8300
  (Drugs, chems, health care prdts, consumer prdts)
    Calox Ecuatoriana, Casilla Postal 955, Guayaquil, Ecuador

NABISCO BRANDS INC   Nabisco Brands Plaza, East Hanover, NJ 07936,
  Tel: (201) 503-2000
  (Mfr food prdts)
    Fleischmann Ecuatoriana S.A., Costanera 504 & Ave. de las Monjas, Urdesa Central,
      Aptdo. 340, Guayaquil, Ecuador
    Fleischmann Ecuatoriana S.A., Plant Ciudadela, El Recreo,
      Eloy Alfaro (Duran) Aptdo. 340,
    Fleischmann Ecuatoriana S.A., Guayaquil, Ecuador
    Fleischmann Ecuatoriana S.A., Km. 11 Via A Bados Totoras, Ambato, Aptdo. 147,
      Guayaquil, Ecuador

NALCO CHEMICAL CO   One Nalco Center, Naperville, IL 60566-1024,
  Tel: (708) 305-1000
  (Chems for water & waste water treatment, oil prod & refining, ind processes;
  water/energy mgmt serv)
    Nalquimica del Ecuador S.A., Casilla 4918 CCI, Quito, Ecuador

NATIONAL CAR RENTAL SYSTEM INC   7700 France Ave S, Minneapolis, MN 55435,
  Tel: (612) 830-2121
  (Car rental)
    Natl. Car Rental, Madrid 1471 y 12 de Octobre, Quito, Ecuador

NUIR INTL INC   1424 LeJeune Rd, Miami, FL 33126, Tel: (305) 871-3563
  (Exporters of constr materials)
    Interbiotic S.A., Aptdo. 4011, Guayaquil, Ecuador
    Nuir Intl. Ecuatoriana Co., Ltda., Edif. Baca, 3er Piso, Avda. 10 de Agosto 1865,
      P.O. Box 3194, Quito, Ecuador

ONAN CORP   1400 73rd Ave NE, Minneapolis, MN 55432, Tel: (612) 574-5000
  (Electric generators, ind engines & controls)
    Redelec Cia. Ltda., Ave. Kennedy 32, Centro. Com. Olimpico, Casilla, Correo 9196,
      Guayaquil, Ecuador

ORYX ENERGY CO   PO Box 2880, Dallas, TX 75221-2880, Tel: (214) 890-6000
(Explor/prod oil & gas)
   Oryx Ecuador Energy Co., AV. NN UU #685 y Shyris, Edificio Cordiez- 60 Piso, Quito,
   Ecuador

OTIS ELEVATOR CO   10 Farm Springs, Farmington, CT 06032, Tel: (203) 674-4047
(Elevators & escalators)
   Otis Elevator Co., General Veintimilla 539 y Seis De Diciembre, Aptdo. 3046, Quito,
   Ecuador

PAN-AMERICAN LIFE INSURANCE CO   Pan American Life Center, New Orleans,
   LA 70130, Tel: (504) 566-1300
(Insurance)
   Pan-American Life Insurance Co., Calle Corea 126 y Av. Amazonas, Edificio Belmonte,
   Ofic. 505, Quito Ecuador

PARKER DRILLING CO   8 E Third St, Tulsa, OK 74103, Tel: (918) 585-8221
(Oil well drilling)
   Parker Drilling Co., Avda. Amazonas 648, P.O. Box 3644, Quito, Ecuador

PETROLEUM HELICOPTERS INC   5728 Jefferson Hwy, Box 23502, Harahan, LA 70183,
   Tel: (504) 733-6790
(Aerial transp, helicopter charter)
   Ecuavia-Oriente S.A., P.O. Box 3418, Quito, Ecuador

PETROLITE CORP   100 N Broadway, St Louis, MO 63102, Tel: (314) 241-8370
(Specialty chem treating programs, performance-enhancing additives & related equip)
   Ecuatoriana de Petroquimicos Petrolite S.A., P.O. Box 11026, Ulloa 1736, Quito,
   Ecuador

PFIZER INC   235 E 42nd St, New York, NY 10017, Tel: (212) 573-2323
(Mfr pharms, hosp prdts, chems, consumer & animal health prdts)
   Pfizer C.A., P.O. Box 8392, Quito, Ecuador

PHELPS DODGE CORP   2600 N Central Ave, Phoenix, AZ 85004-3014,
   Tel: (602) 234-8100
(Minerals, metals & spec engineered prdts for trans & elect mkts)
   Cables Electricos Ecuatorianos C.A. (CABLEC), Casilla Postal 2730, Quito, Ecuador

RORER GROUP INC   500 Virginia Dr, Ft Washington, PA 19034,
   Tel: (215) 628-6000
(Mfr ethical & consumer pharms)
   Rorer de Ecuador S.A., Guayaquil, Ecuador

SYDNEY ROSS CO   90 Park Ave, New York, NY 10016, Tel: (212) 907-2000
(Pharms, toiletries & cosmetics)
   Agencias de Sydney Ross Co., P.O. Box 990, Guayaquil, Ecuador
   Sydney Ross Co., 9 de Octobre 1503, P.O. Box 990, Guayaquil, Ecuador
   Winthrop Products, Inc., 9 de Octobre 1503, P.O. Box 3738, Guayaquil, Ecuador

SQUARE D CO   Executive Plaza, Palatine, IL 60067, Tel: (708) 397-2600
(Power distribution & elec/electr ind control equip)
   Square D Co. Andina S.A., P.O. Box 6466 CCI, Quito, Ecuador

STANDARD FRUIT & STEAMSHIP CO   50 California St, San Francisco, CA 94111,
   Tel: (415) 986-3000
(Shipping, banana & pineapple production & distr)

(cont)

Standard Fruit Co. (Ecuador), Malecon Simon Bolivar 1004, P.O. Box 500, Guayaquil,
Ecuador

STERLING DRUG INC   90 Park Ave, New York, NY 10016, Tel: (212) 907-2000
(Pharms, chems, cosmetics, household cleaners & waxes)
Sterling Products Intl. Inc., 9 de Octobre 1503, P.O. Box 3738, Guayaquil, Ecuador

SYSTEMS ENGINEERING LABS INC   6901 W Sunrise Blvd, Fort Lauderdale,
FL 33313, Tel: (305) 587-2900
(Digital computers)
Interface C.A., Veintimilla 325, Oficina 101, Aptdo. 1355, Quito, Ecuador

TED BATES WORLDWIDE INC   1515 Broadway, New York, NY 10036,
Tel: (212) 869-3131
(Advertising agency)
Zabala/Ted Bates, Winperm 184 y Orellana, Quito, Ecuador

TEXACO INC   2000 Westchester Ave, White Plains, NY 10650, Tel: (914) 253-4000
(Explor/mktg crude oil & its prdts, petro-chems)
Lubricantes y Tambores del Ecuador C.A. (LYTECA), End of Mons. Domingo Comin Ave.,
P.O. Box 6071, Guayaquil, Ecuador
Texaco Petroleum Co., Edif. Perez Guerrero, Calle Jorge Washington 715,
Esq. de Amazona, P.O. Box 1006, Quito, Ecuador

THOMAS BUILT BUSES INC   1408 Courtesy Rd, PO Box 2450, High Point, NC 27261,
Tel: (919) 889-4871
(Mfr buses)
Carrocerias Ecuatorianas Thomas S.A., Casilla 4880, Cotocallao, Quito, Ecuador

TRANS WORLD AIRLINES INC   605 Third Ave, New York, NY 10158,
Tel: (212) 557-6107
(Air transp, hotel, food serv, real estate)
Trans World Airlines, Robles 653 y Ave. Amazonas, Edif. Promco Calisto 7 Piso,
Quito, Ecuador

UNION CARBIDE CORP   Old Ridgebury Rd, Danbury, CT 06817, Tel: (203) 794-2000
(Carbon prdts, chems, plastics, gases & related prdts, etc)
Union Carbide Ecuador C.A., Avda. de las Americas, P.O. Box 5840, Guayaquil, Ecuador

WACKENHUT CORP   1500 San Remo Ave, Coral Gables, FL 33146,
Tel: (305) 666-5656
(Security sys & serv)
Wackenhut del Ecuador S.A., Vallaololid 936 y Cordero, Casilla 4791, Quito, Ecuador

WARNER-LAMBERT CO   201 Tabor Road, Morris Plains, NJ 07950,
Tel: (201) 540-2000
(Mfr ethical & proprietary pharms, confectionary & consumer prdts)
Producto Adams, Casilla 2200, Quito, Ecuador

WESTERN GEOPHYSICAL   PO Box 2469, Houston, TX 77252-2469, Tel: (713) 789-9600
(Geophysical serv)
Western Geophysical, Calle Suecia 227 y Avda. Shyris, Quito, Ecuador

WORLD COURIER INC   46 Trinity Pl, New York, NY 10006, Tel: (718) 978-9400
(Intl courier serv)
World Courier de Ecuador, Robles 653 y Amazonas, Quito, Ecuador
World Courier de Ecuador, Elizalde 1194 Pichincha, Oficina 404, Guayaquil, Ecuador

EGYPT

A-Z INTL TOOL CO   PO Box 7108, Houston, TX 77248-7108, Tel: (713) 880-8888
  (Mfr oil field, milling & casing cutting tools)
    A-Z Intl. Tool Co., c/o Eteco, 6 Dar El Shifa St., Cairo, Egypt

ABBOTT LABORATORIES   Abbott Park, North Chicago, IL 60064,
  Tel: (312) 937-6100
  (Pharm & lab prdts)
    Abbott Laboratories S.A., P.O. Box 678, Morreya, Heliopolis, Cairo, Egypt

ABERCROMBIE & KENT INTL INC   1420 Kensington Rd, Oak Brook, IL 60521-2106,
  Tel: (708) 954-2944
  (Tour wholesaler)
    Abercrombie & Ken (Egypt), 5A Bustan St., Flat 14, Cairo, Egypt

AFIA   110 William St, New York, NY 10038, Tel: (212) 964-4990
  (Insurance)
    Arab Intl. Insurance Co., 28 Talaat Harb St., P.O. Box 2498, Cairo, Egypt

AIR EXPRESS INTL CORP   120 Tokeneke Rd, PO Box 1231, Darien, CT 06820,
  Tel: (203) 655-7900
  (Air frt forwarder)
    Air Express Intl., c/o Misr Condor Impex, 34 El Sayed El Mirghany St., Heliopolis,
      Cairo, Egypt

AIRWAYS ENGINEERING CORP   1700 N Moore St, #810, Arlington, VA 22209,
  Tel: (703) 522-4050
  (Airport planning, design, constr, & supervision)
    Airways Engineering Corp., 52 Nady El Said St., Doky, Giza, Egypt

AMERICAN CYANAMID CO   1 Cyanamid Plaza, Wayne, NJ 07470, Tel: (201) 831-2000
  (Pharms, chems, agric & consumer prdts)
    Cyanamid Intl. Corp., 8 Hoda Shaarawl St., Cairo, Egypt

AMERICAN INTL UNDERWRITERS CORP   70 Pine St, New York, NY 10270,
  Tel: (212) 770-7000
  (General ins)
    Egyptian American Insurance Co., P.O. Box 2012, Talaat Harb St., Cairo, Egypt

ANEMOSTAT PRODUCTS DIV   888 N Keyser Ave, Scranton, PA 18501,
  Tel: (717) 346-6586
  (Mfr air diffusers, grilles & related equip for A/C, heating & ventilation)
    York Mirako, 48 El Batal Ahmed Abdel Aziz St., Madhandessein, Dokki, Guiza, Egypt

ASSOCIATED PRESS   50 Rockefeller Plaza, New York, NY 10020,
  Tel: (212) 621-1500
  (News gathering agency)
    Associated Press, 113 Karr Eo Mil Cairo, Egypt

AT&T INTERNATIONAL   295 N Maple Ave, Basking Ridge, NJ 07920,
  Tel: (908) 221-2000
  (Telecommun)
    AT&T Intl. Inc., El Nasr Bldg., #3, Nite St., Cairo, Egypt

BAKER OIL TOOLS   PO Box 3048, Houston, TX 77253, Tel: (713) 923-9351
  (Oil/gas well completions equip)
    Baker Eastern S.A., 10 Road 262, New Maadi, Cairo, Egypt

BANKAMERICA CORP   PO Box 37000, San Francisco, CA 94137, Tel: (415) 622-3456
  (Financial services)
    Bank of America, 106 Kasr El Ainy St., Cairo, Egypt

BECHTEL GROUP INC   50 Beale St, PO Box 3965, San Francisco, CA 94119,
  Tel: (415) 768-1234
  (Engineering & constr)
    Bechtel Intl. Inc., Cairo Center #5, 2 Abdel Kadar Hamza, Garden City, Cairo Egypt

BELOIT CORP   1st Lawrence Ave, Beloit, WI 53511, Tel: (608) 365-3311
  (Paper making mach & equip)
    Niazi Mostafa, 1282 Immobilia Bldg., Cairo, Egypt

LOUIS BERGER INTL INC   100 Halsted St, East Orange, NJ 07019,
  Tel: (201) 678-1960
  (Consulting engineers, architects, economists & planners)
    Louis Berger Intl. Inc., P.O. Box 2349, Cairo, Egypt

BLACK & VEATCH INTL   PO Box 8405, Kansas City, MO 64114, Tel: (913) 339-8700
  (Engineering/architectural servs)
    AMBRIC, 44 Ramses St 10/F, P.O. Box 2265-11511, Ataba Sq., Cairo, Egypt
    BVI/JMM, 96 Ammar Ibn Yasser St., Nozha, Heliopolis, Cairo, Egypt

BRISTOL LABORATORIES   PO Box 657, Syracuse, NY 13201, Tel: (315) 432-2000
  (Pharm prdts)
    Bristol-Mead Johnson Labs., 16 Sherif St., Cairo, Egypt

BROWN & ROOT INC   4100 Clinton Dr, Houston, TX 77020-6299,
  Tel: (713) 676-4141
  (Engr, constr & maintenance)
    Brown & Root, 10 Kamei Mohamed St., Zamalek, Cairo, Egypt
    Brown & Root (Gulf) E.C., c/o ISS, 16 Mohamed El Mahdy St.,
      Golf Area 92852 RFACO UN, Heliopolis, Cairo, Egypt

LEO BURNETT CO INC   35 West Wacker Dr, Chicago, IL 60601, Tel: (312) 220-5959
  (Advertising agency)
    AMA, Leo Burnett, 21 Ahmed Orabi St., El Nahda Tower, El SahaFeyeen, Cairo, Egypt

CARL BYOIR & ASSOCIATES INC   380 Madison Ave, New York, NY 10017,
  Tel: (212) 986-6100
  (Public relations consultants)
    Radar Public Relations & Research Co, 1 Mestafa El Wakil St., Heliopolis, Cairo,
      Egypt

CALTEX PETROLEUM CORP   PO Box 619500, Dallas, TX 75261, Tel: (214) 830-1000
(Petroleum prdts)
  Caltex (Egypt) S.A.E., 7 Lazoghli St., Garden City, Cairo, Egypt

CAMP DRESSER & MCKEE INTL INC   One Center Plaza, Boston, MA 02108,
  Tel: (617) 742-5151
  (Consulting engineers)
    AMBRIC, P.O. Box 2265, Ataba Sq., Cairo, Egypt
    ARTEC, P.O. Box 413, Dokki, Cairo, Egypt
    Camp Dresser & McKee Inc., 36 Roushdy St., Roushdy Alexandria, Egypt

CANADA DRY INTL CORP   2600 Century Pkwy, Atlanta, GA 30345,
  Tel: (404) 753-2182
  (Carbonated beverages, soft drinks extract)
    Cairo Beverages & Industrial Co., P.O. Box 1556, Cairo, Egypt

CHASE MANHATTAN BANK N A   1 Chase Manhattan Plaza, New York, NY 10081,
  Tel: (212) 552-2222
  (Intl banking)
    Chase Manhattan Overseas Corp., P.O. Box 781, 9 Gamal E.A., Mahassen St.,
      Garden City, Cairo
    Chase National Bank-Egypt, SAE, P.O. Box 2430, 12 El Birgas St., Garden City,
      Cairo, Egypt

CITIBANK NA   399 Park Ave, New York, NY 10043, Tel: (212) 559-1000
  (Intl banking)
    Citibank NA, No. 4 Ahmed Pasha St., Garden CIty, P.O. Box 188, Cairo, Egypt
    Citibank NA, Bourg El-Selsellah 95, July 26 St., P.O. Box 1445, Alexandria, Egypt

COLUMBIA PICTURES INDUSTRIES INC   711 Fifth Ave, New York, NY 10022,
  Tel: (212) 751-4400
  (Producer & distributor of motion pictures)
    Columbia Pictures Inc., 31133 Orabi St., Cairo, Egypt

CONNELL BROTHERS CO LTD   320 California St, San Francisco, CA 94104,
  Tel: (415) 772-4000
  (Exp/imp chems, commodities, minerals, cons materials)
    Connell Brothers Co. Ltd., P.O. Box 133 (Dokki), 12311 Giza, Egypt

CONOCO INC   600 N Dairy Ashford Rd, Houston, TX 77079, Tel: (713) 293-1000
  (Oil, gas, coal, chems, minerals)
    Continental Mid Delta Petroleum Co., P.O. Box 16, 51-A Old Cairo-Helwan Rd., Maadi,
      Cairo, Egypt

CORE LABORATORIES   10205 Westheimer, Houston, TX 77042, Tel: (713) 972-6312
  (Petroleum testing/analysis, analytical chem, environmental servs)
    Core Laboratories, P.O. Box 45, 11431 Maadi, Cairo, Egypt

CPC INTERNATIONAL INC   PO Box 8000, International Plaza, Englewood Cliffs,
  NJ 07632, Tel: (201) 894-4000
  (Mfr consumer food prdts & corn refining prdts)
    National Food Co. S.A.E., P.O. Box 153, Orman Haraneya, Giza, Egypt

EASTMAN KODAK CO   343 State St, Rochester, NY 14650-0518, Tel: (716) 724-4000
  (Devel/mfr photo & chem prdts, info mgmt/video/copier sys, fibers/plastics for
  various ind)
    Kodak S.A., P.O. Box 527, Cairo, Egypt

EG&G INC   45 William St, Wellesley, MA 02181, Tel: (617) 237-5100
(Diversified instru, components, services)
   EG&G Sealol, P.O. Box 151 M. Farid, 139 Mogamah El Masaneh St., Cairo, Egypt

EXXON CORP   225 E John Carpenter Frwy, Irving, TX 75062, Tel: (214) 444-1000
(Petroleum & petroleum prdts)
   Esso Egypt Inc., 10 Tolombat St., P.O. Box 989, Garden City, Cairo, Egypt

FOUR WINDS INTL INC   1 SW Columbia Ave, #1200, Portland, OR 97258,
Tel: (503) 241-2732
(Transp of household goods & general cargo)
   Four Winds Intl., P.O. Box 213, 11A Corniche El Nil, Maadi, Cairo, Egypt

FOXBORO CO   33 Commercial St, Foxboro, MA 02035, Tel: (508) 543-8750
(Mfr prdts/provide servs for ind automation)
   EXE Instrument Scientific Bureau, P.O. Box 1960, Cairo, Egypt
   Lotus Engineering Organization, P.O. Box 1252, Cairo, Egypt

GAMLEN CHEMICAL CO   121 S Maple Ave, S San Francisco, CA 94080,
Tel: (415) 873-1750
(Chems, detergents & tank cleansers)
   National Marine Services Co., 5 El Nasr St., P.O. Box 1362, Alexandria, Egypt
   Sanai Industrial & Marine Supplies, P.O. Box 924, Port Said, Egypt
   Sanai Industrial & Marine Supplies, P.O. Box 5, Suez, Egypt

GENERAL DYNAMICS CORP   Pierre Laclede Center, St Louis, MO 63105,
Tel: (314) 889-8200
(Mfr aircraft, submarines, missiles, space launch vehicles, bldg prdts, info sys)
   General Dynamics Intl., 39 Beirut St., Heliopolis, Cairo, Egypt

GENERAL ELECTRIC CO   3135 Easton Tpk, Fairfield, CT 06431,
Tel: (203) 373-2211
(Diversified mfr, tech & servs)
   GE Technical Services, 1085 Corniche El Nil, Garden City, Cairo, Egypt

GENERAL MOTORS CORP   3044 W Grand Blvd, Detroit, MI 48202,
Tel: (313) 556-5000
(Automotive prdts, electronics)
   General Motors Egypt S.A.E., Cairo, Egypt

GILBERT COMMONWEALTH INTL INC   PO Box 1498, Reading, PA 19603,
Tel: (215) 775-2600
(Studies, engr & design, constr & project mgmt, technologies & training for ind &
govts)
   Gilbert Associates (Middle East) Ltd., 12 Sebaweeh El Masri St., Nasr City, Cairo,
   Egypt

GLOBAL INTERNATIONAL   500 Ygnacio Valley Rd, #175, Walnut Creek, CA 94596,
Tel: (415) 933-2293
(Freight forwarding)
   GVL International BV, 44 Mohamed Mazhar St., Zamalek, Cairo, Egypt

GRAY TOOL CO   PO Box 2291, Houston, TX 77001, Tel: (713) 747-1240
(Oil field equip, pipe connectors, etc)
   Gray Tool Intl. Inc., 48 Kasr El Nil St., P.O. Box 2330, Cairo, Egypt

HOLIDAY INNS INC   3742 Lamar Ave, Memphis, TN 38195, Tel: (901) 362-4001
  (Hotels, restaurants, casinos)
    Holiday Inn, Guiza-Pyramids, P.O. Box 25, Cairo Intl. Airport, Cairo, Egypt

HORWATH & HORWATH INTL   919 Third Ave, New York, NY 10022,
  Tel: (212) 980-3100
  (Public accountants & auditors)
    Youssef Nabih & Co., 22 Kasr El Nil St., Cairo, Egypt

IMCO SERVICES   5950 N Course Dr, Houston, TX 70072, Tel: (713) 561-1300
  (Drilling fluids)
    IMCO Services, P.O. Box 61, Road 108, House #42, Maadi, Cairo, Egypt

INA CORPORATION   1600 Arch St, Philadelphia, PA 19101, Tel: (215) 523-5335
  (Holding co: ins, financial serv)
    P.L. Cappiello, 23 Midan El Tahrir, P.O. Box 55, Alexandria, Egypt

ITT SHERATON CORP   60 State St, Boston, MA 02108, Tel: (617) 367-3600
  (Hotel operations)
    Cairo Sheraton Hotel & Casino, P.O. Box 11, Galae Sq., Giza, Egypt
    Montazah Sheraton Hotel, Corniche Rd., Montazah, Alexandria, Egypt

JEEP CORP   27777 Franklin Rd, Southfield, MI 48034, Tel: (313) 827-1000
  (Automobiles, trucks, utility vehicles)
    American Arab Vehicles, P.O. Box 2419, Horgia, Heliopolis, Cairo, Egypt

JOHNSON & JOHNSON   One Johnson & Johnson Plaza, New Brunswick, NJ 08933,
  Tel: (201) 524-0400
  (Surgical, med & baby prdts)
    Johnson & Johnson (Egypt) S.A.E., Cairo, Egypt

S C JOHNSON & SON INC   1525 Howe St, Racine, WI 53403, Tel: (414) 631-2000
  (Home, auto, commercial & personal care prdts, specialty chems)
    Johnson Wax, 20 Wady el Nil St., Mohandissine, Cairo, Egypt

JOHNSTON PUMP CO   800 Koomey Rd, Brookshire, TX 77423, Tel: (713) 391-6000
  (Mfr vertical turbine pumps)
    J.P.C. Liaison Office, 2 Kamel Mohamed Zamalek, Cairo, Egypt

MANUFACTURERS HANOVER TRUST CO   270 Park Ave, New York, NY 10017,
  Tel: (212) 286-6000
  (Banking)
    Manufacturers Hanover Trust Co., 8 Salah El Din St., Cairo, Egypt

MARATHON OIL CO   539 S Main St, Findlay, OH 45840, Tel: (419) 422-2121
  (Petroleum explor & prod)
    Marathon Petroleum Egypt Ltd., P.O. Box 52, Maadi, Egypt

MASCO CORP   21001 Van Born Rd, Taylor, MI 48180, Tel: (313) 274-7400
  (Mfr building, energy, cold extruded prdts)
    Masco Middle East, 6 Dar El Shifa St., Garden City, Cairo, Egypt

METCALF & EDDY INTL INC   10 Harvard Mill Sq, Wakefield, MA 01888,
  Tel: (617) 246-5200
  (Consulting engineers)
    Canal Cities Consultants, 83 Abdel Hamid Badawi St., Heliopolis, Cairo, Egypt
    WWCG, P.O. Box 2351, Alexandria, Egypt

MILCHEM INC   3900 Essex Lane, PO Box 22111, Houston, TX 77027,
  Tel: (214) 439-8000
  (Gas & oil well drilling fluids & chem additives)
    Milchem Intl. Ltd., 8 Rd. 279, Villa El Baraka, New Maadi, Cairo, Egypt

MOBIL CORP   150 E 42nd St, New York, NY 10017, Tel: (212) 883-4242
  (Petroleum explor, prdts)
    Mobil Exploration Inc., Mobil Oil S.A.A., 1097 Sharia Corniche, El Neil,
    Garden City, Cairo, Egypt

MTS SYSTEMS CORP   PO Box 24012, Minneapolis, MN 55424, Tel: (612) 937-4000
  (Electrohydraulic testing & prod equip, mach controls)
    QUATEC, P.O. Box 2682, Horriya, Heliopolis, Egypt

NATIONAL CAR RENTAL SYSTEM INC   7700 France Ave S, Minneapolis, MN 55435,
  Tel: (612) 830-2121
  (Car rental)
    Natinal Car Rental System Inc., Hotel Indiana, 16 Saraya Str., Dokki, Cairo, Egypt

NCR CORP   1700 S Patterson Blvd, Dayton, OH 45479, Tel: (513) 445-2000
  (Develop/mfr/sell/serv business info processing sys)
    NCR Egypt Ltd., 21, 23 El Giza St, P.O. Bag Cairo, Cairo, Egypt

OTIS ELEVATOR CO   10 Farm Springs, Farmington, CT 06032, Tel: (203) 674-4047
  (Elevators & escalators)
    Otis Elevator Co., S.A.A., 14 Emad el Din St., Cairo, Egypt

PARAMOUNT INTL FILMS INC   1 Gulf & Western Plaza, New York, NY 10023,
  Tel: (212) 333-4600
  (Film prod & distr)
    Paramount Films of Egypt Inc., 35 Talaat Harb St., Cairo, Egypt

PEPSICO INC   700 Anderson Hill Rd, Purchase, NY 10577, Tel: (914) 253-2000
  (Beverages, food prdts & servs, sporting goods)
    Pepsi-Cola Intl. Ltd., 20 St., No. 10, Maadi, P.O. Box 51, Maadi, Cairo, Egypt

PFIZER INC   235 E 42nd St, New York, NY 10017, Tel: (212) 573-2323
  (Mfr pharms, hosp prdts, chems, consumer & animal health prdts)
    Pfizer S.A.E., 47 Ramses St., P.O. Box 2357, Cairo, Egypt

PHILLIPS PETROLEUM CO   Phillips Bldg, Bartlesville, OK 74004,
  Tel: (918) 661-6600
  (Crude oil, natural gas, liquefied petroleum gas, gasoline & petro-chems)
    Phillips Petroleum Co., 32 Lumumba St., P.O. Box 63, Alexandria, Egypt

PIONEER HI-BRED INTL INC   700 Capital Sq, 400 Locust St, Des Moines,
  IA 50309, Tel: (515) 245-3500
  (Seed corn, feed seed, data sys & equip)
    Misr Pioneer Seed Co., Cairo, Egypt

PUROLATOR COURIER CORP   131 Morristown Rd, Basking Ridge, NJ 07980,
  Tel: (201) 953-6400
  (Time-sensitive package delivery)
    Intl. Business Associates, 1079 Corniche el Nil, Garden City, Cairo, Egypt

RCA GLOBAL COMMUNICATIONS INC   60 Broad St, New York, NY 10004,
  Tel: (212) 806-7000
  (Commun serv)
    United Engineering & Marketing Co., 1 El Sad El Ali St., Kobriegalaa Sq., Cairo,
      Egypt

SEA-LAND SERVICE INC   379 Thornall St, Edison, NJ 08837, Tel: (201) 558-6000
  (Container transport)
    Sea-Land Inc., Alexandria, Egypt
    Sea-Land Inc., Port Said, Egypt
    Sea-Land Inc., Suez, Egypt

WILBUR SMITH ASSOCS   NCNB Tower, PO Box 92, Columbia, SC 29202,
  Tel: (803) 738-0580
  (Consulting engineers)
    Wilbur Smith Associates, Mobile Oil Egypt Bldg. 3/F, 1096 Cornish El Nil,
      Garden City (Cairo), Egypt

SONAT OFFSHORE DRILLING INC   PO Box 2765, Houston, TX 77252-2765,
  Tel: (713) 871-7500
  (Offshore oil well drilling)
    Sonat Offshore S.A., P.O. Box 352, Maadi, Cairo, Egypt

SONESTA INTL HOTELS CORP   200 Clarendon St, Boston, MA 02166,
  Tel: (617) 421-5400
  (Hotels)
    Sonesta Hotel Cairo, 4 El Tayaran St., Nasr City, Cairo, Egypt

STANLEY CONSULTANTS INC   225 Iowa Ave, Muscatine, IA 52761,
  Tel: (319) 264-6600
  (Engineering & architectural servs)
    Stanley Consultants, P.O. Box 1457, Nasr City, Cairo 11511, Egypt

TIDEWATER INC   Tidewater Place, 1440 Canal St, New Orleans, LA 70112,
  Tel: (504) 568-1010
  (Marine serv & equip to companies engaged in explor, development & prod of oil, gas &
  minerals)
    Pan Marine Intl., 26 Road 265, New Maadi, Cairo, Egypt

U S WHEAT ASSOCIATES   200 Market Bldg Suite 1020, Portland, OR 97201,
  Tel: (503) 223-8123
  (Market development for wheat prdts)
    U.S. Wheat Associates, Inc., 19 Gamal El Din Abu Al Mahassen St., Garden City,
      No. 21, Cairo, Egypt

UNION CARBIDE CORP   Old Ridgebury Rd, Danbury, CT 06817, Tel: (203) 794-2000
  (Carbon prdts, chems, plastics, gases & related prdts, etc)
    Union Carbide, 6 Ibn el Nabih St., Zamalek, Cairo, Egypt

UNION OIL INTL DIV   Union Oil Center, PO Box 7600, Los Angeles, CA 90017,
  Tel: (213) 977-7600
  (Petroleum prdts, petrochems)
    Unionoil Suez Ltd., 11 Abul Feda St., Zamalek, Cairo, Egypt

WEATHERFORD INTL INC   1360 Post Oak Blvd, PO Box 27608, Houston,
  TX 77227-9917, Tel: (713) 439-9400
  (Tubular & cementation servs, prdts & equip; water jetting servs, mfr marine pedestal

(cont)

cranes)
    Weatherford Oil Tool GmbH, 8 Aswan Sq., P.O. Box 128, Mohandessin, Guiza, Cairo,
    Egypt

WESTERN GEOPHYSICAL   PO Box 2469, Houston, TX 77252-2469, Tel: (713) 789-9600
(Geophysical serv)
    Western Arabian Geophysical Co., Box 443, 12 Tulumbat St., #2/3/4, Garden City,
    Cairo, Egypt

WILLIS DIV   2508 E Palm Dr, Long Beach, CA 90807, Tel: (213) 426-4411
(Oil tools & equip)
    TAM Oilfield Services, 4 Guizira St., Zamalek, Cairo, Egypt

YORK INTERNATIONAL CORP   PO Box 1592, York, PA 17405-1592,
Tel: (715) 771-7890
(Mfr A/C, heating & refrig sys & equip)
    MIRACO, 48 El Batal Ahmed Abdel, Aziz St., Dokki, Giza, Egypt

EL SALVADOR

3M CO   3M Center, St Paul, MN 55144-1000, Tel: (612) 733-1110
(Mfr abrasives, adhesives, chems, ind & consumer tapes/diskettes, health care prdts,
elec connectors)
    3M Interamerica Inc., Km. 5, Carretera Panamerica a Santa Tecla, Aptdo. Postal 681,
    San Salvador, El Salvador

ABBOTT LABORATORIES   Abbott Park, North Chicago, IL 60064,
Tel: (312) 937-6100
(Pharm & lab prdts)
    Abbott Laboratories de El Salvador, S.A., Aptdo. (06) 352, San Salvador, El Salvador

AMERICAN INTL UNDERWRITERS CORP   70 Pine St, New York, NY 10270,
Tel: (212) 770-7000
(General ins)
    La Seguridad Salvadorena, Compania de Seguros, S.A., Edificio The Hanover,
    Insurance Co., P.O. Box 1527, Km. 4B Carretera a Santa Tecla, El Salvador

AMERICAN LIFE INSURANCE CO (ALICO)   PO Box 2226, Wilmington, DE 19899,
Tel: (302) 594-2000
(Life ins, pension & annuity plans, health prdts)
    La Seguridad Salvadorena, Compania de Seguros S.A., P.O. Box (06) 1527, El Salvador

AVON PRODUCTS INC   9 W 57th St, New York, NY 10019, Tel: (212) 546-6015
(Mfr/distr cosmetics, perfumes)
    Productos Avon S.A., San Salvador, El Salvador

AVX CORP   750 Lexington Ave, New York, NY 10022-1208, Tel: (212) 935-6363
  (Mfr multilayer ceramic capacitors)
    AVX Corp., Calle Cojutepeque No. 42, Zona Francesa, San Bartolo, El Salvador

BARDAHL MFG CORP   1400 N W 52nd St, PO Box 70607, Seattle, WA 98107,
  Tel: (206) 783-4851
  (Lubricating oils)
    Ferrometal, S.A., Aptdo. Postal (CC) 772, San Salvador, El Salvador

LOUIS BERGER INTL INC   100 Halsted St, East Orange, NJ 07019,
  Tel: (201) 678-1960
  (Consulting engineers, architects, economists & planners)
    Louis Berger Intl. Inc., 67 Avenida Sur 255, San Salvador, El Salvador

BLACK & DECKER CORP   701 E Joppa Road, Towson, MD 21204, Tel: (301) 583-3900
  (Mfr portable elect & pneumatic power tools, household prdts)
    B&D El Salvador S.A. de C.V., Aptdo. Postal 905, Codigo Postal 01.118,
      San Salvador, El Salvador

CANADA DRY INTL CORP   2600 Century Pkwy, Atlanta, GA 30345,
  Tel: (404) 753-2182
  (Carbonated beverages, soft drinks extract)
    Embotelladora Miguelena, S.A., 3 Avenida Sur y 17 Calle Presidente, San Miguel,
      El Salvador

CITIBANK NA   399 Park Ave, New York, NY 10043, Tel: (212) 559-1000
  (Intl banking)
    First National City Bank, Aptdo. (06) 1324, San Salvador, El Salvador

COLGATE-PALMOLIVE CO   300 Park Ave, New York, NY 10022, Tel: (212) 310-2000
  (Pharms, cosmetics, toiletries, detergents)
    Colgate Palmolive (Central America) Inc., Aptdo. 1178, San Salvador, El Salvador -

COSCO INTERNATIONAL INC   1845 Oak St, #9, Northfield, IL 60093,
  Tel: (708) 446-9390
  (Flavoring extracts, chem spec, franchised soft drinks)
    Sabores Cosco de El Salvador, Aptdo. 647, San Salvador, El Salvador

DOW CHEMICAL CO   2030 Dow Center, Midland, MI 48640, Tel: (517) 636-1000
  (Chems, plastics, fibers, pharms)
    Laboratorios Life de El Salvador, S.A., San Salvador, El Salvador

EXXON CORP   225 E John Carpenter Frwy, Irving, TX 75062, Tel: (214) 444-1000
  (Petroleum & petroleum prdts)
    Esso Chem de Centro America, S.A., Edificio Sisa, Doble Via a Santa
    Esso Standard, S.A., Blvd. del Ejercito Nacional Km. 6.5, San Salvador, El Salvador
    Refineria Petrolera Acajutla, S.A., Edificio Daglio, Avda. Roosevelt,
      & 47a Avda. Sur., Aptdo. 944, San Salvador, El Salvador
    Tecla, San Salvador, El Salvador

FLORIDA INTL FORWARDERS   6905 N W 25th St, PO Box 522085, Miami, FL 33122,
  Tel: (305) 592-6450
  (Air cargo service)
    FIF, Condominio Areadas Arce, 19 Av. Norte & CAlle Arce, Local E-7, San Salvador,
      El Salvador

H B FULLER CO   2400 Energy Park Dr, St Paul, MN 55108, Tel: (612) 645-3401
(Mfr/distr adhesives, sealants, coatings, paints, waxes, sanitation chems)
   H.B. Fuller El Salvador, Apartado 2967, San Salvador, El Salvador

HORWATH & HORWATH INTL   919 Third Ave, New York, NY 10022,
   Tel: (212) 980-3100
   (Public accountants & auditors)
      Horwath & Horwath Intl., Hidalgo, Campos & Asociados, Aptdo. 829, Edificio Cardona,
         Diagonal Centro America 201, San Salvador, El Salvador

INA CORPORATION   1600 Arch St, Philadelphia, PA 19101, Tel: (215) 523-5335
   (Holding co: ins, financial serv)
      La Centro America, S.A., Aptdo 527, San Salvador, El Salvador

KIMBERLY-CLARK CORP   PO Box 619100, Dallas, TX 75261-1200,
   Tel: (214) 830-1200
   (Mfr fiber-based prdts for personal care, pulp & forest prdts; air transport)
      Kimberly-Clark de Centro America, S.A., Sitio del Nino, El Salvador

MONSANTO CO   800 N Lindbergh Blvd, St Louis, MO 63167, Tel: (314) 694-1000
   (Mfr chem & agric prdts, pharms, ind process equip, man-made fibers, plastics)
      Monsanto Centroamerica El Salvador, S.A., Jardines de Cuscatlan, Poliogono B,
         No. 1, Antiguo Cuscatlat, La Liberland, El Salvador

MYERS TIRE SUPPLY INTL   1293 South Main St, Akron, OH 44301,
   Tel: (216) 253-5592
   (Mfr polymer & metal prdts for mat handling, automotive & constr inds)
      Myers De El Salvador, 4A Calle Poniente #2212, Colonia Flor Blanca, San Salvador,
         El Salvador

McCANN-ERICKSON WORLDWIDE   750 Third Ave, New York, NY 10017,
   Tel: (212) 697-6000
   (Advertising)
      McCann-Erickson Centroamericana (EI Salvador), S.A., Metrocentro, Nivel 2,
         P.O. Box 1170, San Salvador, El Salvador

McCORMICK & CO INC   11350 McCormick Rd, Hunt Valley, MD 21031,
   Tel: (301) 771-7301
   (Seasons, flavorings, specialty foods)
      McCormick de Centro America, S.A., 77 Av. Norte & 5a C Pte., 4006 Col. Escalon,
         San Salvador, El Salvador

McKESSON CORP   One Post St, San Francisco, CA 94104, Tel: (415) 983-8300
   (Drugs, chems, health care prdts, consumer prdts)
      Corporation Bonima, Aptdo. Postal (06) 1092, San Salvador, El Salvador

NABISCO BRANDS INC   Nabisco Brands Plaza, East Hanover, NJ 07936,
   Tel: (201) 503-2000
   (Mfr food prdts)
      Pan American Standard Brands Inc., Aptdo. 282, Blvd. Venezuela No. 3067, El Salvador

NATIONAL CAR RENTAL SYSTEM INC   7700 France Ave S, Minneapolis, MN 55435,
   Tel: (612) 830-2121
   (Car rental)
      National Car Rental, Centro Profesional Edificio Mena 1, Centro de, Gobierno,
         San Salvador, El Salvador

ONAN CORP   1400 73rd Ave NE, Minneapolis, MN 55432, Tel: (612) 574-5000
  (Electric generators, ind engines & controls)
    Cia. Importadora de Maquinaria S.A., Alameda Roosevelt & 53 Av. Norte,
      San Salvador, El Salvador

OTIS ELEVATOR CO   10 Farm Springs, Farmington, CT 06032, Tel: (203) 674-4047
  (Elevators & escalators)
    Otis Elevator Co., Aptdo. Postal (06) 1607, San Salvador, El Salvador

PAN-AMERICAN LIFE INSURANCE CO   Pan American Life Center, New Orleans,
  LA 70130, Tel: (504) 566-1300
  (Insurance)
    Pan-American Life Insurance Co., Condominio Torre Roble, Piso 10, Metrocentro,
      Ciudad, San Salvador, El Salvador

PHELPS DODGE CORP   2600 N Central Ave, Phoenix, AZ 85004-3014,
  Tel: (602) 234-8100
  (Minerals, metals & spec engineered prdts for trans & elect mkts)
    Conductores Electricos de Centro America, S.A. (CONELCA), Aptdo. 283, San Salvador,
      El Salvador

RICHARDSON-VICKS INC   Ten Westport Rd, Wilton, CT 06897, Tel: (203) 834-5000
  (Consumer health & personal care prdts)
    Richardson-Vicks Interamericas Inc., Ia. Diagonal No. 431, Urbanizacion,
      La Esperanza, San Salvador, El Salvador

RORER GROUP INC   500 Virginia Dr, Ft Washington, PA 19034,
  Tel: (215) 628-6000
  (Mfr ethical & consumer pharms)
    Rorer de Centro America, S.A. de C.V., San Salvador, El Salvador

SEA-LAND SERVICE INC   379 Thornall St, Edison, NJ 08837, Tel: (201) 558-6000
  (Container transport)
    Transoceanicas Inc., S.A., Condominio los Heroes, Blvd., de los Heroes,
      Aptdo. 2424, San Salvador, El Salvador

TEXACO INC   2000 Westchester Ave, White Plains, NY 10650, Tel: (914) 253-4000
  (Explor/mktg crude oil & its prdts, petro-chems)
    Texaco Inc., Aptdo. (06) 344, San Salvador, El Salvador

ENGLAND

3M CO   3M Center, St Paul, MN 55144-1000, Tel: (612) 733-1110
  (Mfr abrasives, adhesives, chems, ind & consumer tapes/diskettes, health care prdts,
  elec connectors)
    3M (UK) Ltd., 3M House, P.O. Box 1, Bracknell, Berkshire, RG12 1JU, England
    Minnesota 3M Research Ltd., The Pnnacles, Harlow, Essex CH19 5AE, England

AAR CORP   1111 Nicholas Blvd, Elk Grove Village, IL 60007,
  Tel: (708) 439-3939
  (Aircraft prdts & serv, aviation serv)
    AAR Allen Aircraft Intl. Inc., Cardinal Point, Newall Rd., Heathrow Airport,
      Hounslow, Middlesex TW6 2BP, England
    AAR Aviation Services (UK) Ltd., 35 Willow Lane, Mitcham, Surrey CR4 4UQ, England

ABBOTT LABORATORIES   Abbott Park, North Chicago, IL 60064,
  Tel: (312) 937-6100
  (Pharm & lab prdts)
    Abbott Laboratories Ltd., Queenborough, Kent, ME11 5EL, England

ABERCROMBIE & KENT INTL INC   1420 Kensington Rd, Oak Brook, IL 60521-2106,
  Tel: (708) 954-2944
  (Tour wholesaler)
    Aercrombie & Kent Ltd., Sloane Square House, Holbein Pl., London SW1S 8NS, England

ACADEMIC PRESS INC   111 Fifth Ave, New York, NY 10003, Tel: (212) 741-6800
  (Publ scientific books)
    Academic Press Inc. Ltd., 24/28 Oval Rd., London NW1 7OX, England
    Academic Press Inc., Ltd., 24/28 Oval Rd., London, NW1 7OX, England

ACCO INTL INC   770 S Acco Plaza, Wheeling, IL 60090, Tel: (708) 541-9500
  (Paper fasteners & clips, metal fasteners, binders, staplers)
    Intl. Acco Company Ltd., Bretton Way, Bretton Peterborough, PE3 8YE, England

ACCURAY CORP   650 Ackerman Rd, PO Box 02248, Columbus, OH 43202,
  Tel: (614) 261-2000
  (Computer-based process mgmt sys for forest prdts, metals rolling, textiles, tobacco
  ind)
    AccuRay (UK) Ltd., Rickmansworth, England

ACE CONTROLS INC   23435 Industrial Park Dr, Farmington Hills, MI 48024,
  Tel: (313) 476-0213
  (Ind hydraulic shock absorbers, cylinders, valves & automation controls)
    Ace Controls Intl., Belvedere, Newton-le-Willows, Merseyside, WA1 20JJ, England

ACHESON COLLOIDS CO   1600 Washington Ave, PO Box 288, Port Huron, MI 48060,
  Tel: (313) 984-5581
  (Graphite, lubricants & other specialty chems)
    Acheson Colloids Co. (UK), Price Rock, Plymouth, PL4 OSP, England

ACME GENERAL CORP   300 E Arrow Hwy, San Dimas, CA 91773, Tel: (714) 599-6881
  (Proprietary sliding & folding door hdwe sys & access)
    Acmetrack Ltd., Holland Rd., Oxted, Surrey, England

ACME UNITED CORP   425 Post Rd, Fairfield, CT 06430, Tel: (203) 384-1371
  (Shears & scissors, sterile procedure trays)
    Surmanco Ltd., 15/33 Cavendish St., Sheffield, S3 7SA, England

ACOUSTIC RESEARCH   330 Turnpike St, Canton, MA 02021, Tel: (617) 821-2300
  (Mfr high fidelity equip)
    Acoustic Research, High St., Houghton Regis, Dunstable, Bedfordshire LU5 5QJ,
      England

ACTION INSTRUMENTS INC   8601 Aero Dr, San Diego, CA 92123,
Tel: (619) 279-5226
(Mfr electr instru & ind meas computers)
   Action Instruments Ltd., Barbot Hall Industrial State, Mangham Rd.,
   South Yorkshire S61 4RJ, England

ACUFF-ROSE PUBLICATION INC   65 Music Square W, Nashville, TN 37203,
Tel: (615) 321-5000
(Music publisher)
   Acuff-Rose Music Ltd., 129 Park St., London, W1Y 3FA, England

ADC TELECOMMUNICATIONS INC   4900 W 78th St, Minneapolis, MN 55435,
Tel: (612) 835-6800
(Mfr telecom equip)
   ADC Europe, 126/128 Crockhamwell Rd., Woodley, Berkshire RG5 3JY, England

ADDISON-WESLEY PUBLISHING CO   Route 128, Reading, MA 01867,
Tel: (617) 944-3700
(Educational textbook publ)
   Addison-Wesley Publishers Ltd., Finehampstead Rd., Wokingham, Berks., RG11 2NZ,
   England

ADDRESSOGRAPH FARRINGTON INC   300 Pond St, Randolph, MA 02368,
Tel: (617) 963-8500
(Embossing & credit authorization sys)
   Addressograph Farrington, AFI House, Griffin Ind. Estate, Staines Rd., Feltham,
   Middlesex, TW14 0HR, England

ADVANCED MICRO DEVICES INC   PO Box 3453, Sunnyvale, CA 94088-3000,
Tel: (408) 732-2400
(Mfr integrated circuits for commun & computation ind)
   Advanced Micro Devices (UK), Intec Bldg. 4, Wade Rd., Basingstoke, Hants RG2 41,
   England

AEC INC   801 AEC Drive, Wood Dale, IL 60191, Tel: (708) 595-1090
(Mfr/serv aux equip for plastics ind)
   Mannesmann Demag Hamilton Ltd., Sterling House, 20 Station Rd., Gerrads Cross,
   Bucks, SL9 8EW, England

AERO SYSTEMS AVIATION CORP   PO Box 52-2221, Miami, FL 33152,
Tel: (305) 871-1300
(Aviation equip sales & serv sys)
   Aero Systems Aviation Corp, 24 Sussex Rd., Haynards Heath, Sussex RH16 4FA, England

AEROMARITIME INC   11240 Waples Mill Rd, Fairfax, VA 22030,
Tel: (703) 359-6633
(Military electronics)
   Aeromaritime Ltd., Leon House, 11th floor, 233 High St., Croydon, Surrey, CR0 9XT,
   England

AFIA   110 William St, New York, NY 10038, Tel: (212) 964-4990
(Insurance)
   AFIA, Chesterfield House, 26-28 Finchurch St., London, EC3M 3DH, England

AIR EXPRESS INTL CORP   120 Tokeneke Rd, PO Box 1231, Darien, CT 06820,
Tel: (203) 655-7900
(Air frt forwarder)

(cont)

Air Express Intl., Unit 20, Elmdon Trading Estate, Marston Green, Birmingham,
  B37 7HE, England
Air Express Intl., Bristol Airport, Bristol, BS1 93 DS, England
Air Express Intl., Waverley Freight Terminal, Miller Rd., Preston PR1 RQS,
  Lancashire, England
Air Express Intl., Intl. House, Central Trading Estate, Staines, Middlesex,
  TW1 84 DQ, England
Air Express Intl., Intl. House, Roundthorn Industrial Estate, Tilson Rd.,
  Manchester, M23 9PH, England

AIR PRODUCTS & CHEMICALS INC   7201 Hamilton Blvd, Allentown, PA 18195,
  Tel: (215) 481-4911
  (Mfr ind gases & chems)
  Air Product (GB) Ltd., Air Product (UK) Ltd., address as above
  Air Products Ltd., Molesey Rd., Walton-on-Thames, Surrey, KT12 4RZ, England,
  APCEL Ltd., Airproducts Llanwern, Ltd., Ga

AIR-SHIELDS VICKERS   330 Jacksonville Rd, Hatboro, PA 19040,
  Tel: (215) 675-5200
  (Mfr/sales/serv spec med equip, med electr prdts)
  Vickers Plc, Priestley Rd., Basingstoke, Hants RG24 9NP, England

AIRBORNE EXPRESS   3101 Western Ave, PO Box 662, Seattle, WA 98111,
  Tel: (206) 285-4600
  (Air transp serv)
  Airborne Express UK, Heathrow Ind. Trading Estate, Unit 2, Green Lane, Hounslow,
  Middlesex, TW4 6JF, England

AJAX MAGNETHERMIC CORP   1745 Overland Ave NE, PO Box 991, Warren, OH 44482,
  Tel: (216) 372-2529
  (Electric induction heaters)
  Ajax Magnethermic (UK) Ltd., Holland Rd., Oxted, Surrey, RH8 9BA, England

ALARM DEVICE MFG CO   165 Eileen Way, Syosset, NY 11791, Tel: (516) 921-6704
  (Security, fire & burglary sys)
  Ademco-Sontrix (Europe) Ltd., 11 Cradock Rd., Reading, Berkshire, RG2-OJT, England

ALBANY INSURANCE CO   59 John St, New York, NY 10030, Tel: (212) 233-0560
  (Insurance)
  Atlas Assurance Co.Ltd., Royal Exchange, London, England

ALBANY INTL CORP   PO Box 1907, Albany, NY 12201, Tel: (518) 445-2200
  (Paper mach clothing, engineered fabrics, plastic prdts, filtration media)
  Albany Engineered Systems Europe, Ltd., 2 Buckingham Ave., Trading Estate., Slough,
  Berkshire, SL1 4NB, England
  J.K. Industrial Fabrics, Roach Bank Mill, P.O. Box 28, Pimhole Rd. Bury, BL9 7HA,
  Lancashire, England
  James Kenyon & Son (PMC), Pilsworth Mill, P.O. Box 35, Bury BL9 8QE, Lancashire,
  England

ALCO STANDARD CORP   825 Duportail Rd, Wayne, PA 19087, Tel: (215) 296-8000
  (Diversified distr, mfg & resources)
  Alco Standard UK Ltd., 26 Eccleston Sq., London, England
  Big Drum Equipment (England), 5 Kinston Business Center, Fuller's Way,
  S. Chessington, Surrey KT9 1HF, England
  Whitlenge Drink Equipment Ltd., Chancel Way, Halesowen Park, Halesowen,
  W. Midlands, England

ALEXANDER & ALEXANDER INC   1211 Ave of the Americas, New York, NY 10036,
  Tel: (212) 840-8500
  (Ins brokerage, risk & human resource mgmt consult)
    Alexander & Alexander, Aldwych House, Aldwych, London, WC28 4HH, England

ALLEN-BRADLEY CO   PO Box 2086, Milwaukee, WI 53201, Tel: (414) 382-2000
  (Electrical control devices)
    Allen-Bradley Industrial Automation Prdts., Denbigh Rd., Bletchley, Milton Keynes,
      MK1 1EP, England
    Allen-Bradley Intl. Ltd., Chiltern House, 45 Station Rd., Henley-on-Thames,
      Oxon RG9 1AT, England

ALLERGAN PHARMACEUTICALS INTL INC   2525 DuPont Dr, Irvine, CA 92713,
  Tel: (714) 752-4500
  (Pharms, opthalmic & dermatological preparations)
    Allergan Ltd., Fennels Lodge, St. Peters Close, Loudwater - High Wycombe,
      Buckinghamshire, HP 11 1JT, England

ALLIED AFTERMARKET DIV   105 Pawtucket Ave, East Providence, RI 02916,
  Tel: (401) 434-7000
  (Mfr spark plugs, waste treatment sys, filters, brakes)
    Fram Europe Ltd., Llantrisant, Pontyclun, Glamorgan, England

ALLIED GRAPHIC ARTS INC   1515 Broadway, New York, NY 10036,
  Tel: (212) 730-1414
  (Direct sales catalogs, trading stamps, stamp collectors' books)
    Allied Graphic Arts, 72/75 Mary Lebone, High St., London, W1M 3AR, England

ALLIED-SIGNAL INC   Columbia Rd & Park Ave, PO Box 2245R, Morristown,
  NJ 07960, Tel: (201) 455-2000
  (Mfr aerospace & automotive prdts, engineered materials)
    Airsupply Intl., Archway House, 114-116 St. Leonard Rd., Windsor, Berks. SL4 3DG,
      England
    Allied Corp. Intl. NV, S-A7 Intl. House, Bickenhill Lane, Birmingham B37 7HQ,
      England
    Allied-Signal Aerospace Co., 536 Kings Rd., London SW10 0UH, England
    Allied-Signal Aerospace Co., 114-116 St. Leonard Rd., Windsor, Berks. SL4 3DG,
      England
    Bendix Ltd., Douglas Rd., Kingswood, Bristol BS15 2NL, England
    Bendix Safety Restraints Div., Norfolk St., Carlisle, Cumbria CA2 5HX, England
    Garrett Turbo Ltd., Potter Place-West Pimbo, Skelmersdale, Lancs. WN8 9PH, England
    Normalair-Garrett Ltd., Yeovil, Somerset BA20 2YD, England
    Norplex/Oak UK Ltd., Stone Circle Rd., Round Spinney, Northampton NN3 4RX, England

ALLIS-CHALMERS CORP   PO Box 512, Milwaukee, WI 53201, Tel: (414) 475-4011
  (Heavy mach, equip & serv)
    A-C Project Systems Ltd., Southampton, Hampshire, England
    Allis-Chalmers Great Britain Ltd., Allis-Chalmers House, Girling Way,
      Great Southwest Rd., Bedford Feltham, Middlesex, TW1 40PH, Engla

ALPHA WIRE CORP   711 Lidgerwood Ave, Elizabeth, NJ 07207, Tel: (201) 925-8000
  (Mfr wire & cable prdt)
    Alpha Wire Ltd., Alpha House, Central Way, North Feltham Trading Estate, Feltham,
      Middlesex TW14 0XQ, England

AM INTL INC   333 W Wacker Dr, #900, Chicago, IL 60606-1265,
   Tel: (312) 558-1966
   (Mfr/sale/serv commun graphics, info handling equip & sys)
      AM Internationl (Holdings) Ltd., P.O. Box 17, Maylands Ave., Hemel Hempstead,
         Hertfordshire, HP2 7ET, England
      AM Intl. (Holdings), Ltd., other locations in England

AMAX INC   200 Park Ave, New York, NY 10166, Tel: (212) 856-4200
   (Metals & energy)
      Climax Molybdenum UK Ltd., Needham Rd., Stowmarket, Suffolk, IP14 2AE, England,
         Hemerdon Mine, Hemerdon, Plympton, Plymouth PL7

AMDAHL CORP   1250 East Arques Ave, PO Box 3470, Sunnyvale, CA 94088-3470,
   Tel: (408) 746-6000
   (Mfr large scale computers, complementary software storage & commun prdts)
      Amdahl (UK) Ltd., Viking House, 29/31 Lampton Rd., Hounslow, Middlesex, TW3 1JD,
         England
      Amdahl Intl. Mgmt. Services Ltd., Dogmersfield Park, Hartley Eintney, Basingstoke,
         Hamps. RG27 8TE, England

AMERACE CORP   Newburgh Rd, Hackettstown, NJ 07840, Tel: (201) 852-1122
   (Chems, rubber prdts, plastics, electrical components & controls)
      Aerotarget Ltd., 25 Victoria St., London, England

AMERADA HESS CORP   1185 Ave of the Americas, New York, NY 10036,
   Tel: (212) 997-8500
   (Crude oil, natural gas)
      Amerada Petroleum Corp. of U.K., Ltd., 2 Stephen St., Tottenham Court Rd.,
         London W1P 1PL, England

AMERICAN & EFIRD INC   PO Box 507, Mt Holly, NC 28120, Tel: (704) 827-4311
   (Mfr ind thread, yarn & consumer sewing prdts)
      American & Efird (GB) Ltd., Bankside Mills, Chapelfield, Radcliffe, Manchester,
         England

AMERICAN AIR FILTER CO INC   215 Central Ave, PO Box 35690, Louisville,
   KY 40277, Tel: (502) 637-0011
   (Air cleaning equip)
      AAF-Ltd., Bassington Industrial Estate, Cramlington, Northumberland, England

AMERICAN AIRLINES INC   PO Box 619616, Dallas-Ft Worth Arpt, TX 75261-9616,
   Tel: (817) 355-1234
   (Air transp)
      American Airlines, 7 Albemarle St., London, W1X 3AF, England
      American Airlines, Rm. 6, Level 7, Manchester Airport, Cheshire M22 5PA, England

AMERICAN APPRAISAL ASSOCS INC   525 E Michigan St, Milwaukee, WI 53202,
   Tel: (414) 271-7240
   (Valuation consulting serv)
      American Appraisal (UK) Ltd., 49 Whitehall, London SW1A 2BX, England

AMERICAN BANKERS INSURANCE GROUP   11222 Quail Roost Dr, Miami, FL 33157,
   Tel: (305) 253-2244
   (Insurance)
      Bankers Insurance Co. Ltd., 37/39 Lime St., London EC3, England

AMERICAN BRANDS INC   1700 E Putnam Ave, Old Greenwich, CT 06870-0811,
Tel: (203) 698-5000
(Mfr diversified consumer prdts)
  Gallaher Ltd., Members Hill, Brooklands Rd., Weybridge, Surrey KT13 OQU, England

AMERICAN BUREAU OF SHIPPING   45 Eisenhower Dr, Paramus, NJ 07653-0910,
Tel: (201) 368-9100
(Classification/certification of ships & offshore structures, devel & tech assistance)
  American Bureau of Shipping, ABS House, 1 Frying Pan Alley, London E1 7HR, England

AMERICAN COLLOID CO   1500 W Shure Dr, Arlington Hgts, IL 60004,
Tel: (708) 966-5720
(Bentonite mining)
  Volclay Ltd., Birkenhead Rd., Wallasey-Merseyside, L44 7BU, England

AMERICAN CYANAMID CO   1 Cyanamid Plaza, Wayne, NJ 07470, Tel: (201) 831-2000
(Pharms, chems, agric & consumer prdts)
  Cyanamid Intl. Clinical Research, Shearwater House, The Green, Richmond, Surrey,
    England
  Cyanamid of Great Britain Ltd., P.O. Box 7, Gosport, Hants, OAS, England

AMERICAN EXPRESS CO   American Express Tower, New York, NY 10285-4765,
Tel: (212) 640-2000
(Diversified fin & travel-related serv)
  American Express, Trafalgar House, 11 Waterloo Place, London, SW1Y 4AS, England
  American Express, Knightsbridge, 78 Brompton Rd., London, SW3, England

AMERICAN FILTRONA CORP   PO Box 31640, Richmond, VA 23294, Tel: (804) 346-2400
(Diversified manufacturing)
  Dollinger Intl., Bridgegate Gambers, Duke St., Chester CH1 1RP, England

AMERICAN GENERAL CORP   2727 Allen Parkway, Houston, TX 77019,
Tel: (713) 522-1111
(Life & health ins, financial serv)
  Albany Life Assurance Co., Ltd., 31 Old Burlington St., London, England

AMERICAN GREETINGS CORP   10500 American Rd, Cleveland, OH 44144,
Tel: (216) 252-7300
(Mfr/distr greeting cards, gift wrappings, tags, seals, ribbons & party goods)
  Carlton Cards Ltd., Mill St East, Newsbury, W. Yorkshire WF12 9AW, England

AMERICAN HOME PRODUCTS CORP   685 Third Ave, New York, NY 10017,
Tel: (212) 878-5800
(Drugs, food, household prdts)
  American Home Products Ltd., Accrington, England
  American Home Products Ltd., Avonmouth, England
  American Home Products Ltd., London, England
  American Home Products Ltd., Cradley, England
  American Home Products Ltd., Kingswood, England

AMERICAN INTL UNDERWRITERS CORP   70 Pine St, New York, NY 10270,
Tel: (212) 770-7000
(General ins)
  American Intl. Underwriters (London) Ltd., 120 Fenchurch St., London, EC3M 5BP,
    England
  American Intl. Underwriters (London) Ltd., American Intl. Building,
    12/14 Sydenham Rd., Croydon, CR92LG, Surrey, England

AMERICAN LIFE INSURANCE CO (ALICO)   PO Box 2226, Wilmington, DE 19899,
  Tel: (302) 594-2000
  (Life ins, pension & annuity plans, health prdts)
    American Life Insurance Co., American Intl. Building, 2-8 Altyre Rd.,
    Croydon Surrey, England

AMERICAN LOCKER GROUP INC   15 W Second St, Jamestown, NY 14702,
  Tel: (716) 664-9600
  (Mfr coin-oper locks, office furniture)
    Helmsman Coin Controlled Lockers Ltd., Morthern Way, Mildenhall Rd.,
    Bury St. Edmunds, Suffolk, England

AMERICAN MANAGEMENT SYSTEMS INC   1777 North Kent St, Arlington, VA 22209,
  Tel: (703) 841-6000
  (Design/serv computer sys)
    AMS Management Systems UK Ltd., 2 London Wall Bldg., London Wall, London EC2M 5PP,
    England

AMERICAN METER CO   13500 Philmont Ave, Philadelphia, PA 19116,
  Tel: (215) 673-2100
  (Meas & control serv for natural gas inds)
    International Gas Apparatus Ltd., Glebeland Rd., Yorktown Industrial Estate,
    Camberley Surrey, GU 153 EX, England

AMERICAN MUTUAL SERVICES CORP   100 Crossways Park Dr W, PO Box 304, Woodbury,
  NY 11797, Tel: (516) 921-2540
  (Consumer credit)
    American Mutual Services Corp., 222 Grand Bldgs., Trafalgar Sq., London, WC2,
    England

AMERICAN NATL BANK & TRUST CO OF CHICAGO   33 N LaSalle St, Chicago,
  IL 60690, Tel: (312) 661-5000
  (Banking serv)
    American National Bank & Trust Co. of Chicago, 15 St. Swithin's Lane, London,
    EC4N 8AN, England

AMERICAN OPTICAL CORP   14 Mechanic St, Southbridge, MA 01550,
  Tel: (617) 765-9711
  (Ophthalmic lenses, frames & cases, sunglasses)
    British American Optical Co., Radlett Rd., Watford/Herts, WD2 4LJ, England

AMERICAN PRECISION INDUSTRIES INC   2777 Walden Ave, Buffalo, NY 14225,
  Tel: (716) 684-9700
  (Mfr heat transfer equip, coils, capacitors, electro-mech clutches & brakes)
    American Precision Ind., (UK) Ltd., Aldwych House, Aldwych, London, WC2B4 JP,
    England

AMERICAN RE-INSURANCE CO   One Liberty Plaza, 91 Liberty St, New York,
  NY 10006, Tel: (212) 766-6700
  (Reinsurance)
    American Re-Insurance Co. (UK) Ltd., 8 Lime St., London EC3M 7AD, England

AMERICAN STANDARD INC   40 W 40th St, New York, NY 10018, Tel: (212) 840-5100
  (Heating & sanitary equip)
    Ideal Standard Ltd., P.O. Box 60, National Ave., Hull HU5 4JE, England

AMES TEXTILE CORP   720 Suffolk St, Lowell, MA 01854, Tel: (617) 458-3321
(Textile prdts)
  Ames Mills Victoria Mill, Church St., Westhoughton, Bolton, Lancs. BL5 3QP, England

AMETEK INC   Station Sq, Paoli, PA 19301, Tel: (215) 647-2121
(Mfr instru, elect motors, engineered materials)
  Scama Ltd., Eastern Way, Bury St. Edmunds, Suffolk 1P32 7AQ, England

AMICON CORP   182 Conant St, Danvers, MA 01923, Tel: (617) 777-3622
(Research apparatus)
  Amicon Ltd., Amicon House, 2 Kingsway, Woking Surrey, GU21 1UR, England

AMOCO OIL CO   200 E Randolph Dr, Chicago, IL 60601, Tel: (312) 856-5111
(Petroleum mfg & refining)
  Amoco (UK) Ltd., 1 Olympic Way, Wembley, Middlesex HA9 OND, England

AMP INC   470 Friendship Rd, Harrisburg, PA 17111, Tel: (717) 564-0100
(Mfr electrical wiring devices)
  AMP Services Ltd., 20 Queensmere, Slough, Berkshire, SL1 1YZ, England
  AMP of Great Britain Ltd., Terminal House, Stanmore, Middlesex HA7 4RS, England

AMPCO METAL INC   1745 S 38th St, PO Box 2004, Milwaukee, WI 53201,
Tel: (414) 645-3750
(Cast & wrought copper-based alloys)
  Ampco Metal Ltd., 17 Binns Close off Torington Ave., Coventry CV4 9TB, England

AMPEX CORP   401 Broadway, Redwood City, CA 94063-3199, Tel: (415) 367-2011
(Mfr professional audio/visual sys, magnetic recording media, data-memory prdts)
  Ampex Europe, Africa, Middle East, same address, England
  Ampex Great Britain Ltd., same address, England
  Ampex Systems Group, Acre Rd., Reading, Berks. RG2 OQR, England

AMPHENOL PRODUCTS   4300 Commerct Ct, Lisle, IL 60532, Tel: (708) 983-3500
(Elect interconnect/penetrate sys & assemblies)
  Amphenol Ltd., Romsey Ind. Estate, Greatbridge Rd., Romsey, Hamps. SO5 OHR, England
  Amphenol Ltd., Thanet Way, Whitstable, Kent CT5 3JF, England

AMSTED INDUSTRIES INC   205 N Michigan, Chicago, IL 60601, Tel: (312) 645-1700
(Steel castings for railroad & ind use)
  Hydromation Co., 450 Blandford Rd., Poole, Dorset, BN16 5BN, England

AMWAY CORP   7575 E Fulton Rd, Ada, MI 49355, Tel: (616) 676-6000
(Distr household cleaning, nutrition & diet prdts)
  Amway (UK) Ltd., Snowdon Dr., Winterhill, Milton Keynes MK6 1AR, England

ANACON INC   117 South St, Hopkinton, MA 01748, Tel: (508) 435-6973
(Mfr process control instru)
  Anacon Corp. Ltd., St.Peters Rd., Maidenhead Berks, SL6 7QA, England

ANACONDA CO   555 17th St, Denver, CO 80202, Tel: (303) 575-4000
(Copper mining)
  Anaconda, Collier House 3rd Floor, 163/69 Brompton Rd., London, SW3 1PZ, England

ANALOG DEVICES INC   1 Technology Way, Box 9106, Norwood, MA 02062,
Tel: (617) 329-4700
(Analog digital converters)
  Analog Devices Ltd., Central Ave., East Molesey, Surrey, England

ANALYTICAL MEASUREMENTS INC   31 Willow St, Chatham, NJ 07928,
  Tel: (201) 273-7500
  (PH meters & electrometers)
    Analytical Measurements Ltd., Spring Corner, Felham, Middlesex, London, TW13 4PE,
    England

ANAREN MICROWAVE INC   6635 Kirkville Rd, E Syracuse, NY 13057,
  Tel: (315) 432-8909
  (Mfr/serv microwave components)
    Anaren Microwave Ltd., Frimley Business Park, Frimley Camberley, Surrey GU16 5SG,
    England

ANCHOR HOCKING CORP   109 N Broad St, PO Box 600, Lancaster, OH 43132,
  Tel: (614) 687-2111
  (Mfr glassware & dinnerware, plastic prdts)
    Anchor Hocking Corp. UK, 271 High St., Berkhamsted, Herts., HP4 1AA, England

ANDREW CORP   10500 W 153rd St, Orlando Park, IL 60462, Tel: (708) 349-3300
  (Antenna sys)
    Andrew Antenna, Lochgelly, Fife, KY5 9HG, England

ANHEUSER-BUSCH INTL INC   One Busch Place, St Louis, MO 63118-1852,
  Tel: (314) 577-2591
  (Beer)
    Anheuser-Busch Europe Inc., Radgemore House, Henley-on-Thames, Oxon,RG9 4NP, England

ANIXTER BROS INC   4711 Golf Rd, Skokie, IL 60076, Tel: (708) 677-2600
  (Dist wiring sys/prdts for voice, video, data & power applications)
    Anixter United Kingdom Headquarters, Anixter House, Prescott Rd., Colnbrook,
    Slough SL3 0AE, England

ANTHONY INDUSTRIES INC   4900 S Eastern Ave, Los Angeles, CA 90040,
  Tel: (213) 724-2800
  (Pool constr & equip, fishing tackle, athletic apparel)
    Shakespeare Co., U.K. Branch, Worcestershire, England

APPLE COMPUTER INC   20525 Mariani Ave, Cupertino, CA 95014,
  Tel: (408) 996-1010
  (Personal computers, peripherals & software)
    Apple Computer (UK) Ltd., Eastman Way, Helem, Hempstead, Herts. HP2 7HQ, England

ARCHER-DANIELS-MIDLAND CO   4666 Faries Pkwy, Decatur, IL 62525,
  Tel: (217) 424-5200
  (Flours, grains, oils, flax fibre)
    British Arkady Co., Ltd., Old Trafford, Manchester, M16 0NJ, England

ARKWRIGHT   PO Box 9198, Waltham, MA 02254-9198, Tel: (617) 890-9300
  (Property ins, risk mgmt serv)
    FM Insurance Co. Ltd., 105 Victoria St., London SW1E 6QT, England

ARMCO INTL INC   703 Curtis St, PO Box 700, Middletown, OH 45042,
  Tel: (513) 425-6541
  (Sheet steel & steel prdts, constr, oil field equip, ins, finance leasing)
    Armco Ltd., Jubilee Rd., P.O. Box 11, Letchworth, Herts, SG6 1NQ, England

ARMSTRONG WORLD INDUSTRIES INC   PO Box 3001, Lancaster, PA 17604,
    Tel: (717) 397-0611
    (Mfr/mkt interior furnishings & spec prdts for bldg, auto & textile inds)
        Armstrong World Industries Ltd., Armstrong House, 3 Chequers Sq., Uxbridge,
            Middlesex UB8 1NG, England

ARO INTL CORP   One Aro Center, Bryan, OH 43506, Tel: (419) 636-4242
    (Mfr portable air tools, drills, motors, fluid handling pumps)
        Aro Corp. (UK) Ltd., Walkers Rd., N. Moons Moat, Industrial Park, Redditch, Worcs.,
            B98 9HE, England

ARROW ELECTRONICS INC   25 Hub Dr, Melville, NY 11747, Tel: (516) 391-1300
    (Distr electron parts & components)
        Arrow Electronics (UK) Ltd., St. Martins Way, Cambridge Rd., Bedford MK4 20LF,
            England

ARVIN INDUSTRIES INC   One Noblitt Plaza, Columbus, IN 47201,
    Tel: (812) 379-3000
    (Mfr auto OEM & replacement parts & fabricated metal parts, R&D & testing)
        Bainbridge Silencers Ltd., Ribchester House, Lancaster Rd., Preston,
            Lancs. PR1 2QL, England

ASHLAND CHEMICAL CO   5200 Paul G Blazer Memorial Pkwy, Columbus, OH 43216,
    Tel: (614) 889-3333
    (Chemicals)
        Ashland Chemical Ltd., 58 James St., London, SW1 A1PR, England

ASK MR FOSTER TRAVEL CORP   7833 Haskell Ave, Van Nuys, CA 91406,
    Tel: (818) 988-0181
    (Travel service)
        Ask Mr. Foster/Fits Travel Ltd., 12-14 Argyll St., London W1, England

ASSOCIATED MERCHANDISING CORP   1440 Broadway, New York, NY 10018,
    Tel: (212) 536-4000
    (Retail service organization)
        Associated Merchandising Corp., 32 Wigmore St., London W1H 0DB, England

ASSOCIATED PRESS   50 Rockefeller Plaza, New York, NY 10020,
    Tel: (212) 621-1500
    (News gathering agency)
        The Associated Press Ltd., 83 Farringdon St., London, EC4A 4BR, England

AST RESEARCH INC   16215 Alton Parkway, PO Box 19658, Irvine, CA 92713-9658,
    Tel: (714) 727-4141
    (Mfr personal computers enhancement & data commun prdt)
        AST Europe Ltd., AST House Goat Wharf, Brentford, Middlesex TW8 0BA, England

AT&T INTERNATIONAL   295 N Maple Ave, Basking Ridge, NJ 07920,
    Tel: (908) 221-2000
    (Telecommun)
        AT&T Intl. (UK) Ltd., Norfolk House, 31 St. James Sq., London, SW1Y 4JR, England

AT&T PARADYNE   8550 Ulmerton Rd, PO Box 2826, Largo, FL 34294-2826,
    Tel: (813) 530-2000
    (Mfr data commun prdts & serv)
        AT&T Paradyne (UK), Paradyne House, 14 Upton Rd., Watford, Herts., WD1 7EP, England

(cont)

AT&T Paradyne Ltd., 14 Upton Rd., Paradyne House, Watford, Hartfordshire WD1 7EP, England

AUGAT INC   89 Forbes Blvd, Mansfield, MA 02048, Tel: (508) 543-4300
(Interconnection prdts)
   Augat Ltd., Sunrise Pkwy., Linford Wood East, Milton Keynes, Bucks., England

THE AUSTIN CO   3650 Mayfield Rd, Cleveland, OH 44121, Tel: (216) 382-6600
(Conslt, design, engr & constr serv)
   The Austin Co. of UK Ltd., 35 Ballards Lane, London, N3 1XW, England

AUTOMATIC SWITCH CO   Hanover Rd, Florham Park, NJ 07932, Tel: (201) 966-2000
(Valves & switches)
   Asco (UK) Ltd., 2 Pit Hey Pl., West Pimbo, Skelmersdale, Lancs., WN8 9PG, England

AVCO FINANCIAL SERVICES INC   3349 Michelson Dr, Irvine, CA 92715,
Tel: (714) 553-1200
(Fin serv, loans)
   Avco Trust Ltd., Avco House, Castle St., Reading, Berks., RG1 7DW, England

AVERY INTL CORP   150 N Orange Grove Blvd, Pasadena, CA 91103,
Tel: (213) 304-2000
(Mfr self-adhesive labels & marking equip)
   Avery Label Europe, 48 West St., Marlow, Buckinghamshire, SL7 2NB, England

AVMARK INC   1911 North Ft Myer Dr, #1000, Arlington, VA 22209,
Tel: (703) 528-5610
(Aviation consult, aircraft appraisal, aviation related pub)
   Avmark International Ltd., 26 Eccleston Square, London SW1V 1NS, England

AVON PRODUCTS INC   9 W 57th St, New York, NY 10019, Tel: (212) 546-6015
(Mfr/distr cosmetics, perfumes)
   Avon Overseas Ltd., Imperial House, Imperial Dr., Payners Lane, Harrow, Middlesex, England

AVX CORP   750 Lexington Ave, New York, NY 10022-1208, Tel: (212) 935-6363
(Mfr multilayer ceramic capacitors)
   AVX Ltd., AVX House, Manor Park, Aldershot, GU12 4RG, England

AYERST LABORATORIES   145 King of Prussia Rd, Radnor, PA 19087,
Tel: (215) 688-4400
(Biologicals & pharms)
   Ayerst Laboratories Ltd., Farnborough, England

THE BADGER CO INC   One Broadway, Cambridge, MA 02142, Tel: (617) 494-7312
(Engr & const serv to process ind)
   Badger Catalytic Ltd., C.I. Tower, High St., New Malden, Surrey KT3 4HH, England

BAILEY CONTROLS CO   29801 Euclid Ave, Wickliffe, OH 44092,
Tel: (216) 943-5500
(Mfr analog & digital instru, controls & control sys)
   ICS Bailey Controls Ltd., Hortonwood 37, Telford, Shropshire TF1 4EX, England

BAIRD CORP   125 Middlesex Turnpike, Bedford, MA 01730, Tel: (617) 276-6000
(Scientific instru)
   Baird-Atomic Ltd., Warner Dr., Braintree, Essex, CM7 7YL, England

BAKER & McKENZIE   2800 Prudential Plaza, Chicago, IL 60601,
   Tel: (312) 861-8000
   (Intl attorneys)
      Baker & McKenzie, Aldwych House, Aldwych, London, WC2 B4JP, England

J T BAKER INC   222 Red School Lane, Phillipsburg, NJ 08865,
   Tel: (201) 859-2151
   (Mfr/sale/serv lab & process chems)
      J.T. Baker U.K., P.O. Box 9, Hayes Gate House, Hayes, Middlesex Ub4 OJD, England

BAKER OIL TOOLS   PO Box 3048, Houston, TX 77253, Tel: (713) 923-9351
   (Oil/gas well completions equip)
      Baker Oil Tools (UK) Ltd., Admiralty Rd., Great Yarmouth, Norfold NR30 3NR, England

BAKER PERKINS INC   100 Hess Ave, Saginaw, MI 48601, Tel: (517) 752-4121
   (Food, chem processing)
      Baker Perkins Holding Ltd., Peterborough, England

BAKER PRODUCTION TECHNOLOGY   PO Box 40129, Houston, TX 77240-0129,
   Tel: (713) 943-0170
   (Inflatable packers, instru well testing)
      Baker Production Services (UK) Ltd., Berkshire House, Queen St., Maidenhead,
      Berks., SL6 1NF, England
      Baker Production Services (UK) Ltd., Hudson House, Hudson Eurocentre, North,
      River Rd., Great Yarmouth, Norfolk, NR30 1TA, England
      Lynes Inc., Unit 5, Bessemer Way, Harfreys Ind. Estate, Great Yarmouth, Norfolkd,
      England

BALFOUR MACLAINE CORP   Wall Street Plaza, New York, NY 10005,
   Tel: (212) 269-0800
   (Commodity brokers)
      Balfour Maclaine Intl. (UK) Ltd., Europe House, World Trade Centre, London E1 9AA,
      England

BALTIMORE AIRCOIL CO INC   PO Box 7322, Baltimore, MD 21227,
   Tel: (301) 799-6200
   (Evaporative condensers, cooling, towers, ind fluids)
      Baltimore Aircoil Ltd., Princewood Rd., Earlstress Ind. Est., Corby, Northants.,
      NN17 2AP, England

BAND-IT IDEX CORP   4799 Dahlia St, Denver, CO 80216, Tel: (303) 320-4555
   (Mfr pressure clamps)
      Band-It Co., Ltd., Speedwell Industrial Estate, Staveley near Chesterfield S43 3PF,
      England

THE BANK OF CALIFORNIA NA   400 California St, San Francisco, CA 94104,
   Tel: (415) 765-0400
   (Banking)
      Bank of California, P.O. Box 72, 13 Moorgate, London, EC2P 2NX, England

BANK OF NEW ENGLAND NA   28 State St, Boston, MA 02106, Tel: (617) 742-4000
   (Full service bank)
      Bank of New England NA, Veritas House, 119 Finsbury Pavement, Longon EC2A 1NQ,
      England

THE BANK OF NEW YORK   48 Wall St, New York, NY 10286, Tel: (212) 530-1784
  (Banking)
    The Bank of New York, 46 Berkeley St., London W1X 6AA, England

BANKAMERICA CORP   PO Box 37000, San Francisco, CA 94137, Tel: (415) 622-3456
  (Financial services)
    Bank of America Intl. Ltd., 1 Alie St., London E1 8DE, England

BANKERS TRUST CO   280 Park Ave, New York, NY 10017, Tel: (212) 775-2500
  (Banking)
    Bankers Trust Co., 9 Queen Victoria St., London, EC4P 4DB, England
    Bankers Trust Co., 34-40 Temple St., Birmingham, B2 5DP, England
    Bankers Trust Co., Suite 3B Brook House, 77-79 Fountain St., Manchester, M2 2EE,
      England
    Bankers Trust Co., Dashwood House, 69 Old Broad St., London, EC2P ZEE, England

BANTAM BOOKS INC   666 Fifth Ave, New York, NY 10103, Tel: (212) 765-6500
  (Publ)
    Transworld Publishers, Ltd., 61/63 Uxbridge Rd., Ealing, London, W5 5SA, England

BARBER STEAMSHIP LINES INC   17 Battery Place, New York, NY 10004,
  Tel: (212) 908-1234
  (Steamship line)
    Barber Wilhelmsen Agencies Ltd., 12 Cambridge House, Cambridge Rd., Barking Essex,
      1G11 8EE, England

BARBER-COLMAN CO   555 Colman Center Dr, Rockford, IL 61125,
  Tel: (815) 397-7400
  (Mfr controls, motors)
    Barber & Colman Ltd., Marsland Rd., Brooklands, Sale Cheshire, M33 1UL, England

BARBER-GREENE CO   3000 Baraber-Greene Rd, DeKalb, IL 60115,
  Tel: (815) 756-5600
  (Mfr heavy road constr equip)
    Barber-Green England Ltd., Saxham, Bury St. Edmunds, Suffolk IP33 3TA, England
    Barber-Greene England Ltd., Risby, Bury St. Edmunds, Suffolk, IP28 6RX, England

C R BARD INC   731 Central Ave, Murray Hill, NJ 07974, Tel: (201) 277-8000
  (Health care prdts)
    C.R. Bard Intl. Ltd., Pennywell Industrial Estate, Sunderland, SR4 9EW, England

BARDAHL MFG CORP   1400 N W 52nd St, PO Box 70607, Seattle, WA 98107,
  Tel: (206) 783-4851
  (Lubricating oils)
    Southern Lubricants Ltd., 32 Newton Rd., Kingskerwell, S. Devon, TQ12 5AG, England

THE BARDEN CORP   200 Park Ave, PO Box 2449, Danbury, CT 06813-2449,
  Tel: (203) 744-2211
  (Precision ball bearings)
    Barden Corp. (UK) Ltd., Western Rd., Brackwell, Berkshire, RG12 IQU, England

BARNES-HIND INC   895 Kifer Rd, Sunnyvale, CA 94086, Tel: (408) 736-5462
  (Contact lenses & accessories, opthalmic & dermatology prdts)
    Barnes-Hind Ltd., St. Leonard's House, St. Leonard's Rd., Eastbourne,
      E. Sussex BN21 3YG, England

BARRY CONTROLS INC   700 Pleasant St, Watertown, MA 02172, Tel: (617) 923-1150
  (Mfr/sale vibration isolation mounting devices)
     Barry Controls Ltd., Molesey Rd. Hersham, Walton-on-Thames, Surrey KT12 3PQ, England

BARRY WRIGHT CORP   1 Newton Executive Park, Newton, MA 02162,
  Tel: (617) 965-5800
  (Shock & vibration equip)
     Muffelite Ltd., Walton-on-Thames, Surrey KT12 3PQ, England

BARRY-WEHMILLER CO   4660 W Florissant Ave, St Louis, MO 63115,
  Tel: (314) 381-1504
  (Bottling mach, bottle inspection & washing)
     Barry-Wehmiller Ltd., Atlantic St., Broadheath Altrincheam, Cheshire, WA14 5EW,
        England

BARTON BRANDS LTD   55 E Monroe St, Chicago, IL 60603, Tel: (312) 346-9200
  (Bourbon & blended whiskey)
     Barton Intl. Ltd., 5th Floor, Sackville House, 40 Piccadilly, London, W1V 9PA,
        England

BASE TEN   1 Electronic Dr, PO Box 3151, Trenton, NJ 08619,
  Tel: (609) 586-7010
  (Mfr electronics devices & sys, custom computers)
     Base Ten Systems Ltd., 12 Eelmoor Rd, Farmborough, Hampshire, GU14 7QN, England

BATTELLE MEMORIAL INSTITUTE   505 King Ave, Columbus, OH 43201,
  Tel: (614) 424-6424
  (Tech devel, commercialization & mgmt)
     Battelle Institute Ltd., 15 Hanover Sq., London, W1R 9AJ, England

BAUSCH & LOMB INC   1 Lincoln First Sq, Rochester, NY 14601-0054,
  Tel: (716) 338-6000
  (Mfr healthcare & optics prdts)
     Bausch & Lomb Ltd., Hampton, Middlesex, England
     Bausch & Lomb UK Ltd., London, England

BAXTER TRAVENOL LABORATORIES INC   1 Baxter Pky, Deerfield, IL 60015,
  Tel: (708) 948-2000
  (Pharm & disposable med prdts)
     Travenol Laboratories, Ltd., Hayes Gate House, 27 Uxbridge Rd., Hayes, Middlesex,
        UB4 OJN, England
     Travenol Laboratories, Ltd., Edward St., Nelson, Lancashire, England
     Travenol Laboratories, Ltd., Claxton Way, Thetford, Norwalk, England

BEAR STEARNS & CO INC   245 Park Ave, New York, NY 10167, Tel: (212) 272-2000
  (Invest banking & trading)
     Bear Stearns Home Loans Ltd., South Quay Plaza, 183 Marsh Wall, London E14 9FX,
        England
     Bear, Stearns Intl., Ltd.,, 9 Devonshire Sq., London EC2M 4YL, England

BEATRICE MEATS INC INTL   1919 Swift Dr, Oak Brook, IL 60522-9010,
  Tel: (708) 850-5801
  (Meats, poultry, cheese)
     Beatrice Swift Ltd., 10 Charterhouse Sq., London, England

BECHTEL GROUP INC   50 Beale St, PO Box 3965, San Francisco, CA 94119,
Tel: (415) 768-1234
(Engineering & constr)
  Bechtel Great Britain, Bechtel House, P.O. Box 739, 245 Hammersmith Rd., London,
  W6 8DP, England

BECKMAN INSTRUMENTS INC   2500 Harbor Blvd, Box 3100, Fullerton, CA 92634,
Tel: (714) 871-4848
(Mfr/distr/serv research & clinical lab instru, sys, software & reagents)
  Beckman Instruments (UK) Ltd., Industrial Estate, High Wycombe, Buckinghamshire,
  HP12 4JL, England

BEE CHEMICAL CO   2700 E 170th St, Lansing, IL 60438, Tel: (708) 758-0500
(Coatings & finishes for plastics & metals)
  Bee Chemical UK, Kangley Bridge Rd., Lower Sydenham, London SE26, England

BELL & HOWELL CO   5215 Old Orchard Rd., Skokie, IL 60077, Tel: (708) 470-7684
(Diversified info prdts & servs)
  Bell & Howell Ltd., 33-35 Woodthorpe Rd., Ashford, Middlesex TW15 2RZ, England
  Micromeida Ltd., Telford Rd., Bicester, Oxon, OX6 0UP, England

BELLSOUTH INTERNATIONAL   1155 Peachtree St NE, #400, Atlanta, GA 30367,
Tel: (404) 249-4800
(Mobile commun, telecom network sys)
  Air Call Communications Ltd., Unit 6, Air Call Business Center, Colindeep Lane,
  Colindale, London, England
  BellSouth Intl., London, England

BELOIT CORP   1st Lawrence Ave, Beloit, WI 53511, Tel: (608) 365-3311
(Paper making mach & equip)
  Beloit Walmsley Ltd., Wood St., Bury, Lancashire, BL8 2QT, England
  Lenox Machine Co., Ltd., Mistral House, Parsons Lane, Hinckley, LE10 1XT, England

BENTLEY LABORATORIES INC   17502 Armstrong Ave, Irvine, CA 92714,
Tel: (714) 546-8020
(Mfr para-med devices)
  Bentley Labs., Ltd., 267 Cranbrook Rd., Ilford, Essex, England

BENTLY NEVADA CORP   PO Box 157, Minden, NV 89423, Tel: (702) 782-3611
(Electronic monitoring system)
  Bently Nevada (UK) Ltd, 2 Kelvin Close, Science Park N., Birchwood, Warrington,
  Cheshire, WA3 7PB, England

LOUIS BERGER INTL INC   100 Halsted St, East Orange, NJ 07019,
Tel: (201) 678-1960
(Consulting engineers, architects, economists & planners)
  Louis Berger Intl. Inc., The Studio, Crown Reach, 149A Grosvenor, London SW1V 3JY,
  England

BERKEY-COLORTRAN INC   1015 Chestnut St, Burbank, CA 91502,
Tel: (213) 843-1200
(Lighting equip)
  Berkey-Colortran Intl., P.O. Box 5, Burrell Way, Thetford, Norfolk
  IP24 3RB, England

BEROL USA   Eagle Rd, Danbury, CT 06810, Tel: (203) 744-0000
(Writing instru, sharpeners, drafting prdts, templates)
    Berol Ltd., Oldmeadow Rd., King's Lynn, Norfolk PE30 4JR, England

SAMUEL BINGHAM CO   479 Business Center Dr, Mt Prospect, IL 60056,
Tel: (708) 298-6777
(Print & ins rollers, inks)
    Usher-Walker-Bingham Ltd., Chancery House, Chancery Lane, London, WC2A 1SA, England

BINGHAM DANA & GOULD   150 Federal St, Boston, MA 02110, Tel: (617) 951-8000
(Law firm)
    Bingham, Dana & Gould, 39 Victoria St., London SW1H OEE, England

BINKS MFG CO   9201 W Belmont Ave, Franklin Park, IL 60131,
Tel: (708) 671-3000
(Mfr of spray painting & finishing equip)
    Binks-Bullows Ltd., Pelsall Rd., Brownhills, Walsall, Staffs, WS8 7HW, England

BINNEY & SMITH INC   1100 Church Lane, PO Box 431, Easton, PA 18042,
Tel: (215) 253-6271
(Mfr art supplies, craft kits)
    Binney & Smith (Europe) Ltd., Ampthill Rd., Bedford, MK42 9RS, England

BIO-RAD LABORATORIES   2200 Wright Ave, Richmond, CA 94804,
Tel: (415) 234-4130
(Spec chems, clinical diagnostic prdts, test kits)
    Bio-Rad Lab., Ltd., Caxton Way, Holywell Ind. Estate, Watford, Herts., WD1 8RP, England
    Polaron Equip. Ltd., 21 Greenhill Cres., Holywell Ind. Estate, Watford, Herts., WD1 8XG England

BISON INSTRUMENTS INC   5708 W 36th St, Minneapolis, MN 55416,
Tel: (612) 926-1846
(Geophysical instru)
    Oceanics PLC., Oceanic House, 89 High St., Alton, Hampshire, GU34 1LG, England

BISSELL INC   2345 Walker Road, NW, Grand Rapids, MI 49504,
Tel: (616) 453-4451
(Mfr home cleaning prdts)
    Bissell Appliances Ltd., Highams Park, London, E4 9HN, England

BIW CABLE SYSTEMS INC   22 Joseph E Warner Blvd, N Dighton, MA 02764,
Tel: (508) 822-6600
(Mfr elect wire & cable, cable assemblies & connectors)
    Boston Insulated Wire (UK) Ltd., Lower Mills, Mill Rd., Esher, Surrey, England

BLACK & DECKER CORP   701 E Joppa Road, Towson, MD 21204, Tel: (301) 583-3900
(Mfr portable elect & pneumatic power tools, household prdts)
    Black & Decker Ltd., Westpoint, The Grove, Slough, Berks. SL1 1QQ, England
    Black & Decker Ltd., Meadowfield Ind. Estate, Durham, DH7 8RL, England
    Black & Decker Ltd., Harmondsworth, Hatch Lane, Middlesex, UB7 OBX, England
    Black & Decker Ltd., Green Lane, Spennymore, Durham, England

BLACK & VEATCH INTL   PO Box 8405, Kansas City, MO 64114, Tel: (913) 339-8700
(Engineering/architectural servs)
    Black & Veatch (UK) Ltd., P.O. Box 486, Threehouseholds, Chalfont St., Giles, Bucks. HP8 4NA, England

BLACK CLAWSON CO   666 Third Ave, New York, NY 10017, Tel: (212) 972-4440
(Paper & pulp mill mach)
   Black-Clawson Intl. Ltd., 20/26 Wellesley Rd., Croydon, Surrey, CR9 2BT, England

BLACK SIVALLS & BRYSON INC   PO Box 27125, Houston, TX 77227,
Tel: (713) 981-8303
(Oil & gas prod equip, engineering serv, constr mgt)
   Black, Sivalls & Bryson (GB) Ltd., 36 Paradise Rd., Richmond, Surrey TW9 1SA,
   England

BLOUNT INC   4520 Executive Park Drive, Montgomery, AL 36116-1602,
Tel: (205) 244-4370
(Mfr cutting chain & equip, timber harvest/materials handling equip, sporting ammo,
gen contracting)
   Omark UK Ltd., 6 Station Dr., Bredon, Tewkesbury, Gloucestershire GL20 7HQ, England

BOOZ ALLEN & HAMILTON INC   101 Park Ave, New York, NY 10178,
Tel: (212) 697-1900
(Mgmt consultants)
   Booz, Allen & Hamilton Inc. Intl. (UK) Ltd., 100 Piccadilly, Mayfair,
   London W1V 9HA, England

BORDEN CHEMICAL DIV   180 East Broad St, Columbus, OH 43215,
Tel: (614) 225-4000
(Chems, tapes, resins)
   Borden UK Ltd., P.O. Box 10, Romsey, Hants, SO5 9XW, England

BORDEN INC   420 Lexington Ave, New York, NY 10170, Tel: (212) 573-4000
(Milk processing, dairy foods, specialty foods, chems, plastics)
   Borden (UK) Ltd., N. Baddesley, Southampton, SO5 9ZB, England

BORG-WARNER CORP   200 S Michigan Ave, Chicago, IL 60604, Tel: (312) 322-8500
(Mfr A/C equip, chem & plastics, ind prdts, trans equip)
   Borg-Warner Ltd., 715 North Circular Rd., London, NW2 7AU, England
   Borg-Warner Ltd., Gardiners Lane South, Basildon, Essex, SS14 3HE, England
   Borg-Warner Ltd., Leamington Spa, Warwickshire, CV32 7JW, England
   Borg-Warner Ltd., Jubilee Rd., Letchworth, Herts, SG6 1NH, England
   Borg-Warner Ltd., Eldon Way, Langford Rd., Biggleswade, Beds, SG18 8NG, England
   Borg-Warner Ltd., P.O. Box 18, Works Rd., Letchworth, Herts, SG6 1NH, England

BORN INC   408 N Boston Ave, PO Box 102, Tulsa, OK 74103-1404,
Tel: (918) 582-2186
(Design/mfr direct fired heaters)
   Born Heaters, Ltd., P.O. Box 171, Europa House, Southwick Sq., Sussex BN4 4UA,
   England

BOSE CORP   100 The Mountain Rd, Framingham, MA 01701, Tel: (617) 879-7330
(Electronic equip)
   Bose UK Ltd., Trinity Trading Estate, Sittingbourne, Kent, ME10 2PD, England

BOSTITCH DIV   815 Briggs St, East Greenwich, RI 02818, Tel: (401) 884-2500
(Stapling machs & supplies, wire)
   Bostitch UK, Station Rd., Edenbridge, Kent, England

BOURNS INC   1200 Columbia Ave, Riverside, CA 92507, Tel: (714) 781-5960
(Mfr resistive com & networks, precision potentiometers, panel controls)
   Bourns Electronics Ltd., 90 park St., Chamberley, Surrey GU15 3NY, England

R R BOWKER CO   245 W 17th St, New York, NY 10011, Tel: (212) 337-6903
  (Publishers)
    Butterworths, Borough Green, Sevenoaks, Kent TN15 8PH, England

BOWMAR INSTRUMENT CORP   531 Main St, Acton, MA 01720, Tel: (617) 263-8365
  (Electronic displays, precision mech components)
    Bowmar Instrument Ltd., 43/45 High St., Weybridge, Surrey, KT1 38BB, England

BOYDEN ASSOCIATES INC   260 Madison Ave, New York, NY 10016,
  Tel: (212) 685-3400
  (Mgt consultants, exec search)
    Boyden Intl. Ltd., 148 Buckingham Palace Rd., London SW1W 9TR, England

BOZELL JACOBS KENYON & ECKHARDT INC   40 West 23rd St, New York, NY 10010,
  Tel: (212) 206-5400
  (Advertising agency)
    Bozell Jacobs & Partners Ltd., St. Ann's House, 3-4 Diadem Court Dean St., London,
    W1V 3AP, England

W H BRADY CO   727 W Glendale Ave, PO Box 571, Milwaukee, WI 53201,
  Tel: (414) 332-8100
  (Wire markers, name plates)
    W.H. Brady Co., Ltd., Daventry Rd. Industrial Estate, Banbury, Oxfordshire,
    OX16 7JU, England

BRANSON ULTRASONICS CORP   Eagle Rd, Danbury, CT 06810, Tel: (203) 796-0400
  (Ultrasonic & vibratory plastics assembly mach)
    Lucas Dawe Ultrasonics Ltd., Concord Rd., Western Ave., London W3 0SD, England

C F BRAUN & CO   1000 S Fremont Ave, Alhambra, CA 91802, Tel: (213) 570-1000
  (Engineering/constr/mgmt for energy & power ind)
    Taywood-Santa Fe Ltd., 309 Ruislip Rd. East, Greenford, Middlesex, UB6 9BQ, England

BRIDGE INFORMATION SYSTEMS INC   717 Office Parkway, St Louis, MO 63141,
  Tel: (314) 567-8300
  (Invest info & serv)
    Bridge Information Systems (UK) Ltd., 2 Lanark Square, Limeharbour, London E14 9RE,
    England

BRIGGS & STRATTON CORP   PO Box 702, Milwaukee, WI 53201, Tel: (414) 259-5333
  (Mfr engines, auto locking devices)
    Briggs & Stratton U.K. Ltd., all mail to: U.S. address

BRINK'S INC   Thorndal Circle, Darien, CT 06820, Tel: (203) 655-8781
  (Security transportation)
    Brink's-Mat Ltd., London, England

BRISTOL BABCOCK INC   1100 Buckingham St, Watertown, CT 06795,
  Tel: (203) 575-3000
  (Mfr process control instru & intelligent digital prdts)
    Babcock-Bristol Ltd., 218 Purley Way, Croydon, Surrey, CR9 4HE, England
    Babcock-Bristol Ltd., Process Ind. Div., Oldington Vale Trading Estate,
      Stourport Rd., Kidderminster, Worcs., DY11 7QP England
    Bristol Babcock Ltd., Parsonage House, Parsonage Sq., Dorking, Surrey RH4 1UP,
      England

BRK ELECTRONICS   780 McClure Rd, Aurora, IL 60504-2495, Tel: (708) 851-7330
(Mfr smoke detectors, fire extinguishers, lights, timers & sensor sys)
   BRK Electronics (UK) Ltd., 4 The Paddock, Hambridge Rd., Newbury, Berks.,
   RG14 5TQ England

BROWN & ROOT INC   4100 Clinton Dr, Houston, TX 77020-6299,
   Tel: (713) 676-4141
   (Engr, constr & maintenance)
      Brown & Root (UK) Ltd., 150 The Broadway, Wimbledon, London SW19 1RX, England
      Brown & Root (UK) Ltd., 17 Hanover Sq., London W1R 0EL, England
      Brown & Root Vickers Ltd., Wessex House, Market St., Eastleigh, Hants SO5 4FD,
      England
      Devonport Management Ltd., Devonport Royal Dockyard, Devonport, Plymouth,
      Devon PL1 4SG, England
      European Marine Contractors Ltd., Millers Mead, 200 High St., Colliers Wood,
      London SW19 2JR, England
      Howard Humphreys Group Ltd., Thorncroft Manor, Thorncroft Dr., Dorking Rd.,
      Leatherhead, Surrey KT22 8JB, England
      Integrated Documatics Ltd., Olympic House, 196-200 The Broadway, Wimbledon,
      London SW19 1SN, England

BROWN & SHARPE MFG CO   Precision Park, North Kingston, RI 02852,
   Tel: (401) 886-2000
   (Mfr machine tools & metrology equip)
      Brown & Sharp Ltd., Derby Rd., Melbourne, Derby DE7 1FF, England
      Tesa Metrology Ltd., P.O. Box 418, Halesfield 8, Telfond, Shropshire TF7 4QN,
      England

BROWN BROTHERS HARRIMAN & CO   59 Wall St, New York, NY 10005,
   Tel: (212) 483-1818
   (Financial serv)
      Brown Brothers Harriman Ltd., Garden House, 18 Finsbury Circus, London EC2M 7BP,
      England

BRUSH WELLMAN INC   17876 St Clair Ave, Celeveland, OH 44110,
   Tel: (216) 486-4200
   (Beryllium metal, alloys & compounds; friction prdts, cutting edges)
      Brush Wellman Ltd., 2405 Ely Rd., Theale Com'l. Est., Theale, Reading,
      RG7 4BQ England

BUCK CONSULTANTS INC   Two Pennsylvania Plaza, New York, NY 10121,
   Tel: (212) 330-1000
   (Employee benefit, actuarial & compensation conslt serv)
      Buck Paterson Consultants Ltd., 10 Buckingham Place, London SW1E 6HT, England

BUCKHORN INC   55 W TechneCenter Dr, Milford, OH 45150, Tel: (513) 831-4402
   (Mfr/serv plastic containers & pallets)
      Buckhorn Ltd., Witney Trading Estate, Station Lane- Unit 4, Witney, Oxon OX8 6YT,
      England

BUCYRUS-ERIE CO   PO Box 56, Milwaukee, WI 53172, Tel: (414) 768-4000
   (Shovels, cranes)
      Ruston-Bucyrus Ltd., Lincoln, England

BUDGET RENT-A-CAR CORP OF AMERICA   200 N Michigan Dr, Chicago, IL 60601,
   Tel: (312) 580-5000
   (Self-drive car hire)

Budget Rent-A-Car Intl. Inc., 85 Great N. Rd., Intl. House, Hatsfield, Herts, AL9 5EF, England

BULAB HOLDINGS INC   1256 N McLean Blvd, Memphis, TN 38108,
Tel: (901) 278-0330
(Mfr microbicides, biocides, additives, corrosion inhibitors, chems)
   Buckman Laboratories Ltd., Enterprise House, Manchester Science Park, Lloyd St. N., Manchester M15 4EN, England

BURLINGTON AIR EXPRESS   18200 Van Karman Ave, Irvine, CA 92715,
Tel: (714) 752-1212
(Air freight)
   Burlington Air Express, Unitair Centre, Great South West Rd., Feltham, Middlesex TW14 8NT, England

BURNS INTL SECURITY SERVICES   2 Campus Dr, Parsippany, NJ 07054,
Tel: (201) 397-2000
(Provider of security officers)
   Burn Intl. Security Services UK Ltd., 100 Warwick Rd., Ealing, London, W5 5PT, England

BURR-BROWN RESEARCH CORP   PO Box 11400, Tucson, AZ 85734, Tel: (602) 746-1111
(Electronic components & sys modules)
   Burr-Brown Intl. Ltd., 1 Millfield House, Woodshots Meadow, Watford Herts WD1 8YX, England

BURSON-MARSTELLER   230 Park Ave, New York, NY 10003-1566, Tel: (212) 614-4000
(Public relations/public affairs consultants)
   Burson-Marsteller Ltd., 24-28 Bloomsbury Way, London WC1A 2PX, England

BUSINESSLAND INC   1001 Ridder Park Dr, San Jose, CA 95131,
Tel: (408) 437-0400
(Distr, integration & support microcomputer sys)
   Businessland (UK) Ltd., Network House, Langley Business Centre, Station Rd., Langley, Berkshire SL3 8YS, England
   Businessland (UK) Ltd., other locations in England

BUSSMANN   PO Box 14460, St Louis, MO 63178-4460, Tel: (314) 394-2877
(Mfr electr fuses & acces, terminal strips, interconnect devices & circuit breakers)
   Bussmann, Frome, Somerset, England

BUTTERICK FASHION MARKETING CO   161 Ave of the Americas, New York, NY 10013,
Tel: (212) 620-2500
(Sewing patterns)
   Butterick Fashion Marketing Ltd., New Lane, Havant, Hants, PO9 2ND, England

CARL BYOIR & ASSOCIATES INC   380 Madison Ave, New York, NY 10017,
Tel: (212) 986-6100
(Public relations consultants)
   CBA-Welbeck Intl. Communications, 11A W. Halkin St., London SW1X 8JL, England
   Carl Byoir & Associates Ltd., 11A W. Halkin St., London SW1X 8JL, England
   Welbeck Public Relations Ltd., 2 Endell St., London WC2H 9EW, England

CABLE DATA INTL   11020 Sun Center Dr, Ranch Cordova, CA 95670,
Tel: (916) 636-5830
(Mgt/serv software & hardware for cable TV, satellite & telecom ind)
   British Satellite Systems Ltd., Arlington Business Centre, Millshaw Park,

(cont)

Leeds LS11 OL1, England
Cable Date Europe Ltd. (UK), Arlington Business Centre, Millshaw Park,
  Leeds LS11 OLT, England

CABOT CORP   950 Winter St, PO Box 9073, Waltham, MA 02254,
  Tel: (617) 890-0200
  (Mfr carbon blacks, plastics; oil & gas, info sys)
    BOCMIN Metals Ltd. (Cabot Mineral Resources), Broadway Chambers,
      Hammersmith Broadway, London, W67 AF England
    Cabot Alloys Europe (Engineered Products), Cabot House, William St., Windsor,
      Berkshire, SL4 1BA, England
    Cabot Alloys UK Ltd. (HiTec Div.), Earlstrees Rd., Corby, Northants, NN17 2AZ,
      England
    Cabot Europe Ltd., Cabot Plastics Europe (Energy), Silk House, 6 Park Green,
      Macclesfield, Cheshire, SK11 7NA, England
    Cabot Plastics Division (Energy), Gate St., Dukinfield, Cheshire, SK14 4RZ, England
    Cabot Safety Ltd. (E-A-R), First Ave., Poynton, Stockport, Cheshire, SK12 1YJ,
      England
    Deloro Stellite (WearTec Div.), Stratton St. Margaret, Swindon, Wiltshire, SN3 4QA,
      England

CADILLAC PLASTIC & CHEMICAL CO   143 Indusco Ct, Troy, MI 48083,
  Tel: (313) 583-1200
  (Dist plastic basic shapes)
    Cadillac Plastic Ltd., Rivermead Dr., Westlea, Swindon, Wittshire SN5 7YT, England

CALCOMP   2411 W La Palma Ave, PO Box 3250, Anaheim, CA 92801,
  Tel: (714) 821-2142
  (Mfr computer graphics)
    Calcomp Europe Ltd, 75/77 High St., Tunbridge Wells, Kent TN1 1X2, England
    Calcomp Ltd., Cory House, The Ring, Bracknell, Berks. RG12 1ER, England,
      Calcomp Europe, 4 The Courtyard, Denmark

CALGON CORP   PO Box 1346, Pittsburgh, PA 15230, Tel: (412) 777-8000
  (Mfr. cosmetic, personal care & water treatment prdts)
    Chemviron Specialty Chemicals Ltd., 1-3 Upperhead Row, Huddersfield HD1 2JL,
      W. Yorkshire, England

CALIFORNIA CEDAR PRODUCTS CO   PO Box 528, Stockton, CA 95201,
  Tel: (209) 464-9881
  (Incense cedar & pencil slats)
    California Cedar Products Co., 12 Goodwin's Court St. Martin's Lane, London,
      WC2N 4LL, England

CALIFORNIA PELLET MILL CO   221 Main St, #420, San Francisco, CA 94105,
  Tel: (415) 431-3800
  (Mfr mach for pelleting)
    CPM/Europe Ltd., West March, Daventry, Northants, NN11 4SA, England

CALTEX PETROLEUM CORP   PO Box 619500, Dallas, TX 75261, Tel: (214) 830-1000
  (Petroleum prdts)
    Caltex Trading *UK) Ltd., Griffin House, 161 Hammersmith Rd., Hammersmith,
      London W6 8B6, England

CAMCO INC   7010 Ardmore St, Houston, TX 77021, Tel: (713) 747-4000
 (Oil field equip)
    Camco Ltd., Unit 9c, Harfrey's Rd., Harfrey Industrial Estate, Great Yarmouth,
      Norfolk, NR31 OLS, England

CAMP INTL INC   PO Box 89, Jackson, MI 49204, Tel: (517) 787-1600
 (Mfr orthotics & prosthetics)
    Camp Ltd., Northgate House, Staple Gardens, Winchester, Hamshire, SO23 8ST,England

CAMPBELL SOUP CO   Campbell Place, Camden, NJ 08101, Tel: (609) 342-4800
 (Food prdts)
    Campbell's Soups Ltd., Hardwick Rd., King's Lynn, Norfolk, PE30 4HS, England
    Campbell's UK Ltd., Kennet House, 80 King's Rd., Reading, Berks. RG1 3BS, England
    Unger Meats Ltd., Unger House, Derby St., Manchester M8 8HE, England

CANADA DRY INTL CORP   2600 Century Pkwy, Atlanta, GA 30345,
 Tel: (404) 753-2182
 (Carbonated beverages, soft drinks extract)
    Canada DT Intl. Inc., 1-11 Hayhill, London, WIX 7LF, England
    Canada Dry (UK) Ltd., 8-12 Station Rd., Kettering, Norchants, NN15 7HH, England

CANBERRA INDUSTRIES INC   One State St, Meriden, CT 06450, Tel: (203) 238-2351
 (Mfr instru for nuclear research)
    Canberra-Packard Ltd.Ltd., Book House, 14 Station Rd., Pangbourne, Berks. RG8 7DT,
      England

CANNY BOWEN INC   425 Park Ave, New York, NY 10022, Tel: (212) 758-3400
 (Mgmt consultants)
    Canny, Bowen & Associates Ltd., 83 Pall Mall, London, SW1Y 5ES, England

CAPITAL CONTROLS CO INC   3000 Advance Lane, PO Box 211, Colmar,
 PA 18915-0211, Tel: (215) 822-2901
 (Mfr/serv water disinfection prdts & sys)
    Capital Controls Co. Ltd., Crown Quay Lane, Sittingbourne, Kent ME10 3JG, England

CAPITAL GROUP INC   333 S Hope, Los Angeles, CA 90071, Tel: (213) 486-9401
 (Investment mgmt)
    Capital Intl. Ltd., One St. Paul's Churchyard, London EC4 8AN, England

CAPITOL-EMI MUSIC INC   1750 N Vine St, Hollywood, CA 90028,
 Tel: (213) 462-6252
 (Production/dist recorded music)
    EMI Records (UK), 20 Manchester Sq., London, W1A 1ES, England

CARAVAN TOURS INC   401 N Michigan Ave, Chicago, IL 60611, Tel: (312) 321-9800
 (Tour operator)
    Caravan Ltd., 41/47 Strand, London WC2 5LB, England

CARGILL   PO Box 9300, Minneapolis, MN 55440, Tel: (612) 475-7575
 (Food prdts, feeds, animal prdts)
    Cargill UK Ltd., 3 Chortlands, Hammersmith, London W6 8RT, England

CARPCO INC   4120 Haines St, Jacksonville, FL 32206, Tel: (904) 353-3681
 (Design/mfr separation equip & sys; lab & pilot plant testing, flowsheet design for
 mineral recovery)
    Boxmag-Rapid Ltd., Chester St., Aston, Birmingham B6 4AJ, England
    Richard Mozley Ltd., Woodlane, Falmouth, Cornwall TR15 4SS, England

CARPENTER TECHNOLOGY CORP   101 W Bern St, PO Box 14662, Reading, PA 19612,
   Tel: (215) 371-2000
   (Mfr specialty steel & alloy prdts)
      Carpenter Technology (UK) Ltd., 6 Royal House, 11 Market Pl., Redditch,
      Worcs. B98 8AA, England

CARRIER INTERNATIONAL CORP   PO Box 4806, Syracuse, NY 13221,
   Tel: (315) 432-6000
   (A/C, heating, refrig & power equip)
      Carrier Intl. Ltd., London, England

CARTER CONTROLS INC   3000-170th Street, Lansing, IL 60438,
   Tel: (708) 474-3305
   (Pneumatic hydraulic controls)
      Carter Controls UK Ltd., 2 Charles St., Sheffield, S1 2HS, England

CARTER-WALLACE INC   2 Research Way, Princeton, NJ 08450-6628,
   Tel: (609) 520-3100
   (Mfr pharms, diagnostics, toiletries)
      Carter-Wallace Ltd., Wear Bay Rd., Folkestone, Kent CT19 6PG, England

CASCADE CORP   2020 SW 4th Ave, Portland, OR 97201, Tel: (503) 227-0024
   (Lift truck attachments)
      Cascade (UK) Ltd., Bassington Industrial Estate, Cramlington, New Town,
      Northumberland, NE23 8AE, England

J I CASE CO   700 State St, Racine, WI 53404, Tel: (414) 636-6011
   (Mfr/sale agric & constr equip)
      J I Case Europe, Wheatley Hall Dr., Doncaster, S. Yorkshire DN2 4PG, England
      J.I. Case Co., Meltham, Huddersfield, HD7 3AR, England

CAT PUMPS CORP   1681 94th Lane NE, Minneapolis, MN 55434, Tel: (612) 780-5440
   (Mfr/distr pumps)
      Cat Pumps U.S. Ltd., 27 Station Industrial Estate, Fleet Hampshire GU1 38QY, England

CATERPILLAR INC   100 N E Adams St, Peoria, IL 61629, Tel: (309) 675-1000
   (Mfr earth/material-handling & constr mach & equip, engines, generators)
      Caterpillar Tractor Co. Ltd., Desford, Leicester LE9 9JT, England

CBI INDUSTRIES INC   800 Jorie-Blvd, Oak Brook, IL 60521, Tel: (708) 654-7000
   (Holding co: metal plate fabricating, constr, oil & gas drilling)
      CBI Constructors Ltd., 48 Leicester Sq., London, WC2H 7LF, England

CCS COMMUNICATIONS CONTROL INC   633 Third Ave, New York, NY 10017,
   Tel: (212) 682-4637
   (Mfr electronic security prdts)
      CCS Counterspy Shop, 62 S. Audley St., London W1, England

CDI CORP   10 Penn Center Plaza, Philadelphia, PA 19103, Tel: (215) 569-2200
   (Engr, design, drafting & tech serv)
      CDI Techniscope Ltd., Hanover House 73/74, High Holborn, London WC1V 6LS, England

CEILCOTE CO   140 Sheldon Rd, Berea, OH 44017, Tel: (216) 243-0700
   (Mfr corrosion-resistant material, air pollution control equip, cons serv)
      Ceilcote UK Ltd., London Rd. So., Poynton, Stockport, Cheshire, SK12 1LH, England

CELOTEX CORP   1500 N Dale Mabry Hwy, Tampa, FL 33607, Tel: (813) 871-4414
  (Building materials)
     Celotex Ltd., Warwick House, 27/31 St. Mary's Rd., London, W5, England
     Celotex Ltd., Warwick House, 27/31 St.Mary's Rd., London W5, England

CENTRAL NATIONAL-GOTTESMAN INC   100 Park Ave, New York, NY 10017,
  Tel: (212) 532-7300
  (Pulp & paper prdts)
     Central National (UK) Ltd., Rythe House, Littleworth Rd., Esher, Surrey KT10 9PN,
     England

CENTURY 21 REAL ESTATE CORP   2601 SE Main, PO Box 19564, Irvine,
  CA 92713-9564, Tel: (714) 553-2100
  (Real estate)
     Century 21 Real Estate Agency Ltd., Roberts House, Station Close, Potters Bar,
     Herts. EN6 3JW, England

CETEC CORP   9900 Baldwin Place, El Monte, CA 91731, Tel: (213) 442-8840
  (Misc plastic prdts, elect components, radio & TV commun equip)
     Cetec Intl. Ltd., Unit 2F, 15 North Field Industrial Estate, Beresford Ave.,
     Wembley, Middlesex, HAO 1YB, England

CHAMPION SPARK PLUG CO   PO Box 910, Toledo, OH 43661, Tel: (419) 535-2567
  (Mfr spark plugs, wiper blades & related prdts)
     Champion Spark Plug Co., Ltd., Arrowebrook Rd., Upton, Wirral, Merseyside L49 OUQ,
     England

CHARLES OF THE RITZ GROUP LTD   625 Madison Ave, New York, NY 10022,
  Tel: (212) 527-4000
  (Fine fragrances & cosmetics)
     Charles of the Ritz Ltd., 51 Charles St., London, W1X 7PA, England
     Charles of the Ritz Ltd., Victoria Rd., Burgess Hill, Sussex, England

CHARTER MEDICAL CORP   577 Mulberry St, PO Box 209, Macon, GA 31298,
  Tel: (912) 742-1161
  (Intl hospital mgmt)
     Charter Medical Corp. of the UK Ltd., 1-5 Radnor Walk, Box 323, London, SW3 4PB,
     England

CHASE MANHATTAN BANK N A   1 Chase Manhattan Plaza, New York, NY 10081,
  Tel: (212) 552-2222
  (Intl banking)
     Interactive Data Corp., 80 Coleman St., London, EC2R 5BJL:, England
     Intl. Investment Corp., S.A., 14/16 Cockspur St., London, SW1Y SBL, England
     The Chase Manhattan Bank, N.A., Woolgate House, Coleman St., London, EC2P 2HD,
     England
     The Chase Manhattan Bank, N.A., P & O Bldg., Leaden Hall St., London, EC3P 3JL,
     England

CHECK TECHNOLOGY CORP   1284 Corporate Center Dr, St Paul, MN 55121,
  Tel: (612) 454-9300
  (Mfr computer controlled check/coupon print sys)
     Check Technology Ltd., 3/4 Satellite Bus. Village, Fleming Way, Crawley,
     W. Sussex RH10 2NE, England

CHEMICAL BANK   277 Park Ave, New York, NY 10172, Tel: (212) 310-6161
(Banking & financial serv)
   Chemical Bank, Chemical Bank House, 180 Strand, London WC2R 1ET, England
   Chemical Bank Trustee Co. Ltd., Union Court, 53 Old Broad St., London EC2N 1EA,
   England

CHEMINEER INC   PO Box 1123, Dayton, OH 45401-1123, Tel: (513) 454-3200
(Mfr fluid agitators & stataic mixers for chem processing)
   Chemineer Ltd., 7 Cranmer Rd., West Meadows, Derby DE2 6XT, England

CHEMTEX INTL   560 Lexington Ave, New York, NY 10022, Tel: (212) 752-5220
(Mfr fibers & films)
   Chemtex Overseas Inc., Freeland House, Freeland, Oxford, England

THE CHERRY CORP   3600 Sunset Ave, PO Box 718, Waukegan, IL 60087,
Tel: (708) 662-9200
(Mfr switches, keyboards, etc)
   Cherry Electrical Products Ltd., Coldharbour Lane, Harpenden,
   Hertfordshire AL5 4UN, England

CHESEBROUGH-POND'S INC   33 Benedict Place, Greenwich, CT 06830,
Tel: (203) 661-2000
(Cosmetics, consumer prdts)
   Chesebrough-Pond's Ltd., 63 Windsor Rd., Slough, Berkshire,England

CHEVRON CHEMICAL CO   PO Box 5047, San Ramon, CA 94583-0947,
Tel: (415) 842-5500
(Chemicals)
   Octel Associates, 20 Berkeley Sq., London W1X 6DT, England
   The Associated Octel Co., 20 Berkeley Sq., London W1X 6DT, England

CHICAGO PNEUMATIC TOOL CO   2200 Bleeker St, Utica, NY 13501,
Tel: (315) 792-2600
(Mfr air tools & equip)
   Consolidated Pneumatic Tool Co., Ltd., P.O. Box 241, CP House, Mark Court,
   37 Mark Rd., Hemel Hempstead, Herts HP2 7RN, England

CHIEF INDUSTRIES INC   3942 W Old Highway 30, PO Box 2078, Grand Island,
NE 68802-2078, Tel: (308) 382-8820
(Mfr grain bins, steel bldg, mobile/modular homes, rec vehicles, wastewater & electr
display sys)
   Chief Industries UK Ltd., Bentall Industrial Estate, Maldon, Essex CM9 7NW, England

CHRISTENSEN INTL   PO Box 26135, Salt Lake City, UT 84126, Tel: (801) 487-5371
(Diamond drills)
   Christensen Diamond Products (UK) Ltd., Govett Ave., Shepperton, Middlesex,
   TW17 8AH, England
   Christensen Diamond Products (UK) Ltd., Greener House, 66-68 Haymarket, London,
   SWI, England

CHRISTIAN SCIENCE PUBLISHING SOCIETY   1 Norway St, Boston, MA 02115,
Tel: (617) 262-2300
(Publishing)
   Christian Science Publishing Society, 108 Palace Gardens, Terrace, London, W8 4RT,
   England

THE CHUBB CORP   15 Mountain View Rd, Warren, NJ 07060, Tel: (201) 580-2000
(Holding co: property/casualty ins)
   Chubb Insurance Co. of Europe, England

CIGNA CORP   One Liberty Place, 1650 Market St, Philadelphia, PA 19101,
Tel: (215) 523-4000
(Ins, invest, health care & other fin servs)
   Cigna Insurance Co. of Europe SA-NV, Cigna House, 8 Lime St., London EC3M 7NA,
   England
   Cigna Reinsurance Co. (UK) Ltd., Cigna House, 8 Lime St., London EC3M 7NA, England
   Cigna Services UK Ltd., Cigna House, 8 Lime St., London EC3M 7NA, England
   Cigna U.K. Holding Ltd., Cigna House, 8 Lime St., London EC3M 7NA, England
   Cigna Unit Trust Managers Ltd., Crusader House, Reigate, Surrey RH2 8BL, England
   Crusader Managed Pension Funds Ltd., Crusader House, Reigate, Surrey RH2 8BL,
   England
   Crusader Staff Pension Investments Ltd., Crusader House, Reigate, Surrey RH2 8BL,
   England
   Ernest Linsdell Ltd., Commonwealth House, 1-19 New Oxford St., London WCIA 1NB,
   England
   Esis Intl., Inc., Chesterfield House, 26-28 Fenchurch St., London EC3M 3DH, England
   Growth Property Management Co. Ltd., Crusader House, Reigate, Surrey RH2 8BL,
   England
   Insurance Co. of North America, Cigna House/ 8 Lime St., London EC3M 7NA, England
   Insurance Co. of North America (UK) Ltd., Cigna House, 8 Lime St., London EC3M 7NA,
   England
   Plough Investment Properties Ltd., Crusader House, Reigate, Surrey RH2 8BL, England

CINCINNATI MILACRON INC   4701 Marburg Ave, Cincinnati, OH 45209,
Tel: (513) 841-8256
(Mfr mach tools, robots, plastic mach, metrology equip)
   Cincinnati Milacron Ltd., P.O. Box 505, Birmingham, B4 0QU, England

CINCOM SYSTEMS INC   2300 Montana Ave, Cincinnati, OH 45211,
Tel: (513) 662-2300
(Computer software)
   Cincom Systems (UK) Ltd., The Cincom Bldg., 99/105 King St., Maidenhead,
   Berkshire SL6 IDP, England

CIT FINANCIAL CORP   650 Madison Ave, New York, NY 10022, Tel: (212) 572-6500
(Finance, ins, loans)
   CIT (UK) Ltd., 10 Charles 11 St., London, SW1Y 4AB, England

CITIBANK NA   399 Park Ave, New York, NY 10043, Tel: (212) 559-1000
(Intl banking)
   Citibank N.A., Citibank House, 336 Strand, P.O. Box 78, London, WC2R 1HB,England
   Citibank N.A., Abbey House, 2nd Floor, 74-76 Mosley St., Manchester, M2 3EH, England
   Consumer Services Group, European Div., 364-366 Kensington High St., London, W14,
   England

CLARKSON INDUSTRIES INC   30 Buxton Farm Rd, Stamford, CT 06905-1206,
Tel: (203) 322-3990
(Mfr centrifugal blowers, compressors, handling equip)
   R. Mclvor & Sons, Ltd., Hoffman Air & Filtration Systems Ltd, Unit 1, Ashton Rd.,
   Bredbury Stockport, Cheshire, England

CLEARY GOTTLIEB STEEN & HAMILTON   1 State Street Plaza, New York, NY 10004,
Tel: (212) 344-0600
(Law firm)
  Cleary Gottlieb Steen & Hamilton, Winchester House, 77 London Wall,
  London EC2N 1DA, England

CLIMAX MOLYBDENUM CORP   One Greenwich Plaza, Greenwich, CT 06830,
Tel: (203) 629-6400
(Molybdenum, tungsten)
  Climax Molybdenum Co., Ltd., Imperial House, 1/3 Grosvenor Place, London, SWIX 7DL,
  England

COBE LABORATORIES INC   1185 Oak St, Lakewood, CO 80215, Tel: (303) 232-6800
(Mfr med equip & supplies)
  COBE Laboratories Ltd., Eastbrook Rd., Eastern Ave., Gloucester GL4 7DB, England

COGSDILL TOOL PRODUCTS INC   PO Box 7007, Camden, SC 29020,
Tel: (803) 438-4000
(Roller burnishing mach)
  Cogsdill-Nuneaton Ltd., Tenlons Rd., Nuneaton, England

THE COLEMAN CO INC   250 N St Francis Ct, PO Box 1762, Wichita, KS 67201,
Tel: (316) 261-3485
(Mfr camping, outdoor & water recreation prdts)
  Coleman UK Inc., Parish Wharf Estate, Harbor Rd., Portishead, Bristol, BS20 9DA,
  England

COLGATE-PALMOLIVE CO   300 Park Ave, New York, NY 10022, Tel: (212) 310-2000
(Pharms, cosmetics, toiletries, detergents)
  Colgate-Palmolive Ltd., 76 Oxford St., London, W1A 1EN, England

COLLAGEN CORP   1850 Embarcadero Rd, Palo Alto, CA 94303, Tel: (415) 856-0200
(Mfr prod for repair/replacement of damaged human tissue)
  Collagen UK Ltd., Longwich Rd., Princess Risborough, Buckinghamshire HP17 9RR,
  England

COLLOIDS INC   394-400 Frelinghuysen Ave, Newark, NJ 07114,
Tel: (201) 926-6100
(Chem prdts)
  Barrow Hepburn Group Ltd., 73 S. Audley St., London, W1Y 6JR, England

COLT INDUSTRIES INC   430 Park Ave, New York, NY 10022, Tel: (212) 940-0400
(Pumps, water sys, engines, motor arms, etc)
  Grusteel Ltd., Rutland Way, Sheffield, Yorkshire, S3 8DG, England

COLUMBIA PICTURES INDUSTRIES INC   711 Fifth Ave, New York, NY 10022,
Tel: (212) 751-4400
(Producer & distributor of motion pictures)
  Columbia Pictures Corp., Ltd., 19/23 Wells St., London, W1P 3FP, England
  Columbia-EMI-Warner Distributors Ltd., 135 Wardour St., London, W1V 4AP, England

COMBINED INSURANCE CO OF AMERICA   123 N Wacker Dr, Chicago, IL 60606,
Tel: (312) 701-3000
(Insurance)
  Combined Insurance Co. of America, 15 Fairfield West, Kingston Upon Thames, Surrey,
  KT1 2PA, England

COMBUSTION ENGINEERING INC 900 Long Ridge Road, Stamford, CT 06902,
Tel: (203) 329-8771
(Tech constr)
  C-E Lummus - The Lummus Co., Ltd., 100 Fetter Lane, P.O. Box 64, London,
  E.C. 4P 4BA, England
  C-E Natco (UK) Ltd., 24 Nutford Place, London W1H 5YN, England
  C-E Refractories Ltd., East Common Lane, Scunthorpe, Humberside, DN16 1XD, England
  C-E Vefco Services, Ventura House, 72/74 Station Rd., Hayes, UB3 4DP, England
  Combustion Engineering Inc., 100 Fetter Lane, London, E.C. 4P 4BA, England
  Crest Engineering (UK) Inc., P.O. Box 82, 43 Fetter Lane, London, EC4A 1NQ, England
  Gray Tool Co. (Europe) Ltd., Boundary Rd., Harfreys Industrial Estate,
  Great Yarmouth, Norfolk, England

COMMERCE CLEARING HOUSE INC 4025 W Peterson Ave, Chicago, IL 60646,
Tel: (312) 583-8500
(Pub topical law report, computer serv)
  CCH Editions Ltd., Telford Rd., Bicester, Oxon OX6 OXD, England

COMMERCIAL INTERTECH CORP 1775 Logan Ave, Youngstown, OH 44501,
Tel: (216) 746-8011
(Mfr hydraulic com, metal stampings, pre-engr metal bldgs, fluid purification prdts)
  Commercial Hydraulic Bedford Ltd., Shuttleworth Rd., Goldington Estate, Bedford,
  England
  Commercial Hydraulic Gloucester Ltd., Gloucester Trading Estate, Hucclecote,
  Gloucester, GL3 4XE, England

COMPTON INTERNATIONAL 625 Madison Ave, New York, NY 10022,
Tel: (212) 754-1100
(Advertising)
  Saatchi & Saatchi Compton Ltd., 80 Charlotte St., London, W1A 1AQ, England

COMPUCORP 1901 S Bundy Dr, Los Angeles, CA 90025, Tel: (213) 478-9761
(Minicomputers; data & word processing)
  Compucorp European Support Centre, 1 Blenheim Rd., Cressex Estate, High Wycombe,
  Bucks, HP 123 RS, England

COMPUGRAPHIC CORP 200 Ballardvale St, Wilmington, MA 01887,
Tel: (617) 658-5600
(Mfr computerized composition & typesetting sys)
  Compugraphic (UK) Ltd., Sandbeck Way, Wetherby, W. Yorks, LS22 4DN, England

COMPUTER ASSOCIATES INTL INC 711 Stewart Ave, Garden City, NY 11530,
Tel: (516) 227-3300
(Devel/mkt/mgt info mgt & bus applications software)
  C.A. Computer Associates Ltd., Computer Associates House, 183-187 Bath Rd., Slough,
  Berkshire SL1 4AA, England

COMPUTER SCIENCES CORP 2100 E Grand Ave, El Segundo, CA 90245,
Tel: (213) 615-0311
(Software servs, sys integration)
  Computer Sciences Co. Ltd., Heathcoat, House, 20 Savile Row, London, W1X 1AE,
  England

COMPUTERVISION CORP 201 Burlington Rd, Bedford, MA 01730,
Tel: (617) 275-1800
(Automation sys, semiconductors)
  Computervision (Europe) Inc., Point West, 1040 Uxbridge Rd., Hayes, Middlesex,

(cont)

England
Computervision Ltd., Penn St., Village Amersham, Burks, England
Computervision Ltd., Elmden House, Coventry Rd., Sheldon, Burmingham, England

CONDE NAST PUBLICATIONS INC   350 Madison Ave, New York, NY 10017,
Tel: (212) 880-8800
(Publ)
Conde Nast Publications Ltd., Vogue House, Hanover Sq., London, WIR OAD, England

CONOCO INC   600 N Dairy Ashford Rd, Houston, TX 77079, Tel: (713) 293-1000
(Oil, gas, coal, chems, minerals)
Conch Methane Services Ltd., c/o Shell Intl. Gas Ltd., Shell Centre, London,
   SE1 7NA, England
Conoco (UK) Ltd., South Denes Rd., Great Yarmouth, Norfolk, NR30 3QD, England
Conoco Ltd., Park House, 116 Park St., London, WIY 4NN, England
Conoco Ltd., Conoco House, 230 Blackfriars Rd., London, SE1 8NR, England
Continental Oil Holdings Ltd., 103/105 Wigmore St., London, W1H OEL, England
Humber Refinery, South Killingholme, South Humberside, DN40 3DW, England
Vinatex Ltd., New Lane, Havant, Hampshire, PO9 2NQ, England

CONSTRUCTION SPECIALTIES INC   55 Winans Ave, Cranford, NJ 07016,
Tel: (201) 272-5200
(Aluminum architectural prdts)
Construction Specialties Ltd., Conspec House, Springfield Rd., Chesham,
   Bucks. HP5 1PW, England

CONTINENTAL BANK NA   231 S Lasalle St, Chicago, IL 60697, Tel: (312) 828-2345
(Coml banking servs)
Continental Bank Corp., Continental Bank House, 162 Queen Victoria St.,
   London EC4V 4BS, England
Continental Capital Markets Ltd., Continental Bank House, 162 Queen Victoria St.,
   London EC4V 4BS, England
First Options of Chicago Ltd., 1/2 Royal Exchange Bldg., London EC3V 3LD, England

CONTINENTAL CAN CO   PO Box 5410, Stamford, CT 06856, Tel: (203) 357-8110
(Packaging prdts & mach, metal, plastic & paper containers)
Continental Can Co. (UK) Ltd., Coburg House, 10 Sheet St., Windsor, Berks. SL4 1BG,
   England

THE CONTINUUM CO INC   9500 Arboretum Blvd, Austin, TX 78759,
Tel: (512) 345-5700
(Design & mkt software for life ins industry)
Continuum London, 423 London Rd., Camberley, Surrey GU1 53QP, England

CONTROL DATA CORP   8100 34th Ave S, Minneapolis, MN 55440,
Tel: (612) 853-8100
(Control data equip, computer sys serv & financial serv)
Computing Devices Co., Ltd., Castle Ham Rd., St. Leonards-on-Sea, P.O. Box 10,
   East Sussex, TN38 9NJ, England
Control Data Ltd., 22A St. James Sq., London, SW1, England
Control Data Ltd., Arena House Broadway, Letchworth, Harts, SG3 3BX, England
Data Peripherals Ltd., Bessemer Dr., Stevenage, Hertfordshire, SG1 2DX, England
First Fortum Holding Ltd., Fortune House, 137-132 Park Lane, London, W14 3AD,
   England

COOPER ELECTRICAL DISTRIBUTION PRODUCTS   PO Box 9050, Charlottesville,
VA 22906-9050, Tel: (804) 973-4411
(Mfr wiring devices, spec switches, circuit breakers & ind control)
  Cooper Electrical Distribution Products, Plymouth, England

COOPER LIGHTING GROUP   400 Busse Rd, Elk Grove Village, IL 60007-2195,
Tel: (312) 956-8400
(Mfr indoor & outdoor lighting prdts)
  Cooper Lighting Group, Milton Keynes, England

COOPERTOOLS   PO Box 30100, Raleigh, NC 27622, Tel: (919) 781-7200
(Mfr hand tools)
  CooperTools, Wear Industrial Estate, District 6, Washington, Tyne & Wear, NE37 1NA,
    England

CORE INDUSTRIES INC   PO Box 2000, Bloomfield Hills, MI 48013,
Tel: (313) 642-3400
(Electronics, agric equip, fluid controls, vehicle & constr prdts)
  Anilam Electronics-Europe, 3 Stockwood Rise, Camberley, Surrey, England

CORESTATES FINANCIAL CORP   PO Box 7618, Philadelphia, PA 19101,
Tel: (215) 973-3100
(Banking)
  Philadelphia National Ltd., Philadelphia National House, 3 Gracechurch St.,
    Longon EC3V OAD, England

CORNING CORP   Houghton Park, PO Box 2000, Corning, NY 14831,
Tel: (617) 974-9000
(Mfr glass, ceramic materials)
  Corning Europe Inc., Corning House 339/341 Bath Rd., Slough, Berkshire SL1 5PR,
    England
  Corning Ltd., Wear Glass Works, Sunderland, Tyne & Wear SR4 6EJ, England

CORROON & BLACK INTL   Wall Street Plaza, New York, NY 10005,
Tel: (212) 363-4100
(Ins brokers)
  Minet Intl. Ltd., Minet House, 100 Leman St., London, E1 8HG, England

COURTAULDS PERFORMANCE FILMS   PO Box 5068, Martinsville, VA 24115,
Tel: (703) 629-1711
(Mfr solar control & dyed polyester/metal window films)
  Martin Processing Inc., Beech Ave., Lower Bourne, Farnham, Surrey GU10 3J2, England

CPC INTERNATIONAL INC   PO Box 8000, International Plaza, Englewood Cliffs,
NJ 07632, Tel: (201) 894-4000
(Mfr consumer food prdts & corn refining prdts)
  CPC (UK) Ltd., P.O. Box 16c, Claygate House, Esher, Surrey KT10 9PN, England

CR INDUSTRIES   900 N State St, Elgin, IL 60123, Tel: (708) 742-7840
(Mfr shaft & face seals)
  CR Industrial Prdts. Ltd., Unit 30, Elmdon Trading Estate, Bickenhill Lane,
    Marston Green, Birmingham B37 7HE, England

CRANE CO   757 Third Ave, New York, NY 10017, Tel: (212) 415-7300
(Diversified mfr/distr engineered prdts for ind)
  Crane Ltd., Audrey House, Ely Place, London EC1N 6SN, England
  UMC Industries Ltd., Dock Rd., Lytham, Lancs. FY8 5BD, England

JOHN CRANE INC   6400 Oakton St, Morton Grove, IL 60053, Tel: (708) 967-2400
(Mfr engineering seals)
   Deep Sea Seals Ltd., 4 Marples Way, Havant, Hants PO9 1NX, England
   John Crane UK Ltd., Crossbow House, Liverpool Rd., Slough, SL1 4QX, England
   John Crane UK Ltd., Tilson Rd., Roundthorn Industrial Estate, Wythenshawe,
      Manchester M23 9PH, England
   Lapmaster Intl. Ltd., Lee Mill Industrial Estate, Ivybridge, Devon PL21 9EN, England

CRESAP McCORMICK & PAGET INC   245 Park Ave, New York, NY 10167,
   Tel: (212) 953-7000
   (Mgmt consultants)
   Cresap, McCormick & Paget Inc., 30-32 Mortimer St., London, WlN 7RA, England

CROCKER BANK INTERNATIONAL   299 Park Ave, New York, NY 10017,
   Tel: (212) 980-5500
   (Intl banking serv)
   Crocker Bank Intl. Ltd., 34 Great St. Helen's, London, EC3A 6EP, England

CROSS & TRECKER CORP   PO Box 925, Bloomfield Hills, MI 48013,
   Tel: (313) 644-4343
   (Automated mfg sys, computer- controlled mach tools)
   Cross Intl., Knowsley, Prescot, Merseyside L34 9E2, England

CROSS CO   17801 Fourteen Mile Rd, Fraser, MI 48026, Tel: (313) 293-3000
   (Metal working machs)
   Cross Intl., Knowsley, Prescot, Merseyside, L34 9EZ, England

CROWN CENTRAL PETROLEUM CORP   One North Charles, PO Box 1168, Baltimore,
   MD 21203, Tel: (301) 539-7400
   (Petroleum prdts & petrochems)
   Crown Central Intl. (UK) Ltd., 6-8 Sackville St., Picadilly, London, WlX 1DD,
      England

CRSS INC   1177 W Loop So, PO Box 22427, Houston, TX 77227,
   Tel: (713) 552-2000
   (Arch, engr, const & project mgt serv; project financing)
   CRSS (UK) Ltd., Westgate House, Ealing Rd., Brentford, Middlesex TW8 0QZ, England
   Mowlem+CRSS Ltd., Westgate House, Ealing Rd., Brentford, Middlesex TW8 0QZ, England
   Mowlem+CRSS Ltd., 20 Mason Yard, Duke St., St. James, London SW1 6BU, England

CUBIC CORP   9333 Balboa Ave, PO Box 85587, San Diego, CA 92123,
   Tel: (619) 277-6780
   (Automatic fare collection equip, training sys)
   Cubic Tiltman Langley, 177 Nutfield Rd., Merstham, Surrey, RHI 3HH, England

CULLIGAN INTL CO   One Culligan Parkway, Northbrook, IL 60062,
   Tel: (708) 205-6000
   (Water treatment prdts & serv)
   Culligan Intl. Co., Blenheim Rd., Cressex Industrial Estate, High Wycombe,
      HP12 3RS, England

CUMMINS ENGINE CO INC   PO Box 3005, Columbus, IN 47202, Tel: (812) 377-5000
   (Mfr diesel engines)
   Cummins Engine Co. Ltd., 46-50 Coombe Rd., New Malden, Surrey KT3 4QL, England

CURTISS-WRIGHT CORP   1200 Wall St, W Lyndhurst, NJ 07071, Tel: (201) 896-8400
(Aircraft engines)
Dorr-Oliver Co., Ltd., Crosden, England
Memi Improvement Co., Ltd., Derby, England

CYBEREX INC   7171 Industrial Park Blvd, Mentor, OH 44060, Tel: (216) 946-1783
(Mfr uninterruptible power supplies & power conditioning equip)
Cyberex Intl., Covenant House, 12-18 Warwick Rd., Beaconsfield, Bucks., HP9 2PE,
England

CYCLOPS INDUSTRIES INC   650 Washington Rd, Pittsburgh, PA 15228,
Tel: (412) 343-4000
(Prod of stainless/carbon steel, alloy & tubular prdts, mfr metal panels for bldgs)
Cyclops Intl., 14 Chapelside, Chapel St., Spondon Derbyshire DE2 7JQ, England

D'ARCY MASIUS BENTON & BOWLES INC (DMB&B)   1675 Broadway, New York,
NY 10019, Tel: (212) 468-3622
(Advertising & communications)
DMB&B Ltd., 2 St.James' Sq., London SW1Y 4JN, England
Yellowhammer Advertising Ltd., 76 Oxford St., London W1A 1DT, England

D-M-E COMPANY   29111 Stephenson Highway, Madison Heights, MI 48071,
Tel: (313) 398-6000
(Basic tooling for plastic molding & die casting)
DME Europe UK, Halifax Rd., Cresex Industrial Estate, High Wycombe, Bucks,
HP12 3TN, England

DAMES & MOORE   911 Wilshire Blvd, Los Angeles, CA 90017, Tel: (213) 683-1560
(Consulting engineers)
Dames & Moore, Booth House, 15-17 Church St., Twickenham TW1 3NJ, England
Dames & Moore, Blackfriar's House, St. Mary's Parsonage, Manchester M3 2JA, England
Europa Research Laboratories, Thames House, Wood Lane, Slough SL1 9EB, England
Food & Agriculture Intl. Ltd., Chiltern House, Oxford Rd., Aylesbury,
Bucks. HP19 3EQ, England

DAMON CORP   115 Fourth Ave, Needham Heights, MA 02194, Tel: (617) 449-0800
(Clinical diagnostic labs)
Damon/IEC (UK) Ltd., Unit 7, Lawrence Way, Brewers Hill Rd., Dunstable,
Bedfordshire LU6 1BD, England

DANCER FITZGERALD SAMPLE INTL   405 Lexington Ave, New York, NY 10174,
Tel: (212) 661-0800
(Advertising agency)
Dorland Advertising Ltd., 121-141 Westbourne Ter., London W2 6JR, England

DANIEL INTERNATIONAL CORP   Daniel Bldg, Greenville, SC 29602,
Tel: (803) 298-2500
(Gen contractor, engr & constr)
IMO Ltd., Fluor House, Euston Sq., P.O. Box 309, London, NW1 2DJ, England

DATA GENERAL CORP   4400 Computer Dr, Westboro, MA 01580, Tel: (617) 366-8911
(Design, mfr gen purpose computer sys & peripheral prdts & servs)
Data General Ltd., Hounslow House, 721-734 London Rd., Hounslow, Middlesex,
TW3 1PD, England

DATA MEASUREMENT CORP   15884 Gaither Dr, Gaithersburg, MD 20877,
Tel: (301) 948-2450
(Mfr quality/process control gauges)
DMC UK, Ltd., Burch Rd., Northfleet, Kent DA11 9NE, England

DATAEASE INTL INC   7 Cambridge Dr, Trumbull, CT 06611, Tel: (203) 374-8000
(Mfr applications devel software)
Sapphire Intl., 1 Coventry Rd., Ilford, Essex IG1 4QR, England

DATAGRAPHIX INC   PO Box 82449, San Diego, CA 92138, Tel: (714) 291-9960
(Mfr electronic computing equip)
Datagraphix Ltd., New Lodge, Drift Rd., Windsor, Berkshire, SL4 4RQ, England

DATAPRODUCTS CORP   6200 Canada Ave, PO Box 746, Woodland Hills, CA 91365,
Tel: (818) 887-8000
(Mfr computer printers & supplies)
Dataproducts Intl. Ltd., Dataproducts House, 136-138 High St., Egham,
Surrey TW20 9HL, England
Dataproducts Ltd., Unit 1, Heron Ind. Estate, Spencers Wood, Reading, Berkshire,
RG7 1PJ, England

DATASCOPE CORP   14 Philips Pkwy, Montvale, NJ 07645, Tel: (201) 391-8100
(Mfr medical devices)
Datascope Medical Co. Ltd., Cambridge, England

DAVIS POLK & WARDWELL   1 Chase Manhattan Plaza, New York, NY 10005,
Tel: (212) 530-4000
(Law firm)
Davis Polk & Wardwell, 1 Fredericks Place, London EC2R 8AB, England

DAY INTL   333 W First St, Dayton, OH 45412, Tel: (513) 226-7000
(Diversified auto, ind & household prdts)
Dayco Rubber (UK) Ltd., St. James's House, Wellington Rd., North, Stockport,
SK4 2RH, England

DAYTON PROGRESS CORP   500 Progress Rd, Dayton, OH 45449, Tel: (513) 859-5111
(Punches, dies & guide bushings)
Dayton Progress (UK) Ltd., Powerscroft Rd., Sidcup, Kent, England

DAYTON-WALTHER CORP   PO Box 1022, Dayton, OH 45401, Tel: (513) 296-3113
(Mfr heavy duty components for truck/trailer chassis)
Dayton-Walther Ltd., 75/76 Brindley Rd., Astmoor Industrial Estate, Runcorn-,
Cheshire, WA7 1BR, England

DDB NEEDHAM WORLDWIDE INC   437 Madison Ave, New York, NY 10022,
Tel: (212) 415-2000
(Advertising)
BMP DDB Needham Worldwide Ltd., 12 Bishop's Bridge Rd., London W2 6AA, England
DDB Needham Worldwide Inc., 54 Baker St., London W1M 1DJ, England

DE VILBISS CO   300 Phillips Ave, Toledo, OH 43612, Tel: (419) 470-2169
(Mfr spray painting & finishing equip)
The DeVilbiss Co., Ltd., Ringwood Rd., Bournemouth, Hants, BH11 9LH, England

DE ZURIK CORP   250 Riverside Ave, Sartell, MN 56377, Tel: (612) 259-2000
(Mfr manual, process & control valves)
  DeZurik Intl., Nelson Way, Nelson Industrial Estate, Cramlington,
    Northumberland NE23 9BJ, England

DEAK & CO INC   29 Broadway, New York, NY 10006, Tel: (212) 635-0515
(Foreign exchange specialists)
  Deak-Perera Ltd., 18 St. Swithin's Lane, London, EC4N 8AH, England

DEARBORN DIV   300 Genesse St, Lake Zurich, IL 60047, Tel: (708) 438-1800
(Mfr water treatment chems & serv)
  Dearborn Chemical Co., Ltd., Foundry Lane, Widnes, Cheshire, 2A8 82Z, England

DEBEVOISE & PLIMPTON   875 3rd Ave, New York, NY 10022, Tel: (212) 909-6000
(Law firm)
  Debevoise & Plimpton, 5 Ludgate Hill, London EC4M 7AA, England

DEERE & CO   John Deere Rd, Moline, IL 61265, Tel: (309) 752-8000
(Mfr/sale agri/constr/utility/forestry & lawn/grounds care equip)
  John Deere Ltd., Harby Rd., Langar, Nottingham NG13 9HT, England

DEL MONTE CORP   1 Market Plaza, PO Box 3575, San Francisco, CA 94119,
  Tel: (415) 442-5120
(Fresh/frozen foods, distribution serv)
  Del Monte Foods Ltd., Artronaut House, Hounslow Rd., Feltham, Middlesex, TW14 9AE,
    England

DELAVAN INC   811 4th St, West Des Moines, IA 50265-0100, Tel: (515) 274-1561
(Mfr heating equip, nozzles, hydraulic pumps)
  Delavan Ltd., Gorsey Lane, Widnes, Cheshire, WA8 ORJ, England

DELL COMPUTER CORP   9505 Arboretum Blvd, Austin, TX 78759,
  Tel: (512) 338-4400
(Design/mfr personal computers)
  Dell Computer Corp., Ltd., Melbanke House, Western Rd., Bracknell,
    Berkshire RG12 1RW, England

DENNISON MFG CO   300 Howard St, Framingham, MA 01701, Tel: (617) 879-0511
(Paper prdts & office supplies)
  Dennison Mfr. Co. Ltd., Colonial Way, Watford Herts, WD2 4JY, England

DENTSPLY INTL INC   PO Box 872, York, PA 17405, Tel: (717) 845-7511
(Mfr dental, medical & ind supplies & equip)
  Ash Instruments/Dentsply, Unit 9, Madleaze Trading Estate, Bristol Rd.,
    Gloucester GL1 5SG, England
  CMW Labs/Dentsply, Cornford Rd., Blackpool FY4 4QQ, England
  Dentsply Ltd., Hamm Moor Lane, Addlestone, Weybridge, Surrey KT15 2SE, England
  Dentsply Ltd., Diamond Bldg., Coombe Rd., Brighton, Sussex BN2 4ER, England
  M&IE/Dentsply, Falcon Rd., Sowton Industrial Estate, Exeter, Devon EX2 7NA, England

DENVER EQUIPMENT DIV   PO Box 340, Colorado Springs, CO 80901,
  Tel: (303) 471-3443
(Ind process equip)
  Joy Process Equip. Ltd., Stocks House, 9 North St., Leatherhead, Surrey, England

DEVCON CORP   30 Endicott St, Danvers, MA 01923, Tel: (617) 777-1100
(Mfr filled epoxies, urethanes, adhesives & metal treatment prdts)
    Devcon Ltd., Brunel Close, Park Farm Estate, Wellingborough, Northants., England

DEWITT INTERNATIONAL CORP   5 N Watson Rd, Taylors, SC 29687,
    Tel: (803) 244-8521
(Mfr over-counter pharms)
    E.C. DeWitt & Co. Ltd., Seymour Rd., Leyton, London E10 7LX, England

DHJ INDUSTRIES INC   1040 Ave of the Americas, New York, NY 10018,
    Tel: (212) 944-4500
(Mfr of knit fabrics, interlinings plastic chips & denim)
    DHJ Industries (UK) Ltd., 2 Wardrobe Pl., London EC4V 5HL, England

DIAMOND CHAIN CO   402 Kentucky Ave, Indianapolis, IN 46225,
    Tel: (317) 638-6431
(Mfr roller chains)
    Alremco Engineering (UK) Ltd., Unit 5, The Furlong, Berry Hill Industrial Estate,
       Droitwich, Worcs. WR9 9AR, England

DIAMOND SHAMROCK CORP   1100 Superior Ave, Cleveland, OH 44114,
    Tel: (216) 694-5000
(Organic & inorganic chems & specialties, agric chems)
    Diamond Shamrock Agrochemicals Ltd., Bayheath House, 4 the fairway, Petts wood,
       Kent, BR51 EG, England
    Diamond Shamrock Overseas Ltd., P.O. Box 1, Eccles, Manchester, England

DICTAPHONE CORP   3191 Broadbridge Ave, Stratford, CT 06497-2559,
    Tel: (203) 381-7000
(Mfr/sale dictation, tel answering & multi-channel voice commun recording sys)
    Dictaphone Co. Ltd., Regent Sq. House, The Parade, Royal Leamington Spa.,
       Warwickshire, CV32 4NL, England

DIGICON INC   3701 Kirby Drive, Houston, TX 77096, Tel: (713) 526-5611
(Geophysical services)
    Digital Exploration Ltd., East Grinstead, Susses RH19 4HG, England

DIGITAL EQUIPMENT CORP   129 Parker St, Maynard, MA 01754, Tel: (617) 897-5111
(Digital computers, digital circuit modules, memory elec- tronic system)
    Digital Equipment Co. Ltd., Fountain House, Butts Centre. Reading, Berkshire,
       RG1 7QN, England

DILLON READ & CO INC   535 Madison Ave, New York, NY 10022,
    Tel: (212) 906-7000
(Investment banking)
    Dillon Read Overseas Corp., 10 Chesterfield, London, W17 HF, England

WALT DISNEY PRODUCTIONS   500 S Buena Vista St, Burbank, CA 91521,
    Tel: (818) 560-1000
(Film/TV prod, amusement parks, land mgmt)
    Walt Disney Productions Ltd., 68 Pall Mall, London, SW1Y 5EX, England

DIXON TICONDEROGA CO   2600 Maitland Center Pkwy, #200, Maitland, FL 32751,
    Tel: (407) 875-9000
(Mfr/serv writing implements & art supplies)
    Dixon Wearever Ltd., 36 Stapledon Rd., Peterboro PE2 OTD, England

DO ALL COMPANY   254 N Laurel Ave, Des Plaines, IL 60016, Tel: (708) 824-1122
(Distributors of mach tools, metal cutting tools, instru & ind supplies)
    DoAll Co. (UK) Ltd., Unit 9, Beldray Industrial Park, Mount Pleasant, Bilston,
        West Midlands WV14 7NH, England

DOBOY PACKAGING MACHINERY DIV   869 S Knowles Ave, New Richmond, WI 54017,
    Tel: (715) 246-6511
    (Mfr packaging machinery)
        Doboy Ltd., 13 Sunderland Rd., Middlefield Industrial Estate, Sandy, Bedfordshire,
        England

DOMINICK & DOMINICK INC   90 Broad St, New York, NY 10090, Tel: (212) 558-8800
    (Brokers)
        Dominick & Dominick Ltd., 8 Little Trinity Lane, London, EC4, England

DONALDSON CO INC   PO Box 1299, Minneapolis, MN 55440, Tel: (612) 887-3131
    (Filtration prdts & sys)
        Donaldson Filter Components Ltd., Osla Rd., Sutton Fields Estate, Hull, HU8 OXN,
        England

DONALDSON LUFKIN & JENRETTE INC   140 Broadway, New York, NY 10005,
    Tel: (212) 504-3000
    (Investment mgmt)
        Donaldson, Lufkin & Jenrette, Inc., Ltd., 22 Austin Friars, London, EC2 N2HY,
        England

R R DONNELLEY & SONS CO   2223 King Dr, Chicago, IL 60616, Tel: (312) 326-8000
    (Coml printing, alied commun servs)
        Ben Johnson & Co. Ltd., Boroughbridge Rd., York YO2 5SS, England
        R. R. Donnelley (UK) Ltd., Donnelley House, 25 Worship St., London EC2A 2DX, England

DONNELLY DIRECTORY   287 Bowman Ave, Purchase, NY 10577, Tel: (914) 933-6800
    (Telephone directories, direct mail, merchandising serv)
        Thomson Directories Ltd., 296 Farnborough Rd., Farnborough, Hants GU14 7NU, England

DOREMUS & CO INC   120 Broadway, New York, NY 10271, Tel: (212) 964-0700
    (Advertising & public relations)
        Doremus & Co., 5/11 Theobalds Rd., London WC14 8S8 England

DORR-OLIVER INC   612 Wheeler's Farm Rd, PO Box 3819, Milford, CT 06460,
    Tel: (203) 876-5400
    (Mfr process equip for food, pulp & paper, mineral & chem ind; & municipal/ind waste
    treatment)
        Dorr-Oliver Co., Ltd., NLA Tower, 12/16 Addiscombe Rd., Croydon CR9 2DS, England

DOUBLEDAY & CO INC   245 Park Ave, New York, NY 10167, Tel: (212) 953-4561
    (Book publ)
        Doubleday & Co, Inc., 100 Wigmore St., London, W1, England

DOW CHEMICAL CO   2030 Dow Center, Midland, MI 48640, Tel: (517) 636-1000
    (Chems, plastics, fibers, pharms)
        Dow Chemical Co., Ltd., Meadow Bank, Bath Rd., Hounslow, TW5 9QY, England

DOW CORNING CORP   2220 W Salzburg Rd, PO Box 1767, Midland, MI 48640,
    Tel: (517) 496-4000
    (Silicones, silicon chems, solid lubricants)
        Dow Corning Ltd., Reading Bridge House, Reading, RCI 8PW, England

DOW JONES & CO INC   200 Liberty St, New York, NY 10281, Tel: (212) 416-2000
(Publisher)
   AP-Dow Jones, 76 Shoe Lane, London, EC4 A3JB, England

DRAKE BEAM MORIN INC   100 Park Ave, New York, NY 10017, Tel: (212) 692-7700
(Human resource mgmt consulting & training)
   Drake Beam Morin Ltd., 41/42 Dover St., London W1, England

DRESSER INDUSTRIES INC   1600 Pacific Bldg, PO Box 718, Dallas, TX 75221,
   Tel: (214) 740-6000
(Diversified supplier of equip & tech serv to energy & natural resource ind)
   Boyles Bros. Div., Dresser Europe S.A., Bowes St., South Gosforth,
      Newcastle Upon Tyne, Northumberland, NE3 1TH, England
   British Jeffrey Diamond, Thornes Works, Wakefield, West Yorkshire, WF2 8PT, England
   Dewrance & Co., Ltd., Trevithick Works, Gillibrands Estate, Shelmersdale,
      Lancashire, WN8 9TU, England
   Dresser Atlas Div., Dresser Europe S.A., 197 Knightsbridge, London, SW7, England
   Dresser Europe S.A., 187 Knightsbridge, London, SW7 1RJ, England
   Dresser Europe S.A., Milton House, Queen St., Morley, Leeds, Yorkshire, LS27 9EB,
      England
   Dresser Minerals Intl. Inc., Ryder Point Plant, Wirksworth, Derbyshire, DE4 4ES,
      England
   Dresser Wayne Div., Dresser Europe S.A., Western Rd., Brackell, Berkshire,
      RG12 IRJ, England
   Industrial Specialty Products Div., Dresser Europe S.A., Warington Service Center,
      29/31 Hardwick Grange, Warrington, WA1 4RF, England
   Lodge Cottrell Ltd., UK., George St., Parade, Birmingham, B3 IQQ, England
   P & M Manufacturing Div., Dresser Europe S.A., Whitworth St., Openshaw, Manchester,
      M11 2NJ, England

DREVER COMPANY   PO Box 98, Huntington Valley, PA 19006, Tel: (215) 947-3400
(Mfr industrial furnaces)
   Drever U.K., Corner Sandwell/Newhall Sts., Walsall, West Midlands, England

DREW CHEMICAL CORP   One Drew Plaza, Boonton, NJ 07005, Tel: (201) 263-7600
(Spec chems for ind water & fuel treatment, chem processing)
   Drew Ameroid UK Ltd., Barton Ave., Eccles, Manchester M30 OHN, England

DRIVER-HARRIS CO   308 Middlesex St, Harrison, NJ 07029, Tel: (201) 483-4800
(Wire, cables, etc)
   British Driver-Harris Co. Ltd., Cheadle Heath, Stockport, Cheshire, SK3 OSB, England
   British Driver-Harris Co. Ltd., Cable Div., Road Four Industrial Estate, Winsford,
      Cheshire, CW7 3QR, England

DU BOIS INTL INC   1100 DuBois Tower, Cincinnati, OH 45202,
   Tel: (513) 762-6000
(Mfr spec chems & maintenance prdts)
   DuBois Chemicals Ltd., Swan House, Peregrine Business Park, Gomm Rd., High Wycombe,
      Bucks. HP13 7YZ, England

E I DU PONT DE NEMOURS & CO   Du Pont Bldg, 1007 Market St, Wilmington,
   DE 19898, Tel: (302) 774-1000
(Mfr/sale diversified chems, plastics, specialty prdts & fibers)
   Du Pont (UK) Ltd., Du Pont House, 18 Bream's Bldgs., Fetter Lane, London, EC4A 1HT,
      England

DUNHAM-BUSH INC   175 South St, West Hartford, CT 06110, Tel: (203) 249-8671
(Ind & commercial refrigeration, heating & A/C equip)
   Dunham-Bush Ltd., Fitzherbert Rd., Farlington, Portsmouth, England

DURACELL INTL INC   Berkshire Industrial Park, Bethel, CT 06801,
Tel: (203) 796-4000
(Mfr batteries)
   Duracell Batteries Ltd., Mallory House, Hazelwick Ave., Three Bridges, Crawley,
   West Susses RH10 1FQ, England

DURAMETALLIC CORP   2104 Factory St, Kalamazoo, MI 49001, Tel: (616) 382-8720
(Mfr mech seals, compression packings, auxiliaries)
   Durametallic UK, Unit 13B, United Trading Estate, Old Trafford, Manchester, le,
   M16 ORJ, England

DURIRON CO INC   425 N Findlay St, PO Box 1145, Dayton, OH 45401,
Tel: (513) 226-4000
(Mfr chem equip, pumps, valves, filters, fans, heat exchangers)
   Durco Processe Equipment Ltd., 23 Heathfield, Stacey Bushes, Milton, Keynes,
   MK12 6HR, England

E-Z-EM INC   7 Portland Ave, Westbury, NY 11590, Tel: (516) 333-8230
(Mfr prdts for med contrast media, lead protective wear & surg prdts)
   E-Z-EM, Ltd., London, England

EALING CORP   22 Pleasant St, S Natick, MA 01760, Tel: (617) 655-7000
(Research instru)
   Ealing Beck Ltd., Greycaine Rd., Watford, WD2 4PW, England

EASTMAN & BEAUDINE INC   111 W Monroe, Chicago, IL 60603, Tel: (312) 726-8195
(Investments)
   Eastman & Beaudine Inc. (UK), DeWalden Court, 85 New Cavendish St., London,
   W1M 7RA, England

EASTMAN KODAK CO   343 State St, Rochester, NY 14650-0518, Tel: (716) 724-4000
(Devel/mfr photo & chem prdts, info mgmt/video/copier sys, fibers/plastics for
various ind)
   Kodak Ltd., Kodak House, Box 66, Station Rd., Hemel Hempstead, Herts, HP1 1JU,
   England

EATON CORP   100 Erieview Plaza, Cleveland, OH 44114, Tel: (216) 523-5000
(Advanced tech prdts for transp & ind mkts)
   Eaton Ltd., Eaton House, Staines Rd., Hounslow, Middlesex, TW4 5DX, England

ECHLIN INC   100 Double Beach Rd, Branford, CT 06405, Tel: (203) 481-5751
(Mfr motor vehicle replacement parts)
   Grau Ltd., Fountain Works, Carluke St., Blackburn, Lancs. BB1 3JR, England
   Hobourn Group Ltd., Temple Farm Works, Priory Rd., Strood, Rochester, Kent ME2 2BD,
      England
   Lipe Ltd., York Ave., Haslingden, Rossendale, Lancs. BB4 4HN, England
   Quinton Hazell PLC, Hazell Way, Bermuda Rd., Numeaton, Warwickshire CV10 7QQ,
      England

ECLIPSE INC   1665 Elmwood Rd, Rockford, IL 61103, Tel: (815) 877-3031
(Mfr ind process heating equip & hdwe for natural gas utils)
   Eclipse Thermal Systems Ltd., Wassage Way, Hampton Lovett Ind. Estate,
   Kidderminster Rd., Droitwich, Worc. WR9 0NX, England

ECOLAB INC   370 Wabasha St, St Paul, MN 55102, Tel: (612) 293-2233
(Ind & household detergents, cleaning agents & equip)
   E.L. Europe Ltd., Boundary House, Cricketfield Rd., Uxbridge, Middlesex, UB8 ITB,
   England
   Soilax Ltd., 830 Yeovil Rd., Slough, Berkshire, SL1 4JL, England

ECONOMY FORMS CORP - EFCO   4301 NE 14th St, Des Moines, IA 50316-0386,
Tel: (515) 266-1141
(Mfr steel forms for concrete construction)
   Economy Forms Corp/EFCO UK Ltd., 35 Stilebrook Rd., Yardley Road Industrial Estate,
   Olney, Bucks. MK46 7EA, England

EG&G INC   45 William St, Wellesley, MA 02181, Tel: (617) 237-5100
(Diversified instru, components, services)
   EG&G Astrophysics Research Ltd., Vale Rd., Windsor, Berks. SL2 5JP, England
   EG&G Electro Optics, 8 Broadstone Park Rd., Livermead, Torquay, Devon TQ2 6TY,
   England
   EG&G Fiber Optics/Geometrics/Instruments, Sorbus House, Mulberry Business Park,
   Wokingham, Berks. RG11 2GY, England
   EG&G Ltd./Sealol Div., Coronation Rd., Cressex Industrial Estate, High Wycombe,
   Bucks. HP12 3, England
   EG&G Reticon, 34/35 Market Pl., Wokingham, Berks. RG11 1AT, England
   EG&G Sealol, Coronation Rd., Cressex Industrial Estate, High Wycombe,
   Bucks. HP12 3TP, England

ELDON INDUSTRIES INC   9920 La Cienega Blvd, Inglewood, CA 90301,
Tel: (213) 757-2151
(Soldering & desoldering equip, sign boards, office furniture & accessories)
   Eldon Office Products, Unit 3, Clifton Rd., Shefford, Bedfordshire, SG17 5AG,
   England

ELECTRO-CRAFT CORP   1600 South Second St, Hopkins, MN 55343,
Tel: (612) 931-2700
(Mfr servo motors & sys, optical encoders, electronic components)
   Electro-Craft Ltd., Third Ave., Crewe CW1 XU, England

ELECTRONIC ASSOCIATES INC   185 Monmouth Park Hwy, West Long Branch,
NJ 07764, Tel: (201) 229-1100
(Analog/hybrid computers, training simulators, energy measurement sys)
   Electronic Associates, Ltd., Burgess Hill, Sussex, England

ELECTRONICS CORP OF AMERICA   265 Winter St, Waltham, MA 0215442,
Tel: (617) 466-8000
(Mfr electrical ind apparatus, electronic sys & controls)
   Electronics Corp. of America Ltd., Tuition House, St. Georges Rd., Wimbledon,
   SW19 4XE, England

ELIZABETH ARDEN INC   55 East 52nd St, New York, NY 10055-0191,
Tel: (212) 407-1000
(Cosmetics, fragrances, toiletries)
   Elizabeth Arden Ltd., 140 Wales Farm Rd., Acton, London W3 6jXL, England

EMCO WHEATON INC   50 Chamberlain Blvd, PO Box 688, Conneaut, OH 44030,
Tel: (216) 599-8151
(Mfr petroleum handling equip- ment)
   Emco Wheaton, UK, Ltd., Westwood, Margate, Kent, CT9 4JR, England

EMERSON & CUMING DEWEY & ALMY CHEMICAL CO   59 Walpole St, Canton, MA 02021,
   Tel: (617) 828-3300
   (Plastics & ceramics for electr shielding materials)
      Emerson & Cuming (UK) Ltd., 866/868 Uxbridge Rd., Hayes, Middlesex, UB4 ORR, England

EMERY WORLDWIDE   3350 W Bayshore Rd, Palo Alto, CA 94304, Tel: (415) 855-9100
   (Expedited heavy air freight)
      Emery Worldwide, Ashford House, 41-45 Church Rd., Ashford, Middlesex TW15 2TY,
      England
      Emery Worldwide, Units 3, 4 & 5, Bldg. 303, Manchester Airport,
      Manchester WA15 8UX, England

ENCYCLOPEDIA BRITANNICA INC   425 N Michigan Ave, Chicago, IL 60611,
   Tel: (312) 321-7000
   (Book publ)
      Encyclopaedia Britannica Intl. Ltd., Mappin House, 156-162, Oxford St., London,
      W1N 9DL, England

ENERPAC   13000 W Silver Spring Dr, Butler, WI 53007, Tel: (414) 781-6600
   (Mfr/sale high pressure hydraulic maint tools)
      Enerpac, Leacon Rd., Ashford, Kent TN23 2TU, England

ENGELHARD CORP   Menlo Park, CN 40, Edison, NJ 08818, Tel: (201) 632-6000
   (Mfr spec chem prdts & engineered materials for ind; precious metal mgmt serv)
      Engelhard Ltd., Chancery House, St. Nicholas Way, Sutton, Surrey SM1 1SB, England

ENSEARCH INTL DEVELOPMENT INC   300 South St Paul, Dallas, TX 75201,
   Tel: (214) 651-8700
   (Div energy operations)
      Humphreys & Glasgow Ltd., 253 Vauxhall Bridge Rd., Chestergate House, London,
      England

ENVIROTECH CORP   3000 Sand Hill Road, Menlo Park, CA 94025,
   Tel: (415) 854-2000
   (Supplier of equip & tech for underground mining, ind processing & pollution control)
      Eimco (Great Britain) Ltd., Barlsway, Team Valley, Gateshead, NE11 0SB, England
      Sparling Envirotech Ltd., Victoria Rd., Burgess Hill, Sussex, RH15 9LL, England

A EPSTEIN & SONS INTL INC   600 W Fulton St, Chicago, IL 60606-1199,
   Tel: (312) 454-9100
   (Engr, arch, constr & devel)
      A. Epstein & Sons (UK) Ltd., Vincent House, Vincent Sq., London SW1P 2NB, England

EPSTEIN ENGINEERING EXPORT LTD   600 W Fulton St, Chicago, IL 60606-1199,
   Tel: (312) 454-9100
   (Engr & constr)
      A. Epstein & Sons (UK) Ltd., Vincent House, Vincent Sq., London SW1P 2NB, England

ERICO PRODUCTS INC   34600 Solon Road, Cleveland, OH 44139,
   Tel: (216) 248-0100
   (Mfr electric welding apparatus & hardware, metal stampings, specialty fasteners)
      Erico Europa (UK) Ltd., 59/61 Milford Rd., Reading, Berkshire, England

ESTERLINE CORP   10800 NE 8th St, #600, Bellevue, WA 98004,
   Tel: (206) 453-6001
   (Mfr equip & instru for ind automation, precision meas, data acquisition)
      Excellon Intl., Dominion Way, Rustington, Littlehampton, West Sussex BN16 3HQ,

(cont)

England
    Federal Gauges Ltd., Brick Knoll Park, Ashley Rd., St. Albans, Herts. AL1 5PL,
    England
    Hollis Europe Ltd., Unit 1, Riverside, Sir Thomas Langey Rd., Nedway City Estate,
    Strood, Kent M22 4DP, England

ETHYL PETROLEUM ADDITIVES INC   20 S 4th St, St Louis, MO 63102-1886,
    Tel: (314) 421-3930
    (Mfr lubricant & fuel additives)
    Ethyl Petroleum Additives Ltd., London Rd., Bracknell, Berks. RG12 2UW, England

EXCELLON AUTOMATION   23915 Garnier, Torrance, CA 90509, Tel: (213) 534-6300
    (PCB drilling & routing machs; optical inspection equip)
    Excellon Intl., Dominion Way, Rustington, Littlehampton, W., Sussex, BN16 3HQ,
    England

EXXON CORP   225 E John Carpenter Frwy, Irving, TX 75062, Tel: (214) 444-1000
    (Petroleum & petroleum prdts)
    Esso Europe Inc., 50 Stratton St., London, W1X 6AU, England

FAFNIR BEARING CO   37 Booth St, New Britain, CT 06050, Tel: (203) 225-5151
    (Ball bearings)
    Fafnir Bearing Div. of Textron, Ltd., GPO Box 18, Upper Villiers St.,
    Wolverhampton, WVZ 4NT, England

FAIRCHILD AIRCRAFT CORP   PO Box 32486, San Antonio, TX 78284,
    Tel: (512) 824-9421
    (Mfr turboprop aircraft)
    Fairchild Aircraft Corp., 1 Lavender Park, Swinley Rd., Ascot, Berks. SL5 8BD,
    England

FAIRCHILD PUBLICATIONS INC   7 East 12th St, New York, NY 10003,
    Tel: (212) 741-4000
    (Publishers)
    Fairchild Publications Inc., 3 Buckingham Gate, London, SW1E 6JN, England

FANSTEEL INC   1 Tantalum Pl, North Chicago, IL 60064, Tel: (708) 689-4900
    (Mfr refractory metals, cutting & mining tools, aerospace fabrications)
    Titanium Intl. Ltd., Thornhill Rd., Solihull, West Midlands B9I 2HF, England

FARAH INC   8889 Gateway Blvd W, El Paso, TX 79925, Tel: (915) 593-4000
    (Mfr wearing apparel)
    Farah Manufacturing (UK) Ltd., Unit 2a Gatwick, Gate Estate, Charlwood Rd.,
    Lowfield Heath, Crawley Sussex, RH11 OJS, England

FARR CO   2301 E Rosecrans Ave, El Segundo, CA 90245, Tel: (213) 772-5221
    (Filtration equip)
    Farr Filtration Ltd., 272 Kings Rd., Tyseley, Birmingham B11 2AB, England

FARREL CORP   25 Main St, Ansonia, CT 06401, Tel: (203) 734-3331
    (Mfr polymer processing equip)
    Farrel Ltd., Queensway, Castleton, P.O. Box 27, Rochdale, Lancs. OL11 2PF, England

FEDERAL EXPRESS CORP   PO Box 727, Memphis, TN 38194-4212, Tel: (901) 922-6900
    (Package air express svc)
    Federal Express (UK) Ltd., 1A Girling Way, Feltham, Middlesex, TW14 OPH, England

Federal Express (UK) Ltd., 48-49 Westbrook Rd., Trafford Park, Manchester, M17 1AY, England

FEHR BROS INC   110 Wall St, New York, NY 10005, Tel: (212) 825-0850
(Mfr/distr steel/steel prdts, chems, plastics)
Frank Fehr & Co. Ltd., Prince Rupert House, 64 Queen St., London, EC4R 1ER, England

FELTON INTERNATIONAL INC   599 Johnson Ave, Brooklyn, NY 11237,
Tel: (212) 497-4664
(Essential oils & extracts, perfumes & flavor material, aromatic chems)
Felton Co. (UK) Ltd., Pond Wood Close, Moulton Park, Northampton, NN3 1RT, England

FENWALL INC   400 Main St, Ashland, MA 01721, Tel: (617) 881-2000
(Temperature controls, ignition sys, fire/smoke detection & supression sys)
Fenwal Intl., Lyons House, 2A Station Rd., Frimley, Camberley, Surrey GU16 5HP, England

FERRANTI ELECTRIC INC   87 Modular Ave, Commack, NY 11725, Tel: (516) 543-0200
(Electronic equip)
Ferranti Ltd., Hollinwood, Lancs, OL9 7JS, England

FERREX INTL INC   17 Battery Pl, New York, NY 10004, Tel: (212) 509-7030
(Mfg/distr of road maint mach, welding & ind equip & supplies)
Ferrex-Europe, London, England

FERRO CORPORATION   One Erieview Plaza, Cleveland, OH 44114,
Tel: (216) 641-8580
(Chems, coatings, plastics, refractories)
Ferro (Great Britain) Ltd., Ounsdale Rd., Wombourne, Wolverhampton, WV5 8DA, England

FIDELITY BANK   135 S Broad St, Philadelphia, PA 19109, Tel: (215) 985-6000
(Investments & banking)
Fidelity Bank, 1 Bishopsgate, London EC2N 3AB, England

FIGGIE INTERNATIONAL INC   4420 Sherwin Rd, Willoughby, OH 44094,
Tel: (216) 946-9000
(Fire protection, safety & security, consumer/recreation prdts, electrical &
electronic instru)
Fred Perry Sportswear Ltd., Meyer Dumore, England

FINNIGAN CORP   355 River Oaks Parkway, San Jose, CA 95134-1991,
Tel: (408) 433-4800
(Mfr mass spectrometers, data handling sys, methodology devel)
Finnigan MAT Ltd., Paradise, Hemel Hempstead, Herts, HP2 4TG, England
Finnigan MAT Ltd., Unit 14, Howard Court, Manor Park, Runcorn, Cheshire WA7 1SJ, England

FIRST CITY NATIONAL BANK   1001 Main St, Houston, TX 77002,
Tel: (607) 772-2011
(Commercial banking)
First City National Bank of Houston, 99 Bishopsgate, 20th Floor, London EC2M 3XD, England

FIRST INTERSTATE BANCORP   633 W 5th St, Los Angeles, CA 90071,
Tel: (213) 614-3001
(Banking)

(cont)

First Interstate Bank, Ltd., First Interstate House, 6 Agar St., London WC2H 4HN, England

THE FIRST NATIONAL BANK OF ATLANTA   PO Box 4148, Atlanta, GA 30302,
Tel: (404) 332-5000
(Commercial banking)
The First National Bank of Atlanta, 7 Albemarle St., London W1X 3HF, England

FIRST NATIONAL BANK OF BOSTON   100 Federal St, Boston, MA 02110,
Tel: (617) 434-2200
(Commercial banking)
Africa Private Banking, 12 Cadogan Pl., London SW1 9HX, England
Boston Financial Co. Ltd., Spencer House, 23 Sheen Rd., Richmond, Surrey, TW9 1BG, England
Boston Trust & Savings Ltd., Boston House, Lower Dagnall St., St. Albans, Herts. AL3 4PG, England
First Boston Corp.Ltd., 16 Finsbury Circus, London EC2M 7RY, England
First National Bank of Boston, Box 155, 5 Cheapside, London, EC2P 2DE, England
First National Bank of Boston, 31 Lowndes St., London, SW1X 9HX, England

FIRST NATIONAL BANK OF CHICAGO   One First National Plaza, Chicago, IL 60670,
Tel: (312) 732-4000
(Financial services)
First Chicago Ltd., First Chicago House, 90 Long Acre, London WC2E 9RB, England
First National Bank of Chicago, First Chicago House, 90 Long Acre, London WC2E 9RB, England

FISCHER & PORTER CO   125 E County Line Rd, Warminster, PA 18974,
Tel: (215) 674-6000
(Design/mfr meas, recording & control instru & sys; mfr ind glass prdts)
Fischer & Porter Ltd., Salterbeck Trading Estate, Workington, Cumbria, CA14 5DS, England

FISHER CONTROLS INTL INC   8000 Maryland Ave, Clayton, MO 63105,
Tel: (314) 694-9900
(Ind process control equip)
Fisher Controls Ltd., 6 Whitworth Rd., S.W. Ind. Estate, Peterlee, Co. Durham, SR8 2LY, England
Fisher Controls Ltd., Medway House, Knight Rd., Strood, Rochester, Kent, ME2 2EZ, England
Fisher Controls Ltd., Meriden East, Leicester LE3 2WU, England

FISHER-PRICE   636 Girard Ave, East Aurora, NY 14052, Tel: (716) 687-3000
(Mfr toys & games)
Fisher-Price, Northwest Industrial Estate, Mill Hill Rd., Peterlee, County Durham SR8 2HY, England
Fisher-Price, Fisher-Price House, Oaklands Park, Fishponds Rd., Wokingham RG11 2FD, England

FLAREGAS CORP   100 Airport Executive Park, Spring Valley, NY 10977,
Tel: (914) 352-8700
(Flare sys)
Flaregas Engineering Ltd., Bentinck House, Bentinck Rd., W. Drayton, Middlesex, England

FLEET/NORSTAR FINANCIAL GROUP INC   50 Kennedy Plaza, Providence, RI 02903,
  Tel: (401) 278-5800
  (Banking, financial serv)
    Fleet National Bank, 40-41 St. Andrews Hill, London ED4V 5DE, England

FLORASYNTH INC   410 E 62nd St, New York, NY 10021, Tel: (212) 371-7700
  (Mfr aromatic chems, fra- grances & flavors)
    Florasynth Ltd., 327 Oldfield Lane, Greenford, Middlesex, UB6 0AH, England

FLORIDA INTL FORWARDERS   6905 N W 25th St, PO Box 522085, Miami, FL 33122,
  Tel: (305) 592-6450
  (Air cargo service)
    Florida Intl. Forwarders Ltd., Hill & Delamain, Concord House, Colndale Rd.,
    Colnbrook, SL3 0HO, England

FLOW LABORATORIES INC   7655 Old Springhouse Rd, McLean, VA 22102,
  Tel: (703) 893-5900
  (Mfr/distr biotechnology)
    Flow Laboratories Ltd., Woodcock Hill, Harefield Rd., Rickmansworth, Herts WD3 1PQ,
    England

FLUOR CORP   3333 Michelson Dr, Irvine, CA 92730, Tel: (714) 975-2000
  (Engr/constr & related services; coal & lead)
    Fluor Daniel Ltd., London, England

FLYING TIGER LINE INC   7401 World Way W, Los Angeles, CA 90009,
  Tel: (213) 646-6161
  (Air frt carrier, air cargo service worldwide)
    Flying Tiger Line (UK) Ltd., Cargo Terminal, Heathrow Airport-London, Hounslow,
    Middlesex, England

FMC CORP   200 E Randolph Dr, Chicago, IL 60601, Tel: (312) 861-6000
  (Mach & chem for industry, agric & govt)
    FMC Corp. (UK) Ltd., Brunswick Rd., Cobbs Wood Ind. Estate, Ashford, Kent TN23 1DY,
    England

FMC MATERIAL HANDLING EQUIP DIV   57 Cooper Ave, Homer City, PA 15748-9234,
  Tel: (412) 479-8011
  (Mfr bulk material handling & automation equip)
    Riley Automation Ltd., Sinfin Lane, Foresters Park, Derby DE3 8AG, England

FOOTE CONE & BELDING COMMUNICATIONS INC   101 E Erie St, Chicago,
  IL 60611-2897, Tel: (312) 751-7000
  (Advertising agency)
    FCB Direct, 82 Baker St., London W1M 2AE, England
    FCB/MM, 82 Baker St., London WIM 2AE, England
    Garratt Baulcombe Associates, Bridgeford House, Trent Bridge, Nottingham NG2 5HP,
    England
    Publicis, 67 Brompton Rd., London SW3 1EF, England

FORD MOTOR CO   The American Road, Dearborn, MI 48121, Tel: (313) 322-3000
  (Mfr automobiles, trucks)
    Ford Motor Co. Ltd., Eagle Way, Brentwood, Essex CM13 3BW, England

FOREST LABORATORIES INC   150 E 58th St, New York, NY   10155,
Tel: (212) 421-7850
(Pharms)
    Pharmax Ltd., 5 Bourne Rd., Bexley, Kent, DA5 1NX, England

L B FOSTER CO   415 Holiday Dr, Pittsburgh, PA   15220, Tel: (713) 966-2730
(Steel pipe, railroad rail & acces)
    L.B. Foster Co., European Div., 40 Charlwood Rd., Putney, London SW15, England

FOSTER WHEELER CORP   Perryville Corporate Park, Clinton, NJ   08809-4000,
Tel: (201) 730-4000
(Engr, constr, mfg)
    FW Management Operations (UK) Ltd., Foster Wheeler House, Station Rd., Reading,
      Berks, RG1 1LX, England
    Foster Wheeler Ltd., Foster Wheeler House, Station Rd., Reading RG1 1LX, England
    Foster Wheeler Petroleum Development Ltd., Foster Wheeler House, Station Rd.,
      Reading RG1 1LX, England

FOUR WINDS INTL INC   1 SW Columbia Ave, #1200, Portland, OR   97258,
Tel: (503) 241-2732
(Transp of household goods & general cargo)
    Intl. Moving Services Ltd., Acorn House, Longshot Lane, Bracknell,
      Berks. RG12 1RL. England

FOXBORO CO   33 Commercial St, Foxboro, MA   02035, Tel: (508) 543-8750
(Mfr prdts/provide servs for ind automation)
    Foxboro Intercontinental Ltd., Redhill, Surrey RH1 2HL, England
    Foxboro Intl Ltd., Wiggie House, Redhill, Surrey RH1 2HL, England
    Foxboro Yoxall, Redhill, Surrey RH1 2HL, England

FRANK RUSSELL CO   909 A St, PO Box 1616, Tacoma, WA   98401-9949,
Tel: (206) 572-9500
(Investment services)
    Frank Russell Co., 75 Wimpole St., London W1M 7DD, England

THE FRANKLIN MINT   Franklin Center, PA   19091, Tel: (215) 459-6000
(Creation/mfr/mktg collectible items)
    Franklin Mint Ltd., 138 Bromley Rd., London, SE6 2XG, England

FRIES & FRIES INC   110 East 70th St, Cincinnati, OH   45216,
Tel: (513) 948-8000
(Flavoring compounds for food & pharm industries)
    Fries & Fries Ltd., 813 Bath Rd., Brislington, Bristol, BS4 5NL, England

FULLER CO   2040 Ave C, PO Box 2040, Bethlehem, PA   18001, Tel: (215) 264-6011
(Ind processing equip & sys, conveying & blending sys, etc)
    Gatx-Fuller Ltd., 7-15 Lansdowne Rd., Croydon CR9 2JD, England

H B FULLER CO   2400 Energy Park Dr, St Paul, MN   55108, Tel: (612) 645-3401
(Mfr/distr adhesives, sealants, coatings, paints, waxes, sanitation chems)
    H.B. Fuller U.K. Ltd., Greenhill Lane, Leabrooks, Derbyshire DE5S 4BR, England

FULTON BOILER WORKS INC   Port & Jefferson Sts, PO Box 257, Polaski,
NY 13142, Tel: (315) 298-5121
(Mfr steam & hot water boilers)
    Fulton Boiler Works (GB) Ltd., Unity St., St. Philip's, Bristol, England

FURON CO   29982 Ivy Glenn Dr, Laguna Niguel, CA 92677, Tel: (714) 831-5350
  (Mfr of ind components)
    Furon Felsted UK, Crusader House High St., Maxey, Peterborough PE6 9HQ, England

GAB BUSINESS SERVICES INC   123 William St, New York, NY 10038,
  Tel: (212) 306-8000
  (Ins adjustment)
    GAB Business Services Ltd., 105 Central Park Rd., London E6 3DW, England

GAF CORP   1361 Alps Rd, Wayne, NJ 07470, Tel: (201) 628-3000
  (Chems, bldg materials, commun)
    GAF (Great Britain) Co. Ltd., Tilson Rd., Roundthorn, Wythenshawe,
      Manchester M23 9PH, England
    GAF Europe, Rythe House, 12 Littleworth Rd., Esher, Surrey KT10 9PD, England

GAFFNEY CLINE & ASSOCIATES INC   PO Box 796309, Dallas, TX 75379,
  Tel: (214) 733-1183
  (Consultants to energy & mineral ind)
    Gaffney Cline & Assoc., Bentley Hall, Blacknest, Alton, Hamps. GU34 4PU, England

GALVESTON-HOUSTON CO   4900 Woodway, PO Box 2207, Houston, TX 77056,
  Tel: (713) 966-2500
  (Mfr ind equip)
    Bettis Actuators & Controls Ltd., Brunel Way, Fareham, Hants PO15 5SA, England

GAMLEN CHEMICAL CO   121 S Maple Ave, S San Francisco, CA 94080,
  Tel: (415) 873-1750
  (Chems, detergents & tank cleansers)
    Gamlen Chemical Co. (UK) Ltd., 15 Bevis Marks, London, EC3, England
    Gamlen Chemical Co. (UK) Ltd., London, Milford Haven, England
    Gamlen Chemical Co. (UK) Ltd., 351/353 Westminster Rd., Liverpool, Kent, 4, England
    Gamlen Chemical Co. (UK) Ltd., Liverpool, Hull, England
    Gamlen Chemical Co. (UK) Ltd., Wallingford Rd., Uxbridge, UB8 2TD, England
    H.W. Goodwin, "D" Warehouse, Eastern Dock, Southampton, England
    Harding Bros. Ltd., 2nd Way, Avonmouth, England
    James McReady & Sons, Corporation St., Belfast, Northern Ireland, England

GANNETT CO INC   1100 Wilson Blvd, Arlington, VA 22224, Tel: (703) 284-6000
  (Newspaper pub, opinion research)
    Louis Harris & Associates Inc., London, England
    USA Today Intl., London, England

GARDNER-DENVER MINING & CONSTRUCTION   1700 Blue Hills Dr, NE, Roanoke,
  VA 24012-8601, Tel: (703) 343-1837
  (Mfr portable air compressors & related drilling access)
    Gardner-Denver Mining & Construction, Sheffield, England

GARNAR BOOTH INC   24 Main St, PO Box 367, Peabody, MA 01960,
  Tel: (617) 531-3730
  (Leather & leather raw stock brokers)
    Garnor Booth Ltd., Grange House, 84/86 Borough High St., London, SE1 1LN, England

THE GATES RUBBER CO   PO Box 5887, Denver, CO 80217, Tel: (303) 744-1911
  (Mfr auto/ind belts & hose, hydraulic hose & couplings, molded rubber prdts)
    Gates Hydraulics Ltd., Station Rd., St. Neots, Huntingdon, Cambs. PE19 1QF, England

GATX CORP   120 S Riverside Plaza, Chicago, IL 60606, Tel: (312) 621-6200
  (Railcar leasing, maint & mgmt, bulk liquid storage, fin serv, shipping, mineral
  processing)
      GATX Fuller Ltd., Radnor House 1272 London Rd., London SW16 4DX, England
      GATX Lease Finance Ltd., 10-12 Cork St., London W1X 1PD, England

GCA CORP   7 Shattuck Rd, Andover, MA 01810, Tel: (508) 837-3000
  (Mfr imaging sys for semiconductor ind)
      General Signal SEG Ltd., Berk House, Basing View, Basingstoke, Hampshire RG21 2HZ,
      England

GELMAN SCIENCES INC   600 South Wagner St, Ann Arbor, MI 48106,
  Tel: (313) 665-0651
  (Laboratory prdts)
      Gelman Sciences Ltd. UK, 10 Harrowden Rd., Brackmills, Northampton NN4 OE2, England

GENERAL AUTOMATION INC   1055 S East St, Anaheim, CA 92806,
  Tel: (714) 778-4800
  (Computer hardware & serv)
      General Automation Ltd., 43-45 Windsor Rd., Slough, Berkshire, SL1 2DY, England

GENERAL BINDING CORP   One GBC Plaza, Northbrook, IL 60062,
  Tel: (708) 272-3700
  (Binding & laminating equip & associated supplies)
      General Binding Co., Ltd., Rutherford Rd., Basingstoke, Hants RG24 OPD, England
      General Binding Corp., Rutherford Rd., Basingstoke, Hants. RG24 OPD, England

GENERAL DATACOMM INDUSTRIES INC   1579 Straits Turnpike, Middlebury,
  CT 06762-1299, Tel: (203) 574-1118
  (Mfr trans equip for commun networks)
      General DataComm Ltd., Molly Millar Lane, Wokingham, Berkshire RG11 2QF, England

GENERAL ELECTRIC CO   3135 Easton Tpk, Fairfield, CT 06431,
  Tel: (203) 373-2211
  (Diversified mfr, tech & servs)
      GE Intl. Operations, Shortlands, Hammersmith, London W6 8BX, England

GENERAL FOODS CORP   250 North St, White Plains, NY 10625, Tel: (914) 335-2500
  (Processor, distributor & mfr of foods)
      General Food Ltd., Banbury, Oxon OX16 7QU, England

GENERAL INSTRUMENT CORP   767 Fifth Ave, New York, NY 10153-0082,
  Tel: (212) 207-6200
  (Electronic components & sys)
      GI Jerrold Div., 95 Farnham Rd., Slough, Berks. SL1 4UN, England
      General Instrument Lamps, Beetons Way, Bury St. Edmunds, Suffolk, IP32 6RA, England

GENERAL MONITORS INC   3037 Enterprise St, Costa Mesa, CA 92626,
  Tel: (714) 540-4895
  (Combustible/toxic gas monitors, UV/IR flame detection)
      General Monitors, Queens Ave., Hurdsfield Ind. Estate, Macclesfield,
        Ches. SK10 2BN, England

GENERAL MOTORS ACCEPTANCE CORP   3044 West Grand Blvd, Detroit, MI 48202,
  Tel: (313) 556-5000
  (Automobile financing)
      GMAC UK Ltd., Oakland House, Talbot Rd., Old Trafford, Manchester M16 OPQ, England

GMAC UK Ltd., Aire House, Swinegate, Leeds LS1 4AG, England
GMAC UK Ltd., Bridge House 121, Smallbrook, Queensway, Birmingham, B5 4JP, England
GMAC UK Ltd., Wesley House, 19 Chapel St., P.O. Box 11, Luton, Beds. LU1 2SE, England
GMAC UK Ltd., Kings House, Bond St., Briston BS1 2AE, England

GENERAL MOTORS CORP   3044 W Grand Blvd, Detroit, MI 48202,
Tel: (313) 556-5000
(Automotive prdts, electronics)
  Delco Electronics Overseas Corp., Moorgate Rd., Kirkby, Liverpool, L33 7XL, England
  Delco Products Overseas Corp., P.O. Box 4, High St. North, Dunstable, LU6 1BQ, England
  General Motors Overseas Commercial Vehicle Corp., same address
  Group Lotus PLC, Norwich, Norfolk NR14 8E2, England
  Saginaw Overseas Corp., 1/8 Capitol Way, London NW9 OEH, England
  Vauxhall Motors Ltd., P.O. Box 3, Kimpton Rd., Luton LU2 0SY, England

GENERAL RAILWAY SIGNAL CO   PO Box 20600, Rochester, NY 14602-0600,
Tel: (716) 783-2000
(Railway, rapid transit & vehicle control sys)
  GEC-General Signal Ltd., Elstree Way, Borehamwood, Hertfordshire, WD6 1RX, England

GENERAL REINSURANCE CORP   PO Box 10350, Stamford, CT 06904,
Tel: (203) 328-5000
(Reinsurance)
  General Reinsurance Lrd., 16/18 London St., London EC3R 7JP, England

GENRAD INC   300 Baker Ave, Concord, MA 01742, Tel: (508) 369-4400
(Mfr automatic test equip)
  Cirrus Designs Ltd., Monmouth House, Monmouth Rd., Cheadle Hulme, Cheshire SK8 7AY, England
  GenRad Fareham Ltd., Waterside Gardens, Fareham, Hants PO16 8RR, England
  GenRad Ltd., 3 Rosborough Way, Foundation Park, Maidenhead, Berkshire, SL6 3U0, England

GERBER SCIENTIFIC INSTRUMENT CO   83 Gerber Rd West, So Windsor, CT 06074,
Tel: (203) 644-1551
(CADICAM for electronic & graphic arts ind)
  Gerber Scientific UK Ltd., Clive House, 12/18 Queens Rd., Weybridge, Surrey, KT13 9XD, England

GETTY OIL CO   3810 Wilshire Blvd, Los Angeles, CA 90010, Tel: (213) 739-2100
(Petroleum & petroleum prdts)
  Getty Oil (Britain) Ltd., 1 Butter Place, London, SW1A OPS, England

GETZ CORP   150 Post St, San Francisco, CA 94108, Tel: (415) 772-5500
(Marketing/distribution serv)
  Getz Brox & Co. Inc., 63 Grosvenor St., London W1X 9DA, England

GILBARCO INC   PO Box 22087, Greensboro, NC 27420, Tel: (919) 292-3011
(Service station equip)
  Gilbarco Ltd., Crompton Close, Basildon, Essex, SS14 3BA, England

GILBERT COMMONWEALTH INTL INC   PO Box 1498, Reading, PA 19603,
Tel: (215) 775-2600
(Studies, engr & design, constr & project mgmt, technologies & training for ind & govts)

(cont)

Gilbert Assoc. (Europe) Ltd., Fraser House, London Rd., Twickenham, Middlesex,
 TW1 3ST, England
Halcrow Gilbert Associates Ltd., Burderop park, Swindon, Wiltshire SN4 0QD, England

GILFORD INSTRUMENT LABS INC   132 Artino St, Oberlin, OH 44074,
 Tel: (216) 774-1041
 (Med electronic instru)
 Corning Medical Scientific, Halstead, Essex, CO9 2DX, England

THE GILLETTE CO   Prudential Tower, Boston, MA 02199, Tel: (617) 421-7000
 (Mfr/distr shaving prdts, toiletries & cosmetics, stationery prdts)
 Gillette Ind. Ltd., Great West Rd., Isleworth, Middlesex,TW7 5NP, England

THE GLEASON WORKS   1000 University Ave, Rochester, NY 14692,
 Tel: (716) 473-1000
 (Mfr mfg machines, tooling & services)
 Gleason Works, Ltd., Plymbridge Rd., Estover, Plymouth, Devon PL6 7LQ, England

GLENDINNING COMPANIES INC   Glendinning Place, Westport, CT 06880,
 Tel: (203) 226-4711
 (Marketing consultants)
 Glendinning Associates Intl., 9 Savoy St., London, WC2R 0BB, England

GLENOIT MILLS INTL CORP   111 West 40th St, New York, NY 10018,
 Tel: (212) 391-3915
 (Synthetic pile fabrics)
 Glenoit (UK) Ltd., Aberford Rd., Woodlesford, Leeds, LS26 8PX, England

GLOBAL INTERNATIONAL   500 Ygnacio Valley Rd, #175, Walnut Creek, CA 94596,
 Tel: (415) 933-2293
 (Freight forwarding)
 Global International Forwarding Ltd., 16 Perivale Ind. Park, Horsenden Lane S.,
  Greenford, Middlesex UB7 7RW, England

GLOBAL MARINE DRILLING CO   777 N Eldridge, Houston, TX 77079,
 Tel: (713) 496-8000
 (Offshore drilling)
 Global Marine Europe Ltd., Standbrook House, 2 Old Bond St., London, W1X 4GH,
  England

GOODYEAR TIRE & RUBBER CO   1144 E Market St, Akron, OH 44316-0001,
 Tel: (216) 796-2121
 (Mfr tires, rubber prdts)
 Goodyear Great Britain Ltd., Stafford Rd., Bushbury, Wolverhampton WV10 6D4, England

W R GRACE & CO   1114 Ave of the Americas, New York, NY 10036,
 Tel: (212) 819-5500
 (Specialty chems, natural resources, consumer serv)
 Dearborn Chemicals Ltd., Widnes, Cheshire, WA8 8TZ, England
 DuBois Chemicals, Ltd., DuBois House, 498 Sunleigh Rd., Wembley, Middlesex,
  HA0 4PT, England
 Emerson & Cuming (UK) Ltd., Colville Rd., Acton, London, W3 8BU, England
 W.R. Grace Ltd., Norhtdale House, North Circular Rd., London NW10 7UH, England

GRACO INC 4040 Olson Memorial Hwy, PO Box 1441, Minneapolis, MN 55440-1441,
Tel: (612) 623-6000
(Mfr/serv fluid handling equip & sys)
Graco UK Ltd., Wednesfield Rd., Wolverhampton, West Midlands, WV10 0DR, England

GRANT HARDWARE CO High St, W Nyack, NY 10994, Tel: (914) 358-4400
(Mfr door, drawer & shelf hdwe)
Grant Slides Ltd., Unit 10, Brunswick Industrial Centre, Cobbs Wood, Ashford,
Kent TN23 1EH, England

GRANT THORNTON INTL Prudential Plaza, Chicago, IL 60601, Tel: (312) 856-0001
(Intl accountants)
Grant Thornton, Ltd., Fairfax House, Fulwood Place, High Holborn, London, WC1V 6DW,
England

GREAT LAKES CARBON INTL CORP 320 Old Briarcliff Rd, Briarcliff Manor,
NY 10510, Tel: (914) 941-7800
(Mfr carbon prdts, petroleum)
Anglo Great Lakes Corp. Plc., Newburn Haugh, Newcastle-upon-Tyne NE15 8SU, England
Great Lakes Carbon Intl. Corp., 14 Waterloo Place, London, SW1Y 4AR, England

GREAT LAKES CHEMICAL CORP PO Box 2200, W Lafayette, IN 47906,
Tel: (317) 463-2511
(Bromine & bromine derivatives)
Great Lakes Chemical (Europe) Ltd., Belmont Chambers #7, Baker R.D., Uxbridge,
Middlesex, England

GREEFF FABRICS INC 150 Midland Ave, Port Chester, NY 10573,
Tel: (914) 939-6200
(Fabrics, wallcoverings)
Warner & Sons Ltd., 7-11 Noel St., London, W1V 4AL, England

A P GREEN INDUSTRIES Green Boulevard, Mexico, MO 65265, Tel: (314) 473-3626
(Mfr refractories & lime)
A.P. Green Refractories Ltd., Dock Road South, Bromborough, Wirral,
Merseyside L62 4SP, England

GREY ADVERTISING INC 777 Third Ave, New York, NY 10017, Tel: (212) 546-2000
(Advertising)
Grey Advertising Ltd., 50 Conduit St., London, W1R 0AR, England

GREYHOUND CORP Greyhound Tower, Phoenix, AZ 85077, Tel: (602) 248-4000
(Mfr consumer prdts, transportation, consumer & fin services)
Greyhound Financial & Leasing Corp. AG, 11 Albemarle St., London W1X 3HE, England
Greyhound Intl. Travel Inc., Sussex House, London Rd., East Grinstead,
West Sussex RH19 1LD, England

GRIFFITH LABORATORIES INC I Griffith Center, Alsip, IL 60658,
Tel: (708) 371-0900
(Ind food ingredients & equip)
Griffith Laboratories (UK) Ltd., Cotes Park Estate, Somercotes, Derby, DE5 4NN,
England

GROLIER INC Old Shereman Tpk, Danbury, CT 06816, Tel: (203) 797-3500
(Publishers)
Franklin Watts Ltd., 8 Cork St., London, W1X 2HA, England

(cont)

The House of Grolier, Ltd., Intl. House, 85 Great North Rd., Hatfield, Herts, AL9 5EH, England

GTE CORP   One Stamford Forum, Stamford, CT 06904, Tel: (203) 965-2000
(Electr prdts, telecom sys, publ & commun)
    General Telephone & Electronic Corp., Wyke, England
    General Telephone & Electronic Corp., Shipley, England
    General Telephone & Electronic Corp., Bedford, England

GUARDIAN ELECTRIC MFG CO   1425 Lake Ave, Woodstock, IL 60098,
  Tel: (815) 337-0050
(Mfr ind controls, electrical relays & switches)
    Guardian Intl. Sales, Thrumsdorm House, Collafield, Littledean, Glos. GL14 3LG, England

GULTON INDUSTRIES INC   212 Durham Ave, Metuchen, NJ 08840,
  Tel: (908) 548-6500
(Electr instru & controls, commun equip)
    Gulton Intl., The Hyde, Brighton, BN2 4JU, England

FRANK B HALL & CO INC   549 Pleasantville Rd, Briarcliff Manor, NY 10510,
  Tel: (914) 769-9200
(Insurance)
    Frank B. Hall, P.O. Box 219, 6 Braham St., London E1 8ED, England
    Leslie & Godwin (Holding) Ltd., Dunster House, Mark Lane, London EC3P 3AD, England

HALLIBURTON CO   3600 Lincoln Plaza, Dallas, TX 75201-3391,
  Tel: (214) 978-2600
(Oil field serv, engineering & constr)
    Brown & root (UK) Ltd., B&R House, 125 High St., Colliers Wood, London SW19 2JR, England

HALLMARK CARDS INC   PO Box 419580, Kansas City, MO 64141, Tel: (816) 274-5100
(Mfr greeting cards & related prdts)
    Hallmark Cards Ltd., Hallmark House, Station Rd., Henley-On-Thames, Oxfordshire RG9 1LQ, England
    W.N. Sharp Ltd., Bingley Rd., Heaton, Bradford BD9 6SD, England

HAMLIN INC   612 E Lake St, Lake Mills, WI 53551, Tel: (414) 648-3000
(Mfr position sensors, switches, relays)
    Hamlin Electronics Europe Ltd., Park Rd., Diss, Norfolk IP22 3AY, England

HANDY & HARMAN   850 Third Ave, New York, NY 10022, Tel: (212) 752-3400
(Precious & specialty metals for industry, refining, scrap metal)
    Rigby Maryland (Stainless) Ltd., Crystal Works, Union Rd., Liversedge, WF15 7JU, England

J E HANGER INC   40 Paterson St, NE, Washington, DC 20002, Tel: (202) 789-0050
(Artificial limbs)
    J.E. Hanger & Co. Ltd., Reehampton Lane, SW15 5PL, England

HARBRIDGE HOUSE INC   11 Arlington St, Boston, MA 02116, Tel: (617) 267-6410
(Mgmt consulting & training)
    Harbridge House Inc., 3 Hanover Sq., London W1R 9RD, England

HARCOURT BRACE JOVANOVICH INC   Harcourt Brace Jovanovich Bldg, Orlando,
  FL 32887, Tel: (305) 345-2000
  (Book publ, tests & related serv, journals, facisimile reprints, mgmt consult,
  operates parks/shows)
    Grune & Stratton Ltd., same address

HARLEY-DAVIDSON INTL   3700 W Juneau Ave, Milwaukee, WI 53208,
  Tel: (414) 935-4071
  (Mfr motorcycles, recreational & coml vehicles, parts & accessories)
    Harley-Davidson U.K. Ltd., P.O. Box 27, Daventry, Northamptonshire NN11 5RW, England

HARPER & ROW PUBLISHERS INC   10 E 53rd St, New York, NY 10022,
  Tel: (212) 593-7000
  (Book publishers)
    Harper & Row Ltd., 28 Tavistock St., London, WC2E, 7PN, England

THE HARPER GROUP INC   260 Townsend St, PO Box 77933, San Francisco,
  CA 94107, Tel: (415) 978-0600
  (Ocean/air freight fwdg, customs brokerage, packing & whse, logistics mgt, ins)
    Baxter Hoare Ltd., UK, International House, 2 Balford Rd., Ilford, Essex IG1 4JL,
      England
    Circle Freight Intl. UK, Ltd., Haslemere Ind. Estate, Unit 6, Armadale Rd.,
      Feltham, Middlesex TW14 OLW, England
    Circle Las Air Cargo, Heathrow Intl. Trading Estate, Green Lane, Hounslow,
      Middlesex TW4 6HB, England

HARPER-WYMAN CO   2150 Western Ct, Hinsdale, IL 60532, Tel: (708) 960-9500
  (Mfr thermostatic & electr controls, valves, combustion prdts)
    Diamond Controls Ltd., Vulcan Rd., Norwich NR6 6AH, Englandire, England

HARRIS CORP   1025 W NASA Blvd, Melbourne, FL 32919, Tel: (305) 961-9100
  (Communications & information handling equip)
    Harris-Intertype Ltd., Farnham Rd., Slough, Berks, England

HARRIS PRC INC   300 E 42nd St, New York, NY 10017, Tel: (212) 986-2700
  (Engineering consultants)
    PRC Harris Inc., 200 Great Dever St., London, SE1 4YB, England

HARSHAW/FILTRO PARTNERS   30100 Chagrin Blvd, Cleveland, OH 44124,
  Tel: (216) 292-9200
  (Ind chems)
    Harshaw Chemicals Ltd., P.O. Box 4, Daventry, Northamptonshire, NN11 4HF,England

HARVEY HUBBELL INC   584 Derby-Milford Road, Orange, CT 06477,
  Tel: (203) 789-1100
  (Electrical wiring components)
    Harvey Hubbell Ltd., Minehead, Somerset, England

HAYNES INTL INC   1020 W Park Ave, PO Box 9013, Kokomo, IN 46904-9013,
  Tel: (317) 456-6000
  (Mfr cobalt & nickel-base alloys for aerospace & chem inds)
    Haynes Intl., Inc., PO Box 10, Parkhouse St., Openshaw, Manchester M11 2ER, England

HAYSSEN MFG CO   5300 Hwy 42 North, Sheboygan, WI 53081, Tel: (414) 458-2111
  (Mfr automatic packaging mach)
    Hayssen Europe Ltd., Fison Way, Thetford, Norfolk, IP24 IHT, England

HAZLETON CORP   13873 Park Center Rd, Herndon, VA 22071, Tel: (703) 478-9450
  (R&D)
    Hazleton Europe, Otley Rd., Harrogate HG3 1PY, England

HCA INTL CO   1 Park Plaza, PO Box 550, Nashville, TN 37202,
  Tel: (615) 327-9551
  (Hospital & health care mgmt)
    HCA Intl Ltd., 49 Wigmore St., London W1A 9LE, England

HCC INDUSTRIES INTL   16311 Ventura Blvd, Encino, CA 91436,
  Tel: (818) 995-4131
  (Glass-to-metal thremetically sealed connectors, leaders & terminals (components))
    HCC Ind. Intl., Beaver House, Victoria Rd., Swindon, Wiltshire SN1 3BV, England

H J HEINZ CO   PO Box 57, Pittsburgh, PA 15230, Tel: (412) 456-5100
  (Food prdts)
    H.J. Heinz Co., Ltd., Hayes Park, Hayes, Middlesex, W34 8AL, England

HENNINGSEN FOODS INC   2 Corporate Park Dr, White PLains, NY 10604,
  Tel: (914) 694-1000
  (Dehyd egg, poultry & meat prdts)
    Henningsen Foods Ltd., 168 Sloane St., London SW1, England

HERCULES INC   Hercules Plaza, Wilmington, DE 19894, Tel: (302) 594-5000
  (Mfr spec chems, plastics, film & fibers, coatings, resins, food ingredients)
    Hercules Ltd., PFW Ltd., Bletchley, Milton Keyes MK1 1JR, England

HERTZ CORP   225 Brae Blvd, Park Ridge, NJ 07656-0713, Tel: (201) 307-2000
  (Automobile rental)
    Hertz Rent A Car, Radnor House, 1272 London Rd., Norbury SW16 4DQ, England

HEWLETT-PACKARD CO   3000 Hanover St, PO Box 10301, Palo Alto, CA 94303-0890,
  Tel: (415) 857-1501
  (Mfr measurement & computation prdts & sys)
    Hewlett-Packard Laboratories, same address
    Hewlett-Packard Ltd., Nine Mile Ride, Wokingham RG11 3LL, England

HEXCEL CORP   20701 Nordhoff St, Chatsworth, CA 91311, Tel: (213) 882-3022
  (Honeycomb core materials, specialty chems, resins & epoxies)
    Hexcel UK, Catherine House, 63 Guilford Rd., Lightwater, Surrey, England

HICKORY RECORDS INC   2510 Franklin Rd, Nashville, TN 37204,
  Tel: (615) 297-8558
  (Phonograph records, tapes, etc)
    Acuff-Ross Music Ltd., 16 St. George St., London, W1, England

HIGH VOLTAGE ENGINEERING CORP   S Bedford St, PO Box 416, Burlington,
  MA 01803, Tel: (617) 272-1313
  (Irradiated plastics, electrical connectors & switches, instru)
    Anacon (Instruments) Ltd., Maidenhead, England

HIGHLANDS INSURANCE CO   600 Jefferson St, Houston, TX 77002,
  Tel: (713) 659-5541
  (Property & casualty ins)
    Highlands Ins. Co. (UK) Ltd., 117 Fenchurch St., London EC3M 5EJ, England

HILL & KNOWLTON INC   420 Lexington Ave, New York, NY 10017,
 Tel: (212) 697-5600
 (Public relations, public affairs, comm counseling)
   Hill & Knowlton (UK) Ltd., 5-11 Theobalds Rd., London WC1X 8SH, England

HOBART INTL INC   World Headquarters Ave, Troy, OH 45374, Tel: (513) 335-7171
 (Food preparation & processing equip)
   Hobart Brothers (Gt. Britain) Ltd., P.O. Box 28, Unit 4, Dunhams Lane, Letchworth,
     SG6 1LJ, England

HOKE INC   1 Tenakill Rd, Cresskill, NJ 07626, Tel: (201) 568-9100
 (Valves, fittings, fluid control specialties)
   Hoke Intercontinental, 1-3 Bouverie Rd., Harrow, Middlesex HA1 4HB, England

A J HOLLANDER & CO INC   257 Park Ave So, New York, NY 10010,
 Tel: (212) 353-8000
 (Hides, skins & leather)
   Hollander Hyams Ltd., 20-22, Bedford Row, London, WC1R 4ET, England

HOLLINGSWORTH & VOSE CO   112 Washington St, East Walpole, MA 02032,
 Tel: (508) 668-0295
 (Mfr tech & ind papers & non-wovens)
   Hollingsworth & Vose Co. Ltd., Postlip Mills, Winchcombe, Cheltenham,
     Gloucestershire GL54 5BB, England

HOLOPHANE CO INC   214 Oakwood Ave, Newark, OH 43055, Tel: (614) 345-9631
 (Lighting equip)
   Holophane Ltd., Box 36, Bond Ave., Bletchley, Milton, Keynes, MK1 1JG, England

HOMELITE TEXTRON   14401 Carowinds Blvd, Charlotte, NC 28217,
 Tel: (704) 588-3200
 (Mfr pumps, generators, lawn/garden equip, outdoor power equip)
   Homelite Div. of Textron Ltd., Unit 22, Hitcher Green Ind. Estate, Clevedon,
     Bristol, Avon BS21 6XV, England

THE HOOVER GROUP   403 W 4th St N, Newton, IA 50208, Tel: (515) 792-8000
 (Mfr floor care prdts, laundry & refrig appliances)
   Hoover Ltd., Perivale, Greenford, Middlesex, UB6 8DX, England

HORWATH & HORWATH INTL   919 Third Ave, New York, NY 10022,
 Tel: (212) 980-3100
 (Public accountants & auditors)
   Horwath & Horwath (UK) Ltd., 84 Baker St., London, W1M 1DL, England
   Stoy Hayward & Co., 54 Baker St., London, W1M 1DJ, England

E F HOUGHTON & CO   PO Box 930, Valley Forge, PA 19482-0930,
 Tel: (215) 666-4000
 (Mfr spec chems, hydraulic fluids, lubricants)
   E.F. Houghton & Co. Ltd., Copthall House, Station Sq., Coventry, CV1 2FZ, England
   E.F. Houghton & Co. Ltd., Third Ave., Trafford Park, Manchester, M17 1JA, England
   E.F. Houghton & Co. Ltd., Shortroods Rd., Paisley, PA3 2NR, England
   E.F. Houghton & Co. Ltd., High Wycombe, Sands Industrial Estate, High Wycombe,
     England
   Edgar Vaughan & Co., Legge St., B'ham, B4 7EU, England
   Evco Seals Ltd., New Rd., Burntwood, England

HOUSEHOLD INTL INC   2700 Sanders Rd, Prospect Heights, IL 60070,
  Tel: (708) 564-5000
  (Financial services)
    HFC Bank, North St., Winkfield, Windsor, Berks. SL4 4TD, England

HOWE-BAKER ENGINEERS INC   PO Box 956, Tyler, TX 75710, Tel: (214) 597-0311
  (Design, fabricate, erect process sys for petroleum ind)
    Howmar Intl. Ltd., Albany Park Estate, Frimley Rd., Camberley, Surrey, GU15 2UD,
    England

HUBBARD FARMS INC   PO Box 415, Walpole, NH 03608, Tel: (603) 756-3311
  (Poultry breeding R&D, poultry foundation breeding stock)
    British United Turkeys Ltd., Warren Hall, Broughton Nr. Chester CH4 OEW, England

HUCK MFG CO   PO Box 19590, Irvine, CA 92713, Tel: (714) 855-9000
  (Mfr fasteners & fastening sys)
    Huck UK Ltd., Unit C, Stafford Park 7, Telford, Shropshire TF3 3BQ, England

HUGHES AIRCRAFT CO   PO Box 45066, Los Angeles, CA 90045, Tel: (213) 568-7200
  (Aircraft & aerospace sys & equip)
    Hughes Aircraft UK, 140 Park Lane, Suite 4, London, W1 England

HUGHES TOOL CO   PO Box 2539, Houston, TX 77001, Tel: (713) 924-2222
  (Equip & serv to oil & gas explor & prod ind)
    BJ Hughes B.V., 25/28 Old Burlington St., London, W1X 1LB, England
    Hughes Tool Co. Ltd., AMF House, 25/28, Old Burlington St., London, W1X 1LB, England

HUMANA INC   500 W Main St, Louisville, KY 40201, Tel: (502) 580-1000
  (Integrated health care)
    Humana Hospital-Wellington, Wellington Pl., London NW8 9LE, England

HUNKAR LABORATORIES INC   7007 Valley Ave, Cincinnati, OH 45244,
  Tel: (513) 272-1010
  (Process equip for plastics industry)
    Hunkar UK Ltd., Royex House, Aldermanbury Sq., London, EC2V 7LD, England

HYATT INTL CORP   200 West Madison St, Chicago, IL 60606, Tel: (312) 750-1234
  (Intl hotel mgmt)
    Hyatt Carlton Tower London, 2 Cadogan Pl., London SW1X 9PY, England

HYDROMATION FILTER CO   39201 Amrhein Rd, Livonia, MI 48150,
  Tel: (313) 464-0600
  (Ind filter sys)
    Hydromation Engineering Co. (UK) Ltd., 450 Blandford Rd., Hamworthy, Poole, Dorset,
    BH16 5BN, England

HYSTER CO   PO Box 2902, Portland, OR 97208, Tel: (503) 280-7000
  (Fork lifts, trucks, trailers, towing winches, personnel lifts, compaction equip)
    Hyster Europe Ltd., Berk House, Basing View, Basingstoke, Hants, RG21 2HQ, England

ICF KAISER ENGINEERS   1800 Harrison St, Oakland, CA 94612,
  Tel: (415) 268-6000
  (Engineering & constr)
    Kaiser Engineers Ltd., Regal House, London Rd., Twickenham, Middlesex, TW1 3QQ,
    England

ICI AMERICAS INC   Wilmington, DE 19897, Tel: (302) 575-3000
  (Chems, pharms, dyes, plastics, films, etc)
     Imperial Chemical Industries Ltd., Imperial Chemical House, Millbank, London, SW1,
     England

ICP   9100 Keystone Crossing, PO Box 40946, Indianapolis, IN 46240,
  Tel: (317) 844-7461
  (Magazines/directories for computer software mkt)
     ICP Publishing Ltd., 37 Albert Embankment, London SE1 7TL, England

IDEAL TOY CORP   184-10 Jamaica Ave, Hollis, NY 11423, Tel: (212) 454-5000
  (Toys, games, dolls)
     Ideal Toy Co. Ltd., Coronation St., Cressex, High Wycombe, Bucks, England

IDEX CORP   630 Dundee Rd, #400, Northbrook, IL 60062, Tel: (708) 498-7070
  (Mfr ind pumps, lubrication sys, metal fabrication equip, bending & clamping devices)
     Band-It Co., Ltd., Speedwell Industrial Estate, Staveley, Chesterfield, England

ILLINOIS TOOL WORKS INC   8501 West Higgins Rd, Chicago, IL 60631,
  Tel: (312)693-3040
  (Metal cutting tools, fasteners, sealants, gear measuring instru)
     ITW Ltd., 470 Bath Rd., Cippenham, Slough, Berks, SL1 6BJ, England

IMC MAGNETICS CORP   100 Jericho Quadrangle, Jericho, NY 11753,
  Tel: (516) 938-0800
  (Airmovers, elec motor driven fans, blowers; computer equip, etc)
     A.K. Fans Ltd., 32/34 Park Royal Rd., London NW10 7LN, England

IMCO SERVICES   5950 N Course Dr, Houston, TX 70072, Tel: (713) 561-1300
  (Drilling fluids)
     IMCO Services Div. Halliburton Mfg. Svcs. Ltd., 17 Hanover Sq., London, W1R OEL,
     England
     IMCO Services Div. Halliburton Mfg. Svcs. Ltd., Farraday Rd., Gapton Hall,
     Ind. Estate, Great Yarmouth, Norfolk NR31 ONF, England

IMODCO INC   23901 Calabasas Rd, #2090, Calabasas, CA 91302,
  Tel: (818) 713-8603
  (Single point mooring sys)
     Imodco Ltd., Tavistock House, Tavistock Sq., London WC1H 9LG, England

INA CORPORATION   1600 Arch St, Philadelphia, PA 19101, Tel: (215) 523-5335
  (Holding co: ins, financial serv)
     Brodrick, Leitch & Kendall Ltd., 655 Sefton House, Exchange Bldg., Liverpool,
     L2 3SE, England
     Commodore Shipping Co. Ltd., Commodore House, St. Sampson's, Guernsey, England
     Hodder Whitwill, Ltd., Gloucester Rd., Avonmouth, Bristol, BS1 1BA, England
     INA Universal Corp., 18 Finsbury Circus, London, EC2M 7DE, England
     Insurance Co. of North America (UK) Ltd., Bank House, Eight Cherry St., Birmingham,
     B25AL, England
     Insurance Co. of North America (UK) Ltd., Bridge House, Baldwin St., Bristol,
     BS1 1BA, England
     Insurance Co. of North America (UK) Ltd., Yorkshire House, Greek St., Leeds,
     LS1 5SX, England
     Insurance Co. of North America (UK) Ltd., Carlton House, 28 Regent St., Leicester,
     LE1 6YH, England
     W. Cockrill & Son, Oriel Chambers, 27 High St., Hull, England

INCOM INTERNATIONAL INC   3450 Princeton Pike, Lawrenceville, NJ 08648,
   Tel: (609) 896-7600
   (Roller & motorcycle chains, drive components, marine controls, etc)
      Locker Air Maze, Ltd., P.O. Box 17, Folly Lane, Warrington, WA5 5NP, England
      Teleflex-Morse, Ltd., Christopher Martin Rd., Basildon, Essex, SS14 3ES, England

INDUCTOTHERM CORP   10 Indel Ave, Rancocas, NJ 08073, Tel: (609) 267-9000
   (Mfr induction melting furnaces)
      Inductoheat Banyard Ltd., 16 Nuttfield Rd., Poole, Dorset BH17 7RD, England
      Inductotherm Europe, The Furlong, Droitwich, Worcestershire WR9 9AH, England

INDUSTRIAL ACOUSTICS CO   1160 Commerce Ave, Bronx, NY 10462,
   Tel: (212) 931-8000
   (Design/mfr acoustic structures for sound conditioning & noise control)
      Industrial Acoustics Co. Ltd., Walton House, Central Trading Estate, Staines,
         Middlesex, England

INFORMATION BUILDERS INC   1250 Broadway, New York, NY 10001,
   Tel: (212) 736-4433
   (Devel/serv computer software)
      Information Builders (UK) Ltd., Station House, Harrow Rd., Wembley, Middlesex,
         England

INFORMATION HANDLING SERVICES   15 Inverness Way E, Englewood, CO 80150,
   Tel: (303) 790-0600
   (Mfr indexed info databases)
      Technical Indexes Ltd., Willoughby Rd., Bracknell, Berkshire RG12 4DW, England

INFOTRON SYSTEMS CORP   Cherry Hill Ind Center-9, Cherry Hill, NJ 08003,
   Tel: (609) 424-9400
   (Data commun equip)
      Infotron Systems Ltd., Poundsbury Rd., Dorchester, Dorset DT1 1TQ, England

INGERSOLL ENGINEERS INC   1021 N Mulford Rd, Rockford, IL 61107,
   Tel: (815) 395-6440
   (Mgmt consultants to mfg businesses)
      Ingersoll Engineers Inc., Bourton Hall, Bourton on Dunsmore, Rugby,
         Warwickshire CV23 9SD, England

INGERSOLL-RAND CO   200 Chestnut Ridge Rd, Woodcliff Lake, NJ 07675,
   Tel: (201) 573-0123
   (Mfr compressors, rock drills, pumps, air tools)
      Ingersoll-Rand Co. Ltd., Horwich, Bolton Lancashire, England

INSTRON CORP   100 Royall St, Canton, MA 02021, Tel: (617) 828-2500
   (Testing instru)
      Instron Ltd., Coronation Rd., High Wycombe, Bucks. HP12 3SY, England

INSTRUMENTATION LABORATORY   113 Hartwell Ave, Lexington, MA 02173-3190,
   Tel: (617) 861-0710
   (Med & sci analyzers & meas instru)
      Instrumentation Laboratory (UK) Ltd., Kelvin Close, Birchwood Science Park,
         Warrington, Cheshire WA3 7PB, England

INTERCONEX INC   52 Vanderbilt Ave, New York, NY 10017, Tel: (212) 490-7444
   (Frt forwarding)
      Interconex Inc., Spilsby Rd., Harold Hill Ind. Estate, Harold Hill, Romford,
         Essex RM3 8SB, England

INTERFLORA INC   29200 Northwestern Hwy, Southfield, MI 48037,
   Tel: (313) 355-9300
   (Intl flowers by wire)
      Interflora British Unit, Sleaford House, Sleaford, Lincolnshire NG34 7TB, England

THE INTERLAKE CORP   550 Warrenville Rd, Lisle, IL 60532-4387,
   Tel: (708) 852-8800
   (Mfr handling/packaging sys, engr mat)
      Dexion Group PLC, Marylands Ave., Hemel Hempstead, Hertfordshire HP2 7EW, England
      Pakseal Industries Ltd., Pakseal House, Cordwallis Estate, Maidenhead,
         Berkshire SL6 7DB, England

INTERMEC CORP   6001 36th Ave West, Everett, WA 98203-9280,
   Tel: (206) 348-2600
   (Mfr automated data collection sys)
      Intermec UK Ltd., Attenborough House, 15 Bennett Rd., Reading, Berkshire RG2 OQX,
         England

INTERNATIONAL BUSINESS MACHINES (IBM)   Old Orchard Rd, Armonk,
   NY 10504-1783, Tel: (914) 765-1900
   (Info-handling sys, equip & serv)
      IBM United Kingdom Holdings Ltd., North Harbour, Portsmouth, Hants. PO6 3A4, England

INTERNATIONAL FLAVORS & FRAGRANCES INC   521 W 57th St, New York, NY 10019,
   Tel: (212) 765-5500
   (Create/mfr flavors, fragrances & aroma chems)
      Intl. Flavors & Fragrances, Ltd., Crown Rd., Southbury Rd., Enfield, Middlesex,
         England

INTERNATIONAL MAILING SYSTEMS INC   19 Forest Parkway, Shelton, CT 06484,
   Tel: (203) 926-1087
   (Mfr gummed tape dispensers, postal meters & scales, mailing machines)
      Better Packages (UK) Ltd., Powder Mill Lane, Dartford, Kent DA1 1NN, England

INTERNATIONAL MINERALS & CHEMICALS CORP   2315 Sanders Rd, Northbrook,
   IL 60062, Tel: (708) 564-8600
   (Fertilizers, chems, ind materials)
      IMC Europe, 19 Grafton St., London, W1X 4HL, England

INTERNATIONAL PAINT CO INC   PO Box 386, Union, NJ 07083, Tel: (212) 825-0800
   (Paints)
      Intl. Paint Co. Ltd., Henrietta House, 9 Henrietta Place, London, W1A 1AD, England

INTERNATIONAL PAPER   2 Manhattanville Rd, Purchase, NY 10577,
   Tel: (914) 397-1500
   (Mfr/distr container board, paper, wood prdts)
      Anitec Image (Great Britain) Ltd., 3&4 Suffolk Way, Drayton Rd.,
         Abingdon-Oxon OX14 5JX, England
      Bergvik Sales Ltd., Glen House, Stag Place, Victoria, Longon SW1E 5A6, England
      Boardcraft Ltd., West Wing, Jason House, Kerry Hill, Horsforth, Leeds LS18 4JR,
         England
      Hardboard Servicing Ltd., West Wing, Jason House, Kerry Hill, Horsforth,

(cont)

Leeds LS18 4JR, England
IPI Investments (UK) Ltd., 4/5 Grosvenor Place, London SW1X 7HD, England
International Paper Co. (UK) Ltd., 4/5 Grosvenor Pl., London SW1X 7HD, England
Strathmore-Beckett Intl. Ltd., DMR House, Oaklands Parks, Fishponds Rd., Wokingham, Berks. RC11 2FD, England
lford Ltd., 14-22 Tottenham St., London W1P OAH, England

INTERNATIONAL RECTIFIER CORP   233 Kansas St, El Segundo, CA 90245,
Tel: (213) 772-2000
(Mfr power semiconductors)
Intl. Rectifier Co. Ltd., Hurst Green, Oxted, Surrey RH8 9BB, England

INTERNATIONAL ROBOMATION INTELLIGENCE   2281 Las Palmas Dr, Carlsbad,
CA 92008, Tel: (619) 438-4424
(Vision sys, PCB inspectors)
IRI Ltd., 85 Shakespeare Dr., Shirley, Solihull, West Midlands B90 2AT, England

INTRALOX INC   PO Box 50699, New Orleans, LA 70150, Tel: (504) 733-0463
(Mfr plastic, modular conveyor belts & access)
Intralox, Ltd., 3rd Ave.- Bldg. 69, Pensnett Trading Estate, Kingswinford, West Midlands DY6 7PP, England

INVACARE CORP   899 Cleveland St, PO Box 4028, Elyria, OH 44036,
Tel: (216) 329-6000
(Mfr patient-care prdts)
Cartera J&A Ltd., Aintree Ave., White House Bus. PK., N. Bradley, Trowbridge, Wiltshire BA14 OXA, England

INVENTION SUBMISSION CORP   903 Liberty Ave, Pittsburgh, PA 15222,
Tel: (412) 288-1300
(Inventor assistance services)
Intromark Inc., 99/101 Regent St., London W1R 7HB, England
Invention Submission Corp., 99/101 Regent St., London W1R 7HB, England

IOMEGA CORP   1821 W 4000 South, Roy, UT 84067, Tel: (801) 778-4494
(Mfr data storage prdts)
Iomega, 7 Mt. Mews, High St., Hampton-On-Thames, Middlesex, England

IPSEN INDUSTRIES INC   PO Box 6266, Rockford, IL 61125, Tel: (815) 332-4941
(Heat treating equip)
Ipsen Industries Ltd., 26 Brighton Rd., Surbiton, Surrey, England

IRVIN INDUSTRIES INC   630 Fifth Ave, New York, NY 10111, Tel: (212) 977-2500
(Parachutes, cargo handling equip, life-saving devices)
Irvin (UK) Ltd., Icknield Way, Letchworth, Herts. SG6 1EY, England

IRVING TRUST CO   1 Wall St, New York, NY 10015, Tel: (212) 487-2121
(Intl banking)
Irving Trust Co., 36/38 Cornhill, London, EC3V 3NT, England

ITEL CONTAINERS INTL CORP   55 Francisco St, San Francisco, CA 94133,
Tel: (415) 984-4400
(Leasing, repair, storage of ocean-going containers)
Itel Containers Corp. Intl., Northside House, 69 Tweedy Rd., Bromley, Kent BR1 3WA, England

ITEL CORP   2 N Riverside Plaza, Chicago, IL 60606, Tel: (312) 902-1515
  (Transport & equip leasing & serv)
    Itel (UK) Ltd., England
    SSI Container Ltd., England

ITT CORP   1330 Ave of the Americas, New York, NY 10019, Tel: (212) 258-1000
  (Diversified mfr, tech & services)
    Intl. Telephone & Telegraph Co. Ltd., 190 Strand, London, WC2R 1DU, England

ITT RAYONIER INC   1177 Summer St, Stamford, CT 06904, Tel: (203) 348-7000
  (Chem cellulose, paper pulps, logs, lumber)
    Rayonier Industries Ltd., 17A Curson St., London, W1, England

ITT SHERATON CORP   60 State St, Boston, MA 02108, Tel: (617) 367-3600
  (Hotel operations)
    Sheraton Sales Center, The Kiln House, 210 New Kings Rd., London SW6 4NZ, England

ITW MAGNAFLUX   7300 W Lawrence Ave, Chicago, IL 60656, Tel: (708) 867-8000
  (Mfr testing & inspection equip)
    ITW Magnaflux Ltd., Faraday Rd., South Dorcan Industrial Estate, Swindon, Wilts,
      SN3 5HE, England

ITW SWITCHES   6615 W Irving Park Rd, Chicago, IL 60634, Tel: (312) 282-4040
  (Mfr precision switches)
    ITW Switches, Norway Rd., Portsmouth PO3 5HT, England

JAMESBURY CORP   640 Lincoln St, Worcester, MA 01605, Tel: (617) 852-0200
  (Mfr valves & accessories)
    Jamesbury Ltd., Unit A1, Rustington Trading Estate, Dominion Way, Rustington,
      W. Sussex BN16 3HQ, England

JESUP & LAMONT INTL INC   360 Madison Ave, New York, NY 10017,
  Tel: (212) 907-0100
  (Investment bankers, brokers)
    Jessup & Lamont Intl. Ltd., 44 Hill St., London, W1X 7FR, England

JET-LUBE INC   PO Box 21258, Houston, TX 77026, Tel: (713) 674-7617
  (Grease & lubricants)
    Jet-Lube Lubricants Ltd., Redform Rd., Maidenhead, Berkshire, England

JETBORNE INC   4010 NW 36th Ave, Miami, FL 33142, Tel: (305) 635-6060
  (Aircraft sales, leasing, support)
    Jetborne UK Ltd., Unit 12, Hampton Farm Ind. Estate, Hampton Rd. West, Hanworth,
      Middlesex TW13 6DH, England

JIM WALTER INTL SALES CORP   1500 N Dale Mabry, Tampa, FL 33607,
  Tel: (813) 871-4212
  (Bldg materials, home constr gas & oil explor, sugar growing & refining, chems,
  minerals)
    Celotex Ltd., Warwick House, 27-31 St. Mary's Rd., London, W5S PR, England
    Jim Walter Intl. Sales, 27 St. Mary's Rd., London, W5 5PR, England

JMK INTERNATIONAL INC   4800 Bryant Irvin Ct, Fort Worth, TX 76107,
  Tel: (817) 737-3703
  (Holding co)
    Jamak Fabrication Europe Ltd., Europa Trading Estate, Stonechough Rd., Raddiffe,
      Manchester MZ6 9HE, England

JOHN HANCOCK MUTUAL LIFE INSURANCE CO   200 Clarendon St, PO Box 111, Boston,
MA 02117, Tel: (617) 572-6000
(Life ins)
   John Hancock Mutual Life Insurance Co. Ltd., 38 Trinity Sq., London, England

JOHNSON & JOHNSON   One Johnson & Johnson Plaza, New Brunswick, NJ 08933,
Tel: (201) 524-0400
(Surgical, med & baby prdts)
   Cilag Ltd., High Wycombe, England
   Codman Ltd., Maidenhead, England
   Critikon Ltd., Ascot, England
   Iolab U.K., Maidenhead, England
   Janssen Pharmaceutical Ltd., Oxon, England
   Johnson & Johnson Ltd., Maidenhead, England
   Johnson & Johnson Orthopaedics Ltd., New Milton, England
   Johnson & Johnson Patient Care Ltd., Ascot, England
   Ortho Diagnostic Systems Ltd., Box 79, Saunderton, High Wycombe, Bucks, HP14 4HJ,
      England
   Vistakon Ltd., Maidenhead, England

S C JOHNSON & SON INC   1525 Howe St, Racine, WI 53403, Tel: (414) 631-2000
(Home, auto, commercial & personal care prdts, specialty chems)
   Johnson Wax Ltd., Frimley Green, Camberley, Surrey, GU16 5AJ, England

JOHNSON CONTROLS INC   5757 W Green Bay Ave, PO Box 591, Milwaukee, WI 53201,
Tel: (414) 228-1200
(Mfr facility mgmt & control sys, auto seating, batteries & plastics)
   Johnson Control Systems Ltd., Stonehill Green, Weatlea Down, Swindon,
      Wilts. SN5 7DD, England

THE JOHNSON CORP   805 Wood St, Three Rivers, MI 49093, Tel: (616) 278-1715
(Mfr rotary joints & syphon sys)
   Johnson Corp (JOLO) Ltd., Little Lane, Ilkley, West Yorkshire LS29 8HY, England

THE JOURNAL OF COMMERCE   110 Wall St, New York, NY 10005, Tel: (212) 425-1616
(Business newspaper & journal pub)
   Derek Wood Associates, P.O. Box 4, Faversham, Kent, England

K-TEL INTL INC   15525 Medina Rd, Plymouth, MN 55447, Tel: (612) 559-6800
(Packaged consumer entertainment & convenience prdts)
   K-Tel Intl. (UK) Ltd., 620 Western Ave., London, W3 OTU, England

KAISER ALUMINUM & CHEMICAL CORP   300 Lakeside Dr, Oakland, CA 94643,
Tel: (415) 271-3300
(Aluminum & aluminum prdts, chems)
   Kaiser Trading (UK) Ltd., 11A W. Halkin St., London, SW1X 8JL, England

KAMDEN INTL SHIPPING INC   167-41 147th Ave, Jamaica, NY 11434,
Tel: (718) 917-8181
(Freight forwarding servs)
   Kamden Intl. Shipping Ltd., Heathrow Intl. Trading Estate Unit 12, Green Lane,
      Hounslow, Middlesex TW4 6HB, England
   Kamden Intl. Shipping, Ltd., Bldg. 305, Cargo Centre- #108, Manchester Airport,
      Altrincham, Cheshire WA1S 8UX, England

KATY INDUSTRIES INC   853 Dundee Ave, Elgin, IL 60120, Tel: (708) 697-8900
(Holding company: transp, electronics, ind prdts)
   British LaBour Pump Co., Ltd., Denington Estate, Wellingborough, Northants, England

KAWNEER CO INC   555 Guthridge Ct, Norcross, GA 30092, Tel: (404) 449-5555
(Mfr arch aluminum prdts for commercial constr)
   Kawneer UK Ltd., Astmoor Rd., Astmoor, Runcorn, Cheshire WA7 1QQ, England

KAY CORP INTL   Wall St Plaza, New York, NY 10005, Tel: (212) 425-2100
(Wearing apparel, jewelry)
   De Monchy Aromatics Ltd., 119/123 Richmond Rd., Kingston-upon-Thames, Surrey,
      KT2 5BX, England

KAYNAR CO   PO Box 3001, Fullerton, CA 92634, Tel: (714) 871-1550
(Mfr fasteners, self-locking nuts)
   Kaynar (UK) Ltd., Gaw House, Alperton Lane, Wembley, Middlesex, England

KDI CORP   5721 Dragon Way, Cincinnati, OH 45227, Tel: (513) 272-1421
(Holding co: diversified mfg)
   IDM Electronics Ltd., 30 Suttons Park Ave., Suttons Ind. Park, Reading, Berks.,
      RG6 1AZ, England

A T KEARNEY INC   222 S Riverside Plaza, Chicago, IL 60606,
Tel: (312) 648-0111
(Mgmt consultants)
   A.T. Kearney Inc. Ltd., 134 Piccadilly, London, W1V 9FJ, England

KEENE CORP   200 Park Ave, New York, NY 10166, Tel: (212) 557-1900
(Mgmt consultants)
   Keene Corp. Ltd., Bowser Progress House, 21 Progress Way, Croydon, Surrey, CRO 4XD,
      England

KEITHLEY INSTRUMENTS INC   28775 Aurora Rd, Cleveland, OH 44139,
Tel: (216) 248-0400
(Mfr electr test/meas instru, PC-based data acquisition hdwe/software)
   Keithley Instruments Ltd., The Minister, 58 Portman Rd., Reading RG3 1ES, England

KELLOGG CO   235 Porter St, Battle Creek, MI 49016, Tel: (616) 966-2000
(Food prdts)
   Kellogg Co. (UK) Ltd., Stretford, Manchester, England

THE M W KELLOGG CO   3 Greenway Plaza, Houston, TX 77046-0395,
Tel: (713) 960-2000
(Design, engr, procurement & constr for process & energy ind)
   Kellogg Intl. Corp., The M.W. Kellogg Bldg., Stadium Way, Wembley, Middlesex,
      HA9 OEE, England
   M. W. Kellogg Ltd., Stadium Way, Wembley, Middlesex HA9 OEE, England

KENDA SYSTEMS INC   One Stiles Rd, Salem, NH 03079, Tel: (603) 898-7884
(Software & programming servs)
   Kenda Systems Ltd., 9 Lork St.- 2nd Fl., London W1X 1PD, England

THE KENDALL CO   PO Box 10, Boston, MA 02101, Tel: (617) 423-2000
(Surgical dressings, baby prdts)
   Kendall Co. (UK) Ltd., First Field Lane, Braunton, Devon, England

KENNAMETAL INC   PO Box 231, Latrobe, PA 15650, Tel: (412) 539-5000
(Tools, hard carbide & tungsten alloys)
   Bristol Erickson Ltd., Tower Rd. N., Warmley, Bristol BS15 2XF, England
   Kennametal Ltd., Box 29, Kingswinford, West Midland, DY6 7NP, England

KENNECOTT CORP   1717 Midland Bldg, Cleveland, OH 44115, Tel: (203) 964-3000
(Minerals & metals)
   Metal Sales Co. Ltd., Essex House, 27 Temple St., Birmingham, B2 5DF, England

KENT-MOORE CORP   28635 Mound Rd, Warren, MI 48092, Tel: (313) 574-2332
(Mfr service equip for auto, constr, recreational, military & agric vehicles)
   Kent-Moore UK Ltd., 86 Wharfdale Rd., Tyseley, Birmingham B11 2DD, England

KEPNER-TREGOE INC   Research Rd, PO Box 704, Princeton, NJ 08542,
Tel: (609) 921-2806
(Mgmt & organizational devel)
   Kepner-Tregor Ltd., 13-15 Victoria St., Windsor, Berks. SL4 1HB, England

KERR-McGEE CORP   PO Box 25861, Oklahoma City, OK 73125, Tel: (405) 270-1313
(Mfr oil, gas, & refined petroleum prdts, ind chems, coal)
   Kerr-McGee Oil (UK) PLC, 75 Davies St., Mayfair, London W1Y 1FA, England

KETCHUM COMMUNICATIONS   4 Gateway Center, Pittsburgh, PA 15222,
Tel: (412) 456-3500
(Advertising, public relations)
   David Williams & Ketchum, 52 Bedford Row, London, WC1R 4LX, England

KEYES FIBRE CO   3003 Summer St, Stamford, CT 06905, Tel: (203) 357-9100
(Molded containers)
   Keyes Fibre Co. Ltd., Sperry House, 78 Portsmouth Rd., Cobham, Surrey KT11 1JZ,
   England
   Keyes UK Ltd., 1 Pikelaw Pl., West Pimbo, Skelmersdale, Lancs. WN8 9PP, England

KIDDER PEABODY GROUP INC   10 Hanover Sq, New York, NY 10005,
Tel: (212) 510-3000
(Investment banking)
   Kidder, Peabody & Co. Ltd., 107 Cheapside, London EC2V 6DD, England
   Kidder, Peabody Intl. Ltd., 107 Cheapside, London EC2V 6DD, England
   Kidder, Peabody Securities Ltd., 107 Cheapside, London EC2V 6DD, England

KIMBALL INTERNATIONAL INC   1600 Royal St, Jasper, IN 47546,
Tel: (812) 482-1600
(Mfr office furn & seating, pianos, wood veneers, plywood prdts)
   Herrburger Brooks Ltd., Meadow Lane, Long Eaton, Nottingham, NG10 2FG,England
   Kimball Europe Ltd., 21-27 Marylebone Ln., London W1M 5FG, England

KIMBERLY-CLARK CORP   PO Box 619100, Dallas, TX 75261-1200,
Tel: (214) 830-1200
(Mfr fiber-based prdts for personal care, pulp & forest prdts; air transport)
   Kimberly-Clark Ltd., Larkfield, Kent, England

KIRBY BUILDING SYSTEMS INC   555 Marriott Dr, PO Box 140700, Nashville,
TN 37214, Tel: (615) 889-0020
(Steel building sys)
   Kirby Bldg. Systems Ltd., 39-40 Thames St., Windsor, Berkshire, SL4 1PR, England

KNOGO CORP   350 Wireless Blvd, Hauppauge, NY 11788, Tel: (516) 232-2100
(Mfr electr article surveillance sys)
    Knogo UK Ltd., Harleyford, Henley Rd., Marlow, Buckinghamshire SL7 2DY, England

KNOLL INTL   655 Madison Ave, New York, NY 10021, Tel: (212) 826-2400
(Furniture & fabrics)
    Form Intl Ltd., Whittingford House, 19-30 Alfred Place, London, WC1E 7EA, England

KNOTT HOTELS CORP   840 Madison Ave, New York, NY 10021, Tel: (212) 535-2000
(Hotels)
    Knott Hotels Co. Ltd., The Westbury, New Bond St., London, W1Y OPD, England

KNOWLES ELECTRONICS INC   3100 N Mannheim Rd, Franklin Park, IL 60131,
Tel: (708) 455-3600
(Microphones & loudspeakers)
    Knowles Electronics Ltd., Victoria Rd., Burgess Hill, Sus$ex, RH15 9LP, England

KOLLMORGEN CORP   66 Gate House Rd, Stamford, CT 06902, Tel: (203) 327-7222
(Printed circuits, elec motors & controls, electro-optical instru)
    Kollmorgen (UK) Ltd., 219 Kings Rd., Reading, Berks, England

KOLMAR LABORATORIES INC   123 Pike St, Port Jervis, NY 12771,
Tel: (914) 856-5311
(Contract mfr: cosmetics, pharms, household prdts)
    Kolmar Cosmetics Ltd., Derby Rd., Ashby de la Zouch, Leicestershire LE6 5HG, England

KORN/FERRY INTL   237 Park Ave, New York, NY 10017, Tel: (212) 687-1834
(Executive search)
    Korn/Ferry Intl. Ltd., Pepys House, 12 Buckingham St., London WC2N 6DF, England

KRAFT INC   Kraft Court, Glenview, IL 60025, Tel: (708) 998-2000
(Dairy prdts, processed food, chems)
    Kraft Foods Ltd., St. George's House, Bay Hill Rd., Cheltenham, Gloucester, England

KRATOS ANALYTICAL   170 Williams Dr, Ramsey, NJ 0744637, Tel: (201) 934-9000
(Mfr liq chromatography, mass spectrometry & surface analysis instru)
    Kratos Analytical, Barton Dock Rd., Urmston, Manchester M31 2LD, England

KULICKE & SOFFA INDUSTRIES INC   2101 Blair Mill Rd, Willow Grove, PA 19090,
Tel: (215) 784-6000
(Mfr assembly equip for semiconductor ind)
    Kulicke & Soffa (UK) Ltd., Denton Island, Newhaven, East Sussex BN9 98A, England

THE KULJIAN CO   3624 Science Center, Philadelphia, PA 19104,
Tel: (215) 243-1900
(Studies, design, engineeering, constr mgmt, site supervision)
    Kuljian Corp., 500 Chesham House, 150 Regent St., London, WIR 5FA, England

LAMBDA ELECTRONICS INC   515 Broad Hollow Rd, Melville, NY 11747,
Tel: (516) 694-4200
(Power supplies, semiconductors, test equip)
    Coutant-Lambda Ltd., Kingsley Ave., Ilfracombe, Devon EX34 BES, England

LANDIS TOOL CO   20 E Sixth St., Waynesboro, PA 17268, Tel: (717) 762-2161
(Mfr precision cylindrical grinding mach)
    Landis Lund Ltd., Cross Hills, Keighley, Yorks BD20 7SD, England

LANSDOWNE STEEL & IRON CO   Highland Ave & Alfa Terrace, Morton, PA 19070,
Tel: (215) 543-8800
(Looms & allied mach)
   Wilson Longbottom & Lansco Ltd., Barnsley, Yorkshire, England

LAWTER INTERNATIONAL INC   990 Skokie Blvd, Northbrook, IL 60062,
Tel: (708) 498-4700
(Resins, pigments, coatings)
   Lawter Chemicals Ltd., Murdock Rd., Bicester, Oxon, England

LE TOURNEAU INC LONGVIEW DIV   PO Box 2307, Longview, TX 75606,
Tel: (214) 753-3449
(Heavy constr, mining mach & equip)
   Contramine Contractors & Mining Equipment Ltd., Ingersoll House, Kingsway,
   London WC2 BGFA, England
   Le Tourneau Ltd., Blockwood-Hodge, Hunsbury, Hill Ave., Northampton, NN4 9QT,
   England

LEACH CORP   6900 Orangethorpe Ave, Buena Park, CA 90620, Tel: (714) 739-0770
(Mfr aerospace electromechan & solid state comp)
   LRE Relays & Electronics Ltd., The Dean, Alresford, Hamps. SO24 9BH, England

LEARONAL INC   272 Buffalo Ave, Freeport, NY 11520, Tel: (516) 868-8800
(Chem specialties)
   LeaRonal (UK) Ltd., High Peak Laboratories, Ashbourne Rd., Buxton, Derbyshire,
   SK17 9SS, England

LEBUS INTL INC   PO Box 2352, 25 Ind St, Longview, TX 75601,
Tel: (214) 758-5512
(Wire line spooling sys)
   Lebus Intl. Engineers Ltd., Dane Works, Trinity Trading Estate, Sittingbourne,
   Kent, England

LEEDS & NORTHRUP CO   Sumneytown Pike, North Wales, PA 19454,
Tel: (215) 699-2000
(Mfr process control instru & sys)
   Leeds & Northrup Ltd., Wharfdale Rd., Tyseley, Birmingham, B11 2DJ, England

LENNOX INDUSTRIES INC   Box 809000, Dallas, TX 75380-9000, Tel: (214) 980-6000
(Mfr heating & A/C equip)
   Lennox Industries Ltd., Box 43, Lister Rd., Basingstoke, Hampshire, England

LEP TRANSPORT INC   160 Varick St, New York, NY 10013, Tel: (212) 807-7200
(Forwarding & air frt agent)
   Lep Transport Ltd., Sunlight Wharf, Upper Thames St., London, EC4P 4AD, England

LEVI STRAUSS & CO   1155 Battery, San Francisco, CA 94111, Tel: (415) 544-6000
(Mfr wearing apparel)
   Levi Strauss (UK) Ltd., Levi's House, Moulton Park, Northampton, NN3 1QA, England

ELI LILLY & CO   307 E McCarty St, Indianapolis, IN 46285, Tel: (317) 261-2000
(Pharms, agric & cosmetic prdts)
   Eli Lilly Intl. Corp., Lilly House, 13 Hanover Sq., London, W1R OPA, England

THE LINCOLN ELECTRIC CO   22801 St Clair Ave, Cleveland, OH 44117,
    Tel: (216) 481-8100
    (Mfr arc welding equip & consumables, elec motors)
      Lincoln WeldRo Ltd., Mansfield Rd., Ashton, Sheffield S31 OBS, England

LINCOLN ST LOUIS DIVISION   1 Lincoln Way, St Louis, MO 63120,
    Tel: (314) 679-4200
    (Lubrication equip, materials dispensing equip)
      Lincoln GmbH (UK), 16/17 Lower Cherwell St., Banbury, Oxs. OX16 8AY, England

LINTAS:WORLDWIDE   1 Dag Hammarskjold Plaza, New York, NY 10017,
    Tel: (212) 605-8000
    (Advertising agency)
      Still Price Court Twivy D'Souza:Lintas, 80 Eccleston Sq., London SW1V 1PX, England

ARTHUR D LITTLE INC   25 Acorn Park, Cambridge, MA 02140-2390,
    Tel: (617) 864-5770
    (Technology & mgmt consulting)
      Arthur D. Little Ltd., Berkeley Sq. House, Berkeley Sq., London, W1X 6EY, England
      Cambridge Consultants Ltd., Unit 3, Lightning Way, Alvechurch Rd., West Heath,
        Bilmingham B31 3PH, England

LITTON INDUSTRIES INC   360 N Crescent Dr, Beverly Hills, CA 90210,
    Tel: (213) 859-5000
    (Elec sys, ind automation, resource explor)
      Aero Products, 36 Hertford St., London, W1, England
      Aero Service, c/o Western Geophysical Co., 288/290 Worton Rd., Isleworth,
        Middlesex, TW7 6EN, England
      Litton Precision Products Intl., 95 High St., 6B Slough, Berks, SL1 DH, England

LNP ENGINEERING PLASTICS   475 Creamery Way, Exton, PA 19341,
    Tel: (215) 363-4500
    (Mfr thermoplastic composites)
      LNP Engineering Plastics, Unit 25, Monkspath Business Park, Highlands Rd.,
        Solihull, West Midlands, England

LOCKHEED CORP   2555 N Hollywood Way, Burbank, CA 91520, Tel: (213) 847-6121
    (Aircraft, missiles, etc)
      Lockheed Aircraft (Europe) SA., 1 Mount St., London, W1Y 5AA, England

LOCTITE CORP   705 North Mountain Rd, Newington, CT 06111, Tel: (203) 278-1280
    (Adhesives, sealants)
      Loctite (UK) Ltd., Walchmead, Welwyn, Garden City, Hertfordshire, AL7 1JB, England

LOFFLAND BROTHERS CO   8301 E 51st St, PO Box 2847, Tulsa, OK 74101,
    Tel: (918) 622-9330
    (Oil & gas well drilling contractor)
      Loffland Brothers Eastern Hemisphere, Inc., Newmark House, 143 Great Portland,
        Road, London, WIN 6JX, England

LORAL INTL INC   999 Central Park Ave, Yonkers, NY 10704, Tel: (914) 964-6520
    (Comm sys, computers, instru equip)
      Loral Intl. Ltd., Windsor House, 83 Kingsway, London WC2B 65D, England
      Loral Intl. Systems Ltd., Windsor House, 83 Kingsway, London WC2B 65D, England
      Loral Mil - Spec Computers, UK Ltd., Dorna House, Guildford Rd., West End, Woking,
        Surrey GU24 9PW, England

(cont)

Loral Mil-Spec Computers UK Ltd., Dorna House, Guildford Rd., West End, Woking, Surrey GU24 9PW, England

LORD CORP   2000 W Grandview Blvd, Erie, PA 16514, Tel: (814) 868-0924
(Adhesives, coatings, chems, film prdts)
Durham Chemicals Ltd., Birtley, Chester-le-Street, County Durham DH3 1QX, England
Hughson Chemicals Co, Stretford Motorway Estate, Barton Dock Rd., Stretford, Manchester M32 0ZH, England

LORIMAR PRODUCTIONS INC   10202 W Washington Blvd, Culver City, CA 90232, Tel: (213) 202-2000
(Motion pictures, TV films)
Lorimar Ltd., 16 Berkeley St., London, W1, England

LOUISIANA LAND & EXPLORATION CO   PO Box 60350, 909 Poydras St, New Orleans, LA 70160, Tel: (504) 566-6500
(Oil & gas explor)
LL & E (Europe, Africa, Middle East) Inc., LL & E House, London, England

THE LOVABLE CO   2121 Peachtree Ind Blvd, Buford, GA 30518, Tel: (404) 945-2171
(Mfr women's undergarments)
The Lovable Co. Ltd., Faringdon Ave., Harold Hill, Romford, Essex, England

LUBRIZOL CORP   29400 Lakeland Blvd, Wickliffe, OH 44092, Tel: (216) 943-4200
(Chem additives for lubricants & fuels)
Lubrizol (UK) Ltd., Waldron House, 57 Old Church St., London, SW3 5BS, England

LUCAS AVITRON   PO Box 120039, Stamford, CT 06912, Tel: (203) 351-8400
(Distr elec generating & fluid handling sys)
Lucas Avitron, 8 Airlinks Estate, Spitfire Way, Heston, Middlesex TW5 9NR, England

LUNDY ELECTRONICS & SYSTEMS INC   1 Robert Lane, Glen Head, NY 11545, Tel: (516) 671-9000
(CAD/CAM prdts, defense & financial automation prdts)
Lundy-Farrington Ltd., Lundy House, 18 Ordnance Row, Portsmouth, Hamps., PO1 3DN, England

LYKES BROS STEAMSHIP CO INC   Lykes Center, 300 Poydras St, New Orleans, LA 70130, Tel: (504) 523-6611
(Ocean frt trans)
Lykes Lines Agency Inc., 73 Leman St., P.O. Box 115, London, E1 8ET, England

M&T CHEMICALS INC   PO Box 1104, Rahway, NJ 07065, Tel: (201) 499-0200
(Specialty chems & application technologies)
M & T Chemicals Ltd., William St., W. Bromwich, W. Midlands B70 0BE, England

R H MACY & CO INC   51 West 34th St, New York, NY 10001, Tel: (212) 560-3600
(Department stores, importers)
R.H. Macy & Co. Inc., Elsley House, 24/30 Great Titchfield St., London, WIP 8AO, England

MAGNETEK UNIVERSAL ELECTRIC   300 E Main St, Owosso, MI 48867, Tel: (517) 723-7866
(Mfr fractional horsepower elect motors)
MagneTek Universal Electric Ltd., P.O. Box 8, Peatham Rd., Gainsborough, Lincolnshire DN21 1XU, England

MAGNETROL INTERNATIONAL   5300 Belmont Rd, Downers Grove, IL 60515-4499,
    Tel: (708) 969-4000
    (Mfr level & flow process instru)
        Magnetrol Intl. UK, Regents Bus. Centre Unit 1, Jubilee Rd., Burgess Hill,
        W. Sussex RH15 9TL, England

MALLINCKRODT INC   675 McDonnell Blvd, PO Box 5840, St Louis, MO 63134,
    Tel: (314) 895-2012
    (Med/ind chems, organics, pharms)
        BYK-Mallinckrodt (UK) Ltd., Houndslow, England
        Mallinckrodt (UK) Ltd., Bristol, England
        Perry Bros. (Perfume Bases) Ltd., Bury St., Edmunds, England

MANITOWOC CO INC   500 S 16th St, Manitowoc, WI 54221-0066,
    Tel: (414) 684-6621
    (Mfr cranes, ice-making mach & contract prdts; ship repair & conversion)
        Manitowoc (UK) Ltd., St. James Mill Rd., Northampton NN5 5JW, England

MANPOWER INC   5301 N Ironwood Rd, PO Box 2053, Milwaukee, WI 53201-2053,
    Tel: (414) 961-1000
    (Temporary help)
        Manpower Ltd., Manpower House, 270/272 High St., Slough, Berks. SL1 1QD, England

MANUFACTURERS HANOVER TRUST CO   270 Park Ave, New York, NY 10017,
    Tel: (212) 286-6000
    (Banking)
        M.H. Credit Corp., Ltd., 1 Gerry Raffles Sq., London, E15 1XG, England
        Manufacturers Hanover Trust Co., 7 Princes St., London, EC2P 2LR, England
        Manufacturers Hanover Trust Co., 88 Brook St., London, W1A 4NF, England

MANUFACTURERS NATIONAL BANK OF DETROIT   Renaissance Bank Tower, Detroit,
    MI 48243, Tel: (313) 222-4000
    (Banking)
        Atlantic Intl. Banking Ltd., London, England

MANVILLE CORP   PO Box 5108, Denver, CO 80217-5108, Tel: (303) 978-2000
    (Mfr fiber glass prdts, paper & forest prdts, roofing & insulation material, ind
    minerals)
        Holophane Europe Ltd., Bond Ave., Bletchley, Milton-Keynes MK1 1JG, England
        John-Manville Ltd., Parkbridge House, The Little Green, Richmond, Surrey, TW9 IQU,
            England
        Manville (Great Britain) Ltd., Regal House, London Rd., Twickenham,
            Middlesex TW1 3QE, England
        Manville (Great Britain) Ltd., Livingstone Rd., Hessle, N. Humberside, England

MARATHON OIL CO   539 S Main St, Findlay, OH 45840, Tel: (419) 422-2121
    (Petroleum explor & prod)
        Marathon Intl. Petroleum Ltd., 174 Marylebone Rd., London, NW1 5AT, England

MARK CONTROLS CORP   5202 Old Orchard Rd, Skokie, IL 60077,
    Tel: (708) 470-8585
    (Process equip for petroleum & power ind, water sys & comp)
        Mark Controls Corp., Foundry Ln., Horsham, Sussex RH13 5PX, England

MARKEM CORP   150 Congress St, Keene, NH 03431, Tel: (603) 352-1130
    (Marking and printing mach; hot stamping foils)
        Markem Systems Ltd., Ladywell Trading Estate, Eccles New Rd., Salford, England

MARLEY CO   1900 Johnson Dr, Mission Woods, KS 66205, Tel: (913) 362-5440
(Cooling & heating towers, waste treatment sys)
  The L.T. Mart Co. Ltd., Brocades House, Pyrford Rd., W. Byfleet, Weybridge, Surrey,
    KT14 6RB, England

MARRIOTT CORP   Marriott Dr, Washington, DC 20058, Tel: (301) 897-9000
(Lodging, contract food & beverage serv, restaurants)
  Marriott-DeMontis In-Flite Services Ltd., Faggs Rd., Feltham, Middlesex, England

MARS INC   6885 Elm St, McLean, VA 22101, Tel: (703) 821-4900
(Mfr candy, snack foods, cat food)
  Mars Ltd., Dundee Rd., Trading Estate, Slough, Bucks, England

MARSH & McLENNAN COS INC   1221 Ave of the Americas, New York, NY 10020-1011,
Tel: (212) 997-2000
(Insurance)
  Marsh & McLennan Bowring, The Bowring Bldg., Tower Place, London EC3P 3BE, England
  William M. Mercer Fraser Ltd., Burwood House, 16 Caxton St., London, SW1H OQV,
    England

MARSTELLER INTL   1 E Wacker Dr, Chicago, IL 60601, Tel: (312) 329-1100
(Advertising, marketing research, sales promotion)
  Marsteller Ltd., 2 Basil St., London, SW3 1AA, England

MARTIN MARIETTA CORP   6801 Rockledge Dr, Bethesda, MD 20817,
Tel: (301) 897-6000
(Design/mfr/mgmt of sys in fields of space, defense, energy, electronics, commun)
  EO Systems Int. Ltd., 10 Fitzroy Sq., London W1P 6AB, England
  Hoskyns Group Ltd., Africa House, 64/78 Kingsway, London WC2B 6BL, England, Surrey,
    England
  PGM Systems Ltd., 91-93 Farrington Rd., London EC1M 3LB, England

MARTIN MARIETTA DATA SYSTEMS   PO Box 2392, Princeton, NJ 08540,
Tel: (609) 799-2600
(Computer softward, computing & professional serv)
  Martin Marietta Data Systems, 79-83 Great Portland St., London W1N 5RA, England

MARTIN PROCESSING INC   PO Box 5068, Martinsville, VA 24112,
Tel: (703) 629-1711
(Solar control polyester window films, dyed & metallized polyester films, dyed carpet
yarns)
  Martin Processing Inc., Beech Ave., Lower Bourne, Farnham, Surrey GU10 3JZ, England

MARTIN-DECKER CO   1200 Cypress Creek Rd, Cedar Park, TX 78613,
Tel: (512) 331-0411
(Oilfield & ind weight & meas sys)
  Martin-Decker Overseas Corp., Chester House, 76-86 Chertsey Rd., Woking,
    Surrey GU21 5BJ, England

MASCO CORP   21001 Van Born Rd, Taylor, MI 48180, Tel: (313) 274-7400
(Mfr building, energy, cold extruded prdts)
  Masinco Ltd., Banda House, Cambridge Grove, London W6 OLE, England

MASONEILAN DIV   275 Turnpike St, Canton, MA 02021, Tel: (617) 821-5100
(Mfr control, safety & safety relief valves)
  Masoneilan Ltd., Controls House, Park Royal Dr., London, NW10 7LD, England

MATHEMATICA PRODUCTS GROUP   PO Box 2392, Princeton, NJ 08540,
  Tel: (609) 799-2600
  (Computer softwear, policy research, analysis, etc)
    Mathematica Products Group, 79-73 Great Portland St., London, W1N 5RA, England

MAYFRAN INC   PO Box 43038, Cleveland, OH 44143, Tel: (216) 461-4100
  (Conveyors for metal working & refuse)
    Mayfran UK Ltd., Queens House, Queens Rd., Coventry CV1 3HR, England

MBANK DALLAS   1704 Main St, Dallas, TX 75201, Tel: (214) 698-6364
  (Banking)
    MBank Dallas, 7 Birchin Ln., London EC3V 9BY, England

MEAD CORP   Courthouse Plaza, NE, Dayton, OH 45463, Tel: (513) 222-6323
  (Mfr paper, packaging, pulp, lumber & other wood prdts, school & office prdts; electr
  pub, distri)
    Mead Coated Board U.K. Ltd., London, England
    Mead Packaging Ltd., 1 Great Western Way, Briston, England

MEASUREX CORP   One Results Way, Cupertino, CA 95014, Tel: (408) 255-1500
  (Mfr computer integrated mfg sys)
    Measures U.K., Units 15/16 Greenwood Close, Taylor Industrial Estate, Risley,
      Warrington, Cheshire WA3 6BL, England
    Measurex U.K., Windsor House, Reading Rd., Winnersh, Wokingham, Berks. RG11 5UJ,
      England
    Measurex UK, Measurex Intl. Systems Ltd., Measurex House, Slough Rd., Datchet,
      Slough, Berkshire, SL3 9AJ, England

MEDTRONIC INC   7000 Central Ave, NE, Minneapolis, MN 55432,
  Tel: (612) 574-4000
  (Mfr med devices, med serv)
    Medtronic Ltd., Marlin House, Marlins Meadows, Watford, Herts. WD1 8RG, England

MEEHANITE METAL CORP   9909 Clayton Rd, St Louis, MO 63124,
  Tel: (314) 994-3570
  (Castings)
    Intl. Meehanite Metal Co. Ltd., Meerlon House, 38 Albert Rd., N. Reigate, Surrey,
      England

ROBERT MELLIN MUSIC PUBLISHING CORP   1841 Broadway, New York, NY 10023,
  Tel: (212) 757-3287
  (Music publ)
    Robert Mellin Ltd., 24 Parkside, Knightsbridge, London, SW1, England

MELLON BANK NA   One Mellon Bank Center, Pittsburgh, PA 15258,
  Tel: (412) 234-5016
  (Commercial & trade banking, foreign exchange)
    Mellon Bank, 6 Devonshire Sq., London EC2M 4LB, England
    Mellon Bank NA, 15 Trinity Sq., London, EC3N 4AP, England
    Mellon-Picket Intl. Mngmt. Ltd., Cutlers Gardens, 5 Devonshire Sq.,
      London EC2M 4LD, England

MEMOREX CORP   San Thomas at Central Expressway, Santa Clara, CA 95052,
  Tel: (408) 987-1000
  (Magnetic recording tapes, etc)
    Memorex UK Ltd., Hounslow House, 730 London Rd., Hounslow, Middlesex, England
    Memorex UK Ltd., 96-102 Church St., Staines, Middlesex, England

MENTHOLATUM CO   1360 Niagara St, Buffalo, NY 14213, Tel: (716) 882-7660
  (Proprietary medicines, drugs)
    Mentholatum Co. Ltd., Longfield Rd., Twyford, Beakshire, RG10 GAU, England

MERCK SHARP & DOHME INTL   PO Box 2000, Rahway, NJ 07065, Tel: (201) 574-4000
  (Pharms, chems & biologicals)
    Merck, Sharp & Dohme Ltd., Hoddesdon Herts, Herford Rd., Herts, EN11 9BU, England

MERISEL INC   200 Continental Blvd, El Segundo, CA 90245, Tel: (213) 615-3080
  (Distr software & hardware)
    Softsel Computer Products, Ltd., Syon Grate Way, 941 Great West Rd., Brentford,
      Middlesex, London, England

MERRILL LYNCH PIERCE FENNER & SMITH   World Financial Center, 225 Liberty St,
  New York, NY 10080, Tel: (212) 449-1000
  (Brokers, securities, commodities)
    Merrill Lynch & Co. Ltd., 27-28 Finsbury Sq., London, EC2, England
    Merrill Lynch & Co. Ltd., Merrill Lynch House, 3 Newgate St., London, EC1A 7DA,
      England
    Merrill Lynch & Co. Ltd., Time-Life Building, 153 New Bond St., London, W1Y 9PA,
      England
    Merrill Lynch & Co. Ltd., 25 Davies St., London, W1, England
    Merrill Lynch & Co. Ltd., 27 Finsbury Sq., London, EC2A 1AQ, England

METAL IMPROVEMENT CO   10 Forest Ave, Paramus, NJ 07652, Tel: (201) 843-7800
  (Shot peening)
    Metal Improvement Co., Hambridge Lane, Unit 3, Newbury, Berks., England
    Metal Improvement Co., Ascot Dr., Derby DE2 8ST, England

METAL-CLADDING INC   PO Box 630, 470 Niagara Way, North Tonawanda, NY 14120,
  Tel: (716) 693-6205
  (FRP tanks & custom constr, scrubbers, odor control equip)
    Forbes Plastics Ltd., Denver Downham Mkt., Norfolk PE38 0DR, England

METALLURG INC   25 E 39th St, New York, NY 10016, Tel: (212) 686-4010
  (Mfr ferrous & nonferrous alloys & metals)
    London & Scandinavian Metallurgical Co. Ltd., 45 Wimbledon Hill Rd.,
      London SW19 7LZ, England

METCO DIV OF PERKIN-ELMER   1101 Prospect Ave, Westbury, NY 11590,
  Tel: (516) 334-1300
  (Mfr/serv thermal spray coating equip & supplies)
    Metco Ltd., Chobham,. Woking, Surrey, GU24 8RD, England

GEORGE J MEYER MFG CO   PO Box 10208, Charleston, SC 29411,
  Tel: (803) 572-6640
  (Mfr high speed packaging equip)
    Meyer-Mojonnier, Abbey Rd., Park Royal, London NW10, England

MGM/UA COMMUNICATIONS CO   10000 W Washington Blvd, Culver City, CA 90230,
  Tel: (213) 280-6000
  (Motion picture, home video & pay TV prod & distr)
    MGM/UA Home Video U.K., 113/117 Wardour St., London W1V 3TD, England
    MGM/US Telecommunications Inc., 37-41 Mortimer St., London W1A 2JL, England
    United International Pictures, Mortimer House, 37-41 Mortimer St., London W1A 2JL,
      England
    United International Pictures, 45 Beadon Rd., Hammersmith, London, W6 0EG, England

MICRODOT INC   Two First National Plaza, 20 S Clark St, Chicago, IL 60603,
Tel: (312) 899-1925
(Connectors, cables, automotive fasteners)
  Kaynar UK Ltd., Blackthorne Rd., Colnbrook, Slough, SL3 OHG, England

MICROMERITICS INSTRUMENT CORP   One Micromeritics Dr, Norcross,
GA 30093-1877, Tel: (404) 662-3620
(Mfr analytical instruments)
  Micromeritics Ltd., The Ringway Centre, Edison Rd. Houndmills, Basingstoke,
    Hampshire RG21 2YH, England

MIDLAND-ROSS CORP   20600 Chagrin Blvd, Cleveland, OH 44122,
Tel: (216) 491-8400
(Thermal processing sys, steelcast- ings, elect pdts, mech controls)
  Cambion Electronic Products Ltd., Castleton Near Sheffield, S30 2WR, England
  Stein Atkinson Stordy Ltd., Ounsdale Rd., Wombourne, Wolverhampton, WV5 8BY, England

MIDLANTIC CORP   PO Box 600, Metro Park Plaza, Edison, NJ 08818,
Tel: (908) 321-8000
(Banking)
  Midlantic National Bank, Prince Rupert House, 64 Queen St., London EC4R 1AD, England

MIKROPUL CORP   10 Chatham Rd, Summit, NJ 07901, Tel: (201) 273-6360
(Air pollution control & particle reduction sys)
  Mikropul Ltd., Towerfield Industrial Estate, Shoeburyness, Essex, England

MILCHEM INC   3900 Essex Lane, PO Box 22111, Houston, TX 77027,
Tel: (214) 439-8000
(Gas & oil well drilling fluids & chem additives)
  Milchem Drilling Fluids, 6 Babmaes St., London SW14 6HD, England
  Milchem Drilling Fluids, East Quay, S. Denes Rd., Great Yarmouth, Norfolk, England

HERMAN MILLER INC   8500 Byron Rd, Zeeland, MI 49464, Tel: (616) 772-3300
(Office furnishings)
  Herman Miller Ltd., Lower Bristol Rd., Bath BA2 3ER, England

MILTON ROY CO   PO Box 12169, St Petersburg, FL 33733, Tel: (813) 823-4444
(Med & ind equip, process control instru)
  LDC UK, Milton Roy House, 52 High St., Stone Staffordshire, ST15 8AR, England

MISSION DRILLING PRODUCTS DIV   PO Box 40402, Houston, TX 77240,
Tel: (713) 460-6200
(Oilfield equip, drilling & mining equip, ind valves)
  TRW Mission Ltd., Keswick House, 207 Anerley Rd., London SE20 8ER, England

MISSION MFG CO   PO Box 40402, Houston, TX 77040, Tel: (713) 460-6200
(Oil field equip)
  Mission Manufacturing Co. Ltd., Berkeley Sq. House, Berkeley Sq., London, W1,
    England

MMOS INC   15219 Michigan Ave, Dearborn, MI 48126, Tel: (313) 582-9480
(Marine accessories)
  M.M.O.S. Inc., 216 Fair Oak Rd., Eastleigh, Hampshire, SO5 6NJ, England

MNC INTERNATIONAL BANK   2 N Charles St, Baltimore, MD 21201,
  Tel: (301) 244-6804
  (Intl banking)
    Maryland Bank Intl. S.A., Mercury House, 195 Knightsbridge, London SW7 1RE, England

MOBIL CORP   150 E 42nd St, New York, NY 10017, Tel: (212) 883-4242
  (Petroleum explor, prdts)
    Mobil Data Services Ltd., Becket House, Vestry Rd., Seven Oaks, Kent, TN14 5EJ,
      England
    Mobil Services Co. Europe/Africa, York House 23 Kingsway, London, WC2B 6UE, England
    Mobil Shipping Co. Ltd., Mobil House, 54/60 Victoria St., London, SW1E 6QB, England
    Mobil Tankships (UK) Ltd., Mobil Court, 3 Clements Inn, London, WC2A 2EB, England

MODERN CONTROLS INTL INC   6820 Shingle Creek Pkwy, Minneapolis, MN 55430,
  Tel: (612) 560-2900
  (Packaged goods testing equip, pharm weighing equip)
    Mocon UK, Fryern House, 125 Winchester Rd., Chandlers Ford, Southampton,
      Hampshire S05 2DR, England

MONARCH MACHINE TOOL CO   PO Box 668, Sidney, OH 45365-1335,
  Tel: (513) 492-4111
  (Mfr metalcutting lathes, machining centers, coil processing equip)
    Dean Smith & Grace Ltd., P.O. Box 15, Worth Valley Works, Pitt St., Keighley,
      West Yorkshire BD21 4PG, England
    Stamco UK, Ltd., Bath House, Bath St., Walsall, West Midlands WS1 3BD, England

MONSANTO CO   800 N Lindbergh Blvd, St Louis, MO 63167, Tel: (314) 694-1000
  (Mfr chem & agric prdts, pharms, ind process equip, man-made fibers, plastics)
    Monsanto Ltd., 2nd floor, Thames Tower, Burleys' Way, Leicester,
      Leicestershire LE1 3TP, England
    Monsanto Ltd., Monsanto House, 10-18 Victoria St., London SW1H ONQ, England

MOOG INC   East Aurora, NY 14052-0018, Tel: (716) 652-2000
  (Mfr precision control components & sys)
    Moog Controls Ltd., Ashchurch, Tewkesbury, Gloucester GL20 8NA, England

MOORE PRODUCTS CO   Summeytown Pike, Spring House, PA 19477,
  Tel: (215) 646-7400
  (Mfr process control instru)
    Moore Products Co. UK Ltd., Copse Rd., Lufton Industrial Estate, Yeovil,
      Somerset BA22 8RN, England

MORGAN ADHESIVES CO   4260 Darrow Rd, Stow, OH 44224, Tel: (216) 688-1111
  (Self-adhesive print stock & emblem materials)
    Morgan Adhesives of Canada Ltd., Henry St., Northampton, NN1 4JD, England

MORGAN EQUIPMENT CO   1550 Evans Ave, PO Box 7802, San Francisco, CA 94124,
  Tel: (415) 826-9200
  (Engineers, builders)
    Morgan Equipment (UK) Ltd., 26 Maryland Rd., Tongwell, Milton Keynes, Bucks. MK15,
      England

MORGAN GUARANTY TRUST CO   23 Wall St, New York, NY 10015, Tel: (212) 483-2323
  (Banking)
    Morgan Grenfell Holdings Ltd., 23 Great Winchester St., London, EC2P 2AX, England
    Morgan Guaranty Ltd., 306 South State St., Dover, DE19 901, England
    Morgan Guaranty Ltd., 30 Throgmorton St., London, EC2N 2NT, England

Morgan Guaranty Ltd., 31 Berkeley Sq., London, W1X 6EA, England
Morgan Guaranty Ltd., 1 Angel Court, London, EC2R 7AE, England
Saudi Intl. Bank, 99 Bishopsgate, London, EC2M 3TB, England

MORRISON KNUDSEN CORP   1 Morrison Knudsen Plaza, PO Box 73, Boise, ID 83707,
Tel: (208) 386-5000
(Design, procurement, constr)
Morrison Knudsen Intl., 21 Dartmouth Pl., Chiswick, London W4 2KH, England

MORTON INTERNATIONAL INC   100 N Riverside Plaza, Chicago, IL 60606,
Tel: (312) 807-2000
(Mfr adhesives, coatings, finishes, spec chems, advanced & electr materials, auto
safety prdts)
Morton Intl. Ltd., University of Warwick Science Park, Sir Wm. Lyons Rd.,
Coventry CV4 7EZ, England
Morton Intl. Ltd., Greville House, Hibernia Rd., Hounslow, Middlesex TW3 3RX,
England
Morton Intl. Ltd., 18 Chesford Grance, Woolston, Warrington, Cheshire WA1 4RQ,
England

MOSTEK CORP   1215 W Crosby Rd, Carrollton, TX 75006, Tel: (214) 466-6000
(Integrated circuits, micro computer sys, semiconductors, etc)
Mostek UK Ltd., Masons House, 1-3 Valley Dr., Kingsbury Rd., London, NW9, England

MOTION PICTURE EXPORT ASSN OF AMERICA   522 Fifth Ave, New York, NY 10036,
Tel: (212) 840-6161
(Motion picture trade association)
MPEAA, 162/170 Wardour St., London, W1V 4AB, England

MOTOROLA COMPUTER SYSTEMS DIV   10700 N De Anza Blvd, Cupertino, CA 95014,
Tel: (408) 255-0900
(Mfr computer sys)
Motorola Ltd., 27 Market St., Maidenhead, Berkshire SL6 8AE, England

MOTOROLA INC   1303 E Algonquin Rd, Schaumburg, IL 60196, Tel: (708) 397-5000
(Mfr commun equip, semiconductors, cellular phones)
Motorola Information Systems, 27 Market St., Maidenhead, Berks, SL6 8AE, England
Motorola Ltd., Jays Close, Viables Ind. Estate, Basingstoke, Hamps., RG22 4PD,
England
Motorola Ltd., Taylors Rd., Stotfold, Hitchin, Herts., SG5 4AY, England

MSI DATA CORP   340 Fischer Ave, Costa Mesa, CA 92626, Tel: (714) 549-6000
(Portable data entry terminals)
MSI Data Intl. (UK), Data House, St. Ives Rd., Maidenhead, Berkshire, SL6 IQX,
England

MTS SYSTEMS CORP   PO Box 24012, Minneapolis, MN 55424, Tel: (612) 937-4000
(Electrohydraulic testing & prod equip, mach controls)
MTS Systems Ltd., Tricorn House, Cainscross, Stroud, Glos. GL5 4LF, England

MULTIGRAPHICS DIV   1800 W Central Rd, Mt Prospect, IL 60056,
Tel: (708) 398-1900
(Offset duplicating & graphic commun sys)
AM Intl. Information System Ltd., P.O. Box 17, Maylands Ave., Hemel, Hempstead,
Hertfordshire, HP2 7ET, England

MUNFORD INC   1860-74 Peachtree Rd, NW, Atlanta, GA   30309, Tel: (404) 352-6641
(Convenience & specialty stores)
   Majik Markets Inc., 127 Lodge Causeway, Fish Ponds, Bristo BS 16 3JY, England

MacANDREWS & FORBES GROUP INC   36 E 63rd St, New York, NY   10021,
   Tel: (212) 688-9000
   (Jewelry, watches, chocolate, cocoa)
   MacAndrews & Forbes Co. Inc., Pembroke House, 44 Wellesley Rd., Croydon, CR9 3QE,
      England

MacDERMID INC   245 Freight St, Waterbury, CT   06702, Tel: (203) 575-5700
   (Chem processing for metal ind, plastics, electronics cleaners, strippers)
   MacDermid Ltd., Stafford Park, 18 Telford, Shropshire TF3 3BN, England

E F MacDONALD CO   129 S Ludlow St, Dayton, OH   45401, Tel: (513) 226-5000
   (Trading stamps, travel & sales incentives)
   E.F. MacDonald Incentive Co., 58 Davies St., London, WIY 1LB, England
   E.F. MacDonald Incentive Co., Belgrave House, Grosvenor Center, Northampton, England
   E.F. MacDonald Incentive Co., Cannon House, 2255 Conventry Rd., Sheldon,
      Birmingham 26, England
   E.F. MacDonald Incentive Co., Mint House, 6 Stanley Park Rd., Wallington, Surrey,
      SM6 OEU, England
   E.F. MacDonald Intl. Inc., 58 Davies St., London, WIY 1LB, England

McCANN-ERICKSON WORLDWIDE   750 Third Ave, New York, NY   10017,
   Tel: (212) 697-6000
   (Advertising)
   McCann Direct, Haddon House, 2-4 Fitzroy St., London W1A 1AT, England
   McCann-Erickson Advertising Ltd., McCann-Erickson House, 36 Howland St., London,
      W1A 1AT, England
   McCann-Erickson Advertising Ltd., other locations in England
   McCann-Erickson Network Ltd., 36 Howland St., London, W1A 1AT, England
   Salesdesk Ltd., Haddon House, 2-4 Fitzroy St., London W1A 1AT, England
   The Harrison Agency, Haddon House, 2/4 Fitzroy St., London, W1A 1AT, England

McCORMICK & CO INC   11350 McCormick Rd, Hunt Valley, MD   21031,
   Tel: (301) 771-7301
   (Seasons, flavorings, specialty foods)
   McCormick U.K. PLC, High Wycombe, Bucks., England

McDONNELL DOUGLAS CORP   Box 516, St Louis, MO   63166, Tel: (314) 232-0232
   (Military & comm aircraft, space vehicles, electronics, missiles, data processing)
   McDonnell Douglas Info Systems Ltd., Maylands House, Hemel Hempstead,
      Herts. HP2 4RL, England

McGRAW-HILL INC   1221 Ave of the Americas, New York, NY   10020,
   Tel: (212) 512-2000
   (Books, magazines, info sys, financial serv, b/cast operations)
   DRI Europe Ltd., 30 Old Queen St., St. James Park, London SW1 H9HP, England
   McGraw-Hill Book Co. UK Ltd., McGraw-Hill Intl. Trainins Sys, Shoppenhangers Rd.,
      Maidenhead, Berks. SL6 2Q1, England
   McGraw-Hill Intl. Publications Co. Ltd., 34 Dover St., London W1X 4BR, England

McKINSEY & CO INC   55 E 52nd St, New York, NY   10022, Tel: (212) 909-8400
   (Mgmt consultants)
   McKinsey & Co., 74 St. James's St., London, SW1A 1PS, England

NABISCO BRANDS INC   Nabisco Brands Plaza, East Hanover, NJ 07936,
Tel: (201) 503-2000
(Mfr food prdts)
   Intl. Standard Brands Management Ltd., Wing #1 - 7th floor, Berkeley Sq. House,
      Berkeley Sq., London, W1X 5LB, England
   Nabisco Ltd., Welwyn Garden City, Hertfordshire, England
   Romix Foods Ltd., Atherton Rd., Liverpool, L9 7AQ, England
   Standard Brands Ltd., St. Crispin's Way, Thurmaston, Leicester, LE4 8BR,England
   Standard Brands Ltd., P.O. Box 14, Chichester, West Sussex, PO18 8PX, Lngland:
   Walkers Crisps Ltd., Feature Rd., Thurmaston, Leicester, LE4 8BS, England

NALCO CHEMICAL CO   One Nalco Center, Naperville, IL 60566-1024,
Tel: (708) 305-1000
(Chems for water & waste water treatment, oil prod & refining, ind processes;
water/energy mgmt serv)
   Nalfloc Ltd., P.O. Box 11, Northwich, Cheshire CW8 4DX, England

NAMCO CONTROLS   7567 Tyler Blvd, Mentor, OH 44060, Tel: (216) 946-9900
(Mfr sensors, switches, encoders)
   Namco Machinery Ltd., 27 Cardiff Rd., Luton, Beds., England

NASH INTL CO   310 Wilson Ave, Norwalk, CT 06856, Tel: (203) 852-5700
(Mfr vacuum pumps & compressors)
   Nash Engineering Co. Ltd., Road One, Industrial Estate, Winsford, Cheshire,
      CW7 3PL, England

NASHUA CORP   44 Franklin St, Nashua, NH 03061, Tel: (603) 880-2323
(Mfr/distr/serv office copier sys & supplies)
   Nashua Copycat Ltd., Cory House, The Ring, Bracknell, Berks. RG12 1ET, England
   Nashua Copycat Ltd., The Washington Center, Lincoln House, 100 Broadway,
      Salford M5 2UW, England
   Nashua Photo Products Ltd., Brunel Rd., Newton Abbot, Devon TQ12 4PB, England
   Nashua UK Ltd., Bldg. 685, 7 Steyning Way, Green Lane, Hounslow, Middlesex TW4,
      England

NATCO   PO Box 1710, Tulsa, OK 74101, Tel: (918) 663-9100
(Mfr/sale/serv oil & gas prdts)
   NATCO (UK) Ltd., Station House, Harrow Rd. Wembley, Middlesex HA9 6EN, England

NATIONAL BANK OF DETROIT   611 Woodward, PO Box 116, Detroit, MI 48232,
Tel: (313) 225-1000
(Banking)
   National Bank of Detroit, 28 Finsbury Circus, London EC2M 7AU, England

NATIONAL CAN CORP   8101 W Higgins Rd, Chicago, IL 60631, Tel: (312) 399-3000
(Metal, glass & plastic containers, closures)
   Nacanco Ltd., Salhouse Rd., Norwich, NOR 82R, England

NATIONAL CAR RENTAL SYSTEM INC   7700 France Ave S, Minneapolis, MN 55435,
Tel: (612) 830-2121
(Car rental)
   National Car Rental UK, Davis House, Wilton Rd., London, SWI, England

NATIONAL DATA CORP   National Data Plaza, Atlanta, GA 30329,
Tel: (404) 728-2000
(Provider of info & transaction serv to fin, retail, health care & commun sectors)
   NDC Intl. Ltd., Windsor Plaza, 72 Hammersmith Rd., London W14 8YD, England

NATIONAL GYPSUM CO   4500 Lincoln Plaza, Dallas, TX 75201, Tel: (214) 740-4500
  (Building prdts & servs)
    The Austin Co. of U.K. Ltd., London, England

NATIONAL SCREEN SERVICE CORP   1600 Broadway, New York, NY 10019,
  Tel: (212) 246-5700
  (Film trailers & advertising displays, etc)
    National Screen Service Ltd., Nascreno House, Soho Sq., London, W1, England

NATIONAL SUPPLY CO   PO Box 4638, Houston, TX 77210, Tel: (713) 984-4000
  (Oilfield drill & prod equip)
    National Supply Co. Ltd., 76 Jermyn St., London, SW1Y 6NP, England

NATIONAL-STANDARD CO   1618 Terminal Rd, Niles, MI 49120, Tel: (616) 683-8100
  (Mfr wire, wire related prdts, mach & med prdts)
    National-Standard Co. Ltd., Stourport Rd., P.O. Box 23, Kidderminster,
      Worcestershire, England
    National-Standard Co. Ltd., Heslop, Halesfield Industrial Estate, Telford,
      Shropshire, England
    National-Standard Co. Ltd., Stourport on Severn, England

NCR CORP   1700 S Patterson Blvd, Dayton, OH 45479, Tel: (513) 445-2000
  (Develop/mfr/sell/serv business info processing sys)
    NCR Ltd., 206 Marylebone Rd., London NW1 6LY, England

NEPTUNE INTL CORP   4360 Chamblee Dr, Atlanta, GA 30341, Tel: (404) 458-1212
  (Mfr liquid meters, electr control devices, scales)
    Neptune Measurement Ltd., Tameside Works, Dobcross, Near Oldham, Lancashire, England

NEW BRUNSWICK SCIENTIFIC CO INC   44 Talmadge Rd, Edison, NJ 08818-4005,
  Tel: (201) 287-1200
  (Mfr research & production equip for life sciences)
    New Brunswick Scientific (UK) Ltd., 163 Dixons Hill Rd., North Mymms,
      Hatfield AL9 75E, England

NEW YORK NAVIGATION CO INC   420 Lexington Ave, New York, NY 10017,
  Tel: (212) 490-3490
  (Shipping agents)
    New York Navigation Co. Inc., 123 Pall Mall, London SW1, England

NEWSWEEK INTL INC   444 Madison Ave, New York, NY 10022, Tel: (212) 350-2000
  (Publ)
    Newsweek Inc., 25 Upper Brook St., London, England

NICO INC   345 Hudson St, New York, NY 10014, Tel: (212) 620-8200
  (Constr mgt, contracting & consult servs)
    Nico Construction PLC, City Tangent, 25 Lavington St., London SE1 0NZ, England

NICOLET INSTRUMENT CORP   5225 Verona Rd, Madison, WI 53711-4495,
  Tel: (608) 271-3333
  (Mfr infrared spectrometers, oscilloscopes, med electro-diag equip)
    Nicolet Instrument Ltd., Budbrooke Rd., Warwick, Warwickshire, CV34 5XH, England

A C NIELSEN CO   Nielsen Plaza, Northbrook, IL 60062, Tel: (708) 498-6300
  (Marketing research)
    A.C. Nielsen Co. Ltd., Nielsen House, Headington, Oxford, OX3 9RX, England

Petroleum Information Ltd., Green Dragon House, 64/70 High St., Croydon, Surrey CRO 9XN, England

NORDA INC   140 Route 10, East Hanover, NJ 07936, Tel: (201) 887-5600
(Aromatic chems, flavors)
Norda Intl. Ltd., Stirling Rd., Slough, Bucks, England

NORDSON CORP   28601 Clemens Rd, Westlake, OH 44145, Tel: (216) 892-1580
(Mfr ind application equip & packaging mach)
Nordson U.K. Ltd., Ashurst Dr., Cheadle Heath, Stockport, Cheshire SK3 0RY, England
Nordson U.K. Ltd., Wenman Rd., Thame, Oxfordshire OX9 3SW, England

NORTH AMERICAN VAN LINES INC   5001 US 30 West, Fort Wayne, IN 46818,
Tel: (219) 429-2511
(Household goods movers, trucking, frt forwarding, brokerage serv)
North American Van Lines, 15/16 Chestnut Way, Felthambrook Industrial Estate, Feltham, Middlesex, England

NORTON CO   1 New Bond St, Worcester, MA 01606, Tel: (508) 795-5000
(Abrasives, drill bits, constr & safety prdts, plastics)
Christensen Diamond Products (UK) Ltd., Kirkhill Rd., Kirkhill Industrial, Estate, Dyce Aberdeen, England
Christensen Diamond Products (UK) Ltd., Govett Ave., Shepperton, Walton-on-Thames, Middlesex, England
Clipper Mfr. Co., Thurmaston Blvd., Barkby Rd., Leicester, LE4 7JB, England
Norton Abrasives Ltd., Bridge Rd., East Welwyn Garden City, Herts, AL7HZ, England
Norton Chemical Process Products Ltd., King St., Fenton, Stroke-on-Trent, ST4 3LY, England
Norton Industrial Ceramics Ltd., King St., Fenton, Stroke-on-Trent, ST4 3LY, England
Norton Intl., Cartwright House, 39/43 Monument Hill, Weybridge, Surrey, KT13 8RN, England

NORWICH EATON PHARMACEUTICALS INC   17 Eaton Ave, Norwich, NY 13815,
Tel: (607) 335-2111
(Mfr pharms, chems, health prdts)
Eaton Laboratories, Regent House, The Broadway Woking, Surrey, GU21 5AP, England

NUMATICS INC   1450 N Milford Rd, Highland, MI 48031, Tel: (313) 887-4111
(Mfr control valves & manifolds)
Numatics Ltd., P.O. Box 18, 23/24 Acacia Close, Cherrycourt Way, Leighton Buzzard, Beds. LU7 7DJ, England

NYNEX CORP   1113 Westchester Ave, White Plains, NY 10604, Tel: (914) 397-1200
(Telecom & info servs)
BIS Group Ltd., London, England

OAK INDUSTRIES INC   16935 W Bernardo Dr, Rancho Bernardo, CA 92127,
Tel: (619) 485-9300
(Switch sys components, appliance controls, comm hdwe & software, pay TV)
Diamond H Controls Ltd., Vulcan Rd. North, Norwich, Norfolk, NR6 6AH, England

OAKITE PRODUCTS INC   50 Valley Rd, Berkeley Heights, NJ 07922,
Tel: (201) 464-6900
(Mfr chem prdts for ind cleaning & metal treating)
Oakite Ltd., West Carr Rd. Industrial Estate, Retford, Notts, DN22 7SN, England

OCCIDENTAL PETROLEUM CORP   10889 Wilshire Blvd, Los Angeles, CA 90024,
  Tel: (213) 879-1700
  (Petroleum & petroleum prdts, chems, plastics)
    Enoxy Chemical Ltd., Watling House, 35/37 Cannon St., London, EC4M 5SD, England
    Occidental Intl. Oil Inc., 16 Palace St., London, SW1 E5BQ, England

OCEAN DRILLING & EXPLORATION CO INC   PO Box 61780, New Orleans, LA 70161,
  Tel: (504) 529-2811
  (Offshore drilling contractors)
    ODECO (UK) Ltd., 37 Park St., London, W1, England

ODI   25 Mall Rd, Burlington, MA 01803, Tel: (617) 272-8040
  (Mgt & consul serv)
    ODI Ltd., Company House Tower Hill, Bristol, Avon BS2 0EQ, England

C M OFFRAY & SON INC   Route #24, Box 601, Chester, NJ 07930-0601,
  Tel: (201) 879-4700
  (Mfr narrow fabrics)
    C.M. Offray & Son Ltd., Fir Tree Pl., Church Rd., Ashford, Middlesex TW15 2PH,
    England

OGILVY & MATHER INC   2 E 48th St, New York, NY 10017, Tel: (212) 907-3400
  (Advertising agency)
    Foster Turner & Benson Ltd., Chancery House, Chancery Lane, London, WC2A 1QU,
    England
    Mathers & Bensons Advertising Ltd., 8G Lambs, Conduct Passage, London, WC1R 4RH,
    England
    Mathers Advertising Ltd., Chancery House, Chancery Lane, London, WC2A 1QU, England
    Ogilvy Benson & Mather Ltd., Brettenham House, Lancaster Place, London, WC2E 7EZ,
    England
    Ogilvy Benson & Mather Ltd., 4-6 Castle Arcade Bldg. Belfast, BT1 5DG, England

OHAUS SCALE CORP   29 Hanover Rd, Florham Park, NJ 07932, Tel: (201) 377-9000
  (Balances & scales for labs & industry)
    Ohaus Scale Europe Ltd., Broad Lane, Cottenham, Cambridge CB4 4SW, England

OIL-DRI CORP OF AMERICA   520 N Michigan Ave, Chicago, IL 60611,
  Tel: (312) 321-1515
  (Oil & grease absorbants, soil conditioners, etc)
    Oil-Dri UK Ltd., c/o Consolidated Land Services, Humber Rd., South Killingsholme,
    Grimsby, DN40 3DU, England

OLIN CORP   120 Long Ridge Rd, Stamford, CT 06904-1355, Tel: (203) 356-2000
  (Chems, metals, applied physics in elect, defense, aerospace inds)
    Olin UK Ltd., Site 7, Kidderminster Rd., Cutnall Green, Worcs. WR9 0NS, England

OMARK INDUSTRIES INC   5550 SW Macadam Ave, Portland, OR 97201,
  Tel: (503) 796-1400
  (Mfr chain & accessories for chain saws, welding equip, power tools)
    KSM Stud Welding Ltd., Old Boston Trading Estate, Penny Lane, Haydock, England

OMNI-SPECTRA INC   21 Continental Blvd, Merrimack, NH 03054,
  Tel: (617) 272-4046
  (Electronic components, connectors & subsys)
    Omni Spectra Ltd., 1 Loverock Rd., Battle Farm Estate, Reading, Berkshire, RG3 1DQ,
    England

ON-LINE SOFTWARE INTL INC   2 Executive Dr, Fort Lee, NJ 07024,
Tel: (201) 592-0009
(Software & related servs; consult & educ servs)
   On-Line Software (UK) Ltd., Tenterden House, 3 Tenterden St., Hanover Square,
   London W1R 9AH, England

ONAN CORP   1400 73rd Ave NE, Minneapolis, MN 55432, Tel: (612) 574-5000
(Electric generators, ind engines & controls)
   Onan Europe Div., 48, High St., Slough, Berks, SL1 1EL, England
   Trident Equipment Power Ltd., The Airport, Southampton, S02 28G, England

OPPENHEIMER CASING CO   5201 W 65th St, Chicago, IL 60638, Tel: (708) 458-0333
(Mfr sausage casings)
   Oppenheimer Casing.Co. (UK) Ltd., 320 Kilburn High Rd., London, NW6 2QP, England

ORGANIZATIONAL DYNAMICS INC   5 Burlington Woods Dr, Burlington, MA 01803,
Tel: (617) 272-8040
(Quality/productivity consultants)
   ODI Ltd., Waterloo House, 58-60 High St., Witney, Oxon OX8 6HJ, England

ORIEL CORP   250 Long Beach Blvd, Stratford, CT 06497, Tel: (203) 377-8282
(Mfr optical goods)
   Oriel Scientific Ltd., P.O. Box 31, 1 Mole Business Park, Leatherhead,
   Surrey KT22 7AN, England

ORYX ENERGY CO   PO Box 2880, Dallas, TX 75221-2880, Tel: (214) 890-6000
(Explor/prod oil & gas)
   Oryx UK Energy Co., The Charter Place, Vine St., Uxbridge, Middlesex UB8 1EZ,
   England

OTIS ELEVATOR CO   10 Farm Springs, Farmington, CT 06032, Tel: (203) 674-4047
(Elevators & escalators)
   Otis Elevator Co. Ltd., The Otis Bldg., 43/59 Clapham Rd., London, SW9 0JZ, England
   Otis Elevator Co. Ltd., Moorgate Rd., Kirby, Near Liverpool, Lancaster, L33 7XW,
   England

OTIS ENGINEERING CORP   PO Box 819052, Dallas, TX 75381-9052,
Tel: (214) 418-3932
(Mfr oil/gas field equip; service well completion & maint)
   Otis Pressure Control Ltd., 17 Hanover Sq., London W1R 0EL, England

OWENS-CORNING FIBERGLAS CORP   PO Box 901, Fiberglas Tower, Toledo, OH 43659,
Tel: (419) 248-8000
(Mfr insulation, building materials, glass fiber prdts)
   Owens-Corning Fiberglas (G.B.) Ltd. (U.K.), England
   Owens-Corning Fiberglas (U.K.) Ltd., England
   Regina Fibreglass Ltd. (U.K.), England
   Scanglas. Ltd. (U.K.), England
   Wrexham A.R. Glass Ltd. (U.K.), England

PACIFIC TELESIS GROUP   130 Kearney St, San Francisco, CA 94108,
Tel: (415) 394-3000
(Telecommun & info sys)
   One-to-One Ltd., Scorpio House, 102 Syndey St., London SW3 6NL, England

PACKAGING CORP OF AMERICA   1603 Orrington Ave, Evanston, IL 60204,
  Tel: (708) 492-5713
  (Mfr custom packaging, aluminum & plastic molded fibre, corrugated containers)
    Alcan Ekco Ltd., 90 Asheridge Rd., Chesham, Bucks. HP5 2QE, England
    Omni-Pac UK Ltd., Marine Parade, South Denes, Great Yarmouth, Norfolk NR30 3QH,
      England

PAINEWEBBER GROUP INC   1285 Ave of the Americas, New York, NY 10019,
  Tel: (212) 713-2000
  (Stock brokerage serv & invest)
    PaineWebber Intl., 1 Finsbury Ave., London EC2M 2PA, England
    PaineWebber Intl. (UK) Ltd., 1 Finsbury Ave., London EC2M 2PA, England
    PaineWebber Intl. Bank Ltd., 47 Berkeley Sq., London W1X 5DB, England

PALL CORP   30 Sea Cliff Ave, Glen Cove, NY 11542, Tel: (516) 671-4000
  (Filters & related fluid clarification equip)
    Pall Europe Ltd., Havant St., Portsmouth, PO6 1TD, England

PANALARM DIV   7401 N Hamlin Ave, Skokie, IL 60076, Tel: (708) 675-2500
  (Elec alarm sys, temp monitors, display sys, sensors)
    Scama Ltd., Eastern Way, Bury St., Edmunds, Suffolk, 1P32 7AQ, England

PANDUIT CORP   17301 Ridgeland Ave, Tinley Park, IL 60477, Tel: (708) 532-1800
  (Mfr elec/electr wiring comps)
    Panduit Ltd., 61-65 Revenge Rd., Chatham, Kent ME5 8YT, England

PANGBORN CO   Pangborn Blvd, PO Box 380, Hagerstown, MD 21740,
  Tel: (301) 739-3500
  (Blast cleaning sys)
    Pangborn UK/Spencer & Halstead Ltd., Bridge Works, Ossett, Yorkshire, England

PAPER CONVERTING MACHINE CO   PO Box 889, Green Bay, WI 54305,
  Tel: (414) 494-5601
  (Paper converting mach)
    Paper Converting Machine Co. Ltd., Southway Dr., Plymouth, Devon, England

PARAMOUNT INTL FILMS INC   1 Gulf & Western Plaza, New York, NY 10023,
  Tel: (212) 333-4600
  (Film prod & distr)
    Paramount Television Ltd., 23 Berkeley House, 15 Hay Hill, London, W1X 8JB, England

PARK ELECTROCHEMICAL CORP   5 Dakota Dr, Lake Success, NY 11042,
  Tel: (516) 354-4100
  (Multi-layer laminate printed circuit materials, ind comps, plumbing hdwe prdts)
    New England Laminates (UK) Ltd., 1 Paddock Rd., W. Pimbo, Skelmersdale, Lancashire,
      England

PARKER HANNIFIN CORP   17325 Euclid Ave, Cleveland, OH 44112,
  Tel: (216) 531-3000
  (Mfr motion-control prdts)
    Parker Digiplan Ltd., 21-22 Balena Close, Creekmoor, Poole, Dorset BH17 7DX, England
    Parker Hannifin Corp., Paraker House, 55 Maylands Ave., Hemel Hempstead,
      Herts. HP2 4SJ, England
    Parker Hannifin PLC, Walkmill Lane, Bridgtown, Cannock, Staffs WS11 3LR, England
    Parker Hannifin PLC, other locations in England

PARKER PEN CO   One Parker Place, Janesville, WI 53545, Tel: (608) 755-7000
(Writing instru, temporary help, leisure apparel & equip)
   Parker Pen Co. Ltd., 15 Grosvenor Gardens, London, SW1W OBL, England

PARKS-CRAMER CO   P O Drawer 2200, Fitchburg, MA 01420, Tel: (617) 343-3796
(Textile traveling cleaners, valves, fittings, cranes, etc)
   Parks-Cramer Ltd., Suther St., Oldham, Lancashire, OL9 7TF, England

PARSONS CORP   100 W Walnut St, Pasadena, CA 91124, Tel: (818) 440-2000
(Engineering & constr)
   Ralph M. Parsons Co. Ltd., Parsons House, Kew Bridge Rd., Brentford,
      Middlesex TW8 OEH, England

BRUCE PAYNE CONSULTANTS INC   140 West End Ave, New York, NY 10023,
   Tel: (212) 799-8255
(Mgmt consultants)
   Bruce Payne Consultants Ltd., 1 Puddle Dock, Blackfriars, London EC4V 3PD, England
   Bruce Payne Consultants, Inc., 99-101, St. Leonard's Rd., Windsor, Berkshire,
      London, SC4 3BS, England

PENTON PUBLISHING CO   1100 Superior Ave, Cleveland, OH 44114,
   Tel: (216) 696-7000
(Pub industrial magazines)
   Industrial Publishing Co., 14 Broadway, Lond   W1, England

PEPSICO FOOD SERVICE INTL   9111 E Douglas, Wichita, KS 67207,
   Tel: (316) 681-9793
(Operates restaurants)
   PepsiCo Food Service Intl., Eurafme House 2, Woodgrange Ave., Kenton,
      Middlesex HA3 OXD, England

PEPSICO INC   700 Anderson Hill Rd, Purchase, NY 10577, Tel: (914) 253-2000
(Beverages, food prdts & servs, sporting goods)
   PepsiCo, Ltd., 2 Basil St., London, SW3 1AA, England

PERKIN-ELMER CORP   761 Main Ave, Norwalk, CT 06859, Tel: (203) 762-1000
(Analytical instru, computers, semiconductor prod equip, avionics, electro-optical
sys, etc)
   Perkin-Elmer Ltd., P.O. Lane, Beaconsfield, Buckinghamshire, HP9 1QA, England

PET INC   400 S 4th St, St Louis, MO 63102, Tel: (314) 622-6358
(Process/mktg specialty foods)
   C. Shippam Ltd. (England), Post Office #3, East Walls, Chichester,
      W. Sussex PO19 1PQ, England
   Pet Intl., Europe, 10-16 Castle St., Kingston-upon-Thames, Surrey KT1 1SS, England

PETERSON SPRING CORP   800 W Broadway, Three Rivers, MI 49093,
   Tel: (616) 273-1515
(Springs & small metal prdts)
   Mepla, Ltd., Telford. Rd., Bicester, Oxon, England

PETROLITE CORP   100 N Broadway, St Louis, MO 63102, Tel: (314) 241-8370
(Specialty chem treating programs, performance-enhancing additives & related equip)
   Petrolite Ltd., Kirkby Bank Rd., Knowsley Industrial Park, Liverpool L33 7S4,
      England

PFIZER INC   235 E 42nd St, New York, NY 10017, Tel: (212) 573-2323
(Mfr pharms, hosp prdts, chems, consumer & animal health prdts)
   Pfizer Ltd., Ramsgate Rd., Sandwich. Kent, CT13 9NJ, England

PHELPS DODGE CORP   2600 N Central Ave, Phoenix, AZ 85004-3014,
   Tel: (602) 234-8100
   (Minerals, metals & spec engineered prdts for trans & elect mkts)
      Sevalco Ltd., Severn Rd., Avonmouth, Bristol BS11 OVL, England

PHILIPP BROTHERS CHEMICALS INC   1 Parker Plaza, Fort Lee, NJ 07029,
   Tel: (201) 944-6020
   (Mfr ind & agric chems)
      Ferro Metal & Chemical Corp., Crompton House, Aldwych, WC2B 4JF, England

PHILIPP BROTHERS INC   1221 Ave of the Americas, New York, NY 10020,
   Tel: (212) 575-5900
   (Mktg ind raw materials, minerals, agric prdts)
      Philipp Brothers Ltd., 111 Buckingham Palace Rd., London SW1W OSL, England

PHILLIPS PETROLEUM CO   Phillips Bldg, Bartlesville, OK 74004,
   Tel: (918) 661-6600
   (Crude oil, natural gas, liquefied petroleum gas, gasoline & petro-chems)
      Phillips Petroleum Co., Portland House, Stag Place, London, SW1E 5DA, England

PILLAR INDUSTRIES INC   N92 W15800 Megal Dr, Menomonee Falls, WI 53051,
   Tel: (414) 255-6470
   (Mfr induction heating & melting equip)
      Pillar Europe Ltd., Unit 6, Wye Estate, London Rd., High Wycombe, Bucks. HP11 1LH,
      England
      Pillar Industries Europe, 15 Avon Business Park, Wolverhampton Rd., Cannock,
      Staffs. WS11 1LT, England

PILLSBURY CO   Pillsbury Center, Minneapolis, MN 55402, Tel: (612) 330-4966
   (Baking mixes, canned & frozen foods, restaurants & food shops)
      Geo. Browick & Sons Ltd., Portland Rd., Hove 3, Sussex, England

PINKERTON'S INC   6727 Odessa Ave, Van Nuys, CA 91406, Tel: (818) 373-8800
   (Security & investigations)
      Pinkerton's of UK Ltd., Ferrare House, 102 College Rd., Harrow, London,
      Borough of Harrow, HAI, England

PITNEY BOWES INC   World Headquarters, Stamford, CT 06926-0700,
   Tel: (203) 356-5000
   (Postage meters, mailroom equip, copiers, bus supplies & servs)
      Pitney-Bowes Ltd., The Pinnacles, Harlow, Essex, England

PITTSBURGH-DES MOINES CORP   Neville Island, Pittsburgh, PA 15225,
   Tel: (412) 331-3000
   (Water & petroleum storage sys, low temp & cryogenic tanks & sys, waste water
   treatment facilities)
      PDM (UK) Ltd., 9/11 Kensington High St., London W8 5NP, England

PLACID OIL CO   1601 Elm St, Dallas, TX 75201, Tel: (214) 741-3081
   (Petroleum explor)
      Placid Oil Co. (UK), 192 Sloane St., London, SWL, England

PLASTIGLIDE MFG CORP   2701 W E Segundo Blvd, Hawthorne, CA 90250,
Tel: (213) 777-8108
(Furniture component parts, indus- trial plastic & metal parts)
    Plastiglide Products Ltd., Masons Rd., Stratford-upon-Avon, Warwicks, England

PLIBRICO CO   1800 Kingsbury St, Chicago, IL 60614, Tel: (312) 549-7014
(Refractories, engineering, constr)
    Plibrico Co. Ltd., 33/35 Upper George St., Luton, Beds. LU1 2RD, England

PLOUGH INC   PO Box 377, Memphis, TN 38151, Tel: (901) 320-2011
(Proprietary drug & cosmetic prdts)
    Scholl (UK) Ltd., 204 St. John St., London, EC1P 1DH, England

POLAROID CORP   549 Technology Sq, Cambridge, MA 02139, Tel: (617) 577-2000
(Photographic and optical prdts)
    Polaroid (UK) Ltd., Ashley Rd., St. Albans, Herts, England

R L POLK & CO   1155 Brewery Park Blvd, Detroit, MI 48207-2697,
Tel: (313) 961-9470
(Directories, direct mail advertising)
    R.L. Polk & Co. Ltd., 294-304 St. James Rd., London, SE1 5JZ, England
    R.L. Polk & Co. Ltd., Sudbury, Suffolk, England

POLYCHROME CORP   On the Hudson, Yonkers, NY 10702, Tel: (914) 965-8800
(Metal offset plates, coating specialties, graphic arts films)
    Polychrome Corp, Ltd., Sandown Rd., Watford, Herts, WD2 4XA, England

POMEROY INC   PO Box 1377, Stamford, CT 06904, Tel: (203) 324-6775
(Building hardware)
    Pomeroy Inc. (UK), Box 5, Yeovil, 13A 202XA, England

PORTA SYSTEMS CORP   575 Underhill Blvd, Syosset, NY 11791,
Tel: (516) 364-9300
(Designs/mfr protection & testing equip for telecom ind)
    Porta Systems Ltd., Royal Oak Way N., Royal Oak Ind. Est., Daventry NN1 15PQ,
    England

PORTER PRECISION PRODUCTS CO   2734 Banning Rd, Cincinnati, OH 45239,
Tel: (513) 923-3777
(Mfr piercing punches & die supplies for metal stamping & tool/die ind)
    Porter Precision Products Ltd., Masons Rd., Stratford-upon-Avon,
    Warwickshire CV37 9NF, England

POTTERS INDUSTRIES INC   20 Waterview Blvd, Parsippany, NJ 07054,
Tel: (201) 299-2900
(Mfr glass spheres for road marking & ind applications)
    Potters Ballotini, Ltd., Darlington Rd., West Auckland, Durham D114 9PR, England
    Potters-Ballotini Ltd., Pontefract Rd., Barnsley/South Yorkshire, S71 1HJ, England

PPG INDUSTRIES   One PPG Place, Pittsburgh, PA 15272, Tel: (412) 434-3131
(Mfr flat glass, fiber glass, chems, coatings, med electr)
    PPG Glass Fibers Ltd., P.O. Box 132, Leigh Rd., Hindley Green, Wigan,
    Lancashire WN2 4X2, England
    PPG Industries (UK) Ltd., P.O. Box 359, Rotton Park St., Birmingham B16 0AD, England

PRECISION CASTPARTS CORP   4600 SE Harney Dr, Portland, OR 97206,
Tel: (503) 653-8210
(Metal castings)
   Precision Castparts Corp. UK, Parkway Ind. Estate, Sheffield, S9 4WA, England

PRECISION RUBBER PRODUCT CORP   Hartman Dr, Lebanon, TN 37087,
Tel: (615) 444-0191
(Rings, seals & custom molded rubber prdts)
   Precoril Seals (UK) Ltd., 459 London Rd., (0276) 24676 Camberley, Surrey, GU15 3JA,
   England

PRECISION VALVE CORP   PO Box 309, Yonkers, NY 10702, Tel: (914) 969-6500
(Mfr aerosol valves)
   Precision Valve UK Ltd., Unit C, Newcombe Way, Orton Southgate, Peterborough,
   Cambs PE2 0SF, England

PREFORMED LINE PRODUCTS CO   PO Box 91129, Cleveland, OH 44101,
Tel: (216) 461-5200
(Mfr pole line hardware for elec transmission lines; splice closures & related prdts
for telecom)
   Preformed Line Products, Ltd., Andover, Hants, England

PREMARK INTL INC   1717 Deerfield Rd, Deerfield, IL 60015, Tel: (708) 405-6000
(Mfr/sale diversified consumer & coml prdts)
   Dart Industries Ltd., 130 College Rd., Harrow, Middlesex HA1 1BQ, England

PREMIX INC   PO Box 281, N Kingsville, OH 44068, Tel: (216) 224-2181
(Mfr molded fiber glass, reinforced thermoset molding compounds & plastic parts)
   Permali-Premix Ltd., 125 Bristol Rd., Gloucester GL 15TT, England

PRIME COMPUTER INC   Prime Park, Natick, MA 01760, Tel: (617) 655-8000
(Mfr minicomputers, hardware & software)
   Prime Computer Inc. (UK) Ltd., Primos House, 2-4 Lampton Rd., Hounslow,
   Middlesex TW3 1JW, England

PRINTRONIX INC   17500 Cartwright Rd, Irvine, CA 92715, Tel: (714) 863-1900
(Mfr computer printers)
   Printronix UK, Loddon Vale House- Ste. B, Hurricane Way, Woodley,
   Berkshire RG5 4UX, England

PROCTER & GAMBLE CO   One Procter & Gamble Plaza, Cincinnati, OH 45202,
Tel: (513) 983-1100
(Personal care, food, laundry, cleaning & ind prdts)
   Procter & Gamble Ltd., St. Nicholas Ave., Gosforth, Newcastle-upon-Tyne, Tyne,
   NE9 1EE, England

PRODUCT RESEARCH & CHEMICAL CORP   5430 San Fernando Rd, Glendale, CA 91203,
Tel: (213) 240-2060
(Sealants, coatings & adhesives)
   PRC (UK) Ltd., Portland Rd., Newcastle-upon-Tyne NE2 1BL, England

PROSERV INC   1101 Wilson Blvd, #1800, Arlington, VA 22209,
Tel: (703) 276-3030
(Sports mktg, mgt & consult)
   ProServ UK, 14-15 Craven St., London WC2N 5AD, England

PSI INDUSTRIES INC   3333 N Fernando Blvd, Burbank, CA 91504,
Tel: (213) 843-5831
(Cathodic protection of gas/oil)
    Pipeline Seal & Insulator Co. Ltd., Davis House, 8 Scrubbs, London, NW10, England

PURE INDUSTRIES INC   441 Hall Ave, Saint Marys, PA 15857, Tel: (814) 781-1573
(Mfr carbon graphite & silicon carbide com)
    Pure Industries Ltd., 12 & 13 Madeley Rd., North Moons Moat, Redditch,
       Worcestershire B98 9NB, England

PUROLATOR COURIER CORP   131 Morristown Rd, Basking Ridge, NJ 07980,
Tel: (201) 953-6400
(Time-sensitive package delivery)
    Purolator Services Ltd., Coinbrook, Slough, Berks, SL3 OAE, England

PYLE-NATIONAL INC   1334 N Kostner Ave, Chicago, IL 60651-1697,
Tel: (312) 342-6300
(Mfr elec, electr & military specification connectors)
    Pyle-National Ltd., Sherbrook Rd., Daybrook, Nottingham NG5 68T, England

QUAKER CHEMICAL CORP   Elm & Lee Sts, Conshohocken, PA 19428,
Tel: (215) 828-4250
(Mfr chem specialties)
    Quaker Chemical Ltd., Woodchester, Stroud, Gloucestershire, England

QUAKER OATS CO   345 Merchandise Mart Plaza, Chicago, IL 60654,
Tel: (312) 222-7111
(Foods, pet foods, toys, chems)
    Quaker Oats Ltd., Bridge Rd., Southall, Middlesex, UB2 4AG, England

QUIGLEY CO INC   235 E 42nd St, New York, NY 10017, Tel: (212) 573-3444
(Mfr refractory specs, application equip)
    Pfizer-Quigley UK Ltd., Aldwarke Rd., Rawmarsh, Rotherham, S. Yorks. S65 3SR,
       England

QUIGLEY PUBLISHING CO   159 W 53rd St, New York, NY 10019, Tel: (212) 247-3100
(Publisher)
    Quigley Publications Ltd., 15 Samuel Rd., Langdon Hills, Basildon New Town, Essex,
       England

RAMSEY TECHNOLOGY INC   1853 W County Rd, St Paul, MN 55113,
Tel: (612) 633-5150
(Mfr scales & mining equip)
    Ramsey Process Controls Ltd., 109 Oyster Lane, Byfleet, Surrey KT14 9JS, England

RANCO INC   555 Metro Pl N, PO Box 248, Dublin, OH 43017, Tel: (614) 764-3733
(Controls for appliance, automotive, comfort, commercial & consumer mkts)
    Ranco Controls Ltd., Southway Dr., Southway, Plymouth, PL6 6QT, England

RANSBURG CORP   3939 W 56th St, Indianapolis, IN 46208, Tel: (317) 298-5000
(Mfr electrostatic coating sys)
    Ransburg-Gema UK Ltd., 52-54 Hamm Moor Ln., Weybridge, Surrey KT1S 2SF, England

RAYOVAC CORP   601 Rayovac Dr, Madison, WI 53711, Tel: (608) 275-3340
(Mfr batteries & lighting devices)
    Rayovac Ltd., King St., Mainstone, Kent ME14 1BG, England

(cont)

Rayovac Micro Power Ltd., Tyne & Wear, Washington, England
Rayovac Vidor Ltd., Newton Aycliffe, England

RAYTHEON CO   141 Spring St, Lexington, MA 02173, Tel: (617) 862-6600
(Mfr diversified electronics & apppliances; aviation, ind & constr services,
publishing)
A.C. Cossor Ltd., The Pinnacles, Elizabeth Way, Harlow, Essex, CM19 5BB, England
Data Logic Ltd., The Pinnacles, Harlow, Essex CM19 5BB, England
Electrical Installations Ltd., 65 Vincent Sq., Westminster, London, SW1P 2NX,
    England
Seismograph Service Ltd., Holwood, Westerham Rd., Keston, Kent, BR2 6HD, England

RCA GLOBAL COMMUNICATIONS INC   60 Broad St, New York, NY 10004,
Tel: (212) 806-7000
(Commun serv)
RCA Ltd., Norfolk House, 31 St. James Sq., London SW1Y 4JR, England

READER'S DIGEST ASSOCIATION INC   PO Box 235, Pleasantville, NY 10570,
Tel: (914) 238-1000
(Global publisher & direct mail marketer)
Reader's Digest Association Ltd., 25 Berkeley Sq., London, W1X 6AB, England

READING & BATES CORP   2200 Mid-Continent Tower, Tulsa, OK 74103,
Tel: (918) 583-8521
(Oil & gas explor & prod, offshore contract drilling, water mgmt sys)
Reading & Bates (UK) Ltd., Seymour Mews House, Seymour Mews, London, England

RECOGNITION EQUIPMENT INC   PO Box 222307, Dallas, TX 75222,
Tel: (214) 579-6000
(Optical character recognition sys & equip for document processing & computer data)
Recognition Equip. Ltd., Queen's House, 2 Holly Rd., Twickenham, Middlesex,
    TW1 4EW, England

REDKEN LABORATORIES INC   6625 Variel Ave, Canoga Park, CA 91303,
Tel: (818) 992-2700
(Mfr hair & skin care prdts)
Redken Laboratories Inc. Ltd., Precedent Dr., Milton Keynes MK13 8PF, England

THE REECE CORP   800 South St, Waltham, MA 02254-9168, Tel: (617) 894-9220
(Mfr apparel mach)
Reece Machinery Co. Ltd., 32/30 Leman St., London, E1 8EZ, England

REEVES BROTHERS INC   1271 Ave of the Americas, New York, NY 10020,
Tel: (212) 573-8600
(Woven cotton & synthetic fabrics, textile job finishing, filter cloth, ind fabric
prdts)
Textile Laminations Ltd., Portman House, George St., Aylesbury, Bucks, England

REICHHOLD CHEMICALS INC   RCI Bldg, 525 N Broadway, White Plains, NY 10603,
Tel: (914) 682-5700
(Synthetic resins & specialty chems)
Doverstrand Ltd., England
Sterling Varnish Co. Ltd., Fraser Rd., Trafford Park, Manchester, M17 1DU, England

RELIABILITY INC   PO Box 218370, Houston, TX 77218, Tel: (713) 492-0550
(Mfr burn-in & burn-in test sys & related equip/serv; DC/DC converters)
Reliability Europe Ltd., 69 Buckingham Ave., Slough SL1 4PN, England

RELIANCE ELECTRIC CO   24701 Euclid Ave, Cleveland, OH 44117,
  Tel: (216) 266-7000
  (Equip & sys for ind automation, telecom equip)
    Reliance Electric Ltd., Hales Field 19, Telfurd, Shopshire TF7 4PT, England
    Toledo Scale Ltd., Boston Rd., Gorse Hill Ind. Estate, Beamont Leys,
      Leicester LE4 1AW, England

RELIANCE GROUP INC   55 E 52nd St, New York, NY 10055, Tel: (212) 909-1100
  (Financial serv, ins, mgmt serv)
    Fuel & Energy Consultants Ltd., Wellington House, Queens Rd., Oldham, Lancashire,
      OLS 2BA, England
    Inbucon Ltd., 197 Knightsbridge, London, SW7 IRN, England
    John Evans Companies, Systems House, Great Hampton St., Birmingham 18, England
    Leasco Software Ltd., Reliance House, 150-152 Bath Rd., Maidenhead, Berks, SL6 4LD,
      England

REMINGTON PRODUCTS INC   60 Main St, Bridgeport, CT 06602, Tel: (203) 367-4400
  (Mfr home appliances, electric shavers)
    Remington Consumer Products Ltd., High St., New Malden, Surrey, England

REPUBLIC TELCOM SYSTEMS CORP   6150 Lookout Rd, Boulder, CO 80301,
  Tel: (303) 530-8600
  (Mfr packet-switched voice & data networking sys)
    Republic Telcom Systems, 53-54 Haymarket, London SW1Y 4RP, England

REPUBLICBANK DALLAS NA   310 N Ervay St, Dallas, TX 75265, Tel: (214) 922-5000
  (Banking)
    Republic Bank Dallas, 51 Grace Church St., London EC3V OBN, England

REVLON INC   767 Fifth Ave, New York, NY 10153-0033, Tel: (212) 572-5000
  (Cosmetics, health care prdts)
    Revlon Intl. Corp. Ltd., 86 Brook St.,-London, W1, England

REXNORD CORP   PO Box 2022, Milwaukee, WI 53201, Tel: (414) 643-3000
  (Mfr power transmission prdts)
    Rexnord (UK) Ltd., 14 Stadium Way, Stadium Industrial Estate, Reading, Berkshire,
      RG3 6BX, England
    Rexnord UK Ltd., Joseph's Well #2D, Hanover Walk, Park Lane, Leeds LS3 1AB, England

RICHARDSON-VICKS INC   Ten Westport Rd, Wilton, CT 06897, Tel: (203) 834-5000
  (Consumer health & personal care prdts)
    Vicks Ltd., Rusham Park, Whitehall Lane, Egham Surrey, TW20 9NM, England

RICHTON INTL CORP   1345 Ave of the Americas, New York, NY 10115,
  Tel: (212) 765-6480
  (Nondurable consumer wearables, active sportswear jewelry & accessories)
    Corocraft Ltd., Palladium House, 1-4 Argyll St., London, W1V 2EU, England

RIDGE TOOL CO   400 Clark St, Elyria, OH 44035, Tel: (216) 323-5581
  (Hand & power tools for working pipe, drain cleaning equip, etc)
    Ridge Tool Ltd., Royston Rd., Baldock, Herts, England

RIGHT ASSOCIATES   1818 Market St, 14th Fl, Philadelphia, PA 19103-3614,
  Tel: (215) 988-1588
  (Outplacement & human resources consult servs)
    Right Associates, 21 Rosedale Pannal, Harrogate, Yorkshire HG3 1LB, England
    Right Associates, other locations in England

RIKER LABORATORIES INC   Bldg 225-1N-07, 3M Center, St Paul, MN 55144,
Tel: (612) 733-9577
(Specialty pharms)
  Riker Laboratories, 1 Morley St., Loughborough, Leics. LE11 1EP, England

RMS GROUP INC   43-59 10th St, Long Island City, NY 11101, Tel: (718) 361-9756
(Intl market devel)
  Loader Chemicals & Plastics, Ltd., 13 Headley Chase, Warley, Brentwood,
    Essex CM14 5BN, England

ROBERT HALF INTL INC   2884 Sand Hill Rd, #200, Menlo Park, CA 94025,
Tel: (415) 854-9700
(Personnel servs)
  Robert Half Intl., Inc., 63 Temple Row, Birmingham B2 5LS, England
  Robert Half Intl., Inc., other locations in England
  Robert Half-London, Walter House, 418 Strand, London WC2R OPT, England

H H ROBERTSON CO   Two Gateway Center, Pittsburgh, PA 15222,
Tel: (412) 281-3200
(Mfr roof & wall prdts, cellular steel floor sys, ventilation equip)
  H.H. Robertson Ltd., Cromwell Rd., Ellesmere Port, Wirral, Cheshire, L65 4DS,
    England

A H ROBINS CO INC   1407 Cummings Dr, PO Box 26609, Richmond, VA 23261-6609,
Tel: (804) 257-2000
(Mfr ethical pharms & consumer prdts)
  A.H. Robins Co. Ltd., Gatwick Rd., West Sussex, England

ROCHESTER INSTRUMENT SYSTEMS INC   255 N Union St, Rochester, NY 14605,
Tel: (716) 263-7700
(Electronic alarms & monitors in- cluding annunciators, event recorders, etc)
  Rochester Instrument Systems Ltd., Maxim Rd., Crayford, Kent, DA1 4BG, England

ROCKWELL GRAPHIC SYSTEMS   700 Oakmont Lane, Westmont, IL 60559-5546,
Tel: (708) 850-5600
(Mfr printing equip)
  Rockwell Graphic Systems Ltd., Greenbank St., Preston, Lancs. PR1 7LA, England
  Rockwell Graphic Systems Ltd., Central House, 3 Lampton Rd., Middlesex TW3 1HY,
    England

ROCKWELL INTL CORP   2230 E Imperial Hwy, El Segundo, CA 90245,
Tel: (213) 647-5000
(Prdts & serv for aerospace, automotive, electronics, graphics & automation inds)
  Rockwell Graphic Systems Ltd., Greenbank St., Preston, Lancashire, PR1 7LA, England
  Rockwell Intl. Ltd., Central House, 3 Lampton Rd., Hounslow, Middlesex TW3 1HY,
    England
  Rockwell-Collins (UK) Ltd., Rockwell House, Suttons Park Ave., Earley, Reading,
    Berks. RG6 1LA, England
  Rockwell-Maudslay Ltd., Alcester, Warwickshire, B49 6HT, England

R A RODRIGUEZ INC   320 Endo Blvd, Garden City, NY 11530, Tel: (516) 832-2617
(Export mgt: bearings & power trans equip)
  R. A. Rodriguez (UK) Ltd., Icknield House, Eastcheap, Letchworth, Herts SG6 3DF,
    England

ROGERS CORP   One Technology Dr, Rogers, CT 06263, Tel: (203) 774-9605
  (Mfr flexible, molded, die-stamped & microwave circuits; engineered polymer prdts)
    Mektron Circuit Systems Ltd., 119 Kingston Rd., Leatherhead, Surrey, KT22 7SU,
      England

ROHM & HAAS CO   Independence Mall West, Philadelphia, PA 19105,
  Tel: (215) 592-3000
  (Mfr ind & agric chems, plastics)
    EMCA UK, The Grip Industrial Estate, Station Rd., Linton, Cambridge CB1 6NW, England
    Rohm & Haas (UK) Ltd., Lennig House, 2 Mason's Ave., Croydon, Surrey CR9 3NB,
      England
    Rohm & Hass Co., Chesterfield House, Bloomsbury Way, London WC1A 2TP, England

RONCO TELEPRODUCTS INC   1200 Arthur Ave, Elk Grove Village, IL 60007,
  Tel: (708) 640-0700
  (Consumer prdts, housewares & record albums)
    Ronco Inc., Ltd., 111 Mortlkae Rd., Kew Richmond, Surrey, TW9 4AB, England

RORER GROUP INC   500 Virginia Dr, Ft Washington, PA 19034,
  Tel: (215) 628-6000
  (Mfr ethical & consumer pharms)
    Radio Chemicals Ltd., Witham, Essex, England

ROSEMOUNT INC   12001 Technology Dr, Eden Prairie, MN 55344,
  Tel: (612) 941-5560
  (Mfr aerospace & ind instrumentation)
    Rosemount Ltd., Heath Pl., Bognor Regis, Sussex, PO22 9SH, England

ROSS OPERATING VALVE CO   PO Box 7015, Troy, MI 48007, Tel: (313) 362-1250
  (Mfr air valves, pneumatic controls & accessories)
    Ross Valve U.K. Ltd., 94 Alston Dr., Bradwell Abbey, Milton Kenyes MK13 9HF, England

ROWAN COMPANIES INC   5051 Westheimer St, Houston, TX 77056,
  Tel: (713) 621-7800
  (Contract drilling & air charter service)
    British American Offshore Ltd., 43 Upper Grosvenor Sq., London W1X 9P6, England

ROWLAND INC   222 Dividend Rd, Rocky Hill, CT 06067, Tel: (203) 563-6000
  (Extruded, laminated & co-extruded thermoplastic sheet & film)
    Rocel Ltd., Box 13, Old Church Rd., Coventry, CV6 7DW, England

RUDER FINN INC   301 E 57th St, New York, NY 10022, Tel: (212) 593-6400
  (Public relations serv, broadcast commun)
    Sterling Hewland, Ruder & Finn Intl. Ltd., 1 Lowther Gardens, Prince, Consort Rd.,
      London, SW7 2AA, England

RUSSELL REYNOLDS ASSOCIATES INC   200 Park Ave, New York, NY 10166,
  Tel: (212) 351-2000
  (Exec recruiting services)
    Russell Reynolds Associates Ltd., 24 St. James Sq., London SW1Y 4HZ, England

SAFETY-KLEEN CORP   777 Big Timber Rd, Elgin, IL 60123, Tel: (708) 697-8460
  (Solvent based parts cleaning serv, sludge/solvent recycling serv)
    Safety-Kleen Parts Washer Svce. Ltd., Box 14, Worton Hall, Worton Rd., Isleworth,
      Hounslow, Middlesex, England

SALEM CORP   PO Box 2222, Pittsburgh, PA 15230, Tel: (412) 923-2200
  (Mfr ind furnaces, coal processing equip, metal finishing equip)
    Salem Engineering Co. Ltd., Milford House, Milford, Nr. Derby, England
    Salem Herr-Voss Co. Ltd., Eastgate House, Derby, England

SALOMON BROS INC   1 New York Plaza, New York, NY 10004, Tel: (212) 747-7000
  (Securities dealers & underwriters)
    Salomon Brothers Intl. Ltd., 1 Angel Ct., London, EC2 CR7HS, England

SAMSONITE CORP   11200 E 45th St, Denver, CO 80239, Tel: (303) 373-7159
  (Mfr luggage & leather goods)
    Samsonite Ltd., Block E, Meridian Gate, Marsh Wall, West India Dock, London E14,
    England

SARGENT & GREENLEAF INC   1 Security Dr, Nicholasville, KY 40356,
  Tel: (606) 885-9411
  (Security locking mechanisms)
    Sargent & Greenleaf Inc. Ltd., 468 Ewell Rd., London, KT6 7EL, England

W B SAUNDERS CO   W Washington Sq, Philadelphia, PA 19105, Tel: (215) 574-4700
  (Med & tech book publishers)
    W.B. Saunders Co. Ltd., 12 Dyott St., London, WC1, England

SAVAIR PRODUCTS CO   33200 Freeway Dr, St Clair Shores, MI 48082,
  Tel: (313) 296-7390
  (Welding mach components, air & hydraulic cylinders)
    Savair Products Ltd., Black Moor Rd., Ebb Lake Industrial Estate, Verwood,
    Wimborne, Dorset BH21 6AX, England

SCHENECTADY CHEMICALS INC   PO Box 1046, Schenectady, NY 12301,
  Tel: (518) 370-4200
  (Mfr elec insulating varnishe, enamels, resins, alkylated phenol)
    Schenectady-Midland Ltd., Four Ashes, Wolverhampton WV10 7BT, England

R P SCHERER CORP   2075 W Big Beaver Rd, Troy, MI 48084, Tel: (313) 649-0900
  (Mfr soft gelatin & two-piece hard shell capsules)
    R.P. Scherer Ltd., Frankland Rd., Blagrove, Swindon, Wilts. SN5 8YS, England

SCHLEGEL CORP   400 East Ave, Rochester, NY 14607, Tel: (716) 546-6260
  (Engineered perimeter sealing systems for residential & commercial constr)
    Schiegel (UK) Ltd., Ring Rd., Seacroft, Leeds 14, England

SCHOLASTIC INC   730 Broadway, New York, NY 10003, Tel: (212) 505-3000
  (Pub educational magazines, books, software)
    Scholastic Publications Ltd., Marlborough House, Holly Walk, Leamington Spa,
    Warwickshire CV32 4D, England

SCHRADER BELLOWS DIV   200 W Exchange St, Akron, OH 44309, Tel: (216) 375-1263
  (Pneumatic & hydraulic valves & cylinders, FRL units & accessories)
    Schrader Bellows Div., Walkmill Lane, Bridgtown, Cannock, Staffs, WS11 3LR, England

SCIENCE MANAGEMENT CORP   PO Box 0600, Basking Ridge, NJ 07920,
  Tel: (201) 647-7000
  (Human/mgmt resources, info technology, engr & technology services)
    SMC Intl., 148 Buckingham Palace Rd., London, SW1W 9TR, England

SCIENTIFIC ATLANTA INC   1 Technology Pkwy, PO Box 105600, Atlanta, GA 30348,
Tel: (404) 441-4000
(Telecommun instru & equip, energy mgmt & home security equip, test & measurement
instru)
    Scientific-Atlanta (UK) Ltd., Horton Manor, Stanwell Rd., Horton, Slough, SL3 9PA,
    England

SCIENTIFIC DESIGN CO   2 Park Ave, New York, NY 10016, Tel: (212) 689-3000
(Engineering & constr of chem plants; organic chems, petrochems)
    Scientific Design Co. Ltd., Bush House, Aldwych, London, WC2 B4 QB, England
    Scientific Design Co. Ltd., 9 Kingsway, London WC2B 6XF, England

SCM CORP   299 Park Ave, New York, NY 10171, Tel: (212) 752-2700
(Business equip, chems, coatings & resins, foods, paper prdts)
    SCM (UK) Ltd., SCM House, North Circular Rd., Stonebridge Park, London, NW10 7SS,
    England

SCOTT WORLDWIDE INC   Scott Plaza, Philadelphia, PA 19113, Tel: (215) 521-5000
(Paper & paper prdts, bleached pulp)
    Scott Ltd., England

SCRIPTURE PRESS PUBLICATIONS INC   1825 College Ave, Wheaton, IL 60187,
Tel: (708) 668-6000
(Publ Christian education materials)
    Scripture Press Foundation (UK) Ltd., Raans Rd., Amersham-on-the-Hill,
    Bucks HP6 6JQ, England

SEA-LAND SERVICE INC   379 Thornall St, Edison, NJ 08837, Tel: (201) 558-6000
(Container transport)
    Freight Sales Intl. Ltd., Port of Preston, Authority Bldg., Watery Lane, Preston,
    Lancashire, England
    Freight Sales Intl. Ltd., c/o Sea-Land Terminal, New South Quay Dock, Felixstowe,
    Suffolk, England
    Sea-Land Containerships Ltd., Napier House 24-28, High Holburn, London, WC1, England
    Sea-Land Containerships Ltd., c/o British Roas Services, High St., Turnstall,
    Stoke-on-Trent, Stafes, England

SEALECTRO CORP   225 Hoyt St, Mamaroneck, NY 10543, Tel: (914) 698-5600
(Electronic components, programming & data collection deviccs)
    Sealectro Ltd., Walton Rd., Farlington, Portsmouth, Hants, PO6 1TB, England

SEALED AIR CORP   Park 80 Plaza E, Saddle Brook, NJ 07662-5291,
Tel: (201) 791-7600
(Mfr protective packaging prdts)
    Sealed Air Ltd., Telford Way, Kettering, Northants NN16 8UN, England

SEAQUIST DIV   1160 N Silver Lake Rd, Cary, IL 60013, Tel: (708) 639-2126
(Aerosol valves, closures, pump dispensers)
    Perfect-Valois UK Ltd., 26 Edison Rd., Rabans Lane, Aylesbury, England

G D SEARLE & CO   PO Box 1045, Skokie, IL 60076, Tel: (708) 982-7000
(Pharms, health care & optical prdts, specialty chems)
    G.D. Searle & Co. Ltd., P.O. Box 53, Lane End Rd., High Wycombe, Buckinghamshire,
    HP12 4HL, England
    Pearle Vision Center Ltd., Broadfield's House, Headstone Lane, Harrow, Middlesex,
    England
    Searle Medical Products, P.O. Box 88, Lane End, High Wycombe, Buckinghamshire,

(cont)

HP12 4HL, England
Searle Research & Development, P.O. Box 53, Lane End Rd., High Wycombe,
Buckinghamshire, HP12 4HL, England

SEARS WORLD TRADE   633 Pennsylvania Ave, NW, Washington, DC 20004,
Tel: (202) 626-1600
(Consumer & light ind goods, processed foods)
Price & Pierce, 51 Aldwych, London WC2B 4AZ, England

SEATRAIN LINES INC   270 Sylvan Ave, Englewood Cliffs, NJ 07632,
Tel: (201) 871-8900
(Containerized shipping, ship chartering)
Seatrain Ltd., Albany House, Hurst St., Birmingham, 5, England
Seatrain Ltd., Stock Exchange House, 69 St. Geroge's Place, Glasgow, G2 1QY, England
Seatrain Ltd., Clyde Port Container Terminal, Containerway, Laird St., Greenock,
Renfrewshire, England
Seatrain Ltd., Norwich Union House, Water St., Liverpool, L2 3SP, England
Seatrain Ltd., 1st Floor, St. Clare House, 30/33 The Minories, London, EC3 1DD,
England
Seatrain Ltd., 9th Floor, Arndale House, Arndale Centre, Manchester, M4 3AP, England

SEATTLE FIRST NATIONAL BANK   1001 4th Ave, PO Box 3586, Seattle, WA 98124,
Tel: (206) 583-3131
(Bank holding company, financial serv)
Seattle-First National Bank, Tribute House, 120 Moorgate, London, EC2M 6TE, England

SECURITY PACIFIC NATIONAL BANK   333 S Hope St, Los Angeles, CA 90071,
Tel: (213) 345-6211
(Banking)
Security Pacific National Bank, 4 Broadgate, London EC2M 7LE, England

SEISMOGRAPH SERVICE CORP   PO Box 1590, Tulsa, OH 74112, Tel: (918) 627-3330
(Geophysical contractor)
Seismograph Service Ltd., Holwood, Westerham Rd., Keston, Kent BR2 6HD, England

SELAS CORP OF AMERICA   Dreshertown Rd & Limekiln Pike, Dresher, PA 19025,
Tel: (215) 646-6600
(Mfr heat treating equip for metal, glass, ceramic & chem inds)
Nordsea Gas Appliance Co. Ltd., 42 Hyde Rd., Denton, Manchester, M34 3AE, England
Priest Furnaces Ltd., P.O. Box S., Bank 18, The Grange Eston, Middlesbrough,
Cleveland, TS6 8DJ, England

SEMICONDUCTOR SPECIALISTS INC   195 W Spangler, Elmhurst, IL 60126,
Tel: (708) 279-1000
(Electr distr)
Semiconductor Specialists (UK) Ltd., Carroll House, 159 High St., Yiewsley,
West Drayton, Middlesex, UB7 7XB, England

SENCO PRODUCTS INC   8485 Broadwell Rd, Cincinnati, OH 45244,
Tel: (513) 388-2000
(Mfr ind nailers, staplers, fasteners & accessories)
Senco Pneumatics (UK) Ltd., 211 Europa Blvd., Westbrook, Warrington,
Cheshire WA5 5TN, England

SEQUA CORP   200 Park Ave, New York, NY 10166, Tel: (212) 986-5500
   (Aerospace prdts & sys, machinery & metal coatings, transp, spec chems, professional
   & fin serv)
      Warwick Intl. Ltd., Wortley Moor Rd., Leeds LS12 4JE, England

SERVICEMASTER INDUSTRIES INC   2399 Warrensville Rd, Downers Grove, IL 60515,
   Tel: (708) 964-1300
   (Mgmt serv to health care, school & ind facilities; home, ind & commercial cleaning
   serv)
      Servicemaster Ltd., 50 Commercial Sq., Freeman 5 Commons, Leicester, LE2 7SR,
      England

SEVEN-UP INTL   120 Park Ave, New York, NY 10017, Tel: (212) 880-4100
   (Soft drinks)
      Seven-Up Inc. Ltd., Philip Morris House 21-47 High St., Feltham, Middlesex, England

SEVERE ENVIRONMENT SYSTEMS CO   PO Box 668, Chatsworth, CA 91311,
   Tel: (213) 998-9090
   (Computer prdts for space, mili- tary, commercial avionics & severe environment ind
   applications)
      EMM Ltd., 122 Bridge Rd., Maidenhead, Berkshire, SL6 8NA, England

SGS CONTROL SERVICES INC   42 Broadway, New York, NY 10004,
   Tel: (212) 482-8700
   (Complete range of quality & quantity control checks & related tech serv)
      Cargo Superintendents Ltd., 29, Cambridge Park, Wanstead, London, E11 2PU, England
      SGS Freight Services Ltd., 29, Cambridge Park, Wanstead, London, E11 2PU, England
      SGS Inspection Services Ltd., Nr. Windsor, Berkshire, Winkfield, SL4 4RT, England
      SGS Inspection Services Ltd., Industrial Div., Valzan House, 201-205 London Rd.,
      Camberley, Surrey, England

SHAKESPEARE FISHING TACKLE GROUP   611 Shakespeare Rd, Columbia, SC 29204,
   Tel: (803) 754-7000
   (Mfr fishing tackle)
      Shakespeare Co. (UK), Broad Ground Rd., Lakeside, Redditch, Worcestershire,
      B98 8NQ, England

SHEAFFER EATON INC   1 Crown Mark Dr, Lincoln, RI 02865, Tel: (401) 333-0303
   (Mfr writing instruments)
      Sheaffer Pen, Hemel Hempstead, Herts, HP2 7ER, England

SHEARMAN & STERLING   599 Lexington Ave, New York, NY 10022,
   Tel: (212) 848-4000
   (Lawyers)
      Shearman & Sterling, St. Helen's, 1 Undershaft, London EC3A 8HX1, England

SHEARSON/AMERICAN EXPRESS   American Express Tower, New York, NY 10285,
   Tel: (212) 298-2000
   (Investment banking, financial serv)
      Shearson/American Express, 55 Grosvenor St., London, WU1X 9DB, England
      Shearson/American Express, 16 Moorfields Highwalk, London, EC2Y 9DH, England
      Shearson/American Express, St. Alphage House, 2 Fore St., London, EC24 5DA, England

SHELLER-GLOBE CORP   1641 Porter St, Detroit, MI 48216, Tel: (313) 962-7311
   (Mfr auto components, ind prdts)
      Sheller-Clifford Ltd., Spring Rd., Hall Green, Birmingham, B11 3DN, England

SHIPLEY CO INC   2300 Washington St, Newton, MA 02162, Tel: (617) 969-5500
   (Mfr chems for printed circuit boards & microelectronic mfg)
      Shipley Europe Ltd., Herald Way, Coventry, CV3 2RQ, England

SHULTON INC   1 Cyanamid Plaza, Wayne, NJ 07470, Tel: (201) 831-2000
   (Health, beauty & grooming prdts)
      Shulton Ltd., Trevor House, 100 Brompton Rd., London, SW3 1EW, England

SIMMONDS PRECISION GROUP   Norwick-Oxford Rd, Norwich, NY 13815,
   Tel: (607) 335-5000
   (Design/mfr aerospace sys, instru & components, ind control sys)
      Simmonds Precision Prdts. Ltd., The Runnymede Malt House, Runnymede,
      Surrey TW2 09B, England

SIMMONS INTL   1 Gulf & Western Plaza, New York, NY 10023, Tel: (212) 333-3511
   (Bedding prdts)
      Sleepeezee Ltd., 61 Morden Rd., Merton, London, SW19 3XP, England

SIMON & SCHUSTER INC   1230 Ave of the Americas, New York, NY 10020,
   Tel: (212) 245-6400
   (Publisher)
      Prentice-Hall Intl. (UK) Ltd., 66 Wood Lane End, Hemel Hempstead, Herts., HP2 4RG,
      England

SIMPLEX TIME RECORDER CO   Simplex Plaza, Gardner, MA 01441,
   Tel: (617) 632-2500
   (Time recorders & stamps, master time sys, alarm, security, monitor & control sys)
      Simplex Management Services Ltd., 114 Cromwell Rd., London, SW7, England
      Simplex Time Recorder Co., Ltd., Holmfield Industrial Estate, Haldsworth, Halifax,
      York, W1, England

SIMPLICITY PATTERN CO INC   200 Madison Ave, New York, NY 10016,
   Tel: (212) 481-3737
   (Dress patterns)
      Simplicity Patterns Ltd., Metropolis House, 39-45 Tottenham Court Rd., London,
      W1P 9RD, England

SIRCO INTL CORP   700-718 S Fulton Ave, Mt Vernon, NY 10550,
   Tel: (914) 664-4400
   (Imp of handbags, totes, wallets)
      Sirco Leatherwares Ltd., No. Circular Rd., Finchly, London, N12, England

SKIDMORE OWINGS & MERRILL   33 W Monroe St, Chicago, IL 60603,
   Tel: (312) 641-5959
   (Architects, engineers)
      SOM Inc., Devonshire House, Mayfair Place, London W1X 5FH, England

WILBUR SMITH ASSOCS   NCNB Tower, PO Box 92, Columbia, SC 29202,
   Tel: (803) 738-0580
   (Consulting engineers)
      Wilbur Smith Associates Inc. Intl., Premier House #422, 10 Greycoat Pl.,
      London SW1P 1SB, England

A O SMITH CORP   PO Box 584, Milwaukee, WI 53201, Tel: (414) 447-4000
   (Auto & truck frames, motors, water heaters, computer serv, etc)
      A.O. Smith Harvester Products Ltd., Eye Suffolk, IP23 7HS, England

SMITH INTL INC   16740 Hardy St, Houston, TX 77032, Tel: (713) 443-6470
  (Mfr/serv downhole drilling equip)
    Smith Intl. (North Sea) Ltd., 7 Balfour Place- 1st Fl., London W1Y 5RY, England

SMYTH MFG CO   85 Granby St, Bloomfield, CT 06002, Tel: (203) 242-2201
  (Bookbinding mach)
    Smyth-Horne Ltd., 2 Pegamoid Rd., Edmonton, London N18 2LW, England

SNAP-ON TOOLS CORP   2801 80th St, Kenosha, WI 53141-1410, Tel: (414) 656-5200
  (Mfr automotive & ind maint serv tools)
    Snap-On Tools Corp., Palmer House, 150-154 Cross St., Sale, Cheshire M33 1FV,
      England

SOLIDYNE INC   60 Spence St, Bay Shore, NY 11706, Tel: (516) 231-7800
  (Heat sealing generators, dielectric equip)
    Stanelco Ltd., 4 Elstree Way, Boreham Wood, Herts, WD6 1SE, England

SONOCO PRODUCTS CO   North Second St, PO Box 160, Hartsville, SC 29550,
  Tel: (803) 383-7000
  (Mfr packaging for consumer & ind mkt)
    Sonoco Capseals Liners, Greenock Rd., Trading Estate, Slough, Berkshire SL1 4QQ,
      England
    Sonoco Europe, Oakwood Rd., Romiley Stockport, Cheshire, SK6 4DY, England
    Sonoco Europe Board Mills, Stainland, NR Halifax, Yorkshire, England
    Sonoco Liquid Packaging, Oakwood Rd., Romiley, Stockport, Cheshire SK6 4DY, England
    Sonoco Packaging Tapes, Bridge St., Horwich, Bolton, Lancashire BL6 7BT, England
    Sonoco Reels, Weston Rd., Trading Estate, Slough, Berkshire SL1 4HR, England

SPALDING & EVENFLO COS INC   5750A N Hoover Blvd, Tampa, FL 33614,
  Tel: (813) 887-5200
  (Mfr sports equip, infant & juvenile furniture & accessories)
    Spalding Sports (UK) Ltd., 16 Trafalgar Way, Ball Hill, Cambridge, CB3 8SQ, England

SPECTRA-PHYSICS   3333 N First St, San Jose, CA 95134, Tel: (408) 946-6080
  (Lasers, optical components & coatings, data sys)
    Spectra-Physics Ltd., 17 Brick Knoll Park St., Albans, Herts, ALI 5UF, England

SPECTRAL DYNAMICS CORP   4141 Ruffin Rd, San Diego, CA 92123,
  Tel: (619) 496-3400
  (Mfr Vibration monitoring, analysis & control equip)
    Scientific-Atlanta Ltd., Home Park Estate, Kings Langley, Herts WD4 8LZ, England

SPEIZMAN INDUSTRIES INC   508 W Fifth St, Charlotte, NC 28231,
  Tel: (704) 372-3751
  (Textile mach & components)
    Speizman Industries (UK) Ltd., 114 Milligan Rd., Leicester, England

THE SPERRY & HUTCHINSON CO   330 Madison Ave, New York, NY 10017,
  Tel: (212) 983-2000
  (Trading stamps, incentive programs)
    Sperry & Hutchinson Co. Ltd., 162 Regent St., London, W1R 6BX, England

SPRINGS INDUSTRIES INC   205 N White St, Fort Mill, SC 29715,
  Tel: (803) 547-2901
  (Mfr & sales finished fabrics, home furnishings, ind fabrics)
    Springs Ltd., 50 Conduit St., London W1R 9FB, England

SPS TECHNOLOGIES INC   900 Newtown-Yardley Rd, Newtown, PA 18940,
  Tel: (215) 860-3000
  (Mfr aerospace & ind fasteners, precision components, superalloys, magnetic
  materials, fastening sys)
      Alexander Socket Screws Ltd., P.O. Box 76, Cranford St., Smethwick, Warley,
      W. Mids. B66 2TA, England
      SPS Technologies Ltd., P.O. Box 38, Burnaby Rd., Coventry CV6 4AE, England
      T.J. Brooks Ltd., 191 Barkby Rd., Leicester LE4 7HX, England

SPX CORP   700 Terrace Point Dr, Muskegon, MI 49443, Tel: (616) 724-5000
  (Mfr spec repair equip & repair parts)
      Bear Automotive (UK) Ltd., Mercers Row, Cambridge CB5 8HY, England
      SPX United Kingdom Ltd., 19-21 Stockfield, Acocks Green, Birminghim B27 6AJ, England
      V.L. Churchill Ltd., P.O. Box 3, London Rd., Daventry, Northant NN11 4NF, England

SQUARE D CO   Executive Plaza, Palatine, IL 60067, Tel: (708) 397-2600
  (Power distribution & elec/electr ind control equip)
      Lircon Ltd., Unit 6, Park Rd., Swanley, Kent, England
      Square D Co. United Kingdom, Swindon, England

SRI INTL   333 Ravenswood Ave, Menlo Park, CA 94025, Tel: (415) 326-6200
  (Intl consulting & research)
      SRI Europe-London, Menlo Park House, 4 Addiscombe Rd., London, England

ST JOE MINERALS CORP   250 Park Ave, New York, NY 10017, Tel: (212) 953-5000
  (Coal, oil, gas, iron ore, metals & minerals)
      St. Joe Petroleum (UK) Corp., 32/33 Lowndes St., London, SW1X 9HX, England

STA-RITE INDUSTRIES INC   777 E Wisconsin Ave, Milwaukee, WI 53202,
  Tel: (414) 276-6888
  (Mfr water pumps & filters, water treatment equip, fluid power components)
      Sta-Rite Industries Overseas Corp., Newton Court, High St., Huntingdon, Cambs,
      PE18 6NE, England

STANDARD COMMERCIAL CORP   PO Box 450, Wilson, NC 27893, Tel: (919) 291-5507
  (Leaf tobacco dealers/processors, wool processors)
      Standard Commercial Tobacco Service Ltd., Godalming, Surrey, England

STANDARD OIL CO OF CALIFORNIA   225 Bush St, San Francisco, CA 94104,
  Tel: (415) 894-7700
  (Oil explor & prod, petroleum prdts)
      Chevron Petroleum Ltd., London, England

STANDARD PRODUCTS CO   2130 W 110th St, Cleveland, OH 44102,
  Tel: (216) 281-8300
  (Molded & extruded rubber & plastic prdts, cartage & warehousing)
      Silent Channel Products Ltd., Ferrars Rd., Huntington, England

STANGE CO   342 N Western Ave, Chicago, IL 60612, Tel: (312) 733-6945
  (Seasonings, food colors & flavorings)
      McCormick Foods (UK) Ltd., Ellesmere Port, England

THE STANLEY WORKS   1000 Stanley Dr, PO Box 7000, New Britain, CT 06050,
  Tel: (203) 225-5111
  (Mfr hand tools & hardware)
      Stanley Curtain Companions Ltd., Woodside, Sheffield S3 9PD, England
      Stanley Magic Door Ltd., 802 Osford Ave., Slough, Berks, SL1 4LN, England

Stanley Power Tools Ltd., Nelson Way, Cramlington, Northumberland, NE23 9JS, England
Stanley Tools Ltd., Woodside, Sheffield, S3 9PD, England
Stanley Tools-Europe, Cory House, The Ring, Bracknell, Berks. RG12 1AS, England
Stanley-Bostitch Ltd., Station Rd., Edenbrigde, Kent, England

STATE STREET BANK & TRUST CO   225 Franklin St, Boston, MA 02101,
  Tel: (617) 786-3000
  (Banking servs)
    State Street Global Advisors UK Ltd., Birchin Ct., 20 Birchin Lane,
    London EC3A 1NQ, England
    State Street London Ltd., Lloyds Chambers, 1 Portsoken St., London E1 8DF, England

STEARNS CATALYTIC DIV OF UNITED ENGINEERS & CONSTRUCTORS   30 S 17th St,
  Philadelphia, PA 19101, Tel: (215) 422-3000
  (Engineering & construction)
    Badger Catalytic Ltd., C.I. Tower, St. George's Sq., High St., New Malden,
    Surrey KT3 4HH, England

STEINER CORP   PO Box 2317, 505 E South Temple St, Salt Lake City, UT 84102,
  Tel: (801) 328-8831
  (Linen supply service)
    Steinerco (UK) Ltd., 6 Albemarle St., London, W1X 3HF, England

STEMCO INC   PO Box 1989, Longview, TX 75606, Tel: (214) 758-9981
  (Mfr automotive seals, mufflers, spec prdts for heavy duty trucks, buses, trailers)
    Garlock GB-Stemco Prdts., Hambridge Rd., Newbury, Berkshire, England

STERLING DIV   1977 Ohio River Rd, Sewickley, PA 15143, Tel: (412) 766-7600
  (Elect varnishes, epoxy compounds, resins, protective coatings)
    The Sterling Varnish Co. Ltd., Manchester, M17 1DU, England

STERLING DRUG INC   90 Park Ave, New York, NY 10016, Tel: (212) 907-2000
  (Pharms, chems, cosmetics, household cleaners & waxes)
    Sterling-Winthrop Group Ltd., Winthrop House, Surbiton-upon-Thames, Surrey, England

STERLING SOFTWARE INC   8080 N Central Expy, #1100, Dallas, TX 75206-1895,
  Tel: (214) 891-8600
  (Sales/serv software prdts; tech servs)
    Sterling Software Intl. Div., Africa House, 64/78 Kingsway, London WC2B 6AL, England

STEWART-WARNER CORP   1826 Diversey Pkwy, Chicago, IL 60614,
  Tel: (312) 883-6000
  (Lubrication equip sys, ind tools & controls, castors, pressure switches)
    Steward-Warner Ltd., Tynemouth, Tyne & Wear NE29 7UE, England

STIEFEL LABORATORIES INC   S/S Route 45, Oak Hill, NY 12460,
  Tel: (518) 239-6901
  (Dermatologicals, soaps, health & diet prdts)
    Stiefel Laboratories Ltd., 825 Yeovil Rd., Slough Trading Estate, Slough , Bucks,
    England

STOKES DIV   5500 Tabor Rd, Philadelphia, PA 19120, Tel: (215) 289-5671
  (Vacuum pumps & components, vacuum dryers, oil-upgrading equip)
    Pennwalt Ltd., Tower Works Doman Rd., Camberley, Surrey, Camberley, GU15 3DN,
    England
    Pennwalt Ltd., Tower Works, Doman Rcl., Camberley, Surrey, GU15 3DN, England

STONE & WEBSTER ENGINEERING CORP   245 Summer St, Boston, MA 02107,
Tel: (617) 973-5111
(Engineering, constr & consulting serv)
  Stone & Webster Engineering Ltd., Stone & Webster House, 500 Elder Gate,
  Milton Keynes, Bucks MK9 1BA, England
  Stone & Webster Engineering Ltd., 500 Elder Gate, Milton Keynes, Bucks., MK9 1BA,
  England

STORAGE TECHNOLOGY CORP   2270 S 88th St, Louisville, CO 80028-0001,
Tel: (303) 673-5151
(Mfr/mkt/serv info storage & retrieval sys)
  Storage Technology Ltd., StorageTek House, Woking Business Park, Albert Dr.,
  Woking, Surrey GU21 5JY, England

STRATEGIC PLANNING ASSOCIATES INC   2300 N St NW, Washington, DC 20037,
Tel: (202) 778-7000
(Mgmt consulting)
  Strategic Planning Associates, 1-3 Grosvenor Pl., London SW1X 7HJ, England

STRATOFLEX INC   220 Roberts Cut-Off Rd, PO Box 10398, Fort Worth, TX 76114,
Tel: (817) 738-6543
(Hose assemblies, self-sealing & quick disconnect couplings, swivels, etc)
  TMU Ltd., Unit 2, Martin Court, Blenheim Ind. Estate, Bulwell, Nottingham NG6 8U8,
  England

STREETER RICHARDSON DIV   680 Van Houten Ave, Clifton, NJ 07015,
Tel: (201) 471-3400
(Ind weighing & packaging equip)
  Chronos Richardson Ltd., Arnside Rd., Bestwood Estate, Nottingham, NG5 5HD, England
  Chronos Richardson Ltd., Arnside Rd., Bestwood Estate, Nottingham, NG5 5HD, England

STSC INC   2115 East Jefferson St, Rockville, MD 20852, Tel: (301) 984-5000
(Computer software devel servs)
  STSC International Ltd., Royal Albert House, Sheet St., Windsor, Berkshire SL4 1BE,
  England

SUDLER & HENNESSEY   1633 Broadway, New York, NY 10019, Tel: (212) 265-8000
(Healthcare prdts advertising)
  Sudler & Hennessey Ltd., 24-28 Bloomsbury Way, London WC1A 2PX, England

SULLAIR CORP   3700 E Michigan Blvd, Michigan City, IN 46360,
Tel: (219) 879-5451
(Refrigeration sys, vacuum pumps, generators, etc)
  Sullair (UK) Ltd., 274 High St., Uxbridge, Middlesex, UB8 ILQ, Lngland

SUN CO INC   100 Matsonford Rd, Radnor, PA 19087, Tel: (215) 293-6000
(Petroleum & petroleum prdts)
  Sun Intl. Exploration & Production Co., 80 Hammersmith Rd., London W14 8YS, England

SUN ELECTRIC CORP   One Sun Pkwy, Crystal Lake, IL 60014, Tel: (815) 459-7700
(Mfr auto tune-up, diagnostic & emission testing equip)
  Suntester (UK) Ltd., Oldmedow Rd., Hardwick Estate, King's Lynn, Norfolk, PE30 4JW,
  England

SUN EXPLORATION & PRODUCTION CO   PO Box 2880, Dallas, TX 75221-2880,
  Tel: (214) 890-2300
  (Oil & gas explor & prod)
    North Sea Sun Oil Co. Ltd., 90 Long Acre, London WC2E 9RG, England

SUNRISE MEDICAL INC   2355 Crenshaw Blvd, #150, Torrance, CA 90501,
  Tel: (213) 328-8018
  (Mfr medical prdts)
    Sunrise Medical Ltd., Fens Pool Ave., Brierly Hill, West Midlands DY5 1QA, England

SUPERIOR BRANDS INC   122 Quincy Shore Dr, Quincy, MA 02171,
  Tel: (617) 770-0880
  (Mfr rawhide pet treats, cat litter, dog biscuits)
    Superior Pet Products Ltd., Rose Hill Works, Nelson St., Bolton, Lancashire,
    BL3.2JW, England

SUPERIOR TUBE CO   Norristown, PA 19494, Tel: (215) 275-2070
  (Seamless tubes)
    Fine Tubes Ltd., Estober Works, Plymouth, PL6 7LJ, England

SWIFT & CO   115 W Jackson Blvd, Chicago, IL 60604, Tel: (312) 431-2000
  (Meat & poultry, food prdts)
    Swift & Co. Ltd., 10 Charterhouse Sq., London, EC1, England

SYBRON CORP   411 E Wisconsin Ave, Milwaukee, WI 07662, Tel: (414) 274-6600
  (Professional health prdts, spec chems, instru, water & waste water treatment sys)
    Tanatex Chemical Co. Ltd., Swinton House, Cromwell Rd., Salford, M6 6DF, England

SYSTEM INDUSTRIES INC   560 Cottonwood Dr, Milpitas, CA 95035,
  Tel: (408) 432-1212
  (Value added third party vendor high performance data storage sybsys)
    System Industries Birmingham, Unit 5, Gunbarrell Ind. Estate, hayseech,
    Cradley Heath, Warley, West Midlands B64 7JS, England
    System Industries Europe, System House, Guildford Rd., Woking, Surrey, GU22 7QQ,
    England
    System Industries Manchester, Unit 2A, Windsor Ct., Christopher St., Salford,
    Manchester M9 4PT, England

SYSTEMS ENGINEERING LABS INC   6901 W Sunrise Blvd, Fort Lauderdale,
  FL 33313, Tel: (305) 587-2900
  (Digital computers)
    SEL Computer Ltd., Third Floor, Raffety House, 2/4 Sutton Court Rd., Sutton,
    Surrey, SM1 4SY, England

TALLY CORP   8301 SE 180th St, Kent, WA 98031, Tel: (206) 251-5500
  (Data preparation & transmission equip)
    Tally Ltd., 7 Cremyll Rd., Reading, RG1 8NQ, England

TANDEM COMPUTERS INC   19333 Vallco Parkway, Cupertino, CA 95014,
  Tel: (408) 725-6000
  (Computer sys)
    Tandem Computers Ltd., Northolt, London, High Wycombe, England

TANDY CORP   1800 One Tandy Center, Fort Worth, TX 76102, Tel: (817) 390-3700
  (Electronic & acoustic equip)
    Memtek UK Div., 2 Ascot Rd., Bedfont, Feltham, Middlesex TW14 8QH, England
    Tandy Corp., Tameway Tower, Bridge St., Walsallow WS1 1LA, England

TATE ACCESS FLOORS INC   7510 Montevideo Rd, Jessup, MD 20794,
  Tel: (301) 799-4200
  (Mfr access flooring for computers & offices)
    Tate Access Floors ltd., Carrier House, 1-9 Warwick Row, London SW1E 5ER, England

TAYLOR INSTRUMENT CO   99 Ames St, PO Box 110, Rochester, NY 14601,
  Tel: (716) 235-6806
  (Instru for process control inds)
    Taylor Instrument Ltd., Gunnels Wood Rd., Stevenage, Herts. SG1 2EL, England
    Taylor Instrument Ltd., Analytical Div., Rotherfield Rd., Jarvis Brook,
      Beaconsfield, Bucks, England

TECH/OPS SEVCON INC   1 Beacon St, Boston, MA 02108, Tel: (617) 523-2030
  (Mfr solid state controllers for elec powered vehicles)
    Tech/Ops Ltd., Kingsway, Gateshead NE11 0QA, England

TECHNICON INSTRUMENTS CORP   511 Benedict Ave, Tarrytown, NY 10591-5097,
  Tel: (914) 631-8000
  (Mfr/serv automated blook anal equip, reagents & diagnostics)
    Technicon Instruments Co. Ltd., Evans House, Hamilton Close, Houndmills,
      Basingstoke, Hants, RG21 2YE, England

TED BATES WORLDWIDE INC   1515 Broadway, New York, NY 10036,
  Tel: (212) 869-3131
  (Advertising agency)
    Moxon, Dolphin & Kerby, 178-202 Great Portland St., London W1N 5TB, England
    Ted Bates Ltd., Fletcher Shelton Delaney, 100 New King's Rd., London, SW6 4LX,
      England
    Ted Bates Ltd., 155 Gower St., London, WC1 E6BJ, England

TEKNIS CORP   PO Box 3189, No Attleboro, MA 02761, Tel: (508) 695-3591
  (Sale advanced technology prdts, fiber optics, materials for semiconductor mfr)
    Teknis Ltd., Teknis House, Meadrow, Godalming, Surrey, GU7 3HQ, England

TEKTRONIX INC   PO Box 500, Beaverton, OR 97077, Tel: (503) 627-7111
  (Mfr test & meas, visual sys & commun prdts)
    Tektronix (UK) Ltd., Fourth Ave., Globe Park, Marlow, Bucks SL7 1YD, England

TELEDYNE COMPONENTS   1300 Terra Bella Ave, Mountain View, CA 94043,
  Tel: (415) 968-9241
  (Mfr data conversion prdts, bipolar interface, etc)
    Teledyne Components, The Harlequin Centre, Southall Lane, Southall,
      Middlesex UB2 5NH, England

TELEDYNE FIRTH STERLING INC   470 Streets Run Rd, Pittsburgh, PA 15236,
  Tel: (412) 464-5200
  (Sintered tungsten carbides for metal cutting, metal forming, etc)
    Teledyne Firth Sterling, 9 Aerodrome Way, Heston Industrial Estate, Hounslow,
      Middlesex, TW5 9QP, England

TELEDYNE INC   1901 Ave of the Stars, Los Angeles, CA 90067,
  Tel: (213) 277-3311
  (Design/mfr electr & aviation control sys & equip, commun & elect prdts)
    Teledyne Acoustic Research, High St., Houghton Regis Dunstable, Bedfordshire,
      LU5 5QJ, England

TELEDYNE LANDIS MACHINE   Fifth & Church St, Waynesboro, PA 17268,
  Tel: (717) 762-3151
  (Mfr screw threading machs & tools)
    Teledyne Landis Machine Ltd., Hyde Cheshire, SK14 1DY, England

TELEFLEX INC   155 S Limerick Rd, Limerick, PA 19468, Tel: (215) 948-5100
  (Designs/mfr/mkt mech & electro-mech sys, meas sys)
    Sermetel (UK) Ltd., High Holborn Rd., Codner, Ripley, Derbyshire, DE5 3NW, England

TELEX COMMUNICATIONS INC   9600 Aldrich Ave S, Minneapolis, MN 55420,
  Tel: (612) 884-4051
  (Mfr audio-visual equip)
    Telex Communications Ltd. U.K., Premier Suites, Exchange House,
    494 Midsummer Blvd., Milton Keynes MK9 2EA, England

TELEX COMPUTER PRODUCTS INC   6422 E 41st St, Tulsa, OK 74135,
  Tel: (918) 627-1111
  (Computer terminals & peripheral prdts)
    GCS/Telex, 226-236 Northfield Ave., London, W13, England

TELXON CORP   3330 W Market St, Akron, OH 44333, Tel: (216) 867-3700
  (Devel/mfr portable computer sys & related equip)
    Telxon Ltd., Old Orchard, High St., Poole, Dorset BH15 1AE, England

C TENNANT SONS & CO OF NY   PO Box 9300, Minneapolis, MN 55440,
  Tel: (612) 475-7340
  (Ferrous & non-ferrous minerals, metals, electronic comps)
    Tennant Europe (UK) Ltd., Staple Hall, 2nd Floor, Stone House Court, London,
    EC3A 7AX, England
    Tennco Exim Ltd., 259 Cranbrook Rd., Liford, Essex, England

TENNECO AUTOMOTIVE   100 Tri-State Intl, #300, Lincolnshire, IL 60069,
  Tel: (708) 948-0900
  (Mfr exhaust sys, ride control prdts, brake components)
    Monroe Europe (UK) Ltd., Manor Lane, Skipton Rd., York YO3 6UA, England
    Tenneco Walker (UK) Ltd., Liverpool Rd., Rosegrove, Burnley BB12 6HJ, England

TENNECO INC   PO Box 2511, Houston, TX 77001, Tel: (713) 757-2812
  (Natural gas pipelines, integrated oil operations, paperboard prdts, agric & land
  devel)
    Albright & Wilson Ltd., 1 Knightsbridge Green, London, England

TENNECO OIL EXPLORATION & PRODUCTION   PO Box 2511, Houston, TX 77001,
  Tel: (713) 757-2131
  (Oil explor & prod)
    Tenneco UK Inc., Castle Yard House, 1 Castle Yard, Richmond, Surrey, England

TENNESSEE ASSOCIATES INTL INC   337 East Broadway Ave, Maryville, TN 37801,
  Tel: (615) 983-4044
  (Mgt consulting servs)
    Tennessee Associates Ltd., 4 Bankside, Lodge Rd., Long Hanborough, Oxford OX7 2LJ,
    England

TERADYNE INC   183 Essex St, Boston, MA 02111, Tel: (617) 482-2700
  (Electronic test equip & blackplane connection sys)
    Teradyne Ltd., Clive House, Queen's Rd., Weybridge, Surrey, England

TESORO PETROLEUM CORP   8700 Tesoro Dr, PO Box 17536, San Antonio, TX 78286,
Tel: (512) 828-8484
(Oil, gas prod & refining)
    Tesoro U.K. Co., 39 Dover St., London W1X 3RB, England

TEXACO INC   2000 Westchester Ave, White Plains, NY 10650, Tel: (914) 253-4000
(Explor/mktg crude oil & its prdts, petro-chems)
    Texaco North Sea UK Co., 1 Knightsbridge Green, London, SW1X 7QJ, England

TEXAS EASTERN TRANSMISSION CORP   PO Box 2521, Houston, TX 77252,
Tel: (713) 759-3131
(Energy pipeliner, oil/gas explor & prod)
    Texas Eastern Intl. Svcs. Ltd., Berkeley Sq. House, Berkeley Sq., London, W1X 5LE,
    England
    Texas Eastern North Sea Inc., same address

TEXAS GAS TRANSMISSION CORP   3800 Frederica St, Owensboro, KY 42301,
Tel: (502) 926-8686
(Natural gas transmission serv, inland waterways serv, trucking, oil & gas explor &
prod)
    Texas Gas Exploration Corp., 7 Old Park Lane, London, WIY 3LJ, England

TEXAS INSTRUMENTS INC   PO Box 655474, Dallas, TX 75265, Tel: (214) 995-2011
(Mfr semiconductor devices, electr/electro-mech sys, instr & controls)
    Texas Instruments Ltd., Manton Lane, Bedford MK41 7PA, England

TEXON INC   Crescent Mills St, Russell, MA 01071, Tel: (413) 862-3652
(Latex & resin impregnated fibre prdts)
    Texon Atlantic Ltd., Radcliffe, England

TEXSCAN CORP   7320 E Butherus Dr, Scottsdale, AZ 85261, Tel: (602) 998-1788
(Electronic test equip, microwave filters & digital display equip)
    Texscan Instruments Ltd., 1 Northbridge Rd., Berkhamsted, Herts, England

THERMADYNE INDUSTRIES INC   101 S Hanley, St Louis, MO 63105,
Tel: (314) 721-5573
(Mfr cutting & welding apparatus & prdts)
    Thermadyne Industries Ltd., Unitie, Deacon Estate, Forstal Rd., Aylesford,
    Kent ME20 7SW, England

THERMAL AMERICAN FUSED QUARTZ CO   4 Baltimore Ave, PO Box 444, Georgetown,
DE 19947, Tel: (302) 856-7741
(Fused quartz & silica)
    TSL Group, Plc, Box 6, Wallsend, Tyne & Wear NE28 6DG, England

THERMCO SYSTEMS INC   1465 North Batavia St, Orange, CA 92668,
Tel: (714) 639-2340
(Microprocessor controlled diffusion furnace sys & vacuum/gas sys for semiconductor
processing)
    Thermco Semiconductor Equipment Ltd., Daux Rd., Billingshurst, Sussex, RH14 9SJ,
    England

THERMO ELECTRIC CO   109 Fifth St, Saddle Brook, NJ 07662, Tel: (201) 843-5800
(Mfr temp/meas control prdts)
    Thermo Electric Intl. Ltd., P.O. Box 10, Sittingbourne, Kent, England

THERMO ELECTRON CORP   101 First Ave, Waltham, MA 02154, Tel: (617) 890-8700
(Devel/mfr of process equip & instru for energy intensive inds)
Thermo Electron Ltd., Woolborough Lane, Crawley, W. Sussex, RH10 2AQ, England
Winterburn Ltd., P.O. Box 6, Riverside Works, Woodhill Rd., Bury, Lancashire,
BL8 1DF, England

THETFORD CORP   7101 Jackson Rd, PO Box 1285, Ann Arbor, MI 48106,
Tel: (313) 769-6000
(Sanitation sys)
Thetford Aqua Products Ltd., Centrovell Ind. Estate, Caldwell Rd., Nuneaton,
Warwickshire, England

THOMAS & BETTS CORP   1001 Frontier Rd, Bridgewater, NJ 08807-0993,
Tel: (201) 685-1600
(Mfr elect/electr connectors & accessories)
T & B Intl. Inc., European Centre, Third Ave., Globe Park, Marlow, Bucks. SL7 1YF,
England

THOR POWER TOOL CO   72 Bayside Rd, Virginia Beach, VA 23455,
Tel: (804) 323-5666
(Mfr portable air-operated & elect tools)
Stewart Warner Ltd., Thor Tool Div., Tyne & Wear, Tynemouth, NE29 7UE, England

THURSTON MOTOR LINES INC   601 Johnston Rd, Charlotte, NC 28206,
Tel: (704) 373-1933
(Motor carrier of general commodities)
British Ceramic Service Co. Ltd., Briticent House, New St., Ringwood, Hants,
BH24 3AE, England

TIDELAND SIGNAL CORP   4310 Directors Row, PO Box 52430, Houston,
TX 77052-2430, Tel: (713) 681-6101
(Mfr aids to navigation)
Tideland Signal Ltd., 15-17 Trowers Way, Redhill, Surrey RH1 2LH, England

TIME WARNER INC   Time Life Bldg, New York, NY 10020, Tel: (212) 522-1212
(Magazine & book publ, communications)
Time-Life Intl. Ltd., Time & Life Bldg., New Bond St., London, W1Y 0AA, England

TIMEPLEX INC   One Communications Plaza, Rochelle Park, NJ 07662,
Tel: (201) 368-1113
(Data commun equip)
Timeplex Ltd., Timeplex House, North Parkway, Leeds LS14 6PX, England
Timeplex Ltd., 77 Boston Manor Rd., Brentford, Middlesex, TW8 95W, England

TIMET CORP   420 Rouser Rd, PO Box 2824, Pittsburgh, PA 15230,
Tel: (412) 262-4200
(Mfr titanium mill prdts)
Titanium Metal & Alloys Ltd., 17 Woodford Trading Estate, Southend Rd.,
Woodford Green, Essex 1G8 8HF, England

THE TIMKEN CO   1835 Dueber Ave SW, Canton, OH 44706-2798, Tel: (216) 438-3000
(Mfr tapered roller bearings & alloy steels)
British Timken, Main Rd., Duston, Northampton NN5 6UL, England

TITAN INDUSTRIAL CORP   745 5th Ave, New York, NY 10151, Tel: (212) 421-6700
(Import & export steel prdts)
Titan Industrial Ltd., Camelot House, 76 Brompton Rd., London, SW3, England

TONKA CORP   6000 Clearwater Dr, Minnetonka, MN 55343, Tel: (612) 936-3300
(Mfr children's toys)
   Tonka Ltd., 17 Market Pl., Henley on Thames, Oxonia RG9 2AA, England

TORIT DIV   1400 W 94th St, Minneapolis, MN 55431, Tel: (201) 573-0123
(Mfr dust collectors, fume extractors)
   Donaldson Torit Ltd., 65 Market St., Hednesford, Staffordshire, England

THE TORO CO   8111 Lyndale Ave S, Minneapolis, MN 55420, Tel: (612) 888-8801
(Mfr outdoor beautification prdts)
   Toro Wheel Horse UK, Unit 7, Heron Ind. Estate, Basingstoke Rd., Spencers Wood,
      Reading, Berks., England

TORRINGTON/FAFNIR   200 Chestnut Ridge Rd, Woodcliff Lake, NJ 07675,
   Tel: (203) 482-9511
(Mfr bearings, precision metal parts & assemblies, universal joints)
   Torrington Co. Ltd., Torrington Ave., Coventry, CV4 9AE, England

TOWERS PERRIN FORSTER & CROSBY INC   245 Park Ave, New York, NY 10167,
   Tel: (212) 309-3400
(Management consulting)
   Towers, Perrin, Forster & Crosby, Inc., Castlewood House, 77-91 New Oxford St.,
      London WC1A 1PX, England

TRACE MOUNTAIN   2190 Bering Dr, San Jose, CA 95131, Tel: (408) 435-7800
(Mfr diskette; tape duplication equip)
   Trace Mountain UK, Porters Wood, St. Albans, Herts AL3 6PP, England

TRACOR INC   6500 Tracor Lane, Austin, TX 78721, Tel: (512) 926-2800
(Time & frequency prdts, gas & liquid chromatographs, eng serv, ship repair)
   Tracor Littelfuse, (UK) Ltd., Crowther District 3, Washington, Tyne & Wear,
      NE38 OAB, England
   Tracor Littelfuse, (UK) Ltd., Tracor Instrument, Tyne & Water, N38 OAB, England

TRADE & INDUSTRIES CORP INC   16 E 34th St, New York, NY 10016,
   Tel: (212) 686-2420
(Finance)
   Trade & Ind. Acceptance Corp., Ltd., 17 Stamford St., London, SE1 9NG, England

TRANE CO   3600 Pammel Creek Rd, La Crosse, WI 54601, Tel: (608) 787-2000
(Mfr A/C equip)
   Trane Ltd., Paul House, Stockport Rd., Timperley, Altrincham, Cheshire, England
   Trane Ltd., 4/5 Hutton Terrace, Jesmond, Newcastle-Upon-Tyne, NE2 4PQ, England
   Trane Ltd., 60 Lenton Blvd., Nottingham, N67 2EN, England
   Trane Ltd., 24 New John St. W., Newtown, Birmingham, B19 3NB, England
   Trane Ltd., Peloquin Chambers, 18 St. Augustines Parade, Bristol, 8S1 4UL, England
   Trane Ltd., 162 Windmill Rd., Sunbury-on-Thames, Middlesex, England

TRANSAMERICA DELAVAL INC   3450 Princeton Pike, PO Box 6550, Lawrenceville,
   NJ 08648, Tel: (609) 896-7600
(Steam turbines, compressors, pumps, filtration sys, power transmission equip)
   Transamerica Instruments, Lennox Rd., Basingstoke, Hampshire RG22 4AW, England

TRANSTECHNOLOGY CORP   15303 Ventura Blvd, 12th Fl, Sherman Oaks, CA 91403,
   Tel: (818) 990-5920
(Mfr diversified coml & ind prdts)

TransTechnology (Europe) Ltd., Warrior House, 12-14 The Hard, Portsmouth,
   Hampshire PO1 3QU, England

TRANTER INC   1054 Claussen Rd, Augusta, GA 30907, Tel: (404) 738-7900
   (Mfr heat exchangers)
   Senior Platecoil Ltd., P.O. Box 38, Calder Vale Rd., Wakefield, West,
   Yorkshire WF1 5P5, England

TREMCO INC   10701 Shaker Blvd, Cleveland, OH 44104, Tel: (216) 229-3000
   (Protective coatings & sealants for building, maint &.constr)
   Tremco Ltd., 27 St. George's Blvd., Wimbledon, London, SW19 4DY, England

TRI-WALL   10507 Timberwood Circle, Louisville, KY 40223, Tel: (502) 429-3300
   (Mfr corrugated containers)
   Tri-Wall Europe, 13 Market Place, Henley-on-Thames, Oxon RG9 2AA, England

TRICO TECHNOLOGIES CORP   1995 Billy Mitchell, Brownsville, TX 78521,
   Tel: (512) 544-2722
   (Mfr windshield wiper sys & components)
   Trico-Folberth Ltd., Great West Rd., Brentford, Middlesex, England

TRINOVA CORP   3000 Strayer, PO Box 50, Maumee, OH 43537, Tel: (419) 867-2200
   (Mfr engr components & sys for ind)
   Aeroquip Ltd., Broad Ground Round, Lakeside, Redditch CB98 8YS, England
   Aeroquip Ltd., Ty-Gas Rd., Cardiff, Llanisheu, Wales CF4 1YL, England
   Vickers Systems Ltd., PO Box 4, New Lane, Havant, Hants PO9 2NB, England
   Vickers Systems Ltd., AMD Div., Larchwood Ave., Bedhampton, Havant, Hants PO9 3QN,
   England
   Vickers Systems Ltd., Lang Pneumatic Div., Halesford 6, Telford,
   Shropshire TF7 4LF, England

TRION INC   101 McNeil Rd, PO Box 760, Sanford, NC 27330, Tel: (919) 775-2201
   (Mfr air cleaners & electrostatic fluid depositors)
   Trion Ltd., Brunel Gate, West Portway Industrial Estate, Andover,
   Hampshire SP1 03TY, England

TRITON ENERGY CORP   4925 Greenville Ave, 1400 One Energy Sq, Dallas,
   TX 75206, Tel: (214) 691-5200
   (Energy explor & prod)
   Triton Europe PLC, 38 Savile Row, London W1X 1AG, England

TRW INC   1900 Richmond Rd, Cleveland, OH 44124, Tel: (216) 291-7000
   (Electr & energy-related prdts, automotive & aerospace prdts, tools & fasteners)
   British Pleuger Submersible Pumps Ltd., Station Rd., Coleshill, Birmingham,
   B46 IJH, England
   Cam Gears Ltd., 45 Wilbury Way, Hitchin, Hertfordshire, SG4 OTU, England
   Hydrosteer, Arundel Rd., Luton, Bedfordshire, England
   Nelson Stud Welding Div. Carr Fastener Co. Ltd., Bessell Lane, Stapleford,
   Nottingham, NG9 7BX, England
   TRW, Clevedon Plant, Kenn Rd., Clevedon, Avon, BS21 GL5, England
   TRW, Hitchin Plant, 45 Wilbury Way, Hitchin, Hertfordshire, SG4 OTO, England
   TRW Clifford Ltd., DuPont House, 101, Vaughan Way, Leicester, LE1 4SA, England
   TRW Datacom Intl., Park House, 191 London Rd., Isleworth, Middlesex, TW7 5BQ,
   England
   TRW Mission Ltd., Berkeley Sq. House, Berkeley Sq., London, W1X 6JE, England
   TRW Reda, Div. TRW Mission Ltd., Suite 8, Westminster Palace Gardens,
   1/7 Artillery Row, London, SW1, England

(cont)

TRW Spares, Furnace Rd., Likeston, Derbyshire, DE7 5EP, England
United-Carr Supplies Ltd., 112 Station Rd., Likeston, Derbyshire, DE7 5LF, England
Ventek Ltd., Station House, Harrow Rd., Wembley, Middlesex, HA9 6ER, England

TUBESALES   2211 Tubeway Ave, Los Angeles, CA 90040, Tel: (213) 728-9101
(Warehousing & distributors of steel, aluminum & nickel alloy tubular prdts)
   Tubesales (UK) Ltd., W. Bay Rd., Southampton, SO9 5HQ, England

TUCK INDUSTRIES INC   1 Lefevre Lane, New Rochelle, NY 10801,
Tel: (914) 235-1000
(Pressure sensitive tapes)
   Technical Tape Ltd., 14 The Broadway, Stanmore, Middlesex, HA7 4DW, England

TURCO PRODUCTS INC   7300 Bolsa Ave, Westminster, CA 92684-3600,
Tel: (714) 890-3600
(Mfr chem cleaning compounds & equip)
   Turco Products Ltd., Clarke House, Brunel Rd., Earlstrees Ind. Estate, Corby,
      Northants, England

U S ELECTRICAL MOTOR CO   326 W Main St, Milford, CT 06460,
Tel: (203) 877-1762
(Mfr elect motors, components)
   U.S. Motor, 5 Reading Arch Rd., Redhill, Surrey RH1 1HG, England

U S INDUSTRIES INC   PO Box 629, Evansville, IN 47704, Tel: (812) 425-2428
(Diversified prdts & sys for industry, agribusiness & retail markets)
   Axelson Intl., Westminster Palace Gardens, Suite 8, 3rd Floor, 1-7 Artillery Row,
      London, SW1P 1RH, England

U S LEASING INTL INC   733 Front St, San Francisco, CA 94111,
Tel: (415) 627-9000
(Equip leasing & financing)
   IR Group, Dorcan House, Meadfield Rd., Berkshire SL3 8AL, England
   U.S. Leasing Ltd., Gateway House, 322 Regents Park Rd., Finchley, London N3 2LP,
      England

U S SAFETY   1535 Walnut St, PO Box 417237, Kansas City, MO 64141,
Tel: (816) 842-8500
(Mfr prdts & equip for personal protection of ind workers)
   Parmelee Ltd., Middlemore Lane W., Redhouse Industrial Estate, Aldridge,
      West Midlands, WS9 8DZ, England

UNION CAMP CORP   1600 Valley Rd, Wayne, NJ 07470, Tel: (201) 628-2000
(Flavors, fragrances, essential oils, aroma chems, corrugated containers)
   Bush, Boake, Allen Ltd., Blackhorse Ln., Walthamstow, London E17 SQP, England
   Union Camp Chemicals (UK) Ltd., Virgo Lane, Chester-le-Street, County Dunham,
      DH3 2RB, England

UNION CARBIDE CORP   Old Ridgebury Rd, Danbury, CT 06817, Tel: (203) 794-2000
(Carbon prdts, chems, plastics, gases & related prdts, etc)
   Horstine Farmery Ltd., North Newbald, GB-York, YO4 3SP, England
   Ore Sales & Services, The African Manganese Co., 7 Old Park Lane, London, W1Y 3LJ,
      England
   UC (UK) Ltd., Fountain Precinct Balm Green, GB, Sheffield, S1 3AE, England
   UC Europe Safety, Direction-Ucore Ltd., 7 Old Park Lane, GB-Lond, W1Y 3LJ, England
   UC Services Ltd., Russell House, 59/61 High St., Rickmansworth, Herts, WD3 1EZ,
      England

Unifos (UK) Ltd., London House, London Rd. South, GB-Poynton, Cheshire, SK12 1YP, England

Viskase Ltd., 185 London Rd., GB-Croydon, CR9 2TT, England

UNION SPECIAL CORP   222 No LaSalle, Chicago, IL 60601, Tel: (312) 606-9500
(Mfr ind sewing machs)
Union Special (UK) Ltd., 22 Mandervell Rd., Oadby, LE2 5LW, England

UNIROYAL INC   World Headquarters, Middlebury, CT 06749, Tel: (203) 573-2000
(Tires, tubes & other rubber prdts, chems, plastics, textiles)
Uniroyal Chemical Div., Uniroyal Ltd., First Ave., Trafford Park, Manchester, M17 1DT, England
Uniroyal Ltd., Monaco House, Bristol St., Birmingham, B5 7AS, England
Uniroyal Ltd., 62/64 Horseferry Rd., London, SW, England

UNISYS CORP   PO Box 500, Blue Bell, PA 19424, Tel: (215) 542-4011
(Mfg/mktg/serv electr info sys)
Burroughs Machines Ltd., Heathrow House, Bath Rd., Hounslow, TW5 9QL, England
Unisys, Stonebridge Park, London NW10 8LS, England

UNITED AIRLINES INC   PO Box 66100, Chicago, IL 60666, Tel: (708) 952-4000
(Air transp)
United Airlines, 718 Conduit St., London W1, England

UNITED BRANDS CO   1271 Ave of the Americas, New York, NY 10020, Tel: (212) 397-4000
(Food prdts)
Fyffes Group Ltd., 15 Stratton St., London, W1A 2LL, England
United Brands Ltd., 1 Queens Way, Southampton, 301 1AQ, England

UNITED CALIFORNIA BANK   PO Box 54191, Los Angeles, CA 90054, Tel: (213) 624-0111
(Banking)
United California Bank, California House, 36/39 Esset St., London, WC2R 3AS, England

UNITED CARGO CORP   40 Rector St, New York, NY 10006, Tel: (212) 766-1808
(Containerized air & sea frt)
United Cargo Ltd., Rainham Rd., South Deganham, Essex, England

UNITED ELECTRIC CONTROLS CO   85 School St, Watertown, MA 02172, Tel: (617) 926-1000
(Electro-mechanical & electronic controls & recorders)
United Electric Controls Co. UK Ltd., Sulby House, North St., Sudbury, Suffolk CO10 6RE, England

UNITED MERCHANTS & MANUFACTURERS INC   1407 Broadway, New York, NY 10018, Tel: (212) 930-3900
(Rayon, cotton, print cloth, nylon, sheeting & drills, glass & plastic fabrics)
United Merchants & Manufacturers (Europe) Ltd., Queensway, Rochdale, Lancashire OL11 2P1, England

UNITED PRESS INTL   220 E 42nd St, New York, NY 10017, Tel: (212) 682-0400
(Collection & distributor of news, newspictures, fin data)
United Press Intl., 8 Bouverie St., London, EC4Y 8BB, England

UNITED TECHNOLOGIES CORP   United Technologies Bldg, Hartford, CT 06101,
Tel: (203) 728-7000
(Mfr aircraft engines, elevators, A/C, auto equip, space & military electr, rocket
propulsion sys)
   Caricor Ltd., Knightsbridge House, 197 Knightsbridge, London, SW7 1RB, England
   Otis Elevator Co. Ltd., Otis Bldg., 43/59 Clapham Rd., London, SW9 0JZ, England
   Porvair Ltd., Estuary Rd., Kings Lynn, Norfolk, PE30 2HS, England

UNIVERSAL GYM EQUIPMENT INC   930 27th Ave, SW, Cedar Rapids, IA 52406,
Tel: (319) 365-7561
(Mfr exercise & gym equip)
   Nisson Intl. Ltd., Tallon Rd., Brentwood, Exxex CM13 1TT, England

UNOCAL CORP   1201 W 5th St, Los Angeles, CA 90017, Tel: (213) 977-7600
(Fully integrated high-tech energy resources devel)
   Unocal (UK) Ltd., 32 Cadbury Rd., Sunbury on Thames, Middlesex TW16 7LU, England

UNUM   2211 Congress St, Portland, ME 04122, Tel: (207) 770-2211
(Financial servs & ins)
   NFL Permanent Health Insurances Ltd., Milton Court, Dorking, Surrey RH4 3LZ, England
   UNUM European Holding Co., Ltd., Hamilton House, 1 Temple Ave.,
      Victoria Embankment, London EC4Y 0HA, England
   UNUM Life Insurance Co., Ltd., Hamilton House, 1 Temple Ave., Victoria Embankment,
      London EC4Y 0HA, England

UOP INC   Ten UOP Plaza, Des Plaines, IL 60016, Tel: (708) 391-2000
(Diversified research, development & mfr of ind prdts & sys mgmt studies & serv)
   Flexonics Div. UOP Ltd., Northampton, England
   Procon Ltd., London, England
   UOP (UK) Ltd., Weedon Rd., Industrial Estate, Northampton, England
   Universal-Matthey Products Ltd., Brimsdown, England

UPJOHN CO   7000 Portage Rd, Kalamazoo, MI 49001, Tel: (616) 323-4000
(Pharms, agric prdts, ind chems)
   Upjohn Intl. Ltd., Fleming Way, Crawley, Sussex, RH10 2NJ, England

URSCHEL LABORATORIES INC   2503 Calumet Ave, PO Box 2200, Valparaiso,
IN 46384-2200, Tel: (219) 464-4811
(Design & mfr precision food processing equip)
   Urschel Intl. Ltd., 6 Groby Trading Estate, Leicester, LE6 0FH, England

USAIR INC   2345 Crystal Dr, Arlington, VA 22227, Tel: (703) 418-7000
(Airline)
   USAir, Inc., N. Office Bldg.- #522, Gatwick, West Sussex RH6 0NP, England

USF&G FINANCIAL SERVICES CORP   100 Light St, Baltimore, MD 21202,
Tel: (301) 547-3000
(Investment mgt, real estate, computer leasing, fin prdt mktg & admin, strategic
consult)
   Axe-Houghton Ltd., 35 Dover St., London W1X 3RA, England
   Megaleasing Holdings Ltd., Heriot House, Guilford St., Chertsey, Surrey KT16 9AD,
      England

UTAH INTL INC   550 California St, San Francisco, CA 94104,
Tel: (415) 981-1515
(Mining, land development, ocean shipping, oil & gas)
   Utah Minerals (UK) Ltd., St. Andrew's House, 40 Broadway, London, SW1H 0BY, England

VAN STRAATEN CHEMICAL CO   630 W Washington Blvd, Chicago, IL 60606,
Tel: (312) 454-1000
(Metalworking fluids, ind cleaners, rust preventives, etc)
   Universal Van Straaten, P.O. Box 60, Doxey Rd., Stafford ST16 1EA, England

VANTON PUMP & EQUIPMENT CORP   Hillside, NJ 07205, Tel: (201) 926-2435
(Mfr commercial & ind pumps, valves & accessories)
   Vanton Pumps Ltd., 26 Sandown Crescent, Unit 6 Radnor Industrial Estate, Congleton,
      Cheshire CW12 4XL, England

VARIAN ASSOCIATES INC   611 Hansen Way, Palo Alto, CA 94304-1030,
Tel: (415) 493-4000
(Mfr microwave tubes & devices, analytical instru, semiconductor process & med equip,
vacuum sys)
   Varian Associates Ltd., 18 Manor Rd., Walton-on-Thames, Surrey KT12 2QF, England
   Varian T.E.M. Ltd., Gatwick Rd., Crawley, Essex RH10 2RG, England

VARITYPER INC   11 Mt Pleasant Ave, E Hanover, NJ 07936, Tel: (201) 887-8000
(Mfr composing & typesetting sys)
   Varityper Ltd., Challenge House #21, Sherwood Dr., Bletchley,
      Milton Keynes MK3 6DP, England

VELSICOL CHEMICAL CORP   5600 N River Rd, Rosemont, IL 60018,
Tel: (708) 698-9700
(Pesticides & ind chems)
   Velsicol Chemical Ltd., 66 Tilehurst Rd., Reading, Berkshire, RG3 2JH, England

VERMONT RESEARCH CORP   Precision Park, N Springfield, VT 05150,
Tel: (802) 882-2256
(Mfr solid-state disk tech, spec memory prdts, disk arrays)
   Vermont Research Ltd., Cleeve Rd., Leatherhead, Surrey, England

VETCO-GRAY INC   250 W Stanley Ave, Ventura, CA 93001, Tel: (805) 653-2500
(Offshore oilfield equip & tools, oilfield inspect & coating serv)
   Vetco Offshore Inc. Ltd., Ventura House, 72/74 Station Rd., Hayes, UB3 4DP, England

VF CORP   PO Box 1022, Reading, PA 19603, Tel: (215) 378-1151
(Mfr/mktg apparel)
   Wrangler Ltd., Park Rd. East, Calverton, Nottingham NG14 6GD, England

VIACOM INTL INC   1211 Ave of the Americas, New York, NY 10036,
Tel: (212) 575-5175
(Diversified entertainment & commun)
   Viacom Intl. Ltd., 40 Conduit St., London, W1R 9FB, England

VIKING CONNECTORS CO   21001 Nordhoff St, PO Box 2379, Chatsworth, CA 91311,
Tel: (818) 341-4330
(Mfr elect/electr interconnect sys)
   Viking Connectors (UK) Ltd., Chatsworth House, Portland Close, Dunstable,
      Beds. LU5 4AW, England

VIRGINIA CHEMICALS INC   3340 W Norfolk Rd, Portsmouth, VA 23703,
Tel: (804) 483-7345
(Ind chems, insecticides, refrigerants, etc)
   R.V. Chemicals Ltd., Moon St., Widnes, Cheshire, WA8 6ND, England
   Virginla Chemicals Ltd., 119/121 Blackfriars Rd., Southsea, Portsmouth, Hants,
      PO5 4NL, England

VITRAMON INC   PO Box 544, Bridgeport, CT 06601, Tel: (203) 268-6261
   (Ceramic capacitors)
      Vitramon Ltd., Wycombe Lane, Wooburn Green, Bucks, England

VIVITAR CORP   9350 Desoto Ave, Chatsworth, CA 91313, Tel: (818) 700-2890
   (Photographic equip, electr supplies)
      Vivitar U.K. Ltd., Vivitar House, Ashfield Trading Estate, Nuffield Wy., Abington,
      Oxon, OX14 1RP, England

WACHOVIA BANK & TRUST CO NA   PO Box 3099, Winston- Salem, NC 27150,
   Tel: (919) 770-5000
   (Commercial banking)
      Wachovia Bank & Trust Co., NA, 7 Albemarle St., London W1X 3HF, England

WACKENHUT CORP   1500 San Remo Ave, Coral Gables, FL 33146,
   Tel: (305) 666-5656
   (Security sys & serv)
      Wackenhut U.K. Ltd., 875 Sidcup Rd., London SE9 3PP, England

WAHL CLIPPER CORP   2902 N Locust St, Sterling, IL 61081, Tel: (815) 625-6525
   (Mfr clippers, soldering irons)
      Wahl Europe Ltd., Herne Bay Trade Park, Sea St., Herne Bay, Kent CT6 8SZ, England

WALKER MFG CO   1201 Michigan Blvd, Racine, WI 53402, Tel: (414) 632-8871
   (Automotive parts, exhaust sys, service equip)
      Harmo Industries Ltd., Stockfield Rd., Tyseley, Birmingham, B27 6AS, England
      Tenneco-Walker (UK) Ltd., Liverpool Rd. B.L., Rose Grove - Burnley, Lancashire,
      BB12 6HJ, England

WALL COLMONOY CORP   30261 Stephenson Hwy, Madison Hghts, MI 48071,
   Tel: (313) 585-6400
   (Mfr metallizing & welding equip, alloys, casting, brazing, aircraft engine parts)
      Wall Colmonoy Ltd., Pontardawe, Swansea, SA8 4HL, England

WANG LABORATORIES INC   1 Industrial Ave, Lowell, MA 01851,
   Tel: (508) 459-5000
   (Mfr computer info processing sys)
      Wang (UK) Ltd., Wang House, 100 George St., London, W10, England

WARD HOWELL INTL INC   99 Park Ave, New York, NY 10016, Tel: (212) 697-3730
   (Executive recruiting)
      Ward Howell Intl., 19 Bentinck St., London, W1M 5RL, England

WARNACO INC   350 Lafayette St, Bridgeport, CT 06601, Tel: (203) 579-8272
   (Intimate apparel, men's & women's shirts, ski & sportswear)
      Warner's (UK) Ltd., Kent House, 87 Regent St., London W1R 7HF, England

WARNER & SWASEY CO   11000 Cedar Ave, PO Box 94531, Cleveland, OH 44101,
   Tel: (216) 432-4009
   (Machine tools, equip)
      Warner Swasey Ltd., Unit D, Stafford Park 2, Telford, Strops TF3 1BA, England

WARNER-LAMBERT CO   201 Tabor Road, Morris Plains, NJ 07950,
   Tel: (201) 540-2000
   (Mfr ethical & proprietary pharms, confectionary & consumer prdts)
      Warner-Lambert (UK) Ltd., Chestnut Ave., Easleigh, Hampshire, S05 3ZO, England

WATERBURY FARREL   785 W Johnson Ave, Cheshire, CT 06410, Tel: (203) 272-3271
  (Machine tools, metal working mach)
    Waterbury Farrel Ltd., Station Tower Block, Station Sq., Coventry, CV1 2GF, England

WATERS CHROMATOGRAPHY DIV   34 Maple St, Milford, MA 01757,
  Tel: (617) 478-2000
  (Mfr/distr liquid chromatographic instru/accessories/tech)
    Millipore (UK) Ltd., Millipore House, Abbey Rd., London, NW10 7SP, England
    Millipore (UK) Ltd., Millipore House, 11-15 Peterborough Rd., Harrow,
      Middlesex HA1 2YH, England
    Waters Associates Ltd., 324 Chester Rd., Hartford, Northwich, Cheshire, CW8 2AH,
      England

WATKINS-JOHNSON CO   3333 Hillview Ave, Palo Alto, CA 94304,
  Tel: (415) 493-4141
  (Defense electronic prdts)
    W-J Intl., Dedworth Rd., Oakley Green, Windsor, Berks. SL4 4LH, England

THE WAYNE GROUP LTD   244 California St, San Francisco, CA 94111,
  Tel: (415) 421-2010
  (Human resources consult)
    The Wayne Group Ltd., Cournswood House, North Dean, Bucks HP14 4NW, England

JERVIS B WEBB CO   34375 W Twelve Mile Rd, Farmington Hills, MI 48331,
  Tel: (313) 553-1000
  (Integrators of material handling sys)
    Jervis B. Webb Co. Ltd., Dawson Rd., Mount Farm, Milton Keynes MK1 1QY, England

WEIGHT WATCHERS INTL INC   Jericho Atrium, 500 North Broadway, Jericho,
  NY 11753-2196, Tel: (516) 939-0400
  (Weight reduction programs, food prdts)
    Weight Watchers (UK) Ltd., Fairacres, Dedworth Rd., Windsor, Berks., SL4 4UY,
      England

WERTHEIM & CO INC   200 Park Ave, New York, NY 10166-0090, Tel: (212) 578-0200
  (Investment banking, security brokers)
    Wertheim Securities Ltd., 55 London Wall, London EC2, England

WEST CO INC   West Bridge St, Phoenixville, PA 19460, Tel: (215) 935-4500
  (Pharm packaging comps)
    West Phamarubber Ltd., Parkside House, Grinstead Rd., London, SE8 5AB, England
    West Pharmaplastics Ltd., Bucklers Lane, Holmbush, St. Austell, Cornwall, PL25 3LP,
      England

WESTERN DIGITAL CORP   2445 McCabe Way, Irvine, CA 92714, Tel: (714) 557-3550
  (Semiconductor devices, electronic components)
    Western Digital Ltd., Crown House, 13th Floor, Morden, Surrey, SM4 5EO, England

WESTERN GEOPHYSICAL   PO Box 2469, Houston, TX 77252-2469, Tel: (713) 789-9600
  (Geophysical serv)
    Western Geophysical Co. (UK), Wesgeco House, Box 18, 455 London Rd., Isleworth,
      Middlesex TW7 5AB, England

WESTERN TEMPORARY SERVICES INC   301 Lennon Lane, Walnut Creek, CA 94598,
  Tel: (415) 930-5300
  (Secretarial & clerical agency)

(cont)

Western Temporary Services Ltd., 43 Clarence St., Gloucester, GL3 IDP, Gloucester, England

WESTERN UNION CORP   One Lake St, Upper Saddle River, NJ 07458,
Tel: (201) 818-5000
(Messaging, financial & other servs)
    Western Union Consumer Services Ltd., Melbray House, 1 Bastwick St.,
    London EC1 3PH, England

WESTINGHOUSE AIR BRAKE CO   40 W 40th St, New York, NY 10018,
Tel: (212) 840-5440
(Equip for transp, constr, mining inds)
    Bridge Foundry Co. Ltd., Bridge St., Wednesbury, West Midlands, WS10 0AN, England
    Clayton Dewandre Co. Ltd., P.O. Box No. 9, Titanic Works, Lincoln, LN5 7JL, England
    Clayton Dewandre Holdings Ltd., 90 Newbold Rd., Rugby, Warwickshire, CV21 2NL,
    England
    Clayton Dewandre Ltd. Service Div., Millroad, Rugby, Warwickshire, England
    Hailwood & Ackroyd Ltd., Beacon Works, Texas St., Morley, Leeds, LS27 0HQ, England
    WABCO Westinghouse, (UK) Ltd., Kiln Farm Industrial Estates, 30 Burners Lane,
    Milton Keynes, MK11 3AT, England

WESTINGHOUSE ELECTRIC CORP   Westinghouse Bldg, Gateway Center, Pittsburgh,
PA 15222, Tel: (412) 244-2000
(TV/radio broadcasting, mfr electr sys for ind/defense, fin & environmental servs)
    Ottermill Ltd., Ottery St. Mary, Devon, Essex 11 1AG, England
    Westinghouse Electronics & Control Co., Haden House, Argyle Way, Stevenage,
    Herts SG1 2AH, England

WHATMAN INC   9 Bridewell Place, Clifton, NJ 07014, Tel: (201) 773-5800
(Laboratory filter paper, chroma- tography prdts)
    Whatman Ltd., Spring Field Mill, Maidstone, Kent, ME14 2LE, England

WHEATON INDUSTRIES   1101 Wheaton Ave, Milville, NJ 08332, Tel: (609) 825-1400
(Glass & plastic containers, glass tableware)
    Rockware Plastics Ltd., Lower Ham Rd., Kingston, KT2 5AE, England

WHITE CONSOLIDATED INDUSTRIES INC   11770 Berea Rd, Cleveland, OH 44111,
Tel: (216) 252-3700
(Major household appliances, ind mach & equip)
    Coles Regulators Ltd., Industrial Estate, Winsfield, Cheshire, CW7 3QL, England
    Kelvinator Ltd., Newcastle Rd., Bromborough, Merceyside, L62 3PE, England

S S WHITE INDUSTRIAL PRODUCTS   151 Old New Brunswick Rd, Piscataway,
NJ 08854, Tel: (201) 752-8300
(Dentistry equip)
    S.S. White Industrial Products, Priory Works, Tombridge, Kent, TN 11 0QL, England
    S.S. White Industrial Products, 3rd Ave., Denbigh Rd., Blelchley, Milton, Keynes,
    MK1 1EJ, England

WICHITA CLUTCH CO   2800 Fisher Road, Wichita Falls, TX 76302,
Tel: (817) 767-2000
(Air-actuated clutches & brakes for ind applications)
    Wichita Co. Ltd., Ampthill Rd., .Bedford, England

JOHN WILEY & SONS INC   605 Third Ave, New York, NY 10158, Tel: (212) 850-6000
(Publishing)
    John Wiley & Sons Ltd., Baffins Lane, Chichester, Sussex, PO19 IUD, England

WILLCOX & GIBBS INC   530 Fifth Ave, New York, NY 10022, Tel: (212) 869-1800
(Distr mach, equip & supplies for apparel ind; mfr computer-based planning & control
sys)
   Willcox & Gibbs Ltd., 60 Worship St., London, EC2 A2EH, England

WILLIAM MORRIS AGENCY INC   1350 Ave of the Americas, New York, NY 10019,
Tel: (212) 586-5100
(Theater, film & TV agents)
   William Morris Agency (UK) Ltd., 31/32 Soho Sq., London W1V 5DG, England

WILLIAMS BROS ENGINEERING CO   6600 S Yale Ave, Tulsa, OK 74136,
Tel: (918) 496-5020
(Engineers, contractors, mgmt serv)
   Williams Brothers Engineering Ltd., 58 St. James St., London SW1A 1PR, England

T D WILLIAMSON INC   PO Box 2299, Tulsa, OK 74133, Tel: (918) 254-9400
(Equip/serv for pipeline maint)
   T.D. Williamson (UK) Ltd., Faraday Rd., Dorcan Way, Swindon, Wilts, SN3 5HF, England

WILLIS DIV   2508 E Palm Dr, Long Beach, CA 90807, Tel: (213) 426-4411
(Oil tools & equip)
   SII-Willis (UK), Nelson Rooms, The Centre, 68 High St., Weybridge, Surrey,
   KT13 8BL, England

WILTEK INC   542 Westport Ave, Norwalk, CT 06851, Tel: (203) 853-7400
(Data communication servs)
   Wiltek (UK) Ltd., 2 Apple Walk, Kembrey Park, Swindon, Wilts SN2 6BL, England

A WIMPFHEIMER & BROS INC   22 Bayview Ave, PO Box 472, Stonington, CT 06378,
Tel: (203) 535-1050
(Velvets)
   Denholme Silk Weavers Ltd., Foreside Mill, Denholme Clough, Near Bradford, Yorks,
   BD13 4EZ, England

WINSOR & NEWTON INC   555 Winsor Drive, Secaucus, NJ 07094,
Tel: (201) 864-9100
(Mfr artists' colors & supplies)
   Winsor & Newton Ltd., Wealdstone, Harrow, Middlesex, HA3 5RH, England

WITCO CORP   520 Madison Ave, New York, NY 10022-4236, Tel: (212) 605-3800
(Mfr chem & petroleum prdts)
   Baxenden Chemical Co. Ltd., Near Accrington, Lancashire BB5 2SL, England

WIX CORP   1301 E Ozark Ave, Gastonia, NC 28052, Tel: (704) 864-6711
(Oil, air & water filters)
   Wix Corp. Ltd., Farm Hill Rd., Waltham Abbey, Essex, EN9 1NL, England

WOLFE LOMBARD INC   220 Fifth Ave, #1201, New York, NY 10001,
Tel: (212) 545-8400
(Public/investor rel & strategic mktg servs)
   Lombard Communications Ltd., 12 Groveland Court, Bow Lane, London EC4M 9EH, England

WOODHEAD INDUSTRIES INC   3411 Woodhead Drive, Northbrook, IL 60062,
Tel: (708) 272-7990
(Elect, mech & telecomm prdts for ind)
   Aero-Motive (UK) Ltd., Fact. No. 9, Rassau Industrial Estate, Ebbw Vale, Gwent,
   NP3 5SD, England

WOODWARD & DICKERSON INC   937 Haverford Road, Bryn Mawr, PA 19010,
  Tel: (215) 527-5200
  (Intl marketing)
    Woodward & Dickerson, 1-2 Rutland Gardens, Knightsbridge, London, SW7 1BX, England

WOODWARD GOVERNOR CO   5001 North 2nd St, PO Box 7001, Rockford,
  IL 61125-7001, Tel: (815) 877-7441
  (Mfr speed control governors)
    Woodward Governor (UK) Ltd., P.O. Box 15, Slough, SL1 4DD, England

WORCESTER CONTROLS CORP   33 Lott Dr, Marlboro, MA 01752, Tel: (508) 481-4800
  (Mfr ball valves, control devices)
    Worcester Valves Co. Ltd., Burrell Rd., Haywards Heath, Sussex, England

WORLD COMMUNICATIONS INC   67 Broad St, New York, NY 10004,
  Tel: (212) 607-2000
  (Intl private line services)
    World Communications Ltd., 4/5 St. Johns Sq., Clerkenwell, London EC1, England

WORLD COURIER INC   46 Trinity Pl, New York, NY 10006, Tel: (718) 978-9400
  (Intl courier serv)
    World Courier (UK) Ltd., Faulkner House, Faulkner St., Manchester, M14DU, England
    World Courier (UK) Ltd., 10-14 Bedford St., Coyent Garden, London, England

WRIGHT LINE INC   160 Gold Star Blvd, Worcester, MA 01606, Tel: (508) 852-4300
  (Mfr filing sys)
    Datafile Ltd., 8D Cosgrove Way, Luton, Bedfordshire LU1 1XL, England

WM WRIGLEY JR CO   410 N Michigan Ave, Chicago, IL 60611-4287,
  Tel: (312) 644-2121
  (Chewing gum)
    Wrigley Co. Ltd., Estover, Plymouth, Devon, PL6 7PR, England

WURLITZER CO   422 Wards Corner Rd, Loveland, OH 45140, Tel: (513) 576-4601
  (Pianos, electronic organs & pianos, vending & pay phonograph machs)
    Wurlitzer Ltd., Parkgate Industrial Estate, Parkgate Lane, Knutsford,
      Cheshire WA16 8DW, England

WWF PAPER CORP   Two Bala Plaza, Bala Cynwyd, PA 19004, Tel: (215) 667-9210
  (Dist paper)
    WWF Paper Sales UK Ltd., Claire House, Bridge St., Leatherhead, Surrey, KT22 8HY,
      England

WYNN OIL CO   2600 E Nutwood Ave, PO Box 4370, Fullerton, CA 92631,
  Tel: (714) 992-2000
  (Chem additives for oil, grease & fuels; hardware)
    Wynn Oil Co. (UK) Ltd., 10 Eaton Place, Reading RG1 71P, England

XEROX CORP   800 Long Ridge Rd, PO Box 1600, Stamford, CT 06904,
  Tel: (203) 968-3000
  (Mfr document processing sys & equip; fin servs)
    Rank Xerox Ltd., Parkway, Marlow, Buckinghamshire SL7 1YL, England

XIDEX CORP   305 Soquel Way, Sunnyvale, CA 94086, Tel: (408) 739-4170
  (Duplicate microfilm)
    Xidex (UK) Ltd., Portreeves House, 1-2 East Bay, Colchester, Essex, England

XYLOGICS INC   53 Third Ave, Burlington, MA 01803, Tel: (617) 272-8140
(Mfr peripheral/commun controllers & terminal servers for open sys buses)
   Xylogics Intl. Ltd., Featherstone Rd., Wolverton Mill, Milton Keynes MK12 5RD,
   England

YORK INTERNATIONAL CORP   PO Box 1592, York, PA 17405-1592,
Tel: (715) 771-7890
(Mfr A/C, heating & refrig sys & equip)
   York Intl. Ltd., Gardiners Lane S., Basildon, Essex SS14 3HE, England

YOUNG & RUBICAM INTL INC   285 Madison Ave, New York, NY 10017,
Tel: (212) 210-3000
(Advertising agency)
   Young & Rubicam Holdings Ltd., Greater London House, Hampstead Rd., London NW1,
   England

YSI INC   1725 Brannum Lane, PO Box 279, Yellow Springs, OH 45387,
Tel: (513) 767-7241
(Mfr analyzers, meas instru & elec components)
   Clandon Scientific Ltd., Lynchford House, Lynchford Lane, Farnborough,
   Hampshire GU14 6LT, England

ZALE CORP   3000 Diamond Park, PO Box 222219, Dallas, TX 75222,
Tel: (214) 634-4011
(Retail jewelry, catalog showrooms, airport newsstands, etc)
   Zale Jewellers Ltd., 18 High Rd., Wood Green, London, England

ZAPATA CORP   Zapata Tower, PO Box 4240, Houston, TX 77001,
Tel: (713) 226-6000
(Offshore drilling & petroleum explor)
   Zapata Off-Shore Service Ltd., Rotherwiek House, 19-21 Old Bond St.,
   London W1X 3DA, England

ZIEBART INTL CORP   1290 E Maple Rd, Troy, MI 48084, Tel: (313) 588-4100
(Auto aftermarket servs)
   Ziebart UK, 3 Downsbrook Estate, Southdownview Way, Worthing, W. Sussex BN14 8NQ,
   England

JOHN ZINK CO   PO Box 7398, Tulsa, OK 74105, Tel: (918) 747-1371
(Central heaters & air conditioners, field flares, etc)
   John Zink Co. Ltd., Acrewood Way, St. Albans, Hertford, England

ETHIOPIA

CROWN CORK & SEAL CO INC   Holmesburg Station, PO Box 6208, Philadelphia,
PA 19136, Tel: (215) 698-5100
(Cans, bottle caps; filling & packaging mach)
   Crown Cork & Can Mfr. Industries, S.C., P.O. Box 5501, Addis Ababa, Ethiopia

HORWATH & HORWATH INTL   919 Third Ave, New York, NY 10022,
  Tel: (212) 980-3100
  (Public accountants & auditors)
    Bocresion Haile & Co., P.O. Box 825, Zewditu Avenue, Addis Ababa, Ethiopia

INA CORPORATION   1600 Arch St, Philadelphia, PA 19101, Tel: (215) 523-5335
  (Holding co: ins, financial serv)
    African Solidarity Insurance Co. Ltd., Afsol House, Haile Selassi Square,
      P.O. Box 2327, Addis Ababa, Ethiopia
    Joseph Hansen & Soehne Ltd., Field Marshall Smuts St., Airport Rd., P.O. Box 1501,
      Addis Ababa, Ethiopia

MOBIL CORP   150 E 42nd St, New York, NY 10017, Tel: (212) 883-4242
  (Petroleum explor, prdts)
    Mobil Oil Ltd., P.O. Box 1365, Addis Ababa, Ethiopia

TRANS WORLD AIRLINES INC   605 Third Ave, New York, NY 10158,
  Tel: (212) 557-6107
  (Air transp, hotel, food serv, real estate)
    Trans World Airlines, Haile Selassie South, Addis Ababa, Ethiopia

FINLAND

3M CO   3M Center, St Paul, MN 55144-1000, Tel: (612) 733-1110
  (Mfr abrasives, adhesives, chems, ind & consumer tapes/diskettes, health care prdts,
  elec connectors)
    OY Suomen 3M Co. AB, P.O. Box 26, 02630 Espoo 63, Finland

ACCURAY CORP   650 Ackerman Rd, PO Box 02248, Columbus, OH 43202,
  Tel: (614) 261-2000
  (Computer-based process mgmt sys for forest prdts, metals rolling, textiles, tobacco
  ind)
    Accuray Finland OY, Helsinki, Finland

AIR EXPRESS INTL CORP   120 Tokeneke Rd, PO Box 1231, Darien, CT 06820,
  Tel: (203) 655-7900
  (Air frt forwarder)
    Air Express Intl. OY, Huolintakeskus AB, Metsalantie 2-4, 00620 Helsinki 62, Finland

ALBANY INTL CORP   PO Box 1907, Albany, NY 12201, Tel: (518) 445-2200
  (Paper mach clothing, engineered fabrics, plastic prdts, filtration media)
    Fennofelt AB OY, BVO Silantie 10, SF-00390 Helsinki 39, Finland

AM INTL INC   333 W Wacker Dr, #900, Chicago, IL 60606-1265,
   Tel: (312) 558-1966
   (Mfr/sale/serv commun graphics, info handling equip & sys)
     AM Intl. OY, Valimotie 1A, 00380 Helsinki 38, Finland

AMP INC   470 Friendship Rd, Harrisburg, PA 17111, Tel: (717) 564-0100
   (Mfr electrical wiring devices)
     AMP Finland OY, P.O. Box 79, SF-00381 Helsinki, Finland

AVERY INTL CORP   150 N Orange Grove Blvd, Pasadena, CA 91103,
   Tel: (213) 304-2000
   (Mfr self-adhesive labels & marking equip)
     Avery Intl., P.O. Box 109, 00101 Helsinki 10, Finland
     Lindell AB OY, Italahdenkatu 15-17, 00210 Helsinki 21, Finland

BARDAHL MFG CORP   1400 N W 52nd St, PO Box 70607, Seattle, WA 98107,
   Tel: (206) 783-4851
   (Lubricating oils)
     El Co. OY, Neitsytpolku 1, 00140 Helsinki 14, Finland

BAUSCH & LOMB INC   1 Lincoln First Sq, Rochester, NY 14601-0054,
   Tel: (716) 338-6000
   (Mfr healthcare & optics prdts)
     Bausch & Lomb Finland AB OY, Helsinki, Finland

BELOIT CORP   1st Lawrence Ave, Beloit, WI 53511, Tel: (608) 365-3311
   (Paper making mach & equip)
     Beloit Corp., Valtameri OY, Pakilantic 61, 00660 Helsinki 66, Finland

BLACK & DECKER CORP   701 E Joppa Road, Towson, MD 21204, Tel: (301) 583-3900
   (Mfr portable elect & pneumatic power tools, household prdts)
     Black & Decker OY, Melkonkatu 16A, 00210 Helsinki 21, Finland

CARL BYOIR & ASSOCIATES INC   380 Madison Ave, New York, NY 10017,
   Tel: (212) 986-6100
   (Public relations consultants)
     Extern OY, Melkonkatu 16, 00210 Helsinki 21, Finland

CANADA DRY INTL CORP   2600 Century Pkwy, Atlanta, GA 30345,
   Tel: (404) 753-2182
   (Carbonated beverages, soft drinks extract)
     Sinebrychoff AB OY, P.O. Box 10024, Helsinki, Finland

CHASE MANHATTAN BANK N A   1 Chase Manhattan Plaza, New York, NY 10081,
   Tel: (212) 552-2222
   (Intl banking)
     Chase Manhattan Bank OY, P.O. Box 50, Kaivokatu 10A,   00100 Helsinki 10, Finland

CITIBANK NA   399 Park Ave, New York, NY 10043, Tel: (212) 559-1000
   (Intl banking)
     Citibank N.A., Pohjoisesplanadi 25B, P.O. Box 180, SF-00131 Helsinki 13, Finland

THE COCA-COLA CO   310 North Ave NW, PO Box Drawer 1734, Atlanta, GA 30313,
   Tel: (404) 676-2121
   (Mfr & sale of soft drink syrups & concentrates, juices & food prdts, motion pic & TV
   prod)
     Coca-Cola, all inquires to: U.S. address

COLUMBIA PICTURES INDUSTRIES INC   711 Fifth Ave, New York, NY 10022,
  Tel: (212) 751-4400
  (Producer & distributor of motion pictures)
    Warner Columbia Felurs AB OY, Pohjoisesplanadi Espcanaadikatu 33, Helsinki 10,
    Finland

COMPTON INTERNATIONAL   625 Madison Ave, New York, NY 10022,
  Tel: (212) 754-1100
  (Advertising)
    Compton Intl., Mannerheimintie 14A, 00100 Helsinki 10, Finland

COMPUTER ASSOCIATES INTL INC   711 Stewart Ave, Garden City, NY 11530,
  Tel: (516) 227-3300
  (Devel/mkt/mgt info mgt & bus applications software)
    Computer Associates Finland Oy, Heikkilantie 2A7, SF-00210 Helsinki, Finland

CONTROL DATA CORP   8100 34th Ave S, Minneapolis, MN 55440,
  Tel: (612) 853-8100
  (Control data equip, computer sys serv & financial serv)
    Control Data AB OY, Veneentekijantie 8A, SF-00210, Helsinki 21, Finland

CPC INTERNATIONAL INC   PO Box 8000, International Plaza, Englewood Cliffs,
  NJ 07632, Tel: (201) 894-4000
  (Mfr consumer food prdts & corn refining prdts)
    CPC Foods OY, Koulutie 4F, SF-02200 Espoo, Finland

D'ARCY MASIUS BENTON & BOWLES INC (DMB&B)   1675 Broadway, New York,
  NY 10019, Tel: (212) 468-3622
  (Advertising & communications)
    DMB&B Oy Ab, Arkadiankatu 4C, 00100 Helsinki, Finland

DANCER FITZGERALD SAMPLE INTL   405 Lexington Ave, New York, NY 10174,
  Tel: (212) 661-0800
  (Advertising agency)
    OY AC-Mainos AB, Pasilanraitio 5, 00240 Halsinki, Finland

DATA GENERAL CORP   4400 Computer Dr, Westboro, MA 01580, Tel: (617) 366-8911
  (Design, mfr gen purpose computer sys & peripheral prdts & servs)
    Data General OY, Nihtisillantie 3D, PL61, SF-02631, Espoo 63, Finland

DATAEASE INTL INC   7 Cambridge Dr, Trumbull, CT 06611, Tel: (203) 374-8000
  (Mfr applications devel software)
    West Soft A/B, Hellerupvej 76, DK-2900 Vantaa, Finland

E I DU PONT DE NEMOURS & CO   Du Pont Bldg, 1007 Market St, Wilmington,
  DE 19898, Tel: (302) 774-1000
  (Mfr/sale diversified chems, plastics, specialty prdts & fibers)
    Suomen Du Pont OY, Finland

ECOLAB INC   370 Wabasha St, St Paul, MN 55102, Tel: (612) 293-2233
  (Ind & household detergents, cleaning agents & equip)
    Soilax AB OY, Makelankatu 54A, 00510 Helsinki 51, Finland

EXXON CORP   225 E John Carpenter Frwy, Irving, TX 75062, Tel: (214) 444-1000
  (Petroleum & petroleum prdts)
    Exxon Corp. OY, Esso AB, Etelaranta 12, 28100 Helsinki 10, Finland

FIRST NATIONAL BANK OF BOSTON   100 Federal St, Boston, MA   02110,
Tel: (617) 434-2200
(Commercial banking)
   First National Bank of Boston, Suomen Interfactors OY, Etelaesplanadi 20,
     00130 Helsinki 13, Finland

FISCHER & PORTER CO   125 E County Line Rd, Warminster, PA   18974,
Tel: (215) 674-6000
(Design/mfr meas, recording & control instru & sys; mfr ind glass prdts)
   Fischer & Porter OY, Kuunkehra 2, 02210 Espoo, Finland

FORD MOTOR CO   The American Road, Dearborn, MI   48121, Tel: (313) 322-3000
(Mfr automobiles, trucks)
   OY Ford AB, Henry Fordin Katu 6, SF-00101 Helsinki 10, Finland

FOXBORO CO   33 Commercial St, Foxboro, MA   02035, Tel: (508) 543-8750
(Mfr prdts/provide servs for ind automation)
   Foxboro Co., Aktiebolaget Ekstroems Maskinalffaer, P.O. Box 41, SF-02101, Esbo 10,
     Finland

GENERAL MOTORS CORP   3044 W Grand Blvd, Detroit, MI   48202,
Tel: (313) 556-5000
(Automotive prdts, electronics)
   Suomen General Motors OY, Kutojantje 8, 02630 Espoo 63, Finland

GERBER SCIENTIFIC INSTRUMENT CO   83 Gerber Rd West, So Windsor, CT   06074,
Tel: (203) 644-1551
(CADICAM for electronic & graphic arts ind)
   Gerber Scientific Instrument OY, Elaesplanadi 14, 00130 Helsinki 13, Finland

W R GRACE & CO   1114 Ave of the Americas, New York, NY   10036,
Tel: (212) 819-5500
(Specialty chems, natural resources, consumer serv)
   W.R. Grace OY, Laivalahdenkatu 4A, 00810 Helsinki 81, Finland

HERCULES INC   Hercules Plaza, Wilmington, DE   19894, Tel: (302) 594-5000
(Mfr spec chems, plastics, film & fibers, coatings, resins, food ingredients)
   OY Hercules AB, Mannerheimintie 14A, 00100 Helsinki 10, Finland

HEWLETT-PACKARD CO   3000 Hanover St, PO Box 10301, Palo Alto, CA   94303-0890,
Tel: (415) 857-1501
(Mfr measurement & computation prdts & sys)
   Hewlett-Packard OY, Piispankalliontie 17, 02200 Espoo, Finland

THE HOOVER GROUP   403 W 4th St N, Newton, IA   50208, Tel: (515) 792-8000
(Mfr floor care prdts, laundry & refrig appliances)
   Hoover OY, Hamina 2, 00100 Helsinki 10, Finland

E F HOUGHTON & CO   PO Box 930, Valley Forge, PA   19482-0930,
Tel: (215) 666-4000
(Mfr spec chems, hydraulic fluids, lubricants)
   OY Terastudnti-Stalimport AB, Kaisanieminkatu 4A, 00100 Helsinki 10, Finland

J M HUBER CORP   PO Box 277, Rumson, NJ   07760, Tel: (201) 291-1880
(Inks, crude oil, gas, carbon black, kaolin clay, rubber & paper pigments, timber &
minerals)
   Zeofinn OY, Hamina 2, 00100 Helsinki 10, Finland

INA CORPORATION   1600 Arch St, Philadelphia, PA 19101, Tel: (215) 523-5335
   (Holding co: ins, financial serv)
      INA Intl., Henrick Krause Etelae Splanadi 12, P.O. Box 276, Helsinki, Finland
      INA Intl., Lakennevakuutusyhdistys Bulevarden 28, Helsinki, Finland
      INA Intl., Vakuutusakeyhtio Pohjola, Lapinmaentie 1, Helsinki, Finland
      INA Intl., Pohjola Insurance Co., Ylloplstonkatu 27, Tusku, Finland

INTERMEC CORP   6001 36th Ave West, Everett, WA 98203-9280,
   Tel: (206) 348-2600
   (Mfr automated data collection sys)
      Bar Code Oy, Nuijamiestentie 5 C, 00400 Helsinki, Finland

INTERNATIONAL BUSINESS MACHINES (IBM)   Old Orchard Rd, Armonk,
   NY 10504-1783, Tel: (914) 765-1900
   (Info-handling sys, equip & serv)
      OY International Business Machines AB, Helsinki, Finland
      Suomi OY, P. Roobertinkatu 8B, 00100 Helsinki 10, Finland

ITT CORP   1330 Ave of the Americas, New York, NY 10019, Tel: (212) 258-1000
   (Diversified mfr, tech & services)
      Standard Electric Puhlinteollisuus OY, Aleksanterinkatu 48A, 00100 Helsinki 10,
         Finland
      Standard Electric Puhlinteollsuus OY, Valimontie 13, 00370 Helsinki 37, Finland

K-TEL INTL INC   15525 Medina Rd, Plymouth, MN 55447, Tel: (612) 559-6800
   (Packaged consumer entertainment & convenience prdts)
      K-Tel Intl. Finland OY, Hameentie 157A, 00560 Helsinki, Finland

KEPNER-TREGOE INC   Research Rd, PO Box 704, Princeton, NJ 08542,
   Tel: (609) 921-2806
   (Mgmt & organizational devel)
      OY Rastor AB, Wavulinintie 3, 00210 Helsinki 21, Finland

KEYSTONE INTL INC   PO Box 40010, Houston, TX 77040, Tel: (713) 466-1176
   (Mfr butterfly valves, actuators & control accessories)
      Keystone Flow Controls, Sepondkatu 6, 53300 Lappeenranta, Finland

LINTAS:WORLDWIDE   1 Dag Hammarskjold Plaza, New York, NY 10017,
   Tel: (212) 605-8000
   (Advertising agency)
      Lintas:Helsinki, Pormestarinrinne 5, 00161 Helsinki, Finland

MANHATTAN INTERNATIONAL   1155 Ave of the Americas, New York, NY 10036,
   Tel: (212) 221-7500
   (Mfr shirts, sweaters, sportswear, table linen)
      Manhattan Industries, Erich Schapira (Lady Manhattan), Finland

MANUFACTURERS HANOVER TRUST CO   270 Park Ave, New York, NY 10017,
   Tel: (212) 286-6000
   (Banking)
      Manufacturars Hanover Trust Co. Marski, 10 Mannerheimintle, 00100, H-10, Helsinki,
         Finland
      Manufacturers Hanover Trust Co. Hesperia, 50 Mannerheimintie, 00260,
         H-26 Inter-Continental, Helsinki, Finland
      Manufacturers Hanover Trust Co. Kalastajatorppa, Munkkiniemi, 00330,
         H-33 Helsinki, Finland
      Manufacturers Hanover Trust Co. Palace, 10 Etelaranta, 00130, H-13 Helsinki, Finland

Manufacturers Hanover Trust Co. Vaakuna, 2 Asema-Aukio, 00100, H-10, Helsinki,
   Finland

MARTIN MARIETTA DATA SYSTEMS   PO Box 2392, Princeton, NJ 08540,
   Tel: (609) 799-2600
   (Computer softward, computing & professional serv)
      Mathematica Scandinavia, Fredrikinkatu 33-B, 00120 Helsinki, Finland

MEASUREX CORP   One Results Way, Cupertino, CA 95014, Tel: (408) 255-1500
   (Mfr computer integrated mfg sys)
      Measurex OY, P.O. Box 91, SF-02631 Espoo, Finland
      Measurex Safecontrol OY, Al-Iljokatu 10, P.O. Box 51, SF-403121 Jyvaskyla, Finland

MEDTRONIC INC   7000 Central Ave, NE, Minneapolis, MN 55432,
   Tel: (612) 574-4000
   (Mfr med devices, med serv)
      Medtronic OY, Etelaranta 4A, 00130 Helsinki, Finland

MEMOREX CORP   San Thomas at Central Expressway, Santa Clara, CA 95052,
   Tel: (408) 987-1000
   (Magnetic recording tapes, etc)
      OY Memorex AB, Hopeatie 1B, P.O. Box 3, SF-00400 Helsinki 40, Finland

MERCK SHARP & DOHME INTL   PO Box 2000, Rahway, NJ 07065, Tel: (201) 574-4000
   (Pharms, chems & biologicals)
      Suomen MSD OY, Maapallonkuja 1, 02210 Espoo 21, Helsinki, Finland

MILLIPORE CORP   Ashley Rd, Bedford, MA 01730, Tel: (617) 275-9205
   (Precision filters)
      Millipore OY, PL 36, 0221 Espoo 21, Finland

MOBIL CORP   150 E 42nd St, New York, NY 10017, Tel: (212) 883-4242
   (Petroleum explor, prdts)
      OY Mobil Oil AB, Keskuskatu B, 00100 Helsinki 10, Finland

MONSANTO CO   800 N Lindbergh Blvd, St Louis, MO 63167, Tel: (314) 694-1000
   (Mfr chem & agric prdts, pharms, ind process equip, man-made fibers, plastics)
      Monsanto OY, Mannerheimintie 15, SF-00100 Helsinki, Finland

McCANN-ERICKSON WORLDWIDE   750 Third Ave, New York, NY 10017,
   Tel: (212) 697-6000
   (Advertising)
      Oy Liikemainonta-McCann AB, Keskuskatu 57, 00100 Helsinki, Finland
      Womena Oy, Yrjonkatu 29A, 00100 Helsinki, Finland

NALCO CHEMICAL CO   One Nalco Center, Naperville, IL 60566-1024,
   Tel: (708) 305-1000
   (Chems for water & waste water treatment, oil prod & refining, ind processes;
   water/energy mgmt serv)
      Suomen Nalco OY, Mikonkatu 8 A 9 KRS, SF-00100 Helsinki, Finland

NATIONAL CAR RENTAL SYSTEM INC   7700 France Ave S, Minneapolis, MN 55435,
   Tel: (612) 830-2121
   (Car rental)
      National Car Rental Systems Inc., Mariankatu 27, Helsinki, Finland

NCR CORP   1700 S Patterson Blvd, Dayton, OH 45479, Tel: (513) 445-2000
   (Develop/mfr/sell/serv business info processing sys)
     NCR Finland OY, Eerikinkatu 3B, SF-00100 Helsinki, Finland

NORDSON CORP   28601 Clemens Rd, Westlake, OH 44145, Tel: (216) 892-1580
   (Mfr ind application equip & packaging mach)
     Nordson Finland OY, PL 119, Vesikuja 1, SF-02201, Espoo, Finland

PARAMOUNT INTL FILMS INC   1 Gulf & Western Plaza, New York, NY 10023,
   Tel: (212) 333-4600
   (Film prod & distr)
     OY Cinema Intl. Corp. AB, Pohjoisesplanadi 33A, 00100 Helsinki 10, Finland

PARKER HANNIFIN CORP   17325 Euclid Ave, Cleveland, OH 44112,
   Tel: (216) 531-3000
   (Mfr motion-control prdts)
     Oy Parker Hannifin (Finland), Tuupakantie 8-10 B, SF-01740 Vantaa, Finland

PERKIN-ELMER CORP   761 Main Ave, Norwalk, CT 06859, Tel: (203) 762-1000
   (Analytical instru, computers, semiconductor prod equip, avionics, electro-optical
   sys, etc)
     Perkin-Elmer OY, Luotelsrinne 4, SF-02270 Espoo, Finland

PLANNING RESEARCH CORP   1500 Planning Research Dr, McLean, VA 22102,
   Tel: (703) 556-1000
   (Consultants in planning, engineering & architecture, information sciences & mgmt)
     OY Mec-Rasto AB, Satamakatu 4, 00160 Helsinki 10, Finland

PROCTER & GAMBLE CO   One Procter & Gamble Plaza, Cincinnati, OH 45202,
   Tel: (513) 983-1100
   (Personal care, food, laundry, cleaning & ind prdts)
     Procter & Gamble OY, Helsinki, Finland

READER'S DIGEST ASSOCIATION INC   PO Box 235, Pleasantville, NY 10570,
   Tel: (914) 238-1000
   (Global publisher & direct mail marketer)
     OY Valitut Palat-Reader's Digest AB, Sentnerikuja 5, SF 00440 Helsinki, Finland

RICHARDSON-VICKS INC   Ten Westport Rd, Wilton, CT 06897, Tel: (203) 834-5000
   (Consumer health & personal care prdts)
     OY Richardson-Vicks AB, Mannerheimintie 15A, SF-00260 Helsinki 26, Finland

H H ROBERTSON CO   Two Gateway Center, Pittsburgh, PA 15222,
   Tel: (412) 281-3200
   (Mfr roof & wall prdts, cellular steel floor sys, ventilation equip)
     OY Finnrobertson AB, Kalevagatan 44 A5, 00180 Helsingfors 18, Finland

THE STANLEY WORKS   1000 Stanley Dr, PO Box 7000, New Britain, CT 06050,
   Tel: (203) 225-5111
   (Mfr hand tools & hardware)
     Suomen Stanley OY, P.O. Box 71, SF-00381 Helsinki 38, Finland

TED BATES WORLDWIDE INC   1515 Broadway, New York, NY 10036,
   Tel: (212) 869-3131
   (Advertising agency)
     Finnad-Bates, Annankatu 42C, 00100 Helsinki, Finland

TEKTRONIX INC   PO Box 500, Beaverton, OR 97077, Tel: (503) 627-7111
  (Mfr test & meas, visual sys & commun prdts)
    Tektronix OY, Larin Kyostintie 4, 00650 Helsinki 4, Finland

THERMO ELECTRIC CO   109 Fifth St, Saddle Brook, NJ 07662, Tel: (201) 843-5800
  (Mfr temp/meas control prdts)
    Thermo Electric Co., Nores & Co. OY, Fabianinkatu 32, Helsinki 10, Finland

TRINOVA CORP   3000 Strayer, PO Box 50, Maumee, OH 43537, Tel: (419) 867-2200
  (Mfr engr components & sys for ind)
    Vickers Systems DY, Virkati 10, Veromiehen, PO Box 12, SF-01511 Vantaa, Finland

VF CORP   PO Box 1022, Reading, PA 19603, Tel: (215) 378-1151
  (Mfr/mktg apparel)
    H.D. Lee Co. Finland OY, Munkinmaki 3, 02400 Kirkkonummi, Finland

WARNER BROS INC   4000 Warner Blvd, Burbank, CA 91522, Tel: (213) 954-6000
  (Prod/dist motion picture films, TV, music recording & pub)
    OY Warner Bros. Films AB, Pesplanadi 33A, 00100 Helsinki, Finland

WEIGHT WATCHERS INTL INC   Jericho Atrium, 500 North Broadway, Jericho,
  NY 11753-2196, Tel: (516) 939-0400
  (Weight reduction programs, food prdts)
    Weight Watchers Suomi OY, Kalevankatu 3A, 00100 Helsinki 10, Finland

WM WRIGLEY JR CO   410 N Michigan Ave, Chicago, IL 60611-4287,
  Tel: (312) 644-2121
  (Chewing gum)
    OY Wrigley Scandinavia AB, IL Poisvagen 9, 20740 Abo 74, Finland

FRANCE

3M CO   3M Center, St Paul, MN 55144-1000, Tel: (612) 733-1110
  (Mfr abrasives, adhesives, chems, ind & consumer tapes/diskettes, health care prdts,
  elec connectors)
    3M France, Blvd. de L'Oise, 95006 Cergy Pontoise Cedex, Cergy, France

AAR CORP   1111 Nicholas Blvd, Elk Grove Village, IL 60007,
  Tel: (708) 439-3939
  (Aircraft prdts & serv, aviation serv)
    Allen Airmotive International SARL, BP 50265, 95957 Roissy Charles de Gaulle Cedex,
    France

ABBOTT LABORATORIES   Abbott Park, North Chicago, IL 60064,
  Tel: (312) 937-6100
  (Pharm & lab prdts)
    Abbott Laboratories, 127 Ave. Charles de Gaulle, 92201, Neuilly, France

ABERCROMBIE & KENT INTL INC   1420 Kensington Rd, Oak Brook, IL 60521-2106,
    Tel: (708) 954-2944
    (Tour wholesaler)
      Abercrombie & Kent (France), 18 Rue Vignon, 75009 Paris, France

ACCO INDUSTRIES INC   101 Oakview Dr, Trumbull, CT 06611, Tel: (203) 371-5439
    (Testing sys, chain, castings, brakes, bridge & jib cranes)
      La Teledynamique SA, 550 Rue St. Just Zone Industrielle, 77 Melun, Vaux-Le-Penil,
      France

ACCO INTL INC   770 S Acco Plaza, Wheeling, IL 60090, Tel: (708) 541-9500
    (Paper fasteners & clips, metal fasteners, binders, staplers)
      Acco France SARL, Entrepot Nord, 11-35 Zone D'Ativite, DuPont-Yblon 93150, France

ACCURAY CORP   650 Ackerman Rd, PO Box 02248, Columbus, OH 43202,
    Tel: (614) 261-2000
    (Computer-based process mgmt sys for forest prdts, metals rolling, textiles, tobacco
    ind)
      Accuray France SARL, 8 Rue Auguste-Renoir 78400, Chatou, France

ACHESON COLLOIDS CO   1600 Washington Ave, PO Box 288, Port Huron, MI 48060,
    Tel: (313) 984-5581
    (Graphite, lubricants & other specialty chems)
      Acheson France SARL, 30 Ave. Admiral Lemonnier, 78160 Marly-le-Roi, France

ACTION INSTRUMENTS INC   8601 Aero Dr, San Diego, CA 92123,
    Tel: (619) 279-5226
    (Mfr electr instru & ind meas computers)
      Action Instruments, SA, 9 Ave. du Canada Parc Hightec, Les Ulis Cedex, France

ACUFF-ROSE PUBLICATION INC   65 Music Square W, Nashville, TN 37203,
    Tel: (615) 321-5000
    (Music publisher)
      Edition Acuff-Rose France SARL, 12 Rue de Penthievre, Paris 8, France

AFIA   110 William St, New York, NY 10038, Tel: (212) 964-4990
    (Insurance)
      American Foreign Insurance Association, 14 Rue Ballu, 75009, Paris, France

AIR EXPRESS INTL CORP   120 Tokeneke Rd, PO Box 1231, Darien, CT 06820,
    Tel: (203) 655-7900
    (Air frt forwarder)
      Air Express International, 59810 Aeroport de Lille Lesquin, France
      Air Express International, B.P. 10406, 95707 Roissy, Aeroport Charles de Gaulle,
      Roissy, France

AIR PRODUCTS & CHEMICALS INC   7201 Hamilton Blvd, Allentown, PA 18195,
    Tel: (215) 481-4911
    (Mfr ind gases & chems)
      Societe des Produits de L'Air, Tour Pleyel Centre Paris, Pleyel 93521, Ste. Denis,
      France

ALBANY INTL CORP   PO Box 1907, Albany, NY 12201, Tel: (518) 445-2200
    (Paper mach clothing, engineered fabrics, plastic prdts, filtration media)
      Postillion SA, 6 Rue Royale, 77300 Fontainebleau, France
      Postillion SA, 24600 Riberac (Dordogne), France

ALCO STANDARD CORP   825 Duportail Rd, Wayne, PA 19087, Tel: (215) 296-8000
  (Diversified distr, mfg & resources)
    Big Drum France SA, Zone Industrielle, Eloyes, F. 88510, France
    Ipsen Industries SARL, 62 Rue de la Colonie, 75013 Paris, France

ALLEN-BRADLEY CO   PO Box 2086, Milwaukee, WI 53201, Tel: (414) 382-2000
  (Electrical control devices)
    Siege et Direction Commerciale de Paris, 8 Rue Paul LaFarque, 92800, Puteaux, France

ALLERGAN PHARMACEUTICALS INTL INC   2525 DuPont Dr, Irvine, CA 92713,
  Tel: (714) 752-4500
  (Pharms, opthalmic & dermatological preparations)
    Allergan SA, B.P. 13, 67401 Illkirch Cedex, France

ALLIED AFTERMARKET DIV   105 Pawtucket Ave, East Providence, RI 02916,
  Tel: (401) 434-7000
  (Mfr spark plugs, waste treatment sys, filters, brakes)
    Fram France, 9 Chaussee Jules-Cesar, 95523 Cergy-Pontoise, France

ALLIED-SIGNAL INC   Columbia Rd & Park Ave, PO Box 2245R, Morristown,
  NJ 07960, Tel: (201) 455-2000
  (Mfr aerospace & automotive prdts, engineered materials)
    Airsupply Intl., 81 Ave. de Marechal Jofre, 92000 Nanterre, France
    Allied-Signal Aerospace Co., 5 Ave. Matignon, 75008 Paris, France
    Bendix Europe, 126 rue de Stalingrad, 93700 Drancy, France
    Bendix France S.A., 224 rue de Stalingrad, 93700 Drancy, France
    Garrett S.A., Route D'Oncourt, BP 19, 88150 Thaon-les-Vosges, France
    Norplex/Oak France, 33 Quai de Dion-Bouton, 92814 Puteaux Cedex, Paris, France

ALLIED-SIGNAL INTL INC   Columbia Rd & Park Ave, PO Box 2000, Morristown,
  NJ 07962, Tel: (201) 455-6034
  (Mfr advanced aerospace, automotive & engineered materials)
    Allied Signal Intl. Inc., 39 Rue Francois 1er, 75008 Paris, France

ALLIS-CHALMERS CORP   PO Box 512, Milwaukee, WI 53201, Tel: (414) 475-4011
  (Heavy mach, equip & serv)
    Allis-Chalmers Process Equipment SARL, 13 Chemin du Levant, Ferney Voltaire 01210,
      France
    Equipment Minier Metallurgique et Industriel SA, 37 Blvd. Malesherbes, Paris, France

AM INTL INC   333 W Wacker Dr, #900, Chicago, IL 60606-1265,
  Tel: (312) 558-1966
  (Mfr/sale/serv commun graphics, info handling equip & sys)
    AM Intl. S.A., B.P. 307, 60 Rue Berthelot, 92402 Courbevoie Cedex, France

AMDAHL CORP   1250 East Arques Ave, PO Box 3470, Sunnyvale, CA 94088-3470,
  Tel: (408) 746-6000
  (Mfr large scale computers, complementary software storage & commun prdts)
    Amdahl France SARL, Maillot 2000, 251 Blvd. Pereire, 75853 Paris, France

AMERACE CORP   Newburgh Rd, Hackettstown, NJ 07840, Tel: (201) 852-1122
  (Chems, rubber prdts, plastics, electrical components & controls)
    Amerace SA, Les Flanades 18, Place de France, Sarcelles, 95200 France

AMERICAN AIR FILTER CO INC   215 Central Ave, PO Box 35690, Louisville,
KY 40277, Tel: (502) 637-0011
(Air cleaning equip)
   AAF SA, Rue William Dian, 27620 Gasny, France

AMERICAN AIRLINES INC   PO Box 619616, Dallas-Ft Worth Arpt, TX 75261-9616,
Tel: (817) 355-1234
(Air transp)
   American Airlines Inc., 82 Ave. Marceau, 75008 Paris, France

AMERICAN BROADCASTING COS INC   1330 Ave of the Americas, New York, NY 10019,
Tel: (212) 887-7777
(Radio/TV prod & broadcast)
   ABC News, 22 Ave. d'Eyleu, Paris 75116, France

AMERICAN CYANAMID CO   1 Cyanamid Plaza, Wayne, NJ 07470, Tel: (201) 831-2000
(Pharms, chems, agric & consumer prdts)
   Cyanamid S.A., same address
   Lab. Lederle SA, 74 Rue d'Arceuil, Silic 275, 94578 Rungis, Cedex, France

AMERICAN EXPRESS CO   American Express Tower, New York, NY 10285-4765,
Tel: (212) 640-2000
(Diversified fin & travel-related serv)
   American Express International Banking Corp., 1 Rue du Boccador, 75008 Paris, France
   American Express International Banking Corp., Antibes & Cannes, France

AMERICAN GREETINGS CORP   10500 American Rd, Cleveland, OH 44144,
Tel: (216) 252-7300
(Mfr/distr greeting cards, gift wrappings, tags, seals, ribbons & party goods)
   Carlton Cards France, 184 Ave. Paul Vaillant Couturier, 93120 La Cournruve, France

AMERICAN HOME PRODUCTS CORP   685 Third Ave, New York, NY 10017,
Tel: (212) 878-5800
(Drugs, food, household prdts)
   American Home Products France, Blois, Brou, Paris, Saint Florent Sur Cher, France
   Ayerst Inc. SA, Hauts-de-Seine, France
   Compgnie Francalse du Golden Fleece SA, Paris, France
   Laboratoires Bismupharm SA, France
   Laboratoires Wyeth-Byla, France
   O-Cedar SA, France
   Prestige France SA, Paris, France
   Societe Civile, Augull Hauts-de-Siene, France

AMERICAN INTL UNDERWRITERS CORP   70 Pine St, New York, NY 10270,
Tel: (212) 770-7000
(General ins)
   American International Underwriters SARL, 24 Ave. de la Grande Armee, Cedex 17,
      75854 Paris, France
   American International Underwriters SARL, 7 Place Vendome, 75001 Paris, France

AMERICAN LIFE INSURANCE CO (ALICO)   PO Box 2226, Wilmington, DE 19899,
Tel: (302) 594-2000
(Life ins, pension & annuity plans, health prdts)
   Compagnie Europeenne d'Assurances sur la Vie (Euravie), 152 Ave. de Malakoff,
      75016 Paris, France

AMERICAN NATIONAL CAN CO   8770 W Bryn Mawr Ave, Chicago, IL 60631,
   Tel: (312) 399-3000
   (Mfr metal, glass & plastic packaging prdt)
      Cotuplas S.A., Zone Industrialle, B.P. 18-51800, Sainte-Menehould, France

AMERICAN OPTICAL CORP   14 Mechanic St, Southbridge, MA 01550,
   Tel: (617) 765-9711
   (Ophthalmic lenses, frames & cases, sunglasses)
      Vergo/AO, B.P. 33, Illkirch-Graffenstaden F. 67401, Strasbourg Cedex, France
      Vergo/AO, Usine de Goetzenbruck F. 57620, Lemberg, France
      Vergo/AO, 327 Rue de Charenton, F. 75012 Paris, France

AMERICAN STANDARD INC   40 W 40th St, New York, NY 10018, Tel: (212) 840-5100
   (Heating & sanitary equip)
      Wabco Westinghouse SA, 2 Blvd. Westinghouse, B.P. 2, F-93270 Freinville Sevaran,
      France

AMERICAN TOOL COMPANIES INC   301 S 13th St, #600, Lincoln, NE 68508,
   Tel: (402) 435-3300
   (Mfr hand tools)
      ATC France SA, 67 Avenue Leon Jouhaux, F-92160 Antony, France

AMERON INC   4700 Ramona Blvd, PO Box 3000, Monterey Park, CA 91754,
   Tel: (213) 268-4111
   (Mfr steel pipe sys, concrete prdts, traffic & lighting poles, protective coatings)
      Tubolining SA, B.P. 43, 13367 Marseille, Cedex 11, France

AMES TEXTILE CORP   720 Suffolk St, Lowell, MA 01854, Tel: (617) 458-3321
   (Textile prdts)
      Ames France, 3 Chemin Departemental, Fallieres, St. Nabord 88200 Remiremont, France

AMICON CORP   182 Conant St, Danvers, MA 01923, Tel: (617) 777-3622
   (Research apparatus)
      Amicon SARL, 63/65 Place de la Reunion, 75020 Paris, France

AMP INC   470 Friendship Rd, Harrisburg, PA 17111, Tel: (717) 564-0100
   (Mfr electrical wiring devices)
      AMP de France, 29 Chaussee Jules-Cesar, B.P. 39, 95301 Pontoise (Val d'Oise), France

AMPCO METAL INC   1745 S 38th St, PO Box 2004, Milwaukee, WI 53201,
   Tel: (414) 645-3750
   (Cast & wrought copper-based alloys)
      Ampco Metal France SARL, 13 Blvd. Malesherbes, 75008 Paris,   France

AMPEX CORP   401 Broadway, Redwood City, CA 94063-3199, Tel: (415) 367-2011
   (Mfr professional audio/visual sys, magnetic recording media, data-memory prdts)
      Ampex SARL, 2 Rue Curnonsky, 75017 Paris, France

AMPHENOL PRODUCTS   4300 Commerct Ct, Lisle, IL 60532, Tel: (708) 983-3500
   (Elect interconnect/penetrate sys & assemblies)
      Amphenol Socapex France, B.P. 349, 3910 Dole, France
      Amphenol Socapex France, B.P. 32, 92151 Suresnes, France
      Amphenol Socapex France, B.P. 29, 74301 Cluses, France

AMWAY CORP   7575 E Fulton Rd, Ada, MI 49355, Tel: (616) 676-6000
   (Distr household cleaning, nutrition & diet prdts)
      Amway France, 14 Ave. Francois Sommer, Zone Industrielle, 92167 Antony Cedex, France

ANALOG DEVICES INC   1 Technology Way, Box 9106, Norwood, MA 02062,
Tel: (617) 329-4700
(Analog digital converters)
    Analog Devices SA, 12 Rue le Corbusier, Silic 204 Batiment Lena, 94518 Rungis,
    Cedex, France

ANDREW CORP   10500 W 153rd St, Orlando Park, IL 60462, Tel: (708) 349-3300
(Antenna sys)
    Antennes Andrew SARL, B.P. 44, 28400 Hogent le-Rotron, France

ANEMOSTAT PRODUCTS DIV   888 N Keyser Ave, Scranton, PA 18501,
Tel: (717) 346-6586
(Mfr air diffusers, grilles & related equip for A/C, heating & ventilation)
    Anemotherm SA, 4749 Rue Jean Bleuzen, 92170 Vanves, France

ANIXTER BROS INC   4711 Golf Rd, Skokie, IL 60076, Tel: (708) 677-2600
(Dist wiring sys/prdts for voice, video, data & power applications)
    Anixter France, ZAC Paris Nord 2, BP 50008, 69 rue de la Belle Etoile,
    95945 Roissy Charles de Gaulle-Cedex, France

APPLE COMPUTER INC   20525 Mariani Ave, Cupertino, CA 95014,
Tel: (408) 996-1010
(Personal computers, peripherals & software)
    Apple Computer France SARL, Ave. de l'Oceanie, Z.I. de Courtaboeuf, B.P. 131,
    91944 Les Ulis, France

ARBOR ACRES FARM INC   41 Marlborough Rd, Glastonbury, CT 06033,
Tel: (203) 633-4681
(Producers of male & female broiler breeders, commercial egg layers)
    Grelier, 49 Saint Laurent de la Plaine, France

ARMSTRONG WORLD INDUSTRIES INC   PO Box 3001, Lancaster, PA 17604,
Tel: (717) 397-0611
(Mfr/mkt interior furnishings & spec prdts for bldg, auto & textile inds)
    Armstrong World Industries, 5 Rue Louis le Jeune, 92128 Montrouge, France

ASGROW SEED CO   7000 Portage Rd, Kalamazoo, MI 49001, Tel: (616) 385-6614
(Growers/breeders agronomic & vegetable seeds)
    Asgrow France SA, B.P. 80, 60304 Senlis, France

ASK MR FOSTER TRAVEL CORP   7833 Haskell Ave, Van Nuys, CA 91406,
Tel: (818) 988-0181
(Travel service)
    Ask Mr. Foster/Novotour SA, 205 Rue St. Honore, 75017 Paris, France

ASSOCIATED MERCHANDISING CORP   1440 Broadway, New York, NY 10018,
Tel: (212) 536-4000
(Retail service organization)
    Associated Merchandising Corp., 14 Rue de Castiglione, 75001 Paris, France

AST RESEARCH INC   16215 Alton Parkway, PO Box 19658, Irvine, CA 92713-9658,
Tel: (714) 727-4141
(Mfr personal computers enhancement & data commun prdt)
    AST Research France SARL, 86-90 Rue Victor Hugo, 93170 Bagnolet Paris, France

AUGAT INC 89 Forbes Blvd, Mansfield, MA 02048, Tel: (508) 543-4300
(Interconnection prdts)
Augat SA, Alle de la Vanne 9, ZI Sofilic 440, 94263 Fresnes, France

AVERY INTL CORP 150 N Orange Grove Blvd, Pasadena, CA 91103,
Tel: (213) 304-2000
(Mfr self-adhesive labels & marking equip)
Eticluettes Avery SA, Rue Blaise-Pascal, Zone Industrial, B.P. 16,
91380 Chilly-Mazarin, France

AVON PRODUCTS INC 9 W 57th St, New York, NY 10019, Tel: (212) 546-6015
(Mfr/distr cosmetics, perfumes)
Avon SA, Rantigny, Claude Noailly, Paris, France

AVX CORP 750 Lexington Ave, New York, NY 10022-1208, Tel: (212) 935-6363
(Mfr multilayer ceramic capacitors)
AVX SA, 76120 Grand Quevilly, Rouen, France

AYERST LABORATORIES 145 King of Prussia Rd, Radnor, PA 19087,
Tel: (215) 688-4400
(Biologicals & pharms)
Laboratoires Auclair, France
Laboratoires Auclair, Montrouge, France

BAKER & McKENZIE 2800 Prudential Plaza, Chicago, IL 60601,
Tel: (312) 861-8000
(Intl attorneys)
Baker & McKenzie, 94 Rue de Faubourg Saint Honore, 75008 Paris, France

BAKER OIL TOOLS PO Box 3048, Houston, TX 77253, Tel: (713) 923-9351
(Oil/gas well completions equip)
Baker Intl. SA, 201 Bureaux de la Colline, 92213 Saint Cloud, France
Baker Intl. SA, Allee des Forges, B.P. 363, 65005 Tarbes Cedex, France

BAKER PRODUCTION TECHNOLOGY PO Box 40129, Houston, TX 77240-0129,
Tel: (713) 943-0170
(Inflatable packers, instru well testing)
Services Petroliers Baker, Zone Industrielle de Lons, Cidex 137 Lons,
64140 Billere, France

BANKAMERICA CORP PO Box 37000, San Francisco, CA 94137, Tel: (415) 622-3456
(Financial services)
Bank of America (France) S.A., 43/37 Ave. de la Grande Armee, 75782 Paris,
Cedex 16, France

BANKERS TRUST CO 280 Park Ave, New York, NY 10017, Tel: (212) 775-2500
(Banking)
Bankers Trust Co., 12-14 Rond-Point des Champs Elysee, Cedex, 75038 Paris, France

BARDAHL MFG CORP 1400 N W 52nd St, PO Box 70607, Seattle, WA 98107,
Tel: (206) 783-4851
(Lubricating oils)
Bardahl Sofra Lus, B.P. 29, 27 Blvd. du General Leclerc, 59051 Rouball, France

BATTEN BARTON DURSTINE & OSBORN INC   1285 Ave of the Americas, New York,
NY 10019, Tel: (212) 459-5000
(Advertising agency)
   Chevalier, Le Forestier, Michel & BBDO SA, 92 Ave. des Ternes, 75017 Paris, France

BAUSCH & LOMB INC   1 Lincoln First Sq, Rochester, NY 14601-0054,
Tel: (716) 338-6000
(Mfr healthcare & optics prdts)
   Bausch & Lomb France SA, Le Mesnil St. Denis, France

BAXTER TRAVENOL LABORATORIES INC   1 Baxter Pky, Deerfield, IL 60015,
Tel: (708) 948-2000
(Pharm & disposable med prdts)
   France Plasir Laboratories Travenol, Rue Descartes, B.P. 26, 78370 Plaisir, France
   Travenol SA, Thevet Saint Julian, La Chatre 36-400, France

BEAR STEARNS & CO INC   245 Park Ave, New York, NY 10167, Tel: (212) 272-2000
(Invest banking & trading)
   Bear Stearns SA, 18 Rue Bayard, 75008 Paris, France

BEARIUM METALS CORP   1170 Chili Ave, Rochester, NY 14624, Tel: (716) 235-5360
(Bearium metal alloys)
   Fonderies de Nogent, 91 Rue Carnot Nogent-Sur Oise, B.P. 57, 60105 Creil, Cedex,
   France

BECKMAN INSTRUMENTS INC   2500 Harbor Blvd, Box 3100, Fullerton, CA 92634,
Tel: (714) 871-4848
(Mfr/distr/serv research & clinical lab instru, sys, software & reagents)
   Beckman Instruments France S.A., 52 Chemin des Bourdons, 93220 Gagny, France

BEE CHEMICAL CO   2700 E 170th St, Lansing, IL 60438, Tel: (708) 758-0500
(Coatings & finishes for plastics & metals)
   Bee Chemical SARL, Place de la Gare, 78590 Noisy le Roi, France

BELL & HOWELL CO   5215 Old Orchard Rd., Skokie, IL 60077, Tel: (708) 470-7684
(Diversified info prdts & servs)
   Bell & Howell France SA, 32/34 Rue Fernand-Pelloutier, 92110 Clichy, France

BELLSOUTH INTERNATIONAL   1155 Peachtree St NE, #400, Atlanta, GA 30367,
Tel: (404) 249-4800
(Mobile commun, telecom network sys)
   BellSouth Intl., Metz, France
   Datech S.A., 1 Rue Marconi, Technopole, Metz 2000, 57070 Metz, France

BELOIT CORP   1st Lawrence Ave, Beloit, WI 53511, Tel: (608) 365-3311
(Paper making mach & equip)
   Beloit Papermachines, SA, Creusot Loire, 15 Rue Pasquier, 75383 Paris, France
   Rader SA, 18-20 Place de la Madeleine, 75008 Paris, France

BENTLEY LABORATORIES INC   17502 Armstrong Ave, Irvine, CA 92714,
Tel: (714) 546-8020
(Mfr para-med devices)
   Bentley Laboratoires SA, 46 Bis Rue Pierre Curie, Z.I. Les Gatines, 78370 Plaisir,
   France

BENTLY NEVADA CORP   PO Box 157, Minden, NV 89423, Tel: (702) 782-3611
  (Electronic monitoring system)
    Bently Nevada France SARL, 30 Ave. de 1, Amiral Lemonnier, 78160, Marly-le-Roi,
    France

LOUIS BERGER INTL INC   100 Halsted St, East Orange, NJ 07019,
  Tel: (201) 678-1960
  (Consulting engineers, architects, economists & planners)
    Louis Berger SARL, 71 Rue Fondary, 75015 Paris, France

BERKEY-COLORTRAN INC   1015 Chestnut St, Burbank, CA 91502,
  Tel: (213) 843-1200
  (Lighting equip)
    Francois Bogard SA, 131 Rue de l'Universitie, 75007 Paris, France

BIJUR LUBRICATING CORP   50 Kocher Dr, Bennington, VT 05201-1994,
  Tel: (802) 447-2174
  (Design/mfr centralized lubrication equip)
    Bijur Products Inc., B.P. 50, Z.I. de Courtaboeuf, F. 91942 Orsay Les Ulis Cedex,
    France

BINKS MFG CO   9201 W Belmont Ave, Franklin Park, IL 60131,
  Tel: (708) 671-3000
  (Mfr of spray painting & finishing equip)
    Binks International, France, Rocade du Parc., Z.I. de Torcy, F. 77200 Torcy, France

BINNEY & SMITH INC   1100 Church Lane, PO Box 431, Easton, PA 18042,
  Tel: (215) 253-6271
  (Mfr art supplies, craft kits)
    Binney & Smith (Europe) Ltd., Succur Sale Francaise, Route de Tricot,
    BP Maigneley-Montigny, France

BIO-RAD LABORATORIES   2200 Wright Ave, Richmond, CA 94804,
  Tel: (415) 234-4130
  (Spec chems, clinical diagnostic prdts, test kits)
    Orimbio SA, 5 Bis, Rue Maurice Rouvier, 75014 Paris, France

BISSELL INC   2345 Walker Road, NW, Grand Rapids, MI 49504,
  Tel: (616) 453-4451
  (Mfr home cleaning prdts)
    Bissell SA, 27 Ave. Ampere, Z.I. de Villemilan, 913 Wissous, France

BLACK & DECKER CORP   701 E Joppa Road, Towson, MD 21204, Tel: (301) 583-3900
  (Mfr portable elect & pneumatic power tools, household prdts)
    Black & Decker (France) SARL, B.P. 417, Lyon R.P., 69218, Lyon Cedex 1, France
    Black & Decker (France) SARL, 38950 St. Etienne de St. Geoirs, France

BLACK CLAWSON CO   666 Third Ave, New York, NY 10017, Tel: (212) 972-4440
  (Paper & pulp mill mach)
    Black Clawson France, 30 Ave. Pierre Curie, B.P. 9, 33270 Floirac/Bordeaux, France

BLACK SIVALLS & BRYSON INC   PO Box 27125, Houston, TX 77227,
  Tel: (713) 981-8303
  (Oil & gas prod equip, engineering serv, constr mgt)
    Black Sivalls & Bryson France SA, 5 et 7 Rue l'Amiral Coubert, Saint Mande,
    94160 Paris, France

BOOZ ALLEN & HAMILTON INC   101 Park Ave, New York, NY 10178,
Tel: (212) 697-1900
(Mgmt consultants)
    Booz Allen, Hamilton, France, 58 Ave. Kleber, Cedex 16, 75784 Paris, France

BORDEN INC   420 Lexington Ave, New York, NY 10170, Tel: (212) 573-4000
(Milk processing, dairy foods, specialty foods, chems, plastics)
    Borden Chemical Co., France SA, Industrial Adhesives Div.,
    20 Rue Dumont du'Urville, 75116 Paris, France

BORG-WARNER CORP   200 S Michigan Ave, Chicago, IL 60604, Tel: (312) 322-8500
(Mfr A/C equip, chem & plastics, ind prdts, trans equip)
    Borg-Warner Chemicals SARL, Le Courcellor 1, 2 Rue Curnonsky, 75017 Paris, France
    Borg-Warner France, 183 Rue Courcelles, 75017 Paris, France

BOSE CORP   100 The Mountain Rd, Framingham, MA 01701, Tel: (617) 879-7330
(Electronic equip)
    Bose SARL, 127 Grand Rue, 93250   Villemomble, France

BOSTITCH DIV   815 Briggs St, East Greenwich, RI 02818, Tel: (401) 884-2500
(Stapling machs & supplies, wire)
    Bostitch Sofrembal, B.P. 24, 112 Ave. Charles de Gaulle, 91 Morangis, France
    SIMAX, Maxonchamp, 88360 Rup. Sur Moselle, France

BOURNS INC   1200 Columbia Ave, Riverside, CA 92507, Tel: (714) 781-5960
(Mfr resistive com & networks, precision potentiometers, panel controls)
    Bourns Ohmic S.A., 21/23 Rue des Ardennes, F-75019 Paris, France

BOYDEN ASSOCIATES INC   260 Madison Ave, New York, NY 10016,
Tel: (212) 685-3400
(Mgt consultants, exec search)
    Boyden International SARL, 13 Rue Madeleine Michelis, 92522 Neuilly, Cedex, France

W H BRADY CO   727 W Glendale Ave, PO Box 571, Milwaukee, WI 53201,
Tel: (414) 332-8100
(Wire markers, name plates)
    W.H. Brady SARL, 109 Ave. Gallouedec, F. 45400 Fleury Les Aubrais, France

BRANSON ULTRASONICS CORP   Eagle Rd, Danbury, CT 06810, Tel: (203) 796-0400
(Ultrasonic & vibratory plastics assembly mach)
    Branson Ultrasons (KBSA), 1 Rue des Pyrenees, Silic 404, 74573 Rungis, Cedex France
    K.B.S.A., Centre Silic 14, 1 Rue des Pyrenees, 94153 Rugis Cedex, France

BRINK'S INC   Thorndal Circle, Darien, CT 06820, Tel: (203) 655-8781
(Security transportation)
    Brink's France, 61 Rue Hautpoul, 75019 Paris, France

BRISTOL BABCOCK INC   1100 Buckingham St, Watertown, CT 06795,
Tel: (203) 575-3000
(Mfr process control instru & intelligent digital prdts)
    Bristol Babcock S.A., 31 rue du General Leclerc, 60250 Mouy, France

BROWN BROTHERS HARRIMAN & CO   59 Wall St, New York, NY 10005,
Tel: (212) 483-1818
(Financial serv)
    Brown Harriman Corp., 12-14 Rond Point des Champs Elysees, 75008 Paris, France

BRUSH WELLMAN INC   17876 St Clair Ave, Celeveland, OH 44110,
    Tel: (216) 486-4200
    (Beryllium metal, alloys & compounds; friction prdts, cutting edges)
        Stainless SA, 114-134 Ave. Laurent Cely, F. 92230 Gennevilliers, France

BURLINGTON AIR EXPRESS   18200 Van Karman Ave, Irvine, CA 92715,
    Tel: (714) 752-1212
    (Air freight)
        Burlington Air Express, Rue Des Deux Cedres, BP 10287,
        95704 Roissy Aeroport Cedex Paris, France

LEO BURNETT CO INC   35 West Wacker Dr, Chicago, IL 60601, Tel: (312) 220-5959
    (Advertising agency)
        Black Pencil S.A.R.L., 14 Rue Alexandre Parodi, 75010 Paris, France
        Bordelais, Lemeunier & Leo Burnett, 185 Ave. Charles de Gaulle,
        92521 Neuilly-sur-Seine, France

BURR-BROWN RESEARCH CORP   PO Box 11400, Tucson, AZ 85734, Tel: (602) 746-1111
    (Electronic components & sys modules)
        Burr Brown International SA, 18 Ave. Dutartre, 78150 Le Chesnay, France

BURSON-MARSTELLER   230 Park Ave, New York, NY 10003-1566, Tel: (212) 614-4000
    (Public relations/public affairs consultants)
        Burson-Marsteller, 11 Rue Paul Baudry, 75008 Paris, France

BUSINESSLAND INC   1001 Ridder Park Dr, San Jose, CA 95131,
    Tel: (408) 437-0400
    (Distr, integration & support microcomputer sys)
        Businessland, Inc., CNIT 2 Place de la Defense, BP 240, 92053 Paris la Defense,
        France

BUTTERICK FASHION MARKETING CO   161 Ave of the Americas, New York, NY 10013,
    Tel: (212) 620-2500
    (Sewing patterns)
        Vogue Pattern Service, 44 Rue la Boetie, 75008 Paris, France

CARL BYOIR & ASSOCIATES INC   380 Madison Ave, New York, NY 10017,
    Tel: (212) 986-6100
    (Public relations consultants)
        TSA Consultants, 35 Rue de Ponthieu, 75008 Paris, France

CABOT CORP   950 Winter St, PO Box 9073, Waltham, MA 02254,
    Tel: (617) 890-0200
    (Mfr carbon blacks, plastics; oil & gas, info sys)
        Berylco-Cabot Metaux Speciaux (Cabot Berylco Div.), B.P. 17, 44220 Coueron, France
        Berylco-Cabot Metaux Speciaux (Cabot Berylco Div.), 76-78 Champs Elyses,
        75008 Paris, France
        Berylco-Cabot Metaux Speciaux, Div. Plastiques, 6 Ave. Charles de Gaulle,
        78150 Le Chesnay, Paris, France

CALCOMP   2411 W La Palma Ave, PO Box 3250, Anaheim, CA 92801,
    Tel: (714) 821-2142
    (Mfr computer graphics)
        CalComp SA, 43 Rue de la Breche-aux-Loups, 75012 Paris, France
        Calcomp SA, 43 Rue de la Breche aux Loups, 75012 Paris, France

CALIFORNIA PELLET MILL CO   221 Main St, #420, San Francisco, CA 94105,
  Tel: (415) 431-3800
  (Mfr mach for pelleting)
    CPM Europe SA, B.P. 35, 34 Ave. Albert I, 92502 Rueil, Malmaison, France

CAMP INTL INC   PO Box 89, Jackson, MI 49204, Tel: (517) 787-1600
  (Mfr orthotics & prosthetics)
    Proteor, 11 Rue de Buttes, 21100 Dijon, France

CAMPBELL SOUP CO   Campbell Place, Camden, NJ 08101, Tel: (609) 342-4800
  (Food prdts)
    Societe Francaise des Biscuits Delacre SA, Rue de Penthievre, F-75008 Paris, France
    Societe Francaise des Biscuits Delacre SA, 2 Rue Belle Vue, 59 Nieppe, France

CANADA DRY INTL CORP   2600 Century Pkwy, Atlanta, GA 30345,
  Tel: (404) 753-2182
  (Carbonated beverages, soft drinks extract)
    Societe Europeenne de Brasseries, 6 Rue des Caues, 92310 Sevres, France

CANBERRA INDUSTRIES INC   One State St, Meriden, CT 06450, Tel: (203) 238-2351
  (Mfr instru for nuclear research)
    Canberra Electronique SARL, Z.I. de Savigny-le-Temple, Rue de l'Etain, B.P. 15,
      77541 Savigny-le-Temple, France
    Packard Instrument S.A., 4 a 10 Rue de la Grosse Pierre, F-94533 Rungis, France

CANDELA LASER CORP   530 Boston Post Rd, Wayland, MA 01778,
  Tel: (508) 358-5700
  (Mfr/serv medical laser systems)
    Candela France Sarl, Le Semanet, 4 Allee de la Combe, 69380 Lissieu, France

CANFIELD CO OF INDIANA INC   PO Box 220, Seymour, IN 47274,
  Tel: (812) 522-2323
  (Ind plastics)
    Canfield Co. (France) SARL, Z.I. du Hello a Lezennes, 59260 Hellemmes-Lille, France

CARBOLINE CO   350 Hanley Ind Court, St Louis, MO 63144, Tel: (314) 644-1000
  (Coatings, sealants)
    Navy Plastic France, Carboline Dept., 8 Sq. Chanton, Neuilly Sur Seine, France

CARGILL   PO Box 9300, Minneapolis, MN 55440, Tel: (612) 475-7575
  (Food prdts, feeds, animal prdts)
    Compagnie Cargill, B.P. 215, 78108 St. Germain-en-laye-Cedex, Paris, France

CARNATION INTL CO   5045 Wilshire Blvd, Los Angeles, CA 90036,
  Tel: (213) 932-6000
  (Milk prdts)
    Gloria, 14 Rue de Bassano, 75783 Paris, Cedex 16, France
    Gloria SA, 14 Rue de Bassano, Cedex 16, 75783 Paris, France

CARRIER INTERNATIONAL CORP   PO Box 4806, Syracuse, NY 13221,
  Tel: (315) 432-6000
  (A/C, heating, refrig & power equip)
    Le Compresseur Frigerifique, Route de Thil, B.P. 6, 91120 Montluel, France

J I CASE CO   700 State St, Racine, WI 53404, Tel: (414) 636-6011
  (Mfr/sale agric & constr equip)
    J I Case Co., Clos Saint Jean, B.P. 37, 52102 St. Dizier, France

J I Case S.A., 71 Ave. Georges Hannart, B.P. 73, 59964 Croix, France
Poclain S.A., Ave. de Poclain, 60330 Le Plessis-Belleville, France

CATERPILLAR INC   100 N E Adams St, Peoria, IL 61629, Tel: (309) 675-1000
  (Mfr earth/material-handling & constr mach & equip, engines, generators)
    Caterpillar France SA, 40-48 Ave. Leon Blum, 38100 Grenoble, France

CCS COMMUNICATIONS CONTROL INC   633 Third Ave, New York, NY 10017,
  Tel: (212) 682-4637
  (Mfr electronic security prdts)
    CCS Communication Controle Securite, 26 Place Vendome, 75001 Paris, France

CENTRAL NATIONAL-GOTTESMAN INC   100 Park Ave, New York, NY 10017,
  Tel: (212) 532-7300
  (Pulp & paper prdts)
    Cenafrance S.A., 38 Rue de Ponthieu, 75008 Paris, France

CENTRAL SOYA CO   PO Box 1400, Ft Wayne, IN 46802, Tel: (219) 425-5100
  (Livestock & poultry feed, soybean meal, grain)
    Central Soya France SA, 9-11 Ave. Arago, B.P. 108, 78191 Trappes Cedex, France

CENTURY 21 REAL ESTATE CORP   2601 SE Main, PO Box 19564, Irvine,
  CA 92713-9564, Tel: (714) 553-2100
  (Real estate)
    Century 21 France S.A., Rue des Cevennes, Batiment 4, Petite Montagne Sud, CE 1701,
      91017 Evry Cedex Lisses, France

CHARLES OF THE RITZ GROUP LTD   625 Madison Ave, New York, NY 10022,
  Tel: (212) 527-4000
  (Fine fragrances & cosmetics)
    Charles of the Ritz SA, 28-34 Blvd. du Parc, 92521 Neuilly-Sur-Seine, Paris, France
    Charles of the Ritz SA, 28-24 Blvd. du Parc, 92521 Neuilly-Sur-Seine, Paris, France

CHARLES RIVER BREEDING LABORATORIES   251 Ballardvale St, Wilmington,
  MA 01887, Tel: (617) 658-6000
  (Scientific research lab animals)
    Charles River France SA, 76410 Saint Aubin-les-Elbeuf, France

CHASE INTERNATIONAL INVESTMENT CORP   1 Chase Manhattan Plaza, New York,
  NY 10081, Tel: (212) 552-4631
  (Investments)
    Chase International Investment Corp., 41 Rue Cambon, Paris, France

CHASE MANHATTAN BANK N A   1 Chase Manhattan Plaza, New York, NY 10081,
  Tel: (212) 552-2222
  (Intl banking)
    Chase Manhattan Bank N.A., 41 Rue Cambon, 75001 Paris, France

CHECK TECHNOLOGY CORP   1284 Corporate Center Dr, St Paul, MN 55121,
  Tel: (612) 454-9300
  (Mfr computer controlled check/coupon print sys)
    Check Technology France SA, Buroparc 1 Batiment 2, Avenue Du Long Rayage,
      91090 Lisses, France

THE CHERRY CORP   3600 Sunset Ave, PO Box 718, Waukegan, IL 60087,
  Tel: (708) 662-9200
  (Mfr switches, keyboards, etc)

(cont)

Cherry S.A.R.L., 1 Ave. des Violettes, Z. A. de Petits Carreaus,
94384 Bonneuil sur Marne Cedex, France

CHESEBROUGH-POND'S INC   33 Benedict Place, Greenwich, CT 06830,
Tel: (203) 661-2000
(Cosmetics, consumer prdts)
Societe Francaise de Distribtion SA, Bis Rue Jean Mermoz, B.P. 751-08, Cedex 08,
75367 Paris, France

CHEVRON CHEMICAL CO   PO Box 5047, San Ramon, CA 94583-0947,
Tel: (415) 842-5500
(Chemicals)
Orogil S.A., 47 rue de Villiers, 92527 Neuilly-sur-Seine, France
Petrosynthese S.A., 47 rue de Villiers, 92527 Neuilly-sur-Seine, France

CHRISTENSEN INTL   PO Box 26135, Salt Lake City, UT 84126, Tel: (801) 487-5371
(Diamond drills)
Christensen Diamond Products Co. (France), Place de la Gare, 78320 La Vierre, France
Christensen Diamond Products Co. (France), Rue Joseph Marie Jacquart,
Zone Industrielle, 64140 Billere, France

CHRISTIAN SCIENCE PUBLISHING SOCIETY   1 Norway St, Boston, MA 02115,
Tel: (617) 262-2300
(Publishing)
Christian Science Committee on Publication or France, 7 Blvd. Flandrin,
75016 Paris, France
The Christian Science Monitor Journal, 4 Rue Castiglione, 75001 Paris, France

THE CHUBB CORP   15 Mountain View Rd, Warren, NJ 07060, Tel: (201) 580-2000
(Holding co: property/casualty ins)
Chubb Insurance Co. of Europe, France

CIGNA CORP   One Liberty Place, 1650 Market St, Philadelphia, PA 19101,
Tel: (215) 523-4000
(Ins, invest, health care & other fin servs)
Cigna France Compagnie D'Assurances, 5 Rue de Turin, 75008 Paris, France
Cigna Insurance Co. of Europe SA-NV, 17 Rue Ballu, F-75008 Paris, France
Cigna Sicav I, 5 Rue de Turin, 75008 Paris, France
Esis Intl., Inc., 5 Rue Kleber, F-93100 Montreuil-Sous-Bois, France
La Nouvelle SA, 14 Rue Ballu, 75009 Paris, France

CINCOM SYSTEMS INC   2300 Montana Ave, Cincinnati, OH 45211,
Tel: (513) 662-2300
(Computer software)
Cincom Systems France SARL, Ilot Des Mariniers, 208 Rue Raymond Losserand,
75680 Paris Cedex 14, France

CITIBANK NA   399 Park Ave, New York, NY 10043, Tel: (212) 559-1000
(Intl banking)
First National City Bank, 60 Ave. des Champs Elysees, 75008 Paris, France

CLARKSON INDUSTRIES INC   30 Buxton Farm Rd, Stamford, CT 06905-1206,
Tel: (203) 322-3990
(Mfr centrifugal blowers, compressors, handling equip)
Hoffmaan Air & Filtration Systems SARL, 179 Ave. Ledru Rollin, Paris, France

CLEARY GOTTLIEB STEEN & HAMILTON   1 State Street Plaza, New York, NY 10004,
  Tel: (212) 344-0600
  (Law firm)
    Cleary, Gottlieb, Steen, & Hamilton, 41 Ave. de Friedland, 75008 Paris, France

CLIMAX MOLYBDENUM CORP   One Greenwich Plaza, Greenwich, CT 06830,
  Tel: (203) 629-6400
  (Molybdenum, tungsten)
    Climax Molybdenum SA, 61 Ave. Victor Hugo, 75116 Paris, France

COBE LABORATORIES INC   1185 Oak St, Lakewood, CO 80215, Tel: (303) 232-6800
  (Mfr med equip & supplies)
    COBE France, 8 Rue des Pyrenees, Silic 513, 94623 Rungis Cedex, France

COLE BUSINESS FURNITURE CO   640 Whiteford Rd, PO Box M-26, York, PA 17405,
  Tel: (717) 854-1545
  (Mfr office furniture)
    ATAL Div. of Joyce Intl., 7 Rue Mariotte 75017, Paris, France

COLGATE-PALMOLIVE CO   300 Park Ave, New York, NY 10022, Tel: (212) 310-2000
  (Pharms, cosmetics, toiletries, detergents)
    Colgate Palmolive, 55 Blvd. de la Mission Marchand, 92401 Courbevoie, France
    Ets. Barbier Dauphin, Route Nationale 96, 13650 Meyrargues, France

COLLOIDS INC   394-400 Frelinghuysen Ave, Newark, NJ 07114,
  Tel: (201) 926-6100
  (Chem prdts)
    Bevaloid SA, 215 Rue de Charenton, 75012 Paris, France

COLT INDUSTRIES INC   430 Park Ave, New York, NY 10022, Tel: (212) 940-0400
  (Pumps, water sys, engines, motor arms, etc)
    Chromex SA, 2 Rue Tirebarbe, 91510 Lardy, France
    Liard SA, 49 Route National, 59570 Bavay, France

COLUMBIA PICTURES INDUSTRIES INC   711 Fifth Ave, New York, NY 10022,
  Tel: (212) 751-4400
  (Producer & distributor of motion pictures)
    Warner Columbia Films, 20 Rue Troyon, 75017 Paris, France

COMBUSTION ENGINEERING INC   900 Long Ridge Road, Stamford, CT 06902,
  Tel: (203) 329-8771
  (Tech constr)
    Combustion Engineering France Europe, SARL, F. 92085 Paris, La Defense Tour,
      Winterthur Cedex 18, France
    Gray Tool Company (Europe) Ltd., 44 Rue Pierre Curle,
      Zone Industrielle les Gatines, Plaisir 78370, France

COMDISCO INC   6400 Shafer Ct, Rosemont, IL 60018, Tel: (708) 698-3000
  (Remarketer used computer equip)
    Comdisco, France SA, Centre d'Affaires, Le Louvre, 2 Place   du Palais Royal,
      75044 Paris Cedex 1, France

COMMERCIAL INTERTECH CORP   1775 Logan Ave, Youngstown, OH 44501,
  Tel: (216) 746-8011
  (Mfr hydraulic com, metal stampings, pre-engr metal bldgs, fluid purification prdts)
    Cuno Europe S.A., 1 Boulevard de L'Oise, 95030 Cergy Pontoise Cedes, France

COMPTON INTERNATIONAL   625 Madison Ave, New York, NY 10022,
  Tel: (212) 754-1100
  (Advertising)
    Dupuy Compton & Associes, 30 Blvd. Vital-Bouhot, 92200 Neuilly-Sur-Seine, France

COMPUGRAPHIC CORP   200 Ballardvale St, Wilmington, MA 01887,
  Tel: (617) 658-5600
  (Mfr computerized composition & typesetting sys)
    Compugraphic Europe & Co., Tour Neptune, Cedex 20, 92086 Paris La Defense, France
    Compugraphic France SA, B.P. 30, 78142 Velizy-Villacoublay Cedex, France

COMPUTER ASSOCIATES INTL INC   711 Stewart Ave, Garden City, NY 11530,
  Tel: (516) 227-3300
  (Devel/mkt/mgt info mgt & bus applications software)
    Computer Associates SA, 14 Avenue Francois Arago, BP 313, 92003 Nanterre Cedex,
      France

COMPUTERVISION CORP   201 Burlington Rd, Bedford, MA 01730,
  Tel: (617) 275-1800
  (Automation sys, semiconductors)
    Computervision SA, 36 Ave. Gallieni, 93170 Bagnolet, France
    Computervision SA, 34 Rue Des Trembles, 38100 Grenoble, France

CONDE NAST PUBLICATIONS INC   350 Madison Ave, New York, NY 10017,
  Tel: (212) 880-8800
  (Publ)
    Les Editions Conde Nast SA, 4 Place de Palais Bourbon, 75007 Paris, France

CONOCO INC   600 N Dairy Ashford Rd, Houston, TX 77079, Tel: (713) 293-1000
  (Oil, gas, coal, chems, minerals)
    Continental Oil Co. of Niger, 17 Ave. Matignon, 75008 Paris, France

CONSTRUCTION SPECIALTIES INC   55 Winans Ave, Cranford, NJ 07016,
  Tel: (201) 272-5200
  (Aluminum architectural prdts)
    Steel et Cie. S.A., B.P. 4, Route de Fourges, Gasny, France

CONTINENTAL BANK NA   231 S Lasalle St, Chicago, IL 60697, Tel: (312) 828-2345
  (Coml banking servs)
    Continental Bank Corp., 20 Rue de la Ville-L'Eveque, 75008 Paris, France

THE CONTINUUM CO INC   9500 Arboretum Blvd, Austin, TX 78759,
  Tel: (512) 345-5700
  (Design & mkt software for life ins industry)
    Continuum France, 15-17 Rue Auber, 75009 Paris, France

CONTROL DATA CORP   8100 34th Ave S, Minneapolis, MN 55440,
  Tel: (612) 853-8100
  (Control data equip, computer sys serv & financial serv)
    Control Data France SA, Tour Gamma A, 195 Rue de Bercy, Cedex 12, 75582 Paris,
      France
    Electrofact SA, 11 Rue Joseph Bouchayer, Grenoble, France 38100

COOPERTOOLS   PO Box 30100, Raleigh, NC 27622, Tel: (919) 781-7200
  (Mfr hand tools)
    Groupe Cooper, 4 Ave. des Coquelicots, 94385 Bonneuil sur Marne, France

COPPERWELD CORP   2 Oliver Plaza, Pittsburgh, PA 15222, Tel: (412) 263-3200
(Copper & steel ingots, wire, cable, tubing)
   Imetal, Tour Maine Montparnasse, 33 Ave. du Maine, 75755 Paris, France

CORE INDUSTRIES INC   PO Box 2000, Bloomfield Hills, MI 48013,
Tel: (313) 642-3400
(Electronics, agric equip, fluid controls, vehicle & constr prtds)
   Amlam Electronique SA, B.P. 84, 2 Ave. de Courtaboeuf, 91943 Les Ullis, France

CORESTATES FINANCIAL CORP   PO Box 7618, Philadelphia, PA 19101,
Tel: (215) 973-3100
(Banking)
   Philadelphia National Bank, 231 Rue Saint Honore, 75001 Paris, France

CORNING CORP   Houghton Park, PO Box 2000, Corning, NY 14831,
Tel: (617) 974-9000
(Mfr glass, ceramic materials)
   Corning France S.A., 44 Ave. de Valvins, B.P. 61, 77211 Avon Cedex, France

COTY INC   235 W 42nd St, New York, NY 10017, Tel: (212) 573-2500
(Fragrance, cosmetics & beauty treatments)
   Coty Div. de Pfizer France, 86 Rue de Paris, 91 101 ORSA 7 Cedex, France

COULTER ELECTRONICS INC   590 W 20th St, Hialeah, FL 33010,
Tel: (305) 885-0131
(Blood cell & particle counters)
   Coultronics France SA, 14 Rue Eugene Legendre-Margency, 95580 Andilly, France

CPC INTERNATIONAL INC   PO Box 8000, International Plaza, Englewood Cliffs,
NJ 07632, Tel: (201) 894-4000
(Mfr consumer food prdts & corn refining prdts)
   CPC France S.A., 379 Ave. du General de Gaulle, 92142 Clamart, France

JOHN CRANE INC   6400 Oakton St, Morton Grove, IL 60053, Tel: (708) 967-2400
(Mfr engineering seals)
   Ropac-John Crane, 15 rue Laterale, 92400 Courbevoie, France

CROWN CORK & SEAL CO INC   Holmesburg Station, PO Box 6208, Philadelphia,
PA 19136, Tel: (215) 698-5100
(Cans, bottle caps; filling & packaging mach)
   Emballages Couronne SA, Crown Cork Co. France, B.P. 1, 91170 Viry Chatillon, France

CULLIGAN INTL CO   One Culligan Parkway, Northbrook, IL 60062,
Tel: (708) 205-6000
(Water treatment prdts & serv)
   Culligan France SA, 4 Ave. du President Kennedy, 78340 Les Clayes sous Bois,
      Yvelines, France

CUMMINS ENGINE CO INC   PO Box 3005, Columbus, IN 47202, Tel: (812) 377-5000
(Mfr diesel engines)
   Cummins Diesel Sales Corp., 39 Rue Ampere, ZI, 69680 Chassieu, France

CURTISS-WRIGHT CORP   1200 Wall St, W Lyndhurst, NJ 07071, Tel: (201) 896-8400
(Aircraft engines)
   Door-Oliver (France) SARL, Paris France

CXR TELCOM CORP   521 Charcot Ave, San Jose, CA 95131, Tel: (408) 263-8520
(Mfr datacom test instru, trans prdts, telecom test sys)
   CXR S.A., Gentilly, France

D'ARCY MASIUS BENTON & BOWLES INC (DMB&B)   1675 Broadway, New York,
NY 10019, Tel: (212) 468-3622
(Advertising & communications)
   DMB&B, 10 Boulevard du Parc, 92521 Neuilly Cedex, France

D-M-E COMPANY   29111 Stephenson Highway, Madison Heights, MI 48071,
Tel: (313) 398-6000
(Basic tooling for plastic molding & die casting)
   DME France SARL, Blvd. Foch 10, F. 93800 Epinay Sur Seine, France

DAMES & MOORE   911 Wilshire Blvd, Los Angeles, CA 90017, Tel: (213) 683-1560
(Consulting engineers)
   Dames & Moore, 2 Rue de Marly-le-Roi, 78150 Le Chesnay, France

DANCER FITZGERALD SAMPLE INTL   405 Lexington Ave, New York, NY 10174,
Tel: (212) 661-0800
(Advertising agency)
   Bazaine DFS, 59 Blvd. Exelmans, 75016 Paris, France

DATA GENERAL CORP   4400 Computer Dr, Westboro, MA 01580, Tel: (617) 366-8911
(Design, mfr gen purpose computer sys & peripheral prdts & servs)
   Data General Europe Inc., Tour Manhattan, 5/6 Place de l'Iris, 92095 Paris, France

DATA MEASUREMENT CORP   15884 Gaither Dr, Gaithersburg, MD 20877,
Tel: (301) 948-2450
(Mfr quality/process control gauges)
   DMC France, SARL, 1 Parc de Diane, BP 30, 78354 Jouyen Josas Cedex, France

DATAEASE INTL INC   7 Cambridge Dr, Trumbull, CT 06611, Tel: (203) 374-8000
(Mfr applications devel software)
   Microformatic, 2 Rue Navoisaau, 93100 Montreuil Sous Bois, France

DATAGRAPHIX INC   PO Box 82449, San Diego, CA 92138, Tel: (714) 291-9960
(Mfr electronic computing equip)
   Datagraphix SARL, 72-74 Quai de la Loire, 75019 Paris, France

DATAPRODUCTS CORP   6200 Canada Ave, PO Box 746, Woodland Hills, CA 91365,
Tel: (818) 887-8000
(Mfr computer printers & supplies)
   Dataproducts S.A.R.L., Zone d'Activites, Ave. de la Republique, E 420,
   91374 Verrieres le

DATASCOPE CORP   14 Philips Pkwy, Montvale, NJ 07645, Tel: (201) 391-8100
(Mfr medical devices)
   Datascope SARL, Paris, France
   InterVascular S.A., La Ciotat, France
   InterVascular SARL, Paris, France

DAVIS POLK & WARDWELL   1 Chase Manhattan Plaza, New York, NY 10005,
Tel: (212) 530-4000
(Law firm)
   Davis Polk & Wardwell, 4 Place de la Concorde, 75008 Paris, France

DAYTON-WALTHER CORP   PO Box 1022, Dayton, OH 45401, Tel: (513) 296-3113
  (Mfr heavy duty components for truck/trailer chassis)
    Dayton-Est SARL, Chassey-Les-Scey, 70170 Port-Sur-Saone, France
    Fiday SA, Rue Anatole France, 70300 Luxeuil, France

DDB NEEDHAM WORLDWIDE INC   437 Madison Ave, New York, NY 10022,
  Tel: (212) 415-2000
  (Advertising)
    DDB Needham Worldwide Inc., 12/14 Rue Mederic, 75849 Paris Cedex 17, France
    DDB Needham Worldwide SA, 12/14 Rue Mederic, 75849 Paris Cedex 17, France

DE VILBISS CO   300 Phillips Ave, Toledo, OH 43612, Tel: (419) 470-2169
  (Mfr spray painting & finishing equip)
    Toussaint de Vilbiss & Cie., 163-171 Ave. des Aureats, Paris, France

DEBEVOISE & PLIMPTON   875 3rd Ave, New York, NY 10022, Tel: (212) 909-6000
  (Law firm)
    Debevoise & Plimpton, 12 Ave. d'Eylau, 75116 Paris, France

DEERE & CO   John Deere Rd, Moline, IL 61265, Tel: (309) 752-8000
  (Mfr/sale agri/constr/utility/forestry & lawn/grounds care equip)
    John Deere France, 10 Rue du Paradis, 45140 St. Jean de la Ruelle Cedex, Ormes,
      France

DEKALB PLANT GENETICS   3100 Sycamore Rd, DeKalb, IL 60115,
  Tel: (815) 753-7333
  (Mfr/genetic res of hybrid corn, sorghum, sunflowers & soybeans)
    SocKalb G.E.E., Siege Social: 18 Rue de Seguret Saincric, 12003 Rodez, France

DEKALB-PFIZER GENETICS   3100 Sycamore Rd, De Kalb, IL 60115,
  Tel: (815) 756-7333
  (Agric seeds)
    Sockalb, Siege Social, 18 Rue de Seguret Saincric, B.P. 326, 12003 Rodez, France

DELL COMPUTER CORP   9505 Arboretum Blvd, Austin, TX 78759,
  Tel: (512) 338-4400
  (Design/mfr personal computers)
    Dell Computer SA, Rue Helene Boucher BP 285, 78053 St. Quentin en Yvelines, Cedex,
      France

DENNISON MFG CO   300 Howard St, Framingham, MA 01701, Tel: (617) 879-0511
  (Paper prdts & office supplies)
    Doret SA, B.P. 23, 8 Rue Montgoltier, 93115 Rosny sous Bols, France

DENTSPLY INTL INC   PO Box 872, York, PA 17405, Tel: (717) 845-7511
  (Mfr dental, medical & ind supplies & equip)
    De Trey Dentsply S.A., 72 Rue de General-Leclerc, 92270 Bois-Colombes, France

DEUTSCH CO   2444 Wilshire Blvd, Santa Monica, CA 90403, Tel: (213) 453-0055
  (Electr components)
    Compagne Deutsch, 10 Rue Lionelterray, 92500 Rueil Malmaison, France

DEVCON CORP   30 Endicott St, Danvers, MA 01923, Tel: (617) 777-1100
  (Mfr filled epoxies, urethanes, adhesives & metal treatment prdts)
    Devcon France SARL, 22 Rue Paul Langevin, 75002 Herblay, France

DHJ INDUSTRIES INC   1040 Ave of the Americas, New York, NY 10018,
   Tel: (212) 944-4500
   (Mfr of knit fabrics, interlinings plastic chips & denim)
      DHJ Ind. Europe SA, 4 Rue Frederic Meyer, 67600 Selestat, France
      DHJ Industries Europe, 92 Tourfiat, Cedex 16, 92084 Paris La Defense, France
      Swift Textiles SA, 29 Rue d'Artois, 75008 Paris, France

THE DIEBOLD GROUP INC   475 Park Ave South, New York, NY 10016,
   Tel: (212) 684-4700
   (Mgmt consultants: info tech)
      Diebold France SA, Puteaux, France (all mail to New York address)

DIGITAL EQUIPMENT CORP   129 Parker St, Maynard, MA 01754, Tel: (617) 897-5111
   (Digital computers, digital circuit modules, memory elec- tronic system)
      Digital Equipment France, 18 Rue Saarinen, Cedex L 225, F. 94528 Rungis, France

WALT DISNEY PRODUCTIONS   500 S Buena Vista St, Burbank, CA 91521,
   Tel: (818) 560-1000
   (Film/TV prod, amusement parks, land mgmt)
      Walt Disney Productions (France) SA, 52 Ave. des Champs-Elysees, 75008 Paris, France

DONALDSON CO INC   PO Box 1299, Minneapolis, MN 55440, Tel: (612) 887-3131
   (Filtration prdts & sys)
      Donaldson France SA, 4 Bis Rue Maryse Bastie, 69500 Bron, France

DONALDSON LUFKIN & JENRETTE INC   140 Broadway, New York, NY 10005,
   Tel: (212) 504-3000
   (Investment mgmt)
      Donaldson Lufkin & Jenrette Inc., 42 Ave. Montaigne, 75008 Paris, France

DONOVAN LEISURE NEWTON & IRVINE   30 Rockefeller Plaza, New York, NY 10112,
   Tel: (212) 489-4100
   (Lawyers)
      Donovan Leisure Newton & Irvine, 130 Rue du Faubourg St. Honore, 75008 Paris, France

DORR-OLIVER INC   612 Wheeler's Farm Rd, PO Box 3819, Milford, CT 06460,
   Tel: (203) 876-5400
   (Mfr process equip for food, pulp & paper, mineral & chem ind; & municipal/ind waste
   treatment)
      Dorr-Oliver SARL, France, Tour Neptune, 92086 Paris La Defense, Cedex 20, France

DOUBLEDAY & CO INC   245 Park Ave, New York, NY 10167, Tel: (212) 953-4561
   (Book publ)
      Doubleday France SARL, 9 Rue du Pre aux Clercs, 75007 Paris, France

DOW CHEMICAL CO   2030 Dow Center, Midland, MI 48640, Tel: (517) 636-1000
   (Chems, plastics, fibers, pharms)
      Dow Chemical France, 64 Rue du Ranelagh, 75016 Paris, France

DOW CORNING CORP   2220 W Salzburg Rd, PO Box 1767, Midland, MI 48640,
   Tel: (517) 496-4000
   (Silicones, silicon chems, solid lubricants)
      Dow Corning SARL, Bureau du Parc, 36-38 Rue de la Princesse, 78430 Lou Viciennes,
      France

DOWNER & CO   695 Atlantic Ave, Boston, MA   02111, Tel: (617) 482-6200
(Investment banking)
   Downer et Cie., 12 Rue de Castiglione, 75001 Paris, France

DRAKE BEAM MORIN INC   100 Park Ave, New York, NY   10017, Tel: (212) 692-7700
(Human resource mgmt consulting & training)
   Drake Beam Morin Europe Inc., 26 Rue de Berri, 75008 Paris, France
   Drake Beam Morin Europe Inc., 99 Rue Nationale, 59800 Lille, France
   Drake Beam Morin Europe Inc., Tour Credit Lyonnais, 69431 Lyon, France
   Drake Beam Morin Europe Inc., 15 Quai Ernest Renaud, 44053 Nantes, France
   Drake Beam Morin Europe Inc., 1 Rue Jacques Duclos, St. Quentin en Yvelnes,
      F-78280 Guyancourt, France

DREW CHEMICAL CORP   One Drew Plaza, Boonton, NJ   07005, Tel: (201) 263-7600
(Spec chems for ind water & fuel treatment, chem processing)
   Drew Ameroid France, c/o Ashland Ave. Bene le Goulet, 27920 St. Pierre,
      de Bailleul, France

DREXEL BURNHAM LAMBERT INC   60 Broad St, New York, NY   10004,
   Tel: (212) 232-5000
(Commission stockbrockers & underwriters)
   Drexel Burnham & CO. SARlL, 17 Ave. George V, 2nd Floor, 75008 Paris, France

L A DREYFUS CO   PO Box 500, South Plainfield, NJ   07080, Tel: (201) 549-1600
(Mfr of chewing gum)
   L.A. Dreyfus Co., Boite Postale 29, 68600 Neuf Brisach, France

DRIVER-HARRIS CO   308 Middlesex St, Harrison, NJ   07029, Tel: (201) 483-4800
(Wire, cables, etc)
   Driver Harris International, Tour Albert 1er, 65 Ave. de France,
      92507 Rueil Malmaison, France
   Driver Harris SA, Rue de Buchelay, 78200 Mantes la Jolie, France
   Resistelec, 232 Rue Paul Bert, 69003 Lyon, France

DU BOIS INTL INC   1100 DuBois Tower, Cincinnati, OH   45202,
   Tel: (513) 762-6000
(Mfr spec chems & maintenance prdts)
   DuBois Chimie SARL, Z.I. du Petit Parc, Rue des Fontenelles, B.P. 7,
      78920 Ecquevilly, France

E I DU PONT DE NEMOURS & CO   Du Pont Bldg, 1007 Market St, Wilmington,
   DE   19898, Tel: (302) 774-1000
(Mfr/sale diversified chems, plastics, specialty prdts & fibers)
   Du Pont de Nemours (France) S.A., France

EASTMAN & BEAUDINE INC   111 W Monroe, Chicago, IL   60603, Tel: (312) 726-8195
(Investments)
   Eastman & Beaudine Inc., 3 Rue de Penthievre, 75008 Paris, France

EASTMAN KODAK CO   343 State St, Rochester, NY   14650-0518, Tel: (716) 724-4000
(Devel/mfr photo & chem prdts, info mgmt/video/copier sys, fibers/plastics for
various ind)
   Kodak Pathe, 8-26 Rue Villiot, 75594 Paris, Cedex 12, France

EATON CORP   100 Erieview Plaza, Cleveland, OH   44114, Tel: (216) 523-5000
(Advanced tech prdts for transp & ind mkts)
   Cutler-Hammer, Europe (Continental), Paris, France

(cont)

Cutler-Hammer, Europe (Continental), Bethime, France
Eaton SA, Zone Industrial de Brais, Saint Nazaire, Loire Atlantique, France

EG&G INC   45 William St, Wellesley, MA 02181, Tel: (617) 237-5100
(Diversified instru, components, services)
EG&G Instruments Div., ZI Petite Montagne Nord, 2 Place de la Vanoise,
91020 Evry Cedex, France
EG&G LMB, 36 Ave. Marie et Pierre Curie, Malemort sur Correze, France
EG&G Sealol S.A.R.L., 18 Rue des Osiers, BP 54, Coignieres, 78314 Maurepas Cedex,
France

ELECTRIC FURNACE CO   435 Wilson St, Salem, OH 44460, Tel: (216) 332-4661
(Design & mfr heat treating furnaces for metals ind)
Electric Furnace (France) SARL, 32 Place St. Georges, 75009 Paris, France

ELECTRO-NITE CO   11601 Caroline Rd, Philadelphia, PA 19154,
Tel: (215) 464-4200
(Expendable sensors & instru for iron & steel ind)
Electro-Nite France SARL, Beau Vallon a Illange, B.P. 25, 57110 Yutz, France

ELECTRONIC ASSOCIATES INC   185 Monmouth Park Hwy, West Long Branch,
NJ 07764, Tel: (201) 229-1100
(Analog/hybrid computers, training simulators, energy measurement sys)
Electronic Associates SARL, 25-27 Rue Ginoux, Cedex 15, F. 75737 Paris, France

ELIZABETH ARDEN INC   55 East 52nd St, New York, NY 10055-0191,
Tel: (212) 407-1000
(Cosmetics, fragrances, toiletries)
SA des Etablissements Elizabeth Arden, 78 Ave. des Champs Elysees, 75008 Paris,
France
SA des Etablissements Elizabeth Arden, Parfums Lagerfeld SAR, 3 rue Edmond Poillet,
29011 Chartres, France

EMCO WHEATON INC   50 Chamberlain Blvd, PO Box 688, Conneaut, OH 44030,
Tel: (216) 599-8151
(Mfr petroleum handling equip- ment)
Emco Wheaton SA, Grue Paul Appell, Parc Moderne, D'Enterprises, Saint Duen,
L'Aumone, France

ENCYCLOPEDIA BRITANNICA INC   425 N Michigan Ave, Chicago, IL 60611,
Tel: (312) 321-7000
(Book publ)
Encyclopaedia Britannica (France) Ltd., Tour Maine Montparnasse, 33 Ave. du Malne,
F. 75755 Paris, France
Encyclopaedia Universales, 110 Rue Vercingetorix, Cedex 14, 75680 Paris, France

ENERPAC   13000 W Silver Spring Dr, Butler, WI 53007, Tel: (414) 781-6600
(Mfr/sale high pressure hydraulic maint tools)
Enerpac, B.P. 200, 91882 Massy Cedes, France

ENGELHARD CORP   Menlo Park, CN 40, Edison, NJ 08818, Tel: (201) 632-6000
(Mfr spec chem prdts & engineered materials for ind; precious metal mgmt serv)
Engelhard SA, 4 Rue Beaubourg, 75004 Paris, France

ENVIROTECH CORP   3000 Sand Hill Road, Menlo Park, CA 94025,
Tel: (415) 854-2000
(Supplier of equip & tech for underground mining, ind processing & pollution control)

Eimco France, 2 Rue de Clichy, 95009 Paris, France
Envirotech Europe, 2 Rue de Clichy, 95009 Paris, France.
Esmil Envirotech SA, 2 Rue de Clichy, 95009 Paris, France
Secoma France, Ave. de Lattre de Tassigny, 69330 Meyzieu, France

A EPSTEIN & SONS INTL INC   600 W Fulton St, Chicago, IL 60606-1199,
  Tel: (312) 454-9100
  (Engr, arch, constr & devel)
    A. Epstein & Sons (France) Inc., Tour Pariferic, 93306 Aubervilliers Cedex, France

EPSTEIN ENGINEERING EXPORT LTD   600 W Fulton St, Chicago, IL 60606-1199,
  Tel: (312) 454-9100
  (Engr & constr)
    A. Epstein & Sons (Paris) Inc., Tour Pariferic, 6 Rue Emile Reynaud,
      93306 Paris Aubervilliers Cedex, France

ERC ENVIRONMENTAL & ENERGY SERVICES CO   3211 Jermantown Rd, Fairfax,
  VA 22053, Tel: (703) 246-0500
  (Engr & conslt serv for energy, envi, & infrastructure engr mkts)
    Evaluations Recherches Conseils, 20 Rue du Faubourg Saint Honore, 75008 Paris,
      France

ERICO PRODUCTS INC   34600 Solon Road, Cleveland, OH 44139,
  Tel: (216) 248-0100
  (Mfr electric welding apparatus & hardware, metal stampings, specialty fasteners)
    Erico France SARL, B.P. 31, Rue Benoit, Fourneyron, One Industrielle Sud,
      42160 Andrezieux-Boutheon, France

ESCO CORP   2141 NW 25th Ave, Portland, OR 97210, Tel: (503) 228-2141
  (Mfr equip for mining, constr, forestry ind)
    Esco SA, B.P. 229, Cedex, 69803 Saint-Priest, France

ESTERLINE CORP   10800 NE 8th St, #600, Bellevue, WA 98004,
  Tel: (206) 453-6001
  (Mfr equip & instru for ind automation, precision meas, data acquisition)
    Auxitrol S.A., 1 rue d'Anjou, BP 241, 92603 Asnieres, France

EXXON CORP   225 E John Carpenter Frwy, Irving, TX 75062, Tel: (214) 444-1000
  (Petroleum & petroleum prdts)
    Esso Standard SA, 6 Ave. Andre Prothin, 92 Courbervoie, France
    SARA/SA, 5 Rue Michel Ange, Cedex 16, 75781 Paris, France
    Societe du Caoutchouc Butyl (Socabu), Cedex 2, 92080 Paris La Defense, France

FAFNIR BEARING CO   37 Booth St, New Britain, CT 06050, Tel: (203) 225-5151
  (Ball bearings)
    Fafnir Roulements Div. of Textron, Atlantic SARL, 1 Rue Jean Perrin,
      93150 Le Blanc-Mesnil, France

FAIRCHILD CAMERA & INSTRUMENT CORP   PO Box 58090, Santa Clara,
  CA 95052-8090, Tel: (408) 743-3355
  (Mfr electr instru & controls)
    Fairchild Semiconducteurs SA, 121 Ave. d'Italie, 75013 Paris, France

FEDERAL EXPRESS CORP   PO Box 727, Memphis, TN 38194-4212, Tel: (901) 922-6900
  (Package air express svc)
    Federal Express (France) SARL, 44/46 Ave. du 8 Mai 1945,
      92390 Villeneuve la Garenne, France

FEDERAL-MOGUL CORP   PO Box 1966, Detroit, MI 48235, Tel: (313) 354-7700
   (Mfr/distr vehicular & ind components for original market & aftermarket)
      Federal Mogul France S.A., P.O. Box 39, 45141 St. Jean de la Ruelle Cedex, France

FELTON INTERNATIONAL INC   599 Johnson Ave, Brooklyn, NY 11237,
   Tel: (212) 497-4664
   (Essential oils & extracts, perfumes & flavor material, aromatic chems)
      Felton Co. France SARL, 34/34 Bis Rue de L'Ermitage, 78000 Versailles, France

FERRO CORPORATION   One Erieview Plaza, Cleveland, OH 44114,
   Tel: (216) 641-8580
   (Chems, coatings, plastics, refractories)
      Alsthom-Ferro Composites (France) S.A., Les Mercuriales, 40 Ave. Jean Jaures,
         93176 Bagnolet Cedex, France
      Eurostar S.A., Zone Industrielle, Rue de la Ferme St-Ladre, B.P. 2, 95470 Fosses,
         France
      Ferro Chemicals S.A., Etang de la Gafette, B.P. 28, 13521 Port-de-Bouc Cedex, France
      SARL Procedes Ferro, 43 Rue Jeanne d'Arc 52100, B.P. 23, 52101 Saint Dizier, France

FINNIGAN CORP   355 River Oaks Parkway, San Jose, CA 95134-1991,
   Tel: (408) 433-4800
   (Mfr mass spectrometers, data handling sys, methodology devel)
      Finnigan MAT SARL, Parc Club Orsay Universite, 2 rue J. Monod, F-91893 Orsay Cedex,
         France

FIRST NATIONAL BANK OF BOSTON   100 Federal St, Boston, MA 02110,
   Tel: (617) 434-2200
   (Commercial banking)
      First National Bank of Boston, 104 Ave. des Champs Elysees, 75008 Paris, France

FISCHER & PORTER CO   125 E County Line Rd, Warminster, PA 18974,
   Tel: (215) 674-6000
   (Design/mfr meas, recording & control instru & sys; mfr ind glass prdts)
      Otic Fischer & Porter, 151 bis, Ave. de la Liberation, 63000 Clermont-Ferrand,
         France

FISHER CONTROLS INTL INC   8000 Maryland Ave, Clayton, MO 63105,
   Tel: (314) 694-9900
   (Ind process control equip)
      Fisher Controls SA, Rue Paul Baudry, B.P. 10, 68700 Cernay, France
      Fisher Controls SA, Rue de la Tour, Abrest, B.P. 24, 03202 Vichy, France

FISHER-PRICE   636 Girard Ave, East Aurora, NY 14052, Tel: (716) 687-3000
   (Mfr toys & games)
      Fisher-Price SARL, B.P. 20, 45801 Saint Jean de Braye, France

FLYING TIGER LINE INC   7401 World Way W, Los Angeles, CA 90009,
   Tel: (213) 646-6161
   (Air frt carrier, air cargo service worldwide)
      Flying Tiger Inc. France, B.P. 95705, Roissy-Alrport Charles de Gaulle, France

JOHN FLYNN & SONS INC   80 Boston St, Salem, MA 09070, Tel: (617) 745-4000
   (Animal skin tanning)
      Flynn France SA, B.C. 16, 81 Graulhet (Tarn) France

FMC CORP   200 E Randolph Dr, Chicago, IL 60601, Tel: (312) 861-6000
(Mach & chem for industry, agric & govt)
   FMC Food Machinery France S.A., B.P. 123, F-93602 Aulnay-sous-Bois, France

FOOTE CONE & BELDING COMMUNICATIONS INC   101 E Erie St, Chicago,
IL 60611-2897, Tel: (312) 751-7000
(Advertising agency)
   FCB Paris, 20 blvd. du Parc, Ile de la Jatte, 92521 Neuilly Cedex, France
   Manuel Noao Direct Marketing, 120 rue du Faubourg Saint-Honore, 75008 Paris, France
   Publicis Conseil, 133 ave des Champs-Elysees, 75380 Paris Cedex 08, France

FORD MOTOR CO   The American Road, Dearborn, MI 48121, Tel: (313) 322-3000
(Mfr automobiles, trucks)
   Ford France SA, 344 Ave. Napoleon Bonaparte, 92506 Rueil Malmaison, Cedex BP 307,
      France

FOSTER WHEELER CORP   Perryville Corporate Park, Clinton, NJ 08809-4000,
Tel: (201) 730-4000
(Engr, constr, mfg)
   Foster Wheeler France S.A., 31 Rue des Bourdonnais, 75021 Paris Cedex 01, France

FOUR WINDS INTL INC   1 SW Columbia Ave, #1200, Portland, OR 97258,
Tel: (503) 241-2732
(Transp of household goods & general cargo)
   Four Winds Intl., 1 bis, Rue de l'Industrie, Z.I. de Courcelles,
      95310 St. Ouen L'Aumone, France

FOXBORO CO   33 Commercial St, Foxboro, MA 02035, Tel: (508) 543-8750
(Mfr prdts/provide servs for ind automation)
   Foxbor France SA, 24 Rue du Vieux-Marche-Aux-Vins, 67000 Strasbourg, France
   Foxboro France SA, 92-98 Blvd. Victor Hugo, 92115 Clichy, France
   Foxboro France SA, Agence Rhone, Alpes et Agence Afrique,
      37 Ave. du General de Gaulle, 69300 Caluire, France
   Foxboro France SA, B.P. 741, 95004 Cergy Pontoise Cedex, France
   Foxboro France SA, Rue des Oziers, ZA du Vert Galant, 95310 Sanit Quen, l'Aumone,
      France
   Foxboro France SA, B.P. 741, 95004 Gergy Pontoise, Cedex, France

THE FRANKLIN MINT   Franklin Center, PA 19091, Tel: (215) 459-6000
(Creation/mfr/mktg collectible items)
   Le Medaillier Franklin S.A., 4 Ave. de L'Escouvrier, 95200 Sarcelles, France

FRUEHAUF TRAILER OPERATIONS   10900 Harper, Detroit, MI 48232,
Tel: (313) 267-1000
(Mfr truck trailers, cargo containers)
   S.E.S.R., 44 Rue Francois Premier, 75008 Paris, France

FULLER CO   2040 Ave C, PO Box 2040, Bethlehem, PA 18001, Tel: (215) 264-6011
(Ind processing equip & sys, conveying & blending sys, etc)
   GATX-Fuller S.A., 45-47 Rue de Villeneuve, Silic 168, 94533 Rungis-Cedex, France

H B FULLER CO   2400 Energy Park Dr, St Paul, MN 55108, Tel: (612) 645-3401
(Mfr/distr adhesives, sealants, coatings, paints, waxes, sanitation chems)
   LW-Fuller France SARL, Zone Industrielle, B.P. 12, 76580 Le Trait, France

GAF CORP   1361 Alps Rd, Wayne, NJ 07470, Tel: (201) 628-3000
   (Chems, bldg materials, commun)
      GAF (France) SA, B.P. 50007, 95945 Roissy Charles de Gaulle Cedex, France

GALVESTON-HOUSTON CO   4900 Woodway, PO Box 2207, Houston, TX 77056,
   Tel: (713) 966-2500
   (Mfr ind equip)
      Compagnie Auxiliarie Industrielle, 57-59 rue Etienne-Marcel, 93100 Montreuil, France

GAMLEN CHEMICAL CO   121 S Maple Ave, S San Francisco, CA 94080,
   Tel: (415) 873-1750
   (Chems, detergents & tank cleansers)
      Fin Arnesen & Son, 4 Rue Lafayette, Bordeaux 33300, France
      Fin Arnesen & Son, in: Brest, Dunkerque, Le Harve, Marseille, Rouen, St. Nazarene
      Gamlen Naintre SA, 2 Rue Huntziger, 92110 Clichy, France

GANNETT CO INC   1100 Wilson Blvd, Arlington, VA 22224, Tel: (703) 284-6000
   (Newspaper pub, opinion research)
      Louis Harris & Associates Inc., Paris, France

THE GATES RUBBER CO   PO Box 5887, Denver, CO 80217, Tel: (303) 744-1911
   (Mfr auto/ind belts & hose, hydraulic hose & couplings, molded rubber prdts)
      Gates France SARL, Zone Industrielle, 95380 Louvres, Paris, France

GATJE PAPACHRISTOU SMITH ARCHITECTS   114 Fifth Ave, New York, NY 10011,
   Tel: (212) 807-7373
   (Architecture, planning, int design)
      MBA Architects, 52 Rue Lhomond, 75005 Paris, France

GATX CORP   120 S Riverside Plaza, Chicago, IL 60606, Tel: (312) 621-6200
   (Railcar leasing, maint & mgmt, bulk liquid storage, fin serv, shipping, mineral
   processing)
      GATX Fuller SA, 45-47 Rue de Villeneuve, 94533 Rungis, Cedex, France

GCA CORP   7 Shattuck Rd, Andover, MA 01810, Tel: (508) 837-3000
   (Mfr imaging sys for semiconductor ind)
      General Signal SEG France, 13 Chemin du Levant, 01210 Ferney-Voltaire, France

GELMAN SCIENCES INC   600 South Wagner St, Ann Arbor, MI 48106,
   Tel: (313) 665-0651
   (Laboratory prdts)
      Gelman Sciences S.A., 108 Rue Auguste Vallaud, 77420 Champs sur Marne, France

GENERAL AUTOMATION INC   1055 S East St, Anaheim, CA 92806,
   Tel: (714) 778-4800
   (Computer hardware & serv)
      General Automation SA, Tour Gallieni 11, 36 Ave. Gallieni F. 93170, Bagnolet, France

GENERAL BINDING CORP   One GBC Plaza, Northbrook, IL 60062,
   Tel: (708) 272-3700
   (Binding & laminating equip & associated supplies)
      GBC France, 44 Rue Maurice de Broglie, Z.A.C. Les Mardelles,
         93602 Aulnay sous Bois - Cedex, France

GENERAL DATACOMM INDUSTRIES INC   1579 Straits Turnpike, Middlebury,
   CT 06762-1299, Tel: (203) 574-1118
   (Mfr trans equip for commun networks)

General DataComm SARL, 3 Batiment Saturne, Parc Club Ariane, Rue Helene Boucher, 78284 Guyancourt Cedex, France

GENERAL ELECTRIC CO   3135 Easton Tpk, Fairfield, CT 06431,
   Tel: (203) 373-2211
   (Diversified mfr, tech & servs)
      GE Information Services, 8 Ave. Franklin Roosevelt, Paris 75008, France

GENERAL FOODS CORP   250 North St, White Plains, NY 10625, Tel: (914) 335-2500
   (Processor, distributor & mfr of foods)
      General Foods France SA, 6 Rue Lionel Terray, 92504 Rueil Malmaison, France

GENERAL INSTRUMENT CORP   767 Fifth Ave, New York, NY 10153-0082,
   Tel: (212) 207-6200
   (Electronic components & sys)
      CP Clare Electronique SARL, Z.I. de Proville, Voie d'Hermenne, B.P. 327,
         59406 Proville, Cambri, France

GENERAL MILLS INC   1 General Mills Blvd, PO Box 1113, Minneapolis, MN 55440,
   Tel: (612) 540-2311
   (Mfr consumer foods; restaurants)
      Biscuiterie Nantaise S.A., Ave. Lotz Cosse 5X, 44040 Nantes Cedex, France

GENERAL MOTORS ACCEPTANCE CORP   3044 West Grand Blvd, Detroit, MI 48202,
   Tel: (313) 556-5000
   (Automobile financing)
      Banque de Credit G.M., 29 Rue de l'Ecole Normale, B.P. 38, 33019 Bordeaux Cedex,
         France
      Banque de Credit General Motors, Tour Manhattan, Cedex 21, Paris La Defense 92095,
         France

GENERAL MOTORS CORP   3044 W Grand Blvd, Detroit, MI 48202,
   Tel: (313) 556-5000
   (Automotive prdts, electronics)
      Delco Remy Div. GM, B.P. 819, 57208 Sarreguemines, France
      Harrison Radiator Div. GM, B.P. 14 Zone Industrielle, 08350 Donchery, France
      Hydra-matic Div. GM, B.P. 33, 67026 Strasbourg Cedex, France

GENEX CORP   16020 Ind Dr, Gaithersburg, MD 20877, Tel: (301) 258-0552
   (Biotechnology research/development)
      Genex Intl. Inc., B.P. 7305, 75223 Paris Cedex 05, France

GENRAD INC   300 Baker Ave, Concord, MA 01742, Tel: (508) 369-4400
   (Mfr automatic test equip)
      Genrad, 96 rue Orfila, 75020 Paris, France

GILFORD INSTRUMENT LABS INC   132 Artino St, Oberlin, OH 44074,
   Tel: (216) 774-1041
   (Med electronic instru)
      Gilford Europe SA, B.P. 138, 91004 Evry Cedex, Paris, France

THE GILLETTE CO   Prudential Tower, Boston, MA 02199, Tel: (617) 421-7000
   (Mfr/distr shaving prdts, toiletries & cosmetics, stationery prdts)
      Gillette France, Boite Postal 26, 74010 Annecy Cedex, France

GILSON MEDICAL ELECTRONICS INC   3000 W Belt Line Hwy, PO Box 27, Middleton,
  WI 53562, Tel: (608) 836-1551
  (Mfr analytical/biomedical instru)
     Gilson Medical Electronics France SA, 72 rue Gambetta, 95400 Villiers-le-Bel, France

GK TECHNOLOGIES INC   500 W Putnam Ave, Greenwich, CT 06830,
  Tel: (203) 661-0100
  (Wire cable, electronic tech serv)
     GK Technologies France SARL, Tours, France

GLENDINNING COMPANIES INC   Glendinning Place, Westport, CT 06880,
  Tel: (203) 226-4711
  (Marketing consultants)
     C.M.P.E., 171 Ave. Charles de Gaulle, 92200 Neuilly/Seine, France

GLOBAL INTERNATIONAL   500 Ygnacio Valley Rd, #175, Walnut Creek, CA 94596,
  Tel: (415) 933-2293
  (Freight forwarding)
     Global International Forwarding, 5 Rue Keppler, 75116 Paris, France

GOODYEAR TIRE & RUBBER CO   1144 E Market St, Akron, OH 44316-0001,
  Tel: (216) 796-2121
  (Mfr tires, rubber prdts)
     Cie. Francaise Goodyear SA, B.P. 310, 92506 Rueil-Malmaison Cedex, France

GOULD INC   10 Gould Center, Rolling Meadows, IL 60008, Tel: (708) 640-4000
  (Electric sys, batteries, etc)
     Compagnie Francaise D'Electro, Chimie, Loiret, France
     Imperial Eastman, Lyon, France

W R GRACE & CO   1114 Ave of the Americas, New York, NY 10036,
  Tel: (212) 819-5500
  (Specialty chems, natural resources, consumer serv)
     Grace SARL, Zone Industrielle, Rue Saint Denis, 28230 Epernon, France
     Societe Atlantique d'Engrais Chimiques (SATEC), B.P. 160, Bayonne, France

GRACO INC   4040 Olson Memorial Hwy, PO Box 1441, Minneapolis, MN 55440-1441,
  Tel: (612) 623-6000
  (Mfr/serv fluid handling equip & sys)
     Graco France S.A., 113 Rue des Solets, Silic 141, 94523 Rungis Cedex, France

GREY ADVERTISING INC   777 Third Ave, New York, NY 10017, Tel: (212) 546-2000
  (Advertising)
     J. Van Aal Grey France, 23 Ruelinois, Cedex 15, 75724 Paris, France

GRUMMAN AEROSPACE CORP   South Oyster Bay, Bethpage, NY 11714,
  Tel: (516) 575-0575
  (Develops & produces military aircraft & spacecraft)
     Grumman International Inc., 26 Rue de la Pepiniers, 74008 Paris, France

GTE CORP   One Stamford Forum, Stamford, CT 06904, Tel: (203) 965-2000
  (Electr prdts, telecom sys, publ & commun)
     General Telephone & Electronics, Barentin, France (Plant)
     General Telephone & Electronics, in: Ivry, Lyon, Nantes, Reims, Rouen & St. Etienne

FRANK B HALL & CO INC   549 Pleasantville Rd, Briarcliff Manor, NY 10510,
Tel: (914) 769-9200
(Insurance)
  Assurances Verspieren SARL, 65 Blvd. du General de Gaulle, 59100 Roubaix, France
  Assurances Verspieren SARL, 9 Rue Buffault, 75009 Paris, France
  Frank B. Hall & Co. Overseas Inc., 4 Rue de Marignan, 75008 Paris, France

HALLMARK CARDS INC   PO Box 419580, Kansas City, MO 64141, Tel: (816) 274-5100
(Mfr greeting cards & related prdts)
  Hallmark Cards, Inc.-French Branch, Rue Eiffel, Zac De Mercieres, 60200 Compiegne,
  France

HAMLIN INC   612 E Lake St, Lake Mills, WI 53551, Tel: (414) 648-3000
(Mfr position sensors, switches, relays)
  Hamilin Electronics SARL, 9 Rue Salvador Allende, 91120 Palaiseau Z.A., France

HARCOURT BRACE JOVANOVICH INC   Harcourt Brace Jovanovich Bldg, Orlando,
FL 32887, Tel: (305) 345-2000
(Book publ, tests & related serv, journals, facisimile reprints, mgmt consult,
operates parks/shows)
  Drake Beam Morin-Europe Inc., 26 Rue de Berri, 75008 Paris, France
  Drake Beam Morin-Europe Inc., Tour Credit Lyonnais, 129 Rue Servient, 69003 Lyon,
  France
  Drake Beam Morin-Europe Inc., 92 Blvd. de Paris, 59100 Roubaix, France

THE HARPER GROUP INC   260 Townsend St, PO Box 77933, San Francisco,
CA 94107, Tel: (415) 978-0600
(Ocean/air freight fwdg, customs brokerage, packing & whse, logistics mgt, ins)
  Circle Freight Intl. France, SA, BP 10169, Roissy CDG 95702 Cedex, France

HARRIS CALORIFIC CO   2345 Murphy Blvd, Gainesville, GA 30501,
Tel: (404) 536-8801
(Mfr gas welding & cutting equip)
  Harris France SARL, 110 Ave. Jean Jaures, B.P. 24, 59880 Saint Saulve, France

HARRIS PRC INC   300 E 42nd St, New York, NY 10017, Tel: (212) 986-2700
(Engineering consultants)
  Harris-Bertin SA, c/o Societe Bertin & Cie, Allee Gabriel Voisin, B.P. 3,
  78370 Plasir, France

HARRIS-INTERTYPE CORP   55 Public Sq, Cleveland, OH 44113, Tel: (216) 771-1718
(Offset presses, cutters)
  Marinoni SA, B.P. 22, 2 Ave. Amberoise Croizat 60160, Montataire, France

HAUSERMAN INC   5711 Grant Ave, Cleveland, OH 44105, Tel: (216) 883-1400
(Steel partitions, cabinets, wall sys)
  Strafor Hauserman SA, 56 Rue Jean Geraudoux, F. 67034 Strasbourg, France

HAYNES INTL INC   1020 W Park Ave, PO Box 9013, Kokomo, IN 46904-9013,
Tel: (317) 456-6000
(Mfr cobalt & nickel-base alloys for aerospace & chem inds)
  Haynes Intl. SARL, 43 Rue de Bellevue, BP 47, 92101 Boulogne Cedex, France

HAZLETON CORP   13873 Park Center Rd, Herndon, VA 22071, Tel: (703) 478-9450
(R&D)
  Hazleton France, Les Oncins BP 118, 69210 L'Arbresle Lyon, France

HEIDRICK & STRUGGLES INC   125 S Wacker Dr, #2800, Chicago, IL 60606,
  Tel: (312) 372-8811
  (Exec search)
    Heidrick & Struggles Intl. Inc., 6 Rond-Point des Champs Elysees, Paris 75008,
    France

H J HEINZ CO   PO Box 57, Pittsburgh, PA 15230, Tel: (412) 456-5100
  (Food prdts)
    H.J. Heinz SARL, 15 Rue Erlanger, F. 75016 Paris, France

HERCULES INC   Hercules Plaza, Wilmington, DE 19894, Tel: (302) 594-5000
  (Mfr spec chems, plastics, film & fibers, coatings, resins, food ingredients)
    Hercules France SA, 3 rue Eugene et Armaud Peugeot, 92508 Rueil-Malmaison Cedex,
    France

HEWLETT-PACKARD CO   3000 Hanover St, PO Box 10301, Palo Alto, CA 94303-0890,
  Tel: (415) 857-1501
  (Mfr measurement & computation prdts & sys)
    Hewlett-Packard France, Parc d'Activites du Bois Briard, 2 Ave. du Lac,
    F-91040 Evry Cedex, France
    Hewlett-Packard France, Lyon Mfg. Systems, Parc d'Activites de Chesnes,
    57 Rue de Maiacombe, 38290 La Verpilliere, France

HEXCEL CORP   20701 Nordhoff St, Chatsworth, CA 91311, Tel: (213) 882-3022
  (Honeycomb core materials, specialty chems, resins & epoxies)
    Hexcel France, Z.I. des Bethunes, Rue de l'Equerre, 95311 Saint Quen l'Auaxne,
    France

HILL & KNOWLTON INC   420 Lexington Ave, New York, NY 10017,
  Tel: (212) 697-5600
  (Public relations, public affairs, comm counseling)
    Hill & Knowlton France, 64 Bis, Rue la Boetle, 75008 Paris, France

HILLERICH & BRADSBY CO INC   PO Box 35700, Louisville, KY 40232-5700,
  Tel: (502) 585-5226
  (Golf, baseball & softball equip)
    Hillerich & Bradsby, Fairgolf, 161 Blvd. Victor Hugo, 92110 Clichy, France

HOBART BROTHERS CO   Hobart Sq, Troy, OH 45373-2928, Tel: (513) 339-6000
  (Arc/automatic welding sys, power sys)
    Hobart Brothers Intl., B.P. 132, 01201 Bellegarde sur Valserine, France

HOLIDAY INNS INC   3742 Lamar Ave, Memphis, TN 38195, Tel: (901) 362-4001
  (Hotels, restaurants, casinos)
    Holiday Inns France, 69 Blvd. Victor, 75015 Port de Versaille, Paris, France
    Holiday Inns France, 110 Rue Jean Joures, 59810 Lesquin, Exit, Autoroute Lille,
    Paris, France
    Holiday Inns France, 4 Ave. Charles Lindberg, 94656 Rungis, Orly Airport, Paris,
    France

A J HOLLANDER & CO INC   257 Park Ave So, New York, NY 10010,
  Tel: (212) 353-8000
  (Hides, skins & leather)
    Hollander France, 10 Rue de la Boetie, 75008 Paris, France

HOMELITE TEXTRON   14401 Carowinds Blvd, Charlotte, NC 28217,
  Tel: (704) 588-3200
  (Mfr pumps, generators, lawn/garden equip, outdoor power equip)
    Homelite Textron SARL, B.P. 7011, 95050 Cercy Pontoise Cedex, France

THE HOOVER GROUP   403 W 4th St N, Newton, IA 50208, Tel: (515) 792-8000
  (Mfr floor care prdts, laundry & refrig appliances)
    SA Hoover, B.P. 9, 21600 Longvic, France

HORWATH & HORWATH INTL   919 Third Ave, New York, NY 10022,
  Tel: (212) 980-3100
  (Public accountants & auditors)
    Cabinet Cauvin Angleys Saint Pierre, 27 Cours Pierre Puget, 13006 Marseille, France
    Horwath & Horwath France, B.P. 425. 40-42 Rue du Rempart, Saint Etienne,
      31008 Toulouse, France

E F HOUGHTON & CO   PO Box 930, Valley Forge, PA 19482-0930,
  Tel: (215) 666-4000
  (Mfr spec chems, hydraulic fluids, lubricants)
    Houghton France SA, Tour Neptune, Cedex 20, 92086 Paris, France

HPD INC   1717 N Naper Blvd, Naperville, IL 60540, Tel: (708) 357-7330
  (Personal processing, recovery/ pollution control sys)
    Compagnie Industrielle, D'Evaporation et de Crystallisa (CIV,
      185 Ave. Charles de Gaulle, 92521 Neuilly-sur-Seine, Cedex, France

HUCK MFG CO   PO Box 19590, Irvine, CA 92713, Tel: (714) 855-9000
  (Mfr fasteners & fastening sys)
    Huck France, Clos D'Asseville, B.P. 4, 95450 Us, France

HUGHES AIRCRAFT CO   PO Box 45066, Los Angeles, CA 90045, Tel: (213) 568-7200
  (Aircraft & aerospace sys & equip)
    Hughes Aircraft International Service Co., 116 Rue de la Tolbiac, 75013 Paris,
      France

HUGHES HUBBARD & REED   1 Wall St, New York, NY 10005, Tel: (212) 943-6500
  (Lawyers)
    Hughes, Hubbard & Reed, 47 Ave. Georges Mandel, 75016 Paris, France

HUGHES TOOL CO   PO Box 2539, Houston, TX 77001, Tel: (713) 924-2222
  (Equip & serv to oil & gas explor & prod ind)
    Brown Oil Tools de France, 16 Rue Franklin, 75016 Paris, France
    Hughes Drill Pipe Assemble SA, 62 Rue de Leval, 59620 Aulnoye Aymeries, France
    Hughes Tool SAF, 12th Floor, Tour Neptune, Cedex 20, LaDefense 92086, Paris, France
    Hughes Tool SAF, Allee des Forges, B.P. 19, Tarbes, Cedex 65001, France

ILLINOIS TOOL WORKS INC   8501 West Higgins Rd, Chicago, IL 60631,
  Tel: (312)693-3040
  (Metal cutting tools, fasteners, sealants, gear measuring instru)
    ITW de France, 20 Rue Fizeau, 75015 Paris, France
    ITW de France, 305 Chaussee Jules Cesar, 95250 Beauchamp, France

INA CORPORATION   1600 Arch St, Philadelphia, PA 19101, Tel: (215) 523-5335
  (Holding co: ins, financial serv)
    Andre Pierron, Comite des Assureurs, Maritimes de Bordeaux, Bourse Maritime,
      Place Laine, Bordeaux, France
    Comite des Assureurs Maritime du Lyon, 11 Rue de l'Arbre Sec, Lyon, France

(cont)

Comite des Assureurs Maritime du Lyon, in: Dunkirk, LeHarve, Marseilles, Mulhouse
Compagnic Nouvelle D'Assurances, 89 Rue Fondaudege F. 3300 Bordeaux, France
DOFINA, 5 Rue de Turin, 75008 Paris, France

INCOM INTERNATIONAL INC   3450 Princeton Pike, Lawrenceville, NJ 08648,
  Tel: (609) 896-7600
  (Roller & motorcycle chains, drive components, marine controls, etc)
    Morse Controls SARL, B.P. 10332-BAT 3417 A, Rue de la Jeune Fille,
      95705 Aeroport de Roissy, France

INDUCTOTHERM CORP   10 Indel Ave, Rancocas, NJ 08073, Tel: (609) 267-9000
  (Mfr induction melting furnaces)
    Inductothermie S.A., 6-10 Quai de Seing, F-93200 St. Denis, France

INFORMATION BUILDERS INC   1250 Broadway, New York, NY 10001,
  Tel: (212) 736-4433
  (Devel/serv computer software)
    Information Builders France SA, 78 Blvd. de la Republique,
      92100 Boulogne-Billancourt, France

INGERSOLL ENGINEERS INC   1021 N Mulford Rd, Rockford, IL 61107,
  Tel: (815) 395-6440
  (Mgmt consultants to mfg businesses)
    Ingersoll Engineers France SARL, Le Concorde, 2 Ave. Zanaroli, 74660 Annecy-Seynod,
      France

INGERSOLL-RAND CO   200 Chestnut Ridge Rd, Woodcliff Lake, NJ 07675,
  Tel: (201) 573-0123
  (Mfr compressors, rock drills, pumps, air tools)
    Compagnie Ingersoll Rand, Ave. Albert Einstein, 78190 Trappes, France

INSTRON CORP   100 Royall St, Canton, MA 02021, Tel: (617) 828-2500
  (Testing instru)
    Instron (France), Rue des Freres Fermen 47, ZI de Buc, 78530 Buc, France

INTERMEC CORP   6001 36th Ave West, Everett, WA 98203-9280,
  Tel: (206) 348-2600
  (Mfr automated data collection sys)
    Intermec Systems SA, Europarc Creteil, 1 Allee des Cerisiers, 94042 Creteil Cedex,
      France

INTERNATIONAL BUSINESS MACHINES (IBM)   Old Orchard Rd, Armonk,
  NY 10504-1783, Tel: (914) 765-1900
  (Info-handling sys, equip & serv)
    Compagnie IBM France SA, 3-5 Place Vendome, 75001 Paris, France
    IBM Europe SA, 3-5 Place Vendome, 75001 Paris, France

INTERNATIONAL PAPER   2 Manhattanville Rd, Purchase, NY 10577,
  Tel: (914) 397-1500
  (Mfr/distr container board, paper, wood prdts)
    Aussedat Rey S.A., Siege Social 1, rue du Petit Clamart, 78141 Velizy-Villacoublay,
      France
    Ilford S.A., B.P. 336, Chemin de la Fouillouse, F-69802 Saint-Priest, Cedex, France
    International Paper (Cellulose) S.A., 36 Ave. Hoche, Paris, France
    International Paper Investments (France) S.A., 36 Avenue Hoche, 75008 Paris, France
    Societe Civile Immoblierer les Semestres Montcale, 25 Rue Michel Salles, St. Cloud,
      France

Societe Mediteraneene d'Emballages, 25 Rue Michel Salles, St. Cloud, France
Societe Moderne d'Emballages, 25 Rue Michel Salles, St. Cloud, France
Societe Normande de Carton Ondule, 25 Rue Michel Salles, St. Cloud, France

INTERNATIONAL STAPLE & MACHINE CO   PO Box 629, Butler, PA 16001,
Tel: (412) 287-7711
(Stapling machs, supplies)
International Stapler & Machine France, 99 Ave. Verdier, 92120 Montrouge, France

INVACARE CORP   899 Cleveland St, PO Box 4028, Elyria, OH 44036,
Tel: (216) 329-6000
(Mfr patient-care prdts)
Invacare France SARL, ZA Beaux Soleils 9, Chausse J. Cesar, BP 404, 95520 Osny,
France

IOMEGA CORP   1821 W 4000 South, Roy, UT 84067, Tel: (801) 778-4494
(Mfr data storage prdts)
Iomega, 70 Ave. du General de Gaulle, 94022 Creteil Cedex, France

ITEL CONTAINERS INTL CORP   55 Francisco St, San Francisco, CA 94133,
Tel: (415) 984-4400
(Leasing, repair, storage of ocean-going containers)
Itel Container France SARL, 182 Bix, Ave. Charles de Gaulle, 92200,
Neuilly sur Seine, France

ITT CORP   1330 Ave of the Americas, New York, NY 10019, Tel: (212) 258-1000
(Diversified mfr, tech & services)
Cie. Generale de Constructions Telephonique, 251 Rue de Vaugirard, 75015 Paris,
France
Flygt France SA, 35 Rue Jean-Jacques Rousseau, 92153 Suresnes, France
Laboratoire Central de Telecommunications, 18-20 Rue Grange Dame Rose 7841,
Velizy Vailla Coublay, Cedex, France

ITT SHERATON CORP   60 State St, Boston, MA 02108, Tel: (617) 367-3600
(Hotel operations)
Sheraton Sales Center, 89 Blvd. Haussmann, 75008 Paris, France

JOHNSON & JOHNSON   One Johnson & Johnson Plaza, New Brunswick, NJ 08933,
Tel: (201) 524-0400
(Surgical, med & baby prdts)
Beghin Say/Johnson & Johnson S.N.C., Paris, France
Cilag SARL, Paris, France
Critikon S.A., Paris, France
Ethnor SA, Paris, France
Iolab S.A., Paris, France
Johnson & Johnson S.A., Paris, France
Laboratoires Janssen S.A., Paris, France
Ortho Diagnostic Systems S.A., Aubervilliers, France
Surgikos S.A.R.L., Viroflay, France

S C JOHNSON & SON INC   1525 Howe St, Racine, WI 53403, Tel: (414) 631-2000
(Home, auto, commercial & personal care prdts, specialty chems)
La Johnson Francaise SA, 10 Rue Saint-Hilaire, Saint-Quen L'Aumone, B.P. 606,
95004 Cergy, Paris, France

JOHNSON CONTROLS INC   5757 W Green Bay Ave, PO Box 591, Milwaukee, WI 53201,
   Tel: (414) 228-1200
   (Mfr facility mgmt & control sys, auto seating, batteries & plastics)
      Johnson Control France S.A.R.L., 357 Rue D'Estiennes D'Orves, 92700 Colombes, France

THE JOURNAL OF COMMERCE   110 Wall St, New York, NY 10005, Tel: (212) 425-1616
   (Business newspaper & journal pub)
      The Journal of Commerce, 6 Rue des Acacias, 91810 Vert-le-Grand, France

KAUFMAN & BROAD HOME CORP   11601 Wilshire Blvd, Los Angeles, CA 90025,
   Tel: (213) 312-1200
   (Housing)
      Bati-Service, 6 Cours Michelet, 92064 Paris la Defense, France
      Kaufman & Broad Developpement, 6 Cours Michelet, 92064 Paris la Defense, France
      Kaufman & Broad S.A., 6 Cours Michelet, 92064 Paris la Defense, France

KAWNEER CO INC   555 Guthridge Ct, Norcross, GA 30092, Tel: (404) 449-5555
   (Mfr arch aluminum prdts for commercial constr)
      Kawneer SA, Zone Industrielle, 24-34740 Vendargues, France

A T KEARNEY INC   222 S Riverside Plaza, Chicago, IL 60606,
   Tel: (312) 648-0111
   (Mgmt consultants)
      A.T. Kearney, Inc. & Cie, 23 Rue du Marignan, 75008, Paris, France

KEITHLEY INSTRUMENTS INC   28775 Aurora Rd, Cleveland, OH 44139,
   Tel: (216) 248-0400
   (Mfr electr test/meas instru, PC-based data acquisition hdwe/software)
      Keithley Instruments SARL, 2 Bis. Rue Leon Blum, B.P. 60, 91121 Palaiseau, Cedex 6,
      France

KEMPER INTL INSURANCE CO   Route 22, Long Grove, IL 60049, Tel: (708) 540-2000
   (Property casualty ins)
      Kemper SA, 56 Rue St. Lazare, 75009 Paris, France

KENNAMETAL INC   PO Box 231, Latrobe, PA 15650, Tel: (412) 539-5000
   (Tools, hard carbide & tungsten alloys)
      Kennametal France SA, Rue de General Leclerc 44, F-91230 Montgeron, France

KEPNER-TREGOE INC   Research Rd, PO Box 704, Princeton, NJ 08542,
   Tel: (609) 921-2806
   (Mgmt & organizational devel)
      Kepner Tregoe France SARL, 6 Rue Paul Gervais, 75013 Paris, France

KETCHUM COMMUNICATIONS   4 Gateway Center, Pittsburgh, PA 15222,
   Tel: (412) 456-3500
   (Advertising, public relations)
      Domino Ketchum, 11 Rue Bailly, 92200 Neuilly sur Seine, Cedex, Paris, France

KEYES FIBRE CO   3003 Summer St, Stamford, CT 06905, Tel: (203) 357-9100
   (Molded containers)
      Societe des Emballages Keyes SA, 37 Rue des Acadias, 75107 Paris, France

KEYSTONE INTL INC   PO Box 40010, Houston, TX 77040, Tel: (713) 466-1176
   (Mfr butterfly valves, actuators & control accessories)
      Keystone Controle des Fluides, 3 Rue Maurice Ravel, 92160 Antony, France

KIDDER PEABODY GROUP INC 10 Hanover Sq, New York, NY 10005,
   Tel: (212) 510-3000
   (Investment banking)
      Kidder, Peabody S.A., 7 Place Vendome, 75001 Paris, France

KIMBERLY-CLARK CORP PO Box 619100, Dallas, TX 75261-1200,
   Tel: (214) 830-1200
   (Mfr fiber-based prdts for personal care, pulp & forest prdts; air transport)
      Kimberly-Clark France S.A.R.L., Paris, France
      Kimberly-Clark Industries S.A., Paris, France
      LTR Industries S.A., Paris, France
      Paperterie de Mauduit SA, Kerisole, 29 S-Quimperle, France
      Papeterie de Malaucene, 84340 Malaucene, France
      Sopalin, Bureaux de la Colline, 92213 Saint Cloud, France

KNOGO CORP 350 Wireless Blvd, Hauppauge, NY 11788, Tel: (516) 232-2100
   (Mfr electr article surveillance sys)
      Knogo France SA, 1 Rue Edmond Michelet, ZNAA Fontaine Du Vaisseau- BP 36,
         93360 Neuilly Plaisance Paris, France

KNOLL INTL 655 Madison Ave, New York, NY 10021, Tel: (212) 826-2400
   (Furniture & fabrics)
      Knoll International, 268 Blvd. Saint Germain, 75007 Paris, France

KOLLMORGEN CORP 66 Gate House Rd, Stamford, CT 06902, Tel: (203) 327-7222
   (Printed circuits, elec motors & controls, electro-optical instru)
      SA Artus, Chemin du Champ des Martyrs, B.P. 9, 49240 Avrille, France

KOLMAR LABORATORIES INC 123 Pike St, Port Jervis, NY 12771,
   Tel: (914) 856-5311
   (Contract mfr: cosmetics, pharms, household prdts)
      Kolmar Cosmetique France SA, 22/24 Rue de la Paix, F-94300 Vincennes, France

KORN/FERRY INTL 237 Park Ave, New York, NY 10017, Tel: (212) 687-1834
   (Executive search)
      Korn/Ferry Intl.SA, 30 Ave. George V, 75008 Paris, France

KRATOS ANALYTICAL 170 Williams Dr, Ramsey, NJ 0744637, Tel: (201) 934-9000
   (Mfr liq chromatography, mass spectrometry & surface analysis instru)
      Kratos SA, 58 Rue Roger Salengro, Le Peripole, 108 BAT, Les Dolomites,
         94126 Fontenay sous Bois Cedex, France

LAMBDA ELECTRONICS INC 515 Broad Hollow Rd, Melville, NY 11747,
   Tel: (516) 694-4200
   (Power supplies, semiconductors, test equip)
      Lambda Electronique SA, Route de Grivery, 91 Gometz le Chatel, B.P. 77,
         91443 Orsay, France

LE TOURNEAU INC LONGVIEW DIV PO Box 2307, Longview, TX 75606,
   Tel: (214) 753-3449
   (Heavy constr, mining mach & equip)
      Blackwood-Hodge/France, B.P. 9, Z.I. Ouest-Rue des Freres Lumiere,
         91162 Longlumeau Cedex, Paris, France
      Ecobem, 8 Rue Lincoln, 75008 Paris, France
      Hamelle Afrique, 31 Quai de Grenelle, Cedex 15, 75738 Paris, France

LEACH CORP   6900 Orangethorpe Ave, Buena Park, CA 90620, Tel: (714) 739-0770
(Mfr aerospace electromechan & solid state comp)
   LRE Relais & Electroniques, 2 Rue Goethe, 57430 Sarralbe, France

LEEDS & NORTHRUP CO   Sumneytown Pike, North Wales, PA 19454,
Tel: (215) 699-2000
(Mfr process control instru & sys)
   Leeds & Northrup France SARL, Z.A. des Bruyeres, 1 Rue Raviov, 78190 Trappes, France

LEVI STRAUSS & CO   1155 Battery, San Francisco, CA 94111, Tel: (415) 544-6000
(Mfr wearing apparel)
   Levi Strauss Continental, 6 Ave. du Pacifique, ZA Courtaboeuf, 91944 Les Ulis,
      France

ELI LILLY & CO   307 E McCarty St, Indianapolis, IN 46285, Tel: (317) 261-2000
(Pharms, agric & cosmetic prdts)
   Eli Lilly France SA, 203 Bureaux de la Colline, 92-213 Saint-Cloud, France

THE LINCOLN ELECTRIC CO   22801 St Clair Ave, Cleveland, OH 44117,
Tel: (216) 481-8100
(Mfr arc welding equip & consumables, elec motors)
   The Lincoln Electric Co. Europe, SA, Ave. Franklin Roosevelt, B.P. 214,
      76120 Grand-Quevilly, France

LINTAS:WORLDWIDE   1 Dag Hammarskjold Plaza, New York, NY 10017,
Tel: (212) 605-8000
(Advertising agency)
   Lintas:Paris, 22 Quai de la Megisserie, Paris 75001, France

ARTHUR D LITTLE INC   25 Acorn Park, Cambridge, MA 02140-2390,
Tel: (617) 864-5770
(Technology & mgmt consulting)
   Arthur D. Little Inc., 230 Rue du Faubourg Saint Honore, 75008 Paris, France

LITTON INDUSTRIES INC   360 N Crescent Dr, Beverly Hills, CA 90210,
Tel: (213) 859-5000
(Elec sys, ind automation, resource explor)
   Litton Precision Products International, 58 Rue Pottier, F. 78150 Le Chesnay, France

LITWIN ENGINEERS & CONSTRUCTORS INC   1250 W Sam Houston Pkwy S, Houston,
TX 77042, Tel: (713) 268-8200
(Heavy constr, design, engr of chem & petrochem facilities)
   Litwin SA, 1 rue des Chauffours, 95020 Cergy-Pontoise, France

LOCKHEED CORP   2555 N Hollywood Way, Burbank, CA 91520, Tel: (213) 847-6121
(Aircraft, missiles, etc)
   Lockheed Aircraft Europe SA, 37 Ave. Pierre les de Serbie, 75008 Paris, France

LONGYEAR CO   PO Box 27314, Salt Lake City, UT 84127, Tel: (801) 972-1395
(Mfr diamond drills, concrete cutting equip; drill serv)
   Longyear France, B.P. 1, 78191 Trappes Cedex, France

LORAL INTL INC   999 Central Park Ave, Yonkers, NY 10704, Tel: (914) 964-6520
(Comm sys, computers, instru equip)
   Loral Mil-Spec Computers-France, 1 Place Gustave Eiffel, Silic 232, F-94578 Rungis,
      Cedex, France
   Loral Mil-Spec Conmputers, 1 Place Gustave Eiffel, Silic 232, F-94578 Rungis, France

LOUIS ALLIS CO   PO Box 2020, Milwaukee, WI 53201, Tel: (414) 481-6000
(Elec motors, adjustable speed drives, generators, compressors)
   Litton Precision Products International Inc., 58 Rue Pottier, F. 78150 de Chesney,
   France

LTV CORP   1600 Pacific St, PO Box 225003, Dallas, TX 75222,
Tel: (214) 746-7711
(Steel, energy prdts, aerospace & ocean shipping)
   LTV Aerospace Corp., 15 Rue de Remusat, 75016 Paris, France

LUBRIZOL CORP   29400 Lakeland Blvd, Wickliffe, OH 44092, Tel: (216) 943-4200
(Chem additives for lubricants & fuels)
   Lubrizol France, Tour Europe, 92400 Courbevole, Cedex 7, Paris La Defense, France

M&T CHEMICALS INC   PO Box 1104, Rahway, NJ 07065, Tel: (201) 499-0200
(Specialty chems & application technologies)
   M&T Chimie SA, B.P. 731, 95004 Cergy Pontoise Cedex, France
   Waldberg SA, B.P. 731, 75004 Cergy Pontoise Cedex, France

R H MACY & CO INC   51 West 34th St, New York, NY 10001, Tel: (212) 560-3600
(Department stores, importers)
   R.H. Macy & Co. Inc., 35 Rue de Ponthieu, 75008 Paris, France

MAGNETROL INTERNATIONAL   5300 Belmont Rd, Downers Grove, IL 60515-4499,
Tel: (708) 969-4000
(Mfr level & flow process instru)
   Magnetrol Intl., 34 Blvd. Haussmann, 75009 Paris, France

MALLINCKRODT INC   675 McDonnell Blvd, PO Box 5840, St Louis, MO 63134,
Tel: (314) 895-2012
(Med/ind chems, organics, pharms)
   Catalysts Intl. SA, Paris, France
   Laboratories Byk-Mallinckrodt France SA, Paris, France

MANPOWER INC   5301 N Ironwood Rd, PO Box 2053, Milwaukee, WI 53201-2053,
Tel: (414) 961-1000
(Temporary help)
   Manpower France SARL, 9 Rue Jacques Bingen, 75017 Paris, France

MANUFACTURERS HANOVER TRUST CO   270 Park Ave, New York, NY 10017,
Tel: (212) 286-6000
(Banking)
   Manufacturers Hanover Banque Bordique, 20 Rue de la Ville l'Eveque, 75008 Paris,
   France

MANVILLE CORP   PO Box 5108, Denver, CO 80217-5108, Tel: (303) 978-2000
(Mfr fiber glass prdts, paper & forest prdts, roofing & insulation material, ind
minerals)
   Johns-Manville de France, 9 & 11 Rue du Colonel de Rochebrune,
     92505 Rueil Malmaison, France
   Manville de France SA, France
   Manville de France SA, B.P. 240, 92504 Rueil-Malmaison, France
   Manville de France SA, B.P. 42, 15300 Murat, France
   Manville de France SA, B.P. 4, 42680 St. Marcellin-en-Forez, France
   Manville de France SA, B.P. G, 67160 Wissembourg, France

MARKEM CORP   150 Congress St, Keene, NH 03431, Tel: (603) 352-1130
 (Marking and printing mach; hot stamping foils)
   Markem France SA, 54 Rue Etienne Dolet, 94230 Cachan, France

MARSTELLER INTL   1 E Wacker Dr, Chicago, IL 60601, Tel: (312) 329-1100
 (Advertising, marketing research, sales promotion)
   Marsteller Intl., 69 Ave. Franklin D. Roosevelt, 95008 Paris, France

MATTEL INC   5150 Rosecrans Ave, Hawthorne, CA 90250, Tel: (213) 644-0411
 (Toys, dolls, games, crafts & hobbies)
   Mattel France SA, Immeuble le Mercure, 10 Bis Rue des Oliviers, Thiais Senia,
     94537 Rungis Cedex, France

MAYTAG CORP   403 W 4th St N, Newton, IA 50208, Tel: (515) 792-8000
 (Mfr home appliances & floor care prdts)
   The Hoover Co., Zone Industrielle De Dijon, Dijon, France

MCI INTERNATIONAL   2 International Dr, Rye Brook, NY 10573,
 Tel: (914) 937-3444
 (Intl telecom servs)
   MCI Intl. (France) SRL, 16 Rue Mederic, 75017 Paris, France

MEAD CORP   Courthouse Plaza, NE, Dayton, OH 45463, Tel: (513) 222-6323
 (Mfr paper, packaging, pulp, lumber & other wood prdts, school & office prdts; electr
 pub, distri)
   Mead Europe Engineering SARL, Blvd. d'Anvaux, 36004 Chateauroux, France
   Mead Holdings SA, 45 rue de Leningrad, Paris, France
   Mead Packaging Europe SARL, Cite Centre, 5 Allee de Bourbonnais, 78310 Maurepas,
     France
   Mead Reassurances SA, Paris, France
   Mead-Emballage SA, Blvd. d'Anvaux, Zone Industrielle, Boite 205, 36 Chateauroux,
     France

MEASUREX CORP   One Results Way, Cupertino, CA 95014, Tel: (408) 255-1500
 (Mfr computer integrated mfg sys)
   Measurex S.A., 8 Rue des Pyrenees, Silic 537, 94633 Rungis Cedex, France

MEDTRONIC INC   7000 Central Ave, NE, Minneapolis, MN 55432,
 Tel: (612) 574-4000
 (Mfr med devices, med serv)
   Medtronic France SA, 52 Bis, Ave. d'Iena 75116, Paris, France

MEMOREX CORP   San Thomas at Central Expressway, Santa Clara, CA 95052,
 Tel: (408) 987-1000
 (Magnetic recording tapes, etc)
   Memorex SA, 25 Blvd. de I'Amiral Bruix, 75016 Paris, France

MENNEN CO   Morristown, NJ 07960, Tel: (201) 631-9000
 (Health & beauty aids)
   Scannon Ltd., 33 Rue Galilee, 75116 Paris, France

MENNEN-MEDICAL INC   10123 Main St, Clarence, NY 14031, Tel: (716) 759-6921
 (Electronic med equip, physiological monitors)
   Mennen Medical France SARL, 20 Rue Benjamin Franklin, 78000 Versailles, France

MERCK SHARP & DOHME INTL   PO Box 2000, Rahway, NJ 07065, Tel: (201) 574-4000
(Pharms, chems & biologicals)
  Merck, Sharp & Dohme-Chibret, 3 Ave. Hoche, 75008 Paris, France

MERGENTHALER LINOTYPE CO   201 Old Country Rd, Melville, NY 11747,
Tel: (516) 673-4197
(Photocomposition machs, sys & equip)
  Linotype France SA, 40 Blvd. Felix-Faur, B.P. 77, 92320 Chatillon, France

MERISEL INC   200 Continental Blvd, El Segundo, CA 90245, Tel: (213) 615-3080
(Distr software & hardware)
  Softsel Computer Products SARL, 124 Boulevard de Verdun, 92411 Courbevoie Paris,
    France

MERRILL LYNCH PIERCE FENNER & SMITH   World Financial Center, 225 Liberty St,
New York, NY 10080, Tel: (212) 449-1000
(Brokers, securities, commodities)
  Merrill Lynch & Co., Hotel Carlton, Cannes 06400, France
  Merrill Lynch & Co., 96 Ave. d'Lena, 75783 Paris Cedex 16, France

METAL IMPROVEMENT CO   10 Forest Ave, Paramus, NJ 07652, Tel: (201) 843-7800
(Shot peening)
  Metal Improvement Co., ZI de St. Etienne, Rue de Cazenave, F-64100 Bayonne, France
  Metal Improvement Co. France, Zone Industrielle, D'Amilly, 45200 Montargis, France

METCO DIV OF PERKIN-ELMER   1101 Prospect Ave, Westbury, NY 11590,
Tel: (516) 334-1300
(Mfr/serv thermal spray coating equip & supplies)
  Perkin-Elmer S.A. Div. Metco, B.P. 61, 95102 Argenteuil Cedex, France

HENRY L MICHAEL & CO INC   PO Box 1915, Deming, NM 88305, Tel: (505) 546-8205
(Electr, med, control equip)
  Henry L. Michael & Co. (Delaware) Inc. SARL, 56 Faubourg Saint Honore, 75008 Paris,
    France

MICRODOT INC   Two First National Plaza, 20 S Clark St, Chicago, IL 60603,
Tel: (312) 899-1925
(Connectors, cables, automotive fasteners)
  Ets. Proner SA, 38 Allee du Closeau, 93160 Noisy le Grand, France

MICROMERITICS INSTRUMENT CORP   One Micromeritics Dr, Norcross,
GA 30093-1877, Tel: (404) 662-3620
(Mfr analytical instruments)
  Micromeritics France SA, Zaet St. Maximin, 181 Rue Henri Bessemer, F-60100 Creil,
    France

MILCHEM INC   3900 Essex Lane, PO Box 22111, Houston, TX 77027,
Tel: (214) 439-8000
(Gas & oil well drilling fluids & chem additives)
  Milchem France SARL, 201 Bureaux de la Colline, 92213 St. Cloud, Paris, France
  Milchem France SARL, 6 Residence du Parc Ave., 64100 Bayonne France

HERMAN MILLER INC   8500 Byron Rd, Zeeland, MI 49464, Tel: (616) 772-3300
(Office furnishings)
  Herman Miller et Cie, B.P. 79, 77312 Marne-le-Vallee Cedex 02, France
  Herman Miller et Cie., Paris France

MILLIPORE CORP   Ashley Rd, Bedford, MA 01730, Tel: (617) 275-9205
(Precision filters)
   Millipore Europe SA, 43 Ave. de L'Europe, 78140 Velizy, France

MILTON BRADLEY CO   1500 Main St, Springfield, MA 01101, Tel: (413) 525-6411
(Jigsaw puzzles, toys, games)
   Milton Bradley France, B.P. 13, 73370 Le Bourget du Lac, France

MILTON ROY CO   PO Box 12169, St Petersburg, FL 33733, Tel: (813) 823-4444
(Med & ind equip, process control instru)
   Dosapro-Milton Roy SA, Pont St., Pierre 27360, France

MINE SAFETY APPLIANCES CO   PO Box 426, Pittsburgh, PA 15230,
   Tel: (421) 273 5000
(Safety equip, ind filters)
   MSA de France, 13 Rue de la Guivernone, B.P. 617, 95004 Cergy, Pontoise, Cedex,
   France

MOBIL CORP   150 E 42nd St, New York, NY 10017, Tel: (212) 883-4242
(Petroleum explor, prdts)
   Mobil Oil Francaise, Tour Septentrion, Cedex 9, 92081 Paris, La Defense, France
   Societe Francaise Soner Mudge, 3 Ave. du General de Gaulle, 92-Puteaux, France

MONSANTO CO   800 N Lindbergh Blvd, St Louis, MO 63167, Tel: (314) 694-1000
(Mfr chem & agric prdts, pharms, ind process equip, man-made fibers, plastics)
   Societe Monsanto, 120 Ave. Charles de Gaulle, 92522 Neuilly s/Seine, Cedex, France

MOOG INC   East Aurora, NY 14052-0018, Tel: (716) 652-2000
(Mfr precision control components & sys)
   Moog SARL, 38 Rue du Morvan, Silic 417, 94573 Rungis, France

MOORE PRODUCTS CO   Summeytown Pike, Spring House, PA 19477,
   Tel: (215) 646-7400
(Mfr process control instru)
   Moore Products of France, 269 Rue Diderot, 94303 Vincennes, France

MORGAN GUARANTY TRUST CO   23 Wall St, New York, NY 10015, Tel: (212) 483-2323
(Banking)
   Morgan & Cie SA, 21 Place du Marche Saint Honore, 75001 Paris, France
   Morgan Guaranty Ltd., France, 14 Place Vendome, 75001 Paris, France

MORTON INTERNATIONAL INC   100 N Riverside Plaza, Chicago, IL 60606,
   Tel: (312) 807-2000
(Mfr adhesives, coatings, finishes, spec chems, advanced & electr materials, auto
safety prdts)
   Morton Intl. S.A., Zone Industrielle, B.P. 36, Igny 91430, France
   Morton Intl. S.A., Place de la Gare, 78590 Noisy le Roi, France
   Morton Intl. S.A., Spec. Chemicals Group, 2 Rue de la Montjoie, B.P. 65,
      93212 La Plaine St.-Denis Cedex, France

MOTOROLA INC   1303 E Algonquin Rd, Schaumburg, IL 60196, Tel: (708) 397-5000
(Mfr commun equip, semiconductors, cellular phones)
   Motorola Electronique Automobile SA, 8 Blvd. Charles Detriche, 49015 Angers, France
   Motorola SA, 14 Allee du Cantal, 91020 Evry, France
   Motorola Semiconducteurs SA, 2 Rue Auguste Conte, 92173 Montrouge, France
   Motorola Semiconducteurs SA, Ave. Gen. Eisenhower, 31300 Toulouse Cedex, France

Motorola systemes d'Information, 5 Rue Louis LeJeune, 92128 Montrouge, France
Tegal Intl. France, Chemin de Malacher, 38240 Meylan, France

MSI DATA CORP   340 Fischer Ave, Costa Mesa, CA 92626, Tel: (714) 549-6000
  (Portable data entry terminals)
    MSI France SARL, 7 Rue des Solets, Silic 426, 94583 Rungis, Cedex, France

MTS SYSTEMS CORP   PO Box 24012, Minneapolis, MN 55424, Tel: (612) 937-4000
  (Electrohydraulic testing & prod equip, mach controls)
    MTS Systems France SARL, Z.A.C. des Cotoaux du Bel-Air, 8 Rue de Temara,
      78100 St. Germain En Lave, France
    MTS Systems France Service, 77231 Marne La Vallee, ZAC du Mandinet (Lognes),
      Cedex 2 Jacques, France

MULTIGRAPHICS DIV   1800 W Central Rd, Mt Prospect, IL 60056,
  Tel: (708) 398-1900
  (Offset duplicating & graphic commun sys)
    AM International SA, B.P. 307, 60 Rue Berthelot, 92402 Courbevoie, Cedex, France

MacDERMID INC   245 Freight St, Waterbury, CT 06702, Tel: (203) 575-5700
  (Chem processing for metal ind, plastics, electronics cleaners, strippers)
    MacDermid France SA, 41 Rue de Chablais, 74100 Annemasse, France

E F MacDONALD CO   129 S Ludlow St, Dayton, OH 45401, Tel: (513) 226-5000
  (Trading stamps, travel & sales incentives)
    E.F. MacDonald France, 111 Rue de Paris, 92100 Boulogne, Paris, France

McCANN-ERICKSON WORLDWIDE   750 Third Ave, New York, NY 10017,
  Tel: (212) 697-6000
  (Advertising)
    Joannis Schneider Conseil S.A., 2 Rue Voltaire, 92309 Levallois Perret Cedex, France
    McCann Erickson S.A., Rue de Villiere, 92309 Levallois Perret Cedex, France

McKINSEY & CO INC   55 E 52nd St, New York, NY 10022, Tel: (212) 909-8400
  (Mgmt consultants)
    McKinsey & Co. Inc., 27-29 Rue de Bassano, 75008 Paris, France

NABISCO BRANDS INC   Nabisco Brands Plaza, East Hanover, NJ 07936,
  Tel: (201) 503-2000
  (Mfr food prdts)
    Biscuits Belin, Ave. Ambroise Croizat, B.P. 93, 91003 Evry, Cedex, France
    Nabisco International Management Inc., 4 Place de la Concorde, 75008 Paris, France

NALCO CHEMICAL CO   One Nalco Center, Naperville, IL 60566-1024,
  Tel: (708) 305-1000
  (Chems for water & waste water treatment, oil prod & refining, ind processes;
  water/energy mgmt serv)
    Nalco Europe SARL, 322 Bureaux de la Colline, 92213 Saint-Cloud Cedex, France
    Nalco France SARL, B.P. 179, Rue Lavoisier, Z.I., de Coignieres-Maurepas,
      78313 Maurepas, Cedex, France

NASHUA CORP   44 Franklin St, Nashua, NH 03061, Tel: (603) 880-2323
  (Mfr/distr/serv office copier sys & supplies)
    Nashua France SA, 70 Ave. General de Gaulle, Echat 652, 94022 Creteil Cedex, France

NATIONAL CAR RENTAL SYSTEM INC   7700 France Ave S, Minneapolis, MN 55435,
  Tel: (612) 830-2121
  (Car rental)
    National Car Rental Systems Inc., B.P. 212, Clamart Cedex, France
    National Car Rental Systems Inc., 13 Rue Sainte Catherine, Abbeville, France

NATIONAL CHEMSEARCH CORP   2727 Chemsearch Blvd, Irving, TX 75061,
  Tel: (214) 438-0211
  (Commercial chem prdts)
    National Chemsearch France, Zone Industrielle, 77160 Provins, France

NCR CORP   1700 S Patterson Blvd, Dayton, OH 45479, Tel: (513) 445-2000
  (Develop/mfr/sell/serv business info processing sys)
    NCR France SA, Tour Neptune, Cedex #20, 92086 Paris La Defense, France

NEWSWEEK INTL INC   444 Madison Ave, New York, NY 10022, Tel: (212) 350-2000
  (Publ)
    Newsweek Inc., 162 Rue du Faubourg, Saint Honore 75008 Paris, France

NICO INC   345 Hudson St, New York, NY 10014, Tel: (212) 620-8200
  (Constr mgt, contracting & consult servs)
    Nico Construction PLC, White Greer, 33 Rue de la Roquette, 75011 Paris, France

NICOLET INSTRUMENT CORP   5225 Verona Rd, Madison, WI 53711-4495,
  Tel: (608) 271-3333
  (Mfr infrared spectrometers, oscilloscopes, med electro-diag equip)
    Nicolet Instruments SARL, A.I. de Pissaloup, B.P. 118, 16 Ave. Jean d'Alembert,
      78192 Trappes Cedex, France

A C NIELSEN CO   Nielsen Plaza, Northbrook, IL 60062, Tel: (708) 498-6300
  (Marketing research)
    A.C. Nielsen Co., 44 Blvd. de Grenelle, 75732 Paris, Cedex 15, France

NORDSON CORP   28601 Clemens Rd, Westlake, OH 44145, Tel: (216) 892-1580
  (Mfr ind application equip & packaging mach)
    Nordson France SA, Zone Industrielle Nord de Torcy, B.P. 8, 77201 Marne La Vallee,
      Cedex 1, France

NORTHERN TELECOM SYSTEMS CORP   PO Box 1222, Minneapolis, MN 55440,
  Tel: (612) 932-8000
  (Remote information processing sys)
    Data 100 SA Europe, La Boursidieri R.N. 186, 92350 Le Plessis, Robinson, France

NORTON CO   1 New Bond St, Worcester, MA 01606, Tel: (508) 795-5000
  (Abrasives, drill bits, constr & safety prdts, plastics)
    Christensen Diamond Products Co., Place de la Gare, 78320, Le Mesnil St.,
      Denis la Verriere, France
    Norton Houard SA, 33 Route de Blois, 37400 Amboise, France
    Norton SA, Rue de I'Ambassadeur, 78702 Couflane Ste. Honorine, France
    Norton SA, 178 Ave. Paul-Vaillant-Couturier, La Courneuve, France

NVF CO   Yorklyn Rd, Yorklyn, DE 19736, Tel: (302) 239-5281
  (Metal containers, steel prdts, laminated plastics, papers)
    NVF Europe, 69540 Irigny, France

OGILVY & MATHER INC   2 E 48th St, New York, NY 10017, Tel: (212) 907-3400
  (Advertising agency)
    Ogilvy & Mather International Inc., 36 Rue Brunel, 75017 Paris, France

OLIN CORP   120 Long Ridge Rd, Stamford, CT 06904-1355, Tel: (203) 356-2000
  (Chems, metals, applied physics in elect, defense, aerospace inds)
    Olin Europe SA, 108-110 Blvd. Haussmann, 75008 Paris, France
    Olin Ski Europe, F-74370 Pringy/Annecy, France

OMARK INDUSTRIES INC   5550 SW Macadam Ave, Portland, OR 97201,
  Tel: (503) 796-1400
  (Mfr chain & accessories for chain saws, welding equip, power tools)
    Titanox SA, 17 Rue de Prony, 92600 Asnieres, France

ONAN CORP   1400 73rd Ave NE, Minneapolis, MN 55432, Tel: (612) 574-5000
  (Electric generators, ind engines & controls)
    Carrier Kheops SA, 12 Villa D'Este Tour Atlas, 75643 Cedex, Paris, France

ORGANIZATIONAL DYNAMICS INC   5 Burlington Woods Dr, Burlington, MA 01803,
  Tel: (617) 272-8040
  (Quality/productivity consultants)
    Groupe G-ODI, 16 Place de la Madeleine, 75008 Paris, France

ORIEL CORP   250 Long Beach Blvd, Stratford, CT 06497, Tel: (203) 377-8282
  (Mfr optical goods)
    Oriel SARL, 9 Ave. de Laponie, Z.A. de Courtaboeuf, 91940 Les Ulis, France

ORTEC INC   100 Midland Rd, Oak Ridge, TN 37830, Tel: (615) 482-4413
  (Scientific instru, electronic & mechanical components)
    Ortec SARL, 2 Quai du Parc, 94100 Saint-Naur, France

OTIS ELEVATOR CO   10 Farm Springs, Farmington, CT 06032, Tel: (203) 674-4047
  (Elevators & escalators)
    Ascinter Otis, 141 Rue de Saussure, B.P. 728, 75822 Paris Cedex 17, France
    European & Transcontinental Operations, Otis Elevator Intern,
      4 Place de La Defense, Cedex 26, 92090 Paris La Defense, France
    Saxby SA, 40 Rue de l'Orillon, B.P. 171, 75526 Paris Cedex 11,   France

OWENS-CORNING FIBERGLAS CORP   PO Box 901, Fiberglas Tower, Toledo, OH 43659,
  Tel: (419) 248-8000
  (Mfr insulation, building materials, glass fiber prdts)
    Owens-Corning Fiberglas France SA, L'Ardoise, France
    Owens-Corning Isolation France S.A., France

PACKAGING CORP OF AMERICA   1603 Orrington Ave, Evanston, IL 60204,
  Tel: (708) 492-5713
  (Mfr custom packaging, aluminum & plastic molded fibre, corrugated containers)
    Omni-Pac SARL, 64 Rue de Miromesnil, F-75008 Paris, France

PAINEWEBBER GROUP INC   1285 Ave of the Americas, New York, NY 10019,
  Tel: (212) 713-2000
  (Stock brokerage serv & invest)
    PaineWebber Intl., 56 rue du Faubourg St. Honore, 75008 Paris, France

PANDUIT CORP   17301 Ridgeland Ave, Tinley Park, IL 60477, Tel: (708) 532-1800
  (Mfr elec/electr wiring comps)
    Panduit SARL, ZA des Marais, 1 Ave. de la Marne, 94124 Fonenay sour Bois, France

PARAMOUNT INTL FILMS INC   1 Gulf & Western Plaza, New York, NY 10023,
  Tel: (212) 333-4600
  (Film prod & distr)
    Films Paramount, 1 Rue Meyerbeer, 75009 Paris, France

PARK ELECTROCHEMICAL CORP   5 Dakota Dr, Lake Success, NY 11042,
  Tel: (516) 354-4100
  (Multi-layer laminate printed circuit materials, ind comps, plumbing hdwe prdts)
    Nelco SA, Rte. de Beze, 213 Mirebeau sur Beze, France

PARKER HANNIFIN CORP   17325 Euclid Ave, Cleveland, OH 44112,
  Tel: (216) 531-3000
  (Mfr motion-control prdts)
    Parker Hennifin RAK S.A., BP 482 Ville-la-Grand, Zone Industriele du Mont Blanc,
      74108 Annemasse, France
    Parker Hennifin RAK S.A., other locations in France

PARKER PEN CO   One Parker Place, Janesville, WI 53545, Tel: (608) 755-7000
  (Writing instru, temporary help, leisure apparel & equip)
    Parker Pen France, Paris, France

PEPSICO INC   700 Anderson Hill Rd, Purchase, NY 10577, Tel: (914) 253-2000
  (Beverages, food prdts & servs, sporting goods)
    Pepsi Cola de France SARL, 41 Ave. Montaigne, 75008 Paris, France

PETROLITE CORP   100 N Broadway, St Louis, MO 63102, Tel: (314) 241-8370
  (Specialty chem treating programs, performance-enhancing additives & related equip)
    Petrolite France SA, 2 Rue de Penthievre, 75008 Paris, France

PFIZER INC   235 E 42nd St, New York, NY 10017, Tel: (212) 573-2323
  (Mfr pharms, hosp prdts, chems, consumer & animal health prdts)
    Pfizer-France SA, 86 Rue de Paris, B.P. 60, 91407 Orsay, Cedex, France

PHELPS DODGE CORP   2600 N Central Ave, Phoenix, AZ 85004-3014,
  Tel: (602) 234-8100
  (Minerals, metals & spec engineered prdts for trans & elect mkts)
    Columbian Carbon Intl. France, 6-12 Rue Raffet, 75016 Paris, France

PHILIPP BROTHERS CHEMICALS INC   1 Parker Plaza, Fort Lee, NJ 07029,
  Tel: (201) 944-6020
  (Mfr ind & agric chems)
    Phibrotec SA, 33 Rue de la Baume, 75008 Paris, France

PHILLIPS PETROLEUM CO   Phillips Bldg, Bartlesville, OK 74004,
  Tel: (918) 661-6600
  (Crude oil, natural gas, liquefied petroleum gas, gasoline & petro-chems)
    Phillips Petroleum International France, 37 Ave. d'Lena, F. 75116 Paris, France

PILLSBURY CO   Pillsbury Center, Minneapolis, MN 55402, Tel: (612) 330-4966
  (Baking mixes, canned & frozen foods, restaurants & food shops)
    Brossard, 19 Rue des Minimes, 92400 Courbevoie, France
    Grincoire SA, 19 Rue des Minimes, 92400 Courbevoie, France

MAURICE PINCOFFS CO INC   2040 North Loop West, #200, Houston, TX 77018,
  Tel: (713) 681-5461
  (Intl marketing & distr)
    Maurice Pincoffs Paris, 27-29 Ave de Saint Mande, 75012 Paris, France

PIONEER HI-BRED INTL INC   700 Capital Sq, 400 Locust St, Des Moines,
  IA 50309, Tel: (515) 245-3500
  (Seed corn, feed seed, data sys & equip)
    GIE Pioneer France, Epuiseau, Ovegues, France

PITNEY BOWES INC   World Headquarters, Stamford, CT 06926-0700,
  Tel: (203) 356-5000
  (Postage meters, mailroom equip, copiers, bus supplies & servs)
    Pitney Bowes France SA, 16 Rue de Toul, 75012 Paris, France

PITTSBURGH NATIONAL BANK   Fifth Ave at Wood, Pittsburgh, PA 15222,
  Tel: (412) 355-2000
  (Banking)
    Pittsburgh National Bank, 20 Place Vendome, 75001 Paris, France

PLAYTEX APPAREL INC   700 Fairfield Ave, Stamford, CT 06904,
  Tel: (203) 356-8000
  (Mfr intimate apparel)
    Playtex France, B.P. 55, Zone Industrielle, 38110 La Tour du Pin, France

PLIBRICO CO   1800 Kingsbury St, Chicago, IL 60614, Tel: (312) 549-7014
  (Refractories, engineering, constr)
    Plibrico Refractories SA, B.P. 27, 76 Ave. Jean-Jaures, 59601 Maubeuge, France

POLAROID CORP   549 Technology Sq, Cambridge, MA 02139, Tel: (617) 577-2000
  (Photographic and optical prdts)
    Polaroid France SA, 57 Rue de Villiers, 92202 Neuilly, France

POTTERS INDUSTRIES INC   20 Waterview Blvd, Parsippany, NJ 07054,
  Tel: (201) 299-2900
  (Mfr glass spheres for road marking & ind applications)
    Potters-Ballotini SA, Z.I. DuPont-Panay, B.P. 67, 03500 Saint-Pourcain-Sur-Sioule,
    France

POWER-PACKER   13000 W Silver Spring Dr, Butler, WI 53007, Tel: (414) 781-6600
  (Mfr OEM hydraulic sys)
    Matairco/Hydro-Air, B.P. 23, 91421 Morangis, France

PPG INDUSTRIES   One PPG Place, Pittsburgh, PA 15272, Tel: (412) 434-3131
  (Mfr flat glass, fiber glass, chems, coatings, med electr)
    Boussois S.A., 126-130 Rue Jules-Guesde, 92302 Levallois-Perret, France
    PPG Europe/PPG Industries Intl., 6 Rue de Penthievre, Paris 75008, France
    PPG Industries (France) S.A., B.P. 377, 59307 Valenciennes, Cedex, France

PRECISION CASTPARTS CORP   4600 SE Harney Dr, Portland, OR 97206,
  Tel: (503) 653-8210
  (Metal castings)
    Precision Castparts Corp. France SA, ZI, 64680 Ogeu Bains, France

PRECISION VALVE CORP   PO Box 309, Yonkers, NY 10702, Tel: (914) 969-6500
  (Mfr aerosol valves)
    Valve Precision SARL, 3 Rue de la Croix Martre, BP 38, 91120 Palaiseau, France

PREMARK INTL INC   1717 Deerfield Rd, Deerfield, IL 60015, Tel: (708) 405-6000
  (Mfr/sale diversified consumer & coml prdts)
    Dart Europe S.A., B.P. 327, F-37303 Joue-Les-Tours, Cedex, France

PRIME COMPUTER INC   Prime Park, Natick, MA 01760, Tel: (617) 655-8000
   (Mfr minicomputers, hardware & software)
      Prime Computer France, 33 Rue Fernanc Forest, B.P. 128, 92154 Suresnes, France

PRINCETON APPLIED RESEARCH CORP   Box 2565, Princeton, NJ 08540,
   Tel: (609) 452-2111
   (Research & analytical instru)
      EG & G Instruments SARL, Silic 428, 4 Place de la Balance 94583, Rungis, Cedex,
         France

PRINTRONIX INC   17500 Cartwright Rd, Irvine, CA 92715, Tel: (714) 863-1900
   (Mfr computer printers)
      Printronix France, 8 Rue Parmentier, F-92800 Puteaux, France

PROCTER & GAMBLE CO   One Procter & Gamble Plaza, Cincinnati, OH 45202,
   Tel: (513) 983-1100
   (Personal care, food, laundry, cleaning & ind prdts)
      Procter & Gamble France, 96 Ave. Charles de Gaulle, 92201, Neuilly Sur Seine,
         France

PROSERV INC   1101 Wilson Blvd, #1800, Arlington, VA 22209,
   Tel: (703) 276-3030
   (Sports mktg, mgt & consult)
      ProServ Europe, 20 Rue de Billancourt, 92100 Boulogne, France

PUROLATOR COURIER CORP   131 Morristown Rd, Basking Ridge, NJ 07980,
   Tel: (201) 953-6400
   (Time-sensitive package delivery)
      Executive Air Express SA, 94200 Ivry Sur Seine, France

QUAKER CHEMICAL CORP   Elm & Lee Sts, Conshohocken, PA 19428,
   Tel: (215) 828-4250
   (Mfr chem specialties)
      Quaker Chemical SARL, 20 Rue Antoine Lavoisier, 95300 Pontoise, France

QUAKER OATS CO   345 Merchandise Mart Plaza, Chicago, IL 60654,
   Tel: (312) 222-7111
   (Foods, pet foods, toys, chems)
      Quaker Oats France, 40 Blvd. de Dunkerque, 13002 Marseille, France

RAIN BIRD SPRINKLER MFG CORP   7045 N Grand Ave, Glendora, CA 91740,
   Tel: (213) 963-9311
   (Lawn sprinklers, irrigation equip)
      Rain Bird Europe, B.P. 72, 13290 Les Milles, France

RALSTON PURINA CO   Checkerboard Sq, St Louis, MO 63164, Tel: (214) 982-1000
   (Poultry & live stock feed, cereals, food prdts)
      Baranne SA, Centre Paris-Pleyel, 1 Rue Pleyel, 93521 Saint Denis, Cedex, France
      Duquesne Purina SA, Cedex 2028, 76040 Roven. Cedex, France

RAMSEY TECHNOLOGY INC   1853 W County Rd, St Paul, MN 55113,
   Tel: (612) 633-5150
   (Mfr scales & mining equip)
      Ramsey Engineering, 63 Place du Commerce, 78370 Plaisir, France

RANCO INC   555 Metro Pl N, PO Box 248, Dublin, OH 43017, Tel: (614) 764-3733
(Controls for appliance, automotive, comfort, commercial & consumer mkts)
   Ranco France SA, Rue Senouque, ZAC, 78530 Buc, France

RANSBURG CORP   3939 W 56th St, Indianapolis, IN 46208, Tel: (317) 298-5000
(Mfr electrostatic coating sys)
   Ransburg-Gema S.A., Ave. Louison Bobet, ZI des Marais, 94124 Fontenay sous Bois,
      Paris, France

RAYTHEON CO   141 Spring St, Lexington, MA 02173, Tel: (617) 862-6600
(Mfr diversified electronics & apppliances; aviation, ind & constr services,
publishing)
   Raytheon Overseas Ltd., 326 Bureaux de la Colline, 92213 Saint Cloud, Cedex, France

RCA GLOBAL COMMUNICATIONS INC   60 Broad St, New York, NY 10004,
   Tel: (212) 806-7000
(Commun serv)
   RCA SA, 57 Rue Vasco de Gama, Paris, France

READER'S DIGEST ASSOCIATION INC   PO Box 235, Pleasantville, NY 10570,
   Tel: (914) 238-1000
(Global publisher & direct mail marketer)
   Selection du Readers Digest SA, 1 a 7 Ave. Louis Pasteur, 92220 Bagneux, France

RECOGNITION EQUIPMENT INC   PO Box 222307, Dallas, TX 75222,
   Tel: (214) 579-6000
(Optical character recognition sys & equip for document processing & computer data)
   Recognition Equipment France SA, 311 Rue Lecourbe 75015, Paris, France

THE REECE CORP   800 South St, Waltham, MA 02254-9168, Tel: (617) 894-9220
(Mfr apparel mach)
   The Reece Machinery Co. France, 19 Ave de la Gare, 94230 Cachan, France

REED TOOL CO   6501 Navigation Blvd, Houston, TX 77001, Tel: (713) 924-5200
(Mfr rock bits for oil & gas explor)
   Reed Tool Co., c/o Rig Service, BP 119, Z.I. Lons, 64143 Pau-Billere-Cedex, France

RELIANCE ELECTRIC CO   24701 Euclid Ave, Cleveland, OH 44117,
   Tel: (216) 266-7000
(Equip & sys for ind automation, telecom equip)
   Toledo SA, 218 Chaussee Jules Cesar, 95250 Beauchamp, France

REVLON INC   767 Fifth Ave, New York, NY 10153-0033, Tel: (212) 572-5000
(Cosmetics, health care prdts)
   Revlon SA, 42 Ave. Montaine, 75008 Paris, France

REXNORD CORP   PO Box 2022, Milwaukee, WI 53201, Tel: (414) 643-3000
(Mfr power transmission prdts)
   Rexnord France SARL, Za les Petits Carreaux, 5 Ave. des Marguerites,
      94380 Bonneuil sur Marne Cedex, France

REXON BUSINESS MACHINES CORP   5800 Uplander Way, Culver City, CA 90230,
   Tel: (213) 641-7110
(Mfr small business computer sys)
   Rexon Intl. Corp., 1 Ave. de St. Cloud, 78000 Versailes, France

RICHARDSON-VICKS INC   Ten Westport Rd, Wilton, CT 06897, Tel: (203) 834-5000
(Consumer health & personal care prdts)
  Vicks International, E/A, 18 Rue Jean Giraudoux, 75116 Paris, France

RICHTON INTL CORP   1345 Ave of the Americas, New York, NY 10115,
Tel: (212) 765-6480
(Nondurable consumer wearables, active sportswear jewelry & accessories)
  Richton International France, 28 Rue Dumont Habor 7500 Paris, France

RIDGE TOOL CO   400 Clark St, Elyria, OH 44035, Tel: (216) 323-5581
(Hand & power tools for working pipe, drain cleaning equip, etc)
  Emerson Electric France SA, Div. Ridge Tool, Morangis, France

RIGHT ASSOCIATES   1818 Market St, 14th Fl, Philadelphia, PA 19103-3614,
Tel: (215) 988-1588
(Outplacement & human resources consult servs)
  Right Associates, 3 Avenue du Pres. Wilson, 75116 Paris, France

RIKER LABORATORIES INC   Bldg 225-1N-07, 3M Center, St Paul, MN 55144,
Tel: (612) 733-9577
(Specialty pharms)
  Laboratoires Riker/3M, 40 Rue Gabriel Crie, 92245 Malakoff Cedex, France

A H ROBINS CO INC   1407 Cummings Dr, PO Box 26609, Richmond, VA 23261-6609,
Tel: (804) 257-2000
(Mfr ethical pharms & consumer prdts)
  Laboratoires Martinet, 222 Blvd. Pereire, 75017 Paris, France

ROCKWELL GRAPHIC SYSTEMS   700 Oakmont Lane, Westmont, IL 60559-5546,
Tel: (708) 850-5600
(Mfr printing equip)
  Rockwell Systems Graphique Nantes S.A., Tour Gan, Cedex 13,
    92082 Paris La Defense 2, France

ROCKWELL INTL CORP   2230 E Imperial Hwy, El Segundo, CA 90245,
Tel: (213) 647-5000
(Prdts & serv for aerospace, automotive, electronics, graphics & automation inds)
  Compagnie Industrielle de Macanismes SA, Tour Gan, Cedex 13,
    92082 Paris La Defense, France
  MGD Graphic Systems SA, 19/21 Rue Remy-Dumoncel, 75014 Paris, France
  Rockwell-Collins France SA, 6 Ave. Didier Daurat-AZC, Aeroport 31700, Blagnac,
    France

R A RODRIGUEZ INC   320 Endo Blvd, Garden City, NY 11530, Tel: (516) 832-2617
(Export mgt: bearings & power trans equip)
  R. A. Rodriguez, 56 Bis Rue Martial Boudet, 92370 Chaville, France

ROGERS CORP   One Technology Dr, Rogers, CT 06263, Tel: (203) 774-9605
(Mfr flexible, molded, die-stamped & microwave circuits; engineered polymer prdts)
  Mektron France SA, ZI de Bellitourne, 53200 Chateau Gintier, France
  Mektron France SA, 9 Allee des Jacheres Sofilie, F-94263 Fresnes Cedex, France

ROHM & HAAS CO   Independence Mall West, Philadelphia, PA 19105,
Tel: (215) 592-3000
(Mfr ind & agric chems, plastics)
  Duolite Intl. SA, La Tour de Lyon, 185 Rue de Bercy, 75579 Paris, France

Rohm & Haas France S.A., 185 Rue de Bercy, 75579 Paris, Cedex 12, France
Rohm & Haas France S.A., Sophia Antipolis, 06565 Valbonne Cedex, France

RORER GROUP INC   500 Virginia Dr, Ft Washington, PA 19034,
   Tel: (215) 628-6000
   (Mfr ethical & consumer pharms)
      Laboratoires Rorer SA, 5 Rue Lacuee, 75012 Paris, France

ROSEMOUNT INC   12001 Technology Dr, Eden Prairie, MN 55344,
   Tel: (612) 941-5560
   (Mfr aerospace & ind instrumentation)
      Rosemount SARL, Silic 265-1 Place des Etats Unis, 94578 Rungis, Cedex, France

RUDER FINN INC   301 E 57th St, New York, NY 10022, Tel: (212) 593-6400
   (Public relations serv, broadcast commun)
      Ruder & Finn SA, 18 Rue Vignon, 75009 Paris, France

RUSSELL REYNOLDS ASSOCIATES INC   200 Park Ave, New York, NY 10166,
   Tel: (212) 351-2000
   (Exec recruiting services)
      Russell Reynolds Assoc. Inc., 7 Place Vendome, 75001 Paris, France

SAFETY-KLEEN CORP   777 Big Timber Rd, Elgin, IL 60123, Tel: (708) 697-8460
   (Solvent based parts cleaning serv, sludge/solvent recycling serv)
      Sopia/Safety-Kleen France, 12 Rue de Tilsitt, 75008 Paris, France

SARA LEE CORP   3 First National Plaza, Chicago, IL 60602, Tel: (312) 726-2600
   (Mfr/distr food & consumer packaged goods)
      Dim, S.A., 24 Rue Marc Sequin, 75018 Paris, France
      Etablissements Lardenois SA, B.P. 1, 60370 Hermes, France

SCHENECTADY CHEMICALS INC   PO Box 1046, Schenectady, NY 12301,
   Tel: (518) 370-4200
   (Mfr elec insulating varnishe, enamels, resins, alkylated phenol)
      Schenectady de France, Ave. George Washington, F-62404 Bethune, France

R P SCHERER CORP   2075 W Big Beaver Rd, Troy, MI 48084, Tel: (313) 649-0900
   (Mfr soft gelatin & two-piece hard shell capsules)
      R.P. Scherer SA, 68 Rue Principale, F-67930 Beinheim Bas-Rhin, France

SCHERING INTL   PO Box 500, Kenilworth, NJ 07033, Tel: (201) 558-4000
   (Pharms, medicines, toiletries, cosmetics, human & animal health prdts)
      Unilabo, 92 Rue Baudin, 92307 Levallois, France

SCHLEGEL CORP   400 East Ave, Rochester, NY 14607, Tel: (716) 546-6260
   (Engineered perimeter sealing systems for residential & commercial constr)
      Schlegel France Technologie SARL, 6 Ave. de Creil, Eoite Postale 61, 60303 Senlis,
      Cedex, France

A SCHULMAN INC   3550 W Market St, Akron, OH 44313, Tel: (216) 666-3751
   (Mfr/sale plastic resins & compounds)
      A. Schulman S.A., 10/12 Rue Andras Beck, 92360 Meudon-La-Foret, Paris, France

SCIENCE MANAGEMENT CORP   PO Box 0600, Basking Ridge, NJ 07920,
   Tel: (201) 647-7000
   (Human/mgmt resources, info technology, engr & technology services)

(cont)

SMC Internationale SARL, 1 Bis, Rue du Petit Clamart, 78140 Velizy-Villacoublay, France

SCIENTIFIC ATLANTA INC   1 Technology Pkwy, PO Box 105600, Atlanta, GA 30348, Tel: (404) 441-4000
(Telecommun instru & equip, energy mgmt & home security equip, test & measurement instru)
   Scientific-Atlanta SA, 129 Ave. du Morechal Foch. 78400 Chatou, France

SCM CORP   299 Park Ave, New York, NY 10171, Tel: (212) 752-2700
(Business equip, chems, coatings & resins, foods, paper prdts)
   Smith Corona Marchant, 19 Rue de 4 Setembre, 75002 Paris, France
   Smith Corona Marchant SA, 86 Ave. de la Republique, 94701 Maison-Alfort, France

SCOTT WORLDWIDE INC   Scott Plaza, Philadelphia, PA 19113, Tel: (215) 521-5000
(Paper & paper prdts, bleached pulp)
   Scott SA, 106 Rue des Dames, 75017 Paris, France

SEA-LAND SERVICE INC   379 Thornall St, Edison, NJ 08837, Tel: (201) 558-6000
(Container transport)
   Agena Container SA, 57 Bis Rue de Villiers, 92200 Neuilly Sur Seine, France
   Agena Container SA, 33075 Bordeaux, France
   Agena Container SA, 17 Rue de Colombier, 69007 Lyon, France
   Agena Container SA, 2 Rue Mazenod, 13002 Marseille, France
   Agena Container SA, Franklin Bldg., 35 Rue de 129 eme, 7600 Le Havre, France
   Agena Container SA, 27 Rue de Fosse des Treize, 6700 Strasbourg, France
   N.A.T., 59650 Rue Van Gogh, Ville Nienve D'Ascq, Lille, France
   R.M.C., 20 Rue de Canton, 16100 Cognac, France
   Sea Land Service Inc., Darse/Graveleau 864, B.P. 44, Port de Fos, Fos-Sur Mer, France
   Sea-Land Agena SA, Paris, France
   Sea-Land Service Inc., 57 Bis Rue de Villiers, 92200 Neuilly Sur Seine, France
   Sea-Land Service Inc., B.P. 1195, 76600 Le Havre, France

SEALECTRO CORP   225 Hoyt St, Mamaroneck, NY 10543, Tel: (914) 698-5600
(Electronic components, programming & data collection deviccs)
   Sealectro, Z.I. de Toulon, Est-83087 Toulon Cedex, France

SEALED AIR CORP   Park 80 Plaza E, Saddle Brook, NJ 07662-5291, Tel: (201) 791-7600
(Mfr protective packaging prdts)
   Douff S.A., B.P. 9009, 3 Avenue de la Mare, Z.I. des Bethunes, 95310 Saint-Ouen-l'Aumone, France
   Sibco SA, B.P. 137, 89300 Joigny, France

SEAQUIST DIV   1160 N Silver Lake Rd, Cary, IL 60013, Tel: (708) 639-2126
(Aerosol valves, closures, pump dispensers)
   Valois SA, Ave. de l'Europe 78, Marly-le-Roi, France

G D SEARLE & CO   PO Box 1045, Skokie, IL 60076, Tel: (708) 982-7000
(Pharms, health care & optical prdts, specialty chems)
   Laboratoire Searle, 7 Blvd. Romain-Rolland, 92128 Montrouge, France
   Searle Medical SA, B.P. 238, 9 Chaussee Jules Cesar, 95523 Cergey Pontoise, France
   Searle Recherche et Development., B.P. 23, Sophia Antipolis 06560, Valbomne, France

SEATRAIN LINES INC   270 Sylvan Ave, Englewood Cliffs, NJ 07632,
  Tel: (201) 871-8900
  (Containerized shipping, ship chartering)
     Seatrain France, Quai de l'Atlantique, B.P. 1092, 76062 Le Havre Cedex, France
     Seatrain France, 32 Rue P. Brosselette, 76600 Le Havre, France
     Seatrain France, 31 Rue du Pont, 92200 Neuilly Sur Seine, France
     Seatrain France, 55 Montee de Choulans, 69323 Lyon Cedex 1, France
     Seatrain France, 1 Rue du Havre, 67100 Strasbourg, France
     Seatrain France, 4 Quai d'Arenc, 13002 Marseille, France

SEISMOGRAPH SERVICE CORP   PO Box 1590, Tulsa, OH 74112, Tel: (918) 627-3330
  (Geophysical contractor)
     Compagnie Francaise de Prospection Sismique, B.P. 16, 06565 Valbonne, Cedex, France

SELAS CORP OF AMERICA   Dreshertown Rd & Limekiln Pike, Dresher, PA 19025,
  Tel: (215) 646-6600
  (Mfr heat treating equip for metal, glass, ceramic & chem inds)
     Selas S.A., 71 Rue Rivay, F-92300 Levallois-Perret, France
     Selas SA, 79 Rue Anatol France, 92300 Levallois, Perret, France

SENSORMATIC ELECTRONICS CORP   500 NW 12th Ave, Deerfield Beach, BF L33341,
  Tel: (305) 427-9700
  (Electronic article surveillance equip)
     Senelco France SA, 19 Ave. Gourgaud, 75017 Paris, France

SEQUA CORP   200 Park Ave, New York, NY 10166, Tel: (212) 986-5500
  (Aerospace prdts & sys, machinery & metal coatings, transp, spec chems, professional
  & fin serv)
     Materiels Equipements Graphiques, 32-34 rue des Malines, Z.I. Les Malines,
        91 Lisses-Evry, France

SGS CONTROL SERVICES INC   42 Broadway, New York, NY 10004,
  Tel: (212) 482-8700
  (Complete range of quality & quantity control checks & related tech serv)
     SGS France SA, 16 Rue du Louvre, F. 75024 Paris Cedex 1, France,
        And more than 30 locations throughout France

SHEAFFER EATON INC   1 Crown Mark Dr, Lincoln, RI 02865, Tel: (401) 333-0303
  (Mfr writing instruments)
     Penco SARL, 8 Rue Martel, Paris 75010, France

SHEARMAN & STERLING   599 Lexington Ave, New York, NY 10022,
  Tel: (212) 848-4000
  (Lawyers)
     Shearman & Sterling, 21 Ave. George V, 75008 Paris, France

SHEARSON/AMERICAN EXPRESS   American Express Tower, New York, NY 10285,
  Tel: (212) 298-2000
  (Investment banking, financial serv)
     Shearson/American Express, 16 Place Vendome, Paris, France

SHELDONS' INC   626 Center St, Antigo, WI 54409-2496, Tel: (715) 623-2382
  (Mfr recreational fishing tackle)
     MEPPS, SA, Quartier Le Gheit, BP 09, 06390 Contes, France

SHELLER-GLOBE CORP   1641 Porter St, Detroit, MI 48216, Tel: (313) 962-7311
  (Mfr auto components, ind prdts)
    Etablissement Mesnel SA, 9-11 Rue de la Riviere, 78420 Carrieres sur Seine, France

SHIPLEY CO INC   2300 Washington St, Newton, MA 02162, Tel: (617) 969-5500
  (Mfr chems for printed circuit boards & microelectronic mfg)
    Shipley SA, Rue du Cap Horn, ZA de Courtaboeuf, F-91940 Les Ulis, France

SHULTON INC   1 Cyanamid Plaza, Wayne, NJ 07470, Tel: (201) 831-2000
  (Health, beauty & grooming prdts)
    Parfums de Prestige International (JV), 3 Rue de Stockholm, 75008 Paris, France

SILICONIX INC   2201 Laurelwood Dr, Santa Clara, CA 95054, Tel: (408) 988-8000
  (Semiconductor components)
    Siliconix SARL, Centre Commercial de l'Echat, Place de l'Europe,
      94019 Creteil Cedex, France

SIMMONS INTL   1 Gulf & Western Plaza, New York, NY 10023, Tel: (212) 333-3511
  (Bedding prdts)
    Compagnie Continentale Simmons, 54 Blvd. Victor Hugo, 93400 S. Ouen,   France

SIMPLEX TIME RECORDER CO   Simplex Plaza, Gardner, MA 01441,
  Tel: (617) 632-2500
  (Time recorders & stamps, master time sys, alarm, security, monitor & control sys)
    Simplex International Time Recorder Co., 106 Bis Rue du General,
      Leclerc 93116 Rosny-Sous-Buis, Cedex, France

SMITH BARNEY HARRIS UPHAM & CO INC   1345 Ave of the Americas, New York,
  NY 10019, Tel: (212) 399-6000
  (Underwriters, stock & bond brokers)
    Smith Barney & Harris Upacon Inc., 7 Place Vendome, Paris, France

SMITH INTL INC   16740 Hardy St, Houston, TX 77032, Tel: (713) 443-6470
  (Mfr/serv downhole drilling equip)
    Smith Intl. France, SARL, BP 217 Lons, 64142 Bellere, France

SMITH TOOL   PO Box C-19511, Irvine, CA 92713, Tel: (714) 540-7010
  (Drilling bits)
    Smith International France SA, Lyons, France

SONOCO PRODUCTS CO   North Second St, PO Box 160, Hartsville, SC 29550,
  Tel: (803) 383-7000
  (Mfr packaging for consumer & ind mkt)
    Sonoco Gunther S.A., 70800 Fontaine les Luxeuil, France

SPECTRA-PHYSICS   3333 N First St, San Jose, CA 95134, Tel: (408) 946-6080
  (Lasers, optical components & coatings, data sys)
    Spectra-Physics France Sud, CIL Rhone Alpes, 14 Rue de Bruxelles,
      St. Quentin Fallavier, 38290 La Verpilliere, France
    Spectra-Physics, SARL, Ave. de Scandinavie, ZI de Courtaboeuf,
      91400 Orsay-les-Ulis, France

SPECTRAL DYNAMICS CORP   4141 Ruffin Rd, San Diego, CA 92123,
  Tel: (619) 496-3400
  (Mfr Vibration monitoring, analysis & control equip)
    Scientific-Atlanta S.A., 4 Ave. Gabariel Peri, 78360 Montesson, France

SPRAGUE ELECTRIC CO   87 Marshall St, North Adams, MA 01247,
  Tel: (413) 664-4411
  (Electronic components)
    Sprague France SARL, Ave. du Danemark, P.O. Box 0143, 37001 Tours-Cedex, France

SPS TECHNOLOGIES INC   900 Newtown-Yardley Rd, Newtown, PA 18940,
  Tel: (215) 860-3000
  (Mfr aerospace & ind fasteners, precision components, superalloys, magnetic
  materials, fastening sys)
    SPS/Unbrako SA, BP 436 Garanor, 73617 Aulnay-sous-Bois, France

SPX CORP   700 Terrace Point Dr, Muskegon, MI 49443, Tel: (616) 724-5000
  (Mfr spec repair equip & repair parts)
    Bear France, SA, BP 39, F-95611 Cergy-Pontoise Cedex, France

SQUARE D CO   Executive Plaza, Palatine, IL 60067, Tel: (708) 397-2600
  (Power distribution & elec/electr ind control equip)
    Square D Co. France S.A., B.P. 76, 92393 Villeneuve La Garenne, France

SRI INTL   333 Ravenswood Ave, Menlo Park, CA 94025, Tel: (415) 326-6200
  (Intl consulting & research)
    SRI France, 6 Ave. Marceau, 75008 Paris, France

ST JOE MINERALS CORP   250 Park Ave, New York, NY 10017, Tel: (212) 953-5000
  (Coal, oil, gas, iron ore, metals & minerals)
    St. Joe Recherches SARL, 78 Blvd. de Sebastopol, F. 75003 Paris, France

THE STANLEY WORKS   1000 Stanley Dr, PO Box 7000, New Britain, CT 06050,
  Tel: (203) 225-5111
  (Mfr hand tools & hardware)
    Bostitch France, B.P. 74, 112 Ave. Charles de Gaulle, 91423 Morangis, Ceded, France
    SICFO SA, Siege Social: 67700 Saverne, RCS Saverne, France
    Societe de Fabrications Bostitch SA, Maxonchamp, 88360 Rupt sur Moselle, France
    Stanley Works Ltd., 20 Ave. Vladimir Komarov, 98192 Trappes Cedex, France
    Stanley-Mabo SA, B.P. 1579, 25009 Besancon, Cedex, France

STEELCASE INC   901 44th St SE, Grand Rapids, MI 49508, Tel: (616) 247-2710
  (Mfr office, computer-support & systems furniture)
    Steelcase Strafor SA, B.P. 6K, 56 Rue Jean Giraudoux, 67035 Strasbourg Cedex, France

STEINER CORP   PO Box 2317, 505 E South Temple St, Salt Lake City, UT 84102,
  Tel: (801) 328-8831
  (Linen supply service)
    Steiner International France, 11 Rue de la Boetie, 75008 Paris, France

STEMCO INC   PO Box 1989, Longview, TX 75606, Tel: (214) 758-9981
  (Mfr automotive seals, mufflers, spec prdts for heavy duty trucks, buses, trailers)
    Liard S.A., Z.I. la Petite Montagne (SUD), 1 Allee du Dauphine, 91018 Evry, France

STEPAN CO   22 W Frontage Rd, Northfield, IL 60093, Tel: (708) 446-7500
  (Mfr basic & intermediate chems)
    Stepan Europe, B.P. 12, 38340 Voreppe, France
    Stepan Europe, Grenoble, France

STERLING DRUG INC   90 Park Ave, New York, NY 10016, Tel: (212) 907-2000
  (Pharms, chems, cosmetics, household cleaners & waxes)
    Sterling-Europa Winthrop Continental, Paris, France

STERLING SOFTWARE INC   8080 N Central Expy, #1100, Dallas, TX 75206-1895,
Tel: (214) 891-8600
(Sales/serv software prdts; tech servs)
   Sterling Software Intl., 21 Rue de Trois Fontanot, 92000 Nanterre, France

STOKES DIV   5500 Tabor Rd, Philadelphia, PA 19120, Tel: (215) 289-5671
(Vacuum pumps & components, vacuum dryers, oil-upgrading equip)
   Sharples-Stokes SA, B.P. 204, 92502 Rueil-Malmaison, Cedex, France

STONE CONTAINER CORP   150 N Michigan Ave, Chicago, IL 60601-7568,
Tel: (312) 346-6600
(Mfr paper & paper packaging)
   Societe Emballages des Cevennes SA, 30410 Molieres-sur-Ceze, France

STORAGE TECHNOLOGY CORP   2270 S 88th St, Louisville, CO 80028-0001,
Tel: (303) 673-5151
(Mfr/mkt/serv info storage & retrieval sys)
   StorageTex France S.A., BP 73, 41 Rue Fourny, 78530 BUC, France

STRATEGIC PLANNING ASSOCIATES INC   2300 N St NW, Washington, DC 20037,
Tel: (202) 778-7000
(Mgmt consulting)
   Strategic Planning Associates, 7 Rue Galilee, 75116 Paris, France

STRATOFLEX INC   220 Roberts Cut-Off Rd, PO Box 10398, Fort Worth, TX 76114,
Tel: (817) 738-6543
(Hose assemblies, self-sealing & quick disconnect couplings, swivels, etc)
   TMU Hydraulics France SARL, 11/13 Blvd. Pacatianus, B.P. 346, 38204 Vienne Cedex,
   France

SUDLER & HENNESSEY   1633 Broadway, New York, NY 10019, Tel: (212) 265-8000
(Healthcare prdts advertising)
   S&H/Paragraphe, 11/15 Ave. Andre-Morizet, 92105 Boulogne Cedex, Paris, France

SULLAIR CORP   3700 E Michigan Blvd, Michigan City, IN 46360,
Tel: (219) 879-5451
(Refrigeration sys, vacuum pumps, generators, etc)
   Sullair France SARL, 40 Rue de la Republique, 78920 Ecquevilly, France

SULLIVAN & CROMWELL   125 Broad St, New York, NY 10004, Tel: (212) 558-4000
(Lawyers)
   Sullivan & Cromwell, 8 Place Vendome, 75001 Paris, France

SUNDSTRAND CORP   PO Box 7003, Rockford, IL 61125-7003, Tel: (815) 226-6000
(Design/mfr proprietary technology based comps & sub-sys for aerospace & ind)
   Sundstrand France, Zone Industrielle, 21600 Longvic, France

SWIFT & CO   115 W Jackson Blvd, Chicago, IL 60604, Tel: (312) 431-2000
(Meat & poultry, food prdts)
   Swift & Co., 16 Rue du Seminaire, 94516 M.I.N. Rungis, France

SYBRON CORP   411 E Wisconsin Ave, Milwaukee, WI 07662, Tel: (414) 274-6600
(Professional health prdts, spec chems, instru, water & waste water treatment sys)
   Gamlen Europe SA, 2 Rue Huntziger, B.P. 38, 92112 Clichy, France
   Gamlen Europe SA, B.P. 405, 27204 Vernon Cedex, France
   Gamlen Europe SA, 62-70 Rue Yvan Tourgueneff, 78380 Bouginal, France
   Tanatex France SARL, 66 Rue Jean-Baptiste Lebas, 599910 Bondues, France

SYSTEM INDUSTRIES INC   560 Cottonwood Dr, Milpitas, CA 95035,
Tel: (408) 432-1212
(Value added third party vendor high performance data storage sybsys)
System Ind. Provence Cote d'Azur, Les Sporades, 2477 Route de Grasse,
06600 Antibes, France
System Industries, 74 Rue Maurice Flandin, 69003 Lyon, France
System Industries SARL, 30 Ave. de L'Amiral Lemonnier, 78160 Marly-Le Roi, France

SYSTEMS ENGINEERING LABS INC   6901 W Sunrise Blvd, Fort Lauderdale,
FL 33313, Tel: (305) 587-2900
(Digital computers)
Systems Engineering Laboratories SA, 29 Rue de Noisy, 78870 Bailly, France

TANDEM COMPUTERS INC   19333 Vallco Parkway, Cupertino, CA 95014,
Tel: (408) 725-6000
(Computer sys)
Tandem Computer SA, Paris, France

TANDY CORP   1800 One Tandy Center, Fort Worth, TX 76102, Tel: (817) 390-3700
(Electronic & acoustic equip)
Tandy France SA, B.P. 147, Cergy Pointoise Cedex, France

TAYLOR INSTRUMENT CO   99 Ames St, PO Box 110, Rochester, NY 14601,
Tel: (716) 235-6806
(Instru for process control inds)
Taylor Instrument France, 89 Rue Damremont, 75018 Paris, France
Taylor Instrument SARL, 27 Allee Leon Gambetta, P.O. Box 206, 92112 Clichy Cedex,
France

TECH/OPS SEVCON INC   1 Beacon St, Boston, MA 02108, Tel: (617) 523-2030
(Mfr solid state controllers for elec powered vehicles)
Tech/Ops SA, 12 Rue Jean Poulmarch, 95100 Argenteuil, France

TECHNICON INSTRUMENTS CORP   511 Benedict Ave, Tarrytown, NY 10591-5097,
Tel: (914) 631-8000
(Mfr/serv automated blook anal equip, reagents & diagnostics)
Compagnie Technicon S.A., 6-10 Quai de Seine, 93206 St. Denis, Cedex 1, France
Compagnie Technicon SA, Route Nationale 1, 95330 Domont, France

TED BATES WORLDWIDE INC   1515 Broadway, New York, NY 10036,
Tel: (212) 869-3131
(Advertising agency)
Agence Francaise de Propagande-Ted Bates & Cie., 3 Rue Bellini, 92806 Puteaux,
France
Ted Bates SA, 3 Rue Bellini, 92806 Puteaux, France

TEKNIS CORP   PO Box 3189, No Attleboro, MA 02761, Tel: (508) 695-3591
(Sale advanced technology prdts, fiber optics, materials for semiconductor mfr)
Teknis SARL, B.P. 85, 78152 Le Chesnay, Cedex, France

TEKTRONIX INC   PO Box 500, Beaverton, OR 97077, Tel: (503) 627-7111
(Mfr test & meas, visual sys & commun prdts)
Tektronix, Z.I. de Courtaboeuf, B.P. 13, 91941 Les Ulis Cedex, France
Tektronix, other locations in France

TELEDYNE COMPONENTS   1300 Terra Bella Ave, Mountain View, CA 94043,
  Tel: (415) 968-9241
  (Mfr data conversion prdts, bipolar interface, etc)
    Teledyne Components, 85 Rue Anatole France, F-92300 Levallois-Perret, France

TELEDYNE INC   1901 Ave of the Stars, Los Angeles, CA 90067,
  Tel: (213) 277-3311
  (Design/mfr electr & aviation control sys & equip, commun & elect prdts)
    Teledyne SA, 75-77 Rue Carnot, 2300 Levallois, Perrep, France

TELXON CORP   3330 W Market St, Akron, OH 44333, Tel: (216) 867-3700
  (Devel/mfr portable computer sys & related equip)
    TELXON FRANCE, Parc Hightec Apogee, Za de Courtaboeuf, 91966 Les Ulis Cedex, France

TENNECO INC   PO Box 2511, Houston, TX 77001, Tel: (713) 757-2812
  (Natural gas pipelines, integrated oil operations, paperboard prdts, agric & land
  devel)
    Poclain S.A., Ave. de Poclain, Le Plessis Belleville, France

TENNESSEE ASSOCIATES INTL INC   337 East Broadway Ave, Maryville, TN 37801,
  Tel: (615) 983-4044
  (Mgt consulting servs)
    TAI France, 43 Blvd. du Marechal Joffre, 92340 Bourg La Reine, France

TERADYNE INC   183 Essex St, Boston, MA 02111, Tel: (617) 482-2700
  (Electronic test equip & blackplane connection sys)
    Teradyne SA, 10/12 Rue de Chartres, Paris, France

TEXACO INC   2000 Westchester Ave, White Plains, NY 10650, Tel: (914) 253-4000
  (Explor/mktg crude oil & its prdts, petro-chems)
    Texaco France SA, 39 Rue Cambon, 75001 Paris, France

TEXON INC   Crescent Mills St, Russell, MA 01071, Tel: (413) 862-3652
  (Latex & resin impregnated fibre prdts)
    Texon France SA, Saint-Rivalain, Morbihan, 56310 Bubry, France
    Texon France SA, 14 Rue Source, 75016 Paris, France

THERMO ELECTRIC CO   109 Fifth St, Saddle Brook, NJ 07662, Tel: (201) 843-5800
  (Mfr temp/meas control prdts)
    Thermo Electric SA, 211 Ave. Aristide Briand, 92160 Antony, France

THETFORD CORP   7101 Jackson Rd, PO Box 1285, Ann Arbor, MI 48106,
  Tel: (313) 769-6000
  (Sanitation sys)
    Thetford Intl. SARL, ZI du Vert Galant, Rue des Oziers, 95310 St. Quen, L'Aumone,
    France

THOMAS & BETTS CORP   1001 Frontier Rd, Bridgewater, NJ 08807-0993,
  Tel: (201) 685-1600
  (Mfr elect/electr connectors & accessories)
    Thomas & Betts France, 57 Place de la Seine, Silic 120, 94513 Rungis, Cedex, France

THOMAS INTL PUBLISHING CO   1 Penn Plaza, New York, NY 10119,
  Tel: (212) 290-7213
  (Publ ind magazines & directories)
    Editions Thomas/Elsevier S.A., 128 Rue Daguesseau, 92100 Boulogne-Billancourt,
    France

THOR POWER TOOL CO 72 Bayside Rd, Virginia Beach, VA 23455,
Tel: (804) 323-5666
(Mfr portable air-operated & elect tools)
Stewart Warner France SA, Rue Des Orteaux 75020 Paris, France

TIME WARNER INC Time Life Bldg, New York, NY 10020, Tel: (212) 522-1212
(Magazine & book publ, communications)
Time Life News Service, 17 Ave. Matignon, 75008 Paris, France

TIMET CORP 420 Rouser Rd, PO Box 2824, Pittsburgh, PA 15230,
Tel: (412) 262-4200
(Mfr titanium mill prdts)
Timet France SARL, B.P. 183, 95023 Cergy Pontoise Cedex, France

TIMEX GROUP LTD Waterbury, CT 06760, Tel: (203) 573-5000
(Watches, clocks, timing instru, cameras, gyroscopes)
Usine Kelton, 1 Rue Denis Papin, 25011 Besancon, France

THE TIMKEN CO 1835 Dueber Ave SW, Canton, OH 44706-2798, Tel: (216) 438-3000
(Mfr tapered roller bearings & alloy steels)
Timken Frnace, 2 Rue Timken, Colmar, 68002 Cedex, France

TOPFLIGHT CORP 200 E 9th Ave, PO Box 472, York, PA 17405,
Tel: (717) 843-9901
(Printed pressure-sensitive adhesive materials)
Topflight France, 105 Ave. des Gresillons, 92 Gennevilliers, France

TORRINGTON/FAFNIR 200 Chestnut Ridge Rd, Woodcliff Lake, NJ 07675,
Tel: (203) 482-9511
(Mfr bearings, precision metal parts & assemblies, universal joints)
Torrington France, 8 Rue Henri Becquerel, Odyssee 2000,
F-92508 Rueil-Malmaison Cedex, Paris, France

TOWERS PERRIN FORSTER & CROSBY INC 245 Park Ave, New York, NY 10167,
Tel: (212) 309-3400
(Management consulting)
Towers Perrin Forster & Crosby, 57 Blvd. de Montmorency, 75016 Paris, France

TRACE MOUNTAIN 2190 Bering Dr, San Jose, CA 95131, Tel: (408) 435-7800
(Mfr diskette; tape duplication equip)
Trace Mountain France, Les Espaces Multiservices, Blvd. de Courcerin,
Zi de Pariest 777325, Mame la Vaue Cedex 2, France

TRACOR INC 6500 Tracor Lane, Austin, TX 78721, Tel: (512) 926-2800
(Time & frequency prdts, gas & liquid chromatographs, eng serv, ship repair)
Tracor France SARL, Cedex L. 202-16, Rue Saarinen, 94533 Silic Rungis, France

TRANE CO 3600 Pammel Creek Rd, La Crosse, WI 54601, Tel: (608) 787-2000
(Mfr A/C equip)
Societe Trane, B.P. 127, 88004 Epinal Cedex, France
Societe Trane, 13 Rue Doct Roux, 75015 Paris, France

TRANS WORLD AIRLINES INC 605 Third Ave, New York, NY 10158,
Tel: (212) 557-6107
(Air transp, hotel, food serv, real estate)
Trans World Airlines, Inc., 101 Ave. des Champs Elysees, 75008 Paris, France

TRIBOL   21031 Ventura Blvd, #600, Woodland Hills, CA 91364,
  Tel: (818) 888-0808
  (Mfr industrial lubricants)
    Tribol SARL, 45 Avenue del Europe, 78142 Velizy Cedex, France

TRINOVA CORP   3000 Strayer, PO Box 50, Maumee, OH 43537, Tel: (419) 867-2200
  (Mfr engr components & sys for ind)
    Aeroquip SA, 14 Rue Du Morvan, 507 Rungis, 94623 Silic, France
    Trinova SA, 9 Rue Michael Faraday, 37173 Chambray-Les-Tours, France

TRITON ENERGY CORP   4925 Greenville Ave, 1400 One Energy Sq, Dallas,
  TX 75206, Tel: (214) 691-5200
  (Energy explor & prod)
    Triton France SA, 109 Rue du Faubourg St. Honore, 75008 Paris, France

TRW INC   1900 Richmond Rd, Cleveland, OH 44124, Tel: (216) 291-7000
  (Electr & energy-related prdts, automotive & aerospace prdts, tools & fasteners)
    Gemmer France, 97 Rue de Verdun, Verdun, 92151 Suresnes (Seine) France
    Le Thillot, Vosges, France
    Societe Hydro-Mecanique Pleuger, 21 Rue de la Mouchetierre, ZI d'Ingres,
      F. 45140 Saint Jean de la Ruelle, Orleans, France
    Societe Metallurgique G. Jeudy, 31 Rue des Forges, 67130 Schirmeck, France
    Societe de Mecanique de Pringy, 74 Pringy (Haute savoie) France
    TRW Composants Electroniques, Ave. de la Jalle Re, 33300 Bordeaux-Lac, France
    TRW Mission Hydrosys. SA, Monceau Commerce Bldg., 38 Rue de Lisbonne 75008, Paris,
      France

TURCO PRODUCTS INC   7300 Bolsa Ave, Westminster, CA 92684-3600,
  Tel: (714) 890-3600
  (Mfr chem cleaning compounds & equip)
    Purex Corp. Turco France SA, 3-5 Impasse du Quai de l'Industrie,
      91200 Athis-Mons (Essonne) France

TURNER MACHINERY CO   181 Elliott, Beverly, MA 01915, Tel: (617) 927-4200
  (Mach for tanning)
    USM France, 5Rue de Dunkerque, 75010 Paris, France

U S INDUSTRIES INC   PO Box 629, Evansville, IN 47704, Tel: (812) 425-2428
  (Diversified prdts & sys for industry, agribusiness & retail markets)
    Big Dutchman France SARL, La Madeleine de Nonancourt 27320, Nonancourt, France

UNION CAMP CORP   1600 Valley Rd, Wayne, NJ 07470, Tel: (201) 628-2000
  (Flavors, fragrances, essential oils, aroma chems, corrugated containers)
    Bush Boake Allen Ltd., 153 Ave. Franklin Roosevelt, 06110 Le Cannet, Rocheville,
      France
    Bush Boake Allen Ltd., 100 Ave. Charles de Gaulle, 92522 Neuilly-Cedex, France

UNION CARBIDE CORP   Old Ridgebury Rd, Danbury, CT 06817, Tel: (203) 794-2000
  (Carbon prdts, chems, plastics, gases & related prdts, etc)
    Biosystemes SA, 45 Rue de Villeneuve, F. 94598 Rungis Cedex, France
    Chemin du Poutingon, Quartier de la Croix d'Argent, F. 34000 Montpellier, France
    Graphite Electrodes Plant, Zone Industrielle des Dunes, Rue des Garennes,
      F. 62100 Calais, France
    Graphite Electrodes Plant, Notre Dame de Briancon, La Lechere,
      F. 73260 Aigueblanche, France
    La Littorale SA, 19 Quai du Port Neuf, F. 34505 Beziers, France

Medical Products, Rue de Puech Villa, Zolad, F. 34000 Montpellier, France
UC France SA, 4 Place des Etats-Unis, Silic 214, 94518 Rungis, Cedex, France

UNION SPECIAL CORP   222 No LaSalle, Chicago, IL 60601, Tel: (312) 606-9500
(Mfr ind sewing machs)
Union Special de France, 91 Ave. de la Republique, 75540 Cedex 11, Paris, France

UNISYS CORP   PO Box 500, Blue Bell, PA 19424, Tel: (215) 542-4011
(Mfg/mktg/serv electr info sys)
SA Unisys, Boulevard de l'Oise, La Palette Orange, 95015 Pontoise, France
Sperry SA, 3 Rue Bellini, 92806 Puteaux, France

UNITED AIRLINES INC   PO Box 66100, Chicago, IL 60666, Tel: (708) 952-4000
(Air transp)
United Airlines, 40 Rue Jean Jaures, 93176 Bagnolet Cedex, France

UNITED BRANDS CO   1271 Ave of the Americas, New York, NY 10020,
Tel: (212) 397-4000
(Food prdts)
Fuffes, Omer Decugis SA, 15 Rue des Antilles-Bat 12, B.P. 315, 94150 Rungis, France

UNITED TECHNOLOGIES CORP   United Technologies Bldg, Hartford, CT 06101,
Tel: (203) 728-7000
(Mfr aircraft engines, elevators, A/C, auto equip, space & military electr, rocket
propulsion sys)
United Technologies Intl. Operations Inc., 141 Rue de Saussure, 75017 Paris, France

UOP INC   Ten UOP Plaza, Des Plaines, IL 60016, Tel: (708) 391-2000
(Diversified research, development & mfr of ind prdts & sys mgmt studies & serv)
Procofrance SA, Paris, France

UPJOHN CO   7000 Portage Rd, Kalamazoo, MI 49001, Tel: (616) 323-4000
(Pharms, agric prdts, ind chems)
Laboratoires Upjohn SARL, Tour Franklin-Cedex 11, 92081 Paris de la Defense, France

URSCHEL LABORATORIES INC   2503 Calumet Ave, PO Box 2200, Valparaiso,
IN 46384-2200, Tel: (219) 464-4811
(Design & mfr precision food processing equip)
Urschel Intl. Ltd., Orly Fret 747, 94398 Orly Aerogare, Cedex, Succursale, France

USF&G FINANCIAL SERVICES CORP   100 Light St, Baltimore, MD 21202,
Tel: (301) 547-3000
(Investment mgt, real estate, computer leasing, fin prdt mktg & admin, strategic
consult)
Quantum Data, 262 Rue du Faubourg Saint Honore, Paris 73008, France

VALERON CORP   750 Stephenson Highway, Troy, MI 48084, Tel: (313) 589-1000
(Cemented carbide, high speed steel, ceramic & diamond cutting tool prdts, etc)
Valenite-Modco SARL, 7 Rue Jean Mace, 69800 Saint Priest, France

VAN STRAATEN CHEMICAL CO   630 W Washington Blvd, Chicago, IL 60606,
Tel: (312) 454-1000
(Metalworking fluids, ind cleaners, rust preventives, etc)
Wynn Oil Co., 41 Rue Parmentier, Asnieres 92600, France

VAREL MFG CO   9230 Denton Rd, PO Box 20156, Dallas, TX 75220,
   Tel: (214) 351-6487
   (Oil, mining, geophysical, water-well & constr equip)
      Varel Europe, 34 Ave. Raspail 94100, Saint Maur (Seine) France

VARIAN ASSOCIATES INC   611 Hansen Way, Palo Alto, CA 94304-1030,
   Tel: (415) 493-4000
   (Mfr microwave tubes & devices, analytical instru, semiconductor process & med equip,
   vacuum sys)
      Varian SA, BP 12, Quartier de Courtaboeuf, F-91941 Les Ulis Cedex, Orsay, France

VEEDER-ROOT CO   125 Powder Forest Dr, PO Box 2003, Simsbury, CT 06070-2003,
   Tel: (203) 651-2700
   (Mfr counting, controlling & sensing devices)
      Veeder Root SARL, 8 Place de la Loire, Silic 422, 94583 Rungis Cedex, France

VENDO CO   7209 N Ingram, Pinedale, CA 93650, Tel: (209) 439-1770
   (Coin-op automatic vending machs)
      Vendo France SA, 10 Place de L'Europe Saint Quentin Fallavier 38290, Laverpilliere,
      France

VISHAY INTERTECHNOLOGY INC   63 Lincoln Highway, Malvern, PA 19355,
   Tel: (215) 644-1300
   (Precision resistors, strain gages instru, educational prdts, etc)
      Vishay Micromesures, 98 Blvd. Gabriel Peri, 92240, Malakoff, France

VIVITAR CORP   9350 Desoto Ave, Chatsworth, CA 91313, Tel: (818) 700-2890
   (Photographic equip, electr supplies)
      Vivitar France SA, 41-43 Rue de Ville Neuve, Silic 197, F. 94563 Rungis, France

WALKER MFG CO   1201 Michigan Blvd, Racine, WI 53402, Tel: (414) 632-8871
   (Automotive parts, exhaust sys, service equip)
      Ets. R. Bellanger SA, B.P. 46, La Croix des Landes, 53940 Saint-Bertheven, France
      Ets. R. Bellanger SA, La Croix des Landes, B.P. 46, 53940 St. Berthevin, France

WARNER BROS INC   4000 Warner Blvd, Burbank, CA 91522, Tel: (213) 954-6000
   (Prod/dist motion picture films, TV, music recording & pub)
      Warner Bros. Columbia Film G.I.E., 20 Rue Troyon, 75017 Paris, France

WARNER ELECTRIC BRAKE & CLUTCH CO   449 Gardner St, South Beloit, IL 61080,
   Tel: (815) 389-3771
   (Automotive & ind brakes & clutches)
      Warner France, B.P. 313, 72007 Lemans, Cedex, France

WARNER-LAMBERT CO   201 Tabor Road, Morris Plains, NJ 07950,
   Tel: (201) 540-2000
   (Mfr ethical & proprietary pharms, confectionary & consumer prdts)
      Warner-Lambert France Ltd., 11 Ave. Dubonnet, 92407, Courbevoie, Cedex, France

WATERS CHROMATOGRAPHY DIV   34 Maple St, Milford, MA 01757,
   Tel: (617) 478-2000
   (Mfr/distr liquid chromatographic instru/accessories/tech)
      Millipore SA, 6 Rue Jean Pierre Timbaud, 78180 Montigny le Bretonneux, France

THE WAYNE GROUP LTD   244 California St, San Francisco, CA 94111,
Tel: (415) 421-2010
(Human resources consult)
    The Wayne Group Ltd., 19 Rue d'Anjou, 75008 Paris, France

WEATHERFORD INTL INC   1360 Post Oak Blvd, PO Box 27608, Houston,
TX 77227-9917, Tel: (713) 439-9400
(Tubular & cementation servs, prdts & equip; water jetting servs, mfr marine pedestal
cranes)
    Weatherford SA, Rue Marie Joliot Curie, Zone Industrielle, BP 130,
      F-64143 Lons Cedex, France

WEIGHT WATCHERS INTL INC   Jericho Atrium, 500 North Broadway, Jericho,
NY 11753-2196, Tel: (516) 939-0400
(Weight reduction programs, food prdts)
    Weight Watchers France SARL, 4 Rue du Colonel Driant, 75001 Paris, France

WERTHEIM & CO INC   200 Park Ave, New York, NY 10166-0090, Tel: (212) 578-0200
(Investment banking, security brokers)
    Wertheim & Cie. SA, 10 Rue Duphot, F. 75001 Paris, France

WESTERN PUBLISHING CO   1220 Mound Ave, Racine, WI 53404, Tel: (414) 633-2431
(Pub children's & adult books; games, educational prdts)
    Les Editions des Deux Coqs d'Or, 28 Rue de la Boetie, 75008 Paris, France

WESTINGHOUSE AIR BRAKE CO   40 W 40th St, New York, NY 10018,
Tel: (212) 840-5440
(Equip for transp, constr, mining inds)
    WABCO Automotive Products Group, Tour Albert 1er, 65 Ave. de Colmar,
      92507 Rueil Malmaison Cedex, France
    WABCO Freinage de Vehicules SA, 124 Ave. Aristide Briand, B.P., 16,
      F. 77410 Claye-Souilly, France

WHEELABRATOR-FRYE INC   11255 N Torrey Pines Rd, La Jolla, CA 92037,
Tel: (603) 926-5911
(Diversified environmental & energy sys, chems, precision & ind equip)
    Wheelabrator Allevard, 58580 Allevard, France

WHITMAN CORP   111 E Wacker Dr, Chicago, IL 60601, Tel: (312) 565-3000
(Strategic mgmt: consumer goods & services)
    Whitman Corp., Tour Albert, 65 ave.de Colmar, 92507 Rueil Malmaison-Cedex, France

WHITTAKER CORP   10880 Wilshire Blvd, Los Angeles, CA 90024,
Tel: (213) 475-9411
(Health care, high tech & spec chems)
    Bennes Marrel SA, Zone Industrielle, 42160 Andrezieux, Bautheon, France

WILLIAMHOUSE-REGENCY INC   28 W 23rd St, New York, NY 10010,
Tel: (212) 691-2000
(Paper converting, thermography)
    Carcy Thermogravure, 75 Ave. Lenine, 92000 Nanterre, France
    Fraire-Part Selection, 13190 Allauch la Pounche, France

HARRY WINSTON INC   718 Fifth Ave, New York, NY 10019, Tel: (212) 245-2000
(Diamonds, lapidary work)
    Harry Winston de New York SARL, 29 Ave. Montaigne, 75008 Paris, France

WITCO CORP   520 Madison Ave, New York, NY 10022-4236, Tel: (212) 605-3800
  (Mfr chem & petroleum prdts)
    Witco Chemical SA, 10 Rue Cambaceres 75008, Paris, France

WORCESTER CONTROLS CORP   33 Lott Dr, Marlboro, MA 01752, Tel: (508) 481-4800
  (Mfr ball valves, control devices)
    Worcester France SARL, Zone d'Activite de Burez Orsay, 91400 Orsay, France

WORLD COMMUNICATIONS INC   67 Broad St, New York, NY 10004,
  Tel: (212) 607-2000
  (Intl private line services)
    World Communications Inc., 172 Rue de Courcelles, F. 75017 Paris, France

WORLD COURIER INC   46 Trinity Pl, New York, NY 10006, Tel: (718) 978-9400
  (Intl courier serv)
    World Courier France, B.P. 10484, Roissy, Paris, France

WM WRIGLEY JR CO   410 N Michigan Ave, Chicago, IL 60611-4287,
  Tel: (312) 644-2121
  (Chewing gum)
    Biesheim, Wrigley France SA, Zone Industrielle, B.P. 29, 68600 Neufbrisach, France

WYNN OIL CO   2600 E Nutwood Ave, PO Box 4370, Fullerton, CA 92631,
  Tel: (714) 992-2000
  (Chem additives for oil, grease & fuels; hardware)
    Wynns France, 41 Rue Parmentier, 92600 Asnieres, Paris, France

YORK INTERNATIONAL CORP   PO Box 1592, York, PA 17405-1592,
  Tel: (715) 771-7890
  (Mfr A/C, heating & refrig sys & equip)
    Le Froid Industriel-York SA, B.P. 10, 44471 Carquefou, Nantes, France

YOUNG & RUBICAM INTL INC   285 Madison Ave, New York, NY 10017,
  Tel: (212) 210-3000
  (Advertising agency)
    Young & Rubicam France, 7-15 Rue du Dome, 92100 Boulogne, France

GABON

BAKER OIL TOOLS   PO Box 3048, Houston, TX 77253, Tel: (713) 923-9351
  (Oil/gas well completions equip)
    Baker Intl. SA, P.O. Box 803, Port Gentil, Gabon

LOUIS BERGER INTL INC   100 Halsted St, East Orange, NJ 07019,
  Tel: (201) 678-1960
  (Consulting engineers, architects, economists & planners)
    Louis Berger Intl. Inc., c/o UNDP, BP 2183, Libreville, Gabon

CHEVRON OVERSEAS PETROLEUM INC   555 Market St, PO Box 7643, San Francisco, CA 94120, Tel: (415) 894-7800
(Petroleum explor)
   Chevron Exploration Corp., Libreville, Gabon

CITIBANK NA   399 Park Ave, New York, NY 10043, Tel: (212) 559-1000
(Intl banking)
   First National City Bank, B.P. 3940, Libreville, Gabon

EXXON CHEMICAL CO   9 Old Kings Hwy S, Darien, CT 06820, Tel: (203) 655-5200
(Mfr & sales of petrochems)
   Exxon Inc., Libreville, Gabon

FIDELITY BANK   135 S Broad St, Philadelphia, PA 19109, Tel: (215) 985-6000
(Investments & banking)
   Fidelty Bank, B.P. 2151, Libreville, Gabon

GAMLEN CHEMICAL CO   121 S Maple Ave, S San Francisco, CA 94080, Tel: (415) 873-1750
(Chems, detergents & tank cleansers)
   Gamlen S.A.M. Daron, P.O. Box 404, Port Gentil, Gabon

FRANK B HALL & CO INC   549 Pleasantville Rd, Briarcliff Manor, NY 10510, Tel: (914) 769-9200
(Insurance)
   Sogerco Gabon, Mbembe Hatton Bldg., P.O. Box 2102, Libreville, Gabon

IMCO SERVICES   5950 N Course Dr, Houston, TX 70072, Tel: (713) 561-1300
(Drilling fluids)
   Halliburton-IMCO (Gabon) SARL, Barge 106, P.O. Box 507, Port Gentil, Gabon

INA CORPORATION   1600 Arch St, Philadelphia, PA 19101, Tel: (215) 523-5335
(Holding co: ins, financial serv)
   INA, Les Commissaires d'Avaries Reunis, B.P. 187, Libreville, Gabon

ITT SHERATON CORP   60 State St, Boston, MA 02108, Tel: (617) 367-3600
(Hotel operations)
   Sheraton Re-Ndama Hotel, B.P. 4064, Libreville, Gabon

MILCHEM INC   3900 Essex Lane, PO Box 22111, Houston, TX 77027, Tel: (214) 439-8000
(Gas & oil well drilling fluids & chem additives)
   Milchem Gabon SARL, B.P. 668, Port Gentil, Gabon

ONAN CORP   1400 73rd Ave NE, Minneapolis, MN 55432, Tel: (612) 574-5000
(Electric generators, ind engines & controls)
   Sogafric/Hydromat Dpt., Boite Postale 613, Libreville, Gabon

TENNECO OIL EXPLORATION & PRODUCTION   PO Box 2511, Houston, TX 77001, Tel: (713) 757-2131
(Oil explor & prod)
   Tenneco Oil of Gabon Inc., B.P. 3921, Libreville, Gabon

TEXACO INC   2000 Westchester Ave, White Plains, NY 10650, Tel: (914) 253-4000
(Explor/mktg crude oil & its prdts, petro-chems)
   Texaco Ltd., P.O. Box 210, Libreville, Gabon

UNION CARBIDE CORP   Old Ridgebury Rd, Danbury, CT 06817, Tel: (203) 794-2000
  (Carbon prdts, chems, plastics, gases & related prdts, etc)
    Union Carbide Corp., Libreville, Gabon

WEATHERFORD INTL INC   1360 Post Oak Blvd, PO Box 27608, Houston,
  TX 77227-9917, Tel: (713) 439-9400
  (Tubular & cementation servs, prdts & equip; water jetting servs, mfr marine pedestal
  cranes)
    Weatherford Intl., BP 654, Port Gentil, Gabon

WESTERN GEOPHYSICAL   PO Box 2469, Houston, TX 77252-2469, Tel: (713) 789-9600
  (Geophysical serv)
    Western Geophysical Co., BP 335, Blvd. de Independance, Libreville, Gabon

GERMANY

3M CO   3M Center, St Paul, MN 55144-1000, Tel: (612) 733-1110
  (Mfr abrasives, adhesives, chems, ind & consumer tapes/diskettes, health care prdts,
  elec connectors)
    3M Deutschland GmbH, Postfach 643, D-4040 Neuss 1, Germany
    3M Electrical Labaoratories GmbH, Georg-Wilhelm-Str. 183-185, D-2102 Hamburg 93,
      Germany

ABBOTT LABORATORIES   Abbott Park, North Chicago, IL 60064,
  Tel: (312) 937-6100
  (Pharm & lab prdts)
    euteche Abbott GmbH, 6507 Ingelheim am Rhein, Germany

ACCO INDUSTRIES INC   101 Oakview Dr, Trumbull, CT 06611, Tel: (203) 371-5439
  (Testing sys, chain, castings, brakes, bridge & jib cranes)
    F. Platen GmbH, 6292 Weilmunster 2, Dusseldorfer Str. 2, Germany

ACCO INTL INC   770 S Acco Plaza, Wheeling, IL 60090, Tel: (708) 541-9500
  (Paper fasteners & clips, metal fasteners, binders, staplers)
    Acco International GmbH, Industrie Str. 25, Postfach 1146, D-6470 Budingen 1,
      Germany

ACCURAY CORP   650 Ackerman Rd, PO Box 02248, Columbus, OH 43202,
  Tel: (614) 261-2000
  (Computer-based process mgmt sys for forest prdts, metals rolling, textiles, tobacco
  ind)
    Accuray Deutschland, GmbH, Siegburg, Germany

ACE CONTROLS INC   23435 Industrial Park Dr, Farmington Hills, MI 48024,
  Tel: (313) 476-0213
  (Ind hydraulic shock absorbers, cylinders, valves & automation controls)
    Ace Stossdampfer GmbH, Postfach 3021, D-4018 Langenfeld, Germany

ACHESON COLLOIDS CO   1600 Washington Ave, PO Box 288, Port Huron, MI 48060,
  Tel: (313) 984-5581
  (Graphite, lubricants & other specialty chems)
    Deutsche Acheson GmbH, Karl Str. 29, Postfach 792, 7900 Ulm, Germany

ACTION INSTRUMENTS INC   8601 Aero Dr, San Diego, CA 92123,
  Tel: (619) 279-5226
  (Mfr electr instru & ind meas computers)
    Action Industrie Computer GmbH, Voltastrasse 8, D-6072 Dreiech, Germany

ACUFF-ROSE PUBLICATION INC   65 Music Square W, Nashville, TN 37203,
  Tel: (615) 321-5000
  (Music publisher)
    Acuff-Rose Musikveriage KG, Heinrich-Barth Str. 30, 2000 Hamburg 13, Germany

ADAMS & ASSOCIATES INTL   978 Hampton Park, Barrington, IL 60010,
  Tel: (708) 304-5300
  (Mgt conslt exec search)
    Feix & Partner Intl., Tolzer Strasse 1 A, Grunwald 6., Munich 8022, Germany

ADDISON-WESLEY PUBLISHING CO   Route 128, Reading, MA 01867,
  Tel: (617) 944-3700
  (Educational textbook publ)
    Addison-Wesley (Deutschland) GmbH, Widemayerstr 17, 8000 Munich 22, Germany
    Addison-Wesley Verlag (Deutschland), Poppelsdorfer Allee 32, D-5300 Bonn 3, Germany

ADDRESSOGRAPH FARRINGTON INC   300 Pond St, Randolph, MA 02368,
  Tel: (617) 963-8500
  (Embossing & credit authorization sys)
    Addressograph Farrington GmbH, Monschauer Str. 1, 4000 Dusseldorf, Germany

AERONAUTICAL INSTRUMENTS & RADIO CO   234 Garibaldi Ave, Lodi, NJ 07644,
  Tel: (201) 473-0034
  (Mfr aeronautical instru)
    Elan GmbH, Freudenber Str. 27, 6200 Weisbaden, Schienstien, Germany

AFIA   110 William St, New York, NY 10038, Tel: (212) 964-4990
  (Insurance)
    AFIA Worldwide Insurance, Aachener Str. 197, 5 Cologne 41, Germany

AIC PHOTO INC   168 Glen Cove Rd, Carle Place, NY 11514, Tel: (516) 742-7300
  (Imp/distr photo equip)
    AIC Fotetechnik GmbH, Schulze-Delitzsch Str. 7, 7022 Stuttgart-Leinfelden, Germany

AIR EXPRESS INTL CORP   120 Tokeneke Rd, PO Box 1231, Darien, CT 06820,
  Tel: (203) 655-7900
  (Air frt forwarder)
    Air Express, Intl. GmbH, 5 Cologne 90, Flughafen Cologne/Bonn, Cologne. Germany
    Air Express, Intl. GmbH, Lufterachtzentrum, 4 Dusseldorf-Flughafen, Dusseldorf,
      Germany
    Air Express, Intl. GmbH, Fasanenweg 4, 6092 Kelsterbach, Germany
    Air Express, Intl. GmbH, Flughafen-Fuhlsbuttez, Luftfrachthof-Halle 119,
      2000 Hamburg 63, Germany

AIR LOGISTICS CORP   3600 E Foothill Blvd, Pasadena, CA 91107,
  Tel: (213) 681-1101
  (Container sys, aircraft instru)
    Air-Log GmbH, Loreleyring 21, 6200 Wiesbaden, Germany

AIR PRODUCTS & CHEMICALS INC   7201 Hamilton Blvd, Allentown, PA 18195,
  Tel: (215) 481-4911
  (Mfr ind gases & chems)
    Air Products GmbH, Klosterstr. 24-28, 4 Dusseldorf, Germany
    Tyczka Industrie-Gase GmbH, Rheinkaistr. 2, 6800 Mannheim 1, Germany

AIRPAX CORP   7 McKee Pl, Cheshire, CT 06450, Tel: (203) 271-6000
  (Mfr small control components)
    Airpax GmbH, Bockenheimer Landstr. 51, 6000 Frankfurt am Main, Germany

ALARM DEVICE MFG CO   165 Eileen Way, Syosset, NY 11791, Tel: (516) 921-6704
  (Security, fire & burglary sys)
    Ademco-Sontrix GmbH, Postfach 4125, D-7302 Ostfildern, Germany
    Ademco-Sontrix GmbH, Oberssestr. 7, 8000 Munich, Germany

ALBANY INTL CORP   PO Box 1907, Albany, NY 12201, Tel: (518) 445-2200
  (Paper mach clothing, engineered fabrics, plastic prdts, filtration media)
    Filtra GmbH, Postfach 5, Filtrastr. 5, 4730 Ahlen 5, Germany
    Filtra GmbH, Postfach 1640, Steinackerstr 20, D-7858 Weil Am Rhein, Germany
    Walters Europa, Postfach 5, 4730 Ahlens, Germany

ALBERTO-CULVER CO   2525 Armitage Ave, Melrose Park, IL 60160,
  Tel: (708) 450-3000
  (Hair sprays)
    Alberto-Culver Co., Kelchstr. 31, 1000 Berlin 41, Germany

ALCO CONTROLS DIV EMERSON ELECTRIC   PO Box 12700, St Louis, MO 63141,
  Tel: (314) 569-4670
  (Mfr/sales refrig & A/C flow controls)
    Alco Controls, Div. Emerson Electric, GmbH, Heerstr. 111, Postfach 1229,
      7050 Waiblingen, Germany

ALCO STANDARD CORP   825 Duportail Rd, Wayne, PA 19087, Tel: (215) 296-8000
  (Diversified distr, mfg & resources)
    Big Drum GmbH, Weinbergstrostrasse 13, D-3505 Gudensberg 1, Germany
    Emerson Electric GmbH, Postfach 1229, 6050 Waiblingen, Germany

ALCOA FUJIKURA LTD   105 Westport Dr, Brentwood, TN 37027, Tel: (615) 370-2105
  (Mfr optical groundwire, wire produce harnesses)
    Alcoa Fujikura Ltd., Robert-Perthel-Strasse 3, D-5000 Koln 60, Germany

ALLEN GROUP INC   534 Broadhollow Rd, Melville, NY 11747, Tel: (516) 293-5500
  (Automotive carwash & diagnostic equip)
    A. Rohe, Branch of The Allen Group International Inc., Nordring 144,
      6050 Offenbach (Main), Germany
    A. Rohe, Branch of The Allen Group International, Inc., 8510 Fuerth,
      Dieselstrabe 5, Germany
    A. Rohe, Branch of The Allen Group International, Inc., Hanoversche Str. 25/7,
      3502 Niestetal, Germany
    California Branch of A. Rohe GmbH, Aschaffenburger Str. 48, 8752 Schoellkrippen,
      Germany
    Romeico, Branch of A. Rohe GmbH, Hanauer Str. 101, Postfach 500145, 8000 Munich 50,

Germany
Tamo, Branch of The Allen Group International, Inc., In de Tarpen 71-99,
2000 Norderstedt 3, Germany

ALLEN-BRADLEY CO   PO Box 2086, Milwaukee, WI 53201, Tel: (414) 382-2000
(Electrical control devices)
Allen-Bradley GmbH, Duesselbergerstr. 15, D-5657 Haan 2 Gruiten, Germany

ALLENBERG COTTON CO INC   104 S Front St, PO Box 254, Memphis, TN 38103,
Tel: (901) 521-1061
(Raw cotton)
Allenberg Baumwoll GmbH, Ostertorsteinweg 57a, 2800 Bremen, Germany

ALLERGAN PHARMACEUTICALS INTL INC   2525 DuPont Dr, Irvine, CA 92713,
Tel: (714) 752-4500
(Pharms, opthalmic & dermatological preparations)
Pharm-Allergan Vertrieb GmbH, Postfach 210-848, D-7500 Karlsruhe 21, Germany

ALLIED-SIGNAL INC   Columbia Rd & Park Ave, PO Box 2245R, Morristown,
NJ 07960, Tel: (201) 455-2000
(Mfr aerospace & automotive prdts, engineered materials)
Airsupply Intl. GmbH, Konradstrasse 9/111, 8000 Munich 40, Germany
Allied-Signal Aerospace Co., Hahnstrasse 40, D-6000 Frankfurt Main 71, Germany
Allied-Signal Aerospace Co., Munchener Freiheit 12, 8000 Munich 40, Germany
Bendix Deutschland GmbH, Postfach 1450, Am Ochsenwald, Neunkirchen 668, Germany
Energit GmbH, EEZ Industriestrasse 20, 7253 Renningen, Baden-Wuerttemberg, Germany
Garrett GmbH, Frankfurterstrasse 4165, Postfach 1150, 6096 Raunheim am Main, Germany
Jurid Werke GmbH, Postfach 1249, Hamburg, Germany

ALLIS-CHALMERS CORP   PO Box 512, Milwaukee, WI 53201, Tel: (414) 475-4011
(Heavy mach, equip & serv)
Allis-Chalmers Mfg. Co., Brennen Deport, Hafenstr. 10/13, Postfach 2058,
2800 Bremen 8, Germany

AM INTL INC   333 W Wacker Dr, #900, Chicago, IL 60606-1265,
Tel: (312) 558-1966
(Mfr/sale/serv commun graphics, info handling equip & sys)
AM International GmbH, Robert-Bosch-Str. 18, Postfach 10-20-08,
6072 Dreieich B. Frankfurt/Main, Germany

AMDAHL CORP   1250 East Arques Ave, PO Box 3470, Sunnyvale, CA 94088-3470,
Tel: (408) 746-6000
(Mfr large scale computers, complementary software storage & commun prdts)
Amdahl Deutschland GmbH, Hauptverwaltung, Arabella Strassse 21, D-8000 Munich 81,
Germany

AMERICAN AIR FILTER CO INC   215 Central Ave, PO Box 35690, Louisville,
KY 40277, Tel: (502) 637-0011
(Air cleaning equip)
AAF-Lufttechnik GmbH, Herner Strasse 57, 4350 Recklinghausen, Germany

AMERICAN AIRLINES INC   PO Box 619616, Dallas-Ft Worth Arpt, TX 75261-9616,
Tel: (817) 355-1234
(Air transp)
American Airlines, Monckebergstr. 31, 2000 Hamburg 1, Germany
American Airlines, Airport Munich, Riem Room 430, 8000 Munich 87, Germany
American Airlines, Terminal C/Rm. 2234, Flughafen, 4000 Duesseldorf 30, Germany

AMERICAN BROADCASTING COS INC   1330 Ave of the Americas, New York, NY 10019,
  Tel: (212) 887-7777
  (Radio/TV prod & broadcast)
    Overseas Media GmbH, Schiller Str. 19-25, 6 Frankfurt/Main, Germany

AMERICAN BUILDINGS CO   State Docks Rd, Eufaula, AL 36027, Tel: (205) 687-2032
  (Metal buildings)
    Akron Standard Mold Co. & Zangl Reifenformenbau GmbH, Frohschammerstr. 14,
      8 Munich 40, Germany

AMERICAN COLLOID CO   1500 W Shure Dr, Arlington Hgts, IL 60004,
  Tel: (708) 966-5720
  (Bentonite mining)
    Bentonit International GmbH, Postfach 120738, 41 Duisburg, Meiderich, Germany

AMERICAN CYANAMID CO   1 Cyanamid Plaza, Wayne, NJ 07470, Tel: (201) 831-2000
  (Pharms, chems, agric & consumer prdts)
    B. Braun - Dexon GmbH, Verladestr. 1, D-3509 Spangenberg, Germany
    Cyanamid GmbH, Pfaffenrieder Str. 7, D-8190 Wolfratshausen, Germany

AMERICAN EXPRESS CO   American Express Tower, New York, NY 10285-4765,
  Tel: (212) 640-2000
  (Diversified fin & travel-related serv)
    American Express International Inc., Kurfuerstendamn 11, Berlin, Germany
    American Express International Inc., Amwall 138, Bremen, Germany
    American Express International Inc., Heinrich Heine-Allee 14, Dusseldorf, Germany
    American Express International Inc., Steinweg 5, Frankfurt, Germany
    American Express International Inc., Friedrich-Ebert-Anlage 16, Heidelberg, Germany
    American Express International Inc., Promenadeplatz 3, Munich, Germany
    American Express International Inc., Heusenstammer Str. 10, Oberishausen, Germany
    American Express International Inc., Lautenschlager Str. 3, Stuttgart, Germany

AMERICAN GAGE & MACHINE CO   853 Dundee Ave, Elgin, IL 60120,
  Tel: (708) 379-1121
  (Aircraft parts)
    Schon & Cie GmbH, Im Cehornerwald 2, 6780 Pirmasems, Germany

AMERICAN HOME PRODUCTS CORP   685 Third Ave, New York, NY 10017,
  Tel: (212) 878-5800
  (Drugs, food, household prdts)
    Durofol Presswerk GmbH, Henckelsstr. 39, 5650 Solingen, Germany
    Wyeth-Pharma GmbH, Schleebrueggenkemp 15, 4400 Muenster/Westf., Germany

AMERICAN LIFE INSURANCE CO (ALICO)   PO Box 2226, Wilmington, DE 19899,
  Tel: (302) 594-2000
  (Life ins, pension & annuity plans, health prdts)
    National Union Lebensversicherungs AG, Hochstr. 43, 6000 Frankfurt/Main, Germany

AMERICAN MANAGEMENT SYSTEMS INC   1777 North Kent St, Arlington, VA 22209,
  Tel: (703) 841-6000
  (Design/serv computer sys)
    AMS Management Systems Deutschland GmbH, Querstrasse 8-16, 6000 Frankfurt 1, Germany

AMERICAN MUTUAL SERVICES CORP   100 Crossways Park Dr W, PO Box 304, Woodbury,
  NY 11797, Tel: (516) 921-2540
  (Consumer credit)
    American Mutual Services Corp GmbH, Adickes Allee 57, 6000 Frankfurt, Germany

AMERICAN NATIONAL CAN CO   8770 W Bryn Mawr Ave, Chicago, IL 60631,
Tel: (312) 399-3000
(Mfr metal, glass & plastic packaging prdt)
   Lamitec Verpackungstechnologien GmbH & Co. KG, Voltastr. 5, D-1000 Berlin 65,
   Germany
   Nacanco GmbH & Co. KG, Emscherstrasse 46, 4650 Gelsenkirchen-Buer, Germany

AMERICAN OPTICAL CORP   14 Mechanic St, Southbridge, MA 01550,
Tel: (617) 765-9711
(Ophthalmic lenses, frames & cases, sunglasses)
   American Optical Co. Deutschland GmbH, Postfach 2145, D-6000 Frankfurt/Main 1,
   Germany

AMERICAN STANDARD INC   40 W 40th St, New York, NY 10018, Tel: (212) 840-5100
(Heating & sanitary equip)
   Ideal Standard GmbH, Euskirchenerstr. 80, Postfach 549, 5300 Bonn, Germany

AMERICAN TOOL COMPANIES INC   301 S 13th St, #600, Lincoln, NE 68508,
Tel: (402) 435-3300
(Mfr hand tools)
   ATC Werkzeuge Vertriebs GmbH, Serrahnstr. 3, D-2050 Hamburg 80, Germany

AMERON INC   4700 Ramona Blvd, PO Box 3000, Monterey Park, CA 91754,
Tel: (213) 268-4111
(Mfr steel pipe sys, concrete prdts, traffic & lighting poles, protective coatings)
   Ameron B.V., Rheinstr. 21, 6000 Frankfurt, Germany

AMETEK INC   Station Sq, Paoli, PA 19301, Tel: (215) 647-2121
(Mfr instru, elect motors, engineered materials)
   Ametek GmbH, Friedrichstrasse 24, 6200 Wiesbaden, Germany

AMICON CORP   182 Conant St, Danvers, MA 01923, Tel: (617) 777-3622
(Research apparatus)
   Amicon GmbH, 5810 Witten (RUHR), Westfalenstr. 11, Germany

AMOCO CHEMICAL CO   200 E Randolph Dr, Chicago, IL 60601, Tel: (312) 856-3200
(Mfr/sale petrol based chems, plastics, chem/plastic prdts)
   Amoco Deutschland GmbH, Germany

AMP INC   470 Friendship Rd, Harrisburg, PA 17111, Tel: (717) 564-0100
(Mfr electrical wiring devices)
   AMP Deutschland GmbH, Postfach Carl Benz Str. 12-14, 6140 Bensheim, Germany

AMPEX CORP   401 Broadway, Redwood City, CA 94063-3199, Tel: (415) 367-2011
(Mfr professional audio/visual sys, magnetic recording media, data-memory prdts)
   Ampex Europa GmbH, Walter-Kolb-Str. 9-11, 6 Frankfurt/Main 70, Germany

AMPHENOL PRODUCTS   4300 Commerct Ct, Lisle, IL 60532, Tel: (708) 983-3500
(Elect interconnect/penetrate sys & assemblies)
   Amphenol-Tuchel Electronics, Tullastr. 20, 7519 Eppingen, Germany
   Amphenol-Tuchel Electronics, Postfach 3469, 7100 Heilbronn, Germany

AMWAY CORP   7575 E Fulton Rd, Ada, MI 49355, Tel: (616) 676-6000
(Distr household cleaning, nutrition & diet prdts)
   Amway GmbH (Germany), Schlag. 5, 8032 Graefelfing, Munich, Germany

ANALOG DEVICES INC   1 Technology Way, Box 9106, Norwood, MA 02062,
  Tel: (617) 329-4700
  (Analog digital converters)
    Analog Devices GmbH, Postfach 15-02-09, D-8000 Munich 15, Germany

ANEMOSTAT PRODUCTS DIV   888 N Keyser Ave, Scranton, PA 18501,
  Tel: (717) 346-6586
  (Mfr air diffusers, grilles & related equip for A/C, heating & ventilation)
    Anemostat Raumlufttechnik, Grafenmuhlenweg 19, 5000 Cologne 80, Germany

ANTHONY INDUSTRIES INC   4900 S Eastern Ave, Los Angeles, CA 90040,
  Tel: (213) 724-2800
  (Pool constr & equip, fishing tackle, athletic apparel)
    Noris Shakespeare GmbH, Cologne, Germany

APPLE COMPUTER INC   20525 Mariani Ave, Cupertino, CA 95014,
  Tel: (408) 996-1010
  (Personal computers, peripherals & software)
    Apple Computers GmbH, Ingolstadterstr. 20, 8000 Munich 45, Germany

ARIES TECHNOLOGY INC   600 Suffolk St, Lowell, MA 01854, Tel: (508) 453-5310
  (Mfr mech computer-aided engr software)
    Aries Technology GmbH, Ismaniuger Strasse 21, 8000 Munich 80, Germany

ARMCO INTL INC   703 Curtis St, PO Box 700, Middletown, OH 45042,
  Tel: (513) 425-6541
  (Sheet steel & steel prdts, constr, oil field equip, ins, finance leasing)
    Armco Eisen GmbH, Sedanstr 37, Armcohaus, Postfach 26, 5000 Koeln 16, Germany
    Armco GmbH, Julius-Kalle-Str. 55, Postfach 100120, D-4220 Dinslaken, Germany

ARMSTRONG WORLD INDUSTRIES INC   PO Box 3001, Lancaster, PA 17604,
  Tel: (717) 397-0611
  (Mfr/mkt interior furnishings & spec prdts for bldg, auto & textile inds)
    Armstrong OK Isoliersysteme GmbH, Leutrirch 3, 7970 Friesenhofen, Germany
    Armstrong World Industries GmbH, Postfach 1433, 4000 Dusseldorf 1, Germany

ARO INTL CORP   One Aro Center, Bryan, OH 43506, Tel: (419) 636-4242
  (Mfr portable air tools, drills, motors, fluid handling pumps)
    Aro GmbH, Kaiserswerther Str. 49-51, Postfach 1152, D-4030 Ratingen 1, Germany

ARROW ELECTRONICS INC   25 Hub Dr, Melville, NY 11747, Tel: (516) 391-1300
  (Distr electron parts & components)
    Spoerle Electronics, Max-Planck-Strasse 1-3, Frankfurt, 6072 Dreiech 6, Germany

ASGROW SEED CO   7000 Portage Rd, Kalamazoo, MI 49001, Tel: (616) 385-6614
  (Growers/breeders agronomic & vegetable seeds)
    Asgrow GmbH, Lusshardstrasse 6, 7520 Bruchsal, Germany

ASK MR FOSTER TRAVEL CORP   7833 Haskell Ave, Van Nuys, CA 91406,
  Tel: (818) 988-0181
  (Travel service)
    Ask Mr. Foster/Poppe Co., Eppichmauergasse 8, 6500 Mainz, Germany

ASSOCIATED MERCHANDISING CORP   1440 Broadway, New York, NY 10018,
  Tel: (212) 536-4000
  (Retail service organization)
    Associated Merchandising Corp., Bleichstrasse 2-4, D-6000 Frankfurt Main 1, Germany

ASSOCIATED METALS & MINERALS CORP   3 N Corporate Park Dr, White Plains,
   NY 10604, Tel: (914) 251-5400
   (Metals & ores)
     Rheinischer Erz-und Metallhandel GmbH, Untersachsenhausen 37, 5000 Cologne, Germany

ASSOCIATED PRESS   50 Rockefeller Plaza, New York, NY 10020,
   Tel: (212) 621-1500
   (News gathering agency)
     The Associated Press GmbH, Moselstr. 27, 6000 Frankfurt/Main, Germany

AST RESEARCH INC   16215 Alton Parkway, PO Box 19658, Irvine, CA 92713-9658,
   Tel: (714) 727-4141
   (Mfr personal computers enhancement & data commun prdt)
     AST Research Deutschland GmbH, Emaniul-Leut-Strasse 1B, D-4000 Dusseldorf 11,
       Germany

ASTRA TRADING CORP   175 Fifth Ave, New York, NY 10010, Tel: (212) 254-9995
   (Intl merchandiser)
     Astra Trading Corp. GmbH, Steinstr. 15, 2000 Hamburg 1, Germany

ASTRONAUTICS CORP OF AMERICA   PO Box 523, Milwaukee, WI 53201,
   Tel: (414) 447-8200
   (Mfr aircraft instru, avionic & electronics sys)
     Astronautics GmbH, Rogerstrasse 27, D-8000 Munich, Germany

AUGAT INC   89 Forbes Blvd, Mansfield, MA 02048, Tel: (508) 543-4300
   (Interconnection prdts)
     Augat GmbH, Westendstr. 272, 8000 Munich 21, Germany

AUTOMATIC SWITCH CO   Hanover Rd, Florham Park, NJ 07932, Tel: (201) 966-2000
   (Valves & switches)
     Asco GmbH, Sandstr. 59, 4030 Ratingen 1, Germany

AVCO CORP   1275 King St, Greenwich, CT 06830, Tel: (203) 966-2800
   (Aircraft engines, gears)
     Avco Lycoming GmbH, Furstenbergerstr. 227, 6 Frankfurt/Main 1, Germany
     MTU-Motoren Und Turbinen-Union Munchen GmbH, Dachauerstr. 665, 8 Munich 50, Germany

AVERY INTL CORP   150 N Orange Grove Blvd, Pasadena, CA 91103,
   Tel: (213) 304-2000
   (Mfr self-adhesive labels & marking equip)
     Avery-Maschinen GmbH, Kollaustr. 105, 2000 Hamburg 61, Germany
     Zweckform-Werk GmbH, Postfach 1280, 8150 Oberlaindern-Holzkierchen, Germany

AVON PRODUCTS INC   9 W 57th St, New York, NY 10019, Tel: (212) 546-6015
   (Mfr/distr cosmetics, perfumes)
     Avon Cosmetics GmbH, Postfach, 8000 Munich 23, Germany
     Avon Cosmetics GmbH, Neufahrn, Germany
     Avon International Services GmbH, Neunkirchern, Germany

BADGER METER INC   4545 W Brown Deer Rd, PO Box 23099, Milwaukee, WI 53223,
   Tel: (414) 355-0400
   (Liquid meters & controls)
     Badger Meter Europe, Talstr. 172, 7024 Filderstadt 1, Stuttgart, Germany

BAKER & McKENZIE   2800 Prudential Plaza, Chicago, IL 60601,
  Tel: (312) 861-8000
  (Intl attorneys)
    Baker McKenzie Steuerberatungsges GmbH, Niddastr. 42-44, 6 Frankfurt/Main, Germany

J T BAKER INC   222 Red School Lane, Phillipsburg, NJ 08865,
  Tel: (201) 859-2151
  (Mfr/sale/serv lab & process chems)
    Baker Chemikaliem, Postfach 1661, 6080 Gross Gerau, Germany

BAKER OIL TOOLS   PO Box 3048, Houston, TX 77253, Tel: (713) 923-9351
  (Oil/gas well completions equip)
    Baker Oil Tools GmbH, Maschweg 9, Postfach 375, D-3100 Celle, Germany

BAKER PRODUCTION TECHNOLOGY   PO Box 40129, Houston, TX 77240-0129,
  Tel: (713) 943-0170
  (Inflatable packers, instru well testing)
    Lynes GmbH, Grafftring 17, D-3100 Celle, Germany

BALDWIN TECHNOLOGY CO INC   65 Rowayton Ave, Rowayton, CT 06853,
  Tel: (203) 838-7470
  (Mfr/serv mat handling, acces, control & prepress equip for print ind)
    Baldwin Gegenheimer GmbH, Derchinger Strasse 137, 8900 Augsburg, Germany

BALL CORP   PO Box 2407, Muncie, IN 47302, Tel: (317) 747-6100
  (Metal beverage containers, injection molded decorated plastics)
    Efratom Elekrontik GmbH, Am Perlacher Forst 186, D-8000 Munich, Germany

THE BANK OF NEW YORK   48 Wall St, New York, NY 10286, Tel: (212) 530-1784
  (Banking)
    The Bank of New York, Niedenau 61-63, D-6000 Frankfurt am Main, Germany

BANKAMERICA CORP   PO Box 37000, San Francisco, CA 94137, Tel: (415) 622-3456
  (Financial services)
    Bank of America, Mainzer Landstr. 46, Postfach 110243, D-6000 Frankfurt, Germany

BANKERS TRUST CO   280 Park Ave, New York, NY 10017, Tel: (212) 775-2500
  (Banking)
    Bankers Trust GmbH, Bockenheimer Landstr. 39, Postfach 2665, 6000 Frankfurt/Main 1,
      Germany

BARBER-COLMAN CO   555 Colman Center Dr, Rockford, IL 61125,
  Tel: (815) 397-7400
  (Mfr controls, motors)
    Barber & Colman GmbH, Kapellenstr. 45, 6239 Kriftel, Germany

BARNES GROUP INC   123 Main St, Bristol, CT 06010, Tel: (203) 583-7070
  (Mfr maint parts & supplies)
    Stumpp & Schuele, Beuren, Germany

BARNES-HIND INC   895 Kifer Rd, Sunnyvale, CA 94086, Tel: (408) 736-5462
  (Contact lenses & accessories, opthalmic & dermatology prdts)
    Barnes-Hind GmbH, Bruchtannenstr. 5, D-8752 Kleinostheim, Germany

BARRY CONTROLS INC   700 Pleasant St, Watertown, MA 02172, Tel: (617) 923-1150
  (Mfr/sale vibration isolation mounting devices)
    Barry Controls Intl. GmbH, Karl Liebknecht strasse 30, D-6096 Raunheim, Germany

BASE TEN   1 Electronic Dr, PO Box 3151, Trenton, NJ 08619,
  Tel: (609) 586-7010
  (Mfr electronics devices & sys, custom computers)
    Base Ten Systems Electronics GmbH, Erfurter Str. 29, 8057 Eching, Germany

BATTELLE MEMORIAL INSTITUTE   505 King Ave, Columbus, OH 43201,
  Tel: (614) 424-6424
  (Tech devel, commercialization & mgmt)
    Battelle Europe, Romerhof 35, 6000 Frankfurt/Main 90, Germany

BAUSCH & LOMB INC   1 Lincoln First Sq, Rochester, NY 14601-0054,
  Tel: (716) 338-6000
  (Mfr healthcare & optics prdts)
    Bausch & Lomb GmbH, Pforzheim, Germany
    Dr. Mann Pharma, Brunsbutteler Damm, Germany

BAXTER TRAVENOL LABORATORIES INC   1 Baxter Pky, Deerfield, IL 60015,
  Tel: (708) 948-2000
  (Pharm & disposable med prdts)
    Travenol GmbH, Nymphenburgerstr. 1, Postfach 202429, 8000 Munich 2, Germany

BECHTEL GROUP INC   50 Beale St, PO Box 3965, San Francisco, CA 94119,
  Tel: (415) 768-1234
  (Engineering & constr)
    Bechtel (Deutschland) GmbH, Inselstr. 34, 4 Dusseldorf, Germany

BECKMAN INSTRUMENTS INC   2500 Harbor Blvd, Box 3100, Fullerton, CA 92634,
  Tel: (714) 871-4848
  (Mfr/distr/serv research & clinical lab instru, sys, software & reagents)
    Beckman Instruments GmbH., 115 Frankfurter Ring, D-8000 Munich, Germany

BELLSOUTH INTERNATIONAL   1155 Peachtree St NE, #400, Atlanta, GA 30367,
  Tel: (404) 249-4800
  (Mobile commun, telecom network sys)
    BellSouth Intl., Bonn, Germany

BELOIT CORP   1st Lawrence Ave, Beloit, WI 53511, Tel: (608) 365-3311
  (Paper making mach & equip)
    Rader International, Am Konigshof 3, D-8400 Regensburg, Germany

BEMIS CO INC   625 Marquette Ave, Minneapolis, MN 55402, Tel: (612) 340-6000
  (Mfr flexible packaging, spec coated & graphics prdts)
    Hayssen Europa GmbH, Postfach 3280, 75 Karlsruhe 1, Germany

BENTLEY LABORATORIES INC   17502 Armstrong Ave, Irvine, CA 92714,
  Tel: (714) 546-8020
  (Mfr para-med devices)
    Bentley Labs GmbH, 111 Ecke Opitzstr., 4000 Dusseldorf 30, Germany

BENTLY NEVADA CORP   PO Box 157, Minden, NV 89423, Tel: (702) 782-3611
  (Electronic monitoring system)
    Bently Nevada GmbH, Postfach 60, Hermannstr. 25, D-6078 Neu-Isenburg, Germany

BICKLEY FURNACES INC   PO Box 6069, 550 State Rd, Philadelphia, PA 19114,
  Tel: (215) 638-4500
  (High temp furnaces)
    Bickley GmbH, 475 Unna, Postfach 2, Westfalia, Germany

BINDICATOR CORP   1915 Dove St, PO Box 9, Port Huron, MI 48060,
  Tel: (313) 987-2700
  (Mfr level control instru for measuring solids & liquids)
    Bindicator Europe GmbH, 18 Karlsruher Str., D-3014 Laatzen 1, Germany

BINKS MFG CO   9201 W Belmont Ave, Franklin Park, IL 60131,
  Tel: (708) 671-3000
  (Mfr of spray painting & finishing equip)
    Binks Deutschland GmbH, Koelnerstr. 339, D-4330 Muelheim (Ruhr) 13, Germany
    Binks International Deutschland GmbH, Suedwall 2, 4150 Krefeld, Germany

BLACK & DECKER CORP   701 E Joppa Road, Towson, MD 21204, Tel: (301) 583-3900
  (Mfr portable elect & pneumatic power tools, household prdts)
    Black & Decker GmbH, Black-&-Decker Str. 40, 6270 Idstein, Germany

BLOUNT INC   4520 Executive Park Drive, Montgomery, AL 36116-1602,
  Tel: (205) 244-4370
  (Mfr cutting chain & equip, timber harvest/materials handling equip, sporting ammo,
  gen contracting)
    Omark Industries GmbH, Postfach 265, D-7032 Sindelfingen, Germany

BOISE CASCADE CORP   One Jefferson Square, PO Box 50, Boise, ID 83728,
  Tel: (208) 384-6161
  (Lumber, paper, related prdts)
    Wellpappe Ansbach, Schumacher GmbH & Co., Robert Bosch Strasse 3, D-8800 Ansbach,
      Germany

BOOZ ALLEN & HAMILTON INC   101 Park Ave, New York, NY 10178,
  Tel: (212) 697-1900
  (Mgmt consultants)
    Booz, Allen & Hamilton Inc., Koenigsallee 98A, 4000 Dusseldorf, Germany

BORG TEXTILE CORP   218 Wisconsin Dr, Jefferson, WI 53549, Tel: (414) 728-5534
  (Knitted fabrics)
    Borg Textil Vertriebs GmbH, Arabellastr. 4 (Sternhaus), 8 Munich 81, Germany

BORG-WARNER CORP   200 S Michigan Ave, Chicago, IL 60604, Tel: (312) 322-8500
  (Mfr A/C equip, chem & plastics, ind prdts, trans equip)
    Borg-Warner Chemicals, Daniel-Goldbachstr. 25, 403 Ratingen, Postfach 1445, Germany
    Borg-Warner International GmbH, Steindamm 71, D-2000 Hamburg 1, Germany
    Borg-Warner International GmbH, Glockengiesserwall 26, Hamburg, Germany
    Borg-Warner-Stieber GmbH, Kurpfalzring, Postfach 101360, Heidelberg 1, Germany
    Brown, Boveri-York Kalte-und Klimatechnick GmbH, Postfach 5180, 6800 Mannheim,
      Germany

BOSE CORP   100 The Mountain Rd, Framingham, MA 01701, Tel: (617) 879-7330
  (Electronic equip)
    Bose GmbH, 118 Ober-Eschbacherstr., 6380 Bad Homburg, Postfach 1160, Germany

BOSTITCH DIV   815 Briggs St, East Greenwich, RI 02818, Tel: (401) 884-2500
  (Stapling machs & supplies, wire)
    Bostitch GmbH, Postfach 1349, Oststr. 26, 2000 Norderstedt. 1, Bez-Hamburg, Germany

BOURNS INC   1200 Columbia Ave, Riverside, CA 92507, Tel: (714) 781-5960
  (Mfr resistive com & networks, precision potentiometers, panel controls)
    Bourns GmbH, Eberhardstrasse 63, Brietestrasse 2, 7000 Stuttgart 1, Germany

BOYDEN ASSOCIATES INC   260 Madison Ave, New York, NY 10016,
  Tel: (212) 685-3400
  (Mgt consultants, exec search)
    Boyden Intl. GmbH, Postfach 1724, D-6370 Bad Homburg, Germany

W H BRADY CO   727 W Glendale Ave, PO Box 571, Milwaukee, WI 53201,
  Tel: (414) 332-8100
  (Wire markers, name plates)
    W. H. Brady GmbH, Odenwaldstr. 71, D-6074 Rodermark, Germany

BRANSON ULTRASONICS CORP   Eagle Rd, Danbury, CT 06810, Tel: (203) 796-0400
  (Ultrasonic & vibratory plastics assembly mach)
    Branson Ultraschall GmbH, Industriestr. 48, Postfach 1367, D-6056 Heusenstamm,
    Germany

BRIGGS & STRATTON CORP   PO Box 702, Milwaukee, WI 53201, Tel: (414) 259-5333
  (Mfr engines, auto locking devices)
    Briggs & Stratton Deutschland GmbH, all mail to: U.S. address

BRUSH WELLMAN INC   17876 St Clair Ave, Celeveland, OH 44110,
  Tel: (216) 486-4200
  (Beryllium metal, alloys & compounds; friction prdts, cutting edges)
    Brush Wellman GmbH, Motorstr. 34, D-7000 Stuttgart 31, Germany

BUCKBEE MEARS CO   2 Appletree Sq, Minneapolis, MN 55425, Tel: (512) 851-6000
  (Glass & metal reticles, scales, grids, electroformed fine mesh, color TV aperture
  masks)
    BMC Europe GmbH, 7840 Mullheim, Postfach 102, Germany

BULAB HOLDINGS INC   1256 N McLean Blvd, Memphis, TN 38108,
  Tel: (901) 278-0330
  (Mfr microbicides, biocides, additives, corrosion inhibitors, chems)
    Buckman Laboratories GmbH, Marienbader Platz 22, D-6379 Bad Homburg v.d.H, Germany

BUNDY CORP   12345 E Nine Mile, Warren, MI 48090, Tel: 313) 758) 6500
  (Small diameter steel tubing, watch cases, etc)
    Mecano-Bundy GmbH, Dischinger Str. 11, 69 Heidelberg, Germany

BURLINGTON AIR EXPRESS   18200 Van Karman Ave, Irvine, CA 92715,
  Tel: (714) 752-1212
  (Air freight)
    Burlington Air Express, c/o Wendschlag & Pohl, Frachthalle Tegel Airport,
      D-1000 Berlin 51, Germany

LEO BURNETT CO INC   35 West Wacker Dr, Chicago, IL 60601, Tel: (312) 220-5959
  (Advertising agency)
    Kastner & Partner GmbHurnett GmbH, Werbeagentur, Kennedyallee 94,
      D-6000 Frankfurt am Main 1, Germany
    Michale Conrad & Leo Burnett GmbH, Feuerbachstrasse 26, D-6000 Frankfurt am Main 1,
      Germany

THOMAS F BUROLA & ASSOCIATES   230 Burnham Rd, Oak View, CA 93022,
  Tel: (805) 647-0155
  (Mgt consulting servs)
    Thomas Burola & Associates, Am Schnepfenweg 41, 8000 Munchen, Germany

BURR-BROWN RESEARCH CORP   PO Box 11400, Tucson, AZ 85734, Tel: (602) 746-1111
(Electronic components & sys modules)
   Burr-Brown International GmbH, Kurze Strasse 40, D-7024 Filderstadt-Bonlanden,
      Germany

BURSON-MARSTELLER   230 Park Ave, New York, NY 10003-1566, Tel: (212) 614-4000
(Public relations/public affairs consultants)
   Burson-Marsteller GmbH, Untermainkai 20, D-6000 Frankfurt/Main 1, Germany

BUSINESSLAND INC   1001 Ridder Park Dr, San Jose, CA 95131,
   Tel: (408) 437-0400
(Distr, integration & support microcomputer sys)
   Businessland SUD GmbH, Welserstrasse 9, D-8906 Gersthofen, Germany
   Businessland SUD GmbH, other locations in Germany

CARL BYOIR & ASSOCIATES INC   380 Madison Ave, New York, NY 10017,
   Tel: (212) 986-6100
(Public relations consultants)
   Welbeck Public Re. GmbH, Falkensteiner Str. 75-77, 6000 Frankfurt am Main, Germany

CABOT CORP   950 Winter St, PO Box 9073, Waltham, MA 02254,
   Tel: (617) 890-0200
(Mfr carbon blacks, plastics; oil & gas, info sys)
   Cabot GmbH, Postfach 901120, Hanau 9, Germany
   Deloro Stellite GmbH (Weartec Div.), Postfach 520, 5400 Koblenz,
      Carl-Spaeterstr. 11, Germany
   Deutssche Beryllium GmbH (Cabot Berylco Div.), Postfach 1620, 637 Oberursel, Germany
   Nickel Contor Deutschland GmbH (Hitec Div.), Taunusanlage 21,
      D-6000 Frankfurt/Main 1, Germany

CALCOMP   2411 W La Palma Ave, PO Box 3250, Anaheim, CA 92801,
   Tel: (714) 821-2142
(Mfr computer graphics)
   CalComp GmbH, Werftstr. 37, 4000 Dusseldorf 11, Germany
   CalComp GmbH, Elmshorner Str. 7-11, 2080 Pinneberg, Germany
   CalComp GmbH, Paul-Gerhardt-Alee 50, 8000 Munich, Germany
   CalComp GmbH, Nikolaus-Otto-Str. 29, 7022 Leinfelden-Echterdigen, Germany
   CalComp GmbH, Schumannstr. 163, 6050 Offenbach, Germany

CALIFORNIA PELLET MILL CO   221 Main St, #420, San Francisco, CA 94105,
   Tel: (415) 431-3800
(Mfr mach for pelleting)
   CPM/Europe (Wesel) GmbH, Hafenstr. 28, D-4230 Wesel, Germany

CAMPBELL SOUP CO   Campbell Place, Camden, NJ 08101, Tel: (609) 342-4800
(Food prdts)
   Deutsche Biscuits Delacre GmbH, Postfach 730249, Frauemhofstr. 4-10,
      6000 Frankfurt, Germany
   Lacroix, Postfach 730229, Frauemhofstr. 4-10, 6000 Frankfurt, Germany

CANADA DRY INTL CORP   2600 Century Pkwy, Atlanta, GA 30345,
   Tel: (404) 753-2182
(Carbonated beverages, soft drinks extract)
   Canada Dry Underberg GmbH, Xantenerstr. 5, 4134 Rheinberg 1, Germany

CANBERRA INDUSTRIES INC   One State St, Meriden, CT 06450, Tel: (203) 238-2351
  (Mfr instru for nuclear research)
    Canberra Elektronik GmbH, Frankfurt, Germany

CANDELA LASER CORP   530 Boston Post Rd, Wayland, MA 01778,
  Tel: (508) 358-5700
  (Mfr/serv medical laser systems)
    Candela Laser Deutchland GmbH, Lilienthalstr. 4, D-8031 Gilching, Germany

CARNATION INTL CO   5045 Wilshire Blvd, Los Angeles, CA 90036,
  Tel: (213) 932-6000
  (Milk prdts)
    Glucksklee GmbH, Mittelweg 36, 2000 Hamburg 13, Germany

CARTER CONTROLS INC   3000-170th Street, Lansing, IL 60438,
  Tel: (708) 474-3305
  (Pneumatic hydraulic controls)
    Carter Controls GmbH, Junkerstr. 92, 7701 Buesingen/Hockrhein, Germany

CASCADE CORP   2020 SW 4th Ave, Portland, OR 97201, Tel: (503) 227-0024
  (Lift truck attachments)
    Cascade GmbH, Haritstr. 36, 4 Dusseldorf, Germany

J I CASE CO   700 State St, Racine, WI 53404, Tel: (414) 636-6011
  (Mfr/sale agric & constr equip)
    Case Vibromax GmbH & Co., KG, Schlueterstrasse 13-19, Postfach 230 149,
      D-4000 Dusseldorf 1, Germany
    J.I. Case Co., Postfach 337, 4040 Neuss Rhein, Germany

CAT PUMPS CORP   1681 94th Lane NE, Minneapolis, MN 55434, Tel: (612) 780-5440
  (Mfr/distr pumps)
    Cat Pumps Deutschland GmbH, Rostocker Strasse 9, 6200 Wiesbaden-Bierstadt, Germany

CBI INDUSTRIES INC   800 Jorie-Blvd, Oak Brook, IL 60521, Tel: (708) 654-7000
  (Holding co: metal plate fabricating, constr, oil & gas drilling)
    CBI Industriestahlbau GmbH, 4650 Gelsenkirchen, Germany

CEILCOTE CO   140 Sheldon Rd, Berea, OH 44017, Tel: (216) 243-0700
  (Mfr corrosion-resistant material, air pollution control equip, cons serv)
    Ceilcote Korrosionstechnik GmbH, D-6083 Biebesheim/Rhein am Brunneweg 10, Germany

CENTRAL NATIONAL-GOTTESMAN INC   100 Park Ave, New York, NY 10017,
  Tel: (212) 532-7300
  (Pulp & paper prdts)
    Central National GmbH, Ferdinandstr. 14, D-6380 Bad Homburg v.d.H. 1, Germany

CHARLES OF THE RITZ GROUP LTD   625 Madison Ave, New York, NY 10022,
  Tel: (212) 527-4000
  (Fine fragrances & cosmetics)
    Novicos Cosmetic GmbH, Bernhard-Feilchenfeld-Str. 11, D-5000 Cologne 51, Zollstock,
      Germany

CHARTPAK CORP   One River Road, Leeds, MA 01053, Tel: (413) 584-5446
  (Pressure sensitive graphic aids prdts)
    Chartpak Rotex GmbH, Lenaustr. 8a, 8 Munich 25, Germany

CHASE MANHATTAN BANK N A   1 Chase Manhattan Plaza, New York, NY 10081,
   Tel: (212) 552-2222
   (Intl banking)
      The Chase Manhattan Bank N.A., Taunusanlage 11, 6 Frankfurt/Main, Germany
      The Chase Manhattan Bank N.A., Bleichstr. 14, 4 Dusseldorf, Germany
      The Chase Manhattan Bank N.A., Maximiliansplatz 9, 8 Munich, Germany
      The Chase Manhattan Bank N.A., Neuer Wall 42, 2 Hamburg 36, Germany

CHEMDYE INTL INC   51 E 42nd St, #1612, New York, NY 10017,
   Tel: (212) 687-3034
   (Rubber prdts)
      Allwetter Sportbelag Vertriebs GmbH, Postfach 101301, D-2000 Hamburg 1, Germany

CHEMICAL BANK   277 Park Ave, New York, NY 10172, Tel: (212) 310-6161
   (Banking & financial serv)
      Chemical Bank, Ulmenstrasse 30, P.O. Box 170251, 6000 Frankfurt am Main 17., Germany
      Chemical Bank AG, P.O. Box 714126, D-6000 Frankfurt am Main 17, Germany

THE CHERRY CORP   3600 Sunset Ave, PO Box 718, Waukegan, IL 60087,
   Tel: (708) 662-9200
   (Mfr switches, keyboards, etc)
      Cherry Mikroschalter GmbH, Industriestr. 19, Postfach 12/20, 8572 Auerbach/OPF,
      Germany

CHESEBROUGH-POND'S INC   33 Benedict Place, Greenwich, CT 06830,
   Tel: (203) 661-2000
   (Cosmetics, consumer prdts)
      Chesebrough-Pond's GmbH, Dachauerstr. 37, Postfach 201928, 8000 Munich 2, Germany

CHEVRON CHEMICAL CO   PO Box 5047, San Ramon, CA 94583-0947,
   Tel: (415) 842-5500
   (Chemicals)
      Orogil KG, Mainzer Str. 172, Postfach 190369, 6000 Frankfurt/Main, Germany

CHICAGO PNEUMATIC TOOL CO   2200 Bleeker St, Utica, NY 13501,
   Tel: (315) 792-2600
   (Mfr air tools & equip)
      Chicago Pneumatic-Germany, Postfach 120251, Hagenauer Strasse 47,
      D-6200 Wiesbaden 12, Germany

CHRISTENSEN INTL   PO Box 26135, Salt Lake City, UT 84126, Tel: (801) 487-5371
   (Diamond drills)
      Christensen Diamond Products GmbH, Braunschweiger Heerstr. 61, Postfach 309,
      3100 Celle, Germany

CHRISTIAN SCIENCE PUBLISHING SOCIETY   1 Norway St, Boston, MA 02115,
   Tel: (617) 262-2300
   (Publishing)
      Christian Science Monitor, Postamt Bundeshaus Schliessf. 9130, 5300 Bonn, Germany

THE CHUBB CORP   15 Mountain View Rd, Warren, NJ 07060, Tel: (201) 580-2000
   (Holding co: property/casualty ins)
      Chubb Insurance Co. of Europe, Germany

CIGNA CORP   One Liberty Place, 1650 Market St, Philadelphia, PA 19101,
   Tel: (215) 523-4000
   (Ins, invest, health care & other fin servs)

Cigna Insurance Co. of Europe SA-NV, Erlenstrasse 2-6, 6000 Frankfurt A/Main, Germany
Esis Intl., Inc., Erlenstrasse 2-6, D-6000 Frankfurt/Main, Germany
Insurance Co. of North America, Direktion Fuer Deutschland, Erlenstrasse 2-6, 6000 Frankfurt/Main, Germany

CINCOM SYSTEMS INC   2300 Montana Ave, Cincinnati, OH 45211,
Tel: (513) 662-2300
(Computer software)
  Cincom Systems GmbH, Postfach 11-04-32, Mainzer Landstrasse 46, D-6000 Frankfurt Am Main 1, Germany

CIRCON ACMI   300 Stillwater Ave, Stamford, CT 06902, Tel: (203) 357-8300
(Mfr med & surgical endoscopes, instru & video sys)
  Circon GmbH, Taunusstrasse 38, 8000 Munich 40, Germany

CIT FINANCIAL CORP   650 Madison Ave, New York, NY 10022, Tel: (212) 572-6500
(Finance, ins, loans)
  Universal Kredit Bank GmbH, Lindenstr. 1, 6 Frankfurt/Main, Germany

CITIBANK NA   399 Park Ave, New York, NY 10043, Tel: (212) 559-1000
(Intl banking)
  First National City Bank, Grosse Gallusstr. 16, 6 Frankfurt/Main 1, Germany
  First National City Bank, Europacenter, 1 Berlin 30, Germany
  First National City Bank, Konigsallee 6, 4 Dusseldorf 1, Germany
  First National City Bank, Ost-West-Str. 51, 2 Hamburg 11, Germany
  First National City Bank, Residenzstr. 22, 8 Munich 1, Germany
  First National City Bank, Theodor-Heuss-Str. 9, 7 Stuttgart, Germany

CLARK EQUIPMENT CO   PO Box 7008, South Bend, IN 46634, Tel: (219) 239-0100
(Mfr ind trucks, skid-steer loaders, heavy duty drive line components)
  Clark Central Parts GmbH, Postfach 010346, Solinberstr. 2, 4330 Mulheim/Ruhr, Germany
  Clark Maschinenfabrik GmbH, Postfach 140220, 4330 Mulheim/Ruhr, Germany

CLARKSON INDUSTRIES INC   30 Buxton Farm Rd, Stamford, CT 06905-1206,
Tel: (203) 322-3990
(Mfr centrifugal blowers, compressors, handling equip)
  Hoffman Air Filtration GmbH, Volmerswertherstr. 040, Neuss, Germany

CLEVELAND TWIST DRILL CO   1242 E 49 St, PO Box 6656, Cleveland, OH 44101,
Tel: (216) 431-3120
(Metal cutting/threading toods related prdts)
  Cleveland Twist Drill GmbH, Postfach 27, 7827 Loeffingen/Schwarzwald, Germany

CLIMAX MOLYBDENUM CORP   One Greenwich Plaza, Greenwich, CT 06830,
Tel: (203) 629-6400
(Molybdenum, tungsten)
  Climax Molybdenum GmbH, Cecilienallee 79, D-4000 Dusseldorf 30, Germany

COBE LABORATORIES INC   1185 Oak St, Lakewood, CO 80215, Tel: (303) 232-6800
(Mfr med equip & supplies)
  COBE GmbH, Henschelring 1-3, 8011 Kirchheim/Munich, Germany
  SECON GmbH, Goettingen, Germany

COIN ACCEPTORS INC   300 Hunter Ave, St Louis, MO 63124, Tel: (314) 725-0100
(Coin mechanisms for vending mach)
  Nalo Coin, Alter Teichweg 11-13, 2000 Hamburg 76, Germany

THE COLEMAN CO INC   250 N St Francis Ct, PO Box 1762, Wichita, KS 67201,
Tel: (316) 261-3485
(Mfr camping, outdoor & water recreation prdts)
  Coleman Deutschland GmbH, Ezetilstr., D-6303 Hungen 3, Germany

COLGATE-PALMOLIVE CO   300 Park Ave, New York, NY 10022, Tel: (212) 310-2000
(Pharms, cosmetics, toiletries, detergents)
  Colgate-Palmolive GmbH, Liebigstr. 2-12, 2 Hamburg 74, Germany

COLUMBIA PICTURES INDUSTRIES INC   711 Fifth Ave, New York, NY 10022,
Tel: (212) 751-4400
(Producer & distributor of motion pictures)
  Warner-Columbia Film Verleih GmbH, Postfach 14-0649, D-8000 Munich 5, Germany

COMBINED INSURANCE CO OF AMERICA   123 N Wacker Dr, Chicago, IL 60606,
Tel: (312) 701-3000
(Insurance)
  Combined Insurance Co of America, Gustav-Stresemann Ring 12-16, 6200 Wiesbaden,
  Germany

COMBUSTION ENGINEERING INC   900 Long Ridge Road, Stamford, CT 06902,
Tel: (203) 329-8771
(Tech constr)
  Kohlenscheigungs GmbH, Postfach 395, Stuttgart, Germany

COMDISCO INC   6400 Shafer Ct, Rosemont, IL 60018, Tel: (708) 698-3000
(Remarketer used computer equip)
  Comdisco (Germany), Buchenhain 9, 5144 Wegberg, Germany

COMPTON INTERNATIONAL   625 Madison Ave, New York, NY 10022,
Tel: (212) 754-1100
(Advertising)
  Compton GmbH, Friedrichstr. 48, 6000 Frankfurt/Main, Germany

COMPUGRAPHIC CORP   200 Ballardvale St, Wilmington, MA 01887,
Tel: (617) 658-5600
(Mfr computerized composition & typesetting sys)
  Compugraphic Deutschland, Ohmstrasse 2, Postfach 1134, 6070 Langen, Germany

COMPUTER ASSOCIATES INTL INC   711 Stewart Ave, Garden City, NY 11530,
Tel: (516) 227-3300
(Devel/mkt/mgt info mgt & bus applications software)
  C.A. Computer Associates GmbH, Hauptverwaltung, Kastanienweg 1, D-6108 Weiterstadt,
  Germany

COMPUTER SCIENCES CORP   2100 E Grand Ave, El Segundo, CA 90245,
Tel: (213) 615-0311
(Software servs, sys integration)
  CSC Computer Sciences GmbH, Garmischer Str. 8, 8000 Munich 2, Germany

COMPUTERVISION CORP   201 Burlington Rd, Bedford, MA 01730,
Tel: (617) 275-1800
(Automation sys, semiconductors)

Computervision GmbH, Berg-am-Laim-Str. 47, D-8000 Munich 80, Germany
Computervision GmbH, Bankstr. 1, 4000 Dusseldorf, Germany

CONOCO INC   600 N Dairy Ashford Rd, Houston, TX 77079, Tel: (713) 293-1000
(Oil, gas, coal, chems, minerals)
CONDEA Petrochemie GmbH, Fritz-Staiger-Str., Postfach 2212, Brunsbuettel, Germany
Conoco Mineraloel GmbH, Hudtwalckerstr. 2-8, 2 Hamburg 39, Germany

CONTINENTAL BANK NA   231 S Lasalle St, Chicago, IL 60697, Tel: (312) 828-2345
(Coml banking servs)
Continental Bank Corp., PO Box 100544, Mainzer Landstrasse 46, 6000 Frankfurt,
Germany

CONTINENTAL CAN CO   PO Box 5410, Stamford, CT 06856, Tel: (203) 357-8110
(Packaging prdts & mach, metal, plastic & paper containers)
Schmalbach-Lubeca AG, Schmalbachstr. 1, Postfach 3307, D-3300 Braunschweig, Germany

THE CONTINUUM CO INC   9500 Arboretum Blvd, Austin, TX 78759,
Tel: (512) 345-5700
(Design & mkt software for life ins industry)
Continuum (Deutschland) GmbH, Tannenwaldallee 76, 6380 Bad Homburg, Germany

CONTROL DATA CORP   8100 34th Ave S, Minneapolis, MN 55440,
Tel: (612) 853-8100
(Control data equip, computer sys serv & financial serv)
Electrofact GmbH, Robert-Bosch-Str. 18, Dormagen 4047, Germany
Magnetic Peripherals Inc. Germany, 9 Tiergartenstr., Heppenheim, Germany

COOPER AIR TOOLS   670 Industrial Dr, PO Box 1410, Lexington, SC 29072-1410,
Tel: (803) 359-1200
(Mfr pneumatic tools, hoists & assembly mach)
Cooper Air Tools, Westhausen, Wurtt, Germany

COOPERTOOLS   PO Box 30100, Raleigh, NC 27622, Tel: (919) 781-7200
(Mfr hand tools)
The Cooper Group, Deutschland GmbH, Postfach 1351, 7122 Besigheim/Wurtt, Germany

CORNING CORP   Houghton Park, PO Box 2000, Corning, NY 14831,
Tel: (617) 974-9000
(Mfr glass, ceramic materials)
Corning GmbH, Abraham-Lincoln Strasse 30, D-6200 Wiesbaden, Germany
Corning Keramik GmbH & Co. KG, Carl-Billand-Strasse 1, D-6750 Kaiserslauten, Germany
QVF Glastechnik GmbH, Corning Process Systems, Schossbergstrasse 11,
  D-6200 Wiesbaden 13, Germany

COSTAR/NUCLEPORE CORP   7035 Commerce Circle, Pleasanton, CA 94566-3294,
Tel: (415) 463-2530
(Mfr membrane filtration sys for lab & process applications)
Nuclepore GmbH, Falkenweg 47, 7400 Tubingen, Germany

COULTER ELECTRONICS INC   590 W 20th St, Hialeah, FL 33010,
Tel: (305) 885-0131
(Blood cell & particle counters)
Coulter Electronics GmbH, Kreuzstr. 93, 4152 Kempen-Huels 2, Germany

COURTAULDS PERFORMANCE FILMS   PO Box 5068, Martinsville, VA 24115,
   Tel: (703) 629-1711
   (Mfr solar control & dyed polyester/metal window films)
      S.L. Martin Processing Folien GmbH, Duisburgerstr. 25, 4800 Bieleteld 14, Germany

CPC INTERNATIONAL INC   PO Box 8000, International Plaza, Englewood Cliffs,
   NJ 07632, Tel: (201) 894-4000
   (Mfr consumer food prdts & corn refining prdts)
      C.H. Knorr GmbH, Knorrstrasse 1, Postfach 2760, D-7100 Heilbronn, Germany

CRANE CO   757 Third Ave, New York, NY 10017, Tel: (212) 415-7300
   (Diversified mfr/distr engineered prdts for ind)
      National Rejectors Inc. GmbH, Zum Fruchthof 6, 2150 Buxtehude, Germany

JOHN CRANE INC   6400 Oakton St, Morton Grove, IL 60053, Tel: (708) 967-2400
   (Mfr engineering seals)
      John Crane GmbH, Postfach 1528, Werner-van-Siemens Strasse, D-6400 Fulda 1, Germany

CROSS & TRECKER CORP   PO Box 925, Bloomfield Hills, MI 48013,
   Tel: (313) 644-4343
   (Automated mfg sys, computer- controlled mach tools)
      Cross Europa-Werk GmbH, Postfach 1252, D-7317 Wendlingen am Neckar, Germany

CROSS CO   17801 Fourteen Mile Rd, Fraser, MI 48026, Tel: (313) 293-3000
   (Metal working machs)
      Cross Europa-Werk GmbH, Postfach 100, D-7317 Wendlingen am Neckar, Germany

CROWN CORK & SEAL CO INC   Holmesburg Station, PO Box 6208, Philadelphia,
   PA 19136, Tel: (215) 698-5100
   (Cans, bottle caps; filling & packaging mach)
      Bender-Werke GmbH, Postfach 245, 6710 Frankenthal/Pfalz, Germany

CULLIGAN INTL CO   One Culligan Parkway, Northbrook, IL 60062,
   Tel: (708) 205-6000
   (Water treatment prdts & serv)
      Culligan Deutschland GmbH, Lise Meitnerstr. 6, Postfach 2240, 4030 Ratingen 2,
      Germany

CUMMINS ENGINE CO INC   PO Box 3005, Columbus, IN 47202, Tel: (812) 377-5000
   (Mfr diesel engines)
      Cummins Diesel Deutschland GmbH, Postfach 1134, D-6080 Gross-Gerau, Germany

CURTISS-WRIGHT CORP   1200 Wall St, W Lyndhurst, NJ 07071, Tel: (201) 896-8400
   (Aircraft engines)
      Dorr-Oliver GmbH, Weisbaden, Germany

D'ARCY MASIUS BENTON & BOWLES INC (DMB&B)   1675 Broadway, New York,
   NY 10019, Tel: (212) 468-3622
   (Advertising & communications)
      DMB&B GmbH, Kaufmannshaus, Bleichenbruecke 10, 2000 Hamburg 36, Germany
      DMB&B IMPARC Werbeagentur GmbH, Karlplatz 21, 4000 Dusseldorf 1, Germany

D-M-E COMPANY   29111 Stephenson Highway, Madison Heights, MI 48071,
   Tel: (313) 398-6000
   (Basic tooling for plastic molding & die casting)
      DME Deutschland, 7106 Neuenstadt am Kocher, Germany

DAMES & MOORE   911 Wilshire Blvd, Los Angeles, CA 90017, Tel: (213) 683-1560
  (Consulting engineers)
    Dames & Moore, Eschersheimer Landstrasse 5-7, D-6000 Frankfurt am Main 1, Germany

DANCER FITZGERALD SAMPLE INTL   405 Lexington Ave, New York, NY 10174,
  Tel: (212) 661-0800
  (Advertising agency)
    DFS & R Werbeagentur GmbH, Possartstr. 1, D-8000 Munich 80, Germany

DANIEL INTERNATIONAL CORP   Daniel Bldg, Greenville, SC 29602,
  Tel: (803) 298-2500
  (Gen contractor, engr & constr)
    Daniel International Construction Co., Postfach 2020, Alwinestr. 24,
      6200 Wiesbaden, Germany

DATA GENERAL CORP   4400 Computer Dr, Westboro, MA 01580, Tel: (617) 366-8911
  (Design, mfr gen purpose computer sys & peripheral prdts & servs)
    Data General GmbH, Kronberger Hang 3, 6231 Schwalbach/TS, Germany

DATAEASE INTL INC   7 Cambridge Dr, Trumbull, CT 06611, Tel: (203) 374-8000
  (Mfr applications devel software)
    Markt & Technik Verlag AG, Hans Pinsel Str. 2, 8013 Haar bei Munchen, Germany

DATAGRAPHIX INC   PO Box 82449, San Diego, CA 92138, Tel: (714) 291-9960
  (Mfr electronic computing equip)
    Data Graphix GmbH, Abraham Lincoln Str. 28, 62 Wiesbaden, Germany

DATAPRODUCTS CORP   6200 Canada Ave, PO Box 746, Woodland Hills, CA 91365,
  Tel: (818) 887-8000
  (Mfr computer printers & supplies)
    Dataproducts GmbH, Otto-Hahn Str. 49, 6072 Dreieich-Sprendingen, Germany

DATASCOPE CORP   14 Philips Pkwy, Montvale, NJ 07645, Tel: (201) 391-8100
  (Mfr medical devices)
    Datascope GmbH, Bremen, Germany
    InterVascular GmbH, Munich, Germany

DAY INTL   333 W First St, Dayton, OH 45412, Tel: (513) 226-7000
  (Diversified auto, ind & household prdts)
    Dayco Corp. GmbH, Daimlerstr. 6, Postfach 36, D-7401 Pliezhausen 1, Germany

DDB NEEDHAM WORLDWIDE INC   437 Madison Ave, New York, NY 10022,
  Tel: (212) 415-2000
  (Advertising)
    Heye & Partner GmbH, Ottobrunner Strasse 28, Unteraching, 8025 Munich, Germany
    Heye & Partner GmbH, Mittelweg 17, 2000 Hamburg 13, Germany
    Wensauer DDB Needham Worldwide GmbH, Schadowstrasse 48/50, 4000 Dusseldorf 1,
      Germany
    Wensauer DDB Needham Worldwide GmbH, Streitfeldstrasse 19, 8000 Munich 80, Germany
    Wensauer DDB Needham Worldwide GmbH, Postfach 1065, Osterholzallee 76,
      7140 Ludwigsburg, Germany

DE VILBISS CO   300 Phillips Ave, Toledo, OH 43612, Tel: (419) 470-2169
  (Mfr spray painting & finishing equip)
    Devilbiss Europa GmbH, Hermannstr 54, D-6078 Neu Isenburg, Germany
    Devilbiss Europa GmbH, Justus-Ven-Liebicstr 31, 6057 Dietzenbach 1, Germany

DEERE & CO   John Deere Rd, Moline, IL 61265, Tel: (309) 752-8000
  (Mfr/sale agri/constr/utility/forestry & lawn/grounds care equip)
    Deere & Co., Steubenstr. 36-42, 6800 Mannheim 1, Germany

DELL COMPUTER CORP   9505 Arboretum Blvd, Austin, TX 78759,
  Tel: (512) 338-4400
  (Design/mfr personal computers)
    Dell Computer GmbH, Monzastr. 4, 6070 Langen, Germany

DENTSPLY INTL INC   PO Box 872, York, PA 17405, Tel: (717) 845-7511
  (Mfr dental, medical & ind supplies & equip)
    Denstsply GmbH, Postfach 101074, Eisenbahntrasse 180, D-6072 Dreieich, Germany
    Dentsply GmbH, Postfach 5346, DeTreystrasse 1, D-7750 Konstane 12, Germany

DEUTSCH CO   2444 Wilshire Blvd, Santa Monica, CA 90403, Tel: (213) 453-0055
  (Electr components)
    Deutsch-Amerikanische Asphalt-Produkte GmbH, Huhnerposten 14, 2 Hamburg 1, Germany

DEVCON CORP   30 Endicott St, Danvers, MA 01923, Tel: (617) 777-1100
  (Mfr filled epoxies, urethanes, adhesives & metal treatment prdts)
    ITW Ateco GmbH, Siemansstr. 15, 4030 Ratingen 4 (Lantare), Germany

DEVLIEG MACHINE CO   Fair St, Royal Oak, MI 48073, Tel: (313) 549-1100
  (Boring & milling machs)
    Devlieg Werkzeugmaschinen GmbH, Wertherstr. 1a, 4290 Bacholt, Germany

DEXTER ELECTRONIC MATERIALS   15051 E Don Julian Rd, Industry, CA 91746,
  Tel: (818) 968-6511
  (Mfr spec coatings for elec/electr ind)
    The Dexter GmbH, Lilienthal Str. 5, 8046 Garching, Germany

DHJ INDUSTRIES INC   1040 Ave of the Americas, New York, NY 10018,
  Tel: (212) 944-4500
  (Mfr of knit fabrics, interlinings plastic chips & denim)
    DHJ Industries Deutschland GmbH, Grafenheiderstr. 105, D-4800 Bielefeld 16, Germany

DIBRELL BROS INC   512 Bridge St, Danville, VA 24543, Tel: (804) 792-7511
  (Sale leaf tobacco, cut flowers)
    Dibrell GmbH, Ostendstrasse 132, 8500 Nurnburg, Germany

THE DIEBOLD GROUP INC   475 Park Ave South, New York, NY 10016,
  Tel: (212) 684-4700
  (Mgmt consultants: info tech)
    Diebold Deutschland GmbH, Frankfurter Str. 27, D-6236 Eschborn bei Frankfurt/Main,
      Germany

DIGITAL EQUIPMENT CORP   129 Parker St, Maynard, MA 01754, Tel: (617) 897-5111
  (Digital computers, digital circuit modules, memory elec- tronic system)
    Digital Equipment GmbH, Rheinstr 28, D-8000 Munich 40, Germany

WALT DISNEY PRODUCTIONS   500 S Buena Vista St, Burbank, CA 91521,
  Tel: (818) 560-1000
  (Film/TV prod, amusement parks, land mgmt)
    Walt Disney Production (Germany) GmbH, Savignystr 76, 6 Frankfurt/Main, Germany

DO ALL COMPANY   254 N Laurel Ave, Des Plaines, IL 60016, Tel: (708) 824-1122
(Distributors of mach tools, metal cutting tools, instru & ind supplies)
  Do All Co., GmbH, Kleberstrasse 5, 4020 Mettmann, Germany

DOBOY PACKAGING MACHINERY DIV   869 S Knowles Ave, New Richmond, WI 54017,
  Tel: (715) 246-6511
(Mfr packaging machinery)
  Doboy Verpackungsmaschinen GmbH, Klebitzweg 16-18, 2 Schensfeld, Germany

DOMINICK & DOMINICK INC   90 Broad St, New York, NY 10090, Tel: (212) 558-8800
(Brokers)
  Dominick & Dominick GmbH, Westendstr. 24, 6 Frankfurt/Main, Germany

DONALDSON CO INC   PO Box 1299, Minneapolis, MN 55440, Tel: (612) 887-3131
(Filtration prdts & sys)
  Donaldson GmbH, Postfach 1149, 4408 Dulmen Dernekamp, Germany

DONN PRODUCTS INC   1000 Crocker Rd, Westlake, OH 44145, Tel: (216) 871-1000
(Suspended ceiling sys)
  Donn Products GmbH, Friedrich Ebert Str. 1, 4 Dusseldorf, Germany

DORR-OLIVER INC   612 Wheeler's Farm Rd, PO Box 3819, Milford, CT 06460,
  Tel: (203) 876-5400
(Mfr process equip for food, pulp & paper, mineral & chem ind; & municipal/ind waste
treatment)
  Door-Oliver GmbH, Friedrich-Bergius Strasse 5, 6200 Wiesbaden-Biebrich (12), Germany

DOW CHEMICAL CO   2030 Dow Center, Midland, MI 48640, Tel: (517) 636-1000
(Chems, plastics, fibers, pharms)
  Dow Chemical GmbH, Kommandantendeich 8, 216 Stade, Germany
  Dow Chemical GmbH, 2160 Stade-Butzfletz, Werk Stade Butzenflether Sand, Germany
  Dow Chemical GmbH, Kommandantendeich 8, 2160 Stade, Germany
  Dow Chemical GmbH, Briennerstr. 44, 8 Munich 2, Germany
  Dow Chemical GmbH, Wiesenhuttenstr. 18, 6 Frankfurt/Main, Germany
  Dow Chemical GmbH, Winterhunder Weg 29/31, 2 Hamburg 76, Germany
  Dow Chemical GmbH, Grunerstr. 46, 4 Dusseldorf 1, Germany
  Dow Chemical GmbH, Gansheidestr. 55, 7 Stuttgart 1, Germany
  Dow Chemical Rheinwerk GmbH, Industriestr. 1, 7581 Rheinmunster, Germany

DOW CORNING CORP   2220 W Salzburg Rd, PO Box 1767, Midland, MI 48640,
  Tel: (517) 496-4000
(Silicones, silicon chems, solid lubricants)
  Dow Corning GmbH, Emanuel-Leutzestr. 1, 4000 Dusseldorf 11, Germany

DRAKE BEAM MORIN INC   100 Park Ave, New York, NY 10017, Tel: (212) 692-7700
(Human resource mgmt consulting & training)
  Drake Beam Morin Europe Inc., Kaiserwerther Str. 13, D-4000 Dusseldorf 30, Germany

DRESSER INDUSTRIES INC   1600 Pacific Bldg, PO Box 718, Dallas, TX 75221,
  Tel: (214) 740-6000
(Diversified supplier of equip & tech serv to energy & natural resource ind)
  Air Tool Div. Europe, S.A., Niederlassuwe Hamburg, Eschelsweg 27, 2000 Hamburg 50,
    Germany
  Dresser Europe, S.A., Postfach 1120, D-5112 Baesweicer, Germany
  Dresser Manuf. Div., Dresser Europe S.A., Postfach 100208, Gueldenwerth 9,
    5630 Remscheid 1, Germany
  Dresser Wayne Germany, Dresser Europe S.A., Postfach 186, Grimsehlstr. 44,

(cont)

D-3352 Einbeck, Germany
Magnesital Feurrfest GmbH, Zum, Eisenhammer 23, 4200 Oberhausen 1, Germany

DREW CHEMICAL CORP   One Drew Plaza, Boonton, NJ 07005, Tel: (201) 263-7600
(Spec chems for ind water & fuel treatment, chem processing)
Drew Ameroid Deutschland GmbH, Rathenaustr. 17, D-6050 Offenbach, Germany

DRG INTL INC   1167 Route 22 East, Mountainside, NJ 07092, Tel: (201) 233-2075
(Sale/serv med diagnostic prdts & equip; biotech prdts)
DRG Instruments GmbH, Frankfurter Str. 59, D-3550 Marburg, Germany

DRIVER-HARRIS CO   308 Middlesex St, Harrison, NJ 07029, Tel: (201) 483-4800
(Wire, cables, etc)
Driver-Harris Deutschland GmbH, Strickerstr 1, 7440 Nurtingen, Germany

DU BOIS INTL INC   1100 DuBois Tower, Cincinnati, OH 45202,
Tel: (513) 762-6000
(Mfr spec chems & maintenance prdts)
DuBois Chemie GmbH, Justus Von Liebig-Str. 24-26, 6057 Dietzenbach, Germany

E I DU PONT DE NEMOURS & CO   Du Pont Bldg, 1007 Market St, Wilmington,
DE 19898, Tel: (302) 774-1000
(Mfr/sale diversified chems, plastics, specialty prdts & fibers)
Du Pont de Nemours (Deutschland) GmbH, Hans-Bocklerstr. 33, 4 Dusseldorf-Nord,
Germany

DUNHAM-BUSH INC   175 South St, West Hartford, CT 06110, Tel: (203) 249-8671
(Ind & commercial refrigeration, heating & A/C equip)
Dunham-Bush GmbH, Wiesenstr. 5, 6140 Bensheim 1, Germany

DURAMETALLIC CORP   2104 Factory St, Kalamazoo, MI 49001, Tel: (616) 382-8720
(Mfr mech seals, compression packings, auxiliaries)
Durametallic Europe GmbH, Blumenstr. 10, Postfach 201108, 6072 Drieich 2, Germany

DURIRON CO INC   425 N Findlay St, PO Box 1145, Dayton, OH 45401,
Tel: (513) 226-4000
(Mfr chem equip, pumps, valves, filters, fans, heat exchangers)
Durco GmbH/Atomac, Von-Braun-Strasse 17, D-4422 Ahaus, Germany

DYN CORP   2000 Edmund Halley Dr, Reston, VA 22091, Tel: (703) 264-0330
(Diversified tech services)
ITS Intl. Service, Schiersteiner Strasse 52, Lindsey Air Station, 6200 Wiesbaden,
Germany

EASTMAN KODAK CO   343 State St, Rochester, NY 14650-0518, Tel: (716) 724-4000
(Devel/mfr photo & chem prdts, info mgmt/video/copier sys, fibers/plastics for
various ind)
Kodak AG, Hedelfingerstr., 7000 Stuttgart 60, Germany

EATON CORP   100 Erieview Plaza, Cleveland, OH 44114, Tel: (216) 523-5000
(Advanced tech prdts for transp & ind mkts)
Eaton GmbH, Am Lindenkamp 31, 5620 Velbert/Rheinland, Germany

EBSCO INDUSTRIES   PO Box 1, Birmingham, AL 35201, Tel: (205) 991-6600
(Serial pub/subscriptions, recreational & educational goods, mfr sheet metal & wire
prdts)
EBSCO Subscription Services, Bodenstedtstr. 6, 62 Wiesbaden, Germany

ECHLIN INC   100 Double Beach Rd, Branford, CT 06405, Tel: (203) 481-5751
  (Mfr motor vehicle replacement parts)
    Graubremse GmbH, Eppelheimer Str. 76, 6900 Heidelberg 1, Germany

ECOLAB INC   370 Wabasha St, St Paul, MN 55102, Tel: (612) 293-2233
  (Ind & household detergents, cleaning agents & equip)
    Ascalia GmbH, Fabrik Chemisch-Technischer Produkte, Amelungstr 2, Postfach 300125,
      2000 Hamburg 36, Germany
    Soilax GmbH, Hammerstr. 1, 6450 Hanau, Germany

ECONOMY FORMS CORP - EFCO   4301 NE 14th St, Des Moines, IA 50316-0386,
  Tel: (515) 266-1141
  (Mfr steel forms for concrete construction)
    Economy Forms Corp/EFCO Schalungsbau GmbH, Landsberger Str. 185, 8000 Munich 21,
      Germany

EG&G INC   45 William St, Wellesley, MA 02181, Tel: (617) 237-5100
  (Diversified instru, components, services)
    EG&G GmbH, Hohenlindenerstr. 12, D-8000 Munich 80, Germany
    EG&G GmbH/Sealol Euroseals, Gagern Ring 5, 6233 Kelkheim, Germany
    EG&G Reticon, Hohenlindener Str. 12, 8000 Munich 80, Germany

ELECTRIC FURNACE CO   435 Wilson St, Salem, OH 44460, Tel: (216) 332-4661
  (Design & mfr heat treating furnaces for metals ind)
    Electric Furnace (Germany) GmbH, Ringstr. 54, Postfach 1327, 419 Kleve, Germany

ELECTROGLASS INC   2902 Coronada Dr, Santa Clara, CA 95051,
  Tel: (408) 246-6500
  (Digital actuators, laser positioners)
    Electroglas GmbH, Hauffstr. 4, 8 Munich 25, Germany

ELECTRONIC ASSOCIATES INC   185 Monmouth Park Hwy, West Long Branch,
  NJ 07764, Tel: (201) 229-1100
  (Analog/hybrid computers, training simulators, energy measurement sys)
    EAI-Electronic Associates GmbH, Franzstr. 107, D-5100 Aachen, Germany

ELECTRONIC ENGINEERING CO OF CALIFORNIA   1441 E Chestnut Ave, PO Box 659,
  Santa Ana, CA 92701, Tel: (714) 835-6000
  (Data processing equip)
    Electronic Engineers International, Postfach 426, 4812 Brackwede, Germany

ELIZABETH ARDEN INC   55 East 52nd St, New York, NY 10055-0191,
  Tel: (212) 407-1000
  (Cosmetics, fragrances, toiletries)
    Elizabeth Arden GmbH, Grafenberger Allee 87, Postfach 1407, D-4000 Dusseldorf,
      Germany

EMCO WHEATON INC   50 Chamberlain Blvd, PO Box 688, Conneaut, OH 44030,
  Tel: (216) 599-8151
  (Mfr petroleum handling equip- ment)
    EMCO Wheaton GmbH, Emcostr. 2-4, Postfach 25 35 75, Kerchhain 1, Germany

EMERSON & CUMING DEWEY & ALMY CHEMICAL CO   59 Walpole St, Canton, MA 02021,
  Tel: (617) 828-3300
  (Plastics & ceramics for electr shielding materials)
    Emerson & Cuming GmbH, Muehlhaldenstr. 14, 7 Stuttgart 80, Germany

ENCYCLOPEDIA BRITANNICA INC   425 N Michigan Ave, Chicago, IL 60611,
   Tel: (312) 321-7000
   (Book publ)
      Els Sprachenistitutu GmbH (Britannica/Liguarama), Rindermarkt 16, 8000 Muchen 2,
      Munich, Germany
      Encyclopaedia Britannica (Germany) Ltd., Berliner Allee 47, Postfach 200 209,
      D-4000, Dusseldorf 1, Germany

ENERPAC   13000 W Silver Spring Dr, Butler, WI 53007, Tel: (414) 781-6600
   (Mfr/sale high pressure hydraulic maint tools)
      Applied Power GmbH, Postfach 30 01 13, D-4000 Dusseldorf 30, Germany

ERC ENVIRONMENTAL & ENERGY SERVICES CO   3211 Jermantown Rd, Fairfax,
   VA 22053, Tel: (703) 246-0500
   (Engr & conslt serv for energy, envi, & infrastructure engr mkts)
      I.E.A.L. Energie Consult GmbH, Komgswintererstrasse 272, 5300 Bonn 3, Germany

ERICO PRODUCTS INC   34600 Solon Road, Cleveland, OH 44139,
   Tel: (216) 248-0100
   (Mfr electric welding apparatus & hardware, metal stampings, specialty fasteners)
      Erico Elektrotechnische, Spezialfabrik GmbH, D679 Schwanenmuehle,
      Postfach Steinalben, Germany

ESTERLINE CORP   10800 NE 8th St, #600, Bellevue, WA 98004,
   Tel: (206) 453-6001
   (Mfr equip & instru for ind automation, precision meas, data acquisition)
      Excellon Europe GmbH, Juston-von-Liebig-Str. 19, D-6057 Dietzenbach, Germany

ETHICON INC   Route 22, Somerville, NJ 08876, Tel: (201) 218-3293
   (Surgical prdts)
      Ethicon GmbH, Robert-Koch-Str. 1, 2 Norderstedt, Germany

EXCELLON AUTOMATION   23915 Garnier, Torrance, CA 90509, Tel: (213) 534-6300
   (PCB drilling & routing machs; optical inspection equip)
      Excellon Europa GmbH, Justus-von-Liebig-Str. 19, D-6057 Dietzenbach, Germany

EXQUISITE FORM INDUSTRIES INC   16 E 40th St, New York, NY 10016,
   Tel: (212) 532-8160
   (Foundation garments)
      Exquisite, Doernerhofstr., Haus Doernerhof, 41 Duisburg, Germany

EXXON CHEMICAL CO   9 Old Kings Hwy S, Darien, CT 06820, Tel: (203) 655-5200
   (Mfr & sales of petrochems)
      Esso Chemie GmbH, Kapstadtring 2, 2 Hamburg 39, Germany

EXXON CORP   225 E John Carpenter Frwy, Irving, TX 75062, Tel: (214) 444-1000
   (Petroleum & petroleum prdts)
      Esso AG, Kapstadtring 2, 2 Hamburg 39, Germany
      Esso Motor Hotel, Effnerstr. 99, 8 Munich 81, Germany
      Esso Motor Hotel GmbH, Isenburger Schneise, 6 Frankfurt/Main, Germany

FAIRCHILD CAMERA & INSTRUMENT CORP   PO Box 58090, Santa Clara,
   CA 95052-8090, Tel: (408) 743-3355
   (Mfr electr instru & controls)
      Fairchild Halbbleiter GmbH, Aarstr. 1, 62 Wiesbaden, Germany

FASTENER CORP   3702 River Rd, Franklin Park, IL 60131, Tel: (708) 678-0100
  (Staplers, tackers, nailers)
    Duo-Fast Europe GmbH, Ruhrstr. 49, 4041 Norf, Germany
    Vessfoff & Co., Duo-Fast GmbH, 5757 Wickede, Germany

FEDERAL EXPRESS CORP   PO Box 727, Memphis, TN 38194-4212, Tel: (901) 922-6900
  (Package air express svc)
    Federal Express (Deutschland) GmbH, Wanheimer Str. 61, 4000 Dusseldorf 30, Germany
    Federal Express (Deutschland) GmbH, Kleiner Kornweg 6-24, 6092 Kezsterbach, Germany
    Federal Express (Deutschland) GmbH, Flughafen, Gebaude 192, 2000 Hamburg, 63,
      Germany
    Federal Express (Deutschland) GmbH, Stahlgruberring 32, 8000 Munich 82, Germany

FERRO CORPORATION   One Erieview Plaza, Cleveland, OH 44114,
  Tel: (216) 641-8580
  (Chems, coatings, plastics, refractories)
    Ferro (Deutschland) GmbH, Postfach 1032, Langenbergstrasse 10,
      D-6750 Kaiserslautern 2, Germany
    Ferro Plastics (Germany) GmbH, Postfach 170125, Werningshof 31, D-4800 Bielefeld,
      Germany
    Ruhr Pulverlack GmbH, Zur Alten Ruhr 4, Postfach 2267, D-5760 Arnsberg, Germany

FINNIGAN CORP   355 River Oaks Parkway, San Jose, CA 95134-1991,
  Tel: (408) 433-4800
  (Mfr mass spectrometers, data handling sys, methodology devel)
    Finnigan MAT GmbH, Postfach 144062, D-2800 Bremen 14, Germany
    Finnigan MAT GmbH, Benzstrasse 28, Postfach 1253, D-8039 Pucheim, Germany
    Finnigan MAT GmbH, Alexandraweg 32, D-6100 Darmstadt, Germany
    Finnigan MAT GmbH, Bernard-Eybergy Str. 74, D-5060 Bergisch/Gladbach, Germany

FIRST NATIONAL BANK OF BOSTON   100 Federal St, Boston, MA 02110,
  Tel: (617) 434-2200
  (Commercial banking)
    First National Bank of Boston, City-Haus, Postfach 2825, Germany
    First National Bank of Boston, Friedrich-Ebert-Anlage 2-14, 6000 Frankfurt/Main 1,
      Germany
    First National Bank of Boston, Ballindamm 13, 2000 Hamburg, Germany

FISCHER & PORTER CO   125 E County Line Rd, Warminster, PA 18974,
  Tel: (215) 674-6000
  (Design/mfr meas, recording & control instru & sys; mfr ind glass prdts)
    Fischer & Porter GmbH, Postfach 1843, D-3400 Goettingen, Germany

FISHER CONTROLS INTL INC   8000 Maryland Ave, Clayton, MO 63105,
  Tel: (314) 694-9900
  (Ind process control equip)
    Fisher Controls GmbH, Albertus-Magnus-Str. 11, D-5650 Solingen 19, Germany
    Fisher Controls GmbH, Apenrader Str. 22, D-2080 Pinneberg, Germany

FISHER-PRICE   636 Girard Ave, East Aurora, NY 14052, Tel: (716) 687-3000
  (Mfr toys & games)
    Fisher-Price Spielwaren GmbH, Schildgesstrasse 71-163, 5040 Bruehl, Germany

FLEER CORP   10th & Somerville Ave, Philadelphia, PA 19141,
  Tel: (215) 455-2000
  (Chewing gum)
    Fleer GmbH, Industriestr. 54, 6909 Walldorf, Germany

FLORIDA INTL FORWARDERS   6905 N W 25th St, PO Box 522085, Miami, FL 33122,
Tel: (305) 592-6450
(Air cargo service)
  Air Cargo System GmbH, Fasanenweg 7, D-6092 Kelsterbach Main, Germany
  Skymater International GmbH, Ltg. Term-Fasaneweg, 10 Kerlsterbach, Germany

FLOW INTERNATIONAL CORP   21440 68th Ave South, Kent, WA 98032,
Tel: (206) 872-4900
(Mfr waterjet sys)
  Flow Europe GmbH, Daimlerweg 6, D-6100 Darmstadt, Germany

FLOW LABORATORIES INC   7655 Old Springhouse Rd, McLean, VA 22102,
Tel: (703) 893-5900
(Mfr/distr biotechnology)
  Flow Laboratories GmbH, Postfach 1249, D-5309 Meckenheim, Germany

FLUOR CORP   3333 Michelson Dr, Irvine, CA 92730, Tel: (714) 975-2000
(Engr/constr & related services; coal & lead)
  Fluor Daniel GmbH, Dusseldorf, Germany

FLYING TIGER LINE INC   7401 World Way W, Los Angeles, CA 90009,
Tel: (213) 646-6161
(Air frt carrier, air cargo service worldwide)
  Flying Tiger Line, Inc., Mainzerlandstr. 27-31, 6000 Frankfurt/Main, Germany

FMC CORP   200 E Randolph Dr, Chicago, IL 60601, Tel: (312) 861-6000
(Mach & chem for industry, agric & govt)
  FMC Machinery Germany GmbH, Achenbachstr. 78, D-4000 Dusseldorf, Germany

FOOTE CONE & BELDING COMMUNICATIONS INC   101 E Erie St, Chicago,
IL 60611-2897, Tel: (312) 751-7000
(Advertising agency)
  Baums, Mang & Zimmermann, Schirmerstrasse 76, 4000 Dusseldorf 1, Germany
  FCB/Direct, Hamburger Strasse 11, 2000 Hamburg 76, Germany
  George Schirmer Business-to-Business, Kaiser-Ludwig-Platz 5/1, 8000 Munich 2,
    Germany
  MWI Markenwerbung Intl., Holstenwall 10, 2000 Hamburg 36, Germany
  Publicis, Lindemannstrasse 75, 4000 Dusseldorf 1, Germany
  Publicis Direct, An der Alster 30, 2000 Hamburg 1, Germany

FORD MOTOR CO   The American Road, Dearborn, MI 48121, Tel: (313) 322-3000
(Mfr automobiles, trucks)
  Ford-Werke AG, Werke Koeln-Niehl, Henry Ford Str., Postfach 604002,
    D-5000 Cologne 60, Germany

FOXBORO CO   33 Commercial St, Foxboro, MA 02035, Tel: (508) 543-8750
(Mfr prdts/provide servs for ind automation)
  Foxboro Deutschland GmbH, Heerdter Lohweg 53-55, D-4000 Dusseldorf 11, Germany

FRANKLIN ELECTRIC CO INC   400 E Spring St, Bluffton, IN 46714,
Tel: (219) 824-2900
(Mfr fractional h.p motors, submersible motors & controls)
  Franklin Electric Europa GmbH, Postfach 1280, Wittlich, Germany

THE FRANKLIN MINT   Franklin Center, PA 19091, Tel: (215) 459-6000
(Creation/mfr/mktg collectible items)
  Franklin Mint GmbH, Alte Landstr. 21, 8012 Ottobrunn b., Munich, Germany

FULLER CO   2040 Ave C, PO Box 2040, Bethlehem, PA 18001, Tel: (215) 264-6011
   (Ind processing equip & sys, conveying & blending sys, etc)
      Gatx-Fuller GmbH, Dusseldorf, Germany

H B FULLER CO   2400 Energy Park Dr, St Paul, MN 55108, Tel: (612) 645-3401
   (Mfr/distr adhesives, sealants, coatings, paints, waxes, sanitation chems)
      H.B. Fuller GmbH, An der Roten Bleiche 2-3, Postfach 2050, D-2120 Lueneburg, Germany

GAF CORP   1361 Alps Rd, Wayne, NJ 07470, Tel: (201) 628-3000
   (Chems, bldg materials, commun)
      GAF (Deutschland) GmbH, Postfach 1380, 5020 Frechen, Germany

GAMLEN CHEMICAL CO   121 S Maple Ave, S San Francisco, CA 94080,
   Tel: (415) 873-1750
   (Chems, detergents & tank cleansers)
      Gamlen Chemie GmbH, 62 Schwarzenbergstr., 21 Hamburg 90, Germany

GARLOCK INC   1250 Midtown Tower, Rochester, NY 14604, Tel: (214) 758-0000
   (Mechanical packings)
      Garlock GmbH, Postfach 300 450, Scheffelstr. 73, 4000 Dusseldorf 30, Germany
      Garlock GmbH, Postfach 300 450, Scheffelstr. 73, 4000 Dusseldorf 30, Germany

THE GATES RUBBER CO   PO Box 5887, Denver, CO 80217, Tel: (303) 744-1911
   (Mfr auto/ind belts & hose, hydraulic hose & couplings, molded rubber prdts)
      Gates GmbH, Eisenbahnweg 50, Postfach 1428, 5100 Aachen, Germany

GATX CORP   120 S Riverside Plaza, Chicago, IL 60606, Tel: (312) 621-6200
   (Railcar leasing, maint & mgmt, bulk liquid storage, fin serv, shipping, mineral
   processing)
      GATX Fuller GmbH, Emanuel-Leutze-Str. 17, 4000 Dusseldorf 17, Germany

GELMAN SCIENCES INC   600 South Wagner St, Ann Arbor, MI 48106,
   Tel: (313) 665-0651
   (Laboratory prdts)
      Gelman Sciences Deutschland GmbH, Max-Planckstr. 19, D-5072 Dreieich, Germany

GENERAL AUTOMATION INC   1055 S East St, Anaheim, CA 92806,
   Tel: (714) 778-4800
   (Computer hardware & serv)
      General Automation GmbH, Heider-Hof-Weg-23, Postfach 465,
      5100 Aachen Verlautenheide, Germany

GENERAL BINDING CORP   One GBC Plaza, Northbrook, IL 60062,
   Tel: (708) 272-3700
   (Binding & laminating equip & associated supplies)
      GBC Deutschland GmbH, Rather Str. 28, D-4000 Dusseldorf 30, Germany
      GBC Deutschland GmbH, Boschstr. 1, D-8901 Konigsbrunn, Germany

GENERAL DYNAMICS CORP   Pierre Laclede Center, St Louis, MO 63105,
   Tel: (314) 889-8200
   (Mfr aircraft, submarines, missiles, space launch vehicles, bldg prdts, info sys)
      General Dynamics Intl. Corp., Buerohaus Am Stadtpark, Koblenzer Str. 99,
      Bad Godesbert, 5300 Bonn 1, Germany

GENERAL ELECTRIC CO   3135 Easton Tpk, Fairfield, CT 06431,
   Tel: (203) 373-2211
   (Diversified mfr, tech & servs)
      GE Germany, Praunheimer Landstrasse 50, 6000 Frankfurt/Main 90, Germany

GENERAL FOODS CORP   250 North St, White Plains, NY 10625, Tel: (914) 335-2500
   (Processor, distributor & mfr of foods)
      HAG GF AG, Hagstrasse 3, 2800 Bremen 1, Germany

GENERAL MOTORS ACCEPTANCE CORP   3044 West Grand Blvd, Detroit, MI 48202,
   Tel: (313) 556-5000
   (Automobile financing)
      Opel Kredit Bank GmbH, Stahlstrasse 34, 6090 Russelsheim, Germany
      Opel Kredit Bank GmbH, Am Fernmeldeamt 15, Postfach 102817, 4300 Essen, Germany
      Opel Kredit Bank GmbH, Grosse Bleichen 21, Postfach 304050, 2000 Hamburg, Germany
      Opel Kredit Bank GmbH, Prielmayerstrasse 1, Postfach 201826, D-8000 Munich, Germany
      Opel Kredit Bank GmbH, Postfach 103643, 7000 Stuttgart 10, Germany
      Opel Kredit Bank GmbH, Postfach 4666, Herschelstrasse 32, Hanover 1, Germany

GENERAL MOTORS CORP   3044 W Grand Blvd, Detroit, MI 48202,
   Tel: (313) 556-5000
   (Automotive prdts, electronics)
      Adam Opel AG, D-6090 Russelsheim, Germany
      Unicables SA, c/o Kabelwerke Reinshagen GmbH, Reinshagenstr. 1,
         D-5600 Wuppertal 21, Germany

GENRAD INC   300 Baker Ave, Concord, MA 01742, Tel: (508) 369-4400
   (Mfr automatic test equip)
      GenRad GmbH, Neumarkter Strasse 83, Postfach 800 711, 8000 Munich 80, Germany

GEORGIA KAOLIN CO INC   2700 US Hwy 22 East, Union, NJ 07083,
   Tel: (201) 851-2800
   (Clay mining)
      Euroclay, c/o Amberger Kaolinwerke GmbH, Schliessfach 1140, D-8452 Hirschau, Germany

GERBER SCIENTIFIC INSTRUMENT CO   83 Gerber Rd West, So Windsor, CT 06074,
   Tel: (203) 644-1551
   (CADICAM for electronic & graphic arts ind)
      Gerber Scientific Germany GmbH, Landsbergerstr. 291, D-8000 Munich 21, Germany

GILBARCO INC   PO Box 22087, Greensboro, NC 27420, Tel: (919) 292-3011
   (Service station equip)
      Gilbarco GmbH, Schierenberg 74, 2000 Hamburg 73, Germany

GILFORD INSTRUMENT LABS INC   132 Artino St, Oberlin, OH 44074,
   Tel: (216) 774-1041
   (Med electronic instru)
      Gilford GmbH, Weibenburgstr. 39, 4000 Dusseldorf, Germany

THE GILLETTE CO   Prudential Tower, Boston, MA 02199, Tel: (617) 421-7000
   (Mfr/distr shaving prdts, toiletries & cosmetics, stationery prdts)
      Braun AG, Postfach 1120, 6242 Kronberg, Germany
      Gillette Deutschland GmbH, Postfach 420831, 1000 Berlin 43, Germany

GLOBAL INTERNATIONAL   500 Ygnacio Valley Rd, #175, Walnut Creek, CA 94596,
   Tel: (415) 933-2293
   (Freight forwarding)

Global Internationale Spedition GmbH, Auf Dem Dransdorferberg 64, D-5300 Bonn 1,
   Germany

GOODYEAR TIRE & RUBBER CO   1144 E Market St, Akron, OH 44316-0001,
   Tel: (216) 796-2121
   (Mfr tires, rubber prdts)
      Deutsche Goodyear GmbH, Xantener Str. 105, Postfach 100508, 5000 Koeln 60, Germany
      Gummiwerke Fulda GmbH, Kuenzellerstr. 59/61, D-6400 Fulda, Germany

W L GORE & ASSOCIATES INC   555 Paper Mill Road, Newark, DE 19711,
   Tel: (302) 738-4880
   (Mfr electr, ind filtration, med & fabric prdts)
      W. L. Gore & Co. GmbH, Glonnerstr., 8011 Putzbrunn, Germany

GOULD INC   10 Gould Center, Rolling Meadows, IL 60008, Tel: (708) 640-4000
   (Electric sys, batteries, etc)
      Ermeto Div., Dielefeld, Germany

W R GRACE & CO   1114 Ave of the Americas, New York, NY 10036,
   Tel: (212) 819-5500
   (Specialty chems, natural resources, consumer serv)
      Grace GmbH, In der Hollerhecke 1, 6520 Worms, Germany
      Grace GmbH, Erlengang 31, 2 Norderstedt 1, Germany
      Teroson GmbH, Mans-Buntestr. 4, 6900 Heidelberg 1, Germany

GRACO INC   4040 Olson Memorial Hwy, PO Box 1441, Minneapolis, MN 55440-1441,
   Tel: (612) 623-6000
   (Mfr/serv fluid handling equip & sys)
      Graco GmbH, Postfach 234, Moselstrasse 19, 4040 Neuss, Germany

GRANT THORNTON INTL   Prudential Plaza, Chicago, IL 60601, Tel: (312) 856-0001
   (Intl accountants)
      Grant Thornton GmbH, Wasserstr. 5, 4000 Dusseldorf 1, Germany

GREY ADVERTISING INC   777 Third Ave, New York, NY 10017, Tel: (212) 546-2000
   (Advertising)
      Gramm & Grey GmbH & Co., KG, Corneliusstr. 18-24, 4 Dusseldorf, Germany

GTE CORP   One Stamford Forum, Stamford, CT 06904, Tel: (203) 965-2000
   (Electr prdts, telecom sys, publ & commun)
      Hopt Electronic GmbH, Koenigsbergerstr. 12, 7210 Rottweil, Germany
      Richard Bosse & Co. GmbH, Telefonbau, Reichenbergerstr. 78, 1 Berlin 36, Germany
      Saba-Werke GmbH, Hermann-Scwer-Str., 7730 Villingen/Schwarzwald, Germany
      Sylvania Lichtlechalk und Elektronik GmbH, Vahrenwalderstr. 205, Postfach 5327,
         3 Hannover 1, Germany

GULTON INDUSTRIES INC   212 Durham Ave, Metuchen, NJ 08840,
   Tel: (908) 548-6500
   (Electr instru & controls, commun equip)
      Electro Voice Div., Unternehmenbereich der Gulton GmbH, Laerchenstr. 99,
         Postfach 831164, 6230 Frankfurt am Main 80, Germany

FRANK B HALL & CO INC   549 Pleasantville Rd, Briarcliff Manor, NY 10510,
   Tel: (914) 769-9200
   (Insurance)
      M.W. Joose & Frank B. Hall Overseas GmbH, Roedingsmarkt 14, 2000 Hamburg, Germany
      M.W. Joose & Frank B. Hall Overseas GmbH, Lange Str. 126, 7570 Baden-Baden, Germany

(cont)

M.W. Joose & Frank B. Hall Overseas GmbH, Kloosterstr. 35, 4000 Dusseldorf 1,
    Germany
M.W. Joose & Frank B. Hall Overseas GmbH, Freiherr-vom-Stein-Str. 24/26,
    6000 Frankfurt 1, Germany
M.W. Joose & Frank B. Hall Overseas GmbH, Franz-Joseph-Str. 1, 8000 Munich, Germany

HALLMARK CARDS INC   PO Box 419580, Kansas City, MO 64141, Tel: (816) 274-5100
(Mfr greeting cards & related prdts)
    Hallmark Cards, Inc.- GmbH, Postfach 700809, 8000 Munchen 70, Germany

HAMLIN INC   612 E Lake St, Lake Mills, WI 53551, Tel: (414) 648-3000
(Mfr position sensors, switches, relays)
    Hamlin Electronics GmbH, Postfach 1306, D-6368 Bad Vilbel, bei Frankfurt/Main,
    Germany

HAMMOND ORGAN CO   4200 Diversey Ave, Chicago, IL 60639, Tel: (312) 283-2000
(Musical instru)
    Deutsche Hammond Instrument GmbH, Spaldingstr. 160, 2 Hamburg 1, Germany

HARCOURT BRACE JOVANOVICH INC   Harcourt Brace Jovanovich Bldg, Orlando,
    FL 32887, Tel: (305) 345-2000
(Book publ, tests & related serv, journals, facisimile reprints, mgmt consult,
operates parks/shows)
    Drake Beam Morin-Europe Inc., Biebricher Allee 30, D-6200 Weisbaden, Germany

HARLEY-DAVIDSON INTL   3700 W Juneau Ave, Milwaukee, WI 53208,
    Tel: (414) 935-4071
(Mfr motorcycles, recreational & coml vehicles, parts & accessories)
    Harley-Davidson GmbH, 7 Industriestrasse, 6096 Raunheim, Germany

HARNISCHFEGER INDUSTRIES INC   PO Box 554, Milwaukee, WI 53201,
    Tel: (414) 671-4400
(Mfr mining & material handling equip, papermaking mach, computer sys)
    Harnischfeger GmbH, Postfach 710411, 6000 Frankfurt/Main, Germany

THE HARPER GROUP INC   260 Townsend St, PO Box 77933, San Francisco,
    CA 94107, Tel: (415) 978-0600
(Ocean/air freight fwdg, customs brokerage, packing & whse, logistics mgt, ins)
    Circle Freight Intl. SP GmbH, PO Box 1333, 6092 Kelsterbach, Germany
    Max Gruenhut GmbH & Co., Billhorner Deich 96, 2000 Hamburg 28, Germany
    Max Gruenhut GmbH & Co. (Germany), Postfach 750269, D-6000 Frankfurt 75, Germany

HARRIS CALORIFIC CO   2345 Murphy Blvd, Gainesville, GA 30501,
    Tel: (404) 536-8801
(Mfr gas welding & cutting equip)
    Harris Calorific Deutschland GmbH, 586 Iserlohn, Masteweg 7, Germany

HARSCO CORP   PO Box 8888, Camp Hill, PA 17011-8888, Tel: (717) 763-7064
(Diversified mfr & serv)
    Heckett Scheackenaufbereitungs Ltd., Postfach 300305, 4600 Dortmund 30, Germany
    TW Cryogenic Products Druckbehaelter GmbH, Postfach 1565, D-2250 Husum/Mildstedt,
    Germany

HARSHAW/FILTRO PARTNERS   30100 Chagrin Blvd, Cleveland, OH 44124,
    Tel: (216) 292-9200
(Ind chems)
    Harshaw Chemie GmbH, Postfach 1360, D-5632 Wermelskirchen 1, Germany

HAUSERMAN INC   5711 Grant Ave, Cleveland, OH 44105, Tel: (216) 883-1400
  (Steel partitions, cabinets, wall sys)
    Strafo-Hausermann GmbH, Stresemann Allee 61, 6000 Frankfurt, Germany

HAZLETON CORP   13873 Park Center Rd, Herndon, VA 22071, Tel: (703) 478-9450
  (R&D)
    Hazleton Deutschland, Kesselfeld 29, 4400 Munster, Germany

HECKETT DIV   PO Box 1071, Butler, PA 16001, Tel: (412) 283-5741
  (Metal reclamation)
    Harsco GmbH, Postfach 30 03005, 4600 Dortmund 30, Germany

HEINECKE INSTRUMENTS CO   3000 Taft St, Hollywood, FL 33021,
  Tel: (305) 987-6101
  (Laboratory glassware, instru)
    Heinicke Instruments of Europa GmbH, Hanauer Landstr. 220, 6000 Frankfurt/Main,
      Germany

H J HEINZ CO   PO Box 57, Pittsburgh, PA 15230, Tel: (412) 456-5100
  (Food prdts)
    H.J. Heinz GmbH, Cologne, Germany
    H.J. Heinz GmbH, Postfach 1672, D-6800 Mannheim 1, Germany
    Nadlerwerke GmbH, Kaefertalerstr. 190, 6800 Mannheim 1, Germany

HERCULES INC   Hercules Plaza, Wilmington, DE 19894, Tel: (302) 594-5000
  (Mfr spec chems, plastics, film & fibers, coatings, resins, food ingredients)
    Hercules GmbH, Curslacker Neur Diech 66, D-2050 Hamburg 80, Germany
    Pomosin AG, Von-Herwath-Strasse, D-2443 Grossenbrode, Germany

HERTZ CORP   225 Brae Blvd, Park Ridge, NJ 07656-0713, Tel: (201) 307-2000
  (Automobile rental)
    Hertz Autovermietung GmbH, Schwalbacher Str. 47-49, 6000 Frankfurt/Main 1, Germany

HILL & KNOWLTON INC   420 Lexington Ave, New York, NY 10017,
  Tel: (212) 697-5600
  (Public relations, public affairs, comm counseling)
    Hill & Knowlton (Frankfurt) GmbH, Bockenheimer Ladnstr. 98-100,
      6000 Frankfurt/Main 1, Germany

HILLERICH & BRADSBY CO INC   PO Box 35700, Louisville, KY 40232-5700,
  Tel: (502) 585-5226
  (Golf, baseball & softball equip)
    VVC/Demitex, Kaninenberghoerne 2, 4300 Essen 1, Germany

HOBART INTL INC   World Headquarters Ave, Troy, OH 45374, Tel: (513) 335-7171
  (Food preparation & processing equip)
    Hobart Maschinen GmbH, Postfach 1620, 76 Offenburg, Baden, Germany

HOKE INC   1 Tenakill Rd, Cresskill, NJ 07626, Tel: (201) 568-9100
  (Valves, fittings, fluid control specialties)
    Hoke Handels GmbH, Hanaver Landstr. 11-13, 6000 Frankfurt/Main, Germany

HOLIDAY INNS INC   3742 Lamar Ave, Memphis, TN 38195, Tel: (901) 362-4001
  (Hotels, restaurants, casinos)
    Holiday Inn Munich, Leapoldstr. 200, 8000 Munich 40, Germany
    Holiday Inn Munich, Schleissheimerstr. 188, 8000 Munich 40, Germany
    Holiday Inn Stuttgart-Munchingen, D 7015 Stuttgart/Munchingen, Siemensstr. 50,

(cont)

Germany
Holiday Inn Stuttgart-Sindelfingen, Schwertstr. 65, 7032 Sindelfingen 3, Germany
Holiday Inn Trier, Zurmaienerstr. 164, D-5500 Trier, Germany
Holiday Inn Viernheim-Mannheim, Bgm Neffstr. 12, D 6806 Viemheim, Germany
Holiday Inn Wolfsburg, Rathausstr. 1, 3180 Wolfsburg 1, Germany

HOLLIS ENGINEERING CO   15 Charron Ave, Nashua, NH 03063, Tel: (603) 889-1121
  (Automatic soldering, cleaning & cutting sys)
    Cooper Industries Electronics, 1081 Westhausen/Kreiss Aalen, Postfach 80, Germany

HOLMES & NARVER INC   999 Town & Country Road, Orange, CA 92668,
  Tel: (714) 567-2400
  (Arch/engr, constr/constr mgmt, O&M serv)
    Holmes & Narver Burton Cohen GmbH, Nordenstr. 2, 6082 Moerfelden, Waldorf, Germany

THE HOOVER GROUP   403 W 4th St N, Newton, IA 50208, Tel: (515) 792-8000
  (Mfr floor care prdts, laundry & refrig appliances)
    Hoover GmbH, Mintropstr. 27, 4000 Dusseldorf 1, Germany

HORWATH & HORWATH INTL   919 Third Ave, New York, NY 10022,
  Tel: (212) 980-3100
  (Public accountants & auditors)
    Dr. Franz Lipfert GmbH, Postfach 444, Alexanderstr. 12B, 7000 Stuttgart 1, Germany
    Dres. Bronner Treuhand-Revision GmbH, Hohenzollerndamm 123, 1000 Berlin 33, Germany
    Horwath & Gelbert GmbH, Ostbahnhofstr. 13, 6000 Frankfurt/Main 1, Germany
    Horwath & Horwath International, Postfach 1414, Graf Adolfstr. 61, Germany
    Horwath & Horwath International, Maximiliansplatz 10, 8000 Munich 2, Germany
    Horwath & Horwath International, Wirtschaftsprufer-Sozietat, Parkstr. 15,
      6200 Wiesbaden, Germany

HOWMEDICA INC   235 East 42nd St, New York, NY 10017, Tel: (212) 573-7575
  (Hospital, med, dental supplies)
    Howmedica International, Inc., Richard-Wagner-Str. 27, 5 Cologne 1, Germany

HUGHES TOOL CO   PO Box 2539, Houston, TX 77001, Tel: (713) 924-2222
  (Equip & serv to oil & gas explor & prod ind)
    Obi-Hughes Germany GmbH, Gross Moorbogen 17, Postfach 901 064, 2100 Hamburg, Germany

ICORE INTERNATIONAL INC   180 N Wolfe Rd, Sunnyvale, CA 94086,
  Tel: (408) 732-5400
  (Harness & conduit sys, battery connectors, etc)
    Icore Industries, Fuhlentwiete 4, 2000 Hamburg 36, Germany

ILLINOIS TOOL WORKS INC   8501 West Higgins Rd, Chicago, IL 60631,
  Tel: (312)693-3040
  (Metal cutting tools, fasteners, sealants, gear measuring instru)
    ITW-Ateco GmbH, Stormannstr. 43, 2 Norderstedt, Germany

IMC MAGNETICS CORP   100 Jericho Quadrangle, Jericho, NY 11753,
  Tel: (516) 938-0800
  (Airmovers, elec motor driven fans, blowers; computer equip, etc)
    IMC Magnetics GmbH, Zwerger Str. 10, D-8014 Unterbiberg, Germany

IMPERIAL SCHRADE CORP   99 Madison Ave, New York, NY 10016,
  Tel: (212) 889-5700
  (Mfr knives, household cutlery)

Imperial Intl. GmbH, Turnich-Industriegelande 1, Postfach 4140, D-5014 Kerpen, Germany

IMS INTERNATIONAL INC   800 Third Ave, New York, NY 10022, Tel: (212) 371-2310
(Market research reports)
  IMS Internationaler Mobeltransport Service GmbH, Larchenstr. 86,
  6000 Frankfurt/Main, Germany

INA CORPORATION   1600 Arch St, Philadelphia, PA 19101, Tel: (215) 523-5335
(Holding co: ins, financial serv)
  Insurance Company of North America, Inselstr. 11, D-4000 Dusseldorf 30, Germany
  Insurance Company of North America, Reuterweg 47, D-6000 Frankfurt/Main, Germany

INCOM INTERNATIONAL INC   3450 Princeton Pike, Lawrenceville, NJ 08648,
  Tel: (609) 896-7600
(Roller & motorcycle chains, drive components, marine controls, etc)
  Morse Controls GmbH, Morsestr. 4, 8044 Unterschleissheim/Munich, Germany

INDUCTOTHERM CORP   10 Indel Ave, Rancocas, NJ 08073, Tel: (609) 267-9000
(Mfr induction melting furnaces)
  HWG Inductoheat GmbH, Postfach 1280, D-7313 Reichenbach/Fil, Germany
  Inductotherm Deutschland GmbH, Haupstrasse 7, 5107 Simmerath, Germany

INDUSTRIAL ACOUSTICS CO   1160 Commerce Ave, Bronx, NY 10462,
  Tel: (212) 931-8000
(Design/mfr acoustic structures for sound conditioning & noise control)
  Industrial Acoustics GmbH, Sohlweg 24, 4055 Niederkruchten, Germany

INFORMATION BUILDERS INC   1250 Broadway, New York, NY 10001,
  Tel: (212) 736-4433
(Devel/serv computer software)
  Information Builders Deutschland GmbH, Munich, Germany

INGERSOLL ENGINEERS INC   1021 N Mulford Rd, Rockford, IL 61107,
  Tel: (815) 395-6440
(Mgmt consultants to mfg businesses)
  Ingersoll Engineers GmbH, Niederkasseler Lohweg 8, 4000 Dusseldorf 11, Germany

INGERSOLL-RAND CO   200 Chestnut Ridge Rd, Woodcliff Lake, NJ 07675,
  Tel: (201) 573-0123
(Mfr compressors, rock drills, pumps, air tools)
  Ingersoll-Rand GmbH, Harortstr. 35, 403 Ratingen-Tiefenbroich, Germany

INSTRON CORP   100 Royall St, Canton, MA 02021, Tel: (617) 828-2500
(Testing instru)
  Instron GmbH, Sanefelderstr. 164, 6050 Offenbach/Main, Germany

INSTRUMENTATION LABORATORY   113 Hartwell Ave, Lexington, MA 02173-3190,
  Tel: (617) 861-0710
(Med & sci analyzers & meas instru)
  Instrumentation Laboratory GmbH, Klausnerring 4, Heinstetten, D-8011 Kirchheim,
  Germany

INTERMEC CORP   6001 36th Ave West, Everett, WA 98203-9280,
  Tel: (206) 348-2600
(Mfr automated data collection sys)

(cont)

Intermec Europe, Schiess-Strasse 44, D-4000 Dusseldorf 11, Germany
Intermec Strichcode Systeme GmbH, Saalburgstrasse 157, D-6380 Bad Hornburg, Germany

INTERMODAL TECHNICAL SERVICES INC   9 Campus Dr, Parsippany, NJ 07054,
Tel: (201) 993-3634
(Damage survey & inspection servs)
Intermodal Technical Services, Inc., Hohe Bleichen 13, D-2000 Hamburg 36, Germany

INTERNATIONAL BUSINESS MACHINES (IBM)   Old Orchard Rd, Armonk,
NY 10504-1783, Tel: (914) 765-1900
(Info-handling sys, equip & serv)
IBM Deutschland GmbH, Pascalstr. 100, Stuttgart, Bad-Wuertt 7000, Germany

INTERNATIONAL FLAVORS & FRAGRANCES INC   521 W 57th St, New York, NY 10019,
Tel: (212) 765-5500
(Create/mfr flavors, fragrances & aroma chems)
International Flavors & Fragrances (Deutschland) GmbH, Postfach 7327, Hamburg 36,
Germany

INTERNATIONAL PAPER   2 Manhattanville Rd, Purchase, NY 10577,
Tel: (914) 397-1500
(Mfr/distr container board, paper, wood prdts)
Anitec Image (Deutschland) GmbH, Dieselstrasse 11, 5014 Kerpen-Sindorf, Germany
Bergvik Chemie GmbH, Schillerstr. 44, 2000 Hamburg 50, Germany
Hammerhill Paper GmbH, Ederburgweg 137, Aachen, Germany
Ilford GmbH, Postfach 124, D-6078 New-Isenberg, Germany
Zanders Feinpapiere AG, Bergisch-Gladbach, Germany

INTERNATIONAL RECTIFIER CORP   233 Kansas St, El Segundo, CA 90245,
Tel: (213) 772-2000
(Mfr power semiconductors)
International Rectifier GmbH, Saalburgstrasse 157, D-6380 Bad Homburg, Germany

INTERNATIONAL STANDARD ELECTRIC CORP   320 Park Ave, New York, NY 10022,
Tel: (212) 752-6000
(Telecommun equip)
Dethloff-Electronic GmbH, Hellmuth-Hirthstr. 42, 7 Stuttgart-Zuffenhausen, Germany

INTERNATIONAL STAPLE & MACHINE CO   PO Box 629, Butler, PA 16001,
Tel: (412) 287-7711
(Stapling machs, supplies)
Ampag & Co. GmbH, 5038 Rodenkirchen, Cologne, Germany

INTRALOX INC   PO Box 50699, New Orleans, LA 70150, Tel: (504) 733-0463
(Mfr plastic, modular conveyor belts & access)
Intralox GmbH, Heinrich-Hertz Str. 44, 4006 Erkrath- Unterfeldhaus, Germany

INVACARE CORP   899 Cleveland St, PO Box 4028, Elyria, OH 44036,
Tel: (216) 329-6000
(Mfr patient-care prdts)
Gunter Meier GmbH, Eschweg 7, 4952 Porta, Westfalica-Holtorf, Germany
Invacare Deutschland GmbH, Eisenstrasse 48, 6090 Russelheim, Germany

IOMEGA CORP   1821 W 4000 South, Roy, UT 84067, Tel: (801) 778-4494
(Mfr data storage prdts)
Iomega, Konigsallee 60/F, 4000 Dusseldorf 1, Germany

IPCO CORP   1025 Westchester Ave, White Plains, NY 10604, Tel: (914) 682-4500
  (Dental & optical prdts)
    Whaledent GmbH Dental Products, Frank Furtherstr. 18, 6360 Freidberg, Germany

IRRIDELCO   440 Sylvan Ave, Englewood Cliffs, NJ 07020, Tel: (212) 532-7070
  (Pumps & irrigation sys)
    Irrigation & Industrial Development Corp. GmbH, Niddastr 42-44, 6000 Frankfurt,
    Germany

IRVING TRUST CO   1 Wall St, New York, NY 10015, Tel: (212) 487-2121
  (Intl banking)
    Irving Trust GmbH, Niedenau 61-63, 6000 Frankfurt/Main, West Germany

ITEL CONTAINERS INTL CORP   55 Francisco St, San Francisco, CA 94133,
  Tel: (415) 984-4400
  (Leasing, repair, storage of ocean-going containers)
    Itel Containers Germany, Kreuzweg 7, 2000 Hamburg 1, Germany

ITEL CORP   2 N Riverside Plaza, Chicago, IL 60606, Tel: (312) 902-1515
  (Transport & equip leasing & serv)
    ITEL Container International GmbH, West Germany

ITT CORP   1330 Ave of the Americas, New York, NY 10019, Tel: (212) 258-1000
  (Diversified mfr, tech & services)
    Flygt Werk GmbH, Adolf Richterstr. 4, 7530 Pforzheim, Germany
    Graetz-Raytronic GmbH, Westigerstr. 172, 5990 Altena, Germany
    ITT Cannon GmbH, Postfach 1120, Postrasste 75, D-7056 Weinstadt, Germany
    Standard Elektrik Lorez AG, Hellmuth-Hirthstr. 42, 7 Stuttgart/Zuffenhausen, Germany
    Transatlantische Versicherungs AG, Repsoldstr 27, 2000 Hamburg 1, Germany

ITT FEDERAL ELECTRIC CORP   621 Industrial Ave, Paramus, NJ 07652,
  Tel: (201) 967-0123
  (Eng, install, support commun & electr sys)
    Federal Electric Intl., Postfach 2430, 675 Kaiserslautern, Germany

ITT SHERATON CORP   60 State St, Boston, MA 02108, Tel: (617) 367-3600
  (Hotel operations)
    Sheraton Sales Center, Ander Hauptwache 11, D-6000 Frankfurt/Main 1, Germany

JAMESBURY CORP   640 Lincoln St, Worcester, MA 01605, Tel: (617) 852-0200
  (Mfr valves & accessories)
    Jamesbury GmbH, Tolnauer Str. 3, Postfach 104, D-7992 Tettnang Buergermoos,
    West Germany

JOHNSON & JOHNSON   One Johnson & Johnson Plaza, New Brunswick, NJ 08933,
  Tel: (201) 524-0400
  (Surgical, med & baby prdts)
    Cilag GmbH, Sulzbach, Germany
    Codman GmbH, Hamburg, Germany
    Critikon GmbH, Norderstedt, Germany
    Devro GmbH, Birkenfeld, Germany
    Dr. Molter GmbH, Neckargemund, Germany
    Ethicon GmbH, Norderstedt, Germany
    Iolab GmbH, Hamburg, Germany
    Janssen GmbH, Rosellen, Germany
    Johnson & Johnson GmbH, Robert-Kochstr. 15, 2000 Norderstedt, Germany
    Johnson & Johnson GmbH, Dusseldorf, Germany

(cont)

Mecron Medical Produkte GmbH, Berlin, Germany
Ortho Diagnostic Systems GmbH, Neckargemund, Germany
Penaten GmbH, Bad Honnef, Germany

S C JOHNSON & SON INC   1525 Howe St, Racine, WI 53403, Tel: (414) 631-2000
(Home, auto, commercial & personal care prdts, specialty chems)
    Johnson Wax GmbH, 5657 Haan (Rhld), Postfach 1100 Solingen, Germany

JOHNSON CONTROLS INC   5757 W Green Bay Ave, PO Box 591, Milwaukee, WI 53201,
    Tel: (414) 228-1200
(Mfr facility mgmt & control sys, auto seating, batteries & plastics)
    JCI Regelungstechnik GmbH, Westendhof 8, D-4300 Essen 1, Germany

THE JOURNAL OF COMMERCE   110 Wall St, New York, NY 10005, Tel: (212) 425-1616
(Business newspaper & journal pub)
    Journal of Commerce, Niedeman 39, 6000 Frankfurt/Main 1, Germany

K-TEL INTL INC   15525 Medina Rd, Plymouth, MN 55447, Tel: (612) 559-6800
(Packaged consumer entertainment & convenience prdts)
    Dominion Vertriebs GmbH, Ramonville Strasse 2 , 3. Stock, 6367 Karben 1, Germany

KAISER ALUMINUM & CHEMICAL CORP   300 Lakeside Dr, Oakland, CA 94643,
    Tel: (415) 271-3300
(Aluminum & aluminum prdts, chems)
    Kaiser Aluminum & Chemical (Europe), Cecilienallee 6-9, D-4000 Dusseldorf 30,
    Germany

KAWNEER CO INC   555 Guthridge Ct, Norcross, GA 30092, Tel: (404) 449-5555
(Mfr arch aluminum prdts for commercial constr)
    Kawneer Aluminum GmbH, Postfach 20 07 45, Erstrasse 75, Monchengladbach 2, Germany

KAYSER-ROTH CORP   2303 W Meadowview Rd, Greensboro, NC 24707,
    Tel: (919) 852-2030
(Mfr hosiery)
    Arlington Socks, Fabrikstr. 1, D-7860 Schopfheim, Germany

A T KEARNEY INC   222 S Riverside Plaza, Chicago, IL 60606,
    Tel: (312) 648-0111
(Mgmt consultants)
    A.T. Kearney GmbH, Jan-Willem-Platz 3, 4000 Dusseldorf, Germany
    A.T. Kearney GmbH, Konigstrasse 43B, 7000 Stuttgart, Germany

KEITHLEY INSTRUMENTS INC   28775 Aurora Rd, Cleveland, OH 44139,
    Tel: (216) 248-0400
(Mfr electr test/meas instru, PC-based data acquisition hdwe/software)
    Keithley Instruments GmbH, Heiglhofstr. 5, D-8000 Munich 70, Germany

KELLOGG CO   235 Porter St, Battle Creek, MI 49016, Tel: (616) 966-2000
(Food prdts)
    Kellogg GmbH, Postfach 20, 2800 Bremen 1, Germany

KEMPER INTL INSURANCE CO   Route 22, Long Grove, IL 60049, Tel: (708) 540-2000
(Property casualty ins)
    Kemper SA, Kaltenbornweg 2, D-5000 Cologne 21, Germany

KENNAMETAL INC   PO Box 231, Latrobe, PA 15650, Tel: (412) 539-5000
  (Tools, hard carbide & tungsten alloys)
    Kennametal GmbH, Max Planck Str. 13, Postfach 1347, D-6382 Friedrichsdorf, Germany

KENT-MOORE CORP   28635 Mound Rd, Warren, MI 48092, Tel: (313) 574-2332
  (Mfr service equip for auto, constr, recreational, military & agric vehicles)
    Kent-Moore Deutschland GmbH, Postfach 1528, Alfred Nobel Strasse 12,
    D-6806 Viernheim, Germany

KEPNER-TREGOE INC   Research Rd, PO Box 704, Princeton, NJ 08542,
  Tel: (609) 921-2806
  (Mgmt & organizational devel)
    Marielvise Bopp, Kirchstr. 18, 6209 Aarbergen 2, Germany

KETCHUM COMMUNICATIONS   4 Gateway Center, Pittsburgh, PA 15222,
  Tel: (412) 456-3500
  (Advertising, public relations)
    Durana Ketchum Werbeagentur GmbH, Cronstettenstr. 6a, 6000 Frankfurt/Main 1, Germany

KEYES FIBRE CO   3003 Summer St, Stamford, CT 06905, Tel: (203) 357-9100
  (Molded containers)
    Van Leer-Keyes GmbH, Postfach 3169, Albert Einstein Str. 5-13, 4006 Erkrath, Germany

KEYSTONE INTL INC   PO Box 40010, Houston, TX 77040, Tel: (713) 466-1176
  (Mfr butterfly valves, actuators & control accessories)
    Keystone Armaturen, Schelsenweg 6, D-4050 Monchengladbach 2, Germany

KIENBAUM INTL GROUP   110 Gibraltar Rd, PO Box 238, Horsham, PA 19044,
  Tel: (215) 674-5210
  (Intl business consulting)
    Kienbaum Unternehmungsberatung GmbH, Fuellenbachstr. 8, 4000 Dusseldorf 30, Germany

KIMBERLY-CLARK CORP   PO Box 619100, Dallas, TX 75261-1200,
  Tel: (214) 830-1200
  (Mfr fiber-based prdts for personal care, pulp & forest prdts; air transport)
    Kimberly-Clark GmbH, 5400 Koblenz, Germany

KNOGO CORP   350 Wireless Blvd, Hauppauge, NY 11788, Tel: (516) 232-2100
  (Mfr electr article surveillance sys)
    Knogo Deutschland GmbH, Rheinallee 109, 6500 Mainz, Germany

KNOLL INTL   655 Madison Ave, New York, NY 10021, Tel: (212) 826-2400
  (Furniture & fabrics)
    Knoll International GmbH, 7141 Murr Murr Siemenstr. 1, Germany

KOCH ENGINEERING CO INC   PO Box 8127, Wichita, KS 67208, Tel: (316) 832-5110
  (Mass transfer prdts, static mixers, mist eliminator sys)
    Koch International GmbH, Neusserstr. Nr. 33, 4000 Dusseldorf 1, Germany

KOLMAR LABORATORIES INC   123 Pike St, Port Jervis, NY 12771,
  Tel: (914) 856-5311
  (Contract mfr: cosmetics, pharms, household prdts)
    Kolmar Kosmetic Deutschland GmbH, Messenhauser Str. 22, D-6057 Dietzenbach 1,
    Germany

KORN/FERRY INTL   237 Park Ave, New York, NY 10017, Tel: (212) 687-1834
  (Executive search)
    Korn/Ferry Intl., Konigsallee 60D, Ko-Galerie, D-4000 Dusseldorf 1, Germany
    Korn/Ferry Intl. GmbH, Bechenheimer Landstr. 42, 6000 Frankfurt/Main, Germany

KRAFT INC   Kraft Court, Glenview, IL 60025, Tel: (708) 998-2000
  (Dairy prdts, processed food, chems)
    Kraft Europe GmbH, Dingolfingerstr. 2, D-8000 Munich 80, Germany
    Kraft GmbH, Hauptstr. 185, 6236 Eschborn 1, Germany

KRATOS ANALYTICAL   170 Williams Dr, Ramsey, NJ 0744637, Tel: (201) 934-9000
  (Mfr liq chromatography, mass spectrometry & surface analysis instru)
    Kratos GmbH, Karlsburgstr. 6, Postfach 410580, Karlsruhe 41, Germany

KYSOR INDUSTRIAL CORP   1 Madison Ave, Cadillac, MI 49601-9785,
  Tel: (616) 779-2200
  (Mfr diversified ind prdts & sys)
    Kysor/Warren Refrigeration GmbH, Postfach 1221, 6250 Limburg, Germany

LAMBDA ELECTRONICS INC   515 Broad Hollow Rd, Melville, NY 11747,
  Tel: (516) 694-4200
  (Power supplies, semiconductors, test equip)
    Lambda Electronics GbmH, Josef Hund Str. 1, D-7590 Achern, Germany

LAMSON & SESSIONS CO   25701 Science Park Dr, Cleveland, OH 44122,
  Tel: (216) 464-3400
  (Mfr thermoplastic electrical conduit & related prdts; prdts for transp equip ind)
    Lamson & Sessions GmbH, Postfach 5144, D-5970 Plettenberg 5, Germany

LAWTER INTERNATIONAL INC   990 Skokie Blvd, Northbrook, IL 60062,
  Tel: (708) 498-4700
  (Resins, pigments, coatings)
    Lawter Chemicals GmbH, Oberusel/Taunus, Germany

LEACH CORP   6900 Orangethorpe Ave, Buena Park, CA 90620, Tel: (714) 739-0770
  (Mfr aerospace electromechan & solid state comp)
    LRE Relais & Elektronik GmbH, Hofer Str. 5, 8860 Nordlingen, Germany

LEEDS & NORTHRUP CO   Sumneytown Pike, North Wales, PA 19454,
  Tel: (215) 699-2000
  (Mfr process control instru & sys)
    Leeds & Northrup GmbH, Fleherstr. 32, 4000 Dusseldorf 1, Germany

LEHN & FINK PRODUCTS CO   225 Summit Ave, Montvale, NJ 07645,
  Tel: (201) 391-8500
  (Cosmetics, pharms)
    Schuelke & Mayer GmbH, Moorfuhrtweg 9, 2000 Hamburg 39, Germany

LEVI STRAUSS & CO   1155 Battery, San Francisco, CA 94111, Tel: (415) 544-6000
  (Mfr wearing apparel)
    Levi Strauss Germany GmbH, Postfach 1451, Grosser Seligenstaedter Grund 10-12,
      6056 Heusenstamm, Germany

ELI LILLY & CO   307 E McCarty St, Indianapolis, IN 46285, Tel: (317) 261-2000
  (Pharms, agric & cosmetic prdts)
    Eli Lilly GmbH, Niederlassung Bad Homburg, 638 Homburg, Marienbader Platz, Germany

LINTAS:WORLDWIDE   1 Dag Hammarskjold Plaza, New York, NY 10017,
  Tel: (212) 605-8000
  (Advertising agency)
    Lintas:Frankfurt, Zeppelinallee 77, D-6000 Frankfurt/Main, Germany
    Lintas:Hamburg, Burchardstr. 8, D-2000 Hamburg 1, Germany

ARTHUR D LITTLE INC   25 Acorn Park, Cambridge, MA 02140-2390,
  Tel: (617) 864-5770
  (Technology & mgmt consulting)
    Arthur D. Little International Inc., Abraham Lincoln Str. 1, 6200 Wiesbaden, Germany

LITTON INDUSTRIES INC   360 N Crescent Dr, Beverly Hills, CA 90210,
  Tel: (213) 859-5000
  (Elec sys, ind automation, resource explor)
    Veam Elektro-Anschulusstechnik GmbH, Postfach 1304, Scharnhaeuserstr. 3,
      D-7024 Eildestadt 1, Stuttgart, Germany
    Winchester Electronics Div. of LPPI GmbH, Otto-Hahn-Str. 8,
      D-7100 Biberach/Heilbronn, Germany

LOCTITE CORP   705 North Mountain Rd, Newington, CT 06111, Tel: (203) 278-1280
  (Adhesives, sealants)
    Loctite Deutschland GmbH, Postfach 810580, 8000 Munich 81, Germany

LODGE & SHIPLEY CO   3055 Colerain Ave, Cincinnati, OH 45225,
  Tel: (513) 541-4774
  (Lathes, packaging & mfg sys & equip)
    Ferdinand Low GmbH, Postfach 3823, Hackethalstr. 2, D-3000 Hannover, Germany

LOGETRONICS CORP   7001 Loisdale Rd, Springfield, VA 22150,
  Tel: (703) 971-1400
  (Mfr cartographic, photographic, graphic arts & computer equip)
    LogEtronics GmbH, Dieselstr. 10, 6242 Kronberg 2, Germany

LONGYEAR CO   PO Box 27314, Salt Lake City, UT 84127, Tel: (801) 972-1395
  (Mfr diamond drills, concrete cutting equip; drill serv)
    Longyearr GmbH, Postfach 460, Grafftring 1, 3100 Celle, Germany

LORAL INTL INC   999 Central Park Ave, Yonkers, NY 10704, Tel: (914) 964-6520
  (Comm sys, computers, instru equip)
    Rolm Mil Spec Computers, Am Kronbergerung 3, Schwalbach/TS D-6231, Germany

LORD CORP   2000 W Grandview Blvd, Erie, PA 16514, Tel: (814) 868-0924
  (Adhesives, coatings, chems, film prdts)
    Agomet Klebstoffe, Postfach 602, D-6450 Hanau 1, Stadtteil Wolfgang, Germany
    Henkel KGaA, Postfach 1100, D-4000 Dusseldorf 1, Germany

LTV CORP   1600 Pacific St, PO Box 225003, Dallas, TX 75222,
  Tel: (214) 746-7711
  (Steel, energy prdts, aerospace & ocean shipping)
    Ling Temco Vought Inc., Adenauerallee 209, 5300 Bonn, Germany

LUBRIZOL CORP   29400 Lakeland Blvd, Wickliffe, OH 44092, Tel: (216) 943-4200
  (Chem additives for lubricants & fuels)
    Lubrizol GmbH, Collonaden 51, 2000 Hamburg 1, Germany

LUCAS AVITRON   PO Box 120039, Stamford, CT 06912, Tel: (203) 351-8400
  (Distr elec generating & fluid handling sys)
    Lucas Aerospace GmbH, Zaubzerstr. 11, D-8000 Munich 80, Germany

LUMMUS CREST   1515 Broad St, Bloomfield, NJ 07003, Tel: (201) 893-1515
  (Engr & constr)
    Lummus Crest GmbH, Abraham-Lincoln-Str. 1, 6200 Wiesbaden, Germany

LYKES BROS STEAMSHIP CO INC   Lykes Center, 300 Poydras St, New Orleans,
  LA 70130, Tel: (504) 523-6611
  (Ocean frt trans)
    Lykes Lines Agency, Inc., 2-12 Faulenstr. IV, Postfach 10 35 20, 2800 Bremen 1,
    Germany

M&T CHEMICALS INC   PO Box 1104, Rahway, NJ 07065, Tel: (201) 499-0200
  (Specialty chems & application technologies)
    M & T Chemicals GmbH, Vor Dem Lauch 10, Postfach 81 04 25,
    7000 Stuttgart 81 (Mohringen), Germany

MAGNETROL INTERNATIONAL   5300 Belmont Rd, Downers Grove, IL 60515-4499,
  Tel: (708) 969-4000
  (Mfr level & flow process instru)
    Magnetrol (Deutschland) GmbH, Schlossstrasse 76, D-5060 Bergisch Gladbach, Germany

MALLINCKRODT INC   675 McDonnell Blvd, PO Box 5840, St Louis, MO 63134,
  Tel: (314) 895-2012
  (Med/ind chems, organics, pharms)
    Mallinckrodt GmbH, Grossostheim und Dieberg, Germany

MANPOWER INC   5301 N Ironwood Rd, PO Box 2053, Milwaukee, WI 53201-2053,
  Tel: (414) 961-1000
  (Temporary help)
    Manpower-Planen-Leisten GmbH, Zeil 65-69V, Postfach 3789, 6000 Frankfurt/Main 1,
    Germany

MANUFACTURERS HANOVER TRUST CO   270 Park Ave, New York, NY 10017,
  Tel: (212) 286-6000
  (Banking)
    Manufacturers Hanover Trust Co., Kaiserswertherstr. 196, 4000 Dusseldorf 30, Germany
    Manufacturers Hanover Trust Co., Fehlandtstr 3, D 2000 Hamburg 36, Germany
    Manufacturers Hanover Trust Co., Georgstr 56, 3000 Hannover 1, Germany
    Manufacturers Hanover Trust Co., 67A Ismaningerstr 80, Germany

MANVILLE CORP   PO Box 5108, Denver, CO 80217-5108, Tel: (303) 978-2000
  (Mfr fiber glass prdts, paper & forest prdts, roofing & insulation material, ind
  minerals)
    Glaswerk Schuller GmbH, Postfach 1292/1293, D-6980 Wertheim/Main, Germany
    Manville Deutschland GmbH, Alte Schmelze 18-20, 6200 Weisbaden, Germany

MARKEM CORP   150 Congress St, Keene, NH 03431, Tel: (603) 352-1130
  (Marking and printing mach; hot stamping foils)
    Markem GmbH, Westpreussenstr. 33, D-4150 Krefeld 12 (Linn) Dusseldorf, Germany

MARLEY CO   1900 Johnson Dr, Mission Woods, KS 66205, Tel: (913) 362-5440
  (Cooling & heating towers, waste treatment sys)
    The Marley Cooling Tower GmbH, Grafenberger Allee 401, 4000 Dusseldorf, Germany

MARS INC   6885 Elm St, McLean, VA 22101, Tel: (703) 821-4900
  (Mfr candy, snack foods, cat food)
    Mars Schokladenvertrieb GmbH, Worringerstr. 7-9, 4000 Dusseldorf, Germany

MARSH & McLENNAN COS INC   1221 Ave of the Americas, New York, NY 10020-1011,
  Tel: (212) 997-2000
  (Insurance)
    Gradmann & Holler Group, Postfach 8 25, 7000 Stuttgart 1, Germany

MARSTELLER INTL   1 E Wacker Dr, Chicago, IL 60601, Tel: (312) 329-1100
  (Advertising, marketing research, sales promotion)
    Marsteller International GmbH, Untermainkai 20, 6000 Frankfurt/Main 1, Germany
    Marsteller International GmbH, Salierstr. 24, D-7012 Fellbach 4, Germany

MARTIN MARIETTA DATA SYSTEMS   PO Box 2392, Princeton, NJ 08540,
  Tel: (609) 799-2600
  (Computer softward, computing & professional serv)
    Mathematica Products Group, Eschenweg 9, 4052 Korschenbroich 2, Germany
    Mathematica Products Group, Heidelberger Landstr. 31, 6100 Darmstadt-Eberstadt,
      Germany
    Mathematica Products Group, Ueberseering 13, 2000 Hamburg 60, Germany
    Mathematica Products Group, Bodenseestr. 19, 8000 Munich, Germany

MARY KAY COSMETICS INC   8787 Stemmons Fwy, Dallas, TX 75247,
  Tel: (214) 630-8787
  (Cosmetics & toiletries)
    Mary Kay Cosmetics GmbH, Fraunhoferstr. 10, 8033 Munich Martinsried, Germany

MATHEMATICA PRODUCTS GROUP   PO Box 2392, Princeton, NJ 08540,
  Tel: (609) 799-2600
  (Computer softwear, policy research, analysis, etc)
    Mathematica Products Group GmbH, Poststr. 44, D-6900 Heidelberg 1, Germany

MATTEL INC   5150 Rosecrans Ave, Hawthorne, CA 90250, Tel: (213) 644-0411
  (Toys, dolls, games, crafts & hobbies)
    Mattel GmbH, Postfach 40, 6113 Babenhausen, Ostheimerweg 3-7, Germany

MAXITROL CO   23555 Telegraph Rd, Southfield, MI 48037, Tel: (313) 356-1400
  (Mfr gas pressure regulators, emergency shut-off valves, electr temp controls)
    Maxitrol GmbH, Industrie Strasse, D-4403 Senden, Germany

MAYFRAN INC   PO Box 43038, Cleveland, OH 44143, Tel: (216) 461-4100
  (Conveyors for metal working & refuse)
    May-Fran GmbH, Fruehlingstr. 52, 4300 Essen, Germany
    Mayfran GmbH, Postfach 230124, Alfredstr. 295, D-4300 Essen, Germany

MCI INTERNATIONAL   2 International Dr, Rye Brook, NY 10573,
  Tel: (914) 937-3444
  (Intl telecom servs)
    MCI Intl. (Deutschland) GmbH, Langstrasse 50, 6450 Hanau, Germany

MEAD CORP   Courthouse Plaza, NE, Dayton, OH 45463, Tel: (513) 222-6323
  (Mfr paper, packaging, pulp, lumber & other wood prdts, school & office prdts; electr
  pub, distri)
    Mead Verpackung GmbH, Postfach 181329, 55 Trier, Ehrang, Germany

MEASUREX CORP   One Results Way, Cupertino, CA 95014, Tel: (408) 255-1500
  (Mfr computer integrated mfg sys)
    Measurex GmbH, Frankfurter Str. 33-35, D-6236 Eschborn/Taunus, Germany

MEDTRONIC INC   7000 Central Ave, NE, Minneapolis, MN 55432,
  Tel: (612) 574-4000
  (Mfr med devices, med serv)
    Medtronic GmbH, Am Seestern 24, Postfach 110738, D-4000 Duseldorf 11, Germany

MELLON BANK NA   One Mellon Bank Center, Pittsburgh, PA 15258,
  Tel: (412) 234-5016
  (Commercial & trade banking, foreign exchange)
    Mellon Bank NA, Postfach 16620, 6000 Frankfurt/Main 16, Germany

MEMOREX CORP   San Thomas at Central Expressway, Santa Clara, CA 95052,
  Tel: (408) 987-1000
  (Magnetic recording tapes, etc)
    Memorex GmbH, Hauptverwaltung, Hahnstr. 41, 6000 Frankfurt/Main 71, Germany

MENNEN CO   Morristown, NJ 07960, Tel: (201) 631-9000
  (Health & beauty aids)
    Hamol International Cosmetics GmbH, Siemensstr. 3, 7401 Pliezhausen Germany

MENNEN-MEDICAL INC   10123 Main St, Clarence, NY 14031, Tel: (716) 759-6921
  (Electronic med equip, physiological monitors)
    Mennen Medical GmbH, fur Medizinisch-Elektronische Gerate Gm, 33 Hagenauer St.,
      D-6202 Wiesbaden, Germany

MERCK SHARP & DOHME INTL   PO Box 2000, Rahway, NJ 07065, Tel: (201) 574-4000
  (Pharms, chems & biologicals)
    Merck, Sharp & Dohme, Intl., Leuchtenbergring 20, D-8000 Munich 80, Germany

MERGENTHALER LINOTYPE CO   201 Old Country Rd, Melville, NY 11747,
  Tel: (516) 673-4197
  (Photocomposition machs, sys & equip)
    Linotype GmbH GmbH, Stuttgart, Rotebuhlplatz 20B, D-7000 Stuttgart 1, Germany

MERISEL INC   200 Continental Blvd, El Segundo, CA 90245, Tel: (213) 615-3080
  (Distr software & hardware)
    DNS-Softsel GmbH, Zur Heupresse 4, Olching, 8037 Munich, Germany

MERRILL LYNCH PIERCE FENNER & SMITH   World Financial Center, 225 Liberty St,
  New York, NY 10080, Tel: (212) 449-1000
  (Brokers, securities, commodities)
    Merrill Lynch & Co., Inc., Karl-Arnold-Platz 2, 4000 Dusseldorf 30, Germany
    Merrill Lynch & Co., Inc., Ulmenstr. 30, 6000 Frankfurt/Main 1, Germany
    Merrill Lynch & Co., Inc., Paulstr. 3, 2000 Hamburg 1, Germany
    Merrill Lynch & Co., Inc., Maximilianstr. 21, 8000 Munich 22, Germany

METAL IMPROVEMENT CO   10 Forest Ave, Paramus, NJ 07652, Tel: (201) 843-7800
  (Shot peening)
    Metal Improvement Co., Inc., Otto-Hahne-Str. 3, 4750 Unna, Germany

METAL-CLADDING INC   PO Box 630, 470 Niagara Way, North Tonawanda, NY 14120,
  Tel: (716) 693-6205
  (FRP tanks & custom constr, scrubbers, odor control equip)
    Hurner GmbH, Eschborner Landstr. 134-138, D-6000 Frankfurt/Main 94, Germany

METALLURG INC   25 E 39th St, New York, NY 10016, Tel: (212) 686-4010
  (Mfr ferrous & nonferrous alloys & metals)
    Elektrowerk Weisweiler GmbH, Postfach 7209, D-5180 Eschweiler, Germany
    Gesellschaft fur Elektrometallurgie mbH, Postfach 3520, 4000 Dusseldorf 1, Germany

METCO DIV OF PERKIN-ELMER   1101 Prospect Ave, Westbury, NY 11590,
  Tel: (516) 334-1300
  (Mfr/serv thermal spray coating equip & supplies)
    Perkin-Elmer-Metco GmbH, Postfach 1280, D-6234 Hattersheim/M-1, Germany

METRIC PRODUCTS INC   4671 Leahy St, Culver City, CA 90230,
  Tel: (213) 870-9121
  (Plastic swimwear, bra cups)
    Metric Products GmbH, 7401 Walddorf, Germany

MICROMERITICS INSTRUMENT CORP   One Micromeritics Dr, Norcross,
  GA 30093-1877, Tel: (404) 662-3620
  (Mfr analytical instruments)
    Micromeritics GmbH, PO Box 100955, Hammfelddamm 10, D-4040 Neuss, Germany

MILLER PRINTING EQUIPMENT CORP   1101 Reedsdale St, Pittsburgh, PA 15233,
  Tel: (412) 237-7500
  (Printing mach)
    Miller Johannisberg Deuckmaschinen GmbH, Friedrich Berguis Str. 5, Postfach 129207,
      D-6000 Weisbaden 12, Germany

MILTON ROY CO   PO Box 12169, St Petersburg, FL 33733, Tel: (813) 823-4444
  (Med & ind equip, process control instru)
    Milton Roy (Deutschland) GmbH, Jahnstr. 22-24, 6467 Hasselroth 2, Germany

MINE SAFETY APPLIANCES CO   PO Box 426, Pittsburgh, PA 15230,
  Tel: (421) 273 5000
  (Safety equip, ind filters)
    Auergesellschaft GmbH, Thiemannstr. 1-11, Postfach 440208, D-1000 Berlin 44, Germany
    MSA Europe, Thiemannstr. 1-11, Postfach 440208, D-1000, Berlin 44, Germany

MIXING EQUIPMENT CO INC   135 Mt Read Blvd, PO Box 1370, Rochester, NY 14611,
  Tel: (716) 436-5550
  (Mfr ind mixing mach, aerators)
    Turbo-Mueller GmbH & Co. KG, Im Westfield 3, D-3101 Nienhagen b. Celle, Germany

MOBIL CORP   150 E 42nd St, New York, NY 10017, Tel: (212) 883-4242
  (Petroleum explor, prdts)
    Mobil Oil AG In Deutschland, Steinstr. 5, 2000 Hamburg 1, Germany
    Mobil Oil AG In Deutschland, Burggrafstr. 1, 3100 Celle, Germany

MODERN CONTROLS INTL INC   6820 Shingle Creek Pkwy, Minneapolis, MN 55430,
  Tel: (612) 560-2900
  (Packaged goods testing equip, pharm weighing equip)
    Lippke KG, Postfach 1760, D-5450 Neuwied 1, Germany
    Paul Lippke GmbH KG, Handelsabtellung, Postfach 1760, D-5450 Neuwied 1, Germany

MOGUL CORP   PO Box 200, Chagrin Falls, OH 44022, Tel: (216) 247-5000
  (Water treatment chems, equip)
    Mogul Eurotherm GmbH, Humboldtstr. 51-55, 2000 Hamburg 76, Germany

MONARCH MACHINE TOOL CO   PO Box 668, Sidney, OH 45365-1335,
  Tel: (513) 492-4111
  (Mfr metalcutting lathes, machining centers, coil processing equip)
    Monarch Werkzeugmaschinen GmbH, Berliner Str. 13, Postfach 1140, D-6944 Hemsbach,
      Germany

MONSANTO CO   800 N Lindbergh Blvd, St Louis, MO 63167, Tel: (314) 694-1000
  (Mfr chem & agric prdts, pharms, ind process equip, man-made fibers, plastics)
    Monsanto (Deutschland) GmbH, Immermannstr. 3-5, D-4000 Dusseldorf 1, Germany

MOOG INC   East Aurora, NY 14052-0018, Tel: (716) 652-2000
  (Mfr precision control components & sys)
    Moog GmbH, Hanns Klemmstr. 28, 7030 Boblingen, Germany

MORGAN GUARANTY TRUST CO   23 Wall St, New York, NY 10015, Tel: (212) 483-2323
  (Banking)
    Morgan Guaranty Trust Co. of New York, Bockenheimer Landstr. 8,
      6000 Frankfurt/Main, Germany
    Morgan Guaranty Trust Co. of New York, Berliner Allee 43, 4000 Dusseldorf, Germany
    Morgan Guaranty Trust Co. of New York, Von-der-Tann-Str. 13, 8000 Munich, Germany

MORGEN DESIGN INC   2060 S 61st St, Milwaukee, WI 53219, Tel: (414) 545-5600
  (Ind design assignments)
    MB-Morgan Ingenieurbuero GmbH, St. Leonhardtstr. 22, Postfach 193, 7410 Reutlingen,
      Germany

MORTON INTERNATIONAL INC   100 N Riverside Plaza, Chicago, IL 60606,
  Tel: (312) 807-2000
  (Mfr adhesives, coatings, finishes, spec chems, advanced & electr materials, auto
  safety prdts)
    Morton Intl. GmbH, Beim Struckengerge 11, D-2800 Bremen 21, Germany
    Morton Intl. GmbH, Elastische Werkstoffe, Sandhofer Str. 96,
      D-6800 Mannheim/Waldhof 31, Germany
    Morton Intl. GmbH, Havesringstrasse 1, D-4500 Osnabruck, Germany
    Morton Intl. GmbH, Am Hirschhuegel 2, 6057 Dietzenbach, Germany

MOSTEK CORP   1215 W Crosby Rd, Carrollton, TX 75006, Tel: (214) 466-6000
  (Integrated circuits, micro computer sys, semiconductors, etc)
    Mostek GmbH, Friedlandstr. 1, D-2058 Quickborn, Plz 1-5, Germany
    Mostek GmbH, Schurwaldstr. 15, D-7303 Neuhauser/Filder, Plz 6-7, Germany

MOTOROLA INC   1303 E Algonquin Rd, Schaumburg, IL 60196, Tel: (708) 397-5000
  (Mfr commun equip, semiconductors, cellular phones)
    Motorola GmbH, Heinrich-Hertz-Str. 1, 6204 Taunusstein-Neuhof, Germany
    Motorola GmbH, Luisenstr. 28, 6200 Wiesbaden, Germany
    Motorola GmbH, Lyoner Str. 11, 6000 Frankfurt-Niederrad 71, Germany
    Motorola GmbH, Muenchnerstr. 18, 8043 Unterfoehring, Germany
    Motorola GmbH, Arabella Str. 17, 8000 Munich, Germany
    Motorola GmbH Specialelektronik, Bonner Str. 47, 5480 Rolandseck, Germany
    Tegal Intl., Rudolf-Diesel-Ring 5, 8029 Sauerlach, Germany

MOUNT HOPE MACHINERY CO   15 Fifth St, Taunton, MA 02780, Tel: (508) 824-6994
  (Web control equip for paper, plastics, textiles)
    Gummiwerke Becker AG, Robert-Koch Str. 3, Postfach 1126, 7920 Heidenhein, Germany

MPB CORP   10 Precision Park, Keene, NH 03431, Tel: (603) 352-0310
  (Bearings, tape guides, sys for missiles, etc)
    MPB International Div. of MPB Corp., Josephinenstr. 10, 8000 Munich 71, Germany

MSI DATA CORP   340 Fischer Ave, Costa Mesa, CA 92626, Tel: (714) 549-6000
  (Portable data entry terminals)
    MSI Data GmbH, Goethestr. 23, 6000 Frankfurt, Germany

MTS SYSTEMS CORP   PO Box 24012, Minneapolis, MN 55424, Tel: (612) 937-4000
  (Electrohydraulic testing & prod equip, mach controls)
    MTS Systems GmbH, Potsdamerstr. 23/24, Postfach 370420, 1000 Berlin 37, Germany
    MTS Systems GmbH, 2870 Delmenhorst, Juetland Str. 32C, Bremen, Germany
    MTS Systems GmbH, Erchanbertstrasse 8, D-8000 Munich 81, Germany
    Thode & Scobel Osthangels GmbH, Heilwigstrasse 31A, 2000 Hamburg 20, Germany

MULTIGRAPHICS DIV   1800 W Central Rd, Mt Prospect, IL 60056,
  Tel: (708) 398-1900
  (Offset duplicating & graphic commun sys)
    Am Interntional GmbH, Robert-Bosch-Str. 5, Postfach 10 20 08,
      6072 Dreieich b. Frankfurt/Main, Germany

MacDERMID INC   245 Freight St, Waterbury, CT 06702, Tel: (203) 575-5700
  (Chem processing for metal ind, plastics, electronics cleaners, strippers)
    MacDermid GmbH, Industriegebiet West, Postfach 2065, 7520 Bruchsal, Germany

E F MacDONALD CO   129 S Ludlow St, Dayton, OH 45401, Tel: (513) 226-5000
  (Trading stamps, travel & sales incentives)
    The E.F. MacDonald Co. Verkaufsforderungs GmbH, Eschersheiner Landstr. 69,
      6000 Frankfurt/Main, Germany

McCANN-ERICKSON WORLDWIDE   750 Third Ave, New York, NY 10017,
  Tel: (212) 697-6000
  (Advertising)
    McCann-Erickson Deutschland GmbH, Postfach 101636, 6000 Frankfurt/Main, Germany
    McCann-Erickson Deutschland GmbH, other locations in Germany
    McCann-Erickson Hamburg GmbH, Neuerwall 41, Postfach 303640, 2000 Hamburg 36,
      West Germany

McCORMICK & CO INC   11350 McCormick Rd, Hunt Valley, MD 21031,
  Tel: (301) 771-7301
  (Seasons, flavorings, specialty foods)
    McCormick GewurzbertriebGmbH & Co. KG, Melle 9 (Wellingholzhausen), Germany
    McCormick GmbH, Eschborn/Taunus, Germany

McDERMOTT INC   1010 Common St, New Orleans, LA 70160, Tel: (504) 587-4411
  (General contractors)
    Deutsch-Amerikanische Isolation GmbH, Huettenstr. 13, 4000 Dusseldorf, West Germany

McGRAW-HILL INC   1221 Ave of the Americas, New York, NY 10020,
  Tel: (212) 512-2000
  (Books, magazines, info sys, financial serv, b/cast operations)
    McGraw-Hill Book Co. GmbH, Lademannbogen 136, Postfach 630520, D-2000 Hamburg 63,
      Germany

McKINSEY & CO INC   55 E 52nd St, New York, NY 10022, Tel: (212) 909-8400
  (Mgmt consultants)
    McKinsey & Co., Cedilienallee 9, 4000 Dusseldorf 30, Germany

                                                                    (cont)

McKinsey & Co., Taunusan Lage 21, 6000 Frankfurt 1, Germany
McKinsey & Co., Koniciustr. 25, 8000 Munich 22, Germany
McKinsey & Co., Esplanade 41, 2000 Hamburg 36, Germany

McLEAN INDUSTRIES INC   4th & Main St, Winston-Salem, NC 27102,
  Tel: (919) 748-4000
  (Steamship line)
    Sea-Land (Germany) Transport GmbH, Knochenhauerstr. 18, 2800 Bremen 1, Germany

JOHN J McMULLEN ASSOCIATES INC   1 World Trade Center, Suite 3000, New York,
  NY 10048, Tel: (212) 466-2200
  (Naval architects)
    John J. McMullen GmbH, Glockengiestr-Wall 20, 2000 Hamburg 1, Germany

NABISCO BRANDS INC   Nabisco Brands Plaza, East Hanover, NJ 07936,
  Tel: (201) 503-2000
  (Mfr food prdts)
    Felix, Postfach 1209, D-5840 Schwerte, Germany
    Felix & Planter, Maulwurfsweg 4a, D-4600 Dortmund 30, Germany
    Planters, Postfach, D-4600 Dortmund 30, Germany
    Planters, Binnerheide, D-5840 Schwerte, Germany

NALCO CHEMICAL CO   One Nalco Center, Naperville, IL 60566-1024,
  Tel: (708) 305-1000
  (Chems for water & waste water treatment, oil prod & refining, ind processes;
  water/energy mgmt serv)
    Deutsche Nalco Chemie GmbH, Postfach 970110, 6000 Frankfurt/Main 90, Germany

NAMCO CONTROLS   7567 Tyler Blvd, Mentor, OH 44060, Tel: (216) 946-9900
  (Mfr sensors, switches, encoders)
    Namco-Wagner GmbH, Mittelfeld 10, 2209 Hezhorn, Germany

NASHUA CORP   44 Franklin St, Nashua, NH 03061, Tel: (603) 880-2323
  (Mfr/distr/serv office copier sys & supplies)
    Nashua Copygraph GmbH, Schuetzenstr. 1C, D-3000 Hannover 1, Germany

NATIONAL BANK OF DETROIT   611 Woodward, PO Box 116, Detroit, MI 48232,
  Tel: (313) 225-1000
  (Banking)
    National Bank of Detroit, Hochstr. 35, 6000 Frankfurt/Main, Germany

NATIONAL CAR RENTAL SYSTEM INC   7700 France Ave S, Minneapolis, MN 55435,
  Tel: (612) 830-2121
  (Car rental)
    National Car Rental GmbH, Franfurter Ring 243, 8000 Munich 46, Germany

NATIONAL DATA CORP   National Data Plaza, Atlanta, GA 30329,
  Tel: (404) 728-2000
  (Provider of info & transaction serv to fin, retail, health care & commun sectors)
    NDC Intl. Ltd., Mainzer Landstr. 97, 6000 Frankfurt/M, Germany

NATIONAL MACHINERY CO   PO Box 747, Tiffin, OH 44883, Tel: (419) 447-5211
  (Mfr forging mach)
    National Machinery GmbH, Regensburgerstr. 420, 8500 Nurnberg, West Germany

NATIONAL SEMICONDUCTOR CORP   2900 Semiconductor Dr, Santa Clara, CA 95051,
  Tel: (408) 721-5000
  (Semiconductors, computers & point-of-sale sys)
    National Semiconductor GmbH, Industriestr. 10, D-8080 Furstenfeldbruck, Germany

NATIONAL-STANDARD CO   1618 Terminal Rd, Niles, MI 49120, Tel: (616) 683-8100
  (Mfr wire, wire related prdts, mach & med prdts)
    Herbert GmbH/National-Standard, Hunfield, Germany

NATIONWIDE INSURANCE   One Nationwide Plaza, Columbus, OH 43216,
  Tel: (614) 249-7111
  (Insurance & fin servs)
    Auto Direkt, Oberstedter Str. 14, Postfach 1480, 6370 Oberursel/ Ts. 1, Germany
    Neckura Lebensversicherung, Oberstedter Str. 14, Postfach 1480,
      6370 Oberursel/ Ts. 1, Germany
    Neckura Versicherungs AG, Oberstedter Str. 14, Postfach 1480,
      6370 Oberursel/ Ts. 1, Germany

NCR CORP   1700 S Patterson Blvd, Dayton, OH 45479, Tel: (513) 445-2000
  (Develop/mfr/sell/serv business info processing sys)
    NCR GmbH, Ulmerstr. 160, P.O. Box 10 00 90, D-8900 Augsburg 1, Germany

NEW BRUNSWICK SCIENTIFIC CO INC   44 Talmadge Rd, Edison, NJ 08818-4005,
  Tel: (201) 287-1200
  (Mfr research & production equip for life sciences)
    New Brunswick Scientific GmbH, Industriestrasse, D-6056 Heusenstamm, Germany

NEW HAMPSHIRE BALL BEARINGS INC   Jaffrey Rd, Route 202, Peterborough,
  NH 03458, Tel: (603) 924-3311
  (Precision bearings)
    Gebr. Reinfurt KG, Gneisenaustr. 10/11, 8700 Wuerzburg, Germany

NICOLET INSTRUMENT CORP   5225 Verona Rd, Madison, WI 53711-4495,
  Tel: (608) 271-3333
  (Mfr infrared spectrometers, oscilloscopes, med electro-diag equip)
    Nicolet Instrument GmbH, Senefelderstr. 162, D-6050 Offenbach am Main, Germany

A C NIELSEN CO   Nielsen Plaza, Northbrook, IL 60062, Tel: (708) 498-6300
  (Marketing research)
    A.C. Nielsen Co. GmbH, Friedrich-Ebert-Anlage 2-14, Postfach 16580,
      D-6000 Frankfurt/Main, Germany
    A.C. Nielsen Co. GmbH, Ludwig-Landmann-Str. 405, D-6000 Frankfurt 16, Germany

NORCO INC   PO Box 406, Georgetown, CT 06829, Tel: (203) 544-3801
  (Electromech actuators, mech sys, hold open rods, reversing mech)
    Flennor GmbH, 81 Hildener Str., D-4000 Dusseldorf 13, Germany

NORDSON CORP   28601 Clemens Rd, Westlake, OH 44145, Tel: (216) 892-1580
  (Mfr ind application equip & packaging mach)
    Nordson GmbH, Heinrich-Hertz-Str. 42, D-4006 Erkrath 1, Germany

NORTHERN PRODUCTS CORP   Terminal Sales Bldg, Seattle, WA 98101,
  Tel: (206) 622-6677
  (General merchandise)
    Rudolf Kanzow, Hammerbrookstr. 90, 2000 Hamburg 1, Germany

NORTHERN TELECOM SYSTEMS CORP   PO Box 1222, Minneapolis, MN 55440,
  Tel: (612) 932-8000
  (Remote information processing sys)
    Data 100 GmbH, Myluisstr. 33-37, 6000 Frankfurt/Main, Germany

NORTON CO   1 New Bond St, Worcester, MA 01606, Tel: (508) 795-5000
  (Abrasives, drill bits, constr & safety prdts, plastics)
    Christensen Diamond Products GmbH, Postfach 309, Heerstr. 61,
      D-3100 Braunschweiger, Germany
    Norton GmbH, Vorgebirgsstr. 10, D-5047 Wesseling, Germany

NUMATICS INC   1450 N Milford Rd, Highland, MI 48031, Tel: (313) 887-4111
  (Mfr control valves & manifolds)
    Numatics GmbH, Otto von Guericke Str. 13, 5205 St. Augustin 3, Germany

NUS CORP   910 Clopper Rd, Gaithersburg, MD 20878-1399, Tel: (301) 258-6000
  (Tech consultants & mgrs in energy & environmental fields)
    Nuclear Ing. Service GmbH, Lyoner Str 22, 6000 Frankfurt 71, Germany

OCCIDENTAL PETROLEUM CORP   10889 Wilshire Blvd, Los Angeles, CA 90024,
  Tel: (213) 879-1700
  (Petroleum & petroleum prdts, chems, plastics)
    Kleinholz Mineraloel GmbH, Huysenallee 66-68, Postfach 856, 4300 Essen, Germany
    Mineraloel KG, Jungfernstieg 51, 2000 Hamburg 36, Germany
    Occidental Oil GmbH, Graf-Adolf-Str. 73, 4000 Dusseldorf, Germany

OGILVY & MATHER INC   2 E 48th St, New York, NY 10017, Tel: (212) 907-3400
  (Advertising agency)
    Focus Werbeagentur GmbH, Goethestr. 7, D-6000 Frankfurt 1, Germany
    Heumann Ogilvy & Mather GmbH & Co., Hainerweg 15, D-6000 Frankfurt/Main 70, Germany
    Ogilvy & Mather Direkt GmbH, Geleitsstr. 14, D-6000 Frankfurt 70, Germany

OHAUS SCALE CORP   29 Hanover Rd, Florham Park, NJ 07932, Tel: (201) 377-9000
  (Balances & scales for labs & industry)
    Ohaus Scale Corp., Postfach 600629, D-6000 Frankfurt 60, Germany

OILGEAR CO   2300 S 51st St, Milwaukee, WI 53219, Tel: (414) 327-1700
  (Hydraulic power transmission mach)
    Oilgear GmbH, Fasaneweg 1, Postfach 6092, Kelsterbach/Main, Germany

OLIN CORP   120 Long Ridge Rd, Stamford, CT 06904-1355, Tel: (203) 356-2000
  (Chems, metals, applied physics in elect, defense, aerospace inds)
    Olin Chemicals GmbH, Harkorstr. 32, 4030 Ratingen, Germany
    Olin Ski Europe, Verdistr. 83, Munich, Germany

OLIVER-BECKMAN INC   250 E 73rd St, New York, NY 10021, Tel: (212) 734-1848
  (Advertising agency)
    Oliver Beckman GmbH, Gagernstr. 25, 6000 Frankfurt/Main 14, Germany

OMARK INDUSTRIES INC   5550 SW Macadam Ave, Portland, OR 97201,
  Tel: (503) 796-1400
  (Mfr chain & accessories for chain saws, welding equip, power tools)
    Omark Industries GmbH, Schliessfuch 265, D-7032 Sindelfingen, Germany

ONAN CORP   1400 73rd Ave NE, Minneapolis, MN 55432, Tel: (612) 574-5000
  (Electric generators, ind engines & controls)
    A.M.A.W. Baune GmbH & Co. KG, Carl Mielestr. 193, 4830 Gutersloh 11, Germany

ORTHOPEDIC EQUIPMENT CO INC   260 Main St, Northport, NY 11768,
  Tel: (516) 754-1702
  (Orthopedic equip)
    Ortopedia GmbH, Salzredder 3, 23 Kieo-Dietrichsdorf, Germany

OTIS ELEVATOR CO   10 Farm Springs, Farmington, CT 06032, Tel: (203) 674-4047
  (Elevators & escalators)
    Flohr Otis GmbH, Wichmannstr. 5/6, D-1000 Berlin 30, Germany
    Flohr Otis GmbH, Flohrstr. 12-24, D-1000 Berlin 27, Germany
    Flohr Otis GmbH, Industriestr. 2, 3060 Stadthagen 1, Germany

OVERSEAS NATIONAL AIRWAYS INC   Kennedy Intl Airport, Jamaica, NY 11430,
  Tel: (212) 632-8200
  (Air carrier)
    Overseas National Airways, Frankfurterstr. 172/176, 6078 Neu-Isenburg, Germany

OWENS-CORNING FIBERGLAS CORP   PO Box 901, Fiberglas Tower, Toledo, OH 43659,
  Tel: (419) 248-8000
  (Mfr insulation, building materials, glass fiber prdts)
    Deutsche Owens-Corning Glasswool GmbH, Germany
    Owens-Corning Fiberglas Deutschland GmbH, Germany

OWENS-ILLINOIS INC   PO Box 1035, Toledo, OH 43666, Tel: (419) 247-5000
  (Glass & plastic containers, house- hold & ind prdts, packaging)
    Actien-GmbH der Gerresheimer Glashuttenwerke vorm. Ferd. Hey, Heyestr. 99,
      4000 Dusseldorf-Gerresheim, Germany
    Buendner Glas GmbH, Postfach 983, 4930 Buende-Suedlengern, Germany

PACIFIC ARCHITECTS & ENGINEERS INC   1111 W Sixth St, Los Angeles, CA 90017,
  Tel: (213) 481-2311
  (Tech engineering serv)
    PAE GmbH Planning & Construction, Eschersheimer Landstrasse 14,
      6000 Frankfurt/Main, Germany

PACKAGING CORP OF AMERICA   1603 Orrington Ave, Evanston, IL 60204,
  Tel: (708) 492-5713
  (Mfr custom packaging, aluminum & plastic molded fibre, corrugated containers)
    Omni-Pac Ekco GmbH, Kajen 12, D-2000 Hamburg 11, Germany
    Omni-Pack GmbH, Am Tidehagen 5, Postfach 360, D-2887 Elsfleth/Weser, Germany

PANDUIT CORP   17301 Ridgeland Ave, Tinley Park, IL 60477, Tel: (708) 532-1800
  (Mfr elec/electr wiring comps)
    Panduit (GmbH), Rudolf Diesel Str. 18, Postfach 18, D-8012 Ottobrunn, Germany

PANTASOTE INC   PO Box 1800, Greenwich, CT 06830, Tel: (203) 661-0400
  (Mfr rubber & plastic)
    Europaeische H.O. Canfield GmbH, Boehmerwaldstr. 47, D-8192 Geretsried 1, Germany

PARAMOUNT INTL FILMS INC   1 Gulf & Western Plaza, New York, NY 10023,
  Tel: (212) 333-4600
  (Film prod & distr)
    Paramount Films of Germany, Inc., Kaiserstr. 48, Postfach 9187,
      D-6000 Frankfurt/Main 9, Germany
    Paramount Films of Germany, Inc., Kurfurstenstr. 131, 1000 Berlin 30, Germany
    Paramount Films of Germany, Inc., Berliner Allee 61, D-4000 Dusseldorf, Germany
    Paramount Films of Germany, Inc., Goethestr. 28, D-8000 Munich 15, Germany
    Paramount Films of Germany, Inc., Spitalerstr. 1, D-2000 Hamburg 1, Germany

PARKER HANNIFIN CORP   17325 Euclid Ave, Cleveland, OH 44112,
  Tel: (216) 531-3000
  (Mfr motion-control prdts)
    Parker Ermeto GmbH, Postfach 120206, Am Metallwerk 9, D-4800 Bielefeld 12, Germany
    Parker Fluid Verbindungstelle GmbH, Postfach 1120, Frieherr-vom Stein Str.,
      D-6315 Mucke, Germany
    Parker Hannifin NMF GmbH, Geestemunderstr. 42, D-5000 Cologne 60, Germany
    Parker Hannifin NMF GmbH, other locations in Germany
    Parker Pradifa GmbH, Postfach 40, Stuifenstrasse 55, D-7127 Pleidelsheim, Germany

PARKER PEN CO   One Parker Place, Janesville, WI 53545, Tel: (608) 755-7000
  (Writing instru, temporary help, leisure apparel & equip)
    Parker Pen GmbH, Ludwig-Wilhelm-Str. 20, 7570 Baden-Baden, Germany

BRUCE PAYNE CONSULTANTS INC   140 West End Ave, New York, NY 10023,
  Tel: (212) 799-8255
  (Mgmt consultants)
    Bruce Payne Consultants GmbH, Kronbergerstr. 49, Frankfurt/Main, Germany

PEGASUS INTERNATIONAL CORP   PO Box 1163, Straube Center, Princeton,
  NJ 08540, Tel: (609) 737-3538
  (Mktg of advanced technology pro- ducts, sys & processes)
    Pegasus International Corp., Spengemann Friedensstr. 4, 635 Bad Nauheim, Germany

PENN ELASTIC INC   PO Box 279, Jamesville, NC 27846, Tel: (919) 729-8167
  (Knitted elastic fabrics)
    Penn Elastic GmbH, An der Tallee 20, 4790 Paderborn, Germany

PENTAIR INC   1700 West Hwy 36, St Paul, MN 55113, Tel: (612) 636-7920
  (Diversified manufacturer)
    Lincoln GmbH, Heinrich-Hertz Strasse, Postfach 1263, D-6909 Walldorf, Germany

PETROLITE CORP   100 N Broadway, St Louis, MO 63102, Tel: (314) 241-8370
  (Specialty chem treating programs, performance-enhancing additives & related equip)
    Petrolite GmbH, Rissener Dorfstr. 51, D-2000 Hamburg 56, Germany

PFAUDLER CO   PO Box 1600, Rochester, NY 14692, Tel: (716) 235-1000
  (Glass lined reactor vessels)
    Pfaudler-Werke AG, Postfach 1780, Scheffelstr. 55, D-6830 Schwetzingen, Germany

PFIZER INC   235 E 42nd St, New York, NY 10017, Tel: (212) 573-2323
  (Mfr pharms, hosp prdts, chems, consumer & animal health prdts)
    Pfizer GmbH, Postfach 4949, D-7500 Karlsruhe 1, Germany

PHELPS DODGE CORP   2600 N Central Ave, Phoenix, AZ 85004-3014,
  Tel: (602) 234-8100
  (Minerals, metals & spec engineered prdts for trans & elect mkts)
    Columbian Carbon Deutschland GmbH, Antwerpenstrasse 1, D-2103 Hamburg 95, Germany
    Columbian Chemicals Europe GmbH, Max-Mueller-Strasse 50-52, D-3000 Hannover 1,
      Germany

PHILADELPHIA FUND INC   50 Broad St, New York, NY 10005, Tel: (212) 425-9655
  (Investments)
    Philadelphia Fund, Inc., Frauenpl. 11, D-8000 Munich 2, Germany

PHILADELPHIA INTL INVESTMENT CORP   Broad & Chestnut Sts, Philadelphia,
   PA 19101, Tel: (215) 629-3817
   (Investments)
     Berenberg Bank, Neuer Jungfernstieg 20, D-2000 Hamburg 36, Germany
     Joh. Behrenberg, Gessler & Co., Alter Wall 32, D-2000 Hamburg 11, Germany

PHILLIPS DRILL CO INC   PO Box 364, Michigan City, IN 46360,
   Tel: (219) 874-4217
   (Concrete anchor sys for constr ind)
     Phillips Drill Co. GmbH, 6791 Hutschenhausen 3 (Katzenbach), Germany

PHILLIPS PETROLEUM CO   Phillips Bldg, Bartlesville, OK 74004,
   Tel: (918) 661-6600
   (Crude oil, natural gas, liquefied petroleum gas, gasoline & petro-chems)
     Phillips Petroleum International GmbH, Ulmenstr. 37, D-6000 Frankfurt/Main, Germany

PICKER CORP   595 Minor Rd, Cleveland, OH 44143, Tel: (216) 449-3000
   (X-ray equip)
     Picker Nuclear GmbH, Feldbergstr. 6, D-6201 Auringen, Germany
     Picker Roentgen GmbH, Postfach 229, 4992 Espelkamp, Germany

PILLSBURY CO   Pillsbury Center, Minneapolis, MN 55402, Tel: (612) 330-4966
   (Baking mixes, canned & frozen foods, restaurants & food shops)
     Paul Erasmi & Co. GmbH, F. Vorbeck GmbH, Geninerstr. 88-100, D-2400 Luebeck, Germany

PIONEER HI-BRED INTL INC   700 Capital Sq, 400 Locust St, Des Moines,
   IA 50309, Tel: (515) 245-3500
   (Seed corn, feed seed, data sys & equip)
     Pioneer Saaten GmbH, Buxtehude, Germany

PITNEY BOWES INC   World Headquarters, Stamford, CT 06926-0700,
   Tel: (203) 356-5000
   (Postage meters, mailroom equip, copiers, bus supplies & servs)
     Adrema Pitney-Bowes GmbH, Tiergartenstr. 7, Postfach 480,
       D-6148 Happenheim/Bergstr., Germany

PLIBRICO CO   1800 Kingsbury St, Chicago, IL 60614, Tel: (312) 549-7014
   (Refractories, engineering, constr)
     Plibrico Co. GmbH, Schleissfach 6307, D-4000 Dusseldorf 1, Germany

PNEUMO ABEX CORP   485 Frontage Rd, Burr Ridge, IL 60521, Tel: (708) 323-4446
   (Mfr aerospace & automotive friction materials & equip)
     Abex GmbH-Aerohydraul, Lorenz-Schott-Str. 9, 6503 Mainz-Kastel, Germany

POLAROID CORP   549 Technology Sq, Cambridge, MA 02139, Tel: (617) 577-2000
   (Photographic and optical prdts)
     Polaroid GmbH, Koenigslacherstr. 15-21, D-6000 Frankfurt-Niederrad 1, Germany

POLYCHROME CORP   On the Hudson, Yonkers, NY 10702, Tel: (914) 965-8800
   (Metal offset plates, coating specialties, graphic arts films)
     Polychrome GmbH, Seesenerstr. 11, 336 Osterrode, Germany

POTTERS INDUSTRIES INC   20 Waterview Blvd, Parsippany, NJ 07054,
   Tel: (201) 299-2900
   (Mfr glass spheres for road marking & ind applications)
     Potters-Ballotini, Theaterstr. 77, Postfach 1164, D-5100 Aachen, Germany

(cont)

Potters-Ballotini GmbH, Morschheimerstr. 9, Postfach 1226, 6719 Kirchheimbolanden,
    Germany

PPG INDUSTRIES   One PPG Place, Pittsburgh, PA 15272, Tel: (412) 434-3131
    (Mfr flat glass, fiber glass, chems, coatings, med electr)
        Hellige GmbH, Heinrich-von-Stephan-Strasse 4, D-7800 Freiburg im Breisgau, Germany
        Lenhardt Maschinenbau GmbH, Industriestrasse 2-4, D-7531 Neuhausen-Hamburg, Germany
        PPG Industries (Deutschland) GmbH, Stackenberg Str. 34, D-5600 Wuppertal 11, Germany

PRECISION VALVE CORP   PO Box 309, Yonkers, NY 10702, Tel: (914) 969-6500
    (Mfr aerosol valves)
        Deutsche Prazisions Ventil GmbH, Schulstr. 33, 6234 Battersheim/Main, Germany

PREMARK INTL INC   1717 Deerfield Rd, Deerfield, IL 60015, Tel: (708) 405-6000
    (Mfr/sale diversified consumer & coml prdts)
        Premark GmbH, Praunheimer Landstrasse 70, Postfach 93-01-20,
        D-6000 Frankfurs/Main 93, Germany

PRIME COMPUTER INC   Prime Park, Natick, MA 01760, Tel: (617) 655-8000
    (Mfr minicomputers, hardware & software)
        Prime Computer GmbH, Gustav-Stresemann-Ring 12-16, 6200 Wiesbaden, Germany

PRINTRONIX INC   17500 Cartwright Rd, Irvine, CA 92715, Tel: (714) 863-1900
    (Mfr computer printers)
        Printronix GmbH, Berliner Str. 175, PO Box 101435, D-6050 Offenbach, Germany

PROCTER & GAMBLE CO   One Procter & Gamble Plaza, Cincinnati, OH 45202,
    Tel: (513) 983-1100
    (Personal care, food, laundry, cleaning & ind prdts)
        Procter & Gamble GmbH, Sulzbacherstr. 40, 6231 Schwalbach/Ts., Germany

PUROLATOR COURIER CORP   131 Morristown Rd, Basking Ridge, NJ 07980,
    Tel: (201) 953-6400
    (Time-sensitive package delivery)
        Executive Air Courier GmbH, D-6000 Frankfurt/Main 1, Germany

QUALITROL CORP   1385 Fairport Rd, Fairport, NY 14450, Tel: (716) 586-1515
    (Gauges, thermometers)
        Qualitrol GmbH, Industriestr., Postfach 1170, D-6222 Geisenheim, Germany

RALSTON PURINA CO   Checkerboard Sq, St Louis, MO 63164, Tel: (214) 982-1000
    (Poultry & live stock feed, cereals, food prdts)
        Latz Purina GmbH, Von-Stephan-Str. 6, D-5350 Euskirchen/Rhld, Germany

RAMSEY TECHNOLOGY INC   1853 W County Rd, St Paul, MN 55113,
    Tel: (612) 633-5150
    (Mfr scales & mining equip)
        Ramsey Engineering GmbH, Max-Eyth-Str. 45, 4200 Oberhausen 11, Germany

RANCO INC   555 Metro Pl N, PO Box 248, Dublin, OH 43017, Tel: (614) 764-3733
    (Controls for appliance, automotive, comfort, commercial & consumer mkts)
        Deutsche Ranco GmbH, Am Neven Rheinhaven 4, Postfach 2009, D-6720 Speyer, Germany

RAND McNALLY & CO   8255 N Central Park Ave, Skokie, IL 60076,
    Tel: (708) 267-6868
    (Maps, publishing)
        Mondadori-McNally GmbH, Kartographische Anstalt, Reinsburgstr. 105,

D-7000 Stuttgart 1, Germany
Rand-McNally GmbH, Reinsburgstr. 105, D-7000 Stuttgart, Germany

RANSBURG CORP   3939 W 56th St, Indianapolis, IN 46208, Tel: (317) 298-5000
(Mfr electrostatic coating sys)
Ransburg-Gema GmbH, Postfach 1152, D-6056 Heusenstamm, Germany

RAY BURNER CO   1301 San Jose Ave, San Francisco, CA 94112,
Tel: (415) 333-5800
(Gas & oil burners, water heaters)
Ray Oel-u. Gasbrenner GmbH, Schloss-Str. 92, D-7000 Stuttgart 1, Germany

RAYTHEON CO   141 Spring St, Lexington, MA 02173, Tel: (617) 862-6600
(Mfr diversified electronics & apppliances; aviation, ind & constr services,
publishing)
Lacroix & Kress, Engterstr. 34, Postfach 160, Bramsche 4550, Germany
Transistor Bau-und. Vertriebs GmbH, Straehlerweg 57, Karlsruhe-Durlach 41, Germany

RCA GLOBAL COMMUNICATIONS INC   60 Broad St, New York, NY 10004,
Tel: (212) 806-7000
(Commun serv)
RCA Global Communications Inc., Mittelweg 45, D-6000 Frankfurt/Main 1, Germany

READER'S DIGEST ASSOCIATION INC   PO Box 235, Pleasantville, NY 10570,
Tel: (914) 238-1000
(Global publisher & direct mail marketer)
Reader's Digest-Verlag Das Beste GmbH, Augustenstr. 1, 7000 Stuttgart 1, Germany

RECOGNITION EQUIPMENT INC   PO Box 222307, Dallas, TX 75222,
Tel: (214) 579-6000
(Optical character recognition sys & equip for document processing & computer data)
Recognition Equipment GmbH, Kaiserleistr. 44, 605 Offenbach/Main, Germany

REDKEN LABORATORIES INC   6625 Variel Ave, Canoga Park, CA 91303,
Tel: (818) 992-2700
(Mfr hair & skin care prdts)
Redken Laboratories GmbH, Friesstr. 15, D-6000 Frankfurt 60, Germany

THE REECE CORP   800 South St, Waltham, MA 02254-9168, Tel: (617) 894-9220
(Mfr apparel mach)
Reece Machinery Co. GmbH, Am Siebenstein 12, D-6072 Dreieich, Germany

REGENT SPORTS CORP   45 Ranick Rd, Hauppauge, NY 11787, Tel: (516) 234-2800
(Sporting goods)
Regent Sports GmbH, Germany, Pfarrweg 1, D-8035 Gauting, Germany

REICHHOLD CHEMICALS INC   RCI Bldg, 525 N Broadway, White Plains, NY 10603,
Tel: (914) 682-5700
(Synthetic resins & specialty chems)
Reichhold Chemie AG, Inersstr. 57, D-2000 Hamburg 70, Germany

RELIANCE ELECTRIC CO   24701 Euclid Ave, Cleveland, OH 44117,
Tel: (216) 266-7000
(Equip & sys for ind automation, telecom equip)
Reliance Electric GmbH, Postfach 2410, Krefeld, Germany
Toledo Merk GmbH, Postfach 451209, 5000 Cologne 41, Germany

REMINGTON ARMS CO INC   1800 Washington Rd, Pittsburgh, PA 05241,
  Tel: (412) 831-4000
  (Mfr sporting firearms & ammunition)
    Remington Arms GmbH, Postfach 3266, Wurzburg, Germany

REMINGTON PRODUCTS INC   60 Main St, Bridgeport, CT 06602, Tel: (203) 367-4400
  (Mfr home appliances, electric shavers)
    Remington Products Inc., Niederlassung Deutschland, Kaiser Str. 67,
      D-7410 Reutlingen, Germany

RESEARCH-COTTRELL COS   PO Box 1500, Somerville, NJ 08876, Tel: (201) 685-4000
  (Design/install air pollution control equip; tech servs)
    Research-Cottrell (Deutschland) GmbH, Koelnerstr. 195,
      D-5000 Cologne 90 (Porz-Westhoven), Germany

REVELL/MONOGRAM   8601 Waukegan Rd, Morton Grove, IL 60053, Tel: (708) 66-3500
  (Mfr plastic hobby kits)
    Revell AG, Henschelstr. 20-30, D-4980 Buende 1, Germany

REVLON INC   767 Fifth Ave, New York, NY 10153-0033, Tel: (212) 572-5000
  (Cosmetics, health care prdts)
    Deutsche Revlon GmbH, Tiefenbroicher Weg 15, D-4000 Dusseldorf-Lichtenbroich,
      Germany

REXNORD CORP   PO Box 2022, Milwaukee, WI 53201, Tel: (414) 643-3000
  (Mfr power transmission prdts)
    Rexnord Antriebstechnik GmbH, Postfach 674, Ueberwasserstr. 64, 4600 Dortmund 1,
      Germany
    Rexnord Kette GmbH & Co. KG, Postfach 120, D-5240 Betzdorf, Germany

R J REYNOLDS TOBACCO INC   Winston-Salem, NC 27102, Tel: (919) 777-5000
  (Tobacco & tobacco prdts)
    Reynolds-Neuerburg GmbH, Guelichplatz 3, D-5000 Cologne, Germany

RICHARDSON-VICKS INC   Ten Westport Rd, Wilton, CT 06897, Tel: (203) 834-5000
  (Consumer health & personal care prdts)
    Richardson GmbH, H.S. Richardson Str. D-6080 Gross-Gerau, Germany

RIDGE TOOL CO   400 Clark St, Elyria, OH 44035, Tel: (216) 323-5581
  (Hand & power tools for working pipe, drain cleaning equip, etc)
    Ridge Tool GmbH, Limburg, Lahn, Germany

RIGHT ASSOCIATES   1818 Market St, 14th Fl, Philadelphia, PA 19103-3614,
  Tel: (215) 988-1588
  (Outplacement & human resources consult servs)
    Right Associates, Senefelderstr. 166, 6050 Offenbach Frankfurt, Germany

RIKER LABORATORIES INC   Bldg 225-1N-07, 3M Center, St Paul, MN 55144,
  Tel: (612) 733-9577
  (Specialty pharms)
    Kettelhack Riker Pharma GmbH, 4280 Borken/Westfalen, Germany
    Ringsdorff Werke GmbH & KG, Koenigswintererstr. 1, 5320 Bad Godesberg-Mehlem,
      Germany

A H ROBINS CO INC   1407 Cummings Dr, PO Box 26609, Richmond, VA 23261-6609,
  Tel: (804) 257-2000
  (Mfr ethical pharms & consumer prdts)

Arzneimittel-Fabrik GmbH, Alpirsbah, Schwarzwald, Germany
Kytta-Werk Sauter GmbH, Alpirssbach/Schwarzwald, Germany

ROCKWELL GRAPHIC SYSTEMS   700 Oakmont Lane, Westmont, IL 60559-5546,
  Tel: (708) 850-5600
  (Mfr printing equip)
    Rockwell Graphic Systems Ltd., Grenzstr 30, Postfach 1268, 6053 Obertshavsen,
      Germany

ROCKWELL INTL CORP   2230 E Imperial Hwy, El Segundo, CA 90245,
  Tel: (213) 647-5000
  (Prdts & serv for aerospace, automotive, electronics, graphics & automation inds)
    Rockwell Graphic Systems Inc., Grenzstr. 30, Postfach 1268, D-6053 Obertshausen,
      Germany
    Rockwell International GmbH, Fraunhoferstr. 11, D-8033 Munich-Martinsried, Germany
    Rockwell-Collins GmbH, Boschstr. 4, D-6054 Rodgau 6, Germany
    Rockwell-Collins GmbH, Gebaeude 112, Dlughafen Rhein-Main, D-6000 Frankfurt 75,
      Germany
    Rockwell-Golde GmbH, Hanauer Landstr. 338 und 437, Postfach 3004, D-6000 Frankfurt,
      Germany

R A RODRIGUEZ INC   320 Endo Blvd, Garden City, NY 11530, Tel: (516) 832-2617
  (Export mgt: bearings & power trans equip)
    R. A. Rodriguez GmbH, Rue De Wattrelos 17, 5180 Eschweiler, Germany

ROGERS CORP   One Technology Dr, Rogers, CT 06263, Tel: (203) 774-9605
  (Mfr flexible, molded, die-stamped & microwave circuits; engineered polymer prdts)
    Mektron GmbH, Escheweg 2-4, D-6108 Weiterstadt 1, Germany

ROHM & HAAS CO   Independence Mall West, Philadelphia, PA 19105,
  Tel: (215) 592-3000
  (Mfr ind & agric chems, plastics)
    Rohm & Haas (Deutschland) GmbH, In Der Kron 4, D-6000 Frankfurt 90, Germany

RORER GROUP INC   500 Virginia Dr, Ft Washington, PA 19034,
  Tel: (215) 628-6000
  (Mfr ethical & consumer pharms)
    Arznei Muller-Rorer-GmbH, Bielefeld, Germany
    Rodler GmbH, Florsheim-Dalsheim, Germany

ROSEMOUNT INC   12001 Technology Dr, Eden Prairie, MN 55344,
  Tel: (612) 941-5560
  (Mfr aerospace & ind instrumentation)
    Rosemount Engineering GmbH, Schulstr. 29, 8031 Wessling bei Munich, Germany

ROSS OPERATING VALVE CO INC   PO Box 7015, Troy, MI 48007, Tel: (313) 362-1250
  (Mfr air valves, pneumatic controls & accessories)
    Ross Europa GmbH, Robert-Bosch-Str. 2, D-6070 Langen, Germany

RUBBERMAID INC   1147 Akron Rd, Wooster, OH 44691, Tel: (216) 264-6464
  (Rubber & plastic home, commercial & ind prdts)
    Dupol-Rubbermaid GmbH, An der Trift, D-6072 Dreieichenhain, Germany

RUDER FINN INC   301 E 57th St, New York, NY 10022, Tel: (212) 593-6400
  (Public relations serv, broadcast commun)
    Dirk Blase Public Relations, Richard-Wagner-Str. 10-11, D-7000 Stuttgart 1, Germany

RUSSELL REYNOLDS ASSOCIATES INC   200 Park Ave, New York, NY 10166,
Tel: (212) 351-2000
(Exec recruiting services)
   Russell Reynolds Assocs. Inc., Triton House, Bockenheimer Landstrasse 42,
      6000 Frankfurt/Main, Germany

SAFETY-KLEEN CORP   777 Big Timber Rd, Elgin, IL 60123, Tel: (708) 697-8460
(Solvent based parts cleaning serv, sludge/solvent recycling serv)
   Safety-Kleen GmbH Reinigungstechnik, Auf dem Huls 16, 4020 Mettmann 1, Germany

SCHENKERS INTL FORWARDERS INC   1 World Trade Center, New York, NY 10048,
Tel: (212) 432-3000
(Shippers)
   Schenker & Co. GmbH, Mannheimerstr. 81-95, D-6000 Frankfurt/Main, Germany

R P SCHERER CORP   2075 W Big Beaver Rd, Troy, MI 48084, Tel: (313) 649-0900
(Mfr soft gelatin & two-piece hard shell capsules)
   R.P. Scherer GmbH, Postfach 1243, D-6930 Eberbach/Baden, Germany

SCHLEGEL CORP   400 East Ave, Rochester, NY 14607, Tel: (716) 546-6260
(Engineered perimeter sealing systems for residential & commercial constr)
   Weill & Reineke GmbH, Elselensweg 17, D-2000 Hamburg 28, Germany

A SCHULMAN INC   3550 W Market St, Akron, OH 44313, Tel: (216) 666-3751
(Mfr/sale plastic resins & compounds)
   A. Schulman GmbH, Huttenstr. 211, D-5014 Kerpen 3, Sindorf, Germany

SCIENCE MANAGEMENT CORP   PO Box 0600, Basking Ridge, NJ 07920,
Tel: (201) 647-7000
(Human/mgmt resources, info technology, engr & technology services)
   SMC Intl. GmbH, Leipziger Str. 3, 6000 Frankfurt/Main 90, Germany

SCIENTIFIC ATLANTA INC   1 Technology Pkwy, PO Box 105600, Atlanta, GA 30348,
Tel: (404) 441-4000
(Telecommun instru & equip, energy mgmt & home security equip, test & measurement
instru)
   Scientific-Atlanta GmbH, Albert Schweitzerstr. 66, Postfach 87 27 20,
      D-8000 Munich 83, Germany

SCM CORP   299 Park Ave, New York, NY 10171, Tel: (212) 752-2700
(Business equip, chems, coatings & resins, foods, paper prdts)
   Hamann-Rechenmaschinen GmbH, Bergmannstr. 102, Berlin 61, Germany
   SCM Deutschland GmbH, Hainerweg 37-53, D-6000 Frankfurt/Main, Germany
   SCM International GmbH, Bockenheimer Landstr. 8, Zuerichhaus,
      D-6000 Frankfurt/Main, Germany

SCOTT WORLDWIDE INC   Scott Plaza, Philadelphia, PA 19113, Tel: (215) 521-5000
(Paper & paper prdts, bleached pulp)
   Scott Paper GmbH, 6680 Muenkirchen-Wellesweiler am Ochsenwald, Germany

SEA-LAND SERVICE INC   379 Thornall St, Edison, NJ 08837, Tel: (201) 558-6000
(Container transport)
   Agena S.A., Strassbourg, Germany
   Network Container Fracht Agentur GmbH, Telzerstr. 8, D-2800 Bremen 1, Germany
   Network Container Fracht Agentur GmbH, Baumweg 19, D-6000 Frankfurt/Main, Germany
   Paul Guenther GmbH & Co., Lister Meile 50, D-3000 Hannover 1, Germany
   Paul Guenther GmbH & Co., Postfach 105 227, Martinistr. 1, D-2800 Bremen, Germany

Paul Guenther GmbH & Co., Postfach 200305, D-4000 Dusseldorf 1, Germany
Paul Guenther GmbH & Co., Zeil 65-69, (Hochhaus zum Bienenkorb),
  D-6000 Frankfurt/Main, Germany
Paul Guenther GmbH & Co., Cremon 3, D-2000 Hamburg 11, Germany
Paul Guenther GmbH & Co., Hauptmannreute 75A, D-7000 Stuttgart 1, Germany
Paul Guenther GmbH & Co., Nymphenburgerstr. 81, D-8000 Munich 19, Germany
Sea-Land Service Inc., Nordhafen, Gatehouse, Postfach 2209, 285 Bremerhaven 12,
  Germany
Sea-Land Service Inc., Altenwal 21, D-2800 Bremen, Germany
Sea-Land Service Inc., Mainz, Germany

SEALED AIR CORP   Park 80 Plaza E, Saddle Brook, NJ 07662-5291,
  Tel: (201) 791-7600
  (Mfr protective packaging prdts)
  Sealed Air GmbH, Am Bruckweg 36, D-6090 Russelsheim, Germany

SEALOL INC   Warwick Industrial Park, PO Box 2158, Providence, RI 02905,
  Tel: (401) 781-4700
  (Mfr seals, joints, valves)
  Sealol GmbH, Gagern Rind 5, 6233 Kelkheim, Germany

SEAQUIST DIV   1160 N Silver Lake Rd, Cary, IL 60013, Tel: (708) 639-2126
  (Aerosol valves, closures, pump dispensers)
  Bielsteiner Verschlusstechnik GmbH, Postfach 310165, D-5270 Gummersbach, 31, Germany
  Perfect-Valois Ventil GmbH, Alte Str. 77A, Dortmund, Germany

G D SEARLE & CO   PO Box 1045, Skokie, IL 60076, Tel: (708) 982-7000
  (Pharms, health care & optical prdts, specialty chems)
  G.D. Searle GmbH, Postfach 70 16 20, Konrad-Celtisstr. 81, D-8000 Munich 70, Germany

SEATRAIN LINES INC   270 Sylvan Ave, Englewood Cliffs, NJ 07632,
  Tel: (201) 871-8900
  (Containerized shipping, ship chartering)
  Seatrain GmbH, Rembertiring 18-26, D-2800 Bremen 1, Germany
  Seatrain GmbH, Loningstr. 34,. D-2800 Bremen 1, Germany
  Seatrain GmbH, Gatehouse 1, Container Terminal, D-2850 Bremerhaven-Nordhafen,
    Germany
  Seatrain GmbH, Haussmannstr. 181, D-7000 Stuttgart, Germany
  Seatrain GmbH, Bismarckstr. 66, D-4000 Dusseldorf, Germany
  Seatrain GmbH, Sphienstr. 44, D-6000 Frankfurt/Main, Germany
  Seatrain GmbH, Kattrepel 2, D-2000 Hamburg 1, Germany
  Seatrain GmbH, Schillerstr. 21, D-8000 Munich 2, Germany

SECURITY PACIFIC NATIONAL BANK   333 S Hope St, Los Angeles, CA 90071,
  Tel: (213) 345-6211
  (Banking)
  Security Pacific Bank AG, Ulmenstr. 30, D-6000 Frankfurt 17, Germany

SELAS CORP OF AMERICA   Dreshertown Rd & Limekiln Pike, Dresher, PA 19025,
  Tel: (215) 646-6600
  (Mfr heat treating equip for metal, glass, ceramic & chem inds)
  Selas Waermetechnik GmbH, Dr. Braun-Angott Div., 4006 Erkrath, 1 Unterfeldhaus,
    Niermannsweg 13, Germany
  Selas Waermetechnik GmbH, Schluterstrasse 95, 4000 Dusseldorf 1, Germany

SEMICONDUCTOR SPECIALISTS INC   195 W Spangler, Elmhurst, IL 60126,
  Tel: (708) 279-1000
  (Electr distr)
     Holbleiter Spezialzertirieb Carroll & Co. GmbH, Vilbeler Landstr. 41,
        6000 Frankfurt, Germany

SENCO PRODUCTS INC   8485 Broadwell Rd, Cincinnati, OH 45244,
  Tel: (513) 388-2000
  (Mfr ind nailers, staplers, fasteners & accessories)
     Deutsche SENCO Industrie-Erzeugnisse GmbH & Co. KG, Gelsenkirchenerstr. 27,
        Postfach 10 68 67, D-2800 Bremen 1, Germany

SENSORMATIC ELECTRONICS CORP   500 NW 12th Ave, Deerfield Beach, BF L33341,
  Tel: (305) 427-9700
  (Electronic article surveillance equip)
     Senelco GmbH, Kaiserswertherstr. 289, D-4000 Dusseldorf 30, Germany

SEVERE ENVIRONMENT SYSTEMS CO   PO Box 668, Chatsworth, CA 91311,
  Tel: (213) 998-9090
  (Computer prdts for space, mili- tary, commercial avionics & severe environment ind
  applications)
     EMM GmbH, Hohemarkstr. 152, D-6370 Oberursel/Taunus, Germany

SGS CONTROL SERVICES INC   42 Broadway, New York, NY 10004,
  Tel: (212) 482-8700
  (Complete range of quality & quantity control checks & related tech serv)
     F.H. Gottfeld GmbH, 21 Wilhelm-Mauser-Str., D-5000 Cologne, Germany
     SGS Control Co. GmbH, 7 Gr. Theaterstr., D-2000 Hamburg, Germany

SHAKESPEARE FISHING TACKLE GROUP   611 Shakespeare Rd, Columbia, SC 29204,
  Tel: (803) 754-7000
  (Mfr fishing tackle)
     Shakespeare Intl. GmbH, Postfach 420 424, D-5000 Cologne 41, Germany

SHEAFFER EATON INC   1 Crown Mark Dr, Lincoln, RI 02865, Tel: (401) 333-0303
  (Mfr writing instruments)
     Sheaffer Pen Vertriebs GmbH, Friedenstr. 4, 8700 Wurzburg, Germany

SHEARSON/AMERICAN EXPRESS   American Express Tower, New York, NY 10285,
  Tel: (212) 298-2000
  (Investment banking, financial serv)
     Shearson American Express GmbH, Mainzer Landstr. 27-31, D-6000, Frankfurt/Main,
        Germany
     Shearson American Express GmbH, Neuer Wall 84, D-2000 Hamburg 36, Germany

SHIPLEY CO INC   2300 Washington St, Newton, MA 02162, Tel: (617) 969-5500
  (Mfr chems for printed circuit boards & microelectronic mfg)
     Shipley GmbH, P.O. Box 50 1022, D-7000 Stuttgart 50, Germany

SHULTON INC   1 Cyanamid Plaza, Wayne, NJ 07470, Tel: (201) 831-2000
  (Health, beauty & grooming prdts)
     Shulton GmbH, Huclacher 230, Postfach 500570, D-8000 Munich 50, Germany

SIGNODE PACKAGING SYSTEMS   3600 W Lake Ave, Glenview, IL 60025,
  Tel: (708) 724-6100
  (Mfr packaging systems)
     Signode System GmbH, Postfach 100480, D-4220 Dinslaken, Germany

SILICONIX INC 2201 Laurelwood Dr, Santa Clara, CA 95054, Tel: (408) 988-8000
  (Semiconductor components)
    Siliconix GmbH, Postfach 1340, Johannesstr. 27, D-7024 Filderstadt, Germany

SIMPLEX TIME RECORDER CO Simplex Plaza, Gardner, MA 01441,
  Tel: (617) 632-2500
  (Time recorders & stamps, master time sys, alarm, security, monitor & control sys)
    Simplex Zeitdienstanlagen GmbH, Alleenstr. 33, D-7300 Esslingen, Germany

SIMPLICITY PATTERN CO INC 200 Madison Ave, New York, NY 10016,
  Tel: (212) 481-3737
  (Dress patterns)
    Simplicity Modeschnitt GmbH, Postfach 101664, D-5000 Cologne 1, Germany

SMITH INTL INC 16740 Hardy St, Houston, TX 77032, Tel: (713) 443-6470
  (Mfr/serv downhole drilling equip)
    Smith Intl. Deutschland GmbH, Grafftring 5-7, Postfach 429, D-3100 Celle, Germany

SMITH TOOL PO Box C-19511, Irvine, CA 92713, Tel: (714) 540-7010
  (Drilling bits)
    Smith International Deutschland GmbH, Celle, West Germany

SNAP-ON TOOLS CORP 2801 80th St, Kenosha, WI 53141-1410, Tel: (414) 656-5200
  (Mfr automotive & ind maint serv tools)
    Snap-On Tools Ltd GmbH, Rudolf Dieselstr. 6, D-7104 Obersulm, Willsbach, Germany

SOABAR 7722 Dungan Road, Philadelphia, PA 19111, Tel: (215) 725-4700
  (Marking machs, labels, etc)
    Soabar GmbH, Bradstr. 32, D-5200 Stegburg, Germany

SONOCO PRODUCTS CO North Second St, PO Box 160, Hartsville, SC 29550,
  Tel: (803) 383-7000
  (Mfr packaging for consumer & ind mkt)
    Sonoco Deutschland GmbH, Fennastr. 94, 4460 Nordhorn, Germany

SPECTRA-PHYSICS 3333 N First St, San Jose, CA 95134, Tel: (408) 946-6080
  (Lasers, optical components & coatings, data sys)
    Spectra Physics GmbH, Siemensstr. 20, D-6100 Darmstadt-Kranichstein, Germany
    Spectra-Physics GmbH, Aus dem Huels 16, D-4020 Mettmann, Germany
    Spectra-Physics GmbH, Ismaningerstr. 21, D-8000 Munich, Germany
    Spectra-Physics GmbH, Buero Hamburg, Cuxhavener Str. 36, 2104 Hamburg 92, Germany

SPECTRAL DYNAMICS CORP 4141 Ruffin Rd, San Diego, CA 92123,
  Tel: (619) 496-3400
  (Mfr Vibration monitoring, analysis & control equip)
    Scientific-Atlanta GmbH, P.O. Box 830935, D-8000 Munich 83, Germany

SPRAYING SYSTEMS CO Schmale Rd & North Ave, Wheaton, IL 60187,
  Tel: (708) 665-5000
  (Fabricated metal prdts)
    Feinbau Maschinen GmbH, Postfach 1340, D-7065 Winterbach, Germany
    Spraying Systems Deutschland, Grossmoorring 9, D-2100 Hamburg 90, Germany

SPS TECHNOLOGIES INC 900 Newtown-Yardley Rd, Newtown, PA 18940,
  Tel: (215) 860-3000
  (Mfr aerospace & ind fasteners, precision components, superalloys, magnetic

(cont)

materials, fastening sys)
    Unbrako Schrauben GmbH, Postfach 2180, 5400 Koblenz, Germany

SPX CORP   700 Terrace Point Dr, Muskegon, MI 49443, Tel: (616) 724-5000
(Mfr spec repair equip & repair parts)
    Bear Deutschland GmbH, Am Muhlplatz 18, 7640 Kehl, Germany
    Kent-Moore Deutschland GmbH, Alfred Nobel Str. 12, Postfach 1528, D-6806 Viernheim,
    Germany

SQUARE D CO   Executive Plaza, Palatine, IL 60067, Tel: (708) 397-2600
(Power distribution & elec/electr ind control equip)
    Square D Co. (Deutschland) GmbH, Landwehrstrasse 48, D-6100 Darmstardt, Germany

SRI INTL   333 Ravenswood Ave, Menlo Park, CA 94025, Tel: (415) 326-6200
(Intl consulting & research)
    SRI Frankfurt, Ulmenstr. 23, 6000 Frankfurt/Main, Germany

ST JOE MINERALS CORP   250 Park Ave, New York, NY 10017, Tel: (212) 953-5000
(Coal, oil, gas, iron ore, metals & minerals)
    St. Joe Explorations GmbH, Weinstr. 20, D-3000 Hannover 1, Germany

STA-RITE INDUSTRIES INC   777 E Wisconsin Ave, Milwaukee, WI 53202,
Tel: (414) 276-6888
(Mfr water pumps & filters, water treatment equip, fluid power components)
    Sta-Rite GmbH Europa, 6103 Griesheim/Darmstadt, Germany

STANDARD COMMERCIAL CORP   PO Box 450, Wilson, NC 27893, Tel: (919) 291-5507
(Leaf tobacco dealers/processors, wool processors)
    Leafco Tradinc GmbH, Hamburg, Germany
    Lohmann & Co. GmbH, Bremen, Germany
    Werkhof GmbH, An der Alster 18, D-2000 Hamburg 1, Germany

STANGE CO   342 N Western Ave, Chicago, IL 60612, Tel: (312) 733-6945
(Seasonings, food colors & flavorings)
    McCormick GmbH, Eschborn/Taunus, Germany

THE STANLEY WORKS   1000 Stanley Dr, PO Box 7000, New Britain, CT 06050,
Tel: (203) 225-5111
(Mfr hand tools & hardware)
    Bostitch Germany GmbH, Postfach 1349, Oststr. 26, 2000 Norderstedt, Bez. Hamburg,
    Germany
    Stanley Hardware Inc., Zweignie der lassung, Velbert, Postfach 100970,
    D-5620 Velbert, Germany

STATE STREET BANK & TRUST CO   225 Franklin St, Boston, MA 02101,
Tel: (617) 786-3000
(Banking servs)
    State Street GmbH, Nymphenberger Str. 70, 8000 Munich, Germany

STEINER CORP   PO Box 2317, 505 E South Temple St, Salt Lake City, UT 84102,
Tel: (801) 328-8831
(Linen supply service)
    Alsco-Berufskleidungs-Service GmbH, Bergisch-Gladbacherstr. 1085, Postfach 21,
    D-5000 Cologne 80, Delbrueck, Germany

STEINWAY & SONS   1 Steinway Pl, Long Island City, NY 11105,
  Tel: (718) 721-2600
  (Mfr pianos)
     Steinway & Sons, Colonnaden 29, D-2000 Hamburg 36, Germany

STEMCO INC   PO Box 1989, Longview, TX 75606, Tel: (214) 758-9981
  (Mfr automotive seals, mufflers, spec prdts for heavy duty trucks, buses, trailers)
     Stem Co. Truck Products Garlock GmbH, Duisburgerstr. 3, D-4040 Neuss, Germany

STERER ENGINEERING & MFG CO   4690 Colorado Blvd, Los Angeles, CA 90039,
  Tel: (213) 245-7161
  (Fluid controls)
     Sterer Regeltechn. Geraete GmbH, Rheydterstr. 251, D-4050 Moen, Germany

STERLING DRUG INC   90 Park Ave, New York, NY 10016, Tel: (212) 907-2000
  (Pharms, chems, cosmetics, household cleaners & waxes)
     Sterling Continental GmbH, Hamburg, Germany

STERLING SOFTWARE INC   8080 N Central Expy, #1100, Dallas, TX 75206-1895,
  Tel: (214) 891-8600
  (Sales/serv software prdts; tech servs)
     Sterling Software Intl., Burqplatz 21-22, D-4000 Dusseldorf, Germany

STEWART-WARNER CORP   1826 Diversey Pkwy, Chicago, IL 60614,
  Tel: (312) 883-6000
  (Lubrication equip sys, ind tools & controls, castors, pressure switches)
     Stewart-Warner Alemite GmbH, Stockshausstr. 9, 401 Hilden, Germany
     Thor Power Tool GmbH, Matthias Bruggenstr. 4, D-5000 Cologne, Germany

STONE CONTAINER CORP   150 N Michigan Ave, Chicago, IL 60601-7568,
  Tel: (312) 346-6600
  (Mfr paper & paper packaging)
     Eruopa Carton AG, Spitalerstrasse 11, 2000 Hamburg 1, Germany

STORAGE TECHNOLOGY CORP   2270 S 88th St, Louisville, CO 80028-0001,
  Tel: (303) 673-5151
  (Mfr/mkt/serv info storage & retrieval sys)
     Storage Technology GmbH, Bernerstrasse 35, Postfach 5600147, 6000 Frankfurt/56,
     Germany

STOTTLER STAGG & ASSOCIATES   8660 Astronaut Blvd, Cape Canaveral, FL 32920,
  Tel: (407) 783-1320
  (Architecture, engineering, planning)
     Stottler Stagg Intl. Architects, Engineers, Planners Inc., Westendstrasse 84,
     6000 Frankfurt/Main 1, Germany

STRATOFLEX INC   220 Roberts Cut-Off Rd, PO Box 10398, Fort Worth, TX 76114,
  Tel: (817) 738-6543
  (Hose assemblies, self-sealing & quick disconnect couplings, swivels, etc)
     Stratoflex Deutchland, TMU Hydraulik, Elisabeth Str. 6, 5020 Frechen bei Koln,
     Germany

STREETER RICHARDSON DIV   680 Van Houten Ave, Clifton, NJ 07015,
  Tel: (201) 471-3400
  (Ind weighing & packaging equip)
     Chronos Richardson GmbH, 5202 Hennef Sieg, Frankfurterstr. 85-95, West Germany
     Chronos Richardson GmbH, Frankfurterstr. 89-95, 5202 Henef Sieg 1, Germany

SUDLER & HENNESSEY   1633 Broadway, New York, NY 10019, Tel: (212) 265-8000
(Healthcare prdts advertising)
   Sudler & Hennessey GmbH, Lersnerstrasse 23, 6000 Frankfurt/Main 1, Germany

SULLAIR CORP   3700 E Michigan Blvd, Michigan City, IN 46360,
Tel: (219) 879-5451
(Refrigeration sys, vacuum pumps, generators, etc)
   Sullair Schraubenkompressoren GmbH, Wallensteinstr. 20, D-8120 Geretsried, Germany

SUN ELECTRIC CORP   One Sun Pkwy, Crystal Lake, IL 60014, Tel: (815) 459-7700
(Mfr auto tune-up, diagnostic & emission testing equip)
   Sun Electric Deutschland GmbH, Postfach 100609, D-4020 Mettamann, Germany

SUNBEAM-OSTER INTL   5055 N Lydell Ave, Milwaukee, WI 53217,
Tel: (414) 361-8223
(Mfr small houseware prdts)
   Oster Intl. GmbH, Schreberstrasse 18, D-6050 Offenbach A.M., Germany

SUPERIOR GRAPHITE CO   120 S Riverside Plaza, Chicago, IL 60606,
Tel: (312) 559-2999
(Natural & synthetic graphites)
   Superior Electric GmbH, Frankfurt, Germany

SWAN SALES CORP   6223 W Forrst Home Ave, Milwaukee, WI 53220,
Tel: (414) 543-5555
(General merchandise)
   Swan Sales Corp., Wolfsbergerstr. 5, D-8000 Munich 60, Germany

SYBRON CORP   411 E Wisconsin Ave, Milwaukee, WI 07662, Tel: (414) 274-6600
(Professional health prdts, spec chems, instru, water & waste water treatment sys)
   Karl Baisch GmbH & KG, Poststr. 76, Postfach 1160, D-7056 Winstadt 1, Germany
   Kerr GmbH, Killisfeldstr. 62, Postfach 410540, D-7500 Karlsruhe 41, Germany
   Reco Dental Laboreinrichtungen GmbH, Killisfeldstr. 64, Postfach 410827,
     D-7500 Karlsruhe 41, Germany
   Ritter AG, Killisfeldstr. 62, Postfach 41 0880, D-7500 Karlsruhe 41, Germany
   Tanatex Chemie GmbH, Cracauerstr. 73, Postfach 28-7, D-4150 Krefeld, Germany

SYSTEM INDUSTRIES INC   560 Cottonwood Dr, Milpitas, CA 95035,
Tel: (408) 432-1212
(Value added third party vendor high performance data storage sybsys)
   System Industries GmbH, AM Forsthaus Gravenbruch 5, 6078 Neu-Isenburg 2, Germany
   System Industries GmbH, Heilvronner Str. 67, 7000 Stuttgart 1, Germany
   System Industries GmbH, Leopold Strasse 28A, 8000 Munich 40, Germany

SYSTEMS ENGINEERING LABS INC   6901 W Sunrise Blvd, Fort Lauderdale,
FL 33313, Tel: (305) 587-2900
(Digital computers)
   Systems Engineering Labs., Landsbergerstr. 441/IV OG, D-8000 Munich 60, Germany
   Systems Engineering Labs. GmbH, Bonnerstr. 7-11, D-4000 Dusseldorf 13, Germany

TALLEY CORP   3303 Conejo Rd, Newbury Park, CA 91320, Tel: (805) 498-2121
(Hot air & chem valves)
   Frank H. Talley Luftfahrtbedarf, Taunusstr. 2, D-6200 Wiesbaden, Germany

TANDEM COMPUTERS INC   19333 Vallco Parkway, Cupertino, CA 95014,
Tel: (408) 725-6000
(Computer sys)

Tandem Computers GmbH, Dortmund, Dusseldorf, Frankfurt, Hamburg, Mannheim, Munich, Neufahrn, Stuttgart, Germany

TANDY CORP   1800 One Tandy Center, Fort Worth, TX 76102, Tel: (817) 390-3700
(Electronic & acoustic equip)
  Memtek Co., Hahnstr. 41, 6000 Frankfurt, Germany
  Tandy Intl. Electronics, Christenenstr. 11, 4030 Ratingen 2, Germany

TAYLOR INSTRUMENT CO   99 Ames St, PO Box 110, Rochester, NY 14601,
  Tel: (716) 235-6806
(Instru for process control inds)
  Taylor Instrument GmbH, Postfach 6080, Daimlerstr. 11, D-6054 Rodgau 6, Germany

TECHNICON INSTRUMENTS CORP   511 Benedict Ave, Tarrytown, NY 10591-5097,
  Tel: (914) 631-8000
(Mfr/serv automated blook anal equip, reagents & diagnostics)
  Technicon GmbH, Im Rosengarten 11, 6368 Bad Vilbel, Germany

TECUMSEH PRODUCTS CO   100 E Patterson St, Tecumseh, MI 49286,
  Tel: (517) 423-8411
(Refrig & A/C compressors & units, small engines, pumps)
  Ho Motorenwerk GmbH, Postfach 1260, D-2080 Pinneberg, Germany
  Tecumseh Engines GmbH, Postfach 1640, D-2080 Pinneberg, Germany

TED BATES WORLDWIDE INC   1515 Broadway, New York, NY 10036,
  Tel: (212) 869-3131
(Advertising agency)
  Ted Bates Werbeagentur GmbH, Bettinastr. 53-55, 6000 Frankfurt/Main 2, Germany

TEEPAK INC   3 Westbrook Corp Center, Westchester, IL 60154,
  Tel: (708) 409-3000
(Mfr cellulose, fibrous, collegen sausage casings & plastic packaging)
  Teepak Zweigniederlassung Der (Teepak, Inc.), Lederstr. 21, Postfach 540244,
    D-2000 Hamburg 54, Germany

TEKNIS CORP   PO Box 3189, No Attleboro, MA 02761, Tel: (508) 695-3591
(Sale advanced technology prdts, fiber optics, materials for semiconductor mfr)
  Teknis GmbH, Postfach 711080, 8000 Munich 71, Germany

TEKTRONIX INC   PO Box 500, Beaverton, OR 97077, Tel: (503) 627-7111
(Mfr test & meas, visual sys & commun prdts)
  Tektronix GmbH, Postfach 101544, D-5000 Cologne, Germany
  Tektronix GmbH, Ernst-Reuter-Platz 3-5, D-1000 Berlin, Germany
  Tektronix GmbH, Schoenhauserstr. 65, D-5000 Cologne, Germany
  Tektronix GmbH, Kieler Str. 407, D-2000 Hamburg 54, Germany
  Tektronix GmbH, Knegsstr. 39, D-7500 Karlsruhe 1, Germany
  Tektronix GmbH, Ehrenbreitsteinerstr. 36, D-8000 Munich, Germany
  Tektronix GmbH, Donaustr. 36, D-8500 Nuremberg 60, Germany

TELEDYNE COMPONENTS   1300 Terra Bella Ave, Mountain View, CA 94043,
  Tel: (415) 968-9241
(Mfr data conversion prdts, bipolar interface, etc)
  Teledyne Components, Abraham Lincoln Strasse 38-42, 6200 Wiesbaden, Germany

TELEDYNE McMAY   850 Grantley Rd, York, PA 17405, Tel: (717) 849-2490
(Mfr welding prdts)
  Teledyne McKay, Abraham Lincoln Strasse 38-42, 6200 Wiesbaden, Germany

TELXON CORP   3330 W Market St, Akron, OH 44333, Tel: (216) 867-3700
(Devel/mfr portable computer sys & related equip)
   Telxon GmbH, Gutenbergring 1-5, 200 Norderstedt, Germany

TENNANT CO   701 N Lilac Dr, Minneapolis, MN 55440, Tel: (612) 540-1200
(Mfr ind floor maint sweepers & scrubbers, roofing machs)
   Tennant N.V., Zweigniederlassung Remscheid, Postfach 12 04 68, Germany

TENNESSEE ASSOCIATES INTL INC   337 East Broadway Ave, Maryville, TN 37801,
   Tel: (615) 983-4044
(Mgt consulting servs)
   TAI Deutschland GmbH, Luegplatz 6, 4000 Dusseldorf 11, Germany

TEXACO INC   2000 Westchester Ave, White Plains, NY 10650, Tel: (914) 253-4000
(Explor/mktg crude oil & its prdts, petro-chems)
   Deutsche Texaco AG, Uberseering 40, Postfach 60 04 49, D-2000 Hamburg 60, Germany

TEXAS INSTRUMENTS INC   PO Box 655474, Dallas, TX 75265, Tel: (214) 995-2011
(Mfr semiconductor devices, electr/electro-mech sys, instr & controls)
   Texas Instruments Deutschland GmbH, Haggertystr. 1, 8050 Freising, Germany

TEXAS IRON WORKS INC   12300 S Main St, PO Box 35729, Houston, TX 77235,
   Tel: (713) 729-2110
(Mfr liner hanger equip, production packers, safety & kelly valves)
   Texas Iron Works GmbH, Vogelberg 33a, 3100 Celle, Germany

TEXON INC   Crescent Mills St, Russell, MA 01071, Tel: (413) 862-3652
(Latex & resin impregnated fibre prdts)
   Texon GmbH, Roigheimerstr., D-7108 Moeckmuehl, Wurttemberg, Germany

THERMCO SYSTEMS INC   1465 North Batavia St, Orange, CA 92668,
   Tel: (714) 639-2340
(Microprocessor controlled diffusion furnace sys & vacuum/gas sys for semiconductor
processing)
   Thermco Products GmbH, Fraunhoferstr. 11A, 8033 Martinsried, Germany

THERMO ELECTRIC CO   109 Fifth St, Saddle Brook, NJ 07662, Tel: (201) 843-5800
(Mfr temp/meas control prdts)
   Thermo Electric GmbH, Postfach 900 406, Neue Eilerstr. 36, D-5000 Cologne 90,
   Germany

THERMO ELECTRON CORP   101 First Ave, Waltham, MA 02154, Tel: (617) 890-8700
(Devel/mfr of process equip & instru for energy intensive inds)
   Van Hengel Instrumente GmbH, Baiertalerstr. 24-26, D-6908 Wiesloch, Germany

THETFORD CORP   7101 Jackson Rd, PO Box 1285, Ann Arbor, MI 48106,
   Tel: (313) 769-6000
(Sanitation sys)
   Thetford GmbH, 4 Dusseldorf Hafen, Dusseldorf, Germany

THOMAS & BETTS CORP   1001 Frontier Rd, Bridgewater, NJ 08807-0993,
   Tel: (201) 685-1600
(Mfr elect/electr connectors & accessories)
   Thomas & Betts GmbH, Postfach 1274, Theodor-Heuss-Str. 7-9, D-6073 Egelsbach,
   Germany

THOMAS INDUSTRIES INC   4360 Brownsboro Rd, #300, Louisville, KY 40207,
  Tel: (502) 893-4600
  (Mfr lighting fixtures, compressors, vacuum pumps, spec prdts)
    ASF Thomas Industries, Postfach 1245, Siemenstrasse 4, 8039 Puchheim, Germany
    Helmut Brey GmbH, Postfach 1214, Ludwigstrasse 28, D-8940 Memmingen, Germany
    Wilhelm Sauer GmbH & Co., Postfach 150220, Hahnerberger Strasse 173,
      D-5600 Wuppertal 12, Germany

THOMAS INTL PUBLISHING CO   1 Penn Plaza, New York, NY 10119,
  Tel: (212) 290-7213
  (Publ ind magazines & directories)
    Elsevier Industrieverlag GmbH, Postfach 1869, D-6500 Mainz, Germany

THOR POWER TOOL CO   72 Bayside Rd, Virginia Beach, VA 23455,
  Tel: (804) 323-5666
  (Mfr portable air-operated & elect tools)
    Thor Power Tool, Mathias-Bruggen-Str. 4, Cologne Bickendorf, Germany

TIME WARNER INC   Time Life Bldg, New York, NY 10020, Tel: (212) 522-1212
  (Magazine & book publ, communications)
    Time Public Relations GmbH, Schwanenmarkt 6, D-4000 Dusseldorf, Germany

TIMET CORP   420 Rouser Rd, PO Box 2824, Pittsburgh, PA 15230,
  Tel: (412) 262-4200
  (Mfr titanium mill prdts)
    Tisto Titan-Edelstahl, Wagnerstr. 4, D-4000 Dusseldorf, Germany

TIMEX GROUP LTD   Waterbury, CT 06760, Tel: (203) 573-5000
  (Watches, clocks, timing instru, cameras, gyroscopes)
    Timex Corp., Wurmbergerstr. 125, 753 Pforzhelm, Germany

TOKHEIM CORP   1602 Wabash Ave, PO Box 360, Fort Wayne, IN 46801,
  Tel: (219) 423-2552
  (Mfr gasoline service station dispensers, access, hand & in-tank fuel pumps)
    Tokheim GmbH, Postfach 224, D-8120 Weilheim, Germany

TORRINGTON/FAFNIR   200 Chestnut Ridge Rd, Woodcliff Lake, NJ 07675,
  Tel: (203) 482-9511
  (Mfr bearings, precision metal parts & assemblies, universal joints)
    Torrington GmbH, Postfach 1220 & 1240, D-5102 Wuerselen, Germany

TOWERS PERRIN FORSTER & CROSBY INC   245 Park Ave, New York, NY 10167,
  Tel: (212) 309-3400
  (Management consulting)
    Towers, Perrin, Forster & Crosby, Im Trutz 55, 6000 Frankfurt/Main 1, Germany

TRACOR INC   6500 Tracor Lane, Austin, TX 78721, Tel: (512) 926-2800
  (Time & frequency prdts, gas & liquid chromatographs, eng serv, ship repair)
    Tracor GmbH, Freiherr Von-Stein-Str. 24, D-6000 Frankfurt/Main, Germany

TRANE CO   3600 Pammel Creek Rd, La Crosse, WI 54601, Tel: (608) 787-2000
  (Mfr A/C equip)
    Trane Klima Technisches Buero GmbH, Herbartstr. 61, D-8500 Nuernberg, Germany
    Trane Klima und Kaeltetechnisches Buero GmbH, Untertaxetweg 122,
      D-8035 Munich-Gautin, Germany
    Trane Technisches Buero Berlin GmbH, Fischottersteig 3, D-1000 Berlin 33, Germany
    Trane Technisches Buero Dusseldorf GmbH, Postfach 321147, Munsterstr. 157,

(cont)

D-4000 Dusseldorf 30, Germany
Trane Technisches Buero Frankfurt GmbH, Schoene Aussicht 6, D-6457 Maintal 1,
   Germany
Trane Technisches Buero Hamburg GmbH, J. Ausschlaeger Weg 71, D-2000 Hamburg 26,
   Germany
Trane Technisches Buero Hannover GmbH, Weihbergstr. 63, D-3000 Hannover, Germany
Trane Technisches Buero Stuttgart GmbH, Langenfeldstr. 55, D-7022 Leinfelden,
   Echterdingen 1, Germany

TRANS WORLD AIRLINES INC   605 Third Ave, New York, NY 10158,
   Tel: (212) 557-6107
   (Air transp, hotel, food serv, real estate)
   Trans World Airlines, Inc., Hamburgealle 2-10, D-60001 rankfurt/Main 90, Germany

TRANSAMERICA DELAVAL INC   3450 Princeton Pike, PO Box 6550, Lawrenceville,
   NJ 08648, Tel: (609) 896-7600
   (Steam turbines, compressors, pumps, filtration sys, power transmission equip)
   Delaval Turbine GmbH, Dorn-Assenheimer-Str. 27, 6361 Reichelsheim 4, Germany
   Transamerica Instruments, Postfach 100262, 6360 Friedberg/Hessen, Germany

TRIBOL   21031 Ventura Blvd, #600, Woodland Hills, CA 91364,
   Tel: (818) 888-0808
   (Mfr industrial lubricants)
   Tribol GmbH, Erkelenzer Strasse 20, D-4050 Moenchengladbach 5, Germany

TRINOVA CORP   3000 Strayer, PO Box 50, Maumee, OH 43537, Tel: (419) 867-2200
   (Mfr engr components & sys for ind)
   Aeroquip GmbH, Ruhrstrasse 11, PO Box 2060, 7570 Baden-Baden, Germany
   Aeroquip Steiling GmbH, Eschborner Lanstr. 145-157, D-6000 Frankfurt/Main, Germany
   IBM Systemtechnik, Jahnstrasse 27, D-6451 Mainhausen 1, Germany
   Vickers Systems GmbH, Frolingstrasse 41, Box 2444, 6380 Bad Homburg, Germany

TRION INC   101 McNeil Rd, PO Box 760, Sanford, NC 27330, Tel: (919) 775-2201
   (Mfr air cleaners & electrostatic fluid depositors)
   Trion GmbH, Kapellenstrasse 95, 5000 Koln 50 (Rondorf), Germany

TRW INC   1900 Richmond Rd, Cleveland, OH 44124, Tel: (216) 291-7000
   (Electr & energy-related prdts, automotive & aerospace prdts, tools & fasteners)
   Repa Feinstanzwerk GmbH, 7071 Lindach Ueber, Schwaebisch Guend, Germany
   TRW Carr Europe, Rennbahnstr. 72, D-6000 Frankfurt 71, Germany
   Teves-Thompson GmbH, 3013 Barsinghausen, Hannover, Germany
   Werner Messmer GmbH, Industriestrasse 2-8, D-7760 Radolfzell am Bodensee, Germany

TURCO PRODUCTS INC   7300 Bolsa Ave, Westminster, CA 92684-3600,
   Tel: (714) 890-3600
   (Mfr chem cleaning compounds & equip)
   Turco Chemie GmbH, Postfach 3233, D-2 Hamburg 76, Germany

U S INDUSTRIES INC   PO Box 629, Evansville, IN 47704, Tel: (812) 425-2428
   (Diversified prdts & sys for industry, agribusiness & retail markets)
   Big Dutchman (Deutschland) GmbH, Postfach 1429, D-2849 Vechta, Germany

UNION CAMP CORP   1600 Valley Rd, Wayne, NJ 07470, Tel: (201) 628-2000
   (Flavors, fragrances, essential oils, aroma chems, corrugated containers)
   Bush Boake Allen GmbH, AM Torfberg 60, D-5166 Kreuzau 2, Germany

UNION CARBIDE CORP   Old Ridgebury Rd, Danbury, CT 06817, Tel: (203) 794-2000
(Carbon prdts, chems, plastics, gases & related prdts, etc)
   UC Deutschland GmbH, Morsenbroicher Weg 200, D-4000 Dusseldorf 30, Germany
   UC Deutschland GmbH, Kaiserswertherstr. 82, D-4030 Ratingen, Germany
   UC Deutschland GmbH, Postfach 360, Maurerstr. 42-44, D-5110 Alsdorf, Germany

UNION SPECIAL CORP   222 No LaSalle, Chicago, IL 60601, Tel: (312) 606-9500
(Mfr ind sewing machs)
   Union Special GmbH, Schwabstr. 33, D-7000 Stuttgart 1, Germany

UNIROYAL INC   World Headquarters, Middlebury, CT 06749, Tel: (203) 573-2000
(Tires, tubes & other rubber prdts, chems, plastics, textiles)
   Uniroyal GmbH, Huttenstr. 44, Aachen 1, Germany

UNISYS CORP   PO Box 500, Blue Bell, PA 19424, Tel: (215) 542-4011
(Mfg/mktg/serv electr info sys)
   Geschaftsbereich, Postfach 1110, 6231 Sulzbach/Ts., Germany

UNITED AIRLINES INC   PO Box 66100, Chicago, IL 60666, Tel: (708) 952-4000
(Air transp)
   United Airlines, Munchenerstr. 7, D-6000 Frankfurt/Main, Germany

UNITED CATALYSTS INC   1227 S 12th St, Louisville, KY 40210,
Tel: (502) 637-9751
(Catalysts for petroleum, chem & food inds)
   Sud-Chemie AG, Sparte Katalysatoren, Postfach 202240, Lenbachplatz 6,
     D-8000 Munich 2, Germany

UNITED INDUSTRIAL CORP   18 E 48th St, New York, NY 10017, Tel: (212) 752-8787
(Hospital equip & supplies, re- search & development of military items under defense
contracts)
   Schlieker Electronic GmbH, Kepserstrasse, D-8050 Freising, Germany

UNITED TECHNOLOGIES CORP   United Technologies Bldg, Hartford, CT 06101,
Tel: (203) 728-7000
(Mfr aircraft engines, elevators, A/C, auto equip, space & military electr, rocket
propulsion sys)
   Carrier GmbH, Beckmesserstr. 4, D-8000 Munich 81, Germany
   Carrier GmbH, Aarstr. 247, D-6204 Taunusstein 4, Germany
   Carrier GmbH, Vogelsbergstr. 3, D-6082 Moerfelden-Walldorf, Germany
   Flohr Otis GmbH, Fichrstr. 1-10, Berlin 27 (Borsigwalde), Germany
   Flohr Otis GmbH, Wichmannstr. 5, D-1000 Berlin 30, Germany
   Flohr Otis GmbH, Industriestr. 2, D-3060 Stadthagen, Germany

UNITEK CORP/3M   2724 S Peck Rd, Monrovia, CA 91016-7118, Tel: (818) 574-4000
(Mfr orthodontic prdts)
   Inter-Unitek GmbH, Boschstrasse 10, 8039 Puchheim, Germany

UOP INC   Ten UOP Plaza, Des Plaines, IL 60016, Tel: (708) 391-2000
(Diversified research, development & mfr of ind prdts & sys mgmt studies & serv)
   Universal Matthey Products (Deutschland) GmbH, Emderstr. 107, D-8000 Koln-Niehl,
     Cologne, Germany

UPJOHN CO   7000 Portage Rd, Kalamazoo, MI 49001, Tel: (616) 323-4000
(Pharms, agric prdts, ind chems)
   Upjohn GmbH, Graf von Galenstr., D-6148 Heppenheim, Germany

USAIR INC   2345 Crystal Dr, Arlington, VA 22227, Tel: (703) 418-7000
  (Airline)
    USAir, Inc., Rhein/Main Flughafen, PO Box 222, D-6000 Frankfurt 75, Germany

USF&G FINANCIAL SERVICES CORP   100 Light St, Baltimore, MD 21202,
  Tel: (301) 547-3000
  (Investment mgt, real estate, computer leasing, fin prdt mktg & admin, strategic
  consult)
    Cocret Leasing GmbH, Ratinger Strasse 23, 4000 Dusseldorf 1, Germany

VALERON CORP   750 Stephenson Highway, Troy, MI 48084, Tel: (313) 589-1000
  (Cemented carbide, high speed steel, ceramic & diamond cutting tool prdts, etc)
    Valentine-Modco GmbH, Zentralverkaufsbuero, Lowenstr. 12, D-6090 Russelsheim/Main,
      Germany

VARIAN ASSOCIATES INC   611 Hansen Way, Palo Alto, CA 94304-1030,
  Tel: (415) 493-4000
  (Mfr microwave tubes & devices, analytical instru, semiconductor process & med equip,
  vacuum sys)
    Varian GmbH, Alsfelderstr. 6, Postfach 111435, D-6100 Darmstadt, Germany

VEEDER-ROOT CO   125 Powder Forest Dr, PO Box 2003, Simsbury, CT 06070-2003,
  Tel: (203) 651-2700
  (Mfr counting, controlling & sensing devices)
    Veeder-Root GmbH, Postfach 1110, D-7303 Neuhausen/Filder, Germany

VELSICOL CHEMICAL CORP   5600 N River Rd, Rosemont, IL 60018,
  Tel: (708) 698-9700
  (Pesticides & ind chems)
    Velsicol Chemical GmbH, Vordenbergstr. 16, D-7000 Stuttgart 1, Germany

VENDO CO   7209 N Ingram, Pinedale, CA 93650, Tel: (209) 439-1770
  (Coin-op automatic vending machs)
    Vendo GmbH, Kleberstr. 2, Postfach 100527, Germany

VF CORP   PO Box 1022, Reading, PA 19603, Tel: (215) 378-1151
  (Mfr/mktg apparel)
    H.D. Lee GmbH, GIB-Gewerbepark Rodenkirchen, Haus 21, Ober Buschweg 54,
      5000 Koln 50, Germany

VITRAMON INC   PO Box 544, Bridgeport, CT 06601, Tel: (203) 268-6261
  (Ceramic capacitors)
    Vitramon GmbH, Muhlbachstr. 7, Postfach 1420, D-7150 Backnang-Waldrems, Germany

VIVITAR CORP   9350 Desoto Ave, Chatsworth, CA 91313, Tel: (818) 700-2890
  (Photographic equip, electr supplies)
    Vivitar Photo-Electronik GmbH, Vivitarstr. 7-9, Postfach 1564, D-6238 Hofheim/Ts,
      Germany

WALKER MFG CO   1201 Michigan Blvd, Racine, WI 53402, Tel: (414) 632-8871
  (Automotive parts, exhaust sys, service equip)
    Walker Deutschland GmbH, Industriestr. 22, D-6806 Vierheim, Germany
    Walker Deutschland GmbH, Industriestr. 22, Postfach 1480, D-6806 Viernheim, Germany

WALLACE & TIERNAN DIV   25 Main St, Belleville, NJ 07109, Tel: (201) 759-8000
  (Chems, instru)
    Wallace & Tiernan Chlorator GmbH, D-7501 Groetzingen, Germany
    Wallace & Tiernan GmbH, Postfach 49, D-8870 Guenzburg/Main, Germany

WANG LABORATORIES INC   1 Industrial Ave, Lowell, MA 01851,
  Tel: (508) 459-5000
  (Mfr computer info processing sys)
    Wang Laboratories GmbH, Lyonerstr. 38, Postfach 710570, D-6000 Frankfurt, Germany

WARD HOWELL INTL INC   99 Park Ave, New York, NY 10016, Tel: (212) 697-3730
  (Executive recruiting)
    Ward Howell International GmbH, Cecilienallee 74, D-4000 Dusseldorf 1, Germany

WARNER BROS INC   4000 Warner Blvd, Burbank, CA 91522, Tel: (213) 954-6000
  (Prod/dist motion picture films, TV, music recording & pub)
    Warner Bros. Continental Inc., Kaiserstr. 66, D-6000 Frankfurt, Germany

WARNER ELECTRIC BRAKE & CLUTCH CO   449 Gardner St, South Beloit, IL 61080,
  Tel: (815) 389-3771
  (Automotive & ind brakes & clutches)
    Warner Electric GmbH, Nutingerstr., D-7440, Postfach 308, Germany

WARNER-LAMBERT CO   201 Tabor Road, Morris Plains, NJ 07950,
  Tel: (201) 540-2000
  (Mfr ethical & proprietary pharms, confectionary & consumer prdts)
    Goedecke AG, Postfach 569, D-7800 Freiburg 1, Germany

WATERS CHROMATOGRAPHY DIV   34 Maple St, Milford, MA 01757,
  Tel: (617) 478-2000
  (Mfr/distr liquid chromatographic instru/accessories/tech)
    Millipore GmbH, Siemensstr. 20, 6078 Neu-Isenburg, Germany
    Millipore GmbH, Hauptstr. 71-79, D-6236 Eschborn, Germany

WATKINS-JOHNSON CO   3333 Hillview Ave, Palo Alto, CA 94304,
  Tel: (415) 493-4141
  (Defense electronic prdts)
    W-J Intl., Deutschherrenstr. 46, 5300 Bonn 2, Germany

WEATHERFORD INTL INC   1360 Post Oak Blvd, PO Box 27608, Houston,
  TX 77227-9917, Tel: (713) 439-9400
  (Tubular & cementation servs, prdts & equip; water jetting servs, mfr marine pedestal
  cranes)
    Weatherford Oil Tool GmbH, Hainhauser Weg 150, D-3012 Langenhagen 6, Germany

WEATHERHEAD DIV   6615 Brotherhood Way, Fort Wayne, IN 46825,
  Tel: (219) 481-3500
  (Mfr fluid power prdts, hose assys, tube & pipe fittings & valves)
    The Weatherhead GmbH, Dieselstr. 14, D-8046 Garching, Germany

WEBER MARKING SYSTEMS INC   711 W Algonquin Rd, Arlington Heights, IL 60005,
  Tel: (708) 364-8500
  (Mfr label printing sys, custom labels)
    Weber Marking Systems GmbH, Postfach 28, D-5463 Unkel/Rhein, Germany

WEIGHT WATCHERS INTL INC   Jericho Atrium, 500 North Broadway, Jericho,
  NY 11753-2196, Tel: (516) 939-0400
  (Weight reduction programs, food prdts)
    Weight Watchers (Deutschland) GmbH, Uhlandstr. 9, 4000 Dusseldorf, Germany

WELCH ALLYN INC   State St Rd, Box 220, Skaneateles Falls, NY 13153,
  Tel: (315) 685-5788
  (Illuminated med devices, fiber optics, miniature lamps, etc)
    Welch Allyn GmbH, Strasse der Republik 17-19, Wiesbaden, Germany

WEST CO INC   West Bridge St, Phoenixville, PA 19460, Tel: (215) 935-4500
  (Pharm packaging comps)
    Pharma-Gummi West GmbH, Postfach 1419/1420, Stolbergerstr. 21-41, 5180 Eschweiler,
      Germany
    Pharma-Metall, Eifelstr. 63, 5190 Stolberg-Vicht, Germany

WESTINGHOUSE AIR BRAKE CO   40 W 40th St, New York, NY 10018,
  Tel: (212) 840-5440
  (Equip for transp, constr, mining inds)
    Continental Automotive Products Group, WABCO Fahrzeugbremsen, Postfach 911280,
      D-3000 Hannover 91, Germany
    WABCO Fluid Power Europe, WABCO Steuerungstechnik GmbH & Co., Postfach 91 12 70,
      Bartweg 13, D-3000 Hannover 91, Germany
    Westinghouse Bremsen-und Apparatebau GmbH, Postfach 21-280, Am Lindener Hafen 21,
      D-3000 Hannover/Linden, Germany

WESTINGHOUSE ELECTRIC CORP   Westinghouse Bldg, Gateway Center, Pittsburgh,
  PA 15222, Tel: (412) 244-2000
  (TV/radio broadcasting, mfr electr sys for ind/defense, fin & environmental servs)
    H. Maihak AG, Samperstr. 38, D-2000 Hamburg 60, Germany
    Westinghouse Controlmatic GmbH, Postfach 560200, D-6000 Frankfurt 56, Germany

WHEELABRATOR-FRYE INC   11255 N Torrey Pines Rd, La Jolla, CA 92037,
  Tel: (603) 926-5911
  (Diversified environmental & energy sys, chems, precision & ind equip)
    Deutsche Wheelabrator, Strahlmittel GmbH, Hansaring 49-51, D-5000 Cologne, Germany
    Wheelabrator Metallreinigungs GmbH, Gruenewalderstr. 14-22, D-5650 Solingen, Germany

WICKMAN CORP   10325 Capital Ave, Oak Park, MI 48237, Tel: (313) 548-3822
  (Imported mach tools)
    A.u.W. Busch Maschinen, Hammerstr. 15, D-5820 Gevelsberg 1, Germany

WINCHESTER ELECTRONICS   400 Park Rd, Watertown, CT 06795, Tel: (203) 274-8891
  (Mfr connectors, component parts)
    Winchester Electronics, Otto-Hahn Strasse 8, D-7100 Heinbronn, Biberach, Germany

WINTHROP LABORATORIES   90 Park Ave, New York, NY 10016, Tel: (212) 907-2000
  (Pharms)
    Winthrop GmbH, Fischerfeldstr. 13, D-6000 Frankfurt/Main, Germany

WOOLWORTH CORP   Woolworth Bldg, 233 Broadway, New York, NY 10279,
  Tel: (212) 553-2000
  (Retail stores)
    F.W. Woolworth Co. GmbH, Buerostadt Niederrad, D-6000 Frankfurt/Main 71, Germany

WORCESTER CONTROLS CORP   33 Lott Dr, Marlboro, MA 01752, Tel: (508) 481-4800
  (Mfr ball valves, control devices)
    Worcester Controls Deutschland GmbH, c/o Coopers & Lybrand, Hansa Allee 2,
      D-6000 Frankfurt, Germany

WORLD COMMUNICATIONS INC   67 Broad St, New York, NY 10004,
  Tel: (212) 607-2000
  (Intl private line services)
    World Communications Inc., Ruester Strasse 13, Frankfurt/Main 6000, Germany

WRIGHT LINE INC   160 Gold Star Blvd, Worcester, MA 01606, Tel: (508) 852-4300
  (Mfr filing sys)
    Wright Line GmbH, Waechtersbacherstr. 61, D-6000 Frankfurt/Main 61, Germany

WM WRIGLEY JR CO   410 N Michigan Ave, Chicago, IL 60611-4287,
  Tel: (312) 644-2121
  (Chewing gum)
    Deutsche Wrigley GmbH, Albert Schweitzer Str. 64, Postfach 830252,
      D-8000 Munich 83, Germany

WURLITZER CO   422 Wards Corner Rd, Loveland, OH 45140, Tel: (513) 576-4601
  (Pianos, electronic organs & pianos, vending & pay phonograph machs)
    Wurlitzer International, Ltd., Postfach 1180, D-4995 Stemwede 1, Germany

YARDNEY TECHNICAL PRODUCTS INC   82 Mechanic St, Pawcatuck, CT 06379,
  Tel: (203) 599-1100
  (Mfr high energy batteries)
    Silberkraft Leichtakkumulatoren GmbH, Meidericher Strabe 6-8, Postfach 100552,
      D-4100 Duisburg 1, Germany

YORK INTERNATIONAL CORP   PO Box 1592, York, PA 17405-1592,
  Tel: (715) 771-7890
  (Mfr A/C, heating & refrig sys & equip)
    Brown Boveri-York, Kalte und Klimatechnik GmbH, Postfach 100465, D-6800 Mannheim 1,
      Germany

YOUNG & RUBICAM INTL INC   285 Madison Ave, New York, NY 10017,
  Tel: (212) 210-3000
  (Advertising agency)
    Young & Rubicam GmbH Werbung, Postfach 4665, Bleichstr. 64, D-6000 Frankfurt/Main,
      Germany

ZIPPERTUBING CO   13000 S Broadway, PO Box 61248, Los Angeles, CA 90061,
  Tel: (213) 321-3901
  (Mfr zip-on plastic tubing, wire markers, pipe insulation)
    Zipper-Technik GmbH, Hugenottenallee 129, D-6078 Neu-Isenburg, Germany

GHANA

AMERICAN STANDARDS TESTING BUREAU INC   40 Water St, New York, NY 10004,
  Tel: (212) 943-3157
  (Consulting engineers)
    Premier Consultancy & Resource Development Ltd., P.O. Box 6729, Accra, Ghana

CIGNA CORP   One Liberty Place, 1650 Market St, Philadelphia, PA 19101,
  Tel: (215) 523-4000
  (Ins, invest, health care & other fin servs)
    Crusader Co. (Ghana) Ltd., Samlotte House, Kwame Nkrumah Ave., Accra, Ghana

DE LEUW CATHER & CO   1133 15th St NW, Washington, DC 20005,
  Tel: (202) 775-3300
  (Consulting engineers)
    De Leuw, Cather Intl. Ltd., P.O. Box 207, Accra, Ghana

FOXBORO CO   33 Commercial St, Foxboro, MA 02035, Tel: (508) 543-8750
  (Mfr prdts/provide servs for ind automation)
    Sonic Control & Engineering Services Ltd., P.O. Box 8232, Tema, Ghana

H J HEINZ CO   PO Box 57, Pittsburgh, PA 15230, Tel: (412) 456-5100
  (Food prdts)
    H.J. Heinz Co, Tema, Ghana

INA CORPORATION   1600 Arch St, Philadelphia, PA 19101, Tel: (215) 523-5335
  (Holding co: ins, financial serv)
    P.J. Everett & Co., Ltd., P.O. Box 199, Granville Ave., Accra, Ghana

S C JOHNSON & SON INC   1525 Howe St, Racine, WI 53403, Tel: (414) 631-2000
  (Home, auto, commercial & personal care prdts, specialty chems)
    Johnson's Wax Ltd., P.O. Box 5249, Accra, Ghana

LINTAS:WORLDWIDE   1 Dag Hammarskjold Plaza, New York, NY 10017,
  Tel: (212) 605-8000
  (Advertising agency)
    Lintas:Accra, Ad Vantage House, Klanaa St., Osu (Ako Adsei Park), Accra, Ghana

MARS INC   6885 Elm St, McLean, VA 22101, Tel: (703) 821-4900
  (Mfr candy, snack foods, cat food)
    Mars Ltd., Airport, P.O. Box M 109, Accra, Ghana

MOBIL CORP   150 E 42nd St, New York, NY 10017, Tel: (212) 883-4242
  (Petroleum explor, prdts)
    Mobil Oil Ghana Ltd., P.O. Box 450, Accra, Ghana

NCR CORP   1700 S Patterson Blvd, Dayton, OH 45479, Tel: (513) 445-2000
(Develop/mfr/sell/serv business info processing sys)
   NCR Ghana Ltd., Kwame Nkrumah Ave., P.O. Box 1010, Accra, Ghana

ONAN CORP   1400 73rd Ave NE, Minneapolis, MN 55432, Tel: (612) 574-5000
(Electric generators, ind engines & controls)
   West Afrika Machinery & Tractor Co., P.O. Box 5896, 13 Abrebresem St., Osu Xborg,
      Ghana

PFIZER INC   235 E 42nd St, New York, NY 10017, Tel: (212) 573-2323
(Mfr pharms, hosp prdts, chems, consumer & animal health prdts)
   Pfizer Ltd., P.O. Box 1610, Accra, Ghana

PHILLIPS PETROLEUM CO   Phillips Bldg, Bartlesville, OK 74004,
   Tel: (918) 661-6600
(Crude oil, natural gas, liquefied petroleum gas, gasoline & petro-chems)
   Phillips Petroleum Co. (Ghana), Private Post Box, Central Post Office, Accra, Ghana

SGS CONTROL SERVICES INC   42 Broadway, New York, NY 10004,
   Tel: (212) 482-8700
(Complete range of quality & quantity control checks & related tech serv)
   S.G.S. Ghana Ltd., No. D 657/4, Kojo Thompson Rd., Tudu, P.O. Box 732, Accra, Ghana

WILBUR SMITH ASSOCS   NCNB Tower, PO Box 92, Columbia, SC 29202,
   Tel: (803) 738-0580
(Consulting engineers)
   Wilbur Smith Associates Inc., 82 Palace St., North Kaneshie, Accra, Ghana

STAR-KIST FOODS INC   180 E Ocean Blvd, Long Beach, CA 90802,
   Tel: (213) 590-7900
(Fish, fish by-prdts, pet foods)
   Star-Kist Intl. S.A., P.O. Box 40, Tema, Ghana

TEXACO INC   2000 Westchester Ave, White Plains, NY 10650, Tel: (914) 253-4000
(Explor/mktg crude oil & its prdts, petro-chems)
   Texaco Ghana Ltd., P.O. Box 526, Texaco Bldg., Derby Ave., Accra, Ghana

UNION CAMP CORP   1600 Valley Rd, Wayne, NJ 07470, Tel: (201) 628-2000
(Flavors, fragrances, essential oils, aroma chems, corrugated containers)
   W. J. Bush & Co. Ltd., P.O. Box 489, Takoradi, Ghana

UNION CARBIDE CORP   Old Ridgebury Rd, Danbury, CT 06817, Tel: (203) 794-2000
(Carbon prdts, chems, plastics, gases & related prdts, etc)
   UC Ghana Ltd., P.O. Box 2085, Accra, Ghana
   UC Ghana Ltd., Plot No. 18/6 Industrial Area, Tema, Ghana

GREECE

3M CO   3M Center, St Paul, MN 55144-1000, Tel: (612) 733-1110
(Mfr abrasives, adhesives, chems, ind & consumer tapes/diskettes, health care prdts, elec connectors)
  3M Hellas Ltd., Kifissias 20, GR151 25 Maroussi, Greece

ABBOTT LABORATORIES   Abbott Park, North Chicago, IL 60064,
Tel: (312) 937-6100
(Pharm & lab prdts)
  Abbott Laboratories (Hellas) S.A., 194 Syngrou Ave., Athens, Greece

ACADEMIC PRESS INC   111 Fifth Ave, New York, NY 10003, Tel: (212) 741-6800
(Publ scientific books)
  Intl. Publishers Representatives, 3 Mitropleos St., Athens 18, Greece

AFIA   110 William St, New York, NY 10038, Tel: (212) 964-4990
(Insurance)
  AIFA Worldwide Insurance, Athens, Greece

ALARM DEVICE MFG CO   165 Eileen Way, Syosset, NY 11791, Tel: (516) 921-6704
(Security, fire & burglary sys)
  Ademc-Middle East Dir., 80 Sp. Merkouri St., Pagrati, Athens 116 34, Greece

ALLIED-SIGNAL INC   Columbia Rd & Park Ave, PO Box 2245R, Morristown,
NJ 07960, Tel: (201) 455-2000
(Mfr aerospace & automotive prdts, engineered materials)
  Allied-Signal Aerospace Co., P.O. Box 65039, 15410 Psychico, Athens, Greece

AMERICAN BUREAU OF SHIPPING   45 Eisenhower Dr, Paramus, NJ 07653-0910,
Tel: (201) 368-9100
(Classification/certification of ships & offshore structures, devel & tech assistance)
  American Bureau of Shipping, Akti Miaouli & Filellinon St. 1-3, P.O. Box 80139,
    GR185 10 Pireaus, Greece

AMERICAN CYANAMID CO   1 Cyanamid Plaza, Wayne, NJ 07470, Tel: (201) 831-2000
(Pharms, chems, agric & consumer prdts)
  American Cyanamid Co., P.O. Box 61009, 15100 Amaroussion, Athens, Greece

AMERICAN EXPRESS CO   American Express Tower, New York, NY 10285-4765,
Tel: (212) 640-2000
(Diversified fin & travel-related serv)
  American Express Intl. A.E., Constitution´Sq., Athens, Greece
  American Express Intl. A.E., 10 Venizelou St., Salonica, Greece
  American Express Intl. Banking Corp., 26 Akti Poseidonos, Piraeus, Greece
  American Express Travel Service, Athens Hilton Hotel, Athens, Greece

AMERICAN HOME PRODUCTS CORP   685 Third Ave, New York, NY 10017,
  Tel: (212) 878-5800
  (Drugs, food, household prdts)
    Wyeth Hellas, Athens, Greece

AMERICAN INTL UNDERWRITERS CORP   70 Pine St, New York, NY 10270,
  Tel: (212) 770-7000
  (General ins)
    N.A. Canellopoulos - Cristos Adamantiades S.A., 8 Dragatsaniou St., Athens 122,
      Greece

AMERICAN LIFE INSURANCE CO (ALICO)   PO Box 2226, Wilmington, DE 19899,
  Tel: (302) 594-2000
  (Life ins, pension & annuity plans, health prdts)
    American Life Insurance Co., P.O. Box 8356, Omonia, Athens 100 10, Greece
    American Life Insurance Co., Alico Bldg., 119 Kifisias Ave., Marousi 151 24,
      Attiki, Greece

AMERICAN STANDARDS TESTING BUREAU INC   40 Water St, New York, NY 10004,
  Tel: (212) 943-3157
  (Consulting engineers)
    American Standards Bureau Inc., 16 Nikis St., Athens 118, Greece

AMPEX CORP   401 Broadway, Redwood City, CA 94063-3199, Tel: (415) 367-2011
  (Mfr professional audio/visual sys, magnetic recording media, data-memory prdts)
    Ampex World Operations S.A., Athens, Greece

ARBOR ACRES FARM INC   41 Marlborough Rd, Glastonbury, CT 06033,
  Tel: (203) 633-4681
  (Producers of male & female broiler breeders, commercial egg layers)
    Hellenic Livestock Development, 28 Vas. Constandinou St., Athens 501, Greece

ARGO INTL   140 Franklin St, New York, NY 10013, Tel: (212) 431-1700
  (Distr mach & elec com for marine & ind use)
    Argo Intl. Corp. (Hellas), 1 Skouze St., Piraeus, Greece

ASSOCIATED MERCHANDISING CORP   1440 Broadway, New York, NY 10018,
  Tel: (212) 536-4000
  (Retail service organization)
    Associated Merchandising Corp., 220 Messagion St., Holargos, GR 155-61 Athens,
      Greece

AT&T INTERNATIONAL   295 N Maple Ave, Basking Ridge, NJ 07920,
  Tel: (908) 221-2000
  (Telecommun)
    AT&T Intl. (Greece) Ltd., 23-25 Lekka St., Athens 105 62, Greece

BAKER OIL TOOLS   PO Box 3048, Houston, TX 77253, Tel: (713) 923-9351
  (Oil/gas well completions equip)
    Baker Eastern S.A., 38 Kifissias Ave., Paradissos-Amaroussiou, Athens, Greece

BALTIMORE SPICE CO   Reisterstown Rd, Harrison, MD 21055, Tel: (301) 363-1700
  (Additives & chem mixtures for food ind)
    Baltimore Spice Hellas Ltd., 88 Levadias St., Nikea, Piraeus, Greece

BANKAMERICA CORP   PO Box 37000, San Francisco, CA 94137, Tel: (415) 622-3456
  (Financial services)
    Bank of America, 39 Panepistomiou St., P.O. Box 630, Athens, Greece

BANKERS TRUST CO   280 Park Ave, New York, NY 10017, Tel: (212) 775-2500
  (Banking)
    Bankers Trust Co., 3 Stadiou St., Athens, Greece

BARDAHL MFG CORP   1400 N W 52nd St, PO Box 70607, Seattle, WA 98107,
  Tel: (206) 783-4851
  (Lubricating oils)
    Biniaris Brothers S.A., 35 Piraeus St., Moschaton, Athens, Greece

BAROID DIV   513 Travis Liberty, PO Box 1675, Houston, TX 77001,
  Tel: (713) 456-0176
  (Specialized materials for use in drilling)
    Baroid Intl., 274 Messoghion, Holargos, Athens, Greece

BENTLEY LABORATORIES INC   17502 Armstrong Ave, Irvine, CA 92714,
  Tel: (714) 546-8020
  (Mfr para-med devices)
    Bentley Labs Ltd., 4 Aphroditi St., Pendeli, Attiki, Greece

BENTLY NEVADA CORP   PO Box 157, Minden, NV 89423, Tel: (702) 782-3611
  (Electronic monitoring system)
    Tesims S.A., P.O. Box 80285, GR-185, 10 Piraeus, Greece

BLACK & DECKER CORP   701 E Joppa Road, Towson, MD 21204, Tel: (301) 583-3900
  (Mfr portable elect & pneumatic power tools, household prdts)
    Black & Decker Ltd., 3-5 Xanthou St., P.O. Box 16, Tavros, Athens, Greece

BOSE CORP   100 The Mountain Rd, Framingham, MA 01701, Tel: (617) 879-7330
  (Electronic equip)
    Bose Greece B.V., 35 Xenokratous St., Kolonaki, Athens, Greece

BRANSON ULTRASONICS CORP   Eagle Rd, Danbury, CT 06810, Tel: (203) 796-0400
  (Ultrasonic & vibratory plastics assembly mach)
    Control Technik, 22 King Georgiou St., Athens 516, Greece

LEO BURNETT CO INC   35 West Wacker Dr, Chicago, IL 60601, Tel: (312) 220-5959
  (Advertising agency)
    EURO/Leo Burnett, 371 Sigrou Ave., 175 64 Athens, Greece

CARL BYOIR & ASSOCIATES INC   380 Madison Ave, New York, NY 10017,
  Tel: (212) 986-6100
  (Public relations consultants)
    C&A Public Relations Svcs., 5 Militiadou St., 155 22 Holargos, Athens, Gerrce

CANADA DRY INTL CORP   2600 Century Pkwy, Atlanta, GA 30345,
  Tel: (404) 753-2182
  (Carbonated beverages, soft drinks extract)
    Can Drinks Hellas, 12 Dimokritou St., Athens 134, Greece

CARNATION INTL CO   5045 Wilshire Blvd, Los Angeles, CA 90036,
  Tel: (213) 932-6000
  (Milk prdts)
    Carnation Hellas A.E.B.E., Marathonos & Anthoussis Ave., Pallini, Attikis, Greece

CHASE MANHATTAN BANK N A   1 Chase Manhattan Plaza, New York, NY 10081,
  Tel: (212) 552-2222
  (Intl banking)
    The Chase Manhattan Bank NA, 3 Korai St., P.O. Box 5, Athens, Greece

CHRISTENSEN INTL   PO Box 26135, Salt Lake City, UT 84126, Tel: (801) 487-5371
  (Diamond drills)
    Christensen Diamond Greece, Athens Tower, Athens 610, Greece

CIGNA CORP   One Liberty Place, 1650 Market St, Philadelphia, PA 19101,
  Tel: (215) 523-4000
  (Ins, invest, health care & other fin servs)
    Cigna Insurance Co. (Hellas) SA, Phidippidou #2, Ampelokipi, 11526 Athens, Greece
    Cigna Insurance Co. of Europe SA-NV, Apollo Tower- 17/F, 115-23 Athens, Greece

CITIBANK NA   399 Park Ave, New York, NY 10043, Tel: (212) 559-1000
  (Intl banking)
    Citibank, N.A., P.O. Box 1617, 8 Othonos St., Athens, Greece
    Citibank, N.A., P.O. Box 1720, 2 Xanthou St., Constitution Sq., Athens, Greece
    Citibank, N.A., P.O. Box 99, 47/49 Akti Miaouli, Piraeus, Greece
    Citibank, N.A., P.O. Box 356, 21 Tsimiski St., Thessaloniki, Greece
    Citibank, N.A., Mid-East/North Africa Div., P.O. Box 1720, 24 Kanari St.,
      Kolonaki Sq., Athens, Greece

CLEMCO INDUSTRIES CORP   2177 Jerrold Ave, San Francisco, CA 94124,
  Tel: (415) 282-7290
  (Sandblast equip & accessories)
    Clemco Hellas Ltd., 46 Alexandras Ave., Athens 707, Greece

THE COCA-COLA CO   310 North Ave NW, PO Box Drawer 1734, Atlanta, GA 30313,
  Tel: (404) 676-2121
  (Mfr & sale of soft drink syrups & concentrates, juices & food prdts, motion pic & TV
  prod)
    The Coca-Cola Co. Greece, all mail to: U.S. address

COLGATE-PALMOLIVE CO   300 Park Ave, New York, NY 10022, Tel: (212) 310-2000
  (Pharms, cosmetics, toiletries, detergents)
    Colgate-Palmolive (Hellas) S.A., 89 Athinon St., Piraeus, Greece

COLUMBIA PICTURES INDUSTRIES INC   711 Fifth Ave, New York, NY 10022,
  Tel: (212) 751-4400
  (Producer & distributor of motion pictures)
    Columbia Pictures Hellas SARL, 2 Capodistria St., Athens 147, Greece

COMBUSTION ENGINEERING INC   900 Long Ridge Road, Stamford, CT 06902,
  Tel: (203) 329-8771
  (Tech constr)
    Combustion Engineering Overseas Inc., 17 Varis Varkizis, Voula, Greece

COMPTON INTERNATIONAL   625 Madison Ave, New York, NY 10022,
  Tel: (212) 754-1100
  (Advertising)
    Adel Hellenic Advertising Co. S.A., 120 Syngrou Ave., Athens, Greece

CONTROL DATA CORP   8100 34th Ave S, Minneapolis, MN 55440,
  Tel: (612) 853-8100
  (Control data equip, computer sys serv & financial serv)
    Control Data Holding A.G., 194 Syngrou Ave., Athens, Greece

CPC INTERNATIONAL INC   PO Box 8000, International Plaza, Englewood Cliffs,
  NJ 07632, Tel: (201) 894-4000
  (Mfr consumer food prdts & corn refining prdts)
    Knorr (Hellas) A.B.E.E., 282 Kifissias, GR-15232 Halandri, Athens, Greece

D'ARCY MASIUS BENTON & BOWLES INC (DMB&B)   1675 Broadway, New York,
  NY 10019, Tel: (212) 468-3622
  (Advertising & communications)
    DMB&B Ergon Ltd., 8 Koumbari St., GR 106 74 Athens, Greece

DDB NEEDHAM WORLDWIDE INC   437 Madison Ave, New York, NY 10022,
  Tel: (212) 415-2000
  (Advertising)
    Olympic DDB Needham SA, 124 Kifissias Ave., 115-26 Athens, Greece

DIAMOND SHAMROCK CORP   1100 Superior Ave, Cleveland, OH 44114,
  Tel: (216) 694-5000
  (Organic & inorganic chems & specialties, agric chems)
    Diamond Shamrock Corp., 255 Syngrou Ave., Athens, Greece

DOW CORNING CORP   2220 W Salzburg Rd, PO Box 1767, Midland, MI 48640,
  Tel: (517) 496-4000
  (Silicones, silicon chems, solid lubricants)
    Dow Corning Europe S.A., 9 Dousmani, Glyfada, Athens, Greece

DRESSER INDUSTRIES INC   1600 Pacific Bldg, PO Box 718, Dallas, TX 75221,
  Tel: (214) 740-6000
  (Diversified supplier of equip & tech serv to energy & natural resource ind)
    Mykobar Mining Co. S.A., 188 El Venizelou Ave., P.O. Box 1603, Kallithea,
      Athens 125, Greece

DREW CHEMICAL CORP   One Drew Plaza, Boonton, NJ 07005, Tel: (201) 263-7600
  (Spec chems for ind water & fuel treatment, chem processing)
    Kranios Chemicals S.A., 12 Akti G. Kondyli, P.O. Box 121, Piraeus, Greece

DRIVER-HARRIS CO   308 Middlesex St, Harrison, NJ 07029, Tel: (201) 483-4800
  (Wire, cables, etc)
    Driver-Harris Hellas Ltd., 55 Amyklon, Halandir, Athens, Greece

DROULIA & CO   120 Broadway, New York, NY 10005, Tel: (212) 349-1144
  (Investments)
    Droulia & Co., 3 Stadiou St., Athens 125, Greece

DUKANE CORP   2900 Dukane Drive, St Charles, IL 60174, Tel: (708) 584-2300
  (Communications & sound equip)
    DuKane Corp., 10 Demokritou, Nea Politia, Athens, Greece

EASTMAN KODAK CO   343 State St, Rochester, NY 14650-0518, Tel: (716) 724-4000
  (Devel/mfr photo & chem prdts, info mgmt/video/copier sys, fibers/plastics for
  various ind)
    Kodak (Near East) Inc., 8 Himaras St., Paradissos-Amaroussion, Athens, Greece

EATON CORP   100 Erieview Plaza, Cleveland, OH 44114, Tel: (216) 523-5000
(Advanced tech prdts for transp & ind mkts)
   Eaton Intl. Inc., 6 Queen Frederikis St., Glyfada, Athens, Greece

EBASCO SERVICES INC   2 World Trade Center, New York, NY 10048,
Tel: (212) 839-2685
(Engineering, constr)
   Ebasco Overseas Inc., c/o Public Power Corp., 30 Chalkokondyli St., Athens 102,
     Greece

ECOLAB INC   370 Wabasha St, St Paul, MN 55102, Tel: (612) 293-2233
(Ind & household detergents, cleaning agents & equip)
   Soilax Hellas Ltd., 72 Morgianni & 2 Milou St., Peristeri, Athens, Greece

ETHYL CORP   330 South 4th St, Richmond, VA 23219, Tel: (804) 788-5000
(Chems & plastics)
   Ethyl Hellas Chemical Co. S.A., P.O. Box 260, Thessaloniki, Greece

EXXON CORP   225 E John Carpenter Frwy, Irving, TX 75062, Tel: (214) 444-1000
(Petroleum & petroleum prdts)
   Esso Pappas Industrial Co. A.E., Athens Tower, Athens 610, Greece
   Thessaloniki Refining Co. A.E., Athens Tower, Athens 610, Greece

FMC CORP   200 E Randolph Dr, Chicago, IL 60601, Tel: (312) 861-6000
(Mach & chem for industry, agric & govt)
   FMC Intl. A.G., Agora Center, 10-12 Kifissias Ave., Paradissos, 15125 Athens, Greece

FOOTE CONE & BELDING COMMUNICATIONS INC   101 E Erie St, Chicago,
IL 60611-2897, Tel: (312) 751-7000
(Advertising agency)
   Gnomi/FCB, 350 Syngrou Ave., 17674 Athens, Greece

FOXBORO CO   33 Commercial St, Foxboro, MA 02035, Tel: (508) 543-8750
(Mfr prdts/provide servs for ind automation)
   E. Mokakos, Plateia Agheion, Theodoron 2, Athens GR 105 61, Greece
   Foxboro Co., c/o C.J. Vamvacas, A. Kikolakis, P.O. Box 3113, Athens, Greece

GAMLEN CHEMICAL CO   121 S Maple Ave, S San Francisco, CA 94080,
Tel: (415) 873-1750
(Chems, detergents & tank cleansers)
   Flame Hellas Ltd., 14 Skouze, Piraeus, Greece

GENERAL DYNAMICS CORP   Pierre Laclede Center, St Louis, MO 63105,
Tel: (314) 889-8200
(Mfr aircraft, submarines, missiles, space launch vehicles, bldg prdts, info sys)
   Hellenic Business Development & Investment Co., S.A., 32 Kitisias Ave., 11/F,
     151125 Marousi, Athens, Greece

GENERAL ELECTRIC CO   3135 Easton Tpk, Fairfield, CT 06431,
Tel: (203) 373-2211
(Diversified mfr, tech & servs)
   GE Technical Services, P.O. Box 14075, Athens 11510, Greece

GENERAL MOTORS CORP   3044 W Grand Blvd, Detroit, MI 48202,
Tel: (313) 556-5000
(Automotive prdts, electronics)

(cont)

General Motors Hellas ABEE, P.O. Box 610-20, Amaroussion 151 10, Attica, Greece
General Motors Hellas ABEE, P.O. Box 61020, Amaroussion 15110, Athens, Greece

GOODYEAR TIRE & RUBBER CO   1144 E Market St, Akron, OH   44316-0001,
  Tel: (216) 796-2121
  (Mfr tires, rubber prdts)
    Goodyear Hellas S.A.I.C., 94 Kifissou Ave., P.O. Box 41092, 122 10 Aibaleo, Athens,
    Greece

W R GRACE & CO   1114 Ave of the Americas, New York, NY   10036,
  Tel: (212) 819-5500
  (Specialty chems, natural resources, consumer serv)
    Grace Hellas L.L.C., 20 Lagoumitzi St., Khukaki, Athens, Greece

GRUBMAN & KONTOS   500 E 77th St, New York, NY   10021, Tel: (212) 879-1111
  (Accountants, auditors)
    Kantos & Grubman (Hellas), 36 Voukourestiou, Athens 136, Greece

FRANK B HALL & CO INC   549 Pleasantville Rd, Briarcliff Manor, NY   10510,
  Tel: (914) 769-9200
  (Insurance)
    Astra Group, 302 Syncrou Ave., P.O. Box 75012, Kallithea GR 176 73, Athens. Greece

THE HARPER GROUP INC   260 Townsend St, PO Box 77933, San Francisco,
  CA 94107, Tel: (415) 978-0600
  (Ocean/air freight fwdg, customs brokerage, packing & whse, logistics mgt, ins)
    Circle Freight Intl. (Greece) SA, Syngrou Av., 226 Athens, Greece

HOLIDAY INNS INC   3742 Lamar Ave, Memphis, TN   38195, Tel: (901) 362-4001
  (Hotels, restaurants, casinos)
    Holiday Inns Inc., Michalacopoulou 50, Ilissia, Athens, Greece

INA CORPORATION   1600 Arch St, Philadelphia, PA   19101, Tel: (215) 523-5335
  (Holding co: ins, financial serv)
    Insurance Co. of North America (Hellas) A.E., 2 Fidipidou St., Athens, Greece
    Macrymichalos Brothers S.A., 196 Syngrou Ave., P.O. Box 958, Athens, Greece

INTERMEC CORP   6001 36th Ave West, Everett, WA   98203-9280,
  Tel: (206) 348-2600
  (Mfr automated data collection sys)
    Intermec Hellas, 125 Michalakopoulou Ave., 115-27 Athens, Greece

INTERNATIONAL ELECTRONICS LTD   2440 Reservoir Ave, Trumbull, CT   06611,
  Tel: (203) 372-6501
  (Cathode ray TV picture tubes)
    International Electronics A.E., 74 Academias St., Athens 142, Greece

INTERNATIONAL FLAVORS & FRAGRANCES INC   521 W 57th St, New York, NY   10019,
  Tel: (212) 765-5500
  (Create/mfr flavors, fragrances & aroma chems)
    Intl. Flavors & Fragrances, 16 Iassiou St., Athens 140, Greece

INTERNATIONAL STANDARD ELECTRIC CORP   320 Park Ave, New York, NY   10022,
  Tel: (212) 752-6000
  (Telecommun equip)
    ITT Hellas S.A.I., Telecommunications Div., 171 Syngrou Ave., Athens, Greece

INTERNATIONAL STAPLE & MACHINE CO   PO Box 629, Butler, PA 16001,
  Tel: (412) 287-7711
  (Stapling machs, supplies)
    Em. Co. Coroneas, 19 Aristotlelesstasse, Athens, Greece

ITT CORP   1330 Ave of the Americas, New York, NY 10019, Tel: (212) 258-1000
  (Diversified mfr, tech & services)
    ITT Hellas S.A., 93 Syngrou Ave., Athens, Greece

JOHNSON & JOHNSON   One Johnson & Johnson Plaza, New Brunswick, NJ 08933,
  Tel: (201) 524-0400
  (Surgical, med & baby prdts)
    Janssen Pharmaceutica S.A.C.I., 282 Kifissias Ave., Halandri, Athens, Greece
    Johnson & Johnson Hellas S.A., 246 Kifissias Ave., Halandri, Athens, Greece

S C JOHNSON & SON INC   1525 Howe St, Racine, WI 53403, Tel: (414) 631-2000
  (Home, auto, commercial & personal care prdts, specialty chems)
    S.C. Johnson & Son (Hellas) E.P.E., Messogion Ave., 210 Holargos, Athens, Greece

KEYES FIBRE CO   3003 Summer St, Stamford, CT 06905, Tel: (203) 357-9100
  (Molded containers)
    Heracles Packing Co. S.A., Attica P.O. Box 3500, Athens, Greece

KNOLL INTL   655 Madison Ave, New York, NY 10021, Tel: (212) 826-2400
  (Furniture & fabrics)
    Varangis Avepe S.A., 40 M. Botsari, Pefki, Attica, Greece

LE TOURNEAU INC LONGVIEW DIV   PO Box 2307, Longview, TX 75606,
  Tel: (214) 753-3449
  (Heavy constr, mining mach & equip)
    Eliopoulos Brothers Ltd., 138 Piraeus St., Athens 308, Greece

LEMMON PHARMACAL CO   PO Box 30, Sellersville, PA 18960, Tel: (215) 723-5544
  (Ethical pharms)
    Lemmon Pharmacal Export Corp., 59 Ypsilanti St., Kolonaki, Athens, Greece

LEVI STRAUSS & CO   1155 Battery, San Francisco, CA 94111, Tel: (415) 544-6000
  (Mfr wearing apparel)
    Intl. Clothing Industry S.A., 18 Alkmanos St., Ilisia, Athens 612, Greece

ELI LILLY & CO   307 E McCarty St, Indianapolis, IN 46285, Tel: (317) 261-2000
  (Pharms, agric & cosmetic prdts)
    Eli Lilly (Hellas) L.L.C., 272 Messogion St., Cho Largos, Athens, Greece
    Eli Lilly (Hellas) L.L.C., P.O. Box 5, Aghia Paraskeivi, Attiki, Athens, Greece

LINTAS:WORLDWIDE   1 Dag Hammarskjold Plaza, New York, NY 10017,
  Tel: (212) 605-8000
  (Advertising agency)
    Lintas:Athens, 32 Kifissias Ave., GR-151 25 Maroussi, Athens, Greece

LUBRIZOL CORP   29400 Lakeland Blvd, Wickliffe, OH 44092, Tel: (216) 943-4200
  (Chem additives for lubricants & fuels)
    Lubrizol Intl. S.A., 10 Kokkoni St., Psychikon, Athens, Greece

LYRIC HIGH FIDELITY INC   1221 Lexington Ave, New York, NY 10028,
   Tel: (212) 535-5710
   (Electrical equip)
      Lyric High Fidelity Center (Athens), 52 Alexandras Ave., Athens, Greece

MANUFACTURERS HANOVER TRUST CO   270 Park Ave, New York, NY 10017,
   Tel: (212) 286-6000
   (Banking)
      Manufacturers Hanover Trust Co., 6 Philhellenon St., Athens 118, Greece

MARRIOTT CORP   Marriott Dr, Washington, DC 20058, Tel: (301) 897-9000
   (Lodging, contract food & beverage serv, restaurants)
      Marriott Hellas Airport Services S.A., Athens Airport, East Terminal, Athens, Greece

MARSH & McLENNAN COS INC   1221 Ave of the Americas, New York, NY 10020-1011,
   Tel: (212) 997-2000
   (Insurance)
      Marsh & McLennan-Hellas L.L.C., 124 Kifissias Ave., Ambelokipi, Athens 11526, Greece

MARWAIS STEEL CO   700 Larkspur Landing Circle, Larkspur, CA 94939,
   Tel: (415) 461-3912
   (Steel shelters, metal coil coating)
      Marwais Intl. S.A., 43 Academias St., Athens 133, Greece

MELLON BANK NA   One Mellon Bank Center, Pittsburgh, PA 15258,
   Tel: (412) 234-5016
   (Commercial & trade banking, foreign exchange)
      Mellon Intl. Finance Corp., Athens Tower B, Suite 401, Athens 610, Greece

MERCK SHARP & DOHME INTL   PO Box 2000, Rahway, NJ 07065, Tel: (201) 574-4000
   (Pharms, chems & biologicals)
      Merck, Sharp & Dohme (Greece) Inc., Athens Tower, Messogion 2-4, Athens 610, Greece

MERRILL LYNCH PIERCE FENNER & SMITH   World Financial Center, 225 Liberty St,
   New York, NY 10080, Tel: (212) 449-1000
   (Brokers, securities, commodities)
      Merrill Lynch, Pierce, Fenner & Smith (Hellas) L.L.C., 17 Valaoritou St.,
         Athens 134, Greece

MOBIL CHEMICAL INTL LTD   150 E 42nd St, New York, NY 10017,
   Tel: (212) 883-4242
   (Paints & finishes)
      Mobil Oil Hellas A.E., P.O. Box 163, Athens 134, Greece

MONSANTO CO   800 N Lindbergh Blvd, St Louis, MO 63167, Tel: (314) 694-1000
   (Mfr chem & agric prdts, pharms, ind process equip, man-made fibers, plastics)
      Monsanto Europe S/A, 36 Kifissias Ave., 151 25 Amaroussion, Athens, Greece

MTS SYSTEMS CORP   PO Box 24012, Minneapolis, MN 55424, Tel: (612) 937-4000
   (Electrohydraulic testing & prod equip, mach controls)
      Neotech O.E., c/o R. Newell & Co., V. Olgas 132, 172 36 Ag. Dimitrios, Athens,
         Greece

McCANN-ERICKSON WORLDWIDE   750 Third Ave, New York, NY 10017,
   Tel: (212) 697-6000
   (Advertising)
      McCann-Erickson (Hellas) L.L.C., 7 Ventiri St., Athens 11528, Greece

NATIONAL CAN CORP   8101 W Higgins Rd, Chicago, IL 60631, Tel: (312) 399-3000
(Metal, glass & plastic containers, closures)
  National Can (Greece) A.B.E., 147 Metaxa St., Kallithea, Athens, Greece

NATIONAL CAR RENTAL SYSTEM INC   7700 France Ave S, Minneapolis, MN 55435,
  Tel: (612) 830-2121
(Car rental)
  National Car Rental, 7 Stadium St., Athens 125, Greece

A C NIELSEN CO   Nielsen Plaza, Northbrook, IL 60062, Tel: (708) 498-6300
(Marketing research)
  A.C. Nielsen Hellas Ltd., 196 Sygrou Ave., G. 176-71 Kallithea, Athens, Greece

NORTH AMERICAN PHILIPS CONSUMER ELECTRONICS CORP   PO Box 6950, Knoxville,
  TN 37914, Tel: (615) 639-1121
(Radio & TV receivers)
  Magnavox Overseas Ltd., 5 Timou Moraitini, Psychiko, Athens, Greece

NORWICH EATON PHARMACEUTICALS INC   17 Eaton Ave, Norwich, NY 13815,
  Tel: (607) 335-2111
(Mfr pharms, chems, health prdts)
  Eaton Laboratories (Hellas), 28 Kapodistriou St., Athens 147, Greece

ONAN CORP   1400 73rd Ave NE, Minneapolis, MN 55432, Tel: (612) 574-5000
(Electric generators, ind engines & controls)
  E. Sidericoudis Ltd., 107 Piraeus St., Athens, Greece

OVERSEAS NATIONAL AIRWAYS INC   Kennedy Intl Airport, Jamaica, NY 11430,
  Tel: (212) 632-8200
(Air carrier)
  Overseas National Airways Inc., Athens Airport, East Terminal, Athens, Greece

PACIFIC ARCHITECTS & ENGINEERS INC   1111 W Sixth St, Los Angeles, CA 90017,
  Tel: (213) 481-2311
(Tech engineering serv)
  Pacific Architects & Engineers Inc., 18 Nea Leoforos Vouliagmenis, 166 75 Glyfada,
    Greece

PAINEWEBBER GROUP INC   1285 Ave of the Americas, New York, NY 10019,
  Tel: (212) 713-2000
(Stock brokerage serv & invest)
  PaineWebber Intl., Koumbari 4, Kolonaki, Athens 138, Greece

PARAMOUNT INTL FILMS INC   1 Gulf & Western Plaza, New York, NY 10023,
  Tel: (212) 333-4600
(Film prod & distr)
  Savas Films S.A., 10 Efpolidos St., Athens 111, Greece

PENROD DRILLING CORP   2200 Thanksgiving Tower, Dallas, TX 75201,
  Tel: (214) 880-1700
(Contract oil/gas well drilling)
  Penrod Intl. Drilling Co., 8 Dagli St., P.O. Box 1055, Kavala, Greece

PEPSICO INC   700 Anderson Hill Rd, Purchase, NY 10577, Tel: (914) 253-2000
(Beverages, food prdts & servs, sporting goods)
  Pepsi-Cola Intl. Inc., 64 Louise Riancourt St., Athens 606, Greece

___

PFIZER INC   235 E 42nd St, New York, NY 10017, Tel: (212) 573-2323
   (Mfr pharms, hosp prdts, chems, consumer & animal health prdts)
      Pfizer Hellas A.E., 5 Alketou St., Athens 116-33, Greece

PHELPS DODGE CORP   2600 N Central Ave, Phoenix, AZ 85004-3014,
   Tel: (602) 234-8100
   (Minerals, metals & spec engineered prdts for trans & elect mkts)
      Viem Metal Works S.A., 115 Kifissias Ave., Athens 11524, Greece

PREMARK INTL INC   1717 Deerfield Rd, Deerfield, IL 60015, Tel: (708) 405-6000
   (Mfr/sale diversified consumer & coml prdts)
      Dart Hellas S.A.I., 4 Academias St., Athens 134, Greece

PROCTER & GAMBLE CO   One Procter & Gamble Plaza, Cincinnati, OH 45202,
   Tel: (513) 983-1100
   (Personal care, food, laundry, cleaning & ind prdts)
      Procter & Gamble Hellas S.A., 165 Syngrou Ave., Athens, Greece

RCA GLOBAL COMMUNICATIONS INC   60 Broad St, New York, NY 10004,
   Tel: (212) 806-7000
   (Commun serv)
      RCA Global Communications Inc., Panepistimiou 59, Athens, Greece

R J REYNOLDS TOBACCO INC   Winston-Salem, NC 27102, Tel: (919) 777-5000
   (Tobacco & tobacco prdts)
      Glenn Tobacco Co. Inc., 10 El Venizelou St., Athens 134, Greece

RICHARDSON-VICKS INC   Ten Westport Rd, Wilton, CT 06897, Tel: (203) 834-5000
   (Consumer health & personal care prdts)
      Vick Hellas S.A., 247 Syngrou Ave., Athens, Greece

A H ROBINS CO INC   1407 Cummings Dr, PO Box 26609, Richmond, VA 23261-6609,
   Tel: (804) 257-2000
   (Mfr ethical pharms & consumer prdts)
      A.H. Robins Intl. Co., Athens, Greece

ROHM & HAAS CO   Independence Mall West, Philadelphia, PA 19105,
   Tel: (215) 592-3000
   (Mfr ind & agric chems, plastics)
      Rohm & Haas Greece Ltd., 9 Leontariou St., Alsoupolis, 142 35 Nea Ionia, Athens,
      Greece

SCHLEGEL CORP   400 East Ave, Rochester, NY 14607, Tel: (716) 546-6260
   (Engineered perimeter sealing systems for residential & commercial constr)
      Schlegel E.P.E., P.O. Box 3010, Ampelokipi, Athens, Greece

SEA-LAND SERVICE INC   379 Thornall St, Edison, NJ 08837, Tel: (201) 558-6000
   (Container transport)
      George A. Callitsis S.A., 54 Filonos St., Piraeus, Greece
      Sea-Land Service Inc., 5 Constantinou, Paleologou, Piraeus, Greece

SGS CONTROL SERVICES INC   42 Broadway, New York, NY 10004,
   Tel: (212) 482-8700
   (Complete range of quality & quantity control checks & related tech serv)
      Societe Hellenique de Surveillance S.A., 3 Alkmanos St., P.O. Box 3140, Ampelokipi,
      Athens 615, Greece

SHEARSON/AMERICAN EXPRESS   American Express Tower, New York, NY 10285,
  Tel: (212) 298-2000
  (Investment banking, financial serv)
     Shearson/American Express, P.O. Box 671, 17 Panepistimiou Ave., Athens, Greece
     Shearson/American Express, P.O. Box 73, 26 Akti Poseidonos, Piraeus, Greece
     Shearson/American Express, P.O. Box 477, 19 Tsimiski St., Salonica, Greece

SOCOTAB LEAF TOBACCO CO INC   122 E 42 St, New York, NY 10168,
  Tel: (212) 687-2590
  (Tobacco dealer)
     Socotab Leaf Tobacco Co., P.O. Box 10007, 54110 Thessaloniki, Greece

STANDARD COMMERCIAL CORP   PO Box 450, Wilson, NC 27893, Tel: (919) 291-5507
  (Leaf tobacco dealers/processors, wool processors)
     Exelka S.A., Salonika, Greece
     Transhellenic Tobacco S.A., Salonika, Greece

THE STANLEY WORKS   1000 Stanley Dr, PO Box 7000, New Britain, CT 06050,
  Tel: (203) 225-5111
  (Mfr hand tools & hardware)
     Stanley Works (Sales) Ltd., P.O. Box 18, Kallithea, Athens, Greece

STERLING DRUG INC   90 Park Ave, New York, NY 10016, Tel: (212) 907-2000
  (Pharms, chems, cosmetics, household cleaners & waxes)
     Sterling Mediterranean, Athens, Greece

STP CORP   J-2, 39 Old Ridgebury Rd, Danbury, CT 06817-0001,
  Tel: (203) 794-3865
  (Fuel additives & filters)
     STP Corp., 3 Panos, Ekali, Athens, Greece

TED BATES WORLDWIDE INC   1515 Broadway, New York, NY 10036,
  Tel: (212) 869-3131
  (Advertising agency)
     Ted Bates & Co. Ltd., 26-28 Mitropoleos St., Athens 126, Greece

TEXACO INC   2000 Westchester Ave, White Plains, NY 10650, Tel: (914) 253-4000
  (Explor/mktg crude oil & its prdts, petro-chems)
     Texaco Greek Petroleum Co. S.A., Katehaki, Athens, Greece

THERMO ELECTRIC CO   109 Fifth St, Saddle Brook, NJ 07662, Tel: (201) 843-5800
  (Mfr temp/meas control prdts)
     Elina Ltd., 59 & 59A Tritis Septemvriou St., Athens 103, Greece

TRANE CO   3600 Pammel Creek Rd, La Crosse, WI 54601, Tel: (608) 787-2000
  (Mfr A/C equip)
     Trane S.A., P.O. Box 38, 319 Mesogion Ave., Aghia Paraskevi, Athens, Greece

TRANS WORLD AIRLINES INC   605 Third Ave, New York, NY 10158,
  Tel: (212) 557-6107
  (Air transp, hotel, food serv, real estate)
     Trans World Airlines Inc., 8 Xenophontos St., Athens 118, Greece

UNION CARBIDE CORP   Old Ridgebury Rd, Danbury, CT 06817, Tel: (203) 794-2000
  (Carbon prdts, chems, plastics, gases & related prdts, etc)
     Union Carbide Africa & Middle East Inc., 55 Vassilissis Sofias Ave., Athens 140,
     Greece

(cont)

Union Carbide Hellas S.A., 10 Kifissias Ave., Paradissos Amaroussion, Athens 100, Greece

UNISYS CORP   PO Box 500, Blue Bell, PA 19424, Tel: (215) 542-4011
(Mfg/mktg/serv electr info sys)
Sperry L.L.C., 28 Karolou St., Athens 107, Greece

UNITED TECHNOLOGIES CORP   United Technologies Bldg, Hartford, CT 06101,
Tel: (203) 728-7000
(Mfr aircraft engines, elevators, A/C, auto equip, space & military electr, rocket propulsion sys)
Carrier Intl. Corp., 2-4 Mesogion St., Athens 610, Greece

UPJOHN CO   7000 Portage Rd, Kalamazoo, MI 49001, Tel: (616) 323-4000
(Pharms, agric prdts, ind chems)
Upjohn A.B.E.E., 16th Km. Marathonos Ave., Pallini, Attikis, Greece

VELSICOL CHEMICAL CORP   5600 N River Rd, Rosemont, IL 60018,
Tel: (708) 698-9700
(Pesticides & ind chems)
Velsicol Overseas Corp., P.O. Box 70, Glyfada, Athens, Greece

WARNER-LAMBERT CO   201 Tabor Road, Morris Plains, NJ 07950,
Tel: (201) 540-2000
(Mfr ethical & proprietary pharms, confectionary & consumer prdts)
Adams Chilcott A.B.E.E., 247 Messogion St., P.O. Box 65044, Neo Psyhico 15451, Athens, Greece

WEIGHT WATCHERS INTL INC   Jericho Atrium, 500 North Broadway, Jericho,
NY 11753-2196, Tel: (516) 939-0400
(Weight reduction programs, food prdts)
Weight Watchers of Greece, Athens Tower, Athens 610, Greece

WORLD COURIER INC   46 Trinity Pl, New York, NY 10006, Tel: (718) 978-9400
(Intl courier serv)
World Courier Hellas, 27 Skoufa St., Athens, Greece

GUAM

3M CO   3M Center, St Paul, MN 55144-1000, Tel: (612) 733-1110
(Mfr abrasives, adhesives, chems, ind & consumer tapes/diskettes, health care prdts, elec connectors)
3M Co., Bldg. 14, 171 Guerrero Dr., P.O. Box 8576, Tamuning, Guam

AMERICAN PRESIDENT LINES LTD   1111 Broadway, Oakland, CA 94607,
Tel: (415) 272-8000
(Intermodal shipping serv)
  American President Lines Ltd., 1026 Cabras Hwy, Suite 115, Piti, Guam 96925

CALIFORNIA FIRST BANK   350 California St, PO Box 3799, San Francisco,
CA 94119, Tel: (415) 445-0200
(Intl bank)
  California First Bank, Hernan Cortes Ave., Agana, Guam 96910

CHASE MANHATTAN BANK N A   1 Chase Manhattan Plaza, New York, NY 10081,
Tel: (212) 552-2222
(Intl banking)
  Chase Manhattan Bank, N.A., PDN Bldg., O'Hara St., P.O. Box AE, Agana, Guam 96910
  Chase Manhattan Bank, N.A., P.O. Box 22229, Guam Main Facility (GMF), Agana,
    Guam 96910

CONNELL BROTHERS CO LTD   320 California St, San Francisco, CA 94104,
Tel: (415) 772-4000
(Exp/imp chems, commodities, minerals, cons materials)
  Connell Bros. Co. Ltd., P.O. Box DS, Agana, Guam 96910

DILLINGHAM CONSTRUCTION CORP   5944 Inglewood Dr, Pleasanton, CA 94566,
Tel: (415) 847-7700
(General contracting)
  Hawaiian Rock Prdts., P.O. Box H, Agana, Guam 96910

GETZ CORP   150 Post St, San Francisco, CA 94108, Tel: (415) 772-5500
(Marketing/distribution serv)
  Getz Bros. & Co. (Guam) Inc., P.O. Box 22198, Tamuning, 96921-2198 Guam

INA CORPORATION   1600 Arch St, Philadelphia, PA 19101, Tel: (215) 523-5335
(Holding co: ins, financial serv)
  Associated Insurance Underwriters, Guiterrez Bldg., P.O. Box 2311, Agana, Guam 96910
  Independent Adjustment Co. Inc., Winner Bldg. 20N, P.O. Box 8680, Tamuning,
    Guam 96911

MOBIL CORP   150 E 42nd St, New York, NY 10017, Tel: (212) 883-4242
(Petroleum explor, prdts)
  Mobil Petroleum Co. Inc., P.O. Box EU, Agana, Guam 96910

NATIONAL CAR RENTAL SYSTEM INC   7700 France Ave S, Minneapolis, MN 55435,
Tel: (612) 830-2121
(Car rental)
  National Car Rental, P.O. Box 8638, Tamuning, Guam 96911

OTIS ELEVATOR CO   10 Farm Springs, Farmington, CT 06032, Tel: (203) 674-4047
(Elevators & escalators)
  Otis Elevator Co., Harmon Plaza, Harmon Industrial Estate, Dededo, P.O. Box 7838,
    Tamuning, Guam 96911

GUATEMALA

3M CO   3M Center, St Paul, MN 55144-1000, Tel: (612) 733-1110
(Mfr abrasives, adhesives, chems, ind & consumer tapes/diskettes, health care prdts,
elec connectors)
    3M Interamerica Inc., Km. 13 Carretera Roosevelt 40-70, P.O. Box 2103,
    Guatemala City, Guatelama

ABBOTT LABORATORIES   Abbott Park, North Chicago, IL 60064,
Tel: (312) 937-6100
(Pharm & lab prdts)
    Abbott Laboratories S.A., Km. Carretera Roosevelt, Zona 7, Guatemala City, Guatemala

AFIA   110 William St, New York, NY 10038, Tel: (212) 964-4990
(Insurance)
    Seguros el Roble S.A., Aptdo. 2513, Guatemala City, Guatemala

ALBERTO-CULVER CO   2525 Armitage Ave, Melrose Park, IL 60160,
Tel: (708) 450-3000
(Hair sprays)
    Alberto-Culver (Guatemala) S.A., Aptdo. 1677, Guatemala City, Guatemala

ALEXANDER & ALEXANDER INC   1211 Ave of the Americas, New York, NY 10036,
Tel: (212) 840-8500
(Ins brokerage, risk & human resource mgmt consult)
    Alexander & Alexander de Centroamerica S.A., 12 Calle 2-04, Zona 9,
        Edificio Plaza del Sol, Guatemala City, Guatemala

AMERICAN CYANAMID CO   1 Cyanamid Plaza, Wayne, NJ 07470, Tel: (201) 831-2000
(Pharms, chems, agric & consumer prdts)
    Cyanamid Interamerican Corp., Aptdo. 556, Guatemala City, Guatemala

AMERICAN HOME PRODUCTS CORP   685 Third Ave, New York, NY 10017,
Tel: (212) 878-5800
(Drugs, food, household prdts)
    American Home Products Corp., Guatemala City, Guatemala

AMERICAN INTL UNDERWRITERS CORP   70 Pine St, New York, NY 10270,
Tel: (212) 770-7000
(General ins)
    American Intl. Underwriters (Guatemala) S.A., Aptdo. 124-A, Guatemala City,
        Guatemala

AMERICAN LIFE INSURANCE CO (ALICO)   PO Box 2226, Wilmington, DE 19899,
Tel: (302) 594-2000
(Life ins, pension & annuity plans, health prdts)
    Administradora Atalaya S.A., Aptdo. 1241-A, Guatemala City, Guatemala

Administradora Atalaya S.A., Edif. Reforma Montufar, Ave. Reforma, Guatemala City, Guatemala

AMERICAN STANDARD INC   40 W 40th St, New York, NY 10018, Tel: (212) 840-5100
(Heating & sanitary equip)
Industria Centroamericana de Sanitarios S.A., Aptdo. 2553, Guatemala City, Guatemala

AMWAY CORP   7575 E Fulton Rd, Ada, MI 49355, Tel: (616) 676-6000
(Distr household cleaning, nutrition & diet prdts)
Amway de Guatemala SA, 7a Avenida 6-69, Zona 9, Guatemala City, Guatemala

ARROW CO   530 Fifth Ave, New York, NY 10036, Tel: (212) 930-2900
(Men's apparel)
Arrow de Centro America Ltd., Ave. 33-67, Zona 7, Guatemala City, Guatemala

AVIS INC   900 Old Country Rd, Garden City, NY 11530, Tel: (516) 222-3000
(Car rental serv)
Avis de Guatemala S.A., 12 Calle 2-73, Zona 9, Guatemala City, Guatemala

AVON PRODUCTS INC   9 W 57th St, New York, NY 10019, Tel: (212) 546-6015
(Mfr/distr cosmetics, perfumes)
Avon Productos de Guatemala, Ruta 7, 4-54, Zona 14, Guatemala City, Guatemala

BANKAMERICA CORP   PO Box 37000, San Francisco, CA 94137, Tel: (415) 622-3456
(Financial services)
Bank of America, 11 Calle 5-07, Zona 1, Apdto. Postal 1335, Guatemala City, Guatemala

BARDAHL MFG CORP   1400 N W 52nd St, PO Box 70607, Seattle, WA 98107,
Tel: (206) 783-4851
(Lubricating oils)
Fritz Ammon/Bardahl Mfg. Corp., Aptdo. 1474, Guatemala City, Guatemala
Roland S.A., Aptdo. 305, Guatemala City, Guatemala

LOUIS BERGER INTL INC   100 Halsted St, East Orange, NJ 07019,
Tel: (201) 678-1960
(Consulting engineers, architects, economists & planners)
Louis Berger Intl. Inc., USAID/ORD, 8 Calle 7-86, Zone 9, Guatemala City, Guatemala

BOSTON OVERSEAS FINANCIAL CORP   100 Federal St, Boston, MA 02110,
Tel: (617) 434-3276
(Ind financial serv)
Servicios Comerciales y Industriales S.A., 6a Ave. 2-73, Zona 4, Guatemala City, Guatemala,

BRUNSWICK CORP   One Brunswick Plaza, Skokie, IL 60077, Tel: (708) 470-4700
(Mfr outboard motors & drives, bowling/fishing equip, valves & pumps)
Brunswick Corp. Medical Group/Argyle & Moneject Div., 1a Calle 8-75, Zona 1, Guatemala City, Guatemala

LEO BURNETT CO INC   35 West Wacker Dr, Chicago, IL 60601, Tel: (312) 220-5959
(Advertising agency)
Comunica Leo Burnett Publicidad, 5Ta Avenida 6-39, Zona 14, Colonia El Campo, Guatemala City, Guatemala

CANADA DRY INTL CORP   2600 Century Pkwy, Atlanta, GA 30345,
Tel: (404) 753-2182
(Carbonated beverages, soft drinks extract)
Fabrica de Bebidas Gaseosas Salvavidas, Aptdo. 65, Guatemala City, Guatemala

CARGILL   PO Box 9300, Minneapolis, MN 55440, Tel: (612) 475-7575
(Food prdts, feeds, animal prdts)
Cargill Americas Inc., Aptdo. 2857, Guatemala City, Guatemala

CHASE MANHATTAN BANK N A   1 Chase Manhattan Plaza, New York, NY 10081,
Tel: (212) 552-2222
(Intl banking)
The Chase Manhattan Bank NA, Aptdo. 40-F, Guatemala City, Guatemala

CITIBANK NA   399 Park Ave, New York, NY 10043, Tel: (212) 559-1000
(Intl banking)
Citibank NA, 3a Calle 7-14, Zona 9, Edificio Buonafina, Guatemala City, Guatemala

CLUETT PEABODY & CO INC   510 Fifth Ave, New York, NY 10036,
Tel: (212) 930-3000
(Wearing apparel)
Arrow de Centro America Ltda., 2A Calle 33-67, Zona 7, Aptdo.138, Guatemala City,
Guatemala

THE COCA-COLA CO   310 North Ave NW, PO Box Drawer 1734, Atlanta, GA 30313,
Tel: (404) 676-2121
(Mfr & sale of soft drink syrups & concentrates, juices & food prdts, motion pic & TV
prod)
The Coca-Cola Co. Guatemala, all mail to: U.S. address

CODELL CONSTRUCTION CO   100 Moundale Ave, Winchester, KY 40391,
Tel: (606) 744-2224
(Constr, engineering)
Codell Construction Corp., Guatemala City, Guatemala

COLGATE-PALMOLIVE CO   300 Park Ave, New York, NY 10022, Tel: (212) 310-2000
(Pharms, cosmetics, toiletries, detergents)
Colgate-Palmolive (Central America) Inc., Aptdo. 765, Guatemala City, Guatemala

COSCO INTERNATIONAL INC   1845 Oak St, #9, Northfield, IL 60093,
Tel: (708) 446-9390
(Flavoring extracts, chem spec, franchised soft drinks)
Sabores Cosco de Guatemala S.A., 27 Avda. 33-34, Zona 12, Guatemala City, Guatemala

CPC INTERNATIONAL INC   PO Box 8000, International Plaza, Englewood Cliffs,
NJ 07632, Tel: (201) 894-4000
(Mfr consumer food prdts & corn refining prdts)
Productos de Maiz y Alimentos S.A., Aptdo. Postal 1765, Guatemala City, Guatemala

DOW CHEMICAL CO   2030 Dow Center, Midland, MI 48640, Tel: (517) 636-1000
(Chems, plastics, fibers, pharms)
Dow Quimica de Guatemala Ltda., Guatemala City, Guatemala

EXXON CHEMICAL CO   9 Old Kings Hwy S, Darien, CT 06820, Tel: (203) 655-5200
(Mfr & sales of petrochems)
Fertica S.A., Edificio Galeria Espana, Zona 9, Guatemala City, Guatemala

EXXON CORP   225 E John Carpenter Frwy, Irving, TX 75062, Tel: (214) 444-1000
  (Petroleum & petroleum prdts)
    Exxon Central America S.A., 12 Calle 7-33, Zona 9, Guatemala City, Guatemala

FLORIDA INTL FORWARDERS   6905 N W 25th St, PO Box 522085, Miami, FL 33122,
  Tel: (305) 592-6450
  (Air cargo service)
    Embarcadores de Guatemala, Aptdo. 1329, Guatemala City, Guatemala

FMC CORP   200 E Randolph Dr, Chicago, IL 60601, Tel: (312) 861-6000
  (Mach & chem for industry, agric & govt)
    FMC Guatemala S.A., Aptdo. 158-A, Guatemala City, Guatemala

FOOTE CONE & BELDING COMMUNICATIONS INC   101 E Erie St, Chicago,
  IL 60611-2897, Tel: (312) 751-7000
  (Advertising agency)
    Foote, Cone & Belding, Av. La Reforma 8-60, Zona 9, Edif. Galerias Reforma,
      Torre 1, Guatemala City, Guatemala

H B FULLER CO   2400 Energy Park Dr, St Paul, MN 55108, Tel: (612) 645-3401
  (Mfr/distr adhesives, sealants, coatings, paints, waxes, sanitation chems)
    Kativo de Guatemala S.A., Aptdo. 2061, Guatemala City, Guatemala

GETTY OIL CO   3810 Wilshire Blvd, Los Angeles, CA 90010, Tel: (213) 739-2100
  (Petroleum & petroleum prdts)
    Getty Oil (Guatemala) Inc., 16 Calle 15-50, Zona 13, Guatemala City, Guatemala

GLIDDEN-COATINGS RESINS DIV   900 Union Commerece Bldg, Cleveland, OH 44115,
  Tel: (216) 344-8167
  (Coatings, resins, adhesives, organic chems, etc)
    Galcasa-Galvanizadora Centroamericana S.A., 14 Calle 6-12, Zona 1, Guatemala City,
      Guatemala
    Servicios Minimax, Ave. Reforma 3-48, Zona 9. Guatemala City, Guatemala

GOODYEAR TIRE & RUBBER CO   1144 E Market St, Akron, OH 44316-0001,
  Tel: (216) 796-2121
  (Mfr tires, rubber prdts)
    Gran Industrial de Neumaticos Centroamericana S.A., Apartado Postal 1946,
      Guatemala, C.A. 01012, Guatemala

W R GRACE & CO   1114 Ave of the Americas, New York, NY 10036,
  Tel: (212) 819-5500
  (Specialty chems, natural resources, consumer serv)
    Productos DAREX S.A. de C.V., Aptdo. 2068, Guatemala City, Guatemala

GROLIER INC   Old Shereman Tpk, Danbury, CT 06816, Tel: (203) 797-3500
  (Publishers)
    Editorial Centroamericana S.A., Aptdo. 7214, Guatemala City, Guatemala

FRANK B HALL & CO INC   549 Pleasantville Rd, Briarcliff Manor, NY 10510,
  Tel: (914) 769-9200
  (Insurance)
    Grupo Profesional en Seguros S.A., 7 Avda. 7-07, Zona 4, Guatemala City, Guatemala

HUGHES TOOL CO   PO Box 2539, Houston, TX 77001, Tel: (713) 924-2222
  (Equip & serv to oil & gas explor & prod ind)
    Superser de Guatemala, 6A Ave. 0-60, Zona 4, Guatemala City, Guatemala

INA CORPORATION   1600 Arch St, Philadelphia, PA 19101, Tel: (215) 523-5335
  (Holding co: ins, financial serv)
     Seguros Cruz Azul S.A., Aptdo. 207, Guatemala City, Guatemala

INTERNATIONAL BUSINESS MACHINES (IBM)   Old Orchard Rd, Armonk,
  NY 10504-1783, Tel: (914) 765-1900
  (Info-handling sys, equip & serv)
     IBM de Guatemala, S.A., Guatemala City, Guatemala

ITT SHERATON CORP   60 State St, Boston, MA 02108, Tel: (617) 367-3600
  (Hotel operations)
     Conquistador Sherator Hotel, Via 5 #4-68, Zona 4, Guatemala City, Guatemala

JOHNSON & JOHNSON   One Johnson & Johnson Plaza, New Brunswick, NJ 08933,
  Tel: (201) 524-0400
  (Surgical, med & baby prdts)
     Johnson & Johnson Guatemala S.A., Aptdo. 2067, Guatemala City, Guatemala

KELLOGG CO   235 Porter St, Battle Creek, MI 49016, Tel: (616) 966-2000
  (Food prdts)
     Kellogg's de Guatemala, Aptdo. 2266, Guatemala City, Guatemala

KOPPERS CO INC   Koppers Bldg, 437 Seventh Ave, Pittsburgh, PA 15219,
  Tel: (412) 227-2000
  (Constr materiald & serv; chem & bldg prdts)
     Impregnadora de Madera de Guatemala S.A., 8a Calle 2-31, Zona 1, Guatemala City,
     Guatemala

ELI LILLY & CO   307 E McCarty St, Indianapolis, IN 46285, Tel: (317) 261-2000
  (Pharms, agric & cosmetic prdts)
     Eli Lilly de Centroamerica S.A., Aptdo. 735, Guatemala City, Guatemala

MONSANTO CO   800 N Lindbergh Blvd, St Louis, MO 63167, Tel: (314) 694-1000
  (Mfr chem & agric prdts, pharms, ind process equip, man-made fibers, plastics)
     Monsanto Guatemala Inc., Aptdo. 2360, Guatemala City, Guatemala

MYERS TIRE SUPPLY INTL   1293 South Main St, Akron, OH 44301,
  Tel: (216) 253-5592
  (Mfr polymer & metal prdts for mat handling, automotive & constr inds)
     Orientadores Comerciales SA, 5ta Calle 1-18 Zona 6, Guatemala City, Guatemala

McCANN-ERICKSON WORLDWIDE   750 Third Ave, New York, NY 10017,
  Tel: (212) 697-6000
  (Advertising)
     McCann-Erickson Centroamericana (Guatemala) S.A., P.O. Box 390, 7a Avda. 5-10,
     Zona 4, Centro Financiero, Torre 11, Guatemala City, Guatemala

NABISCO BRANDS INC   Nabisco Brands Plaza, East Hanover, NJ 07936,
  Tel: (201) 503-2000
  (Mfr food prdts)
     Intl. Standard Brands Inc., Aptdo. 167, Guatemala City, Guatemala
     Pan American Standard Brands Inc., Aptdo. 167, Guatemala City, Guatemala

NATIONAL CAR RENTAL SYSTEM INC   7700 France Ave S, Minneapolis, MN 55435,
  Tel: (612) 830-2121
  (Car rental)
     National Car Rental, 14 Calle 1-42, Zona 10, Guatemala City, Guatemala

NCR CORP   1700 S Patterson Blvd, Dayton, OH 45479, Tel: (513) 445-2000
(Develop/mfr/sell/serv business info processing sys)
   NCR de Guatemala S.A., 5a Ave. 6-71, Zona 9, P.O. Box 348, 01009 Guatemala City,
   Guatemala

ONAN CORP   1400 73rd Ave NE, Minneapolis, MN 55432, Tel: (612) 574-5000
(Electric generators, ind engines & controls)
   Guatemala Tecnica S.A., Calz. Aguilar Batres 38-56, Zona 11, Guatemala City,
   Guatemala

OTIS ELEVATOR CO   10 Farm Springs, Farmington, CT 06032, Tel: (203) 674-4047
(Elevators & escalators)
   Otis Elevator Co., Aptdo. 1516, Guatemala City, Guatemala

PAN-AMERICAN LIFE INSURANCE CO   Pan American Life Center, New Orleans,
   LA 70130, Tel: (504) 566-1300
(Insurance)
   Compania de Seguros Panamericana S.A., Edificio Plaza Panamericana,
   Ave. Reforma 9-00, Zona 9, Guatemala City, Guatemala

PHELPS DODGE CORP   2600 N Central Ave, Phoenix, AZ 85004-3014,
   Tel: (602) 234-8100
(Minerals, metals & spec engineered prdts for trans & elect mkts)
   Facelec S.A., 2L Ave. 33.31, Zona 12, Guatemala City, Guatemala

PILLSBURY CO   Pillsbury Center, Minneapolis, MN 55402, Tel: (612) 330-4966
(Baking mixes, canned & frozen foods, restaurants & food shops)
   Productos Alimenticios Imperial, Guatemala City, Guatemala

THE PROTANE CORP   1400 Smith St, Houston, TX 77210, Tel: (713) 853-6161
(Holding co: foreign invest in LPG ind; appliance mfr & mktg)
   Di Gas, 5a Ave. 2-73, Zona 4, Guatemala City, Guatemala

QUAKER OATS CO   345 Merchandise Mart Plaza, Chicago, IL 60654,
   Tel: (312) 222-7111
(Foods, pet foods, toys, chems)
   Quaker de Centroamerica, Aptdo. 2795, Guatemala City, Guatemala

RALSTON PURINA CO   Checkerboard Sq, St Louis, MO 63164, Tel: (214) 982-1000
(Poultry & live stock feed, cereals, food prdts)
   Purina de Guatemala Ltda, Aptdo. 1028, Guatemala City, Guatemala

RCA GLOBAL COMMUNICATIONS INC   60 Broad St, New York, NY 10004,
   Tel: (212) 806-7000
(Commun serv)
   RCA Global Communications Inc., IAC 18-23, Z-15, VH2, C. Com. V. Hermosa, Of. "B",
   Guatemala City, Guatemala

RIVIANA FOODS INC   2777 Allen Parkway, Houston, TX 77019, Tel: (713) 529-3251
(Rice & rice by-prdts, pet foods)
   Agencia Maritima S.A., 5a Ave. 11-71, Zona 1, Guatemala City, Guatemala

A H ROBINS CO INC   1407 Cummings Dr, PO Box 26609, Richmond, VA 23261-6609,
   Tel: (804) 257-2000
(Mfr ethical pharms & consumer prdts)
   Industrial Santa Agape, S.A., Guatemala City, Guatemala

ROHM & HAAS CO   Independence Mall West, Philadelphia, PA 19105,
   Tel: (215) 592-3000
   (Mfr ind & agric chems, plastics)
      Rohm & Haas Guatemala, 2da Ave. 11-10, Zona 9, Guatemala City, Guatemala

RORER GROUP INC   500 Virginia Dr, Ft Washington, PA 19034,
   Tel: (215) 628-6000
   (Mfr ethical & consumer pharms)
      Rorer de Centro America, Guatemala City, Guatemala

SCM CORP   299 Park Ave, New York, NY 10171, Tel: (212) 752-2700
   (Business equip, chems, coatings & resins, foods, paper prdts)
      Galvanizadora Centro Americana S.A., Guatemala City, Guatemala

SEA-LAND SERVICE INC   379 Thornall St, Edison, NJ 08837, Tel: (201) 558-6000
   (Container transport)
      Navecon S.A., Av. La Reforma 8-60, Zona 9, Guatemala City, Guatemala

G D SEARLE & CO   PO Box 1045, Skokie, IL 60076, Tel: (708) 982-7000
   (Pharms, health care & optical prdts, specialty chems)
      G. D. Searle Intl. Co., Aptdo. 1054, Guatemala City, Guatemala

SEARS ROEBUCK & CO   Sears Towers, Chicago, IL 60684, Tel: (312) 875-2500
   (Diversified general merchandise, ins, real estate, financial serv)
      Sears, Roebuck S.A., Aptdo. 513, Guatemala City, Guatemala

SHULTON INC   1 Cyanamid Plaza, Wayne, NJ 07470, Tel: (201) 831-2000
   (Health, beauty & grooming prdts)
      Shulton S.A., Condominion San Martin de Porres, 2a Calle 21-23, Zona 15,
         Guatemala City, Guatemala

STERLING DRUG INC   90 Park Ave, New York, NY 10016, Tel: (212) 907-2000
   (Pharms, chems, cosmetics, household cleaners & waxes)
      Sterling Products Intl. S.A., Aptdo. 340, Guatemala City, Guatemala

NELLO L TEER CO   PO Box 1131, Durham, NC 27702, Tel: (919) 682-6191
   (Heavy highway constr, building constr)
      Nello L. Teer Co. de Centroamerica, Aptdo. 458, Guatemala City, Guatemala

TEXACO INC   2000 Westchester Ave, White Plains, NY 10650, Tel: (914) 253-4000
   (Explor/mktg crude oil & its prdts, petro-chems)
      Texaco Guatemala Inc., Av. Petapa 23-01, Zona 12, Guatemala City, Guatemala

U S WHEAT ASSOCIATES   200 Market Bldg Suite 1020, Portland, OR 97201,
   Tel: (503) 223-8123
   (Market development for wheat prdts)
      U.S. Wheat Associates Inc., 15 Ave. A 3-67, Zona 13, Guatemala City, Guatemala

UNION CARBIDE CORP   Old Ridgebury Rd, Danbury, CT 06817, Tel: (203) 794-2000
   (Carbon prdts, chems, plastics, gases & related prdts, etc)
      Unicar S.A., Aptdo. 1587, Guatemala City, Guatemala

UNIVERSAL FOODS CORP   433 E Michigan St, Milwaukee, WI 53201,
   Tel: (414) 271-6755
   (Yeast & allied baking prdts, food prdts)
      Levaduras Universal, Km. 16 Carretera Roosevelt, Guatemala City, Guatemala

UPJOHN CO   7000 Portage Rd, Kalamazoo, MI 49001, Tel: (616) 323-4000
  (Pharms, agric prdts, ind chems)
    Compania Farmaceutica Upjohn S.A., Aptdo. 991, Guatemala City, Guatemala

WACKENHUT CORP   1500 San Remo Ave, Coral Gables, FL 33146,
  Tel: (305) 666-5656
  (Security sys & serv)
    Wackenhut de Guatemala S.A., Calle 14 #8-51, Zona 10, Barrio Santa Clara,
      Guatemala City, Guatemala

WARNER-LAMBERT CO   201 Tabor Road, Morris Plains, NJ 07950,
  Tel: (201) 540-2000
  (Mfr ethical & proprietary pharms, confectionary & consumer prdts)
    Laboratorios Laprofa, S.A., Aptdo. 582, Guatemala City, Guatemala

WEST CHEMICAL PRODUCTS INC   1000 Herrontown Rd, Princeton, NJ 08540,
  Tel: (609) 921-0501
  (Sanitary equip & supplies)
    West Chemical Products de Guatemala, 3a Calle 10-25, Zona 12, Guatemala City,
      Guatemala

WORLD COURIER INC   46 Trinity Pl, New York, NY 10006, Tel: (718) 978-9400
  (Intl courier serv)
    World Courier Guatemala S.A., Edificio el Triangulo, 7a Ave. 6-53, Zona 4,
      Guatemala City, Guatemala

GUINEA

LOUIS BERGER INTL INC   100 Halsted St, East Orange, NJ 07019,
  Tel: (201) 678-1960
  (Consulting engineers, architects, economists & planners)
    Louis Berger Intl. Inc., B.P. 383, Conakry, Guinea

GANNETT FLEMING CORDDRY & CARPENTER INC   PO Box 1963, Harrisburg, PA 17015,
  Tel: (717) 763-7211
  (Engr consulting serv)
    Gannett Fleming Transportation Engineers, c/o UNDP B.P. 222, Conakry, Guinea

GUYANA

AMERICAN LIFE INSURANCE CO (ALICO)   PO Box 2226, Wilmington, DE 19899,
  Tel: (302) 594-2000
  (Life ins, pension & annuity plans, health prdts)
    American Life Insurance Co., P.O. Box 10607, Georgetown, Guyana
    American Life Insurance Co., American Life Bldg., 30/31 Regent &, Hincks St.,
      Robbstown, Georgetown, Guyana

BARDAHL MFG CORP   1400 N W 52nd St, PO Box 70607, Seattle, WA 98107,
  Tel: (206) 783-4851
  (Lubricating oils)
    Guyana Stores, Ltd., Box 374, Georgetown, Guyana

CHASE MANHATTAN BANK N A   1 Chase Manhattan Plaza, New York, NY 10081,
  Tel: (212) 552-2222
  (Intl banking)
    Chase Manhattan Bank, N.A., P.O. Box 101080, Georgetown, Guyana

COLGATE-PALMOLIVE CO   300 Park Ave, New York, NY 10022, Tel: (212) 310-2000
  (Pharms, cosmetics, toiletries, detergents)
    Colgate-Palmolive (Guyana), Ltd., Ruimveldt Public Rd., E. Bank Demetara, Guyana

TEXACO INC   2000 Westchester Ave, White Plains, NY 10650, Tel: (914) 253-4000
  (Explor/mktg crude oil & its prdts, petro-chems)
    Texaco West Indies Ltd., 45 Main St., Georgetown, Demerara, Guyana

HAITI

AIRWAYS ENGINEERING CORP   1700 N Moore St, #810, Arlington, VA 22209,
  Tel: (703) 522-4050
  (Airport planning, design, constr, & supervision)
    Airways Engineering Corp., c/o Autorite Portuaire Nationale, P.O. Box 616,
      Port-au-Prince, Haiti

AMERICAN AIRLINES INC   PO Box 619616, Dallas-Ft Worth Arpt, TX   75261-9616,
   Tel: (817) 355-1234
   (Air transp)
     American Airlines, Cite de l'Exposition, Francois Duvalier Intl. Airport,
       Port-au-Prince, Haiti

AMERICAN LIFE INSURANCE CO (ALICO)   PO Box 2226, Wilmington, DE   19899,
   Tel: (302) 594-2000
   (Life ins, pension & annuity plans, health prdts)
     Compagnie d'Assurance d'Haiti, S.A., P.O. Box 554, 158 Rue Ducentre,
       Port-au-Prince, Haiti
     Compagnie d'Assurance d'Haiti, S.A., 21B Ave. Marie Jeanne, Port-au-Prince, Haiti

ARCO PIPE LINE CO   200 Arco Pl, Independence, KS   67301, Tel: (316) 331-1300
   (Pipeline transp of crude & refined oil)
     Arco Pipe Line Co., Rue Dantes Destouches, Port-au-Prince, Haiti

ATLANTIC HOSIERY MILLS INC   4705 N W 132nd St, Opa Locka, FL   33054,
   Tel: (305) 685-7617
   (Stockings, etc)
     Atlantic Enterprises, Delmas Rd., Port-au-Prince, Haiti

AVIS INC   900 Old Country Rd, Garden City, NY   11530, Tel: (516) 222-3000
   (Car rental serv)
     Avis Rent A Car, Rue Mais Gate, Port-au-Prince, Haiti

CANADA DRY INTL CORP   2600 Century Pkwy, Atlanta, GA   30345,
   Tel: (404) 753-2182
   (Carbonated beverages, soft drinks extract)
     Usine A. Glace Nationale S.A., P.O. Box 647, Port-au-Prince, Haiti

CITIBANK NA   399 Park Ave, New York, NY   10043, Tel: (212) 559-1000
   (Intl banking)
     Citibank N.A., Rue du Centre 107, P.O. Box W.88, Delmas, Port-au-Prince, Haltl

EXXON CORP   225 E John Carpenter Frwy, Irving, TX   75062, Tel: (214) 444-1000
   (Petroleum & petroleum prdts)
     Esso Standard Oil S.A., Rue du Magasln de l'Etat, Port-au-Prince, Haiti

FIRST NATIONAL BANK OF BOSTON   100 Federal St, Boston, MA   02110,
   Tel: (617) 434-2200
   (Commercial banking)
     First National Bank of Boston, Rue des Miracles, P.O. Box 2216, Port-au-Prince,
       Haiti
     First National Bank of Boston, 19 Rue Gregoire, Petion-Ville, Haiti

GENERAL TELEPHONE CO OF ILLINOIS   1312 E Empire St, Bloomington, IL   61701,
   Tel: (309) 663-3311
   (Telephone service)
     West Indies Telephone Co., Place Geffrard, Port-au-Prince, Haiti

HOLIDAY INNS INC   3742 Lamar Ave, Memphis, TN   38195, Tel: (901) 362-4001
   (Hotels, restaurants, casinos)
     Holiday Inn, Rue Capois #10, P.O. Box 1429, Dwin, Port-au-Prince, Haiti

___

INA CORPORATION   1600 Arch St, Philadelphia, PA 19101, Tel: (215) 523-5335
   (Holding co: ins, financial serv)
       Professionelle d'Assurance, S.A., Boite Postal 1311, Port-au-Prince, Haiti

LANNON MFG CO   PO Box 550, Tullahoma, TN 37388, Tel: (615) 455-0691
   (Sporting goods)
       Haitian Mfr. Enterprise Co., Martissant, Port-au-Prince, Haiti

LUCKETT TOBACCOS INC   222 S First St, #403, Louisville, KY 40202,
   Tel: (502) 562-9283
   (Whl tobacco, cigarette mfg supplies & equip)
       Compagnie des Tabacs Comme Il Faut, P.O. Box 797, Port-au-Prince, Haiti

NORTON CO   1 New Bond St, Worcester, MA 01606, Tel: (508) 795-5000
   (Abrasives, drill bits, constr & safety prdts, plastics)
       Norton S.A., Meu's Bldg., P.O. Box 652, Port-au-Prince, Haiti

ONAN CORP   1400 73rd Ave NE, Minneapolis, MN 55432, Tel: (612) 574-5000
   (Electric generators, ind engines & controls)
       Haytian Tractor & Equipment Co. S.A., Ave. Haile Selaisse, P.O. Box 1318,
          Port-au-Prince, Haiti

RCA GLOBAL COMMUNICATIONS INC   60 Broad St, New York, NY 10004,
   Tel: (212) 806-7000
   (Commun serv)
       R.C.A., P.O. Box A-153, Rue des Miracles, Port-au-Prince, Haiti

SEA-LAND SERVICE INC   379 Thornall St, Edison, NJ 08837, Tel: (201) 558-6000
   (Container transport)
       Sea-Land Service Inc., P.O. Box 234, Port-au-Prince, Haiti

TEXACO INC   2000 Westchester Ave, White Plains, NY 10650, Tel: (914) 253-4000
   (Explor/mktg crude oil & its prdts, petro-chems)
       Texaco Caribbean Ltd., Rue Roux, P.O. Box 867, Port-au-Prince, Haiti

HONDURAS

AMERICAN BILTRITE INC   57 River St, Wellesley Hills, MA 02181,
   Tel: (617) 237-6655
   (Rubber prdts)
       Compania Hulera S.A., P.O. Box 164, San Pedro Sula, Honduras

AMERICAN INTL UNDERWRITERS CORP   70 Pine St, New York, NY 10270,
   Tel: (212) 770-7000
   (General ins)
       American Intl. Underwriters S.A., P.O. Box 113-C, Seccion Comercial, Hotel Honduras,
          Haya, Tegucigalpa, Honduras

BABY TOGS INC   450 W 33rd St, New York, NY 10001, Tel: (212) 868-2100
(Mfr & importers of infants dresses & suits)
   Novelty Honduras S.A., 12th Ave. #5, San Pedro Sula, Honduras

BARDAHL MFG CORP   1400 N W 52nd St, PO Box 70607, Seattle, WA 98107,
Tel: (206) 783-4851
(Lubricating oils)
   Companis General de Accesorios y   Comercio S.A., Aptdo. #6, San Pedro Sula,
   Honduras
   Repuestos Sula S.A., 5a Avenida, 9a y 10c Calle, Aptdo. Postal 611, Tegucigalpa,
   Honduras

CALMAQUIP ENGINEERING CORP   7240 NW 12th St, Miami, FL 33121,
Tel: (305) 592-4510
(Engineering)
   Calmaquip Ingenieros de Honduras S.A., Aptdo. 845, Boulevard Morazan # 1518,
   Barrio de Guacerique, Comayaguela, Honduras

CARGILL   PO Box 9300, Minneapolis, MN 55440, Tel: (612) 475-7575
(Food prdts, feeds, animal prdts)
   Alcon (Alimentos Concentrados, S.A.), Apartado Postal 283, San Pedro Sula, Honduras)

CHASE MANHATTAN BANK N A   1 Chase Manhattan Plaza, New York, NY 10081,
Tel: (212) 552-2222
(Intl banking)
   Banco Atlantida, Aptdo. Postal 57-C, 5a Calle y 7a. Avenida, San Pedro Sula,
   Honduras

CITIBANK NA   399 Park Ave, New York, NY 10043, Tel: (212) 559-1000
(Intl banking)
   Banco de Honduras S.A., Edificio Midence Soto Frente Parque Central,
   Aptdo. Postal 7-C, Tegucigalpa, Honduras
   Banco de Honduras S.A., Callejon del Mercado 3 Calle S.O., Aptdo. Postal 81,
   San Pedro Sula, Honduras

COLGATE-PALMOLIVE CO   300 Park Ave, New York, NY 10022, Tel: (212) 310-2000
(Pharms, cosmetics, toiletries, detergents)
   Colgate-Palmolive Inc., Barrio la Granja, Comayaguela, Tegucigalpa, Honduras

CPC INTERNATIONAL INC   PO Box 8000, International Plaza, Englewood Cliffs,
NJ 07632, Tel: (201) 894-4000
(Mfr consumer food prdts & corn refining prdts)
   Almidones del Istmo SA de CV (ALISA), Aldea Dos Caminos, Villanueva,
   Dpt. de Cortes, Aptdo. 234, San Pedro Sula, Honduras

EXXON CORP   225 E John Carpenter Frwy, Irving, TX 75062, Tel: (214) 444-1000
(Petroleum & petroleum prdts)
   Exxon Corp., La Burrera, Comayaguela, Honduras

FIRST NATIONAL BANK OF BOSTON   100 Federal St, Boston, MA 02110,
Tel: (617) 434-2200
(Commercial banking)
   First National Bank of Boston, Compania de Credito S.A., 5a Avenida 2a Calle S.E.,
   Aptdo. Postal 321, San Pedro Sula, Honduras

FLORIDA INTL FORWARDERS   6905 N W 25th St, PO Box 522085, Miami, FL 33122,
Tel: (305) 592-6450
(Air cargo service)
   Mundial Express, Aptdo. Postal 1242, Tegucigalpa, Honduras
   Mundial Express S.P.S., Aptdo. 374, 2a Calle 1220, San Pedro Sula, Honduras

H B FULLER CO   2400 Energy Park Dr, St Paul, MN 55108, Tel: (612) 645-3401
(Mfr/distr adhesives, sealants, coatings, paints, waxes, sanitation chems)
   H.B. Fuller Co., Kativo de Honduras, Aptdo. 193, San Pedro Sula, Honduras
   H.B. Fuller Co., Kativo de Honduras, Aptdo. 454, Tegucigalpa, Honduras

GLOBAL ASSOCIATES   2420 Camino Ramon, #236, San Ramon, CA 94583,
Tel: (415) 275-9010
(Logistic support services)
   Global-CIC, all mail to: APO Miami, FL 34042

HOLIDAY INNS INC   3742 Lamar Ave, Memphis, TN 38195, Tel: (901) 362-4001
(Hotels, restaurants, casinos)
   Holiday Inn, Calle Peatonal, P.O. Box 175, Tegucigalpa, Honduras

INTERNATIONAL BUSINESS MACHINES (IBM)   Old Orchard Rd, Armonk,
NY 10504-1783, Tel: (914) 765-1900
(Info-handling sys, equip & serv)
   IBM de Honduras S.A., Tegucigalpa, Honduras

LLOYD CORP   9441 W Olympic Blvd, Beverly Hills, CA 90212, Tel: (213) 879-3080
(Oil explor, etc)
   Lloyd Petroleum Co., Aptdo. 38, Tegucigalpa, Honduras

McCANN-ERICKSON WORLDWIDE   750 Third Ave, New York, NY 10017,
Tel: (212) 697-6000
(Advertising)
   McCann-Erickson Centroamericana S. de R.L. (Honduras),
      8 Piso Edificio Banco Atlantida S.A., Aptdo. 802, P.O. Box 1161, San Pedro Sula,
      Honduras

ONAN CORP   1400 73rd Ave NE, Minneapolis, MN 55432, Tel: (612) 574-5000
(Electric generators, ind engines & controls)
   Casa Comercial Mathews S.A., Barrio la Bolsa, Aptdo. Postal 39, Tegucigalpa,
      Honduras

OTIS ELEVATOR CO   10 Farm Springs, Farmington, CT 06032, Tel: (203) 674-4047
(Elevators & escalators)
   Otis Elevator Co., 9 Avenida 12 y 13 Calles, Comayaguela # 1216, Tegucigalpa,
      Honduras

PAN-AMERICAN LIFE INSURANCE CO   Pan American Life Center, New Orleans,
LA 70130, Tel: (504) 566-1300
(Insurance)
   Pan-American Life Insurance Co., Ave. Republica de Chile 804, Edificio PALIC,
      Tegucigalpa, Honduras

PHELPS DODGE CORP   2600 N Central Ave, Phoenix, AZ 85004-3014,
Tel: (602) 234-8100
(Minerals, metals & spec engineered prdts for trans & elect mkts)
   Electro Conductores de Honduras S.A. de C.V. (ECDHSA), Aptdo. Postal 3192,
      Tegucigalpa, Honduras

ROHM & HAAS CO   Independence Mall West, Philadelphia, PA 19105,
  Tel: (215) 592-3000
  (Mfr ind & agric chems, plastics)
    Rocasa Honduras, P.O. Box 1854, San Pedro Sula, Honduras

SEA-LAND SERVICE INC   379 Thornall St, Edison, NJ 08837, Tel: (201) 558-6000
  (Container transport)
    A. Villafranca & Co. S de RL de CV, P.O. Box 58, Puerto Cortes, Honduras

SEARS ROEBUCK & CO   Sears Towers, Chicago, IL 60684, Tel: (312) 875-2500
  (Diversified general merchandise, ins, real estate, financial serv)
    Sears, Roebuck & Cia., Pasaje Valle, San Pedro Sula, Honduras

SUNRISE FASHIONS INC   500 Seventh Ave, New York, NY 10018,
  Tel: (212) 730-0520
  (Raincoats, other apparel)
    Jazmin S. de R.L., Barrio el Jasmin, Tegucigalpa, Honduras

TEXACO INC   2000 Westchester Ave, White Plains, NY 10650, Tel: (914) 253-4000
  (Explor/mktg crude oil & its prdts, petro-chems)
    Texaco Inc., Aptdo. Postal # 112, San Pedro Sula, Honduras

TIMBERLAND LUMBER CO   310 Garfield, Eugene, OR 97401, Tel: (503) 686-2631
  (Lumber & wood prdts)
    Danli Industrial S.A., Danli, Honduras
    Maya Lumber Co., Carretera al Batallon, Comayaguela, Honduras

HONG KONG

3D/INTERNATIONAL INC   1900 W Loop South, Houston, TX 77027,
  Tel: (713) 871-7000
  (Design, mgmt, environmental servs)
    3D/I-Hong Kong, 2/F New Henry House, 10 Ice House St., Central Hong Kong, Hong Kong

3M CO   3M Center, St Paul, MN 55144-1000, Tel: (612) 733-1110
  (Mfr abrasives, adhesives, chems, ind & consumer tapes/diskettes, health care prdts,
  elec connectors)
    3M Hong Kong, Ltd., Victoria Center 5/F, 15 Watson Rd., Causeway Bay, Hong Kong

ABBOTT LABORATORIES   Abbott Park, North Chicago, IL 60064,
  Tel: (312) 937-6100
  (Pharm & lab prdts)
    Abbott Labs, Ltd., 7th Floor, News Bldg., 322 Java Rd., North Point,
      P.O. Box 14402, Hong Kong

ABERCROMBIE & KENT INTL INC   1420 Kensington Rd, Oak Brook, IL 60521-2106,
  Tel: (708) 954-2944
  (Tour wholesaler)
    Abercrombie & Kent (HK) Ltd., 27th fl. Tai Sang Commercial Bldg.,
    24-34 Hennesy Rd., Wanchai, Hong Kong

ACTION OVERSEAS BUYING LTD   460 Nixon Rd, Allegheny Ind Park, Cheswick,
  PA 15024, Tel: (412) 782-4800
  (Distr/sale housewares, hardware, giftware, light bulbs & crystal)
    China Buying Services Ltd., Suite 1406-8, Harcourt House 14/F, 39 Gloucester Rd.,
    Wanchai, Hong Kong

ADDISON-WESLEY PUBLISHING CO   Route 128, Reading, MA 01867,
  Tel: (617) 944-3700
  (Educational textbook publ)
    Addison-Wesley Publishing Co. Ltd., Suite 811, Tsimshatsui Center East Wing,
    66 Mody Rd., Kowloon, Hong Kong

AFIA   110 William St, New York, NY 10038, Tel: (212) 964-4990
  (Insurance)
    AFIA Worldwide Insurance, 9th Floor, Jardine House 20 Pedder St., Hong Kong
    St. Paul Fire & Marine Insurance Co., 9th Floor, Jardine House, Pedder St.,
    P.O. Box 2308, Hong Kong

AIR EXPRESS INTL CORP   120 Tokeneke Rd, PO Box 1231, Darien, CT 06820,
  Tel: (203) 655-7900
  (Air frt forwarder)
    Air Express Intl Hong Kong, Ltd., KAFAT Bldg., Rm 306, 70-78 Sung Wong Toi Rd.,
    Kowloon, Hong Kong

AIR PRODUCTS & CHEMICALS INC   7201 Hamilton Blvd, Allentown, PA 18195,
  Tel: (215) 481-4911
  (Mfr ind gases & chems)
    Air Products Pacific Inc., 89 Queensway, Central Hong Kong, Hong Kong

AIRBORNE EXPRESS   3101 Western Ave, PO Box 662, Seattle, WA 98111,
  Tel: (206) 285-4600
  (Air transp serv)
    Airborne Freight Corp., Units 204-205, Ahafa Cargo Centre, 12 Kai Shun Rd.,
    Kowloon Bay, Kowloon, Hong Kong

ALARM DEVICE MFG CO   165 Eileen Way, Syosset, NY 11791, Tel: (516) 921-6704
  (Security, fire & burglary sys)
    Ademco Hong Kong Ltd., Silver Cord Tower 1, 30 Canton Rd., Tsimshatsui, Kowloon,
    Hong Kong

ALARON INC   185 Park St, Troy, MI 48084, Tel: (313) 585-8400
  (Mfr/distr consumer electr, phones, ceiling fans)
    Alaron Electronics Far East Ltd., 1402 Silvercord Tower 11, 30 Canton Rd., Kowloon,
    Hong Kong

ALLIED-SIGNAL INC   Columbia Rd & Park Ave, PO Box 2245R, Morristown,
  NJ 07960, Tel: (201) 455-2000
  (Mfr aerospace & automotive prdts, engineered materials)
    Allied Chemical Intl. Corp., 1028/29 New World Office Bldg., 24 Salisbury Rd.,
    Tsim-Shat-Sui, LowKowloon, Hong Kong
    Allied Chemical Intl. Corp., 1028-29 New World Office Bldg., 24 Salisbury Rd.,

Tsim-Shat-Sui, Kowloon, Hong Kong
Norplex/Oak Pacific, 1013-14 World Finance Center, Harbour City, Tsim-Shat-Sui, Kowloon, Hong Kong

AMDAHL CORP   1250 East Arques Ave, PO Box 3470, Sunnyvale, CA 94088-3470,
Tel: (408) 746-6000
(Mfr large scale computers, complementary software storage & commun prdts)
Amdahl Intl. Corp., 3804-06, 38th fl., The Bond Center, West Tower, 89 Queensway, Hong Kong

AMERICAN & EFIRD INC   PO Box 507, Mt Holly, NC 28120, Tel: (704) 827-4311
(Mfr ind thread, yarn & consumer sewing prdts)
American & Efird (UK) Ltd., Tsuen Wan Ind. Centre 15/F, 220-248 Texaco Rd., Tsuen Wan, NT, Hong Kong

AMERICAN AIRLINES INC   PO Box 619616, Dallas-Ft Worth Arpt, TX 75261-9616,
Tel: (817) 355-1234
(Air transp)
American Airlines, Caxton House, 1 Duddell St., Hong Kong

AMERICAN APPRAISAL ASSOCS INC   525 E Michigan St, Milwaukee, WI 53202,
Tel: (414) 271-7240
(Valuation consulting serv)
American Appraisal Holdings Ltd., Suite 503, Hang Chong Bldg., Queen's Rd., Central, Hong Kong

AMERICAN CYANAMID CO   1 Cyanamid Plaza, Wayne, NJ 07470, Tel: (201) 831-2000
(Pharms, chems, agric & consumer prdts)
Cyanamid (Far East), Ltd., 14th Floor, Watson's Estate, Watson Rd., P.O. Box 4217, North Point, Hong Kong

AMERICAN EXPRESS CO   American Express Tower, New York, NY 10285-4765,
Tel: (212) 640-2000
(Diversified fin & travel-related serv)
American Express Leasing Corp., 8/F Alexandra House, 16/20 Chater Rd., P.O. Box 3, Hong Kong

AMERICAN INTL UNDERWRITERS CORP   70 Pine St, New York, NY 10270,
Tel: (212) 770-7000
(General ins)
American Intl Assurance Co. Ltd., AIA Bldg., No. 1 Stubbs Rd., P.O. Box 444, Hong Kong
American Intl. Assurance Co. Ltd., No. 1 Stubbs Rd., P.O. Box 444, Hong Kong

AMERICAN PRESIDENT LINES LTD   1111 Broadway, Oakland, CA 94607,
Tel: (415) 272-8000
(Intermodal shipping serv)
American President Lines, Ltd., P.O. Box 98470, World Shipping Centre, 7 Canton Rd., Kowloon, Hong Kong

AMP INC   470 Friendship Rd, Harrisburg, PA 17111, Tel: (717) 564-0100
(Mfr electrical wiring devices)
AMP Products Pacific Ltd., Room 1301, Ocean Centre, 5 Canton Rd., Tsimshatsui Kowloon, Hong Kong

AMPEX CORP   401 Broadway, Redwood City, CA 94063-3199, Tel: (415) 367-2011
   (Mfr professional audio/visual sys, magnetic recording media, data-memory prdts)
      Ampex Ferrotec Ltd., 603 Tai Nan West St., Kowloon, Hong Kong
      Ampex World Operations SA, 709-711 World Finance Center, Harbour City, Canton Rd.,
      Tsim-Shat-Sui, Kowloon, Hong Kong

AMPHENOL PRODUCTS   4300 Commerct Ct, Lisle, IL 60532, Tel: (708) 983-3500
   (Elect interconnect/penetrate sys & assemblies)
      Amphenol East Asia Ltd., 513-514 World Commerce Centre, Harbor City, 11,
      Canton Rd., Tsim-Shat-Sui, Kowloon, Hong Kong
      Amphenol East Asia Ltd., Wah Leun Ind. Centre, 15-21 Wong Chuk Yeung St., Fotan,
      Sha Tin, Hong Kong

AMREP CORP   10 Columbus Circle, New York, NY 10019, Tel: (212) 541-7300
   (Land developers, builders; magazine distr)
      Amrep Distributors Hong Kong, 1411-3 Melbourne Plaza, 33 Queen's Rd., Central,
      Hong Kong

AMSCO INTL   2222 W Grandview Blvd, Erie, PA 16512, Tel: (814) 452-3100
   (Hospital equip)
      AMSCO Intl Co., Harbour View Commercial Bldg., Rm A, 22 Floor, 2-4 Percival St.,
      Hong Kong

AMTHOR IMPORTS INC   2598 Taylor St, San Francisco, CA 94133,
   Tel: (415) 474-3426
   (Wax candles, shell novelties)
      Mark V Intl., Ltd., 1705-1709 Star House, 3 Salisbury Rd., Kowloon, Hong Kong

AMWAY CORP   7575 E Fulton Rd, Ada, MI 49355, Tel: (616) 676-6000
   (Distr household cleaning, nutrition & diet prdts)
      Amway Hong Kong, Ltd., Block B, Second Floor, Watsons Estate, North Point, Hong Kong

ANTHONY INDUSTRIES INC   4900 S Eastern Ave, Los Angeles, CA 90040,
   Tel: (213) 724-2800
   (Pool constr & equip, fishing tackle, athletic apparel)
      Shakespeare Hong Kong, Ltd., Kwun Tong, Kowloon, Hong Kong

APPLE COMPUTER INC   20525 Mariani Ave, Cupertino, CA 95014,
   Tel: (408) 996-1010
   (Personal computers, peripherals & software)
      Apple Computer Intl. Ltd., 14/f Exchange Tower, 8 Connaught Rd., Hong Kong

ARMSTRONG WORLD INDUSTRIES INC   PO Box 3001, Lancaster, PA 17604,
   Tel: (717) 397-0611
   (Mfr/mkt interior furnishings & spec prdts for bldg, auto & textile inds)
      Armstrong AWI Ltd., Harbour Commercial Bldg., 122-124 Connaught Rd. Central,
      Hong Kong

ASSOCIATED MERCHANDISING CORP   1440 Broadway, New York, NY 10018,
   Tel: (212) 536-4000
   (Retail service organization)
      Associated Merchandising Corp., 5th fl. West Wing - Tsim Sha Tsui Centre,
      66 Mody Rd., Kowloon, Hong Kong

AST RESEARCH INC   16215 Alton Parkway, PO Box 19658, Irvine, CA 92713-9658,
   Tel: (714) 727-4141
   (Mfr personal computers enhancement & data commun prdt)

AST Research Far East Ltd., Vanta Industrial Centre 11/F, 21-33 Tai Lin Pai Rd.,
    Kwai Chung, NT, Hong Kong
AST Research Far East Ltd., Citicorp Centre #2903, 18 Whitfield Rd., Causeway Bay,
    Hong Kong

ASTRA TRADING CORP   175 Fifth Ave, New York, NY 10010, Tel: (212) 254-9995
(Intl merchandiser)
    Astra Hong Kong Trading Corp., 707 Sincere Bldg., 173 Des Voeux Rd.,
        P.O. Box 13337, Central, Hong Kong
    Stellar-Merchandise, Ltd., 707 Sincere Bldg., 173 Des Voeux Rd., P.O. Box 13337,
        Central, Hong Kong

AT&T INTERNATIONAL   295 N Maple Ave, Basking Ridge, NJ 07920,
Tel: (908) 221-2000
(Telecommun)
    AT&T Intl. (East Asia) Inc., 9/F Hong Kong Club Bldg., 3A Chater Rd.,
        Central District, Hong Kong

AT&T PARADYNE   8550 Ulmerton Rd, PO Box 2826, Largo, FL 34294-2826,
Tel: (813) 530-2000
(Mfr data commun prdts & serv)
    AT&T Paradyne Far East Corp., Room 901, Wing On Centre, 111 Connaught Rd., Central,
        Hong Kong

AVIS INC   900 Old Country Rd, Garden City, NY 11530, Tel: (516) 222-3000
(Car rental serv)
    Avis Hong Kong, 85-91 Leighton Rd., Bonaventure House, Causeway Bay, Hong Kong

AVMARK INC   1911 North Ft Myer Dr, #1000, Arlington, VA 22209,
Tel: (703) 528-5610
(Aviation consult, aircraft appraisal, aviation related pub)
    Avmark Asia Ltd., 11D Cindic Tower, 128 Gloucester Rd., Hong Kong

AVON PRODUCTS INC   9 W 57th St, New York, NY 10019, Tel: (212) 546-6015
(Mfr/distr cosmetics, perfumes)
    Avon Cosmetics Hong Kong Ltd., Hong Kong

THE BANK OF NEW YORK   48 Wall St, New York, NY 10286, Tel: (212) 530-1784
(Banking)
    The Bank of New York, 73 New Henry House, 10 Ice House St., Hong Kong
    Wing Hang Bank Ltd., 161 Queen Rd. Central, Hong Kong

BANKAMERICA CORP   PO Box 37000, San Francisco, CA 94137, Tel: (415) 622-3456
(Financial services)
    BankAmerica Trust Co. (Hong Kong) Ltd., Bank of America Tower, 12 Harcourt Rd.,
        GPO Box 311, Hong Kong

BANKERS TRUST CO   280 Park Ave, New York, NY 10017, Tel: (212) 775-2500
(Banking)
    Bankers Trust Co., G.P.O. Box 10098, Hong Kong

BARBER STEAMSHIP LINES INC   17 Battery Place, New York, NY 10004,
Tel: (212) 908-1234
(Steamship line)
    Barber Wilhelmsen Agencies Ltd., 14 F Berwich House, Harbour City, Canton Rd.,
        Hong Kong

BARDAHL MFG CORP   1400 N W 52nd St, PO Box 70607, Seattle, WA 98107,
   Tel: (206) 783-4851
   (Lubricating oils)
      Bardahl Intl. Oil Corp. Hong Kong, Ltd., 27 Ashley Rd., 10th Floor, Kowloon,
      Hong Kong

BAUSCH & LOMB INC   1 Lincoln First Sq, Rochester, NY 14601-0054,
   Tel: (716) 338-6000
   (Mfr healthcare & optics prdts)
      Bausch & Lomb (Hong Kong) Ltd., Shaukeiwan, Hong Kong

BEAR STEARNS & CO INC   245 Park Ave, New York, NY 10167, Tel: (212) 272-2000
   (Invest banking & trading)
      Bear Stearns-Kimbaco Ltd.,, Bank of China Bldg. 60/F, 1 Garden Rd., Central,
      Hong Kong
      Shun Loong-Bear Stearns Ltd., East Tower- #1303, Bond Centre, 89 Queensway,
      Central, Hong Kong

BECKMAN INSTRUMENTS INC   2500 Harbor Blvd, Box 3100, Fullerton, CA 92634,
   Tel: (714) 871-4848
   (Mfr/distr/serv research & clinical lab instru, sys, software & reagents)
      Beckman Instruments (Hong Kong) Ltd., 15th fl., Gee Chang Hong Centre,
      65 Wong Chuk Hang Rd., Aberdeen, Hong Kong

BEL FUSE INC   198 Van Vorst St, Jersey City, NJ 07302, Tel: (201) 432-0463
   (Electronic components)
      Bel Fuse, Ltd., J. Hotung House, 1-C Middle Rd., Kowloon, Hong Kong

BELLSOUTH INTERNATIONAL   1155 Peachtree St NE, #400, Atlanta, GA 30367,
   Tel: (404) 249-4800
   (Mobile commun, telecom network sys)
      BellSouth Intl., Hong Kong

BIO-RAD LABORATORIES   2200 Wright Ave, Richmond, CA 94804,
   Tel: (415) 234-4130
   (Spec chems, clinical diagnostic prdts, test kits)
      Bio-Rad Pacific (HK), Sincere Ins. Bldg., 1-3 Des Voeux Rd. West, Hong Kong

BLACK & DECKER CORP   701 E Joppa Road, Towson, MD 21204, Tel: (301) 583-3900
   (Mfr portable elect & pneumatic power tools, household prdts)
      Black & Decker Hong Kong Ltd./Acceptor Enterprises Ltd., 201 Great China, House,
      14 Queen's Rd., Hong Kong

BONDED SERVICES   2050 Center Ave, Fort Lee, NJ 07024, Tel: (201) 592-7868
   (Storage, distribution & service of film & tape libraries)
      Bonded Services Intl. Ltd., Gee, Chang Industrial Bldg., 4th Floor, Factory C,
      108 Lok Shan Rd., To Kwa Wan, Kowloon, Hong Kong

BOURNS INC   1200 Columbia Ave, Riverside, CA 92507, Tel: (714) 781-5960
   (Mfr resistive com & networks, precision potentiometers, panel controls)
      Bourns Asia Pacific Inc., Citicorp Centre, 14th fl., 18 Whitfield Rd.,
      Causeway Bay, Hong Kong

BOYDEN ASSOCIATES INC   260 Madison Ave, New York, NY 10016,
   Tel: (212) 685-3400
   (Mgt consultants, exec search)
      Boyden Associates Ltd., Bank of America Tower, 12 Harcourt Rd., Hong Kong

BRANSON ULTRASONICS CORP   Eagle Rd, Danbury, CT 06810, Tel: (203) 796-0400
(Ultrasonic & vibratory plastics assembly mach)
   Branson Sonic Power Co., Shop F, Wei Chien Ct., Wyler Garden, Wyler Garden,
   Tokwawan, Kowloon, Hong Kong

BRISTOL LABORATORIES   PO Box 657, Syracuse, NY 13201, Tel: (315) 432-2000
(Pharm prdts)
   Bristol-Myers Hong Kong, Ltd., 4th floor, Sincere Insurance Bldg.,
   4-6 Hennessy Rd., Hong Kong

BRK ELECTRONICS   780 McClure Rd, Aurora, IL 60504-2495, Tel: (708) 851-7330
(Mfr smoke detectors, fire extinguishers, lights, timers & sensor sys)
   BRK Electronics Hong Kong, Rm. 624, Star House, 3 Salisbury Rd., Kowloon, Hong Kong

BROWN & ROOT INC   4100 Clinton Dr, Houston, TX 77020-6299,
Tel: (713) 676-4141
(Engr, constr & maintenance)
   Pypun-Howard Humphreys Ltd., 1/3 flrs., Lockhart Centre, 301-307 Lockhart Rd.,
   Wan Chai, Hong Kong
   Pypun-Howard Humphreys Ltd., 1/3 flrs., Lockhart Centre, 301-307 Lockhart Rd.,
   Wan Chai, Hong Kong

BUCK CONSULTANTS INC   Two Pennsylvania Plaza, New York, NY 10121,
Tel: (212) 330-1000
(Employee benefit, actuarial & compensation conslt serv)
   Buck Consultants, One Exchange Sq. 32/F, 8 Connaught Place, Central, Hong Kong

BULOVA WATCH CO INC   Bulova Park, 75-20 Astoria Blvd, Jackson Heights,
NY 11370, Tel: (718) 565-4200
(Mfr timepieces, watches & clocks, watch parts, batteries, precision defense prdts)
   Bulova Watch Intl. Ltd., 601 Prince's Bldg., Chater Rd., Central, Hong Kong

BURLINGTON AIR EXPRESS   18200 Van Karman Ave, Irvine, CA 92715,
Tel: (714) 752-1212
(Air freight)
   Burlington Air Express, Kowloon Bay Cargo Centre 3/F, Godown A, 59 Tai Yip St.,
   Kowloon Bay, Kowloon, Hong Kong

LEO BURNETT CO INC   35 West Wacker Dr, Chicago, IL 60601, Tel: (312) 220-5959
(Advertising agency)
   Leo Burnett, Ltd., Mount Parker House, 9th fl., 1111 King's Rd., Quarry Bay,
   Hong Kong

BURNS & ROE INC   550 Kinderkamack Rd, Oradell, NJ 07649, Tel: (201) 265-2000
(Consulting engineers)
   Burns & Roe Far East, Ltd., 99 Repulse Bay Rd., Repulse Bay, Hong Kong

BURSON-MARSTELLER   230 Park Ave, New York, NY 10003-1566, Tel: (212) 614-4000
(Public relations/public affairs consultants)
   Burson-Marsteller (HK) Ltd., 23rd fl., United Centre, 95 Queensway, Hong Kong

BUSINESS INTERNATIONAL CORP   1 Dag Hammarskjold Plaza, New York, NY 10017,
Tel: (212) 750-6300
(Intl business info: consulting, forecasting, research, publ)
   Business Intl. Asia/Pacific, Ltd., 1111-1119 Mt. Parker House, City Pl.,
   Taikoo Shing, Quarry Bay, Hong Kong

CARL BYOIR & ASSOCIATES INC   380 Madison Ave, New York, NY 10017,
   Tel: (212) 986-6100
   (Public relations consultants)
      Jeff Mann & Associates Ltd., 1101 Block B, Watson Rd., North Point, Hong Kong

CALTEX PETROLEUM CORP   PO Box 619500, Dallas, TX 75261, Tel: (214) 830-1000
   (Petroleum prdts)
      Caltex Oil Hong Kong Ltd., GPO Box 147, Hong Kong

CAMPBELL SOUP CO   Campbell Place, Camden, NJ 08101, Tel: (609) 342-4800
   (Food prdts)
      Campbell Soup Far East Ltd., Harbour Centre 1806, 25 Harbour Rd., Wanchai, Hong Kong

CARGILL   PO Box 9300, Minneapolis, MN 55440, Tel: (612) 475-7575
   (Food prdts, feeds, animal prdts)
      Cargill Hong Kong Ltd., 36th fl., One Pacific Place, 88 Queensway, Central,
      Hong Kong

CATERPILLAR INC   100 N E Adams St, Peoria, IL 61629, Tel: (309) 675-1000
   (Mfr earth/material-handling & constr mach & equip, engines, generators)
      Caterpillar China Ltd., c/o Caterpillar Far East Ltd., Sun Hung Kai Centre,
      30 Harbour Rd., GPO 3069, Wanchai, Hong Kong
      Caterpillar Far East Ltd., Sun Hung Kai Centre, 30 Harbour Rd., GPO 3069, Wanchai,
      Hong Kong

CENTRAL NATIONAL-GOTTESMAN INC   100 Park Ave, New York, NY 10017,
   Tel: (212) 532-7300
   (Pulp & paper prdts)
      Central National Hong Kong Ltd., c/o Che San & Co. Ltd., 3/F Che San Bldg.,
      10-12 Pottinger St., Central, Hong Kong

CHASE MANHATTAN BANK N A   1 Chase Manhattan Plaza, New York, NY 10081,
   Tel: (212) 552-2222
   (Intl banking)
      The Chase Manhattan Bank N.A., Alexandra House, 7 Des Voeux Rd. Central,
      G.P.O. Box 104, Hong Kong
      The Chase Manhattan Bank N.A., G.P.O. Box 104, 280 Gloucester Rd., Causeway Bay,
      Hong Kong

CHEMICAL BANK   277 Park Ave, New York, NY 10172, Tel: (212) 310-6161
   (Banking & financial serv)
      Chemical Bank Hong Kong, The Landmark, 11 Pedder St., Central, Hong Kong

THE CHERRY CORP   3600 Sunset Ave, PO Box 718, Waukegan, IL 60087,
   Tel: (708) 662-9200
   (Mfr switches, keyboards, etc)
      Cherasia Ltd., 5/F Unit 5-8 Westlands Centre, 20 Westlands Rd., Quarry Bay,
      Hong Kong

THE CHUBB CORP   15 Mountain View Rd, Warren, NJ 07060, Tel: (201) 580-2000
   (Holding co: property/casualty ins)
      Federal Insurance Co., Hong Kong

CIGNA CORP   One Liberty Place, 1650 Market St, Philadelphia, PA 19101,
   Tel: (215) 523-4000
   (Ins, invest, health care & other fin servs)
      Cigna Property & Casualty Insurance Co., Office Tower 29/F, Convention Plaza,

1 Harbour Rd., Wanchaiz, Hong Kong
Cigna Worldwide Insurance Co., East Point Centre 16/F, 555 Hennessy Rd.,
Causeway Bay, Hong Kong
Esis Intl., Inc., Edinburgh Tower 5/F, The Landmark, 15 Queen's Rd., Central,
Hong Kong
Insurance Co. of North America, Office Tower/Convention Plaza 29/F, Wanchai,
1 Harbour Rd., PO Box 703, Hong Kong

CITIBANK NA   399 Park Ave, New York, NY 10043, Tel: (212) 559-1000
(Intl banking)
Citibank, Citibank Tower, 8 Queen's Rd. Central, P.O. Box 14, Hong Kong
Citibank, other locations in Hong Kong

CLEARY GOTTLIEB STEEN & HAMILTON   1 State Street Plaza, New York, NY 10004,
Tel: (212) 344-0600
(Law firm)
Cleary, Gottlieb, Steen & Hamilton, 11th fl. Printing House, 18 Ice House St.,
Hong Kong

THE COCA-COLA CO   310 North Ave NW, PO Box Drawer 1734, Atlanta, GA 30313,
Tel: (404) 676-2121
(Mfr & sale of soft drink syrups & concentrates, juices & food prdts, motion pic & TV
prod)
The Coca Cola Co. Hong Kong, all mail to: U.S. address

COLGATE-PALMOLIVE CO   300 Park Ave, New York, NY 10022, Tel: (212) 310-2000
(Pharms, cosmetics, toiletries, detergents)
Colgate-Palmolive Hong Kong, Ltd., 1423-9 Prince's Bldg., 10 Chater Rd.,
P.O. Box 1324, Hong Kong

COLUMBIA PICTURES INDUSTRIES INC   711 Fifth Ave, New York, NY 10022,
Tel: (212) 751-4400
(Producer & distributor of motion pictures)
Fox-Columbia Film Distributors, Loong San Building, 140-142, Connaught Rd. C,
Hong Kong
Fox-Columbia Film Distributors, G.P.O. Box 397, Hong Kong

COMBUSTION ENGINEERING INC   900 Long Ridge Road, Stamford, CT 06902,
Tel: (203) 329-8771
(Tech constr)
Causeway Bay, Rm 1606, Hanglung Centre, 2-20 Paterson St., Hong Kong

COMMERCIAL METALS CO   PO Box 1046, Dallas, TX 75221, Tel: (214) 689-4300
(Metal collecting/processing, steel mills, metal trading)
CMC Far East Ltd., Unit C, 128 Gloucester Rd., Hong Kong

COMPTON INTERNATIONAL   625 Madison Ave, New York, NY 10022,
Tel: (212) 754-1100
(Advertising)
Chase/Compton Advertising Ltd., 1 Luard Rd., Hong Kong

COMPUTER ASSOCIATES INTL INC   711 Stewart Ave, Garden City, NY 11530,
Tel: (516) 227-3300
(Devel/mkt/mgt info mgt & bus applications software)
Computer Associates, World-Wide House #2303-23/F, 19 Des Voeux Rd., Central,
Hong Kong

CONAIR CORP   11 Executive Ave, Edison, NJ 08817, Tel: (201) 287-4800
  (Mfr hair dryers, shower massage units, cosmetics, hair care prdts)
    Continental Conair, Ltd., Rm 713, New World Centre, Salisbury Rd., T.S.T., Kowloon,
      Hong Kong

CONNELL BROTHERS CO LTD   320 California St, San Francisco, CA 94104,
  Tel: (415) 772-4000
  (Exp/imp chems, commodities, minerals, cons materials)
    Connell Bros. Co., Ltd., GPO Box 88, Hong Kong

CONTINENTAL BANK NA   231 S Lasalle St, Chicago, IL 60697, Tel: (312) 828-2345
  (Coml banking servs)
    Continental Bank Corp., Edinburgh Tower 32/F, 15 Queen's Rd., Central, Hong Kong
    Continental International Securities Ltd., Edinburgh Tower 32/F, 15 Queen's Rd.,
      Central, Hong Kong

CONTINENTAL CAN CO   PO Box 5410, Stamford, CT 06856, Tel: (203) 357-8110
  (Packaging prdts & mach, metal, plastic & paper containers)
    Continental Can Hong Kong Ltd., 8-10 Dai Kuai St., Tai Po Ind. Estate, Tai Po,
      N.T., Hong Kong

CONTROL DATA CORP   8100 34th Ave S, Minneapolis, MN 55440,
  Tel: (612) 853-8100
  (Control data equip, computer sys serv & financial serv)
    Control Data Hong Kong Ltd., 185-187 Wal Yip St., 4th Floor, Kowloon, Hong Kong

CORESTATES FINANCIAL CORP   PO Box 7618, Philadelphia, PA 19101,
  Tel: (215) 973-3100
  (Banking)
    Philadelphia Natl. Bank, Fu House, First Floor, 7 Ice House St., Hong Kong

CORNING CORP   Houghton Park, PO Box 2000, Corning, NY 14831,
  Tel: (617) 974-9000
  (Mfr glass, ceramic materials)
    Corning (HK) Ltd., 21/f Sing Pao Bldg., 101 King's Rd., North Point, Hong Kong

COUDERT BROTHERS   200 Park Ave, New York, NY 10166, Tel: (212) 880-4400
  (Lawyers)
    Coudert Bros., Alexandra House, 31st Floor, 20 Chater Rd., Hong Kong

CPC INTERNATIONAL INC   PO Box 8000, International Plaza, Englewood Cliffs,
  NJ 07632, Tel: (201) 894-4000
  (Mfr consumer food prdts & corn refining prdts)
    Corn Products Co. (Hong Kong) Ltd., 6 Dai Fu St., Tai Po Industrial Estate,
      Tao Po. New Territories, Hong Kong

CROCKER BANK INTERNATIONAL   299 Park Ave, New York, NY 10017,
  Tel: (212) 980-5500
  (Intl banking serv)
    Crocker Bank Intl., 1708 Alexandra House, Chater Rd., Hong Kong

CTS CORP   905 N West Blvd, Elkhart, IN 46514, Tel: (219) 293-7511
  (Electronic components & devices, metal enclosures, store fixtures)
    CTS Fabri-Tek HK Ltd., 11/f Lap Shun Centre, 552-566 Castle Peak Rd., Kwai Chung,
      NT, Hong Kong
    CTS Hong Kong Pte. Ltd., 11/F Mita Centre, 552-566 Castle Peak Rd., Kwai Chung, NT,
      Hong Kong

D'ARCY MASIUS BENTON & BOWLES INC (DMB&B)   1675 Broadway, New York,
  NY 10019, Tel: (212) 468-3622
  (Advertising & communications)
    DMB&B Modern Ltd., 10/F Hennessy Centre, East Wing, 500 Hennessy Rd., Hong Kong

D-M-E COMPANY   29111 Stephenson Highway, Madison Heights, MI 48071,
  Tel: (313) 398-6000
  (Basic tooling for plastic molding & die casting)
    Polymide Intl. Co. Ltd., 27 Des Voeux Rd., West 12/F, Hong Kong

LEO A DALY CO   8600 Indian Hills Dr, Omaha, NE 68114, Tel: (402) 391-8111
  (Plan arch engr & interiors, design servs)
    Leo A. Daly Pacific Ltd., Suite 1011-1019 Mt. Parker House, 1111 King's, Rd.,
      Quarry Bay, Hong Kong

DAMES & MOORE   911 Wilshire Blvd, Los Angeles, CA 90017, Tel: (213) 683-1560
  (Consulting engineers)
    Dames & Moore, Tsim Sha Tsui Centre 233, 66 Mody Rd., Tsim Sha Tsui East, Kowloon,
      Hong Kong

DATA GENERAL CORP   4400 Computer Dr, Westboro, MA 01580, Tel: (617) 366-8911
  (Design, mfr gen purpose computer sys & peripheral prdts & servs)
    Data General HK Sales & Service Ltd., 5/f Wheelock House, 20 Pedder St., Hong Kong
    Data General Hong Kong, Ltd., New World Office Bldg. #1014, 20 Salisbury, Rd.,
      Tsimshatsui, Koloon, Hong Kong

DATAEASE INTL INC   7 Cambridge Dr, Trumbull, CT 06611, Tel: (203) 374-8000
  (Mfr applications devel software)
    Great Code Systems, 2204 Yung Wai Commercial, 109-111 Gloucester Rd., Wanchai,
      Hong Kong

DATAPRODUCTS CORP   6200 Canada Ave, PO Box 746, Woodland Hills, CA 91365,
  Tel: (818) 887-8000
  (Mfr computer printers & supplies)
    Dataproducts Hong Kong, Ltd., 5-11 Fl., Block C&D, Sime Darby Ind. Centre,
      420 Kwun Tong Rd., Hong Kong

DDB NEEDHAM WORLDWIDE INC   437 Madison Ave, New York, NY 10022,
  Tel: (212) 415-2000
  (Advertising)
    DDB Needham Asia Pacific Ltd., Citicorp Centre 17/F, 18 Whitfield Rd.,
      Causeway Bay, Hong Kong
    DDB Needham Worldwide DIK Ltd., Citicorp Centre 17/F, 18 Whitfield Rd.,
      Causeway Bay, Hong Kong

DEAK & CO INC   29 Broadway, New York, NY 10006, Tel: (212) 635-0515
  (Foreign exchange specialists)
    Deak & Co. Far East, Ltd., 406 Shell House, Queen's Rd. Central, Hong Kong

DENTSPLY INTL INC   PO Box 872, York, PA 17405, Tel: (717) 845-7511
  (Mfr dental, medical & ind supplies & equip)
    Dentsply Asia Inc., 23/F Gee Chang Hong Centre, 65 Wong Chuk Hang Rd., Aberdeen,
      Hong Kong

DHJ INDUSTRIES INC   1040 Ave of the Americas, New York, NY 10018,
  Tel: (212) 944-4500
  (Mfr of knit fabrics, interlinings plastic chips & denim)

(cont)

DHJ Industries Ltd., 7/f Wyler Centre, 210 Tai Lin Pai Rd., Kwai Chung, N.T., Hong Kong

R E DIETZ CO   224 Wilkinson St, Syracuse, NY 13204, Tel: (315) 424-7400
(Automotive & safety lighting equip)
    R.E. Dietz Co., Ltd., 1st Floor, Express Industrial Bldg., 43 Heung Uip Rd.,
    P.O. Box 220, Aberdeen, Hong Kong

DILLINGHAM CONSTRUCTION CORP   5944 Inglewood Dr, Pleasanton, CA 94566,
Tel: (415) 847-7700
(General contracting)
    Dillingham Construction (HK) Ltd., 904 Tower Two, South Seas Centre, 75 Mody St.,
    Tsim Sha Tsui East, Kowloon, Hong Kong

DONALDSON CO INC   PO Box 1299, Minneapolis, MN 55440, Tel: (612) 887-3131
(Filtration prdts & sys)
    Donaldson Far East Ltd., 1201 Taikoktsui Center, 11 Kok Cheung St., Kowloon,
    Hong Kong

DONALDSON LUFKIN & JENRETTE INC   140 Broadway, New York, NY 10005,
Tel: (212) 504-3000
(Investment mgmt)
    Donaldson, Lufkin & Jenrette, 19/F Bank of America Tower, 12 Harcourt Rd., Hong Kong

DOW CHEMICAL CO   2030 Dow Center, Midland, MI 48640, Tel: (517) 636-1000
(Chems, plastics, fibers, pharms)
    Dow Chemical Hong Kong, Ltd., Gammon House, 12 Harbour Rd., P.O. Box 711, Hong Kong

DOW CORNING CORP   2220 W Salzburg Rd, PO Box 1767, Midland, MI 48640,
Tel: (517) 496-4000
(Silicones, silicon chems, solid lubricants)
    Dow Corning Asia, Ltd., Rm 802-806, Gloucester Tower, The Landmark, 11 Pedder St.,
    Hong Kong

DOW JONES & CO INC   200 Liberty St, New York, NY 10281, Tel: (212) 416-2000
(Publisher)
    Asian Wall Street Journal, GPO Box 9825, Hong Kong

DRAKE BEAM MORIN INC   100 Park Ave, New York, NY 10017, Tel: (212) 692-7700
(Human resource mgmt consulting & training)
    Drake Beam Morin Hong Kong Ltd., Star House, Salisbury Rd., Kowloon, Hong Kong

DRAVO CORP   1 Oliver Plaza, Pittsburgh, PA 15222, Tel: (412) 777-5000
(Material handling equip, process plants)
    Dravo Corp Hong Kong Ltd., 901 Hutchison House, 10 Harcourt.Rd., Hong Kong

DRESSER INDUSTRIES INC   1600 Pacific Bldg, PO Box 718, Dallas, TX 75221,
Tel: (214) 740-6000
(Diversified supplier of equip & tech serv to energy & natural resource ind)
    Dresser Trading Div., American Chamber of Commerce Bldg., 1030 Swire House, Rm 2,
    Hong Kong

DREW CHEMICAL CORP   One Drew Plaza, Boonton, NJ 07005, Tel: (201) 263-7600
(Spec chems for ind water & fuel treatment, chem processing)
    Tin Sing Chemical Engineering Co., Kung Sheung Bldg., 18 Fenwick St., Wanchai,
    Hong Kong

E I DU PONT DE NEMOURS & CO   Du Pont Bldg, 1007 Market St, Wilmington,
  DE 19898, Tel: (302) 774-1000
  (Mfr/sale diversified chems, plastics, specialty prdts & fibers)
    DuPont Far East, Inc., 915 Prince's Bldg., 10 Chater Rd., Hong Kong

DURACELL INTL INC   Berkshire Industrial Park, Bethel, CT 06801,
  Tel: (203) 796-4000
  (Mfr batteries)
    Duracell Asia Ltd., Unit 1602, World Finance Centre, South Tower, Harbour City,
      Canton Rd., Kowloon, Hong Kong

EASTMAN KODAK CO   343 State St, Rochester, NY 14650-0518, Tel: (716) 724-4000
  (Devel/mfr photo & chem prdts, info mgmt/video/copier sys, fibers/plastics for
  various ind)
    Kodak Far East, Ltd., 321 Java Rd., North Point, Hong Kong

ECOLAB INC   370 Wabasha St, St Paul, MN 55102, Tel: (612) 293-2233
  (Ind & household detergents, cleaning agents & equip)
    Economics Laboratory Hong Kong, Ltd., 103 Wai Yip St., Ground & First Floors,
      Kwun Tong, Kowloon, Hong Kong

ELANCO PRODUCTS CO   PO Box 1750, Indianapolis, IN 46206, Tel: (317) 261-2000
  (Antibiotics, fine chems)
    Elanco Agricultural & Industrial Products, 1026-1030 Prince's Bldg., 10 Chater Rd.,
      Hong Kong

EMERY WORLDWIDE   3350 W Bayshore Rd, Palo Alto, CA 94304, Tel: (415) 855-9100
  (Expedited heavy air freight)
    Emery Worldwide, Suite 1503/1504, Harcourt House, 39 Gloucester Rd., Wanchai,
      Hong Kong

EXXON CHEMICAL CO   9 Old Kings Hwy S, Darien, CT 06820, Tel: (203) 655-5200
  (Mfr & sales of petrochems)
    Essochem Eastern, Ltd., 29th Floor, Connaught Centre, Connaught Rd., P.O. Box 749,
      Central, Hong Kong

EXXON CORP   225 E John Carpenter Frwy, Irving, TX 75062, Tel: (214) 444-1000
  (Petroleum & petroleum prdts)
    Eastern Energy, Ltd., 10th Floor, St. George's Bldg., 2 Ice House St., Hong Kong

FAIRCHILD CAMERA & INSTRUMENT CORP   PO Box 58090, Santa Clara,
  CA 95052-8090, Tel: (408) 743-3355
  (Mfr electr instru & controls)
    Fairchild Semiconductor Hong Kong, Ltd., 135 Hoi Bun Rd., Kwun Tong, P.O. Box 9575,
      Kowloon, Hong Kong

FARAH INC   8889 Gateway Blvd W, El Paso, TX 79925, Tel: (915) 593-4000
  (Mfr wearing apparel)
    Farah (Far East) Ltd., Prince's Bldg., 17th Floor, 10 Charter Rd., Central,
      Hong Kong

FEDERAL EXPRESS CORP   PO Box 727, Memphis, TN 38194-4212, Tel: (901) 922-6900
  (Package air express svc)
    Federal Express (HK) Ltd., 100 Sung Wong Toi Rd., Tokwawan, Kowloon, Hong Kong

FELTON INTERNATIONAL INC   599 Johnson Ave, Brooklyn, NY 11237,
    Tel: (212) 497-4664
    (Essential oils & extracts, perfumes & flavor material, aromatic chems)
       Felton Chemicals (Asia) Ltd., Yee Lim Industrial Bldg. (#3), Kin Hong St.,
       Kwai Chung, N.T., Hong Kong

FERREX INTL INC   17 Battery Pl, New York, NY 10004, Tel: (212) 509-7030
    (Mfg/distr of road maint mach, welding & ind equip & supplies)
       Ferrex-Southeast Asia, Realty Gardens, Hong Kong

FERRO CORPORATION   One Erieview Plaza, Cleveland, OH 44114,
    Tel: (216) 641-8580
    (Chems, coatings, plastics, refractories)
       Ferro Far East Ltd., P.O. Box 98436, Tsim Sha Tsui, Kowloon, Hong Kong

FIDELITY BANK   135 S Broad St, Philadelphia, PA 19109, Tel: (215) 985-6000
    (Investments & banking)
       FIB Asia Ltd, 10/F, One Exchange Sq., 8 Connaught Place, Hong Kong

FIRST INTERSTATE BANCORP   633 W 5th St, Los Angeles, CA 90071,
    Tel: (213) 614-3001
    (Banking)
       First Interstate Bank, Ltd., GPO Box 35, Central, Hong Kong

FIRST NATIONAL BANK OF BOSTON   100 Federal St, Boston, MA 02110,
    Tel: (617) 434-2200
    (Commercial banking)
       The First National Bank of Boston, Connaught Centre, Connaught Rd., Hong Kong

FIRST NATIONAL BANK OF CHICAGO   One First National Plaza, Chicago, IL 60670,
    Tel: (312) 732-4000
    (Financial services)
       First Chicago Hong Kong Ltd., Jardine House/13, 1 Connaught Place, Hong Kong
       First National Bank of Chicago, Jardine House/13, 1 Connaught St., Hong Kong

FIRST NATIONAL BANK OF OREGON   PO Box 3131, Portland, OR 97208,
    Tel: (503) 225-2111
    (Banking)
       First National Bank of Oregon, 3101 Connaught Centre, Connaught Rd., Central,
       Hong Kong

FISHER CONTROLS INTL INC   8000 Maryland Ave, Clayton, MO 63105,
    Tel: (314) 694-9900
    (Ind process control equip)
       Fisher Controls Hong Kong Ltd., Room 2807-8 Windsor House, 311 Gloucester House,
       Causeway Bay, Hong Kong

FLEXTRONICS INC   34551 Ardenwood Blvd, Fremont, CA 94555, Tel: (415) 794-3539
    (Contract mfr for electronics ind)
       Flextronics Hong Kong Ltd., Wo Kee Hong Bldg., 585-609 Castle Peak Rd., Kwai Chung,
       Hong Kong

FLYING TIGER LINE INC   7401 World Way W, Los Angeles, CA 90009,
    Tel: (213) 646-6161
    (Air frt carrier, air cargo service worldwide)
       Flying Tiger Line Inc., New Cargo Complex Office Block, Room 223,
       International Airport, Hong Kong

FMC CORP   200 E Randolph Dr, Chicago, IL 60601, Tel: (312) 861-6000
  (Mach & chem for industry, agric & govt)
    FMC Far East, Ltd., World Shipping Centre 606, Harbour City, 7 Canton Rd.,
    Tsimshatsui, Kowloon, Hong Kong

FOOTE CONE & BELDING COMMUNICATIONS INC   101 E Erie St, Chicago,
  IL 60611-2897, Tel: (312) 751-7000
  (Advertising agency)
    Foote, Cone & Belding Ltd., 2309 Sun Hung Kai Centre, 30 Harbour Rd., Hong Kong

FOUR WINDS INTL INC   1 SW Columbia Ave, #1200, Portland, OR 97258,
  Tel: (503) 241-2732
  (Transp of household goods & general cargo)
    Four Winds Removal Ltd., 5/F Len Shing Ind. Bldg., 4 A Kung Ngam Village Rd.,
    Shaukeiwan, Hong Kong

FOXBORO CO   33 Commercial St, Foxboro, MA 02035, Tel: (508) 543-8750
  (Mfr prdts/provide servs for ind automation)
    Advanced Technology Svcs., Star House #1609, 3 Salisbury Rd., Kowloon, Hong Kong

THE FRANKLIN MINT   Franklin Center, PA 19091, Tel: (215) 459-6000
  (Creation/mfr/mktg collectible items)
    Franklin Mint Ltd., 5/F Wing On Plaza, Tsimshatsui East, Kowloon, Hong Kong

GAMLEN CHEMICAL CO   121 S Maple Ave, S San Francisco, CA 94080,
  Tel: (415) 873-1750
  (Chems, detergents & tank cleansers)
    Gamlen Far East, Suite 1503, Tugu Insurance Bldg., Lockhart Rd., Hong Kong

GANNETT CO INC   1100 Wilson Blvd, Arlington, VA 22224, Tel: (703) 284-6000
  (Newspaper pub, opinion research)
    USA Today Intl., Hong Kong

GCA CORP   7 Shattuck Rd, Andover, MA 01810, Tel: (508) 837-3000
  (Mfr imaging sys for semiconductor ind)
    General Signal Asia, Ltd., Room 1910 Park-In Commercial Centre, 56 Dundas St.,
    Kowloon, Hong Kong

GENERAL AUTOMATION INC   1055 S East St, Anaheim, CA 92806,
  Tel: (714) 778-4800
  (Computer hardware & serv)
    General Automation Hong Kong Ltd., 10th Floor, Pennington Commercial Bldg.,
    17 Pennington St., Causeway Bay, Hong Kong

GENERAL DEVELOPMENT CORP   1111 South Bayshore Drive, Miami, FL 33131,
  Tel: (305) 350-1200
  (Real estate agency)
    General Development Corp. Hong Kong Ltd., 1036 Alexander House, 11-A Des Voeux Rd.,
    Central, Hong Kong

GENERAL ELECTRIC CO   3135 Easton Tpk, Fairfield, CT 06431,
  Tel: (203) 373-2211
  (Diversified mfr, tech & servs)
    GE China Co. Ltd., 1201 Two Exchange Sq., 12/F, GPO 705, Hong Kong

GENERAL FOODS CORP   250 North St, White Plains, NY 10625, Tel: (914) 335-2500
(Processor, distributor & mfr of foods)
   General Foods (Asia) Ltd., Suites 1509-13, Connaught Center, 1 Connaught Pl.,
   Central, Hong Kong

GERBER PRODUCTS CO   445 State St, Fremont, MI 49412, Tel: (616) 928-2000
(Mfr/distr baby food & related prdts)
   Gerber Baby Products Intl. Ltd., 1312 Hang Lung Ctr., 2-20 Paterson St.,
   Causeway Bay, Hong Kong

GETZ CORP   150 Post St, San Francisco, CA 94108, Tel: (415) 772-5500
(Marketing/distribution serv)
   The Getz Corp., 5A Upperground Floor, Far East Financial Centre, 16 Harcourt Rd.,
   Hong Kong
   The Getz Corp. (Hong Kong) Ltd., 8/F Wyler Centre, 210 Tai Lin Pai Rd.,
   Kwain Chung, NT, Hong Kong

GLOBAL INTERNATIONAL   500 Ygnacio Valley Rd, #175, Walnut Creek, CA 94596,
   Tel: (415) 933-2293
   (Freight forwarding)
   Global International Forwarding Ltd., Cheung Lee Industrial Bldg. 18/F,
   #9 Cheung Lee St., Chai Wan, Hong Kong

W R GRACE & CO   1114 Ave of the Americas, New York, NY 10036,
   Tel: (212) 819-5500
   (Specialty chems, natural resources, consumer serv)
   W.R. Grace Far East Investment Co., Ltd., 3rd Floor, Kayamally Bldg.,
   22 Queen's Rd., Central, Hong Kong
   W.R. Grace Hong Kong, Ltd., 3rd Floor, Kayamally Bldg., 22 Queen's Rd., Central,
   P.O. Box 710, Hong Kong

GRACO INC   4040 Olson Memorial Hwy, PO Box 1441, Minneapolis, MN 55440-1441,
   Tel: (612) 623-6000
   (Mfr/serv fluid handling equip & sys)
   Graco Hong Kong Ltd., The Goldmark Bldg. #1203, 502 Hennessy Rd., Causeway Bay,
   Hong Kong

GRAY LINE ASSOCIATION INC   350 Fifth Ave, New York, NY 10022,
   Tel: (212) 714-2120
   (Sightseeing tours)
   Gray Line Tours of Hong Kong, Ltd., 501 Cheong Hing Bldg., 72 Nathan Rd.,
   P.O. Box 6710, Kowloon, Hong Kong

GREY ADVERTISING INC   777 Third Ave, New York, NY 10017, Tel: (212) 546-2000
(Advertising)
   People & Grey Advertising, Ltd., Penthouse, 66 Gloucester Rd., Hong Kong

GRIFFITH LABORATORIES INC   I Griffith Center, Alsip, IL 60658,
   Tel: (708) 371-0900
   (Ind food ingredients & equip)
   Griffith Laboratories Ltd., 8th fl. Unit A-B, Supreme Industrial Bldg.,
   15 Shan Mei St., Fo-Tan, Shatin, N.T., Hong Kong

GROLIER INC   Old Shereman Tpk, Danbury, CT 06816, Tel: (203) 797-3500
(Publishers)
   Grolier Intl., Inc., Suite 2102, Jubilee Bldg., 42-46 Gloucester Rd., Hong Kong

GTE CORP   One Stamford Forum, Stamford, CT 06904, Tel: (203) 965-2000
(Electr prdts, telecom sys, publ & commun)
   GTE Intl. Ltd., 11th floor, Gammon House, 12 Harbour Rd., Hong Kong
   GTE Sylvania Far East Ltd., 10 Ng Fong St., San Po Kong, Kowloon, Hong Kong

GTE DIRECTORIES CORP   West Airport Dr, DFW Airport, TX 75261-9810,
   Tel: (214) 453-7000
(Pub telephone directories)
   GTE Directories (HK) Ltd., 22/23 flr. Fortress Tower, 250 Kings Rd., North Point,
   Hong Kong

FRANK B HALL & CO INC   549 Pleasantville Rd, Briarcliff Manor, NY 10510,
   Tel: (914) 769-9200
(Insurance)
   Frank B. Hall & Co. Far East, Ltd., 1231 Prince's Bldg., Hong Kong
   Frank B. Hall & Co. Ltd., 522 Prince's Bldg., Ice House St., Central, Hong Kong

HAMLIN INC   612 E Lake St, Lake Mills, WI 53551, Tel: (414) 648-3000
(Mfr position sensors, switches, relays)
   Hamlin/Stuart Ltd., 2701 Abba Commercial Bldg., 223 Aberdeen Main Rd., Aberdeen,
   Hong Kong

HANDY & HARMAN   850 Third Ave, New York, NY 10022, Tel: (212) 752-3400
(Precious & specialty metals for industry, refining, scrap metal)
   Handy & Harman (HK) Ltd., 1402 Bank of East Asia Bldg., 10 Des Voeux, Rd., Hong Kong

HARCOURT BRACE JOVANOVICH INC   Harcourt Brace Jovanovich Bldg, Orlando,
   FL 32887, Tel: (305) 345-2000
(Book publ, tests & related serv, journals, facisimile reprints, mgmt consult,
operates parks/shows)
   Drake Beam Morin-Hong Kong Ltd., Star House 1014-5, Salisbury Rd., Kowloon,
   Hong Kong

THE HARPER GROUP INC   260 Townsend St, PO Box 77933, San Francisco,
   CA 94107, Tel: (415) 978-0600
(Ocean/air freight fwdg, customs brokerage, packing & whse, logistics mgt, ins)
   Circle Freight Intl. (HK), World Commerce Ctr. #712-715, 11 Canton Rd.,
      Harbour City Phase I, Tsimshatsui, Kowloon, Hong Kong
   Rhenania Intl. Transport Services (HK) Ltd., 1401-2 Tung Wai Coml. Bldg.,
      109-111 Gloucester Rd., Wan Chai, Hong Kong
   Western Navigation (Global) Ltd., World Commerce Ctr. #712-715, 11 Canton Rd.,
      Harbour City Phase I, Tsimshatsui, Kowloon, Hong Kong

HERCULES INC   Hercules Plaza, Wilmington, DE 19894, Tel: (302) 594-5000
(Mfr spec chems, plastics, film & fibers, coatings, resins, food ingredients)
   Hercochem (HK) Ltd., 11/F Tower 3, China Hong Kong City, 33 Canton Rd.,
      Tsimshatsui, Kowloon, Hong Kong

HEWLETT-PACKARD CO   3000 Hanover St, PO Box 10301, Palo Alto, CA 94303-0890,
   Tel: (415) 857-1501
(Mfr measurement & computation prdts & sys)
   Hewlett-Packard Asia Ltd., GPO Box 863, Hong Kong
   Hewlett-Packard Hong Kong Ltd., Sun Hung Kai Centre 5/F, 30 Harbour Rd., Hong Kong

HILL & KNOWLTON INC   420 Lexington Ave, New York, NY 10017,
Tel: (212) 697-5600
(Public relations, public affairs, comm counseling)
    Hill & Knowlton Asia, Ltd., Windsor House, 35/f., 311 Gloucester Rd., Hong Kong

HILLERICH & BRADSBY CO INC   PO Box 35700, Louisville, KY 40232-5700,
Tel: (502) 585-5226
(Golf, baseball & softball equip)
    K.S. Ahluwalia & Sons, 8C Hankow Rd., Kowloon, Hong Kong

HOLIDAY INNS INC   3742 Lamar Ave, Memphis, TN 38195, Tel: (901) 362-4001
(Hotels, restaurants, casinos)
    Holiday Inn Hong Kong, P.O. Box 95555, 50 Nathan Rd., Hong Kong

HORWATH & HORWATH INTL   919 Third Ave, New York, NY 10022,
Tel: (212) 980-3100
(Public accountants & auditors)
    Horwath & Horwath Intl. Associates, Wong Bros. & Co., 712-714 Marina House,
      Queen's Rd., Central, Hong Kong

E F HOUGHTON & CO   PO Box 930, Valley Forge, PA 19482-0930,
Tel: (215) 666-4000
(Mfr spec chems, hydraulic fluids, lubricants)
    Far East Trading Co. Hong Kong, Ltd., Pedder Bldg., 2nd Floor, Hong Kong
    Houghton China Co. Ltd., 776-778 Nathan Rd 4/F, Mongkok, Kowloon, Hong Kong

HYATT INTL CORP   200 West Madison St, Chicago, IL 60606, Tel: (312) 750-1234
(Intl hotel mgmt)
    Hyatt Regency Hong Kong, 67 Nathan Rd., Kowloon, Hong Kong

ICF KAISER ENGINEERS   1800 Harrison St, Oakland, CA 94612,
Tel: (415) 268-6000
(Engineering & constr)
    Kaiser Engineers Intl., 3/F Hop Hong Centre, 8-12 Hennessy Rd., Wanchai, Hong Kong

IDEAL TOY CORP   184-10 Jamaica Ave, Hollis, NY 11423, Tel: (212) 454-5000
(Toys, games, dolls)
    Ideal Toy Corp., 319-A J. Hotung House, 5 Hankow. Rd., Kowloon, Hong Kong

ILLFELDER TOY CO INC   200 5th Ave, New York, NY 10010, Tel: (212) 691-5898
(Toys)
    Illco Intl., Ltd., 6th Floor, Sincere Insurance Bldg., 4-6 Hennessy Rd., Hong Kong

IMPERIAL TOY CORP   2060 E Seventh St, Los Angeles, CA 90021,
Tel: (213) 489-2100
(Mfr plastic toys & novelties)
    Fred Kort Intl., Ltd., 501-2 Peninsula Centre 67, Mody Rd., T.S.T. East Kowloon,
      Hong Kong

INA CORPORATION   1600 Arch St, Philadelphia, PA 19101, Tel: (215) 523-5335
(Holding co: ins, financial serv)
    Insurance Co. of North America, China Bldg., Rm 602, 29 Queen's Rd., Central,
      G.P.O. Box 703, Hong Kong

INDUSTRIAL ACOUSTICS CO   1160 Commerce Ave, Bronx, NY 10462,
Tel: (212) 931-8000
(Design/mfr acoustic structures for sound conditioning & noise control)

Industrial Acoustics Co. (HK) Ltd., Unit 12, Honour Industrial Centre 15/F,
   6 Sun Yip St., Chai Wan, Hong Kong

INGERSOLL-RAND CO   200 Chestnut Ridge Rd, Woodcliff Lake, NJ 07675,
   Tel: (201) 573-0123
   (Mfr compressors, rock drills, pumps, air tools)
      Ingersoll-Rand Far East, 203 Asian House, 1 Hennessy Rd., Hong Kong

INSTRON CORP   100 Royall St, Canton, MA 02021, Tel: (617) 828-2500
   (Testing instru)
      Instron (HK) Ltd., 2/f Gulestan, 125 Repulse Bay Rd., Hong Kong

INSTRUMENTATION LABORATORY   113 Hartwell Ave, Lexington, MA 02173-3190,
   Tel: (617) 861-0710
   (Med & sci analyzers & meas instru)
      Instrumentation Laboratory (Far East) Ltd., Leader Ind. Bldg. 18/f,
      37 Wong Chuk Hang Rd., Aberdeen, Hong Kong

INTERMEC CORP   6001 36th Ave West, Everett, WA 98203-9280,
   Tel: (206) 348-2600
   (Mfr automated data collection sys)
      Hang Ching Co., Hong Kong Plaza #2514, 186-191 Connaught Rd., W., Hong Kong
      Interface Machines Ltd., Fortress Tower 9/F, 250 King's Rd., Hong Kong

INTERNATIONAL BUSINESS MACHINES (IBM)   Old Orchard Rd, Armonk,
   NY 10504-1783, Tel: (914) 765-1900
   (Info-handling sys, equip & serv)
      IBM Southeast Asia Svcs Ltd., Hong Kong
      ROLM Hong Kong Ltd., Hong Kong

INTERNATIONAL CHEMICAL CORP   720 Fifth Ave, New York, NY 10019,
   Tel: (212) 397-3300
   (Chems, pharms, etc)
      ICC Hong Kong, Ltd., 206 Intl. Bldg., 141 Des Voeux Rd., Central, Hong Kong

INTERNATIONAL FLAVORS & FRAGRANCES INC   521 W 57th St, New York, NY 10019,
   Tel: (212) 765-5500
   (Create/mfr flavors, fragrances & aroma chems)
      Intl. Flavours & Fragrances Far East, Ltd., 4th Floor, Block A, Watson's Estate,
      2 Watson Rd., North Point, Hong Kong

INTERNATIONAL PAPER   2 Manhattanville Rd, Purchase, NY 10577,
   Tel: (914) 397-1500
   (Mfr/distr container board, paper, wood prdts)
      International Paper Co. (Far East) Ltd., 1207 Alexandra House, 16-20 Chater Rd.,
      Hong Kong
      Veratec Intl. (HK) Ltd., c/o Deacons, Alexandra House, Hong Kong

INTRUSION-PREPAKT INC   5353 W 161st St, Cleveland, OH 44142,
   Tel: (216) 623-0080
   (Concrete, grouting, rock anchors, erosion control mats)
      Intrusion-Prepakt (Far East) Ltd., Causeway Bay Commercial Bldg. 19/F, Nos. 1-13,
      Sugar St., Hong Kong

IRVING TRUST CO   1 Wall St, New York, NY 10015, Tel: (212) 487-2121
   (Intl banking)
      Wing Hang Bank, Ltd., 161 Queen's Rd., Central, Hong Kong

ITEL CONTAINERS INTL CORP   55 Francisco St, San Francisco, CA 94133,
Tel: (415) 984-4400
(Leasing, repair, storage of ocean-going containers)
    Itel Containers Corp Intl., 7/f Fung House, 19 Connaught Rd., Central, Hong Kong

ITT CORP   1330 Ave of the Americas, New York, NY 10019, Tel: (212) 258-1000
(Diversified mfr, tech & services)
    ITT Far East & Pacific Inc., 5th Floor, P & O Bldg., 23 Des Voeux Rd., Central,
    Hong Kong
    ITT Transelectronics, Ltd., 23 Hing Yip St., Kwun Tong, Kowloon, Hong Kong

ITT SHERATON CORP   60 State St, Boston, MA 02108, Tel: (617) 367-3600
(Hotel operations)
    Sheraton Corp., Sheraton Hong Kong, 20 Nathan Rd., Kowloon, Hong Kong

ITW MAGNAFLUX   7300 W Lawrence Ave, Chicago, IL 60656, Tel: (708) 867-8000
(Mfr testing & inspection equip)
    Signode Hong Kong Ltd., 9B, Kin Yip Bldg., 9 Cheung Yee St., Kowloon, Hong Kong

JOHNSON & HIGGINS   125 Broad St, New York, NY 10005, Tel: (212) 574-7000
(Ins brokerage, benefit conslt)
    Johnson & Higgins Hong Kong, Ltd., 3702 Windsor House, 311 Gloucester Rd.,
    Causeway Bay, Hong Kong

JOHNSON & JOHNSON   One Johnson & Johnson Plaza, New Brunswick, NJ 08933,
Tel: (201) 524-0400
(Surgical, med & baby prdts)
    Johnson & Johnson Hong Kong, Ltd., Hong Kong

S C JOHNSON & SON INC   1525 Howe St, Racine, WI 53403, Tel: (414) 631-2000
(Home, auto, commercial & personal care prdts, specialty chems)
    S.C. Johnson, Ltd., P.O. Box 98450, Tsimshatsui Central Post Office, Kowloon,
    Hong Kong

JOHNSON CONTROLS INC   5757 W Green Bay Ave, PO Box 591, Milwaukee, WI 53201,
Tel: (414) 228-1200
(Mfr facility mgmt & control sys, auto seating, batteries & plastics)
    Johnson Controls Hong Kong Ltd., 1408 Fortress Tower, 250 Kings Rd., North Point,
    Hong Kong

THE JOURNAL OF COMMERCE   110 Wall St, New York, NY 10005, Tel: (212) 425-1616
(Business newspaper & journal pub)
    Headway Media Services Ltd., Rm. 2101 Causeway Bay Centre, 14-23 Sugar St.,
    Causeway Bay, Hong Kong

KAY CORP INTL   Wall St Plaza, New York, NY 10005, Tel: (212) 425-2100
(Wearing apparel, jewelry)
    Balfour-H-H Trading., Ltd., Wing on Centre, 111 Connaught Rd., Hong Kong

KEPNER-TREGOE INC   Research Rd, PO Box 704, Princeton, NJ 08542,
Tel: (609) 921-2806
(Mgmt & organizational devel)
    Kepner-Tregoe Southeast Asia Ltd., Tower A, Suite A-2, 17th Floor, Elizabeth House,
    250 Gloucester Rd., .Wannchai, Hong Kong

KETCHUM COMMUNICATIONS   4 Gateway Center, Pittsburgh, PA 15222,
Tel: (412) 456-3500
(Advertising, public relations)
    Far East-Ketchum, Dominion Centre, 43-59A Queen's Rd. East, Wanchai, Hong Kong

KEYSTONE INTL INC   PO Box 40010, Houston, TX 77040, Tel: (713) 466-1176
(Mfr butterfly valves, actuators & control accessories)
    Keystone Valve Hong Kong Ltd., Block B, 22/f Tak Lee Comm. Bldg., 115 Wanchai Rd.,
    Hong Kong

KIDDER PEABODY GROUP INC   10 Hanover Sq, New York, NY 10005,
Tel: (212) 510-3000
(Investment banking)
    Kidder, Peabody & Co., Ltd., 1704-9 Jardine House, Connaught Rd., Central, Hong Kong

KNOLL INTL   655 Madison Ave, New York, NY 10021, Tel: (212) 826-2400
(Furniture & fabrics)
    Knoll Intl. Furniture, Ltd., 225 Jaffe Rd., Wanchai, Hong Kong

KORN/FERRY INTL   237 Park Ave, New York, NY 10017, Tel: (212) 687-1834
(Executive search)
    Korn/Ferry Intl. (HK) Ltd., Gloucester Tower, Gloucester, Hong Kong

KRAS CORP   99 Newbold Road, Fairless Hills, PA 19030, Tel: (215) 736-0981
(Mfr precision tools & mach for electr & plastics ind)
    Kras Asia, Ltd., 78 Hung to Rd., Kwun Tong, Kowloon, Hong Kong

KULICKE & SOFFA INDUSTRIES INC   2101 Blair Mill Rd, Willow Grove, PA 19090,
Tel: (215) 784-6000
(Mfr assembly equip for semiconductor ind)
    Kulicke & Soffa (Asia) Ltd., Fook Cheong Bldg. 9/F, 63 Hoi Yuen Rd., Kwun Tong,
    Hong Kong

THE KULJIAN CO   3624 Science Center, Philadelphia, PA 19104,
Tel: (215) 243-1900
(Studies, design, engineeering, constr mgmt, site supervision)
    Development Consultants Intl., Suite 9-C, 9th Floor Hyde Center,
    223 Gloucester Rd., Hong Kong

LE TOURNEAU INC LONGVIEW DIV   PO Box 2307, Longview, TX 75606,
Tel: (214) 753-3449
(Heavy constr, mining mach & equip)
    Wm. Hunt & Co. Intl., Ltd., 608 Hysan Ave., Causeway Bay, Hong Kong

LEASEWAY INTL CORP   3700 Park East Dr, Cleveland, OH 44139,
Tel: (216) 765-5500
(Trucking, warehousing, leasing)
    United Distribution Services Ltd., Wyler Centre, Tai Lin Pai Rd., Kwai Chung, N.T.,
    Kowloon, Hong Kong

HAROLD L LEE & SONS   32 Pell St, New York, NY 10013, Tel: (212) 964-9544
(Travel agency)
    Harold L. Lee & Sons Travel Service Hong Kong, Ltd., 802 Cheong Hing Bldg.,
    72 Nathan Rd., Kowloon, Hong Kong

LEVI STRAUSS & CO   1155 Battery, San Francisco, CA 94111, Tel: (415) 544-6000
(Mfr wearing apparel)
    Levi Strauss, 9/F, Hong Kong Spinners Industrial Bldg., 603 Tai Nan West St.,
    Kowloon, Hong Kong

LINTAS:WORLDWIDE   1 Dag Hammarskjold Plaza, New York, NY 10017,
Tel: (212) 605-8000
(Advertising agency)
    Lintas:Hong Kong, 21/F National Mutual Centre, 151 Gloucester Rd., Hong Kong

LOBUE ASSOCIATES INC   13-15 Broadway, Fair Lawn, NJ 07410,
Tel: (201) 797-7400
(Fin consult servs)
    LoBue Associates, Inc., Central Bldg. 11/F-#1133, #1 Pedder St., GPO Box 11308,
    Central, Hong Kong

LOCKHEED CORP   2555 N Hollywood Way, Burbank, CA 91520, Tel: (213) 847-6121
(Aircraft, missiles, etc)
    Lockheed Aircraft Intl., Ltd., Rm 901, Wing On Centre, 111 Connaught Rd., Central,
    Hong Kong

LYKES BROS STEAMSHIP CO INC   Lykes Center, 300 Poydras St, New Orleans,
LA 70130, Tel: (504) 523-6611
(Ocean frt trans)
    Lykes Lines Agency, Inc., 5th Floor, Printing House, 6 Duddell St., Central,
    G.P.O. Box 879, Hong Kong

M&T CHEMICALS INC   PO Box 1104, Rahway, NJ 07065, Tel: (201) 499-0200
(Specialty chems & application technologies)
    M & T Industries Ltd., Rms. 1204-5 Landwide Comm. Bldg., 118-120 Austin Rd.,
    Kowloon, Hong Kong

MACHINED PARTS CORP   5929 Hampshire Blvd, Ft Worth, TX 76112,
Tel: (817) 457-5060
(Components for auto A/C)
    Machined Parts Hong Kong, Ltd., Ground/Mezz. Floors, Aberdeen Industrial Bldg.,
    19 Wong Chuk Hang Rd., Aberdeen, Hong Kong

R H MACY & CO INC   51 West 34th St, New York, NY 10001, Tel: (212) 560-3600
(Department stores, importers)
    R.H. Macy & Co., Inc., 922-924 Ocean Centre, Canton Rd., Kowloon, Hong Kong

MANHATTAN INTERNATIONAL   1155 Ave of the Americas, New York, NY 10036,
Tel: (212) 221-7500
(Mfr shirts, sweaters, sportswear, table linen)
    Manhattan Industries Far East Ltd., 136-138 Austin Rd., Kowloon, Hong Kong

MANPOWER INC   5301 N Ironwood Rd, PO Box 2053, Milwaukee, WI 53201-2053,
Tel: (414) 961-1000
(Temporary help)
    Manpower, Inc., 2207 Alexandra House, 16-20 Chater Rd., Hong Kong

MANUFACTURERS HANOVER TRUST CO   270 Park Ave, New York, NY 10017,
Tel: (212) 286-6000
(Banking)
    Manufacturers Hanover Asia, Ltd., 18th Floor, Sanwa Bldg., 30 Connaught Rd.,
    Central, Hong Kong

Manufacturers Hanover Asia, Ltd., Alexandra House, 27th Floor, 16-20 Chater Rd., Central, Hong Kong

MARSTELLER INTL   1 E Wacker Dr, Chicago, IL 60601, Tel: (312) 329-1100
(Advertising, marketing research, sales promotion)
 Burson-Marsteller Hong Kong, Ltd., 4 Hennessy Rd., 3rd Floor, Hong Kong

MATTEL INC   5150 Rosecrans Ave, Hawthorne, CA 90250, Tel: (213) 644-0411
(Toys, dolls, games, crafts & hobbies)
 Hong Kong Industrial Co., Ltd., 41A Smithfield Rd., Kennedytown, Hong Kong
 Mattel Electronic, Ltd., Shing Dad Industrial Bldg., 10th & 16th Floors,
  232 Aberdeen Main Rd., Aberdeen, Hong Kong
 Mattel-Marden, Ltd., Wheelock House, Peddar St., Hong Kong
 Pacific American Buying Service, Ltd., 1203 Hang Lung Centre, Palerson St.,
  Causeway Bay, Hong Kong

MAY DEPARTMENT STORES CO   611 Olive St, St Louis, MO 63101-1799,
 Tel: (314) 342-3300
(Retail dept stores)
 Alpha Merchandising Service Ltd., 15F S. Tower, World Finance Center, Harbour City,
  Kowloon, Hong Kong

MEASUREX CORP   One Results Way, Cupertino, CA 95014, Tel: (408) 255-1500
(Mfr computer integrated mfg sys)
 Measurex Asia Inc., 1503 Park Tower, 15 Austin Rd., Kowloon, Hong Kong

MEDTRONIC INC   7000 Central Ave, NE, Minneapolis, MN 55432,
 Tel: (612) 574-4000
(Mfr med devices, med serv)
 Medtronic Intl. Ltd., 2002 C. C. Wu Bldg., 308 Hennessy Rd., Wanchai, Hong Kong

MELLON BANK NA   One Mellon Bank Center, Pittsburgh, PA 15258,
 Tel: (412) 234-5016
(Commercial & trade banking, foreign exchange)
 Mellon Bank, 1728-30 Prince's Bldg., Des Voeux Rd. Central, Hong Kong
 Mellon Bank, 3701 Edinburgh Tower, 15 Queens Rd. Central, Hong Kong

MERCK SHARP & DOHME INTL   PO Box 2000, Rahway, NJ 07065, Tel: (201) 574-4000
(Pharms, chems & biologicals)
 Merck, Sharp & Dohme (Asia), Ltd., 1401 Guardian House, 3201 Kwan Rd., Hong Kong

MERRILL LYNCH PIERCE FENNER & SMITH   World Financial Center, 225 Liberty St,
 New York, NY 10080, Tel: (212) 449-1000
(Brokers, securities, commodities)
 Merrill Lynch, Pierce, Fenner & Smith Intl., Ltd., 15th Floor, St. George's Bldg.,
  2 Ice House St., Hong Kong

MICA CORP   8536 National Blvd, Culver City, CA 90231, Tel: (213) 837-8100
(Epoxy & poly-laminate for printed circuit board ind)
 Mica-Ava (Far East) Industrial Ltd., 52-58 Sha Tsui Rd., Tsuen Wan, N.T., Hong Kong

MICROSEMI CORP   2830 S Fairview St, Santa Ana, CA 92704, Tel: (714) 979-8220
(Mfr seimconductors, microelectr hybrid & surface mount assemblies)
 Microsemi (H.K.) Ltd., 7/F Meeco Industrial Bldg., 53-55 Au Pui Wan St., Fo Tan,
  NT, Hong Kong

MIDLANTIC CORP   PO Box 600, Metro Park Plaza, Edison, NJ 08818,
Tel: (908) 321-8000
(Banking)
    Midlantic (Asia) Ltd., Alexandra House, 16-20 Chater Rd., Central, Hong Kong

MOBIL CORP   150 E 42nd St, New York, NY 10017, Tel: (212) 883-4242
(Petroleum explor, prdts)
    Mobil Oil Hong Kong, Ltd., P.O. Box 86, Hong Kong

MONMOUTH PLASTICS INC   PO Box 921, Asbury Park, NJ 07712, Tel: (201) 775-5100
(Flame retardant concentrates, thermoplastic sys, spec formulations)
    Draco Intl., Ltd., Tong Wah Mansion, 8th Floor, 199 Hennessy Rd., Hong Kong

MONSANTO CO   800 N Lindbergh Blvd, St Louis, MO 63167, Tel: (314) 694-1000
(Mfr chem & agric prdts, pharms, ind process equip, man-made fibers, plastics)
    Monsanto Far East, Ltd., 1304-1308 Great Eagle Center, 23 Harbour Rd., Hong Kong

MONTGOMERY WARD & CO INC   Montgomery Ward Plaza, Chicago, IL 60671,
Tel: (312) 467-2000
(Retail merchandisers)
    Montgomery Ward (Hong Kong) Ltd., 1807-1814 Shui On Centre, 6-8 Harbour Rd.,
    Hong Kong

MOORE SPECIAL TOOL CO   PO Box 4088, Bridgeport, CT 06607, Tel: (203) 366-3224
(Precision jig borers, metal working tools, dies)
    Oriental Machinery, Ltd., Chinese General Chamber of Commerce Bldg., 3/F,
    24 Connaught Rd., Central, Hong Kong

MORGAN GUARANTY TRUST CO   23 Wall St, New York, NY 10015, Tel: (212) 483-2323
(Banking)
    Morgan Guaranty Trust Co. of NY, Alexandra House, Hong Kong

MORTON INTERNATIONAL INC   100 N Riverside Plaza, Chicago, IL 60606,
Tel: (312) 807-2000
(Mfr adhesives, coatings, finishes, spec chems, advanced & electr materials, auto
safety prdts)
    Morton Intl. Inc., 2803 Admiralty Centre, Tower 1, 18 Harcourt Rd., Hong Kong
    Morton Intl. Inc., Room 1404 Silvercord Tower 1, 30 Canton Rd., Tsinshatsui,
    Kowloon, Hong Kong

MOTOROLA INC   1303 E Algonquin Rd, Schaumburg, IL 60196, Tel: (708) 397-5000
(Mfr commun equip, semiconductors, cellular phones)
    Motorola Asia, Ltd., 1-15 Kwai Fung Crescent, Kwai Chung, NT, Hong Kong
    Motorola Semiconductors HK Ltd., 7/f Profit Ind. Bldg., 1-15 Kwai Fund Crescent,
    Kwai Chung, N.T., Hong Kong

MTS SYSTEMS CORP   PO Box 24012, Minneapolis, MN 55424, Tel: (612) 937-4000
(Electrohydraulic testing & prod equip, mach controls)
    MTS Systems Hong Kong Ltd., Units A&B, 6/F, Cindic Tower, 128 Gloucester Rd.,
    Wanchai, Hong Kong

MUNFORD INC   1860-74 Peachtree Rd, NW, Atlanta, GA 30309, Tel: (404) 352-6641
(Convenience & specialty stores)
    On Yun Trading Co. Ltd., Flat 1B, 240 Prince Edward Rd., Kowloon, Hong Kong

MacDERMID INC   245 Freight St, Waterbury, CT 06702, Tel: (203) 575-5700
(Chem processing for metal ind, plastics, electronics cleaners, strippers)
   MacDermid Hong Kong Ltd., 10th fl. Block E, 2-12 Au Pui Wan St., Fo Tan, Sha Tin,
      N.T., Hong Kong

McCANN-ERICKSON WORLDWIDE   750 Third Ave, New York, NY 10017,
   Tel: (212) 697-6000
(Advertising)
   McCann-Erickson (H.K.) Ltd., 1/F Sunning Plaza, 10 Hysan Ave., Hong Kong

McGRAW-HILL INC   1221 Ave of the Americas, New York, NY 10020,
   Tel: (212) 512-2000
(Books, magazines, info sys, financial serv, b/cast operations)
   American Industrial Report Ltd., Suite 905 Guardian House, 32 Oi Kwan St.,
      Happy Valley, Hong Kong

NABISCO BRANDS INC   Nabisco Brands Plaza, East Hanover, NJ 07936,
   Tel: (201) 503-2000
(Mfr food prdts)
   Intl Standard Brands, Inc., Far East/Pacific, G.P.O. Box 10157,
      General Post Office, Hong Kong
   Standard Brands Hong Kong, Ltd., P.O. Box 20415, Hennessy Rd. Post Office, Hong Kong

NALCO CHEMICAL CO   One Nalco Center, Naperville, IL 60566-1024,
   Tel: (708) 305-1000
(Chems for water & waste water treatment, oil prod & refining, ind processes;
water/energy mgmt serv)
   Nalco Chemical (HK) Ltd., Rm. 1806, Tower 6, China Hong Kong City, 33 Canton Rd.,
      Kowloon, Hong Kong

NATIONAL BANK OF DETROIT   611 Woodward, PO Box 116, Detroit, MI 48232,
   Tel: (313) 225-1000
(Banking)
   NBD Asia Ltd., Rm. 805 Tower II, Bond Centre, 91 Queensway, Central, Hong Kong

NATIONAL CHEMSEARCH CORP   2727 Chemsearch Blvd, Irving, TX 75061,
   Tel: (214) 438-0211
(Commercial chem prdts)
   Natl. Chemsearch Corp. Hong Kong, Ltd., 75th Floor, 31 Ng Fong St., San Po Kong,
      Kowloon, Hong Kong

NATIONAL FORGE CO   Front St, Rt No 6, Irvine, PA 16329, Tel: (814) 563-7522
(Forged & cast steel)
   Natl. Forge Export Corp., E-9 Repulse Bay Towers, 119-A Repulse Bay Rd., Hong Kong

NATIONAL SEMICONDUCTOR CORP   2900 Semiconductor Dr, Santa Clara, CA 95051,
   Tel: (408) 721-5000
(Semiconductors, computers & point-of-sale sys)
   Natl. Semiconductor Hong Kong, Ltd., Suite 513, Chinachem Golden Plaza,
      77 Moody Rd., Tsimshatsu, Kowloon, Hong Kong

NCR CORP   1700 S Patterson Blvd, Dayton, OH 45479, Tel: (513) 445-2000
(Develop/mfr/sell/serv business info processing sys)
   NCR (Hong Kong) Ltd., 34/F and 35/F Shun Tak Centre, 200 Connaught Rd. C., Hong Kong

NEWSWEEK INTL INC   444 Madison Ave, New York, NY 10022, Tel: (212) 350-2000
   (Publ)
      Newsweek, Rm 2007, Realty Bldg., 71 Des Voeux Rd., Hong Kong

NORTEK INC   50 Kennedy Plaza, Providence, RI 02903, Tel: (401) 751-1600
   (Mfr residential & coml bldg prdts)
      Linear HK Mfg., Ltd., Honour Industrial Centre 19/F, 6 Sun Yip St., Chai Wan,
      Hong Kong

NORTHERN TRUST BANK   50 S LaSalle St, Chicago, IL 60675, Tel: (312) 630-6000
   (Banking)
      The Northern Trust Co., 1417 Connaught Centre, Connaught Rd., Central, Hong Kong

NORWEST BANK MINNESOTA NA   Norwest Center, 6th & Marquette, Minneapolis,
   MN 55479-0095, Tel: (612) 667-8110
   (Banking)
      Norwest Bank Minnesota, NA, Jardine House 43/F-#4301-4, Connaught Place, Central,
      Hong Kong

NYNEX CORP   1113 Westchester Ave, White Plains, NY 10604, Tel: (914) 397-1200
   (Telecom & info servs)
      NYNEX International Co., Two Exchange Square #1207-1208, Central, Hong Kong
      NYNEX Network Systems Co., Two Exchange Square #1207-1208, Central, Hong Kong

OCCIDENTAL LIFE INSURANCE CO OF CALIFORNIA   Hill & Olive at 12th St,
   Los Angeles, CA 90015, Tel: (213) 742-2111
   (Insurance)
      Occidental Life of California, 1920-21 Prince's Bldg., Chater Rd., Hong Kong

OGILVY & MATHER INC   2 E 48th St, New York, NY 10017, Tel: (212) 907-3400
   (Advertising agency)
      Ogilvy & Mather Hong Kong Pte., Ltd., Centre Point, 181-185 Gloucester Rd.,
      Wanchai, Hong Kong

ONAN CORP   1400 73rd Ave NE, Minneapolis, MN 55432, Tel: (612) 574-5000
   (Electric generators, ind engines & controls)
      Analogue Technical Agencies, Ltd., 8A, Wing Cheong Commercial Bldg.,
      19-25 Jervois St., Hong Kong
      Onan Far East, Ltd., Gilman Marine, 1st Floor, Elizabeth House, 250 Gloucester Rd.,
      Causeway Bay, Hong Kong

ORIENTAL EXPORTERS INC   2 Pennsylvania Plaza, New York, NY 10001,
   Tel: (212) 594-7800
   (Exporters of general merchandise)
      Inter-Islands Metals & Minerals, Ltd., 1103-5 Kowloon Centre, 29-43 Ashley Rd.,
      Kowloon, Hong Kong

OTIS ELEVATOR CO   10 Farm Springs, Farmington, CT 06032, Tel: (203) 674-4047
   (Elevators & escalators)
      Otis Elevator Co. Hong Kong, Ltd., G.P.O. Box 82, Hong Kong

OUTBOARD MARINE CORP   100 Sea Horse Dr, Waukegan, IL 60085,
   Tel: (708) 689-6200
   (Outboard & rotary motors, stern engines, marine parts & accessories)
      Outboard Marine Asia, Ltd., 35-47 Tsing Yi Rd., Tsing Yi Island, NT, Hong Kong

PACIFIC NATIONAL BANK OF WASHINGTON   PO Box 160, Seattle, WA 98101,
  Tel: (206) 292-3111
  (Intl banking)
    Pacific Natl. Bank of Washington, 3101 Connaught Centre, Connaught Rd., Central,
    Hong Kong

PAINEWEBBER GROUP INC   1285 Ave of the Americas, New York, NY 10019,
  Tel: (212) 713-2000
  (Stock brokerage serv & invest)
    PaineWebber Intl., St. George's Bldg., 2 Ice House St., Hong Kong

PANDUIT CORP   17301 Ridgeland Ave, Tinley Park, IL 60477, Tel: (708) 532-1800
  (Mfr elec/electr wiring comps)
    Panduit Trading Pte. Ltd., Nan On Commercial Bldg., 69-A Wuhu St., Hungham,
    Kowloon, Hong Kong

PCA ELECTRONICS INC   16799 Schoenborn St, Sepulveda, CA 91343,
  Tel: (213) 892-0761
  (Electronic equip)
    HPC, Ltd., 10th Floor, Shui Ki Industrial Bldg., 18 Wong Chuk Hang Rd., Aberdeen,
    Hong Kong

PENINSULAR LIFE INSURANCE CO   645 Riverside Ave, Jacksonville, FL 32204,
  Tel: (904) 358-6000
  (Life ins)
    Peninsular Life Insurance Co., 410 Hong Kong Hilton Hotel, 2-A Queen's Rd.,
    Central, Hong Kong

J C PENNEY CO   PO Box 227474, Dallas, TX 75222-7474, Tel: (214) 591-1000
  (Department stores)
    JCPenney Purchasing Corp., Room 617, Peninsula Centre, 67 Mody Rd., Tsimshatsui E.,
    Kowloon, Hong Kong

PEPSICO FOOD SERVICE INTL   9111 E Douglas, Wichita, KS 67207,
  Tel: (316) 681-9793
  (Operates restaurants)
    PepsiCo Food Service Intl., 20/F Harcourt House, 39 Gloucester Rd., Wanchai,
    Hong Kong

PERKIN-ELMER CORP   761 Main Ave, Norwalk, CT 06859, Tel: (203) 762-1000
  (Analytical instru, computers, semiconductor prod equip, avionics, electro-optical
  sys, etc)
    Perkin-Elmer AB, Rm 704, New World Centre, 20 Salisbury Rd., Kowloon, Hong Kong

PHILIP MORRIS COS INC   120 Park Ave, New York, NY 10017, Tel: (212) 880-5000
  (Mfr cigarettes, foods prdts, beer)
    Philip Morris Asia Inc., United Centre 25/F, 95 Queensway, Central, Hong Kong

PHILLIPS PETROLEUM CO   Phillips Bldg, Bartlesville, OK 74004,
  Tel: (918) 661-6600
  (Crude oil, natural gas, liquefied petroleum gas, gasoline & petro-chems)
    Phillips Petroleum Co. Asia, 9th Floor, Citibank Tower, 8 Queen's Rd., Central,
    Hong Kong
    Phillips Petroleum Intl., Inc., 501 Cosmopolitan Bldg., 10 Stanley St., Hong Kong

PITTSBURGH NATIONAL BANK   Fifth Ave at Wood, Pittsburgh, PA 15222,
  Tel: (412) 355-2000
  (Banking)
    Pittsburgh Natl Bank, China Bldg., 19th Floor, 29 Queen's Rd., Central, long Kong

PLAINS COTTON COOPERATIVE ASSOCIATES   3301 E 50th St, Lubbock, TX 79408,
  Tel: (806) 763-8011
  (Merchandisers of raw cotton to domestic & foreign textile mills)
    Amerasia Intl., Ltd., 4th Floor, Solar House, 26 Des Voeux Rd., Central, Hong Kong

PLOUGH INC   PO Box 377, Memphis, TN 38151, Tel: (901) 320-2011
  (Proprietary drug & cosmetic prdts)
    Plough Consumer Products (Asia), Ltd., 304 Watsons Estate B, 6 Watson Rd., Hong Kong

POLAROID CORP   549 Technology Sq, Cambridge, MA 02139, Tel: (617) 577-2000
  (Photographic and optical prdts)
    Polaroid Far East, Ltd., 10th Floor, Block B, Watson's Estate, 8 Watson Rd.,
    North Point, Hong Kong

PREMARK INTL INC   1717 Deerfield Rd, Deerfield, IL 60015, Tel: (708) 405-6000
  (Mfr/sale diversified consumer & coml prdts)
    Dart Industries Hong Kong Ltd., G-12 Ground Fl., Kornhill Plaza North,
    a Kornhill Rd., Quarry Bay, Hong Kong

PRIME COMPUTER INC   Prime Park, Natick, MA 01760, Tel: (617) 655-8000
  (Mfr minicomputers, hardware & software)
    Prime Computer (Hong Kong) Ltd., 801 Citicorp Centre, 18 Whitfield Rd.,
    Causeway Bay, Hong Kong

PROFIT BY AIR INC   1950 Spectrum Circle, Marietta, GA 30067,
  Tel: (404) 951-8100
  (Freight forwarder)
    Profit Express (Hong Kong) Ltd., Hong Kong

PRUDENTIAL INSURANCE CO OF AMERICA   Prudential Plaza, Newark, NJ 07101,
  Tel: (201) 877-6000
  (Life ins, health ins, annuities)
    Prudential Reinsurance Co. (USA), Windsor House, Suite 2906, 29th Floor,
    311 Gloucester Rd., Causeway Bay, Hong Kong

PULSE ENGINEERING INC   7250 Convoy Ct, PO Box 12235, San Diego, CA 92112,
  Tel: (619) 268-2400
  (Mfr delay lines, transformers, inductors)
    Pulse Engineering Hong Kong, 7B Wo Kee Hong Bldg., 585-609 Castle Peak Rd.,
    Kwai Chung, NT, Hong Kong

RAYOVAC CORP   601 Rayovac Dr, Madison, WI 53711, Tel: (608) 275-3340
  (Mfr batteries & lighting devices)
    Rayovac Far East Corp, Box 98874, TST Post Office, Kowloon, Hong Kong

READER'S DIGEST ASSOCIATION INC   PO Box 235, Pleasantville, NY 10570,
  Tel: (914) 238-1000
  (Global publisher & direct mail marketer)
    Reader's Digest Assn. Far East Ltd., 3A Kung Ngam Village Rd., Shaukiwan, Hong Kong

THE REECE CORP   800 South St, Waltham, MA 02254-9168, Tel: (617) 894-9220
(Mfr apparel mach)
    Reece (Far East) Ltd., Hyfco Industrial Bldg., Block IV 11/F, Flats B&C,
      203 Tai Kok Tsui Rd., Kowloon, Hong Kong

REGENT SPORTS CORP   45 Ranick Rd, Hauppauge, NY 11787, Tel: (516) 234-2800
(Sporting goods)
    Benny Sports Intl. Hong Kong, Ltd., 5th Floor, Mon Hing Fty. Bldg.,
      20 Catchick St., Kennedy Town, Hong Kong

REPUBLIC TELCOM SYSTEMS CORP   6150 Lookout Rd, Boulder, CO 80301,
Tel: (303) 530-8600
(Mfr packet-switched voice & data networking sys)
    Republic Telcom Systems, 3715 Sun Hung Kai Centre, 30 Harbour Rd., Wanchai,
    Hong Kong

REVLON INC   767 Fifth Ave, New York, NY 10153-0033, Tel: (212) 572-5000
(Cosmetics, health care prdts)
    Revlon Hong Kong, Ltd., 7th Floor, 64-66 To Kwa Wan Rd., Kowloon, Hong Kong

ROBERTSHAW CONTROLS CO   1701 Byrd Ave, Richmond, VA 23230,
Tel: (804) 281-0700
(Mfr automatic controls & control sys for ind, commercial bldgs & home)
    Robertshaw Controls Asia, Central Bldg., Rm. 808, Pedder St., Central, Hong Kong

H H ROBERTSON CO   Two Gateway Center, Pittsburgh, PA 15222,
Tel: (412) 281-3200
(Mfr roof & wall prdts, cellular steel floor sys, ventilation equip)
    H.H. Robertson Hong Kong, Ltd., Rm 910 Dominion Centre, 37-59 Queen's Rd. East,
    Hong Kong

ROCKWELL INTL CORP   2230 E Imperial Hwy, El Segundo, CA 90245,
Tel: (213) 647-5000
(Prdts & serv for aerospace, automotive, electronics, graphics & automation inds)
    Rockwell Intl. Asia Pacific Ltd., 1306 Harbour Centre, 25 Harbour Rd., Wanchai,
    Hong Kong

ROHM & HAAS CO   Independence Mall West, Philadelphia, PA 19105,
Tel: (215) 592-3000
(Mfr ind & agric chems, plastics)
    Rohm & Haas Hong Kong, Ltd., 1201 Dina House, 11 Duddell St., Central, Hong Kong

ROLLINS BURDICK HUNTER CO   123 N Wacker Dr, Chicago, IL 60606,
Tel: (312) 701-4000
(Ins brokers)
    Heath Langeveldt, Ltd., 12th Floor, Wang Kee Bldg., 34-37 Connaught Rd., Central,
    Hong Kong
    Rollins Heath, Ltd., 12th Floor, Wang Kee Bldg., 34-37 Connaught Rd., Central,
    Hong Kong

RORER GROUP INC   500 Virginia Dr, Ft Washington, PA 19034,
Tel: (215) 628-6000
(Mfr ethical & consumer pharms)
    Rorer Intl., Ltd., Hong Kong

ROSEMOUNT INC   12001 Technology Dr, Eden Prairie, MN 55344,
   Tel: (612) 941-5560
   (Mfr aerospace & ind instrumentation)
      Rosemount China, 38 Gloucester Rd., Fleet House #902, Wanchai, Hong Kong

RUSSELL REYNOLDS ASSOCIATES INC   200 Park Ave, New York, NY 10166,
   Tel: (212) 351-2000
   (Exec recruiting services)
      Russell Reynolds Associates Inc., 4107-4108 Gloucester Tower, 11 Pedder St.,
      Hong Kong

SALOMON BROS INC   1 New York Plaza, New York, NY 10004, Tel: (212) 747-7000
   (Securities dealers & underwriters)
      Salomon Bros. Inc., 2907 Alexandra House, 15-20 Chater Rd., Hong Kong

R P SCHERER CORP   2075 W Big Beaver Rd, Troy, MI 48084, Tel: (313) 649-0900
   (Mfr soft gelatin & two-piece hard shell capsules)
      R.P. Scherer Hong Kong Ltd., Block A, 3/F Kwai Bo Industrial Bldg.,
      40 Wong Chuk Hang Rd., Hong Kong

SCOTT WORLDWIDE INC   Scott Plaza, Philadelphia, PA 19113, Tel: (215) 521-5000
   (Paper & paper prdts, bleached pulp)
      Scott Paper Hong Kong, Ltd., Hong Kong

SEA-LAND SERVICE INC   379 Thornall St, Edison, NJ 08837, Tel: (201) 558-6000
   (Container transport)
      Sea-Land Service, Inc., P.O. Box 531, 19th Floor, Melbourne Plaza, 33 Queen's Rd.,
      Central, Hong Kong

SEALED AIR CORP   Park 80 Plaza E, Saddle Brook, NJ 07662-5291,
   Tel: (201) 791-7600
   (Mfr protective packaging prdts)
      Sealed Air (Far East) Ltd., 9/F Wing Kwai Ind. Bldg., 2-8 Wang Wo Tsai St.,
      Tsuen Wan N.T., Hong Kong

SEATTLE FIRST NATIONAL BANK   1001 4th Ave, PO Box 3586, Seattle, WA 98124,
   Tel: (206) 583-3131
   (Bank holding company, financial serv)
      Seattle-First Asia, Ltd., Rm 4104, Gloucester Tower, The Landmark, 11 Pedder St.,
      Central, Hong Kong

SECURITY PACIFIC NATIONAL BANK   333 S Hope St, Los Angeles, CA 90071,
   Tel: (213) 345-6211
   (Banking)
      Security Pacific Asian Bank Ltd., 42/F Jardine House, Central, Hong Kong
      Security Pacific Natl. Bank, Rm. 3804 Jardine House, Central, Hong Kong

SGS CONTROL SERVICES INC   42 Broadway, New York, NY 10004,
   Tel: (212) 482-8700
   (Complete range of quality & quantity control checks & related tech serv)
      SGS Hong Kong, Ltd., Summit Bldg., 10th Floor, 30 Man Yue St., Hung Hom,
      G.P.O. Box 2244 HK, Kowloon, Hong Kong

SHAKESPEARE FISHING TACKLE GROUP   611 Shakespeare Rd, Columbia, SC 29204,
   Tel: (803) 754-7000
   (Mfr fishing tackle)
      Shakespeare Hong Kong Ltd., 175 Hoi Bun Rd., Jwun Tong, Kowloon, Hong Kong

SHEARMAN & STERLING   599 Lexington Ave, New York, NY 10022,
Tel: (212) 848-4000
(Lawyers)
  Shearman & Sterling, 1801 Gammon House, 12 Harcourt Rd., Hong Kong

SHEARSON/AMERICAN EXPRESS   American Express Tower, New York, NY 10285,
Tel: (212) 298-2000
(Investment banking, financial serv)
  Shearson/American Express, St. George's Bldg., 7th Floor, 2 Ice House St., Hong Kong

SHIPLEY CO INC   2300 Washington St, Newton, MA 02162, Tel: (617) 969-5500
(Mfr chems for printed circuit boards & microelectronic mfg)
  Shipley Chemicals (Hong Kong) Ltd., 5/F, Blk 8, Fuk Keung Ind. Bldg.,
    66-68 Tona Mei Rd., Mongkok, Kowlooon, Hong Kong

SIGNODE PACKAGING SYSTEMS   3600 W Lake Ave, Glenview, IL 60025,
Tel: (708) 724-6100
(Mfr packaging systems)
  Signode Hong Kong Ltd., Unit B, 9/F, Kin Yip Fty. Bldg., 9 Cheung Yee St., Kowloon,
    Hong Kong

SILICONIX INC   2201 Laurelwood Dr, Santa Clara, CA 95054, Tel: (408) 988-8000
(Semiconductor components)
  Siliconix Hong Kong, Ltd., 5/6/7th Floors, Liven House, 61-63 King Yip St.,
    Kowloon, Hong Kong

SIRCO INTL CORP   700-718 S Fulton Ave, Mt Vernon, NY 10550,
Tel: (914) 664-4400
(Imp of handbags, totes, wallets)
  Sirco Industries, Ltd., 22 Ashley Rd., Tsimshatsui, Kowloon, Hong Kong

WILBUR SMITH ASSOCS   NCNB Tower, PO Box 92, Columbia, SC 29202,
Tel: (803) 738-0580
(Consulting engineers)
  Wilbur Smith Associates Inc., 1519 Star House, 3 Salisbury Rd., Kowloon, Hong Kong

SOUNDESIGN CORP   34 Exchange Place, Jersey City, NJ 07302,
Tel: (201) 434-1050
(Radios, electronic prdts)
  Soundesign, Kowloon Centre, 29-43 Ashley Rd., Kowloon, Hong Kong

SPRAGUE ELECTRIC CO   87 Marshall St, North Adams, MA 01247,
Tel: (413) 664-4411
(Electronic components)
  Sprague World Trade Corp., Block E, 8th Floor, Hop Hing Industrial Bldg.,
    702 Castle Peak Rd., Kowloon, Hong Kong

SQUARE D CO   Executive Plaza, Palatine, IL 60067, Tel: (708) 397-2600
(Power distribution & elec/electr ind control equip)
  Square D Co. Hong Kong, Ltd., P.O. Box 97064, Tsim Sha Twui, Kowloon, Hong Kong

THE STANLEY WORKS   1000 Stanley Dr, PO Box 7000, New Britain, CT 06050,
Tel: (203) 225-5111
(Mfr hand tools & hardware)
  The Stanley Works Hong Kong, Ltd., Rm 1433, Central Bldg., Pedder St., Hong Kong

STARLIGHT TRADING INC   1370 Broadway, New York, NY 10018, Tel: (212) 695-3510
   (Wearing apparel)
      Starlight Purchasing Corp., Ltd., 1510 Tung Ying Bldg., 100 Nathan Rd., Kowloon,
      Hong Kong

STATE STREET BANK & TRUST CO   225 Franklin St, Boston, MA 02101,
   Tel: (617) 786-3000
   (Banking servs)
      State Street Asia Ltd., 2807 Alexandra House, 16-20 Chater Rd., Central, Hong Kong

STERLING PRODUCTS INTL CORP   90 Park Ave, New York, NY 10016,
   Tel: (212) 972-4141
   (Pharm prdts)
      Sterling Drug Intl., Inc., 12th Floor, Block A, Watson's Estate, Watson Rd.,
      North Point, Hong Kong

STOKES DIV   5500 Tabor Rd, Philadelphia, PA 19120, Tel: (215) 289-5671
   (Vacuum pumps & components, vacuum dryers, oil-upgrading equip)
      Connell Bros. Co. (HK) Ltd., P.O. Box 88, Hong Kong

SULLAIR CORP   3700 E Michigan Blvd, Michigan City, IN 46360,
   Tel: (219) 879-5451
   (Refrigeration sys, vacuum pumps, generators, etc)
      Sullair Hong Kong, Ltd., Rm 7A, Wing Cheong Bldg., MN, 19-25 Jervois St., Central,
      Hong Kong

SUMMIT INDUSTRIAL CORP   600 Third Ave, New York, NY 10016,
   Tel: (212) 490-1100
   (Pharms, agric chem prdts)
      Summit Asia, Ltd., Watson's Estate, Rm 505, Hong Kong

SYBRON CORP   411 E Wisconsin Ave, Milwaukee, WI 07662, Tel: (414) 274-6600
   (Professional health prdts, spec chems, instru, water & waste water treatment sys)
      Gamlen Hong Kong, Rm 1503, Chung Nam Bldg., No. 1 Lockhart Rd., Hong Kong
      Sybron Asia, Ltd., 8-B Kung Sheung Bldg., 8th Floor, 18 Fenwick St.,
      G.P.O. Box 746, Hong Kong

SYSTEMS ENGINEERING LABS INC   6901 W Sunrise Blvd, Fort Lauderdale,
   FL 33313, Tel: (305) 587-2900
   (Digital computers)
      Comptec Data Corp., 3/F Gaylord Commercial Bldg., 114-120 Lockhard Rd., Wanchai,
      Hong Kong

TANDEM COMPUTERS INC   19333 Vallco Parkway, Cupertino, CA 95014,
   Tel: (408) 725-6000
   (Computer sys)
      Tandem Computers Hong Kong, Ltd., Kowloon, Hong Kong

TANDY CORP   1800 One Tandy Center, Fort Worth, TX 76102, Tel: (817) 390-3700
   (Electronic & acoustic equip)
      A & A Intl. (YICHI-HK), Ltd., 1406-1411 World Commerce Centre, Harbour City,
      Phase 1, Kowloon, Hong Kong

TED BATES WORLDWIDE INC   1515 Broadway, New York, NY 10036,
   Tel: (212) 869-3131
   (Advertising agency)
      Ted Bates, Ltd., Malaysia House, 47-50 Gloucester Rd., Hong Kong

TEKTRONIX INC   PO Box 500, Beaverton, OR 97077, Tel: (503) 627-7111
(Mfr test & meas, visual sys & commun prdts)
   Tektronix Hong Kong Ltd., 18/F Great Eagle Centre, 23 Harbour Rd., Wanchai,
   Hong Kong

TELEDYNE COMPONENTS   1300 Terra Bella Ave, Mountain View, CA 94043,
Tel: (415) 968-9241
(Mfr data conversion prdts, bipolar interface, etc)
   Teledyne Components, 10 Sam Chuk St., San Po Kong, Kowloon, Hong Kong

TELLABS INC   4951 Indiana Ave, Lisle, IL 60532, Tel: (708) 969-8800
(Mfr telecom equip)
   Tellabs HK Ltd., Hop Hing Centre 19/F, 8-12 Hennessy Rd., Wanchai, Hong Kong

TEXACO INC   2000 Westchester Ave, White Plains, NY 10650, Tel: (914) 253-4000
(Explor/mktg crude oil & its prdts, petro-chems)
   Texaco Hong Kong, Ltd., Rm 2005, American Intl. Tower, 16-18 Queen's Rd., Central,
   long Kong

THERMCO SYSTEMS INC   1465 North Batavia St, Orange, CA 92668,
Tel: (714) 639-2340
(Microprocessor controlled diffusion furnace sys & vacuum/gas sys for semiconductor
processing)
   Thermco Systems (Far East) Ltd., Wilson House, 19-27 Wyndham St., Hong Kong

THOMAS INTL PUBLISHING CO   1 Penn Plaza, New York, NY 10119,
Tel: (212) 290-7213
(Publ ind magazines & directories)
   Interasia Publications Ltd., 200 Lockhart Rd., Victoria, Hong Kong
   Pacific Resources Ltd., 200 Lockhart Rd., Victoria, Hong Kong

THOMPSON AIRCRAFT TIRE CORP   7775 NW 12th St, Miami, FL 33126,
Tel: (305) 592-3530
(Retread aircraft tires, aircraft wheel & brake servicing)
   Thompson Aircraft Tire Co. (Asia) Ltd., 22-24 Dai Wang St., Tai Po Industrial,
   Estate, Tai Po, NT, Hong Kong

TIDEL SYSTEMS INC   2615 E Beltline Rd, Carrollton, TX 75006,
Tel: (214) 416-8222
(Mfr oil & gas monitors; cash handling equip)
   Polytek Engineering Ltd., Houster Centre 3/F, 63 Mody Rd., Tsim Sha Tsui East,
   Kewloon, Hong Kong

TIME WARNER INC   Time Life Bldg, New York, NY 10020, Tel: (212) 522-1212
(Magazine & book publ, communications)
   Time-Life News Service, 205 Prince's Bldg., Des Voeux Rd., Central, Hong Kong

TOWERS PERRIN FORSTER & CROSBY INC   245 Park Ave, New York, NY 10167,
Tel: (212) 309-3400
(Management consulting)
   Towers, Perrin, Forster & Crosby, BBC House 1/F, 10 Queen's Rd. Central, Hong Kong

TRADE & INDUSTRIES CORP INC   16 E 34th St, New York, NY 10016,
Tel: (212) 686-2420
(Finance)
   Trade & Industry Acceptance Co. Hong Kong, 617-619 Prince's Bldg., 3 Des Voeux Rd.,
   Central, Hong Kong

TRANE CO   3600 Pammel Creek Rd, La Crosse, WI 54601, Tel: (608) 787-2000
  (Mfr A/C equip)
     Trane S.A., 17th Floor, Harbour View, Commercial Bldg., 2-4 Percival St.,
     Causeway Bay, Hong Kong

TRANS WORLD AIRLINES INC   605 Third Ave, New York, NY 10158,
  Tel: (212) 557-6107
  (Air transp, hotel, food serv, real estate)
     Trans World Airlines, Inc., 1330-1331 Prince's Bldg., Hong Kong

TRINOVA CORP   3000 Strayer, PO Box 50, Maumee, OH 43537, Tel: (419) 867-2200
  (Mfr engr components & sys for ind)
     Vickers Systems Ltd., Chiaphua Centre Yuen 2/F, Shun Circuit Siu Lik Yuen, Shatin,
     NT, Hong Kong

TURNER INTL INDUSTRIES INC   405 Lexington Ave, New York, NY 10174,
  Tel: (212) 286-8990
  (Constr mgrs, general constr)
     Turner East Asia, Ltd., 2302 Melbourne Plaza, 33 Queen's Rd., Central, Hong Kong
     Turner East Asia, Ltd., 2302 Melbourne Plaza, 33 Queens Rd., Central, Hong Kong

TYCO TOYS INC   540 Glen Ave, Moorestown, NJ 08057, Tel: (609) 234-7400
  (Mfr toys, elec racing, trains, building blocks)
     Tyco (Hong Kong) Ltd., 7A/F Roxy Industrial Centre, 58-66 Tia Lin Pai Rd., Hong Kong

UNION CAMP CORP   1600 Valley Rd, Wayne, NJ 07470, Tel: (201) 628-2000
  (Flavors, fragrances, essential oils, aroma chems, corrugated containers)
     Bush Boake Allen Ltd., Texaco Rd. Ind. Centre, Block A, 13/F, Texaco Rd.,
     Tsuan Wan, NT, Hong Kong

UNION CARBIDE CORP   Old Ridgebury Rd, Danbury, CT 06817, Tel: (203) 794-2000
  (Carbon prdts, chems, plastics, gases & related prdts, etc)
     UC Asia, Ltd., 38th Floor, Windsor House, Causeway Bay, Hong Kong
     UC Asia, Ltd., other locations in Hong Kong

UNION OIL INTL DIV   Union Oil Center, PO Box 7600, Los Angeles, CA 90017,
  Tel: (213) 977-7600
  (Petroleum prdts, petrochems)
     Unoco, Ltd., 403 Hang Chong Bldg., 5 Queen's Rd., Central, Hong Kong

UNION SPECIAL CORP   222 No LaSalle, Chicago, IL 60601, Tel: (312) 606-9500
  (Mfr ind sewing machs)
     Union Special Far East, Ltd., 3rd Floor, Watson's Estate, Watson Rd., Hong Kong

UNIROYAL INC   World Headquarters, Middlebury, CT 06749, Tel: (203) 573-2000
  (Tires, tubes & other rubber prdts, chems, plastics, textiles)
     Uniroyal Intl., 1008 Shell House, 26 Queen's Rd., Central, Hong Kong

UNISYS CORP   PO Box 500, Blue Bell, PA 19424, Tel: (215) 542-4011
  (Mfg/mktg/serv electr info sys)
     Sperry Ltd., Sun Hung Kai Centre, 30 Horbour St., Wanchai, Hong Kong

UNITED CALIFORNIA BANK   PO Box 54191, Los Angeles, CA 90054,
  Tel: (213) 624-0111
  (Banking)
     United California Bank, 3101 Connaught Centre, Connaught Rd., Central, Hong Kong
     Western Intl. Capital Ltd., G.P.O. Box 35, Hong Kong

UOP INC   Ten UOP Plaza, Des Plaines, IL 60016, Tel: (708) 391-2000
  (Diversified research, development & mfr of ind prdts & sys mgmt studies & serv)
    Norplex Pacific Div UOP Hong Kong, Ltd., Kowloon, Hong Kong

UP-RIGHT INC   1013 Pardee St, Berkeley, CA 94710, Tel: (415) 843-0770
  (Mfr aluminum scaffolds)
    Up-Right (Far East Serv.) Ltd., c/o Wilkinson & Grist, 601 Prince's Bldg.,
    Chater Rd., Hong Kong

UPJOHN CO   7000 Portage Rd, Kalamazoo, MI 49001, Tel: (616) 323-4000
  (Pharms, agric prdts, ind chems)
    Upjohn Overseas Co., 1001 A.I.A. Bldg., 1 Stubbs Rd., Hong Kong

VALMONT INDUSTRIES INC   Highway 275, Valley, NE 68064, Tel: (402) 359-2201
  (Irrigation sys, corrosion protection & specialized oilfield equip, pipe, lighting
  standards)
    Valmont Industries (Asia/Pacific), Ltd., A.I.E. Bldg., 8/F, 33 Connaught Rd.,
    Central, Hong Kong

VARIAN ASSOCIATES INC   611 Hansen Way, Palo Alto, CA 94304-1030,
  Tel: (415) 493-4000
  (Mfr microwave tubes & devices, analytical instru, semiconductor process & med equip,
  vacuum sys)
    Varian Pacific Inc., Room 1018-20 Tower A, New Mandarin Plaza,
    14 Science Museum Rd., Tsimshatsui E., Kowloon, Hong Kong

VETCO-GRAY INC   250 W Stanley Ave, Ventura, CA 93001, Tel: (805) 653-2500
  (Offshore oilfield equip & tools, oilfield inspect & coating serv)
    Vetco Intl., Inc., Rm 906, Hang Lung Centre, 2-20 Peterson St., Causeway Bay,
    Hong Kong

VF CORP   PO Box 1022, Reading, PA 19603, Tel: (215) 378-1151
  (Mfr/mktg apparel)
    VF (Asia) Ltd., 528 Ocean Centre, 5 Canton Rd., Kowloon, Hong Kong

VICTOR REALTY CO   781 Sacramento St, San Francisco, CA 94108,
  Tel: (415) 989-6575
  (Property mgmt, real estate)
    Victory Realty USA, Ltd., 1305 Universal House, 151 Des Voeux Rd., Central,
    Hong Kong

VIRGINIA INTL CO   2815 N Augusta St, Staunton, VA 24401, Tel: (703) 886-3425
  (Oil & gas explor, development & sales)
    Virginia Trading Co., Ltd., 1305 Universal House, 151 Des Voeux Rd., Central,
    Hong Kong

WACKENHUT CORP   1500 San Remo Ave, Coral Gables, FL 33146,
  Tel: (305) 666-5656
  (Security sys & serv)
    Wackenhut Security (HK) Ltd., 1404 Argyle Centre 1, 688 Nathan Rd., Kowloon,
    Hong Kong

WADDELL & REED INC   One Crown Center, PO Box 1343, Kansas City, MO 64141,
  Tel: (201) 386-9300
  (Mutual funds, life ins)
    Waddell & Reed Intl. Asia, Ltd., 41 New Henry House, 10 Ice House St., 306,
    Hong Kong

WANG LABORATORIES INC   1 Industrial Ave, Lowell, MA 01851,
  Tel: (508) 459-5000
  (Mfr computer info processing sys)
    Wang Pacific, Ltd., 9th Floor, Lap Heng House, 47-50 Gloucester Rd., Hong Kong

WARNER-LAMBERT CO   201 Tabor Road, Morris Plains, NJ 07950,
  Tel: (201) 540-2000
  (Mfr ethical & proprietary pharms, confectionary & consumer prdts)
    Warner-Lambert Hong Kong, Ltd., G.P.O. Box 567, Hong Kong

WEATHERFORD INTL INC   1360 Post Oak Blvd, PO Box 27608, Houston,
  TX 77227-9917, Tel: (713) 439-9400
  (Tubular & cementation servs, prdts & equip; water jetting servs, mfr marine pedestal
  cranes)
    Weatherford Intl., 2803 Admiralty Centre, Tower 1, 18 Harcourt Rd., Hong Kong

WELCH ALLYN INC   State St Rd, Box 220, Skaneateles Falls, NY 13153,
  Tel: (315) 685-5788
  (Illuminated med devices, fiber optics, miniature lamps, etc)
    Welch Allyn Hong Kong Inc.,. 77 B-C Waterloo Rd., 14/F, Kowloon, Hong Kong

WESTINGHOUSE BROADCASTING & CABLE INC   90 Park Ave, New York, NY 10016,
  Tel: (212) 983-6500
  (Radio & TV broadcasting)
    Westinghouse Broadcasting Co., Inc., 1-A Gardena Court, 2 Kennedy Terrace, Hong Kong

WEYERHAEUSER CO   Tacoma, WA 98477, Tel: (206) 924-2345
  (Wood & wood fiber prdts)
    Weyerhaeuser Co., G.P.O. Box 3818, Hong Kong

WILBUR-ELLIS CO   320 California St, San Francisco, CA 94104,
  Tel: (415) 772-4000
  (Zippers & general merchandise)
    Talon Hong Kong, Ltd., 307 Holland House, 9 Ice House St., Hong Kong

WILLCOX & GIBBS INC   530 Fifth Ave, New York, NY 10022, Tel: (212) 869-1800
  (Distr mach, equip & supplies for apparel ind; mfr computer-based planning & control
  sys)
    Willcox & Gibbs Hong Kong, Ltd., 12th Floor, Harrington Bldg., 44-50,
      Wang Wo Tsai St., Tsuen Wan, New Territories, Kowloon, Hong Kong

WOODWARD & DICKERSON INC   937 Haverford Road, Bryn Mawr, PA 19010,
  Tel: (215) 527-5200
  (Intl marketing)
    Woodward & Dickerson Far East Ltd., 3801 Gloucester Tower, Hong Kong

WORLD COURIER INC   46 Trinity Pl, New York, NY 10006, Tel: (718) 978-9400
  (Intl courier serv)
    World Courier, Hong Kong, 404 Air Cargo Terminal Office Bldg.,
      Kaitak Intl. Airport, Hong Kong

WM WRIGLEY JR CO   410 N Michigan Ave, Chicago, IL 60611-4287,
  Tel: (312) 644-2121
  (Chewing gum)
    The Wrigley Co. (HK) Ltd., Hong Kong

YORK INTERNATIONAL CORP   PO Box 1592, York, PA 17405-1592,
  Tel: (715) 771-7890
  (Mfr A/C, heating & refrig sys & equip)
    York Air Conditioning & Refrid. Inc., Unit 5A, Sime Darby Ind. Centre,
      420-424 Kwun Tong Rd., Kowloon, Hong Kong

YOUNG & RUBICAM INTL INC   285 Madison Ave, New York, NY 10017,
  Tel: (212) 210-3000
  (Advertising agency)
    Young & Rubicam Asia/Pacific Headquarters, Tugu Bldg., 8th Floor, 1 Lockhart Rd.,
      Hong Kong
    Young & Rubicam Hong Kong, Ltd., 405 Asian House, 1 Hennessy Rd., Hong Kong

HUNGARY

CANADA DRY INTL CORP   2600 Century Pkwy, Atlanta, GA 30345,
  Tel: (404) 753-2182
  (Carbonated beverages, soft drinks extract)
    Canada Dry Corp., Erdie Termet Vallalat, Huszar U.7, 1074 Budapest, Hungary

DATAEASE INTL INC   7 Cambridge Dr, Trumbull, CT 06611, Tel: (203) 374-8000
  (Mfr applications devel software)
    VT-Soft, KFT, Vorosvari Ut 103-105, 1033 Budapest, Hungary

THE DIEBOLD GROUP INC   475 Park Ave South, New York, NY 10016,
  Tel: (212) 684-4700
  (Mgmt consultants: info tech)
    SZ Diebold Management Consulting Ltd., Budapest,
      Hungary (all mail to New York address)

GETZ CORP   150 Post St, San Francisco, CA 94108, Tel: (415) 772-5500
  (Marketing/distribution serv)
    Intercooperation Co. Ltd., P.O. Box 136, H-1431 Budapest, Hungary

HYATT INTL CORP   200 West Madison St, Chicago, IL 60606, Tel: (312) 750-1234
  (Intl hotel mgmt)
    Atrium Hyatt Budapest, Roosevelt Ter. 2, P.O. Box H-1366, Budapest 5, P.F. 55,
      Hungary

INA CORPORATION   1600 Arch St, Philadelphia, PA 19101, Tel: (215) 523-5335
  (Holding co: ins, financial serv)
    INA, Karbiztosok Testulete, Dorottya U.3, P.O. Box 106, H-1051, Budapest V, Hungary

LE TOURNEAU INC LONGVIEW DIV   PO Box 2307, Longview, TX 75606,
  Tel: (214) 753-3449
  (Heavy constr, mining mach & equip)
    Ing. G. Schlamadinger, all mail to: P.B. 4, A-2320 Schwechat, Vienna, Austria

MACRO INTL INC   8630 Fenton St, Silver Spring, MD 20910, Tel: (301) 588-5484
  (Mkt research, surveys, mgmt consult/training)
    TQ Center, Batthyany Ter 23, 9022 Gyor, Hungary

MTS SYSTEMS CORP   PO Box 24012, Minneapolis, MN 55424, Tel: (612) 937-4000
  (Electrohydraulic testing & prod equip, mach controls)
    MTA-MMSZ, PF.1502, H-1502 Budapest, Hungary

McCANN-ERICKSON WORLDWIDE   750 Third Ave, New York, NY 10017,
  Tel: (212) 697-6000
  (Advertising)
    McCann-Interpress, Budakeszi UT 55, 1021 Budapest 2, Hungary